more

13

chip39

996655

Modern
College Physics

A liquid hydrogen bubble chamber, located at the University of California, Berkeley. Photographed by G. Kagawa. Courtesy of Professor L. Alvarez, the Radiation Laboratory at the University of California, and the Atomic Energy Commission. The bubble chamber, 10 inches in diameter, is located in the large cylinder at the lower right. The compression and expansion cylinders are located just to the left of center. The main control panel is seen in the upper right.

MODERN
COLLEGE PHYSICS

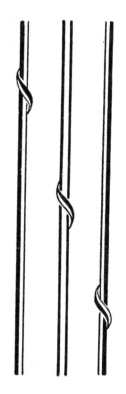

By

HARVEY E. WHITE, PH.D.

PROFESSOR OF PHYSICS
UNIVERSITY OF CALIFORNIA

*Third
Edition*

D. VAN NOSTRAND COMPANY, INC.

PRINCETON, NEW JERSEY

TORONTO   LONDON

NEW YORK

D. VAN NOSTRAND COMPANY, INC.

120 Alexander St., Princeton, New Jersey
257 Fourth Avenue, New York 10, New York
25 Hollinger Rd., Toronto 16, Canada
Macmillan & Co., Ltd., St. Martin's St., London, W.C. 2, England

*All correspondence should be addressed to the
principal office of the company at Princeton, N. J.*

Library of Congress Catalog Card No. 56-6887

First Published February 1948

Six Reprintings

Second Edition March 1953

Five Reprintings

Third Edition January 1956

PRINTED IN THE UNITED STATES OF AMERICA

TO

MY SON

Don

Preface to Third Edition

In this third edition, as in the second, the author has attempted to bring the subjects of atomic and nuclear physics up to date, and to make other changes or modifications in response to suggestions made by some of the many instructors and students using the book as a text. Such changes, for example, are to be found in the treatment of magnetism at the end of Chapter 51, in electromagnetism in Chapters 53 and 55, and in optics in Chapter 44.

Over two hundred new problems have been added to those already given in the second edition bringing the total to well over one thousand. In keeping with previous practices answers are given to all even-numbered problems.

The author wishes to thank the many teachers and students who have written him; their comments and criticisms have been most heartily welcomed.

Harvey E. White

Berkeley, California,
November, 1955.

Preface to Second Edition

In this edition the attempt has been made to improve the text without changing the general outline and scope of the contents of the first edition. The author has been guided principally by the suggestions of the many teachers and students who have used the book as a text; grateful acknowledgment is made here.

Of primary interest to many teachers will be the fact that completely new problems are given at the end of each chapter. The answers to the even-numbered problems only are included; these have been independently checked for accuracy.

Several of the eight chapters on electricity and magnetism have been rewritten, and two additional chapters have been added. These changes are in compliance with numerous requests for a considerable expansion of alternating-current theory and the use of the mks system of units in electricity and magnetism. To compensate for this expansion the three chapters on sources of light and their spectra have been condensed into one. It is sincerely hoped that teachers introducing the mks system for the first time will be as pleased with its success and simplicity as was the author when he tried it for the first time.

The location of the presentation of trigonometry in the treatment of vectors has been shifted from chapter three to chapter eight for the benefit of those students who begin their mathematics course in trigonometry at the same time they begin their physics course. Such students, as well as the others, will have time now to learn, or "brush up" on, the principles of the simplest trigonometry functions.

Perhaps the most difficult task confronting beginning students in college physics courses today is the acquisition of a clear understanding of the difference between weight and mass. Many articles have been written on this subject and there are "pros and cons" for one method or another. To the author it seems pedagogically sound that, because the pound is so commonly used as a unit of weight, and weight is a force, the concept of mass is new and the introduction of the slug as a unit of mass greatly simplifies the problem. This is the procedure that has been followed in this revision, and it is the author's opinion that a difficult subject has been made easier for the student and teacher alike.

Minor changes have been made in the chapters on friction, projectiles, and sound. The last chapters on cosmic rays, nuclear physics, and atomic energy have been brought up to date. I wish to express my sincere thanks to Mr. Herschel Snodgrass for his valuable criticisms of the new material, particularly the chapters on electricity and magnetism.

The frontispiece is used through the courtesy of *Scientific American* (color photograph by Union Carbide and Carbon Corporation).

HARVEY E. WHITE

Berkeley, California,
February, 1953.

Preface

THIS book is designed to be used as a text in the standard one-year college physics course required by most colleges and universities as part of the basic training of students planning to major in one of the physical or life sciences.

The main objective in preparing the manuscript was to bring together under one cover the elementary principles of *classical physics* as well as that branch of modern science called *atomic and nuclear physics*. Two ideas were followed: first, the confinement of all problems and mathematics to elementary algebra, plane geometry, and trigonometry; and second, the inclusion, wherever convenient, of illustrations from the biological and medical sciences as well as from engineering and physics. All too often physics texts present practically all illustrations from the field of engineering in spite of the fact that a relatively large proportion of students planning to major in one of the life sciences is enrolled in most introductory physics courses. As a consequence the pre-medical student, as a typical example, finds little to hold his interest. It appears to him that each new principle encountered and developed applies only to engineering when in reality most physical concepts have some direct application to some phase of medicine or medical research.

The increasing importance of electronics, as well as atomic and nuclear physics, through their application to other branches of knowledge, has given rise to a growing demand for the inclusion of these subjects in the introductory college physics course. Consequently, the last quarter of the book is devoted to an introductory treatment of these subjects. To alleviate the difficulty of having too much material to cover in a one-year course, there are two obvious alternatives. One is for the author to eliminate those subjects in classical physics which he considers of lesser importance, and the other is to retain the standard subjects and let each instructor make his own selections. The author has chosen the second alternative, because instructors differ widely in their ideas as to which subjects are most important and which are not. To this end the book is divided into many chapters, making it possible to eliminate a subject by skipping an entire chapter.

The author wishes to take this opportunity of thanking his colleagues Messrs. L. Alvarez, R. T. Birge, R. B. Brode, D. Cooksey, F. A. Jenkins, E. O. Lawrence, V. F. Lenzen, L. B. Loeb, E. M. MacMillan, J. R. Oppenheimer, G. T. Seaborg, L. L. Skolil, and C. D. Shane, for their valuable criticisms of various portions of the manuscript.

My sincere thanks are also extended to Mr. J. G. Brohl to whom I am indebted for the drawing of many of the diagrams, and to Mrs. R. C. Archibald, Mrs. Caroline Lanham, Mrs. Bay Muldoon and Miss Rebekah Young, for the typing of the manuscript. I also wish to thank the various publishers and commercial laboratories for their permission to reproduce certain illustrations used in the book.

HARVEY E. WHITE

Berkeley, California,
July, 1947.

Contents

Mechanics

Properties of Matter

Contents

Heat

Sound

Light

Electricity and Magnetism

Atomic Physics

Electronics

Quantum Optics

Nuclear Physics

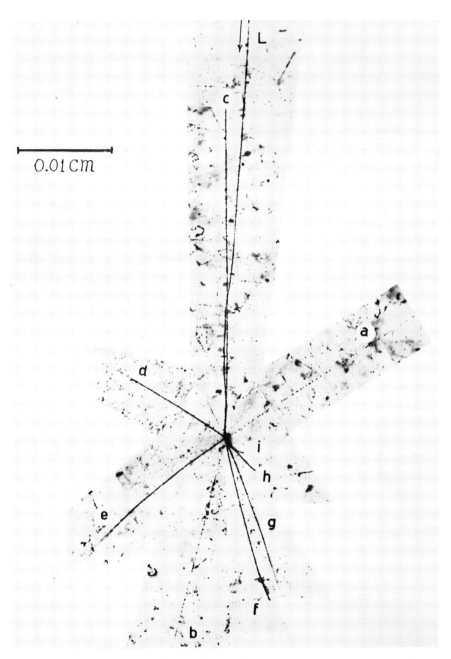

0.01 cm

Antiproton Star observed in a photographic emulsion exposed to high energy particles from the 6 BEV beam of the Bevatron at the University of California, Berkeley. (See *Physical Review,* 101, 1956.) L is the incoming antiproton (negatively charged proton) track. (Track extends 9.31 cm in the original emulsion beyond the top of this photo, a distance equal to 80 ft on this enlargement.) Coming to a stop, the antiproton is captured by a nucleus, resulting in its annihilation and a nuclear explosion. (a) and (b) are pi-meson tracks, (c) is a proton, and (d), (e), (f), (g), (h), and (i) are either protons or alpha particles. Antiprotons were discovered by O. Chamberlain, E. Segre, C. Wiegand, and T. Ypsilantis in October, 1955.

Optical Illusions   Chapter 1

In the early dawn on the morning of July 16, 1945, there occurred in a remote spot on the desert sands of Almagordo, New Mexico, a man-made explosion of enormous magnitude. This, the explosion of the first atomic bomb, marked the culmination of a five-year coordinated research program the size of which in terms of manpower and material is best expressed by its total cost to the United States government of approximately two billion dollars. With the ending of World War II and the subsequent dissemination of many of the scientific and technical developments made during that war the civilized world awakened to the realization that we stand today on the threshold of a scientific era. This is the beginning of an era in which the wonders of television, radar, electronics, atomic energy, jet propulsion and rocket ships will become a commonplace reality.

In all of these developments in the physical sciences, as well as many others in the field of medicine and the life sciences in general, the subject we call physics has played a most important role. So important is this role that many authorities in other fields of knowledge and endeavor consider physics to be the most basic of all the sciences. Certainly a knowledge of the fundamental principles of physics is today an essential part of the education of all who desire to become proficient in the physical and medical professions.

One of the reasons physics is called an exact science is that reproducible experiments are performed and observations are made with high precision measuring instruments. Laws and theories are formulated from the measured results of these experiments and then used to predict the results of new experiments. If these new experimental results do not agree with theory, the theory is either modified and brought into agreement or it is discarded for a new and better theory. Physics may be defined as that branch of knowledge treating the inanimate world and its phenomena and includes the subjects of *mechanics, properties of matter, heat, sound, light, electricity and magnetism, atomic and nuclear structure.*

1.1. Physics as an Objective Method. It has long been known that when experiments are to be performed one cannot rely too much upon the human senses of touch, sight, hearing, etc., to make accurate observations. Methods of measurement which rely upon the senses entirely are called

1

subjective methods. Methods which make use of scientific instruments are generally called *objective methods.*

In the early history of science laws were frequently discovered by the use of subjective methods. Progress was slow, however, until such methods were replaced by objective methods using measuring instruments devised to give greater and greater precision.

It is true that many scientific discoveries have been made in the past with what we now would call the crudest of apparatus and equipment. It is the development of precision instruments and apparatus, however, which has, particularly within the last several decades, led to discoveries which are far-reaching in their theoretical implications and are of extreme practical importance to the advancement of civilization.

As an introduction to the subject of physics we will first consider a num- ber of experiments illustrating the false impressions so easily arrived at from the use of subjective methods of observation. Although these experi- ments are of the nature of an entertainment, they do have more serious aspects, for they demonstrate the necessity for using objective methods in advancing science.

1.2. Subjective Methods. If someone asks you to determine the tem- perature of a pan of water, your first impulse, if the water is not too hot, is to use your hand or your finger-tips and not to bother looking for a ther- mometer. To illustrate the gross inac- curacy of the touch in determining temperature, consider the three pans of water as shown in Fig. 1A. If the hand is first held for some little time in the pan containing *cold* water and then plunged into the *warm* water, the senses tell you it is hot. If, however,

cold   warm   hot

Fɪɢ. 1A—Experiment illustrating the uncertainty of subjective methods of measurement.

the hand is first held in the *hot* water and then plunged into the *warm* water, your senses tell you it is cold. Your conclusion in either case is thus influenced by your experiences immediately preceding your determination of the temperature of the middle pan. When a thermometer is used in this ex- periment the same temperature will be arrived at in either case. Although this latter would be called an objective method of measurement one still relies upon the senses to obtain a reading of the thermometer scale.

If the length and breadth of a table top are to be measured, a *foot rule,* a *yardstick,* or a *meter stick* should be used and not the *span of a hand.* In a similar way the time that it takes a sprinter to run the *"one-hundred yard dash"* is measured by a *clock,* a *watch,* or a *chronometer* and not by the *heart beat* or *pulse.*

1.3. The Eye. In making many scientific measurements the eye is considered as the most useful of all recording instruments. In some instances, however, the eye is not and should not be used directly in making observations, since it cannot be relied upon to observe what is really there. To illustrate how unreliable the sense of vision can be in some cases we will consider in the next section a number of examples commonly referred to as "optical illusions."

Despite its many and sometimes serious imperfections and limitations the human eye is a marvelous optical instrument. It is nature's priceless gift to man enabling him to enjoy the beauties of form, color, and motion made

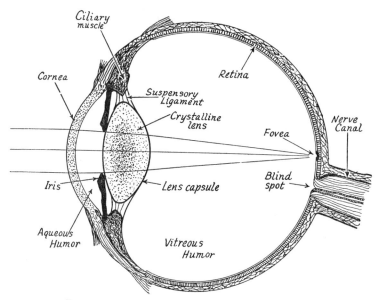

Fig. 1B—Cross-section diagram of the human eye.

possible by light. Optically the eye is like an exceptionally fine camera with an elaborate lens system on the one side and a sensitive screen or photographic film, called the *retina*, on the other. See Fig. 1B. The refracting media of the eye consists of the *cornea*, the *aqueous humor*, the *crystalline lens*, and *vitreous humor*, and its function is to focus an image of the objects to be seen on the retina. Like a camera, the eye contains an *iris diaphragm* which opens wider for faint light and closes down to a bare pinhole opening for very bright sunlight. It is this iris that contains the pigment determining the color of the eye.

In the retina of the eye the light pulses are received by tiny *cones* and *rods* whose function it seems to be to change the light into electricity. Each cone and rod is connected with an individual nerve which conducts the electricity through the nerve canal to the brain. Just how these electrical impulses are produced by the cell-like structures, the cones and rods, and how they are interpreted by the brain as vision is still but vaguely understood by scientists. Experiments seem to indicate that the cones respond only to bright light and are particularly responsible for the detection and distinction of color whereas the rods are sensitive to very feeble light, to motion, and to slight variations in intensity.

At the very center of the retina is a small yellowish-looking spot called the *fovea*. This small region contains a large number of cones, but no rods. It is on this spot in each eye that the words and letters of this page are focused one after the other when reading. Note when scrutinizing one word or particularly a single letter in a word that the rest of the page and even the words and letters close by appear indistinct.

It is customary to divide all sensory data, that contribute to sight perception of any object, into two parts; first, the formation of the retinal image by the light coming from the object, and second, the integrative property of the brain to interpret this image.

1.4. The Blind Spot. Not far from the fovea on the retina of the eye is a small region called the *blind spot*. This spot, which is insensitive to light, is where the nerve canal joins the eyeball. The existence of the blind spot can be demonstrated by closing the right eye, and holding the book at arm's length, looking continuously at the center of the circle of Fig. 1C with the left eye. Both the circle and square will be seen from this distance. If the

Fig. 1C—Experiment illustrating the blind spot of the eye.

book is now moved slowly toward the eye, still fixing the eye upon the circle, a position (about 8 to 10 inches from the eye) will be reached where the square disappears. When both eyes are open no position will be found where either the cross or the square disappears. One eye always sees that part of an object to which the other eye is blind. A similar experiment with the right eye focused on the square will cause the circle to disappear. A further discussion of the human eye and how it functions as an optical instrument is given in Chap. 44.

1.5. Optical Illusions. Of the hundreds of well known optical illusions only a few of the most interesting ones will be presented here. In Fig. 1D is a group of six figures classified as illusions due to *lines* and *angles*. In (a),

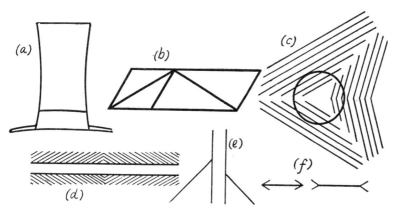

FIG. 1D—Optical illustrations with lines and angles.

the first figure, the brim of the hat is as long as the hat is high; in (b) the diagonal lines of each parallelogram are of the same length; and in (c) the perfect circle appears to be distorted. In figure (d) the two horizontal lines are parallel and straight and in (f) they are of equal length. In (e) the lower right-hand line if extended will intersect the left-hand line where it joins the vertical.

Fig. 1E is an example of *perspective*, an illusion suggesting depth to the picture when in reality it is flat. Actually this figure is a rectangle enclosing three pillars of equal height. By means of slanting lines these pillars are made to appear to have different heights. Experiences from early childhood have trained us to interpret the slanting lines as depth.

The next set of illusions, shown in Fig. 1F, are classified as *equivocal figures*. These illustrate the phenomenon of the *fluctuation* of the process of vision. In figure (a) six cubes may be seen stacked three, two, one, or seven cubes may be seen stacked two, three, two. In (b) a folded sheet of paper is seen opening either toward or away from the reader. In (c) is a flight of steps seen from above looking down, or from below looking up.

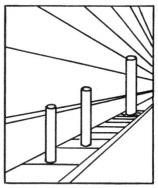

FIG. 1E—Optical illustration in perspective.

Fig. 1F(d) is one of the most interesting of all illusions. To fully appreciate the effect one must himself perform the experiment with a small

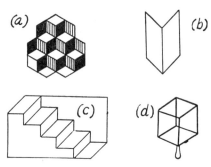

wire cube about one inch in size. The cube is held by a small handle at one corner and viewed with one eye at a distance of from 1 to 2 ft. By the principle of fluctuation the observer next tries to make the farthest corner of the cube appear as the nearest corner. When this condition is attained the cube upon being turned about a horizontal or vertical axis will appear to turn in the opposite direction. A little practice in the fluctuation of the visual senses is required in this experiment and it is well worth performing.

FIG. 1F—Optical illusions illustrating fluctuation of the attention.

In Fig. 1G are two pairs of similar figures of equal area. The slanting lines at the ends make the lower figure in each case appear to be larger than the one immediately above. Such figures should be cut from white cardboard and held one above the other. When the upper figure is interchanged with the corresponding lower figure, one figure seems to grow and the other to shrink before your eyes.

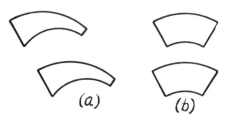

FIG. 1G—Optical illusions of area.

In Fig. 1H(a) are two small squares of equal size, a white square on a black background, and a black square on a white background. When an image of this is formed on the retina of the eye the cones and rods just beyond the white edges are stimulated by those nearby, thus causing the white

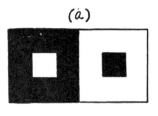

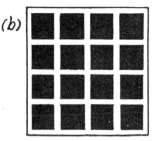

FIG. 1H—Light and dark objects illustrating the phenomenon of irradiation.

square to be larger than the black one. This phenomenon is called *irradiation* or *brightness contrast*. A similar phenomenon is illustrated in Fig. 1H(b) where grey spots are seen at the intersections of the white lines.

1.6. Fatigue and Color Illusions. All of the illusions above have been confined to figures in black and white. There exists a large number of illusions which are classified as *color illusions*. Two of these are diagrammed in Fig. 1I. A disk painted black and white as shown in (a) will appear to be colored when set rotating at a relatively low speed. The colors to be seen are rather faint pastel shades of violet, blue, green, yellow, and pink. The speed of the wheel should be from about 4 to 15 revolutions per second. The explanation usually given for the phenomenon is that the retina of the eye responds more quickly to some colors than to others. Since the white image of the disk moves around on the retina and since white light contains all the colors of the rainbow, some colors are perceived at each given spot on the retina sooner than others and the effect of color is produced.

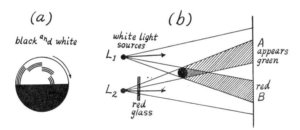

Fig. 1I—Diagrams of experiments demonstrating color illusions.

The second diagram (b) in Fig. 1I illustrates the appearance of color by virtue of contrast. If a white patch of light, for example, is seen on a background of red it will appear to be pale green. If, on the other hand, a white patch is seen on a background of green it will appear to be pink. The experiment may be performed with two similar arc lights producing white light. Each of these is made to cast a shadow of the same rod R on a white screen. If a piece of red glass is placed in front of Light L_2 as shown in the figure, the white patch of light at A will appear to be pale green. If a green glass is inserted in its place the region A will appear pink. In each case, A receives light from L_1 only and must therefore be really white. Red and green of the proper shades are complementary colors and when they are added together produce white light. The subject of the mixing of colors will be taken up in detail in Chap. 45.

1.7. Complementary Images. When the eyes are subjected to bright light for some little time the retina seems to show tiring or *fatigue*. Furthermore continued subjection of any part of the retina to one particular color causes only those cones sensitive to that color to tire. When the same retinal area is subsequently subjected to white light the previously inactive cones respond more strongly than those originally stimulated and a complementary color is seen.

To observe these colored images, fix the attention on the black star in the lower right hand corner of the field of the flag in Fig. 1J and keep it there for about 15 to 20 sec. Then turn the eyes toward a white wall of the room, or toward the open sky, and in one or two seconds the American flag will appear in all of its true colors. Similar effects can be observed with other color photographs.

Delayed images of this kind are always complementary in color to the original pictures, black becomes white, yellow becomes blue, green becomes magenta, magenta becomes green, etc. (For an explanation of complementary colors see Chap. 45.)

1.8. The Stroboscopic Effect. In moving pictures, when a wagon with spoked wheels is coming to a stop the wheels are often noticed to stand still, then turn backward, stop, turn forward, and then stop again. This phenomenon, known as the "stroboscopic effect," is due to interrupted illumination of the moving-picture screen and can be illustrated in many ways. An interesting experiment illustrating the phenomenon is shown in Fig. 1K. Two disks are mounted on the shafts of two separate motors. The smaller

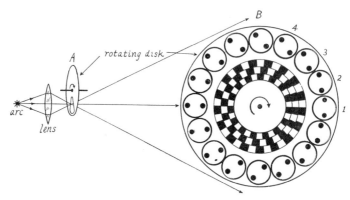

Fig. 1K—Experimental arrangement for demonstrating the stroboscopic effect.

disk A with a narrow slot is used to interrupt the light beam illuminating the larger disk. The disk B is white with black circles and dots arranged exactly as shown. Suppose now that disk A makes sixteen revolutions per second, thus illuminating disk B with sixteen short flashes of light per second. Sup-

Fig. 1J — Fatigue images enable the above objects to appear in their natural colors.

pose also that *B* makes only one revolution per second, and that one flash of light comes when the disk has the position shown in the figure. Confining the attention to the circle at position (1) the two enclosed dots are one above the other. When the second flash of light appears the circle (2) will be in position (1) and the two dots will appear to have shifted slightly clockwise. When the next flash of light comes the circle (3) will be in position (1) and the two dots will have shifted still farther. This process continued shows that the circles will appear to stand still and the dots to rotate within them.

If the light flashes in any such experiment as the one described above are slower than 16 per sec the illuminated object will appear to flicker badly. If, however, the flashes come at an increasingly higher rate, the flicker will

Fig. 1L—Illusion of rotation.

Fig. 1M—Circles appear to be spirals.

soon disappear entirely and the illumination will seem to be steady. The reason for this is that each retinal image is somehow retained by the vision mechanism for about one sixteenth of a second. This is called the *persistence of vision*.

1.9. Circles and Spirals. If this page of the book is held about one foot in front of the observer's eyes and the book moved rapidly in a circle about 2 to 3 inches in diameter the spiral in Fig. 1L will appear to rotate in the direction of motion. A set of alternately dark and light concentric circles will show the same effect, the apparent rotation being due to persistence of vision.

We have seen in the previous illustrations how some optical illusions break down or diminish under critical inspection. There are others, however, that persist. No amount of staring or thought will teach you to see the circles of Fig. 1M as anything other than spirals.

For supplementary reading on optical illusions see Am. J. of Physics, vol. 14, p. 104, 1946.

EXERCISE

1. Using 13 match sticks and some quick drying glue make a small cube as shown in Fig. 1F(d) and carry out the experiment described at the top of page 6. One stick is for handle.

Units of Measurement — Chapter 2

SINCE physics is a science based upon exact measurement it is essential that the student first become familiar with several of the more commonly used measuring devices and the units into which each is usually divided. Every measurement whether it be a distance, a weight, an interval of time, or anything else, requires *two* things: first, a *number;* and second, a *unit.* One might, for example, obtain as the result of the measurement of different distances, *20 feet, 5 miles, 3 rods,* or as the result of the measurement of different weights, *6 pounds, 25 tons, 4½ ounces,* or as the result of the measurement of different time intervals, *7 hours, 26 seconds,* etc. As the result of some experiment or the reading of certain instruments one might obtain the measurements, *10.7 calories, 90 horsepower, 6 volts, 12 kilowatts,* etc. In each case the *unit* is just as essential as the *number* expressing the amount.

Although there are numerous different units, each one can be expressed in terms of not more than three special units. These three, called *fundamental units,* are the units of *length, mass,* and *time.* All other units are called *derived units* since, as we shall see later, they can always be written as some combination of the three fundamental units.

There are in general two widely used sets of fundamental units (a) the *metric,* and (b) the *English.* Throughout the civilized world scientific observations are nearly always expressed in terms of metric units. This set employs the *standard meter* as the unit of length, the *standard kilogram* as the unit of mass, and the *second* as the unit of time.

2.1. The Standard Meter and Yard. The standard meter is a platinum-iridium bar about forty inches long which is kept in the vaults of the International Bureau of Weights and Measures near Paris, France. Three facsimiles of this bar are to be found at the United States Bureau of Standards in Washington, D. C. Each of these duplicate copies may be called an *International Prototype Meter* and is now the standard of length in the United States. From these prototypes all other measuring rods and tapes are standardized.

When the standard meter was first devised it was intended that it have a length equal to one ten-millionth part of the distance from one of the earth's poles to the equator. Although more recent measurements of the earth's dimensions have shown that the distance from pole to equator is about 10,000,880 *standard meters* the two groove marks one on either end of the original platinum-iridium bar are now taken to be exactly one meter apart.

The standard meter is usually divided into one hundred equal parts. Each of these parts is called the *centimeter*.

$$1 \text{ meter} = 100 \text{ centimeters}$$

or, abbreviated,
$$1 \text{ m} = 100 \text{ cm.}$$

inches

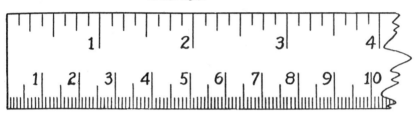

centimeters

Fɪɢ. 2A—Diagram comparing the centimeter scale with the inch scale.

The centimeter is further divided into ten equal parts. Each of these parts is called the *millimeter*. See Fig. 2A.

$$1 \text{ centimeter(cm)} = 10 \text{ millimeters(mm)}$$
$$1000 \text{ millimeters(mm)} = 1 \text{ meter(m).}$$

In civil life in the United States the *yard* is used as the standard unit of length. By an act of Congress in 1866 the standard yard to be used legally in the United States was defined as 3600/3937 part of a standard meter. Since the yard is divided into thirty-six inches.

$$1 \text{ meter(m)} = 39.37 \text{ inches(in.).}$$

With twelve inches to one foot,

$$3 \text{ ft} = 1 \text{ yd}$$
$$1 \text{ ft} = 30.48 \text{ cm}$$

and
$$1 \text{ in.} = 2.54 \text{ cm.}$$

The sizes of the inch, fractions of an inch relative to the centimeter, and millimeter, are illustrated in Fig. 2A.

When large distances are to be measured it is convenient as well as customary to use large units of length. Such units are the *kilometer* in the metric system and the *mile* in the English system. One kilometer is equivalent to one-thousand meters, and one mile is equivalent to five-thousand-two-hundred-and-eighty feet.

$$1000 \text{ meters(m)} = 1 \text{ kilometer(km)}$$
$$1 \text{ mile(mi)} = 5280 \text{ feet(ft)}.$$

The relations between units of length in the metric system as against the English system are given in the following table:

TABLE OF CONVERSION FACTORS FOR UNITS OF LENGTH

		km	m	cm	in.	ft	mi
1 kilometer	=	1	1000	100,000	39370	3280.83	0.62140
1 meter	=	0.00100	1	100	39.370	3.28083	6.21×10^{-4}
1 centimeter	=	1.0×10^{-5}	0.0100	1	0.39370	0.032808	6.21×10^{-6}
1 inch	=	2.54×10^{-5}	0.02540	2.5400	1	0.08333	1.58×10^{-5}
1 foot	=	3.05×10^{-4}	0.30480	30.480	12	1	1.89×10^{-4}
1 mile	=	1.60934	1609.34	160934	63360	5280	1

2.2. The Standard Kilogram and Pound. The standard unit of mass is the *kilogram,* a block of platinum also preserved at the International Bureau of Weights and Measures near Paris. Two copies of this kilogram (which may be called International Prototype Kilograms) are kept in the vaults of the U. S. Bureau of Standards. The kilogram is divided into one-thousand equal parts called *grams.*

$$1000 \text{ grams(gm)} = 1 \text{ kilogram(kg)}.$$

The original intent was to base the standard kilogram upon the gram, the gram being the mass of one cubic centimeter of pure water taken at a temperature of four degrees centigrade.

The standard pound is defined in terms of the standard kilogram by the relation that its mass shall equal 0.4536 kilogram.

Following this we have the relations

$$1 \text{ oz} = 28.35 \text{ gm} \qquad 1 \text{ lb} = 16 \text{ oz}$$
$$1 \text{ ton} = 2000 \text{ lb.}$$

2.3. Historical Time Pieces. Instruments for the measurement of time go back historically to the Babylonians, at least, and probably to the time of the Greeks five centuries B.C. The earliest time pieces on record were chiefly water clocks, some of very simple design and others of more elaborate design. These clocks were based upon the very elementary principle that it takes the same time for equal amounts of water to flow through a small opening. The *hour glass,* employing the same principle and using sand instead of water, is an outgrowth of the water clock and dates back to medieval times.

A water clock of moderately simple design is shown in Fig. 2B(a). Small holes at the edge of the vanes (shown in the detail diagram) allow the water to flow from one compartment to the other. This permits the cylinder to turn slowly, thus unwinding the suspending cords.

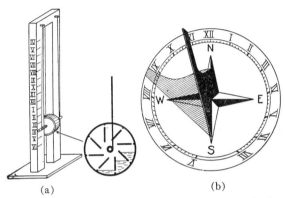

Fig. 2B—Diagrams of two of the early forms of time pieces. (a) a water-clock. (b) a sundial.

The *sundial* dates back to the Chaldean astronomer Berosus who lived about the time of Alexander the Great, 300 B.C. Today, similar instruments serve as ornaments in many of our public parks. A sundial of common design, as shown in Fig. 2B(b), consists essentially of a *pin* called a *gnomon* mounted at an angle on a circular plate called the *dial*. The gnomon is mounted in the vertical North and South plane. The edge of the gnomon is parallel to the earth's rotational axis and its purpose is to cast a shadow on the dial which is marked with the hours of the day. Due to the apparent yearly precessional motion of the earth's axis, small corrections must be made to the time as shown by the shadow. These corrections amounting to several minutes are usually engraved upon every sundial. The sundial on the University of California campus, for example, has the following corrections:

Jan. 10, + 17 min	May 20, + 5 min	Sept. 17, + 4 min
Feb. 9, + 23 "	June 19, + 10 "	Oct. 17, − 5 "
Mar. 11, + 19 "	July 19, + 15 "	Nov. 16, − 6 "
Apr. 10, + 8 "	Aug. 18, + 18 "	Dec. 16, + 5 "

Modern clocks depend for their regulation upon the swinging of a pendulum or the oscillation of a balance wheel. Examples of these are the grandfather clock and the modern wrist-watch. Such devices will be discussed later under the heading of vibrations and waves, Chap. 14. Electric clocks commonly found in the city homes of today are run by tiny electric motors. The speed of these motors is controlled at the city's electric power plant by controlling the frequency of the alternating current supplied to the power lines leading to the house. The master clock at the power house is frequently a pendulum clock.

2.4. Time and the Mean Solar Day. Three kinds of time are always recognized by astronomers: first, *sidereal time;* second, *apparent solar time;* and third, *mean solar time.* The latter is the time used in civil life. If at any given point on the earth's surface we adjust the gnomon of a sundial to lie in the North and South vertical plane, the time interval between two successive transits of the sun's shadow over the twelve o'clock mark is called the apparent solar day. For several reasons, one being that the earth's orbit around the sun is elliptical, this interval of time varies slightly from day to day. An apparent solar day in December is about one minute longer than an apparent solar day in September. It is clear, therefore, why in this day of accurate time pieces we do not regulate our clocks to apparent solar time.

The *average* length of all apparent solar days throughout a solar year is called the *mean solar day.* This is a satisfactory time interval since it is invariable and can be kept by well regulated clocks and watches. The time interval called the *second* is defined as 1/86400th part of a mean solar day.

$$1 \text{ sec} = 1/60 \times 1/60 \times 1/24 = 1/86400 \text{th part of one day.}$$

There are 365.2421 mean solar days in one solar year; that is, with respect to the sun, the earth makes 365.2421 rotations in making one complete revolution in its orbit.

For astronomical purposes a different time scale known as sidereal time is used. There is one more sidereal day in one solar year than there are mean solar days. One solar year equals 366.2421 sidereal days. The reason for the additional day is that in making one complete turn around the sun in its orbit the earth has actually made 366.2421 rotations with respect to the fixed stars. The sidereal second as ticked off by an astronomical clock is therefore slightly shorter than the second given by an ordinary clock keeping mean solar time.

2.5. Metric Units. Nearly all scientific experiments, in the United States as well as abroad, are performed using metric units. In these units distance is usually measured in millimeters, centimeters, meters or kilometers; mass is measured in grams or kilograms; and time is measured in seconds, minutes, or hours. In metric units the abbreviation *cgs,* means *centimeter, gram, second,* and *mks,* means *meter, kilogram, second.*

The English system, as already referred to, uses the foot, yard, and mile as units of length; the ounce, pound, and ton as units of force; and the second as the unit of time. We Americans inherit the English system with all of its cumbersome fractions, and because it is so firmly ingrained in our civil life it will be a difficult task to ever change over completely to the simpler metric system. There is a strong movement today, however, advocating such a change.

The chief advantage of metric units over English units is that all units are divided into ten or one hundred parts. This enables fractional distances and masses to be expressed as decimals. Decimals, it is well known, are easier to manipulate in the addition, subtraction, multiplication, and division of two or more quantities.

2.6. Abbreviated System of Numbers. In speaking of the size and shape of an object or the time interval between the occurrence of two events it is convenient to express very large numbers and very small decimals in an abbreviated form. This is done principally to conserve time and space. It is convenient for the astronomer in the study of stars on the one hand and the physicist and chemist in the study of atoms on the other. The abbreviations in common use are based upon powers of ten as follows:

$$10 = 10^1 \qquad\qquad 1 = 10^0$$
$$100 = 10^2 \qquad\qquad 0.1 = 10^{-1}$$
$$1000 = 10^3 \qquad\qquad 0.01 = 10^{-2}$$
$$10,000 = 10^4 \qquad\qquad 0.001 = 10^{-3}$$
$$100,000 = 10^5 \qquad\qquad 0.0001 = 10^{-4}$$
$$1,000,000 = 10^6 \qquad\qquad 0.00001 = 10^{-5}$$

The abbreviated form on the right side of each equation is mathematically correct. For example

$$10^3 = 10 \times 10 \times 10 = 1000$$

and

$$10^{-3} = \frac{1}{10^3} = \frac{1}{1000} = 0.001.$$

In every case *the exponent is seen to give directly the number of digits the decimal point is moved from unity,* positive integers specifying the number of places the decimal point is moved to the right to make large numbers, and negative integers specifying the number of places it is moved to the left to make small fractions. To illustrate the use of this system suppose we say that a truck weighs three million grams. This can be written

$$3,000,000 \text{ gm} = 3 \times 1,000,000 \text{ gm} = 3 \times 10^6 \text{ gm}.$$

In the abbreviated notation the mass is therefore written 3×10^6 gm. If more than one numeral occurs any one of several abbreviations might be written. For example. in the case of large numbers,

$$840,000,000 = 84 \times 10,000,000 = 84 \times 10^7$$

or, $$840,000,000 = 8.4 \times 100,000,000 = 8.4 \times 10^8.$$

In the case of small numbers, on the other hand,

$$0.0024 = 2.4 \times 10^{-3}, \text{ or } 24 \times 10^{-4}.$$

To illustrate the advantages of this abbreviated notation the mass of the *earth* and the mass of an *electron* are found by experiment to be as follows:

$$\text{mass of the earth, } m = 5.97 \times 10^{24} \text{ kg}$$
$$\text{mass of an electron, } m = 9.11 \times 10^{-31} \text{ kg.}$$

If these are written down in complete decimal form they would appear as follows:

mass of the earth = 5,970,000,000,000,000,000,000,000 kg
mass of the electron = 0.000,000,000,000,000,000,000,000,000,000,911 kg.

2.7. Multiplication and Division of Large and Small Numbers.
The multiplication and division of large and small numbers in the abbreviated notation involves the addition and subtraction of exponents.

Rule 1. When a power number is changed from numerator to denominator, or vice versa, the sign of the exponent is changed. For example,

$$\frac{5}{2 \times 10^{-6}} \text{ equals } \frac{5 \times 10^6}{2}.$$

Rule 2. When two power numbers are multiplied their exponents are added. For example

$$3 \times 10^5 \times 2 \times 10^4 = 3 \times 2 \times 10^{5+4} = 6 \times 10^9.$$

Again:

$$3 \times 10^{17} \times 2 \times 10^{-12} = 3 \times 2 \times 10^{17-12} = 6 \times 10^5.$$

Rule 3. When two power numbers are divided, their exponents are subtracted. For example

$$\frac{8 \times 10^9}{2 \times 10^4} = \frac{8 \times 10^{9-4}}{2} = 4 \times 10^5.$$

Again

$$\frac{6 \times 10^{-7}}{3 \times 10^{-2}} = \frac{6 \times 10^{-7+2}}{3} = 2 \times 10^{-5}.$$

PROBLEMS

1. Find the sum of 5 yards and 3 meters in (a) yards, (b) meters, and (c) centimeters.

2. Find the sum of 208 inches and 629 cm in (a) yards, (b) meters, and (c) centimeters. (*Ans.* (a) 12.66 yds. (b) 11.57 m. (c) 1157 cm.)

3. Find the difference between 10 mi and 20 km in (a) miles, (b) kilometers.

4. Find the difference between 10 km and 7 mi in (a) miles, (b) kilometers. (*Ans.* (a) 0.786 mi. (b) 1.265 km.)

5. Calculate the distance to the moon in m if the distance is 239,000 miles. Express your answer in powers of ten.

6. Calculate the distance to the sun in centimeters if the distance is 90,000,000 miles. (*Ans.* 1.448×10^{13} cm.)

7. If a one pound weight were made only of particles having the mass of an electron, of how many particles would it be composed?

8. The sun's mass is 1.98×10^{33} grams. To how many earth masses is this equivalent? (*Ans.* 3.32×10^{5}.)

9. Calculate the number of seconds in one week and express the answer in powers of ten.

10. Calculate the number of seconds in a life span of 70 years, and express the answer in powers of ten. (*Ans.* 2.21×10^{9} sec.)

11. Solve each of the following equations for x. (a) $\dfrac{x}{a} = \dfrac{2y}{b}$, (b) $\dfrac{x}{a} = \dfrac{2y + 2}{b}$, (c) $\dfrac{5x}{y} = \dfrac{2a}{b}$, (d) $\dfrac{y}{x} = \dfrac{a}{b}$, (e) $\dfrac{a + b}{2} = \dfrac{y}{x}$.

12. Solve each of the following equations for v. (a) $\dfrac{v}{w} = \dfrac{5s}{r}$, (b) $\dfrac{v}{s} = \dfrac{2w + 6}{5r}$, (c) $\dfrac{2v}{p} = \dfrac{s + r}{2w}$, (d) $\dfrac{p}{2v} = \dfrac{q}{s + w}$, (e) $\dfrac{s}{r} = \dfrac{w}{x + v}$.

13. Solve each of the following and give each answer in powers of ten. (a) $3 \times 10^{5} \times 10^{6}$, (b) $2.5 \times 10^{4} \div 5 \times 10^{-2}$, (c) $3.9 \times 10^{8} \times 5 \times 10^{-3}$, (d) $4.2 \times 10^{-6} \div 7 \times 10^{-2}$, (e) $6 \times 10^{-2} \div 1.5 \times 10^{4}$.

14. Solve each of the following and give each answer in powers of ten. (a) $3.2 \times 10^{5} \times 6.0 \times 10^{2}$, (b) $4.2 \times 10^{3} \div 2.0 \times 10^{-2}$, (c) $8.6 \times 10^{6} \times 5 \times 10^{-2}$, (d) $6 \times 10^{-6} \div 1.2 \times 10^{-2}$, (e) $12 \times 10^{-3} \div 3 \times 10^{4}$. (*Ans.* (a) 1.92×10^{8}, (b) 2.1×10^{5}, (c) 4.3×10^{5}, (d) 5×10^{-4}, (e) 4×10^{-7}.)

15. Solve each of the following and give each answer in powers of ten. (a) $4 \times 10^{-2} \times 3.2 \times 10^{6} \div 8 \times 10^{4}$, (b) $2.2 \times 10^{-3} \times 5 \times 10^{-2} \div (4 \times 10^{2} \times 5 \times 10^{-4})$, (c) $9.2 \times 10^{6} \times 3 \times 10^{7} \div 6 \times 10^{-8}$, (d) $3.4 \times 10^{-5} \times 2.8 \times 10^{-2} \div 8 \times 10^{7}$.

16. In performing a certain laboratory experiment the following measurements were made: $W = 25$ lb, $h = 32$ ft, and $t = 40$ sec. If the known physical law concerning this experiment is expressed by the algebraic equation $P = Wh/t$, find the value of P. (*Ans.* $P = 20$ lb-ft/sec.)

17. The following measurements were made in a laboratory experiment: $m = 8$ kg, $s = 6$ m, and $t = 4$ sec. If the known physical law concerning this experiment is expressed by the algebraic equation $F = ms/t^{2}$, find the value of F.

Velocity and Speed   Chapter 3

MECHANICS is defined as that branch of physics dealing with the *motions* or *states* of material bodies. It is generally divided into two parts, the first called *kinematics,* dealing with various kinds of motion, and the second called *dynamics,* dealing with the causes for changes in motion. Dynamics is further divided into two parts, *statics* and *kinetics.*

While statics deals with bodies in a state of equilibrium, a condition brought about by balanced forces, kinetics deals with changes in motion brought about by one or more unbalanced forces. As an introduction to the kinematics of motion, the elementary concepts of *velocity* and *speed* will first be taken up.

3.1. Velocity. *Velocity is defined as the rate of change of position.* Since by *change in position* of a body is meant the distance traveled, this definition of velocity can be written

$$\text{velocity} = \frac{\text{distance traveled}}{\text{time}}. \tag{3a}$$

As an algebraic equation

$$v = \frac{s}{t} \tag{3b}$$

where v is the velocity, s the distance traveled, and t the elapsed time.

Change of position is illustrated in Fig. 3A. A car traveling with uniform velocity along a straight line passes the point A at one instant and the point

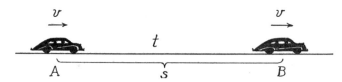

FIG. 3A—Diagram of a body moving with constant velocity.

B at some later instant of time. In substituting in Eq. (3b) the distance traveled is AB, and the time interval between A and B is time t.

Example 1. A man takes 2 hr to drive his car to a distant city 120 mi due East. What is his velocity?

Solution. Here the distance traveled $s = 120$ mi, and the time interval $t = 2$ hr. The velocity therefore is

$$v = \frac{120 \text{ mi}}{2 \text{ hr}} = 60 \frac{\text{mi}}{\text{hr}} . \tag{3c}$$

The answer is *60 mi/hr due East.* The units are just as important as the numbers and must be included in the answer.

If in the answer to the above example the time 1 hr in the denominator is replaced by its equivalent of 3600 sec, a velocity of 60 mi/hr becomes,

$$v = 60 \frac{\text{mi}}{\text{hr}} = 60 \frac{\text{mi}}{3600 \text{ sec}} = 0.0167 \frac{\text{mi}}{\text{sec}} . \tag{3d}$$

If at the same time the distance 1 mi in the numerator is replaced by its equivalent of 5280 ft,

$$v = 60 \frac{\text{mi}}{\text{hr}} = 60 \frac{5280 \text{ ft}}{3600 \text{ sec}} = 88 \frac{\text{ft}}{\text{sec}} . \tag{3e}$$

All three of the answers above, 60 mi/hr, 0.0167 mi/sec and 88 ft/sec, are exactly equal; they are only expressed in different units. This last derived result that 60 mi/hr is equivalent to 88 ft/sec should be memorized, as it is very useful in the solving of many practical problems. A velocity of 120 mi/hr, for example, is equivalent to 2×88 or 176 ft/sec, while a velocity of 30 mi/hr is equivalent to $\frac{1}{2} \times 88$ or 44 ft/sec.

Example 2. A toy train running along a straight track at constant velocity requires 8 sec to travel a distance of 20 m. Find the velocity.

Solution. Since $s = 20$ m and $t = 8$ sec, the velocity

$$v = \frac{20 \text{ m}}{8 \text{ sec}} = 2.5 \frac{\text{m}}{\text{sec}} .$$

The answer is read *two point five meters per second.* To change this answer to centimeters per second the unit 1 m in the numerator is changed to 100 cm, and the answer becomes

$$v = 2.5 \frac{\text{m}}{\text{sec}} = 2.5 \frac{100 \text{ cm}}{\text{sec}} = 250 \frac{\text{cm}}{\text{sec}} .$$

3.2. Distance Traveled. If the velocity of a body is known, the distance traveled can be calculated for any given interval of time. For such problems Eq.(3b) is conveniently changed by solving for s. Multiplying both sides of the equation by t does not alter the equality.

$$vt = \frac{st}{t} .$$

Canceling t's on the right-hand side gives $vt = s$, or

$$s = vt \tag{3f}$$

Example 3. If a body moves with a velocity of 45 cm/sec how far will it travel in 2 min?

Solution. The distance traveled can be determined by Eq.(3f).

$$s = 45 \frac{cm}{sec} \times 2 \text{ min} = 90 \frac{cm \cdot min}{sec} \, .$$

In order to eliminate *time* units in this answer they must both be expressed in the same units. To do this, the minutes may be changed to seconds as follows:

$$s = 45 \frac{cm}{sec} \times 120 \text{ sec} = 5400 \text{ cm}.$$

Note that *sec* in the numerator cancels *sec* in the denominator, leaving *cm* in the answer as the unit of length. This illustrates a common practice that should be followed in the solving of all problems. Always express like quantities in the same units.

Dividing both sides of Eq.(3f) by v and canceling the v's on the right-hand side, gives

$$t = \frac{s}{v} \tag{3g}$$

an equation for the time of travel in terms of s and t.

Example 4. If a car travels with an average velocity of 30 mi/hr, how long will it take to go 175 mi?

Solution. Using Eq.(3g),

$$t = \frac{s}{v} = \frac{175 \text{ mi}}{30 \text{ mi/hr}} = 5.83 \text{ hr}.$$

3.3. Vectors and Scalars. Nearly all physical measurements, whether they are made with the simplest of instruments or with the most complex of apparatus, may be classified as *vector* or *scalar* quantities. *Measurable quantities that have magnitude and direction are called vectors.* Examples of vector quantities are *displacement, velocity, acceleration,* and *force. Measurable quantities that have magnitude only are called scalars.* Examples of scalar quantities are *volume, area,* and *mass.*

The importance of this seemingly trivial distinction between quantities that have direction and those which do not, is realized when in solving certain problems the simple process of the addition of two or more like quantities becomes necessary.

No difficulty is generally encountered with scalars since such quantities are added algebraically. For example, in the addition of volumes, the sum of 2 gallons and 3 gallons is 5 gallons. The addition of two vectors, on the other hand, is more complicated and requires a special process called *vector addition,* and will be treated in detail in Chap. 7.

3.4. Speed and Velocity. The terms *speed* and *velocity* are often used synonymously. Strictly speaking, however, *speed is a scalar quantity* and *velocity is a vector quantity.* In the last section it was explained that vector quantities have magnitude and direction while scalars have magnitude only.

Speed is a term applied only to the magnitude of velocity and does not specify the direction of motion. In moving along a straight line, *speed* and *velocity* are numerically equal to each other. If, however, the speed along a curved path is constant, the velocity is not considered to be constant because of its changing direction.

When a body moves with constant speed along a straight line whose direction is specified, it is customary to speak of its *velocity.* Moving along a straight or curved path, with no reference being made to direction, it is proper to speak of its *speed.*

Speed and velocity always have the *dimensions* of *length divided by time,* i.e., L/T.

TABLE 3A. CONVERSION FACTORS FOR SPEED AND VELOCITY

Velocity	m/sec	ft/sec	km/hr	mi/hr	Knots
1 m/sec =	1	3.281	3.600	2.240	1.940
1 ft/sec =	0.30480	1	1.0973	0.6818	0.5921
1 km/hr =	0.27778	0.9113	1	0.6214	0.5396
1 mi/hr =	0.44704	1.4667	1.6093	1	0.8684
1 knot =	0.51480	1.689	1.853	1.152	1

Example 5. Change 30 mi/hr to kilometers per hour.

Solution. From the table, 1 mi/hr in the left-hand column is (read across to the fourth column) equal to 1.6093 km/hr. Therefore,

$$30 \times 1.6093 = 48.279 \ \frac{\text{km}}{\text{hr}}.$$

Dropping off the last two figures gives the answer to three significant figures as

$$30 \ \frac{\text{mi}}{\text{hr}} = 48.3 \ \frac{\text{km}}{\text{hr}}.$$

The *knot* is a nautical unit of speed, about 15% larger than speed in miles per hour. It is *not* correct to say the speed of a ship is 10 knots/hr; it is correct to say the speed is 10 knots.

3.5. Constant and Variable Velocity. In mechanics it is often convenient to neglect the size and shape of a body and to consider its motion as that of a small *particle* of negligible size. For example, in describing the motion of an airplane flying between two cities, it is not necessary to give a detailed description of the plane to give its position and progress. Hence, it is customary to speak of the motion of a body as the motion of particle.

If the statement is made that a particle travels 30 mi in 1 hr it does not necessarily mean that its speed or velocity is constant. Moving due East in a straight line, the particle either moved with a *constant velocity* or with a *variable velocity*. A constant velocity is defined as one in which equal displacements are traversed in equal intervals of time and the direction is at all times that of the same straight line. In other words, the distance traveled in any 1 sec is equal to that traveled in any other second.

A particle has a *variable velocity* when in equal intervals of time, its displacements are unequal. In such cases it is customary to speak of the *average velocity*. Average velocity, $\bar{v}$, is defined by,

$$\bar{v} = \frac{s}{t}, \tag{3h}$$

where t is the total time required to travel the total distance s.

3.6. Curvilinear Motion. Motion along a curved path is called curvilinear motion. When a particle moves along a curved path as shown in Fig. 3B, it may have a constant or variable speed. The term *speed* is used here in place of velocity since the path is not straight. A *constant speed* is defined as one in which the distances traveled in equal intervals of time are equal, the distances being measured along the curved path.

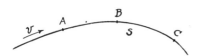

FIG. 3B—Motion along a curved path.

A *variable speed* means that the distances traveled in equal intervals of time are different. It follows from these definitions, by comparison with those for linear motion in the preceding section, that all of the equations in this Chapter apply equally well to constant and average speed.

3.7. Instantaneous Velocity. In describing the curvilinear motion of a particle, it sometimes becomes necessary to specify its *instantaneous velocity*. As shown in Fig. 3C, the instantaneous velocity of a particle at any given point in its path is obtained by drawing a tangent to the curve at the point in question. The magnitude of the instantaneous velocity is equal to the speed of the particle as it passes that point and the direction is that of the tangent to the curve at that point.

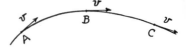

FIG. 3C—Arrows indicate instantaneous velocity.

PROBLEMS

1. An airplane in a steep dive moves with a speed of 570 mi/hr. Compute its speed in (a) ft/sec, (b) km/hr, and (c) knots.

2. A ship sailing from San Francisco to Hawaii makes the trip of 2300 miles in $4\frac{1}{2}$ days. What is its average speed in (a) mi/hr, (b) km/hr, and (c) knots? (*Ans.* (a) 21.3 mi/hr, (b) 34.3 km/hr, (c) 18.5 knots.)

3. It takes a farmer 3 hr to walk the full length of the fence surrounding his farm one mile square. Calculate his average speed in (a) mi/hr, (b) ft/sec, and (c) cm/sec.

4. A circular racetrack is 1500 ft in diameter. A car makes 100 laps around the track in 56 min. Calculate the average speed in (a) mi/hr, (b) ft/sec, and (c) km/hr. (*Ans.* (a) 95.6 mi/hr, (b) 140.25 ft/sec, (c) 154 km/hr.)

5. In a track-meet the 100 yd dash was won in the time of 9.4 sec. Calculate the average speed in (a) ft/sec, and mi/hr.

6. In the Olympic games the 100 meter dash was won in the time of 10.0 sec. Calculate the average speed in (a) ft/sec, and (b) mi/hr. (*Ans.* (a) 32.81 ft/sec, (b) 22.4 mi/hr.)

7. How long will it take a ship traveling at 20 knots to go 525 mi?

8. How long will it take a ship traveling at 25 knots to go 2200 mi? (*Ans.* 3 days 4 hr and 25 min.)

9. A world record in the 10,000 meter run was set in 1924 by P. Nurmi of Finland in the time of 30 min $6\frac{1}{2}$ sec. Calculate his average speed in (a) mi/hr, and (b) ft/sec.

10. In the Olympic games of 1928 the following races were run in the respective times, (a) 100 m in $10\frac{3}{5}$ sec, (b) 200 m in $21\frac{3}{5}$ sec, (c) 400 m in $47\frac{3}{5}$ sec, (d) 800 m in 1 min $51\frac{4}{5}$ sec, (e) 1500 m in 3 min $53\frac{1}{5}$ sec, (f) 5000 m in 14 min $31\frac{1}{5}$ sec, (g) 10,000 m in 30 min $18\frac{4}{5}$ sec, and (h) 15,000 m in 46 min $49\frac{3}{5}$ sec. Calculate the average speed of each in mi/hr. (*Ans.* (a) 21.1 mi/hr, (b) 20.8 mi/hr, (c) 18.8 mi/hr, (d) 16.0 mi/hr, (e) 14.4 mi/hr, (f) 12.9 mi/hr, (g) 12.3 mi/hr, (h) 11.9 mi/hr.

11. Make a graph of the answers in Prob. 10, plotting average speeds vertically and the logarithms of the distances horizontally.

12. Find the cruising range of a plane if its fuel tank contains only 30 gal of gasoline. Assume that at a cruising speed of 80 mi/hr the fuel consumption is 8 gal/hr. (*Ans.* 300 mi).

13. In the Olympic Games of 1936 the marathon, covering a course of 26 mi and 385 yd, was won by Kitei, a Japanese boy of 21 years, in the time of 2 hr, 29 min., 19.2 sec. What was his average speed in mi/hr?

14. An automobile, leaving an airport, averages 45 mi/hr along a straight highway. If a plane leaves the same airport 1 hr later and travels at a rate of 120 mi/hr, (a) how much time will be required for it to overtake the autombile? (b) What will be the distance traveled? (*Ans.* (a) 36 min, (b) 72 mi.)

15. A person drives a car 200 mi at an average speed of 44 mi/hr. What must be his average speed for the next 220 mi if he is to cover the total distance in 9 hr?

16. How much longer would it take to trave a distance of 420 mi at a speed of 45 mi/hr than it would at a speed of 60 mi/hr? (*Ans.* 2 hr and 20 min.)

Acceleration   Chapter 4

4.1. Uniform Acceleration. Whenever the speed or velocity of a body changes, the motion is described as an acceleration. Acceleration is defined as *the rate of change of velocity.* A car "picking up speed" has a *positive acceleration,* while another slowing down has a *negative acceleration.* Standing still or moving with constant velocity a car has no acceleration.

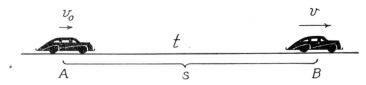

FIG. 4A—A car is accelerated for a period of t seconds.

Consider as an illustration of accelerated motion the car shown in Fig. 4A. Due to a constantly acting force, exerted by the motor through the drive wheels, this car is constantly accelerated as it moves along the straight line AB. As it passes A it has a relatively low velocity v_0, while farther along its path at a point B it is moving faster and has a velocity v. The *initial velocity* is called v_0 and the *final velocity* is called v.

If the time required to go from A to B is t, the acceleration, by the definition given above, is schematically written.

$$\text{acceleration} = \frac{\text{final velocity} - \text{initial velocity}}{\text{time}}$$

or algebraically as,

$$a = \frac{v - v_0}{t}. \tag{4a}$$

Example 1. Suppose at A, in Fig. 4A, that the velocity of the car is 20 ft/sec, that at B it has increased to 40 ft/sec, and that it takes 4 sec to go from A to B. What is the acceleration?

Solution. By direct substitution in Eq.(4a), we obtain,

$$a = \frac{40 \text{ ft/sec} - 20 \text{ ft/sec}}{4 \text{ sec}} = \frac{20 \text{ ft/sec}}{4 \text{ sec}} = 5 \frac{\text{ft}}{\text{sec sec}}.$$

24

The answer is read *five feet per second per second* and means that the velocity increases 5 ft/sec every second of time. Initially the velocity is 20 ft/sec. An increase of 5 ft/sec means that at the end of 1 sec the velocity is 25 ft/sec, at the end of 2 sec it is 30 ft/sec, at the end of 3 sec it is 35 ft/sec, and at the end of 4 sec it is 40 ft/sec. A constant acceleration is, therefore, one in which *the velocity changes by equal amounts each second*.

When a body is slowing down, the initial velocity is greater than the final velocity, and the acceleration, as given by Eq.(4a) is negative.

Example 2. In going up a long steep hill a car slows down from 60 mi/hr to 30 mi/hr in 2 min. Find the acceleration.

Solution. Substitute the foregoing values in Eq.(4a); then

$$a = \frac{30 \text{ mi/hr} - 60 \text{ mi/hr}}{2 \text{ min}} = -15 \frac{\text{mi}}{\text{hr min}}.$$

The velocity thus decreases by 15 mi/hr each minute of time. During the first minute it drops from 60 mi/hr to 45 mi/hr, and during the next minute from 45 mi/hr to 30 mi/hr.

The above answer, as written, has two different units of time in the denominator. It can be left this way or changed to the same units as follows. Replacing 1 hr in the denominator by its equality, 60 min, gives

$$a = -15 \frac{\text{mi}}{60 \text{ min min}} = -0.25 \frac{\text{mi}}{\text{min}^2}.$$

To express this answer in feet and seconds, 1 mi in the numerator is replaced by its equivalent, 5280 ft, and $(1 \text{ min})^2$ in the denominator by $(60 \text{ sec})^2$, to give

$$a = -0.25 \frac{5280 \text{ ft}}{3600 \text{ sec}^2} = -0.367 \frac{\text{ft}}{\text{sec}^2}.$$

This answer is read *minus zero point three six seven feet per second per second*.

4.2. Final Velocity. By transposing Eq.(4a) the formula for acceleration takes on a different aspect. If both sides of the equation are multiplied by t, the two t's on the right side cancel, and there results

$$v - v_0 = at.$$

Transposing v_0 to the other side of the equation,

$$v = v_0 + at. \qquad (4b)$$

Here the final velocity of a body is given as the sum of two terms, the initial velocity v_0 plus the increase in velocity at.

Example 3. A particle with an initial velocity of 50 cm/sec is subject to an acceleration of 8 cm/sec² for 5 sec. What is its final velocity?

Solution. Use Eq.(4b). The known quantities for direct substitution are, $v_0 = 50$ cm/sec, $a = 8$ cm/sec², and $t = 5$ sec.

$$v = 50 \frac{cm}{sec} + 8 \frac{cm}{sec^2} \times 5 \ sec = 50 \frac{cm}{sec} + 40 \frac{cm}{sec} = 90 \frac{cm}{sec} .$$

Note that the product *at* has the dimensions of a velocity; *length* divided by *time*. It can therefore be added to v_0 because it is expressed in the same units (*cm* divided by *sec*). It is a rule well worth remembering when solving a problem by the substitution of known quantities in an equation, that quantities can be added or subtracted only when they are like quantities; that is, they have the same dimensions and the same units.

4.3. Starting from Rest. When a body starting from rest undergoes a constant acceleration the initial velocity v_0 as given in Eq.(4a) is zero, i.e., $v_0 = 0$. The acceleration a is then given by the special equation

$$a = \frac{v}{t} . \tag{4c}$$

Transposed, this takes the form

$$v = at. \tag{4d}$$

Example 4. An airplane starting from rest at one end of a runway acquires its take off speed of 60 mi/hr in 8 sec. What is its acceleration?

Solution. The acceleration is obtained from Eq.(4c).

$$a = \frac{60 \ mi/hr}{8 \ sec} = 7.5 \frac{mi}{hr \ sec} .$$

The answer is read *seven point five miles per hour per second.*

Remembering that 60 mi/hr is equivalent to 88 ft/sec, this same acceleration can be expressed as

$$a = \frac{88 \ ft/sec}{8 \ sec} = 11 \frac{ft}{sec^2} .$$

read *eleven feet per second per second.*

4.4. Average Velocity. While the velocity of an accelerated body is continually changing, the distance traveled in any given time t may be described in terms of its *average velocity*. The average velocity of a particle moving with constant acceleration is given by

$$\bar{v} = \frac{v + v_0}{2} . \tag{4e}$$

The bar over the v indicates an average value. The equation $s = vt$ already given in Chap. 3 to hold for constant velocity also holds for constant acceleration if v is replaced by $\bar{v}$. Thus

$$s = \bar{v}t \qquad \text{or} \qquad s = \frac{v + v_0}{2} t. \tag{4f}$$

Example 5. If 5 sec are required to increase the velocity of a particle from 2 m/sec to 5 m/sec, what are (a) the average velocity, and (b) the distance traveled?

Solution. The given quantities are $t = 5$ sec, $v_0 = 2$ m/sec, and $v = 5$ m/sec. By direct substitution in Eq.(4e),

$$\bar{v} = \frac{5 \text{ m/sec} + 2 \text{ m/sec}}{2} = \frac{7 \text{ m/sec}}{2} = 3.5 \frac{\text{m}}{\text{sec}}.$$

Substitute this answer in Eq.(4f). Then

$$s = \bar{v}t = 3.5 \frac{\text{m}}{\text{sec}} \times 5 \text{ sec} = 17.5 \text{ m}.$$

For the special case of a body starting from rest, $v_0 = 0$; and Eq.(4e) for the average velocity becomes

$$\bar{v} = \frac{v}{2} \tag{4g}$$

4.5 Derived Equations. By combining Eq.(4a) above with Eq.(4f), a new and useful equation is obtained. To do this each of the two equations is solved for t and then set equal to each other as follows:

Eq.(4a) is first transposed and then Eq.(4f) to give

$$t = \frac{v - v_0}{a} \qquad \text{and} \qquad t = \frac{2s}{v + v_0}$$

Since the left-hand sides are both equal to t, the right-hand sides must be equal to each other. By setting them equal and then cross-multiplying, we obtain

$$\frac{v - v_0}{a} = \frac{2s}{v + v_0}, \qquad\qquad (v - v_0)(v + v_0) = 2as.$$

By multiplying out and transposing, we get

$$v^2 - v_0^2 = 2as. \qquad\qquad v^2 = v_0^2 + 2as. \tag{4h}$$

Another useful equation is obtained by eliminating v from the same two original equations. From Eqs.(4a) and (4f) we get separately

$$v = v_0 + at \qquad \text{and} \qquad v = \frac{2s}{t} - v_0.$$

If the right-hand sides of these two equations are set equal to each other, and if v_0 is transposed to the right-hand side,

$$\frac{2s}{t} - v_0 = v_0 + at. \qquad\qquad \frac{2s}{t} = 2v_0 + at.$$

Multiplying through by $t/2$ gives

$$s = v_0 t + \tfrac{1}{2}at^2. \tag{4i}$$

These equations (4h) and (4i) are called *derived equations*. They give no additional information to that given by Eqs.(4a) and (4f); they are only rearrangements of the same quantities. In their new form, however, they are more readily applied to certain types of problems.

For special cases where a body is initially at rest, $v_0 = 0$, Eqs.(4h) and (4i) become

$$v^2 = 2as \tag{4j}$$

and

$$s = \tfrac{1}{2}at^2. \tag{4k}$$

Example 6. A train is making 15 mi/hr when the throttle is suddenly opened full and kept open for a distance of 1 mi. If the acceleration is 0.5 ft/sec², what is the final velocity?

Solution. Since a velocity of 60 mi/hr is equivalent to 88 ft/sec, the given velocity of 15 mi/hr is equivalent to 22 ft/sec. By direct substitution in Eq.(4h), we obtain

$$v^2 = (22 \text{ ft/sec})^2 + 2 \times 0.5 \text{ ft/sec}^2 \times 5280 \text{ ft}$$
$$v^2 = 484 \text{ ft}^2/\text{sec}^2 + 5280 \text{ ft}^2/\text{sec}^2 = 5764 \text{ ft}^2/\text{sec}^2$$
$$v = 76 \text{ ft/sec}, \qquad \text{or } v = 51.8 \text{ mi/hr}.$$

4.6. Acceleration Down an Inclined Plane. A study of acceleration, and an experimental proof of the formulas given above, may be made with an inclined plane. In Fig. 4B a marble is shown rolling down a groove in the

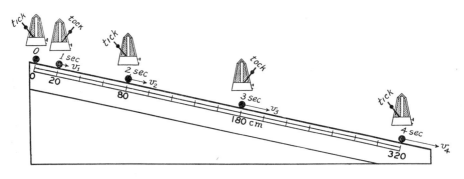

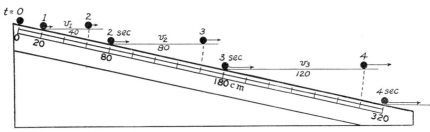

Fig. 4B—Diagram of an inclined-plane experiment showing the numerical distances traveled by a marble for each second of time as it rolls down the plane.

top of a long inclined plane. As the marble moves down with ever-increasing speed, its position is noted at each tick of a *metronome,* or *seconds clock.* In the particular experiment, diagramed here, the angle of the plane has been adjusted so that the distance traveled in the first second is 20 cm. After two seconds the total distance traveled is then measured and found to be 80 cm. After 3 sec, it is 180 cm. etc. These measurements, when tabulated for the first 5 sec, appear as in the first two columns of Table 4A.

TABLE 4A. EXPERIMENTAL AND CALCULATED VALUES DETERMINED FROM THE INCLINED PLANE EXPERIMENT SHOWN IN FIG. 4B

Time t sec	Distance s cm	Velocity v cm/sec	$\dfrac{v}{t}$	at	$\dfrac{s}{t^2}$	t^2	$\dfrac{1}{2}at^2$
0	0	0	—	0	—	0	0
1	20	40	40	40	20	1	20
2	80	80	40	80	20	4	80
3	180	120	40	120	20	9	180
4	320	160	40	160	20	16	320
5	500	200	40	200	20	25	500

To find the velocity attained at the end of each second, a shorter horizontal track is placed first in position 1, then at 2, 3, 4, etc. In each of these positions the distance traveled along the horizontal track in one second is a direct measure of the velocity acquired from the incline. Thus, at the end of one second the velocity is 40 cm/sec, at the end of 2 sec the velocity is 80 cm/sec, etc. These measured values from the experiment are tabulated in column three.

A careful study of the first and third columns shows that the velocity v is directly proportional to the time t.

$$v \propto t.$$

To write this as an algebraic equation, the proportionality sign is replaced by a constant k.

$$v = kt. \tag{4l}$$

The value of k can be determined from the experiment as follows. Divide each value of v in the third column by the corresponding time t in the first column and obtain 40 cm/sec^2 as a common answer. Therefore, $k = 40$ cm/sec^2 and

$$v = 40t. \tag{4m}$$

Referring to Eq.(4d) at the beginning of this chapter, it is seen that the constant 40 is none other than the *acceleration*. In other words it is the increase in velocity per second of time. Each second, the marble on the incline increases its velocity by 40 cm/sec. By replacing 40 in Eq.(4m) by *a*, we find

$$v = at$$

the Eq.(4d).

To find a relation for the distance traveled along the inclined plane, it is observed that *s* in the second column is proportional to the square of *t* listed in the seventh column.

$$s \propto t^2, \quad \text{or} \quad s = kt^2.$$

To find the constant of proportionality *k*, each distance *s* when divided by the corresponding value of t^2 gives 20 cm/sec² as shown in column six. Since this is just half of the acceleration, we may write $\frac{1}{2}a$ for the constant *k* and obtain

$$s = \tfrac{1}{2}at^2.$$

This is the same as Eq.(4k).

PROBLEMS

1. A racing car starting from rest acquires a speed of 100 mi/hr in 8 sec. What is its acceleration and how far did it travel during this time?

2. A train starts from rest and after a constant acceleration for 75 sec acquires a speed of 60 mi/hr. (a) What is the acceleration in ft/sec², and (b) how far does it travel during this time? (*Ans.* (a) 1.173 ft/sec², (b) 3300 ft.)

3. An airplane with a speed of 200 mi/hr goes into a power glide and acquires a speed of 350 mi/hr in 6 sec. Find (a) the acceleration in mi/hr sec, and (b) the distance traveled during this time.

4. A truck with a speed of 15 mi/hr at the top of a long grade starts coasting down and acquires a speed of 60 mi/hr in 30 sec. Assuming constant acceleration find (a) the acceleration in mi/hr sec, and (b) the distance traveled in mi during this time. (*Ans.* (a) 1.5 mi/hr sec, (b) 0.312 mi.)

5. The engine of a train 1000 ft long stands at a road crossing. If the train starts up with an acceleration of 0.25 ft/sec² how long must the motorist wait for the end of the train to cross the intersection?

6. A truck starting from rest maintains a constant acceleration of 0.50 ft/sec². How long will it take the truck to go 1 mi? (*Ans.* 145.3 sec.)

7. A man, driving a car with an initial speed of 60 mi/hr, suddenly applies the brakes bringing the car to a stop in 5 sec. Find (a) the acceleration, (b) the total distance traveled, (c) the speed at the end of 3 sec, and (d) the distance traveled during the first 3 sec.

8. A train, moving 60 mi/hr, is brought to a stop in 32 sec by the sudden application of the brakes. Calculate (a) the acceleration, (b) the total distance traveled after the brakes are applied, (c) the velocity at the end of 10 sec, and (d) the distance traveled during the first 10 sec. (*Ans.* (a) −2.75 ft/sec², (b) 1408 ft, (c) 60.5 ft/sec, (d) 742.5 ft.)

9. A bullet from an army rifle with a barrel 30 in. long has a muzzle velocity of 2600 ft/sec. Find (a) the average speed of the bullet while being accelerated in the gun barrel, (b) the time taken to travel the length of the barrel, and (c) the average acceleration.

10. A passenger car starting from rest has an acceleration of 6 ft/sec² for 11 sec, after which time it continues at constant speed. After 10 sec at this constant speed the brakes are applied bringing the car to rest in 5 sec. Find (a) the constant speed acquired, in mi/hr, and (b) the total distance traveled in ft. (*Ans.* (a) 45 mi/hr, (b) 1188 ft.)

11. A switch engine starting from rest travels with an acceleration of 4 ft/sec² for 6 sec. After traveling with the acquired speed for 13 sec, the brakes are applied, stopping the engine in 4 sec. Find (a) the speed acquired due to the acceleration, (b) the acceleration while the brakes are applied, and (c) the total distance traveled.

12. A rifle bullet with a speed of 900 m/sec strikes the ground and penetrates to a depth of 1 m. Find (a) the average speed while being stopped, (b) the time of stopping, and (c) the acceleration. (*Ans.* (a) 450 m/sec, (b) 0.00222 sec, (c) −405,-000 m/sec².)

13. A box accidentally drops from a truck traveling 30 mi/hr and slides along the ground for a distance of 100 ft. Find (a) the acceleration, (b) the time to come to rest, and (c) the distance traveled the first sec.

14. A marble rolls down an inclined plane acquiring at the end of 5 sec a speed of 0.22 m/sec. Find (a) the acceleration, (b) the total distance traveled, and (c) the distance traveled during the third sec. (*Ans.* (a) 0.044 m/sec², (b) 0.55 m, (c) 0.11 m.)

15. Starting from rest a plane takes off after traveling 3000 ft along a runway. If the plane becomes airborne at speed of 80 mi/hr, find (a) the acceleration, (b) the total time of takeoff, and (c) the distance traveled during the last sec on the ground.

16. A plane coming in for a landing travels a distance of 3500 ft along the runway before coming to rest. Assuming constant acceleration and a landing speed of 75 mi/hr, find (a) the acceleration, (b) the total time for stopping, and (c) the distance traveled during the first 10 sec. (*Ans.* (a) −1.73 ft/sec², (b) 63.6 sec, (c) 1013.6 ft.)

17. A plane starting from rest at the end of a runway maintains a constant acceleration, taking it a distance of 2 ft during the first sec. If the plane becomes airborne at 60 mi/hr (a) what distance is required for takeoff, and (b) what is the total time?

18. In starting from rest, a large ship requires 5 min to acquire its cruising speed of 20 knots. Assuming constant acceleration, calculate (a) the acceleration in knots/hr, and (b) the distance in nautical mi required to reach cruising speed. (*Ans.* (a) 240 knots/hr, (b) 0.833 nautical mi, or 5067 ft.)

19. A jet fighter plane initially at rest is catapulted forward from an aircraft carrier to a speed of 90 mi/hr in 3 sec. Calculate the acceleration in ft/sec².

20. Starting from rest an object A undergoes an acceleration of 2 m/sec². Starting from the same point 4 sec later, object B undergoes an acceleration of 8 m/sec². Find (a) the time required for B to overtake A, and (b) the distance both have traveled. (*Ans.* (a) 4 sec, (b) 64 m.)

21. Starting from rest a locomotive undergoes an acceleration of 2 ft/sec² for 40 sec; then the brakes are applied bringing it to a stop. If the total distance traveled is exactly one-half mile and the total time is exactly 1 min, what was the average acceleration during the time the brakes were applied?

Gravity and Falling Bodies

Chapter 5

NEGLECTING friction, all bodies, large and small, fall with the same acceleration. This, the law of falling bodies, is a physical paradox for it contradicts the conclusion the average person might derive *a priori*. This is not to be wondered at, for centuries ago the great philosopher Aristotle* (384-322 B.C.) taught that heavy bodies fall proportionately faster than lighter ones.

It took the world nearly two thousand years to produce a challenger of Aristotle's scientific teachings. In the year 1590 Galileo † was pondering over the question of falling bodies and found apparent inconsistencies with Aristotle's teachings. As tests, he is said to have dropped various kinds of objects from different levels of the leaning tower of Pisa and to have timed their fall and measured their velocities.

On one occasion, Galileo is alleged to have attracted a large crowd to the leaning tower, where he climbed the spiral staircase to the bell chamber at the top and there through an open archway dropped two stones, one large and one small. These two bodies fell side by side and struck the ground together, thus sounding the deathknell of an old hypothesis and the birth of a new era in science.

Whether this particular incident is true or not, the importance of Galileo's many authentic experiments lies not in the fact that they demonstrated the fallacy of Aristotle's reasoning, but that they presented to the world a new and more reliable scientific method, the method of experimentation.

* Aristotle (384-322 B.C.), famous Greek philosopher, logician, moralist, political thinker, biologist, and founder of literary criticism, spent his early years as a student and fellow worker with Plato. While practically all of Aristotle's teachings concerning physical principles are now known to be erroneous, his contributions to other fields of knowledge have placed him high among the great men of ancient Greece.

† Galileo Galilei (1564-1642), Italian mathematician, astronomer, and experimental physicist. At the early age of twenty-four Galileo wrote a treatise on the center of gravity of solids. This led the following year to his appointment as professor of mathematics at the University of Pisa. A rumor that a Dutch lens grinder had observed that two lenses used together make distant objects appear close at hand led Galileo to construct the first telescope. Successful telescopes of greater and greater magnification enabled him eventually to observe, for the first time, the mountains on the moon, the major satellites of Jupiter, and sunspots. While at Pisa, Galileo carried out many experiments and public demonstrations of principles which laid the foundations of mechanics and the laws of projectiles and falling bodies.

5.1. Gravitation. The principle that all objects fall with the same acceleration can be demonstrated in various ways. One of these is illustrated in Fig. 5A where two steel balls, one large and one small, are supported in the groove of a wooden block 10 or 20 ft above the ground. When the block is tipped by pulling the cord, both balls fall together and strike the ground together. Dropped from a height of 16 ft, the time of fall is just 1 sec. The shaded circles in the figure show the position of the two bodies at the end of each quarter second.

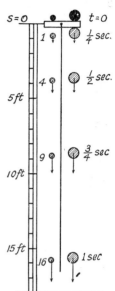

If the balls in the experiment are replaced by two marbles of the same size, one steel and the other wood, they too will fall side by side and strike the ground together. In this case, the steel marble weighs fifteen times as much as the wood. (Density of steel 7.6 gm/cm³: density of wood, 0.5 gm/cm³.)

The question of air friction usually arises in this latter experiment, for careful observation will show that the wooden ball lags ever so slightly behind the steel ball. This lagging due to air friction increases the farther they fall, and is even more pronounced when a still lighter object like a feather or leaf is allowed to fall at the same time. Due to its large surface area, a feather or leaf flutters to the ground, being held back by the large amount of air that must be pushed aside to let it by.

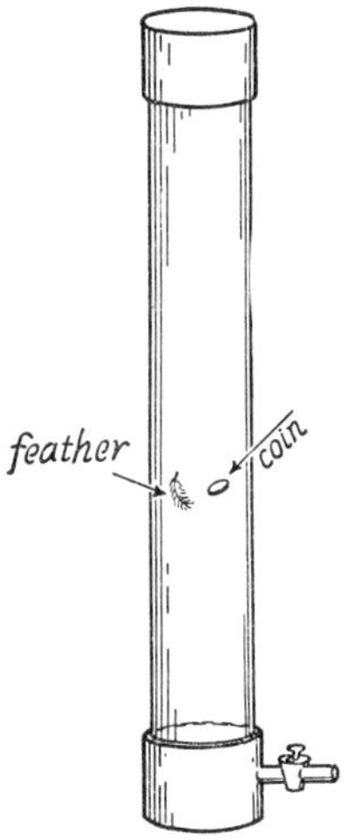

Fig. 5A—All bodies falling freely under the constant pull of gravity fall a distance of 16 ft. in the first second.

In the absence of air, even a feather will fall with the acceleration of a solid steel ball. An experiment illustrating just this is shown in Fig. 5B. A long glass cylinder containing a feather and silver coin is connected by flexible tube to a vacuum pump. If after evacuation the tube is turned upside down, the feather and the coin will be observed to fall together. When the air is once more admitted to the cylinder the feather will again flutter slowly to the bottom. *In the absence of air friction, all bodies fall with the same acceleration.*

Fig. 5B—In a vacuum a feather and a coin fall with the same acceleration and strike the bottom together.

In the treatment of falling bodies given in the remainder of this chapter, air friction is entirely neglected. The formulas presented and used in working problems are known to hold only approximately. In most practical cases, however, the calculated results are so nearly realized experimentally that corrections for air friction need only be made where the distances and velocities involved are large. A detailed discussion of the effects of air friction on falling bodies is given in Chap. 11.

5.2. Free Fall. Many laboratory experiments can be performed to demonstrate the well-established laws of falling bodies. One of these is the inclined plane experiment described at the end of the last chapter. If the angle the plane makes with the horizontal is increased, the acceleration of the ball down the plane will also increase. The velocities as well as the distances traveled will increase in the proper proportions to show that all of the equations summarized at the end of the last chapter are generally valid. This is true even for the limiting angle of 90° where the inclined plane becomes straight up and down and the steel ball falls freely under the full force of gravity.

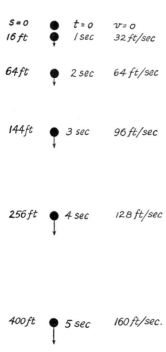

As indicated in Fig. 5C, the measured distance a body falls is 16 ft in the first second; four times sixteen or 64 ft in 2 sec, nine times sixteen or 144 ft in 3 sec, etc. Inserting these distances in Eq.(4k), the constant of acceleration is computed to be $a = 32 \ ft/sec^2$. If the distances are measured in centimeters, the same formula gives the equivalent acceleration as $980 \ cm/sec^2$ or $9.80 \ m/sec^2$.

Fig. 5C—Illustrating the distance and velocity of freely falling bodies at the end of each of the first 5 sec.

5.3. The Acceleration Due to Gravity. Experiments carried on at many points over the earth show that the acceleration due to gravity is not everywhere the same; there are slight variations. While these variations are small and are not of any consequence in most practical problems, they do exist and should be mentioned.

In general, the values of the acceleration due to gravity lie between a minimum of 32.09 ft/sec² or 9.7804 m/sec² at the equator and a maximum of 32.26 ft/sec² or 9.8321 m/sec² at the North and South poles. Referring here to the equator and the poles is only a generalization, for not all points on the equator have the same values as quoted above, nor do all points on any one latitude have the same value. Irregularities of the earth's structure give rise to minute random differences.

The International Committee on Weights and Measures has adopted as a standard or accepted value, 9.80665 m/sec² or 32.174 ft/sec². For practical purposes, however, it is customary to use the even numbered values 9.80 m/sec² and 32 ft/sec², and in formulas for free fall to use the small letter g in place of a as given in the last chapter. For freely falling bodies then

$$g = 980 \text{ cm/sec}^2, \qquad g = 9.80 \text{ m/sec}^2, \quad \text{or} \quad g = 32 \text{ ft/sec}^2,$$

and the equations developed in Chap. 4 to be used are:

General		*Special*	
$v = v_o + at$	(5a)	$v = v_o + gt$	(5a)
$\bar{v} = \dfrac{v + v_o}{2}$	(5b)	$\bar{v} = \dfrac{v + v_o}{2}$	(5b)
$v^2 = v_0^2 + 2as$	(5c)	$v^2 = v_0^2 + 2gs$	(5c)
$s = v_o t + \frac{1}{2} at^2$	(5d)	$s = v_o t + \frac{1}{2} gt^2$	(5d)

Example 1. A boy standing on a bridge 200 ft above a river throws a stone straight downward with a velocity of 50 ft/sec. (a) With what speed will the stone strike the water, and (b) how long will it take to descend?

Solution. To find the answer to (a) use Eq.(5c). The known quantities are $v_o = 50$ ft/sec, $s = 200$ ft, and $g = 32$ ft/sec². Direct substitution gives,

$$v^2 = \left(50 \frac{\text{ft}}{\text{sec}}\right)^2 + 2 \times 32 \frac{\text{ft}}{\text{sec}^2} \times 200 \text{ ft}$$

$$v^2 = 2,500 + 12,800 = 15,300 \text{ ft}^2/\text{sec}^2.$$

If the square root of both sides of the equation is taken, we obtain

$$v = 123.7 \text{ ft/sec.}$$

For the answer to (b) use Eq.(5a). The known quantities are $v = 123.7$ ft/sec, $v_o = 50$ ft/sec, and $g = 32$ ft/sec². By transposing Eq.(5a), we obtain

$$t = \frac{v - v_o}{g}.$$

Then substitute known values in this equation.

$$t = \frac{123.7 \text{ ft/sec} - 50 \text{ ft/sec}}{32 \text{ ft/sec}^2} = \frac{73.7 \text{ ft/sec}}{32 \text{ ft/sec}^2} = 2.3 \text{ sec.}$$

The stone, therefore, hits the water with a speed of 123.7 ft/sec, 2.3 sec after it leaves the boy's hand.

5.4. Projection Straight Upward. When a body is projected straight upward its speed will rapidly diminish until at some point it comes momentarily to rest and then falls back toward the earth, acquiring again at the ground the same speed it had upon projection. Experiment shows that the time taken to rise to the highest point of its trajectory is equal to the time taken to fall from there to the ground. This implies that the upward motions are just the same as the downward motions, but in reverse, and that the time and speed for any point along the path are given by the same equations for free fall, Eqs.(5a), (5b), (5c), and (5d).

In Fig. 5D, a particle is shown projected upward with a velocity of 128 ft/sec. After each second's time, its speed on the way up is shown to be the same as its speed at the same level on the way down.

To treat the motion mathematically it is convenient to use Eqs.(5a), (5b), (5c), and (5d), taking the point of projection as the *origin,* and adopt the following convention of signs: for projection upward

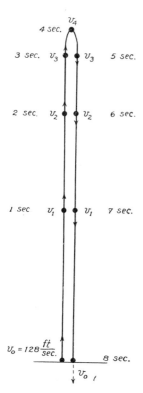

FIG. 5D—The upward motion of a body is just the same as the downward motion but in reverse. A stone thrown upward returns to the ground with the same speed.

(1) *Distances above the origin are positive.*

(2) *Distances below the origin are negative.*

(3) *Velocities upward are positive.*

(4) *Velocities downward are negative.*

(5) *Acceleration downward (gravity) is negative.*

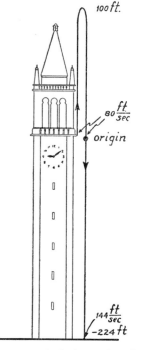

FIG. 5E—A body projected upward rises to a predetermined height, then falls with increasing speed.

Whether a body is moving up or down the acceleration g is always downward.

$$a = -g \qquad (5e)$$

Example 2. A stone is projected upward with a speed of 128 ft/sec. Calculate the time required to reach the highest point.

Solution. The known quantities in this problem are $v_o = 128$ ft/sec, $a = -32$ ft/sec^2, and at the highest point $v = 0$. Since t is the unknown, Eq.(5a) may be used. Direct substitution gives

$$0 = 128 \text{ ft/sec} + (-32 \text{ ft/sec}^2)t$$

Transposing

$$t = \frac{128 \text{ ft/sec}}{32 \text{ ft/sec}^2} = 4 \text{ sec.}$$

In 4 sec, therefore, the stone will reach its highest point. In another 4 sec it will fall to the ground, as shown in Fig. 5D.

Example 3. A baseball is thrown upward with a speed of 80 ft/sec from a point 224 ft above the ground as shown in Fig. 5E. Find (a) the maximum height to which the ball rises, (b) the total time required to reach the point of projection again, (c) the time required to reach a height of 64 ft, (d) the velocity upon arrival at the ground, and (e) the total time in the air.

Solution. (a) The given quantities for part (a) are $v_o = 80$ ft/sec, and $a = -32$ ft/sec^2. At the highest point of the path $v = 0$. Since s is the unknown, Eq.(5c) may be used. By direct substitution

$$v^2 = v_o^2 + 2as$$
$$0 = (80 \text{ ft/sec})^2 + 2(-32 \text{ ft/sec}^2)s$$

Transposing

$$s = \frac{(80 \text{ ft/sec})^2}{2 \times 32 \text{ ft/sec}^2} = \frac{6400 \text{ ft}^2/\text{sec}^2}{64 \text{ ft/sec}^2} = 100 \text{ ft.}$$

(b) Upon returning to its starting point, *the origin*, the ball is at $s = 0$. Since t is the unknown, Eq.(5d) may be used.

$$s = v_o t + \tfrac{1}{2}at^2$$
$$0 = (80 \text{ ft/sec})t + \tfrac{1}{2}(-32 \text{ ft/sec}^2)t^2$$

Transposing,

$$(16 \text{ ft/sec}^2)t^2 = (80 \text{ ft/sec})t$$

Dividing both sides by $16t$,

$$t \text{ ft/sec}^2 = 5 \text{ ft/sec} \qquad \text{or} \qquad t = 5 \text{ sec.}$$

(c) Here the given quantities are $s = 64$ ft, $v_o = 80$ ft/sec, $a = -32$ ft/sec^2, and the unknown is t. Inspection of equations shows that Eq.(5d) may be used. Direct substitution gives

$$64 \text{ ft} = (80 \text{ ft/sec})t + \tfrac{1}{2}(-32 \text{ ft/sec}^2)t^2$$

Transposing

$$(16 \text{ ft/sec}^2)t^2 - (80 \text{ ft/sec})t + 64 = 0$$

Dividing through by 16 ft/sec^2,

$$t^2 - 5 \text{ sec} + 4 \text{ sec}^2 = 0$$

Factoring

$$(t - 1 \text{ sec})(t - 4 \text{ sec}) = 0$$

Giving

$$t = 1 \text{ sec} \qquad \text{and} \qquad t = 4 \text{ sec.}$$

Both of these answers are correct. The first answer, 1 sec, is the time required for the ball to reach the 64 ft level on its way up while the second answer, 4 sec, is the time required to reach the 64 ft level on the way down.

(d) Upon reaching the ground the ball is below the origin, making $s = -224$ ft. Since v is the unknown Eq.(5c) may be used. Substituting directly,

$$v^2 = (80 \text{ ft/sec})^2 + 2(-32 \text{ ft/sec}^2)(-224 \text{ ft})$$
$$v^2 = 20{,}736 \text{ ft}^2/\text{sec}^2$$
$$v = \pm 144 \text{ ft/sec}.$$

Of these two answers only the one $v = -144$ ft/sec is correct; the ball is moving downward.

(e) To find the total flight time we may use Eq.(5a). The known quantities are $v_0 = 80$ ft/sec, $a = -32$ ft/sec^2, and $v = -144$ ft/sec.

$$-144 \text{ ft/sec} = 80 \text{ ft/sec} + (-32 \text{ ft/sec}^2)t$$

from which

$$t = \frac{224 \text{ ft/sec}}{32 \text{ ft/sec}^2} = 7 \text{ sec}.$$

Or we may use Eq.(5d) and obtain

$$-224 \text{ ft} = (80 \text{ ft/sec})t + \tfrac{1}{2}(-32 \text{ ft/sec}^2)t^2$$

from which

$$(16 \text{ ft/sec}^2)t^2 - (80 \text{ ft/sec})t - 224 \text{ ft} = 0$$

Dividing by 16 ft/sec^2, gives

$$t^2 - 5 \text{ sec} - 14 \text{ sec}^2 = 0$$

Factoring

$$(t - 7 \text{ sec})(t + 2 \text{ sec}) = 0$$

giving

$$t = 7 \text{ sec} \qquad \text{and} \qquad t = -2 \text{ sec}.$$

Only the answer $t = 7$ sec is a real answer for this problem.

If a body falls freely from rest so that $v_0 = 0$, the special Eqs.(5e), (5g) and (5h) become,

$$v = gt \qquad\qquad v^2 = 2gs \qquad\qquad s = \tfrac{1}{2}gt^2 \qquad \textbf{(5f)}$$

PROBLEMS

1. A workman accidentally drops a hammer while working on a tall building. If it requires 8 sec to reach the ground (a) how high is the building, and (b) with what speed does the hammer strike the ground?

2. A stone dropped into a well hits the water in 3.5 sec. (a) How deep is the well, and (b) with what speed does the stone hit the water? (*Ans.* (a) 196 ft, (b) 112 ft/sec.)

3. A sandbag dropped from a balloon hits the ground with a speed of 180 mi/hr. (a) How high is the balloon, and (b) how long is the sandbag in falling?

4. An object falls from a bridge 225 ft above the water. (a) With what speed does it hit the water, and (b) how long is it in the air? (*Ans.* (a) 120 ft/sec, (b) 3.75 sec.)

5. An arrow is shot straight upward with a speed of 34.3 m/sec. Find (a) the height to which it rises, and (b) the time required to return to the ground.

6. A stone is thrown vertically upward with speed of 60 mi/hr. Find (a) the height to which it rises, and (b) the total time to reach the ground. (*Ans.* (a) 121 ft, (b) 5.5 sec.)

7. A baseball is hit straight upward with a speed of 39.2 m/sec. Find (a) the maximum height reached, (b) its height at the end of 3 sec, (c) its velocity at the end of 7 sec, and (d) the total time it is in the air.

8. An arrow is shot upward with a speed of 230 ft/sec. Find (a) the maximum height reached, (b) its height at the end of 5.5 sec, (c) its velocity at the end of 10 sec, and (d) the total time of flight. (*Ans.* (a) 827 ft, (b) 781 ft, (c) −90 ft/sec, (d) 14.4 sec.)

9. A stone is thrown upward from the edge of a cliff with a speed of 104 ft/sec. Find (a) the maximum height reached, (b) its velocity at the end of 2 sec, (c) its height at the end of 6 sec, and (d) its height at the end of 8 sec.

10. A boy standing on a bridge 200 ft above the water throws a stone straight upward with a speed of 100 ft/sec. Find (a) the maximum height reached, (b) the time required to reach the bridge level again, and (c) the speed with which it hits the water. (*Ans.* (a) 156 ft, (b) 6.25 sec, (c) 151 ft/sec.)

11. An arrow shot straight upward returns to the ground again in 10.5 sec. Calculate (a) the maximum height reached, and (b) the speed of projection. Use mks units.

12. A baseball hit straight upward is caught 7.5 sec later by the catcher. Find (a) the maximum height reached, and (b) the speed it acquired upon leaving the bat. (*Ans.* (a) 225 ft, (b) 120 ft/sec.)

13. A stone thrown straight upward by a catapult reaches a height of 96 ft in 1 sec. Find (a) the maximum height reached, (b) the total time of flight, and (c) the speed of projection.

14. An arrow shot straight upward reaches a height of 128 ft in one sec. Find (a) the maximum height reached, (b) the total time of flight, and (c) the speed of projection. (*Ans.* (a) 324 ft, (b) 9 sec, (c) 144 ft/sec.)

15. A dart thrown straight upward travels a distance of 19.6 m during the second second. Calculate (a) the maximum height reached, (b) the speed of projection, and (c) the total time of flight.

16. An anti-aircraft shell when shot straight upward travels a distance of 543.9 m during the third second. Neglecting air friction find (a) the total time of flight. (b) the speed of projection, (c) the maximum height reached. (*Ans.* (a) 116 sec, (b) 568.4 m/sec, (c) 16,484 m.)

17. A ball is thrown upward with an initial speed of 120 ft/sec. At the end of 6.5 sec, (a) how far will it be from its starting point, and (b) in what direction will it be moving?

18. Arrows are shot upward at 2-sec intervals with an initial speed of 34.3 m/sec. (a) How long will each arrow be in the air before another passes it, and (b) at what distances above the origin will arrows be passing each other? (*Ans.* (a) 0.5 sec, (b) +15.9 m, and 45.1 m.)

19. Two arrows are shot upward simultaneously, one with a speed of 39.2 m/sec and the other with a speed of 49.0 m/sec. At what time will they be 20 m apart?

Newton's First and Second Laws of Motion

Chapter 6

IN the preceding chapters the motions of bodies have been described in terms of *speed, velocity, acceleration* and *time*. The definitions of these quantities, and the laws and formulas relating to them, are classified as belonging to that branch of mechanics called "kinematics." Here, and in later chapters, the cause of motion is to be treated. Such a treatment involves the introduction of *mass* and *force* into the equations already presented.

To Isaac Newton,* goes the credit of having been the first to systematically introduce these concepts into mechanics and to formulate the fundamental laws governing all motion. These laws constitute the fundamental principles of that branch of mechanics called "dynamics" and resolve themselves into three laws commonly referred to as "Newton's Laws of Motion."

6.1 Newton's First Law. *A body at rest or in uniform motion will remain at rest or in uniform motion unless some external force is applied to it.*† This law can be demonstrated by many simple experiments. In Fig. 6A a card is shown in the process of being snapped from under a coin. With a

---

* Sir Isaac Newton (1642-1727), English physicist and mathematician, was born in England on Christmas day, 1642. He obtained his education at Trinity College, Cambridge, where in 1665 he was awarded the Master of Arts degree. At just this time, the prevalence of the black plague forced him into retirement at his old home in Woolsthorpe where in the two years 1665 and 1666 his genius developed. In this period he invented the calculus, discovered the composition of white light, and conceived the idea of universal gravitation. In the years that followed, he published much of his work on optics and developed his ideas on gravitation which were published in 1687 in his "Principia." At the age of fifty he suffered from a nervous breakdown, and never again did any extensive scientific work, but devoted his time to theology. He became very absent minded and slovenly in his personal appearance. It is needless to say, therefore, that he never married. His "Principia" is considered to be one of the greatest monuments of the human intellect. In it, Newton lays the foundations of mechanics which are broad enough to include all future developments, and these he applies to the motions of heavenly bodies under the law of gravitation. He was elected to Parliament, was president of the Royal Society for twenty-five years, and was knighted by Queen Anne in 1705. The greatness of this modest man is illustrated by a remark of his made on his deathbed, "If I have seen farther than others, it is by standing on the shoulders of giants."

† Newton's First Law of Motion is given in Latin in his famous book "Principia." Lex. I. Corpus omne preserverare in statu suo quiesendi vel movendi uniformiter in directum, nisi quatenus illud a viribus impressis cogitur statum suum mutare.

quick snap of the finger the card slides from under the coin without dislodging it from the pedestal. In diagram (b) a small car is shown free to move on a smooth hard track. If the track is jerked quickly to right or left, the wheels of the car will turn but the car itself will tend to remain at rest.

In both of these experiments the coin and the car are at rest. They tend to remain at rest because the sudden motion of the objects on which they are resting exert no large force for any appreciable length of time. Actually, the coin and the car do move slightly because of frictional forces between the moving parts in contact. The tend-

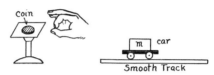

FIG. 6A—A card can be flipped from under a coin without dislodging the coin. The smooth track can be moved quickly without moving the car.

ency for each body to remain at rest is due to that property, common to all material bodies, called *inertia*. The inertia of a body may be defined as that property of a body which tends to resist a change in its state of rest or motion. *Mass* is defined as a quantitative measure of inertia. Inertia and mass are both measured in the same units, in grams, or kilograms.

A third experiment illustrating inertia, and Newton's First Law, is illustrated in Fig. 6B. A small mass M of 100 gm is suspended by a fine thread A, then pulled downward by another piece of the same thread B. If the force F is a slow steady pull, the thread will always break at A; whereas if it is a sudden jerk, it will always break at B. In the first case, the tension in the upper thread is greatest and is equivalent to the force F plus the weight of the mass M. In the second case the force F is momentarily very large causing the thread to break before the mass M has had time to move down far enough to stretch and break the upper thread. It is the inertia of M that permits the very large force F to be momentarily applied to the lower thread only.

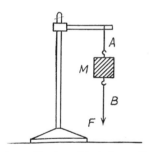

FIG. 6B—A quick jerk at F breaks the thread at B, a slow steady pull at F breaks the thread at A.

If the car in Fig. 6A is started rolling along the track, Newton's First Law states that it should keep moving with the same velocity. The law, of course, neglects friction, for we know that left to itself friction will eventually bring the car to rest. The greater the friction, the sooner will it stop. The smaller the friction, the longer will it move. If friction could be entirely eliminated, the *inertia* of the car would keep it moving indefinitely with constant velocity.

6.2. Newton's Second Law of Motion. Newton's first law, concerning bodies at rest or moving with constant velocity, assumes that no forces are acting to change their state. Newton's second law, however, assumes that such a force is acting and describes the resulting *change in motion*. In

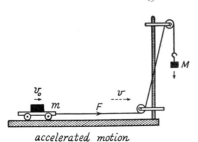

accelerated motion

FIG. 6C—A small car being accelerated by a constant force.

Fig. 6C, for example, a small car of mass m is acted upon by a constant force F. The force is produced by the pull of gravity on the mass M, and is transmitted to the car by a cord passing over pulleys as indicated. If the car is initially at rest, this force will start it moving; if it is already moving with a velocity v_0, the force will increase its velocity. Thus the car is accelerated.

Newton's Second Law of Motion may be stated as follows: *When a body is acted upon by a constant force, its resulting acceleration is proportional to the force and inversely proportional to the mass.*

Symbolically,

$$a \propto \frac{F}{m}.$$

This law is stated as a proportionality because it holds regardless of the units in which each of the three quantities are measured. If the units are properly chosen, an equal sign may be inserted and the law written as an equation,

$$a = \frac{F}{m}.$$

By transposing m to the other side of the equation, the so-called "force equation" which forms the basis of so many principles in mechanics is obtained.

$$F = ma. \tag{6a}$$

force = mass × acceleration

To the above statement of Newton's Second Law should be added the statement that *the acceleration takes place in the direction of the acting force.*

Example 1. Neglecting friction, what constant force will give a mass of 50 gm an acceleration of 5 cm/sec²?

Solution. Substitute the foregoing values into the force equation, Eq.(6a).

$$F = 50 \text{ gm} \times 5 \frac{\text{cm}}{\text{sec}^2} = 250 \frac{\text{gm cm}}{\text{sec}^2}.$$

The answer is a force of 250 gm cm/sec². Thus force is not as simple a concept as it might seem at first hand; it involves all three of the fundamental units, *length, mass,* and *time.*

By definition 1 gm cm/sec² is a unit of force called the *dyne*. According to this definition the answer to the above problem could have been written, *250 dynes. The dyne is a force which, acting on a one gram mass, will give it an acceleration of 1 cm/sec².* 1 dyne $= 1$ gm $\times 1$ cm/sec².

In the cgs system (centimeter-gram-second), the units of Eq.(6a) become: dynes, grams, and centimeters/seconds².

There is a growing movement among scientists and teachers of physics to use the kilogram and meter in place of the gram and centimeter as units of mass and length. According to the meter, kilogram, second system (abbr. *mks system*) unit force is called the "newton" in honor of Sir Isaac Newton. *The newton is defined as that force which, applied to a mass of 1 kilogram, will give it an acceleration of one meter per second per second.*

In the mks system the units of Eq.(6a) become

$$1 \text{ newton} = 1 \text{ kilogram} \times 1 \frac{\text{meter}}{\text{second}^2} .$$

Example 2. Neglecting friction, what constant force in newtons will give a mass of 4 kg an acceleration of 3.8 m/sec²?

Solution. Apply the force equation.

$$F = 4 \text{ kg} \times 3.8 \frac{\text{m}}{\text{sec}^2} = 15.2 \frac{\text{kg m}}{\text{sec}^2} = 15.2 \text{ newtons.}$$

The answer is a constant force of 15.2 newtons.

Dynes and newtons are absolute units of force. They arise from the force equation when the absolute units of *mass* and *time* are used.

Since 1 kg $= 1000$ gm, and 1 m $= 100$ cm, one newton $= 100,000$ dynes.

$$1 \text{ newton} = 10^5 \text{ dynes.}$$

6.3. Weight and Mass. When a mass m is allowed to fall freely, it is the constant downward force of gravity on the mass that gives rise to its constant acceleration. If Newton's Second Law is applied to this motion, the force F is none other than the weight W of the body, and the acceleration a is the acceleration due to gravity g. For falling bodies the force equation, $F = ma$, is written in different symbols.

$$W = mg \tag{6b}$$

weight = mass $\times$ acceleration

In absolute units the weight of a body is expressed in dynes or newtons.

Weight and *force* have both magnitude and direction and are therefore vector quantities. Mass, on the other hand, is a scalar quantity since it has only magnitude. The distinction between *weight* and *mass* is illustrated by imagining a given body to be carried out into free space far removed from other bodies and their gravitational attraction. There, a body at rest will still have its mass but it will have no weight. That such a body has its mass would be demonstrated if another mass were to bump into it. The smaller the mass of the incoming body, the less would be the recoil of the first mass from the impact.

Weight here on the earth is due to the gravitational attraction of the earth upon a mass at its surface, and will be treated in detail in the next chapter. In the equation $W = mg$ we may define g as the *weight per unit mass*. W is equal to the *mass* times the *weight per unit mass*.

Example 3. Calculate the weight of a body having a mass of 1 kg.
Solution. By Eq.(6b),

$$W = 1 \text{ kg} \times 9.80 \, \frac{m}{\text{sec}^2} = 9.80 \, \frac{\text{kg m}}{\text{sec}^2} = 9.80 \text{ newtons.} \qquad (6c)$$

This answer shows that to lift a mass of 1 kg requires an upward force of 9.80 newtons and that the weight and mass differ from each other numerically by the acceleration due to gravity. By similar calculations to the above, the weight of a 1 gm mass is found to be 980 dynes. See Fig. 6E.

6.4. The Engineering System of Units. The engineer seldom uses metric units as described above. He finds it more convenient to measure forces in *pounds* or *tons*. In the construction of buildings, bridges, airplanes, and all kinds of machines, the loads to be carried are usually specified in pounds. To apply Newton's Second Law of Motion, as expressed by the force equation $F = ma$ it is necessary to modify one of the two factors *mass* or *acceleration*.

It is general engineering practice to modify *mass* by defining it not in pounds but in *slugs*. To see how these units are derived from the "force equation," Eqs.(6a) and (6b) are both solved for m, and then set equal to each other.

$$\frac{F}{a} = \frac{W}{g} \qquad (6d)$$

The justification for this is that Newton's Second Law applied to a given mass holds for any force whether it be its own weight W due to the earth's downward pull, or any other applied force F. If the force is F the acceleration is a; if the force is W the acceleration is g. See Fig. 6D. The engineer's form of the force equation evolves from Eq.(6d). By transposing a,

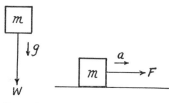

Fig. 6D—A mass m falling freely has an acceleration g: pulled by a force F it has an acceleration a.

$$F = \frac{W}{g} a \qquad (6e)$$

In this relation F and W are to be considered as forces, both measured in pounds, while the accelerations g and a are both measured in the customary units ft/sec². $g = 32$ ft/sec².

Example 4. A small wagon weighing 80 lb stands at rest on a level road. What force is required to give it an acceleration of 3 ft/sec²?

Solution. By direct substitution in the force equation, Eq.(6e),

$$F = \frac{80 \text{ lb}}{32 \text{ ft/sec}^2} \times 3 \text{ ft/sec}^2 = 7.5 \text{ lb.}$$

The answer is a force of 7.5 lb.

The term W/g represents mass in the engineering or British system of units. Such units are called *slugs. Mass in slugs is always obtained by dividing the weight in pounds by the acceleration of gravity, 32 ft/sec².*

In turning this around we may *define unit force (the pound) as that force which, applied to a mass of one slug, will give it an acceleration of one foot per second per second.* Consider now a mass of one slug falling freely under the pull of gravity with an acceleration of 32 ft/sec.² By the above definition of unit force such an acceleration of unit mass (1 slug) could be caused only by a force of 32 lb. In other words, one slug weighs 32 lb. See Fig. 6E.

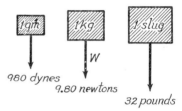

1 newton = 0.224 lb.
1 dyne = 2.24 × 10⁻⁶ lb.
1 slug = 14.6 kg.

FIG. 6E—Weight is a force equal in magnitude to the mass multiplied by the acceleration of gravity. W = mg

6.5. Change in Velocity. In Chap. 4 acceleration was defined as the rate of change of velocity and written algebraically as

$$a = \frac{v - v_0}{t}.$$

If the acceleration a in the force equation $F = ma$, is replaced by $(v - v_0)/t$, Newton's Second Law takes on a new form.

$$F = m \frac{v - v_0}{t}. \tag{6f}$$

This equation is used in solving problems where the initial and final velocities are involved.

Example 5. A 3000 lb automobile is moving with a velocity of 15 mi/hr. What constant force, applied for a period of 12 sec, will increase its velocity to 60 mi/hr?

Solution. In solving this problem, it is convenient to express all quantities in the same units. With the time given in seconds, the velocity is better expressed in feet per second. Since 60 mi/hr is equivalent to 88 ft/sec, 15 mi/hr = 22 ft/sec. Then, by substitution in Eq.(6f), we obtain

$$F = \frac{3000 \text{ lb}}{32 \text{ ft/sec}^2} \times \frac{88 \text{ ft/sec} - 22 \text{ ft/sec}}{12 \text{ sec}} = 515.6 \text{ lb.}$$

6.6. Momentum. When Eq.(6f) is multiplied out, there results an equation involving a new concept; namely, that of *momentum*.

$$F = \frac{mv - mv_0}{t}. \qquad (6g)$$

Momentum is defined as the product *mass times velocity*. According to this definition all moving bodies have momentum. In Fig. 6C, the small car at the left has momentum mv_0. Under the action of a force F it gains in momentum, acquiring, after a time of t seconds, a greater momentum mv. Two masses, one large and one small, moving with the same velocity have quite different momenta: the larger mass has a proportionately larger momentum.

Newton's Second Law of Motion was originally stated in terms of momentum.* *The rate at which the momentum of a body changes is proportional to the impressed force and takes place in the direction of the straight line in which the force acts.*

As an equation in words,

$$\text{force} = \frac{\text{change in momentum}}{\text{time}}.$$

In algebraic symbols, this is Eq.(6g) above.

6.7. Impulse. Transferring t to the left side in Eq.(6g), gives

$$Ft = mv - mv_0. \qquad \textbf{(6h)}$$

This is called the "impulse equation." $F \times t$ is the *impulse* and $mv - mv_0$ is the *change in momentum*. Its meaning is illustrated in Fig. 6F where a

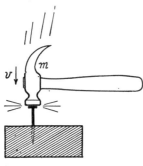

hammer is shown driving a nail into a block of wood. Moving with a velocity v the hammer head of mass m strikes the nail a blow of force F. Lasting for only a fraction of a second, this force has by an impulse driven the nail a short distance into the wood. If F represents the average force, and t the time interval during which the force acts,

$$\text{impulse} = F \times t. \qquad (6i)$$

Fig. 6F—The impulse of a hammer drives a nail into a block of wood.

When a body starts from rest, the initial velocity v_0 of Eq.(6i) is zero, and

$$Ft = mv. \qquad (6j)$$

---

* Newton's Second Law of Motion is stated in Latin in his "Principia." Lex. II. Mutationem motus, proportionalem esse vi motrici impressae, et fieri secundum lineam rectam qua vis illa imprimitur.

As the result of an impulse *Ft,* a body initially at rest acquires a momentum *mv.* Conversely, a body moving with a momentum *mv* can be brought to rest by an impulse — *Ft.* The minus sign indicates that the force is opposite in direction to the velocity.

Example 6. A hammer weighing 2 lb moving with a velocity of 20 ft/sec strikes the head of a spike and drives it into a block of hard wood. If the hammer comes to rest in 0.001 sec, find (a) the impulse, (b) the average force, and (c) the distance the nail is driven into the wood.

Solution. By direct substitution in Eq.(6j),

$$\text{(a)} \quad Ft = -\frac{2 \text{ lb}}{32 \text{ ft/sec}^2} \times 20 \text{ ft/sec} = -1.25 \text{ lb sec.}$$

The average force is

$$\text{(b)} \quad F = -\frac{1.25 \text{ lb sec}}{0.001 \text{ sec}} = -1250 \text{ lb.}$$

That such a large force as this is really exerted is due in part to the very short time in which the force acts and its reality can be demonstrated by trying to push a nail into a block of wood by piling weights on top of it. The minus sign indicates that the force stopping the hammer is opposite in direction to the motion. The hammer velocity is down and the stopping force is up.

To find the distance the nail is driven into the wood in the above example the equations for accelerated motion may be used. From Eq.(4f), substitution of the known quantities gives

$$\text{(c)} \quad s = \bar{v}t = \frac{v + v_0}{2}t = 10 \text{ ft/sec} \times 0.001 \text{ sec} = 0.01 \text{ ft.}$$

which is about one-eighth inch.

PROBLEMS

1. A mass of 2 kg is given a constant acceleration of 0.5 m/sec². Calculate the force required in (a) dynes, and (b) newtons.

2. A mass of 750 gm is given an acceleration of 220 cm/sec². Find the force in (a) newtons, and (b) dynes. (*Ans.* (a) 1.65 newtons, (b) 165,000 dynes.)

3. A motorcycle weighing 350 lb can accelerate at 2.5 ft/sec². Find the force in pounds.

4. A midget car weighing 600 lb can accelerate at 3.25 ft/sec². Find the force in lbs. (*Ans.* 60.9 lb.)

5. A force of 25 newtons acts on a mass of 80 kg. Find the acceleration.

6. A force of 6.05 newtons acts on a mass of 5 kg. Find the acceleration. (*Ans.* 1.21 m/sec².)

7. A mass of 5 kg is acted on by a force of 15,000 dynes. Find the acceleration.

8. A car weighing 3600 lb and traveling 15 mi/hr is accelerated for 8 sec to obtain a speed of 60 mi/hr. Find the force in lb. (*Ans.* 928 lb.)

9. A 5 kg shell traveling 900 m/sec strikes a hillside where it penetrates the ground to a depth of 2 m. Find (a) the time of stopping, and (b) the average force in newtons.

10. A 20 ton passenger plane requires a runway 3000 ft long to acquire its take-off speed of 80 mi/hr. Calculate the total average thrust of its propellers. (*Ans.* 2868 lb.)

11. A 2 kg shell is fired from a 3.2 m gun barrel with a speed of 840 m/sec. Calculate the average force involved.

12. A mortar shell weighing 4.2 lb is fired from a mortar 2.5 ft long. If the muzzle speed is 250 ft/sec, find the average force. (*Ans.* 1641 lb.)

13. A 1.1 oz golf ball lying on the fairway is driven by a golf club with a speed of 140 ft/sec. If the time of impact is 0.012 sec, find (a) the average force in lb, (b) the distance over which the force acts, and (c) the impulse.

14. A body moving with a speed of 4.5 ft/sec has a momentum of 54 slugs ft/sec. Find its mass. (*Ans.* 12 slugs.)

15. A 3000 lb car traveling 30 mi/hr crashes into a stone wall smashing in the front end of the car for 2 ft. Find (a) the momentum, (b) the acceleration, (c) the average force, and (d) the impulse.

16. A hammer of mass 1 kg moving with a speed of 8 m/sec strikes the head of a nail driving it 2 cm into a large block of wood. Neglecting the mass of the nail, calculate (a) the momentum of the hammer before impact, (b) the acceleration during impact, and (c) the time interval during impact. (*Ans.* (a) 8 kg m/sec, (b) −1600 m/sec^2, (c) 0.005 sec.)

17. A constant horizontal force of 20 lb acts on a body on a smooth horizontal plane. The body starts from rest and is observed to move 180 ft in 12 sec. Assuming constant acceleration, what is the mass of the body?

18. A 22-rifle fires a 1.8 gm bullet at 400 m/sec into a block of wood. If the bullet penetrates to a depth of 10 cm, find (a) the average acceleration, and (b) the average force exerted on the bullet. (c) What is the time required in stopping? (*Ans.* (a) −800,000 m/sec^2. (b) −1440 newtons. (c) 0.000514 sec.)

19. A locomotive is capable of exerting a maximum pull of 4 tons. What speed can it give to a passenger train weighing 200 tons in a distance of one-half mile? Assume the train starts from rest.

20. A freight train with a mass of 8×10^5 kg is traveling along a straight and level track at a speed of 90 km/hr. (a) What force applied by the brakes will stop it in a distance of 1 km? (b) Find the time of stopping. (*Ans.* (a) 1×10^4 newtons. (b) 200 sec.)

21. (a) How large a force is required to move a 6 kg mass 2 m along a smooth level surface in 1 sec? (b) How large a force will move this same mass 2 m vertically in 1 sec? Assume the mass initially at rest and no friction.

22. A fireman's hose delivers 240 kg of water per second at a speed of 12 m/sec. If this stream, moving horizontally, strikes a vertical wall, thereby stopping its forward motion, (a) what is the momentum destroyed per second, and (b) what is the force against the wall? (*Ans.* (a) 2880 kg m/sec^2. (b) 2880 newtons.)

23. A horizontal stream of water from a garden hose delivers 1.2 kg of water per second at a speed of 45 m/sec. If this stream, while traveling horizontally, strikes a vertical wall, thereby stopping its forward motion, find (a) the momentum destroyed per second, and (b) the force exerted against the wall.

Vector Addition and Composition of Forces Chapter 7

7.1. Vector Addition. The process of vector addition will be first illustrated by an example involving two displacements. Suppose that a ship starts from a point A and sails due North for a distance of 6 miles to a point B where it changes course and sails due East for a distance of 4 miles to a point C. Although the ship has sailed a total distance of $6 + 4$ (or 10) mi, it is obvious that its distance from the starting point is not given by this arithmetic sum.

To find the actual displacement, that is the distance from the starting point, a scale diagram like that shown in Fig. 7A may be drawn. With a pencil and a ruler (a centimeter scale) a vertical line AB, 6 cm long, is drawn to represent the displacement *6 miles North*. The line BC is next drawn to the right from B and 4 cm long to represent the

4 *miles East*. The triangle is finally completed by joining A and C. With an arrowhead at C, the hypotenuse R, measuring 7.2 cm, represents the resultant displacement of 7.2 miles.

Vectorially written,

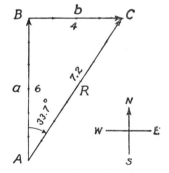

$$\overrightarrow{AB} + \overrightarrow{BC} = \overrightarrow{AC} \quad \text{or} \quad \overrightarrow{R} = \overrightarrow{a} + \overrightarrow{b}.$$

Using a protractor, the angle A is measured to be 33.7°. The direction of the resultant vector R is therefore 33.7° East of North.

It is customary in any vector diagram to

FIG. 7A—Illustrating vector addition as applied to displacements.

represent all vector quantities by arrows, each arrow being drawn in the proper direction and to the proper length. A little practice in drawing will show that regardless of what scale is used to make the diagram, the resultant must be the same in magnitude and direction, and that the more carefully the diagram is drawn, the more accurate will be the measured result.

To calculate the magnitude of the resultant R in Fig. 7A, use is made of

49

the Pythagorean theorem in geometry that for any right triangle *the square of the hypotenuse is equal to the sum of the squares of the other two sides.*

$$R^2 = a^2 + b^2.$$

Substitute the two values of a and b.

$$R^2 = (6)^2 + (4)^2 = 52.$$

By taking the square root* of 52, we finally obtain

$$R = 7.21 \text{ mi.}$$

Example 1. A man walks East for a distance of 10 mi, then turns and walks North-East for a distance of 5 mi. Find the resultant displacement.

Solution. Following the procedure outlined above, a horizontal line *AB* is first drawn 10 units long and labeled as shown in Fig. 7B. The second vector, *BC*, is next

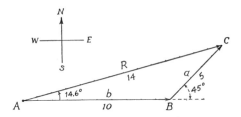

Fɪɢ. 7B—Vector diagram for Example 1.

drawn *NE* in direction, i.e., at 45°, and 5 units long. The resultant *R* is then drawn and measured; its length is found to be 14 units and represents a displacement of 14 mi. The angle at *A* measured with a protractor is found to be 14.6°. The answer, therefore, is 14 mi in direction 14.6° North of East.

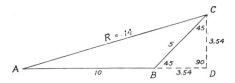

Fɪɢ. 7C—Vector diagram for Example 1.

To calculate the magnitude of *R*, it is seen that a right triangle can be formed as shown in Fig. 7C. The right triangle theorem is then applied to the triangle *BCD*

$$(BC)^2 = (BD)^2 + (CD)^2.$$

* A simplified method for finding the square root of a number to an accuracy of three figures is the following. By inspection, a guess of the square root is made to two figures. For example, if the number is 685, inspection shows that it lies between $(20)^2 = 400$ and $(30)^2 = 900$, and that a reasonable guess might be 25. The original number is then divided by 25 and gives 27.4. The average of these two numbers, 26.2, is then the square root to three figures. If greater accuracy is desired, the averaged number may be assumed to be an original guess and the process repeated.

Since two angles of BCD are equal to each other the triangle is isosceles and the sides BD and CD are equal. $BD = CD$. Therefore,

$$(BC)^2 = 2(BD)^2 = 25,$$

from which

$$(BD)^2 = 25/2,$$

and

$$BD = \sqrt{12.5} = 3.54.$$

Applying the same theorem to the right triangle ADC,

$$R^2 = (3.54)^2 + (13.54)^2 = 195.8$$

from which

$$R = 14.0 \text{ mi.}$$

7.2. The Parallelogram Method of Vector Addition. There are two generally accepted methods of vector addition; namely, the triangle method described in the preceding section and shown in Figs. 7A and 7B, and the parallelogram method described below. Consider as an illustration of the latter the addition of the same two vectors given in Fig. 7B, $b = 10$ mi and $a = 5$ mi, the two making an angle of $45°$ with each other.

As shown at the left in Fig. 7D, the vectors are first drawn outward from the same origin A. From D a dotted line is next drawn parallel to vector b, and from B a dotted line is drawn parallel to vector a, as in the middle diagram. From the point C, where these two lines cross, the diagonal line AC is drawn in and labeled with an arrowhead as the resultant R.

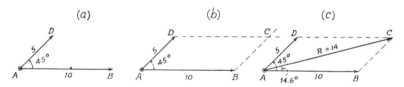

FIG. 7D—Illustrating the parallelogram method of vector addition.

A comparison of the parallelogram with the triangle in Fig. 7B shows that the triangle ABC in both diagrams is identical. Both methods, therefore, lead to the same result. In solving certain problems, the triangle method will be found most convenient, while in solving others the parallelogram is most readily applicable.

There are two common systems by which the directions of vector quantities are designated: one is to refer all angles to the points of the compass as in Figs. 7A and 7B; and the other is to specify all angles with reference to

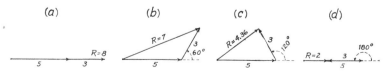

FIG. 7E—Illustrating the triangle method of vector addition.

the *X-axis,* as in Fig. 7D and 7E. In navigation the *true bearing* of a ship is measured from the *North* clockwise around the compass. To sail East is to have a true bearing of 90°, and to sail South-West is to have a true bearing of 225°.

When directions are referred to the *x-axis,* angles measured in a counter clockwise direction from the $+x$ axis are called $+$; those measured clockwise from the same line are called $-$. For example, the direction-angle for the second vector in Fig. 7E is $+60°$, or $-300°$.

7.3. Weight Is a Vector. Everyone knows that when he weighs himself as illustrated in Fig. 7F, he is measuring the downward force he exerts on the foot board of the scales, and that this force causes some mechanism within the scales to indicate his weight. The greater the downward force, the greater is the indicated weight. We are not interested here in the system of levers, weights, or springs within the scales, but rather with the downward force we call our *weight.*

Weight, as explained in the last chapter, is due to the gravitational attraction of the earth for all bodies and is given by the formula,

$$W = mg.$$

As illustrated in Fig. 7G, gravitational forces always act in the direction of a line joining the body and the center of the earth and are, therefore, perpendicular to the earth's surface at the body.

FIG. 7F—Weight is a downward force. The earth attracts all bodies toward its center.

The term force is not confined to weight alone but to the action of any one body upon another. For example, in towing an automobile as shown in Fig. 7H, there are two forces acting, (1) a downward force W due to gravity, and (2) a horizontal force F due to a pull on the tow line. The latter force is supplied by some external object or machine. In pushing a lawnmower there are also two forces, (1) the downward force W due to gravity and (2) a diagonal force F due to some person pushing on the lawnmower handle.

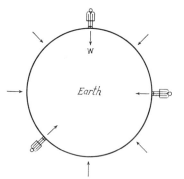

FIG. 7G—Weight is a force due to gravitational attraction and acts in the direction of a line joining the body and the center of the earth.

Regardless of the direction in which a force may act, its magnitude may be expressed in *dynes, newtons,* or *pounds.* The justification for this is illustrated in Fig. 7I where spring scales are used to measure forces. In diagram

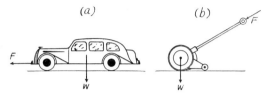

Fig. 7H—Illustrating two independent forces acting on the same body.

(a), the 3 lb weight exerts a downward force of 3 lb. A horizontal force of the same magnitude is produced by running the cord over a pulley as in diagram (b).

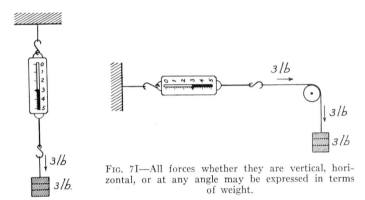

Fig. 7I—All forces whether they are vertical, horizontal, or at any angle may be expressed in terms of weight.

This is not to imply that gravitational attraction is responsible for all forces, for it is not; it is only to indicate that all forces, whatever their origin or direction, may be expressed in terms of weight.

7.4. Forces Are Added Vectorially. Since forces have both magnitude and direction, they are vector quantities and, therefore, subject to the rules of *vector addition.* Consider the diagram in Fig. 7J, illustrating a heavy trunk being pulled along the floor by two ropes. With steady pulls of 40 lb and 25 lb exerted in directions at 90° from each other, the trunk moves in a direction indicated by the dotted arrow. By

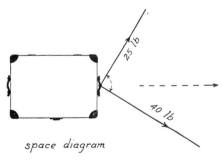

space diagram

Fig. 7J—Two forces acting at an angle are equivalent to a single force acting in a direction lying at some angle between them.

vector addition a *resultant* force can now be found which, upon taking the place of the two forces shown, will produce the same motion.

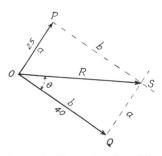

FIG. 7K—Illustrating the addition of two forces acting at an angle of 90° with each other.

The addition of the two force vectors of Fig. 7J is illustrated in Fig. 7K. Starting at O the two vectors a and b are first drawn to scale and in their proper directions. The dotted lines QS and PS are next drawn in to complete the parallelogram, and then followed by the diagonal R. With an arrowhead at S, the diagonal represents the resultant whose magnitude R and direction θ is to be calculated by trigonometry.

Since a and b make an angle of 90° with each other OQS is a right triangle with the sides, a, b, and R. By definition from trigonometry,

$$\frac{a}{b} = \tan \theta.$$

In this equation, substitute known values, as follows:

$$\frac{25}{40} = 0.625 = \tan \theta.$$

Look up 0.625 in the tangent column of Table III in the Appendix. We find that $\theta = 32°$.

Again, by definition,

$$\frac{b}{R} = \cos \theta.$$

Since R is the unknown to be calculated, transposing gives

$$\frac{b}{\cos \theta} = R.$$

Look up the natural cosine of 32° in Table III, then, by substitution,

$$\frac{40}{0.848} = 47.2 \text{ lb.}$$

The resultant force is, therefore, equal to 47.2 lb at an angle of 32° with OQ.

Example 2. A boat is being towed through a canal by two ropes, one on either side of the canal, as shown at the left in Fig. 7L. If the applied forces are 400 and 600 newtons respectively, and the angle between the ropes is 60°, find the magnitude of the resultant force on the boat and the angles the ropes make with the canal. Assume the resultant force to be parallel to the canal.

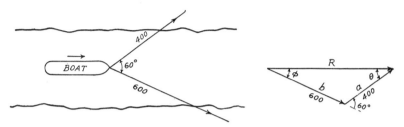

FIG. 7L—The pull of two ropes at an angle on a canal boat is equivalent to a single force straight down the canal.

Solution. The triangle method is applied to the solution of this problem at the right in Fig. 7L. First a vector b, *6 cm* long, is drawn down and to the right to represent the one force of 600 newtons. From the end of this vector, and at an angle of 60°, the second vector a, 4 cm long, is drawn to represent the other force of 400 newtons. The line R is then drawn in with an arrowhead to represent the resultant force on the boat.

By trigonometry the unknown quantities, (1) the magnitude of R, (2) the angle θ, and (3) the angle ϕ, can be calculated as follows.

Use the Law of Cosines for an oblique triangle. (See Appendix II.)

$$R^2 = a^2 + b^2 + 2ab \; cos \; 60°.$$

Look up the cosine of 60° in tables and substitute the value in this equation.

$$R^2 = (400)^2 + (600)^2 + 2(400)(600) \times 0.500$$

from which

$$R^2 = 160{,}000 + 360{,}000 + 240{,}000$$

giving

$$R^2 = 760{,}000 \qquad \text{and} \qquad R = 872 \text{ newtons.}$$

The resultant force $R = 872$ newtons.

To find angles ϕ, and θ, either the Law of Sines or the Law of Cosines may be used. (See Appendix II.) Using the Law of Cosines to find angle ϕ,

$$\cos \phi = \frac{b^2 + R^2 - a^2}{2bR} = \frac{(600)^2 + (872)^2 - (400)^2}{2 \times 600 \times 872}.$$

Thus

$$\cos \phi = 0.9174$$

which from tables of cosines gives

$$\phi = 23.5°.$$

Use the Law of Sines to find angle θ.

$$\frac{a}{\sin \phi} = \frac{b}{\sin \theta}.$$

By transposing and substituting, we find

$$\sin \theta = \frac{b \sin \phi}{a} = \frac{600 \times 0.3987}{400} = 0.5980.$$

From tables of natural sines,

$$\theta = 36.7°.$$

7.5. Force Polygon. When three or more forces act simultaneously upon a body, a single force called their resultant can be found which acting alone upon that body will produce the same result. To find such a resultant force, the *polygon method* of vector addition is often employed. In principle this is an extension of the triangle method and consists of placing the tail of one vector at the head of the one preceding it, and continuing this process until all vectors have been added.

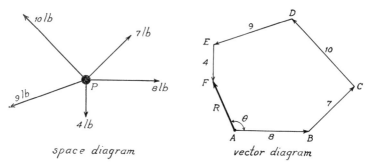

space diagram   *vector diagram*

F_{IG}. 7M—Illustrating the graphical addition of five forces to find their resultant. (The polygon method.)

An illustration of the polygon method applied to five forces is given in Fig. 7M. The space diagram at the left shows the forces acting on a body at P, while the *vector diagram* at the right shows the vector addition and resultant force R. Starting at A as origin, vector AB is drawn 8 cm long and parallel to the 8 lb vector in diagram (a). Vector BC is next drawn 7 cm long and parallel to the 7 lb vector. These are followed in succession by vectors CD, DE, and EF, respectively. With all five vectors added, the resultant R is found by joining the last arrowhead F with the origin A.

Drawn to scale, the measured length of R will give the magnitude of the resultant force and the measured angle θ will give the direction in which it acts.

To calculate the resultant force R in such a problem the polygon may either be divided up into triangles and all sides and angles of the triangles calculated in their turn, or each force can be resolved into components and the components added arithmetically. The latter method is generally the easier of the two, and will be treated in detail in Sec. 8.3.

1. A car averages 40 mi/hr. After traveling east for one hour and thirty minutes it turns and travels north for 45 minutes. What is the resultant displacement?

2. A ship sails north a distance of 200 mi then turns and sails southwest for 80 mi. Apply the triangle method to find the ship's distance from home port. (*Ans.* 154 mi at 21.5° west of north.)

3. An airplane flies due east for a distance of 250 km then turns and flies 60° south of east for 180 km. How far and in what direction is the plane from its starting point?

4. A girl riding a bicycle at the rate of 6 mi/hr rides south for 4 hr then turns and rides east for 3 hr. Determine the displacement graphically, and by calculation. (*Ans.* 30 mi at 36.8° east of south.)

5. A plane flies southwest for a distance of 200 km then turns and flies east for a distance of 200 km when he is forced down. How far and in what direction is the plane from its base?

6. A taxi driver averages 45 mi/hr. After traveling east for 20 min he turns and drives north for 40 min, then east again for 40 min. How far and in what direction is he from his starting point? (*Ans.* 54.1 mi at 33.7° north of east.)

7. Cruising at 300 km/hr a pilot flies southwest for 45 min, then turns and flies north for 1 hr and 15 min then finally turns toward home port and flies for 30 min when he is forced down. How far and in what direction is he from home port?

8. A pilot cruising at 240 mi/hr flies northeast for 1 hr and 20 min, then turns and flies south for 2 hr. Turning then for home base he flies for 50 min before being forced down at sea. How far and in what direction is he from home base? (*Ans.* 140 mi at 41.7° east of south.)

9. An airplane flying 300 mi/hr travels northeast for 10 min, then turns southeast for 20 min, then turns for home. Forced down at sea after a total elapsed time of 40 min the pilot sends out an SOS signal giving his position. How long will it take another plane capable of flying 150 mi/hr to reach the downed ship?

10. A car speeding along the highway at 60 mi/hr travels for 1 hr and 20 min in a direction 35° north of east. Determine graphically and by calculation how far north and how far east the car is from its starting point. (*Ans.* 45.9 mi north and 65.5 mi east.)

11. Two forces, 6 newtons and 8 newtons are exerted simultaneously on the same body. If these two forces make an angle of 60 degrees with each other, what equivalent force would produce the same result?

12. A car is being towed by two ropes making an angle of 90 degrees with each other. If the forces on the ropes are 120 lb and 160 lb, what is the magnitude and direction of the resultant force? (*Ans.* 200 lb at 36.9° with the 160 lb.)

13. Find the resultant of two forces, (a) 5 dynes at 65° and (b) 8 dynes at 155°.

14. Calculate the magnitude and direction of the resultant of the two following forces, (a) 9 newtons at 120° and (b) 14 newtons at 210°. (*Ans.* 16.6 newtons at 177.3°.)

15. Combine the following forces and find their resultant; 50 lb east and 40 lb northwest.

16. Determine the resultant of two forces, (a) 16 lb toward the south, and (b) 20 lb toward the southwest. (*Ans.* 33.3 lb at 25.1° west of south.)

17. Calculate the magnitude and direction of the resultant of two forces, (a) 15 newtons at 205° and (b) 10 newtons at 255°.

18. Find the resultant of two forces, one of 450 newtons vertically upward and the other of 270 newtons making an angle of 35° with the vertical. (*Ans.* 689 newtons making 13° with the vertical.)

19. A horizontal force of 50 newtons is combined with a vertically upward force. If their resultant has a direction of 32°, find the magnitude of (a) the vertical force, and (b) the resultant force.

20. A vertically upward force of 12 newtons is combined with a second force directed at 30°. If their resultant has a direction of 45°, find the magnitude of (a) the second force, and (b) the resultant. (*Ans.* (a) 32.7 newtons, (b) 40.1 newtons.)

21. Find the resultant of the following three forces: (a) 8 lb at 0°, (b) 6 lb at 90°, and (c) 4 lb at 135°.

22. Find the resultant of the following forces: (a) 40 newtons at 30°, (b) 26 newtons at 120°, and (c) 30 newtons at 180°. (*Ans.* 43.3 newtons at 101.2°.)

23. The following four forces are applied to the same body. Graphically determine their resultant. (a) 5 newtons at 20°, (b) 6 newtons at 80°, (c) 3 newtons at 180°, and (d) 4 newtons at 225°.

24. Graphically determine the resultant of the following five coplaner forces: (a) 6.8 newtons at 0°, (b) 40 newtons at 30°, (c) 27 newtons at 90°, (d) 16 newtons at 135°, and 24 newtons at 240°. (*Ans.* 41.7 newtons at 64.2°.)

25. The following five forces act on the same body. Graphically determine their resultant. (a) 4 lb at 120°, (b) 6 lb at 240°, (c) 3 lb at 300°, (d) 7 lb at 30°, and (e) 5 lb at 90°.

26. Graphically determine the resultant of the following coplaner forces: (a) 4 newtons at 0°, (b) 4 newtons at 45°, (c) 6 newtons at 90°, (d) 5 newtons at 180°, (e) 3 newtons at 210°, and (f) 2 newtons at 270°. (*Ans.* 5.38 newtons at 98.1°.)

Vector Resolution and the Method of Components *Chapter 8*

8.1. Resolution of a Force into Components. Many of the problems in mechanics are most easily solved by the so-called *"method of compo-nents."* To apply this method to typical problems it is necessary that we first see how a single vector may be resolved into two components. Consider as an illustration the known force F, making an angle of θ degrees with the x-axis as shown in Fig. 8A.

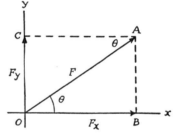

By dropping lines from A, perpendicular to the x- and y-axes, the component forces F_x and F_y are equivalent to the original force F, since by adding them vectorially they give F as a resultant.

FIG. 8A—Illustrating the resolution of a vector into two rectangular components.

With F_x and F_y perpendicular to each other, triangles OAB and OAC are equivalent right triangles with corresponding sides equal. $F_y = $ AB and $F_x = $ AC.

By trigonometry then,

$$\frac{F_y}{F} = \sin \theta, \qquad \frac{F_x}{F} = \cos \theta, \text{ and} \qquad \frac{F_y}{F_x} = \tan \theta \qquad (8a)$$

Since F and θ are usually the known quantities, the first two equations are the most useful in finding the magnitudes of force components. Transposing, they become,

$$F_y = F \sin \theta, \qquad \text{and} \qquad F_x = F \cos \theta. \qquad (8b)$$

Example 1. A force of 50 lb is applied to the handle of a 150 lb lawn roller. See Fig. 8B. Calculate (a) the horizontal and vertical components of this force if the

59

handle makes an angle of 40° with the horizontal, and (b) the force exerted by the roller on the ground.

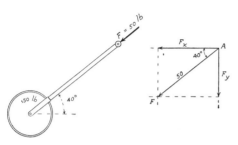

Solution. The graphical solution to (a) is shown at the right in Fig. 8B. The magnitudes of the two components F_x and F_y are calculated by direct substitutions in Eq.(8b).

$$F_x = 50 \text{ lb} \times \cos 40°$$
$$F_y = 50 \text{ lb} \times \sin 40°.$$

From tables of natural sines and cosines, substitution gives

$$F_x = 50 \times 0.766 = 38.3 \text{ lb}$$
$$F_y = 50 \times 0.643 = 32.1 \text{ lb}.$$

FIG. 8B—The force on the handle of a lawn roller is resolved into two components.

The horizontal component, $F_x = 38.3$ lb, is the force causing the roller to move, while the vertical component, $F_y = 32.1$ lb, acting straight downward must be added to the weight of the roller to find the total force exerted by the roller on the ground.

$$\text{Total downward force} = 150 + 32.1 = 182.1 \text{ lb.}$$

8.2. The Sailboat. A problem that puzzles many people, particularly those more or less familiar with sailboats, is that of sailing across the water into the wind. This phenomenon, commonly known as *tacking,* is another illustration of the resolution of a force into rectangular components.

As shown in Fig. 8C, the wind is from the east and the boat is headed *NE.* When the sail is properly set, the wind, in blowing across the canvas, is deflected away in such a way that it exerts a force F normal to the surface as shown. By resolving this force into two rectangular components, one parallel and the other perpendicular to the keel, the force B, responsible for the boat's motion, is found.

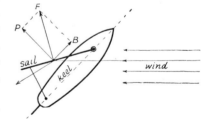

The other component, P, has little effect upon the boat since it is perpendicular to the motion. It is a useless force which tends to tip the boat and move it to leeward. To reduce tipping or being

FIG. 8C—A boat sailing into the wind. An example of the resolution of a force F into two rectangular components, P and B.

pushed sideways, sailboats are equipped with a deep heavy keel. By increasing the angle between the sail and the wind, the force F will increase but the forward component will decrease. If the boat is headed more directly into the wind, without changing the relative position of the sail and the keel, the useful component B will again decrease. Most rapid progress upwind is attained when the wind and keel make an angle of 45° and the sails so rigged that the rudder is parallel to the keel.

8.3. Vector Addition by the Method of Components. When several forces act upon a body simultaneously, their resultant force may be determined by any one of a number of different methods. Some methods involve long and tedious processes of calculation, while others involve a minimum number of simple operations. Of the graphical solutions of force problems, the polygon method just described in Section 7.5 is undoubtedly the simplest. Of the analytical solutions, however, the Method of Components is generally the shortest and is preferred because of its simplicity.

As an illustration of the method of components, consider the example of the four forces shown graphically at the left in Fig. 8D; $F_1 = 5$ lb at 30°, $F_2 = 4$ lb at 90°, $F_3 = 7$ lb at 135°, and $F_4 = 6$ lb at 240°. The problem here is to find the resultant force equivalent to all four together.

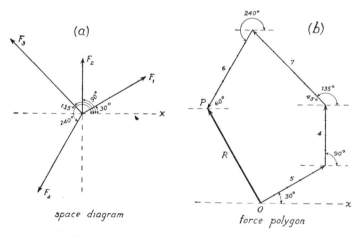

Fig. 8D—Illustrating the polygon method of vector addition for four forces.

The right-hand figure shows the graphical solution with all given angles measured from the *x-axis*. The analytical solution consists of performing the following operations:

(1) Each force is resolved into x- and y-components.
(2) The x-components are added to give a resultant X-component.

(3) *The y-components are added to give a resultant Y-component.*
(4) *The resultant X- and Y-components are combined at right angles to obtain their resultant R.*

The first of these steps is shown graphically in Fig. 8E. Each vector is drawn in its proper direction and the *x*- and *y*-components found separately by using Eq.(8b). For F_1 the *x*-component is 5 cos 30° = 4.33 lb and the *y*-component is 5 sin 30° = 2.5 lb. For F_2 the *x*-component is zero and the

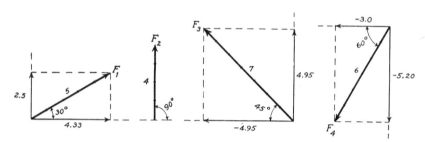

Fɪɢ. 8E—Resolution of all forces into *x*- and *y*-components.

y-component 4 lb. For F_3 the *x*-component is 7 cos 45° = 4.95 lb and the *y*-component is 7 sin 45° = 4.95 lb. Finally for F_4 the *x*-component is 6 cos 60° = 3.0 lb and the *y*-component is 6 sin 60° = 5.20 lb.

Components to the right or up are positive in sign; components to the left or down are negative in sign. The second and third steps of adding *x*- and *y*-components separately are tabulated below, and the fourth step of combining the *X*- and *Y*-components is shown graphically in Fig. 8F.

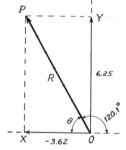

Fɪɢ. 8F—Resultant *X*-and *Y*-components added vectorially to give the resultant *R*.

x-components	*y*-components
+4.33 lb	+2.50 lb
+0.00	+4.00
−4.95	+4.95
−3.00	−5.20
$X = -3.62$ lb	$Y = +6.25$ lb

From the tabulated *x*-components, *X* has the magnitude −3.62 lb; and from the *y*-components, *Y* has the magnitude +6.25 lb.

Since *X* and *Y* are at right angles to each other, the triangle *OPX* is a right triangle and the hypothenuse *R* is given by

$$R = \sqrt{(3.62)^2 + (6.25)^2} = 7.23 \text{ lb.}$$

The angle θ is obtained from the tangent relation in Eq.(8a),

$$\tan \theta = \frac{6.25}{3.62} = 1.726$$

giving $\theta = 59.9°$. The direction angle of R from the $+x$ direction is $180 - 59.9$, or $120.1°$.

The graphs accompanying the solution above may be combined into one diagram as shown in Fig. 8G. In this figure the original space diagram of forces, as well as all the components, are indicated. The x-components are OP, OM, and ON, while the y-components are OA, OB, OC, and OF$_2$.

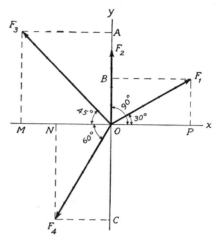

FIG. 8G—Vector diagram showing all forces and the x- and y-components.

A general formula that can be used for solving problems involving many forces by the method of components is the following:

$$X = F_1 \cos \theta_1 + F_2 \cos \theta_2 + F_3 \cos \theta_3 + \cdots + F_n \cos \theta_n \qquad (8c)$$
$$Y = F_1 \sin \theta_1 = F_2 \sin \theta_2 + F_3 \sin \theta_3 + \cdots + F_n \sin \theta_n \qquad (8d)$$
$$\text{and } R^2 = X^2 + Y^2 \qquad \text{and } \tan \theta = Y/X. \qquad (8e)$$

In abbreviated notation,

$$X = \Sigma F \cos \theta \qquad (8f)$$
$$Y = \Sigma F \sin \theta. \qquad (8g)$$

The Greek letter Σ indicates a summation.

PROBLEMS

1. An upward force of 16 newtons makes an angle of 35 with the vertical. Calculate its vertical and horizontal components.

2. A force of 55 dynes makes an angle of 54° with the x-axis. Calculate the x- and y-components. (*Ans.* 32.3 dynes and 44.5 dynes.)

3. A heavy box weighing 100 lb is being pulled across the floor by a 65 lb force inclined at an angle of 40° with the horizontal. Find (a) the vertical and horizontal components of the applied force, and (b) the resultant vertically downward force on the floor.

4. A lawn roller weighing 200 lb is pushed along the ground by a force of 45 lb making an angle of 30° with the horizontal. Find (a) the x- and y-components of the applied force, and (b) the resultant of the two forces F and W. See Fig. 8B. (*Ans.* (a) 39 lb and 22.5 lb, (b) 226 lb at 10° to the vertical.)

5. A 60-lb force makes an angle of 35° with the x-axis. Find the two components of this force acting in directions of 15° and 65° respectively.

6. A single force of 320 lb at 27° is to be resolved into two components whose direction angles are 5° and 76° respectively. Determine their magnitude. (*Ans.* 255 lb and 127 lb.)

7. Apply the method of components to the following three forces, and find their resultant: (1) 8 dynes at 35°, (2) 3 dynes at 125°, and (3) 2 dynes at 165°.

8. Apply the method of components to the following three forces and find their resultant; (1) 4 newtons at 120°, (2) 6 newtons at 30°, and (3) 5 newtons at 340°. (*Ans.* 9.3 newtons at 32°.)

9. The following four forces act on the same body, (a) 20 newtons at 245°, (b) 12 newtons at 340°, (c) 15 newtons at 25°, and (d) 10 newtons at 135°. Apply the method of components to find the resultant.

10. Four forces act on the same body: (a) 40 lb at 315°, (b) 50 lb at 200°, (c) 60 lb at 35°, and (d) 35 lb at 100°. Find their resultant by the method of components. (*Ans.* 33.8 lb at 44°.)

11. A man exerts a force of 250 newtons along the handle of a 150 kg roller. The handle makes an angle of 35° with the ground. Find (a) the horizontal and vertical components of this force, and (b) the force exerted by the roller on the ground.

12. A sailboat is tacking at 45° into the wind. If the resultant force exerted by the wind on the sail is 180 lb and the boom makes an angle of 30° with the keel, find the forward thrust on the boat. (*Ans.* 90 lb.)

13. The wind exerts a resultant force of 500 newtons on the sail of a small boat. If the angle between the wind and keel is 45° and the angle between the boom and keel is 20°, find the forward thrust on the boat.

14. Apply the method of components to find the resultant of the following four forces: (a) 10 newtons at 120°, (b) 5 newtons at 270°, (c) 4 newtons at 45°, and (d) 12.5 newtons at 0°. (*Ans.* 12.2 newtons at 32.1°.)

15. A ball weighing 3.5 lb on a 30° inclined plane rests against a brick lying on the plane. Find the force exerted on the brick by the wall.

16. Four forces act on the same body. Find their resultant. (a) 10 lb at 20°, (b) 6 lb at 90°, (c) 12 lb at 220°, and (d) 2 lb at 0°. (*Ans.* 2.78 lb at 37.7°.)

17. A 50 kg wagon on a 20° inclined plane is kept from rolling down hill by a rope tied to a tree. If the rope is parallel to the incline, what is the tension in the rope?

Newton's Law of Gravitation
and Third Law of Motion   Chapter 9

9.1. Newton's Law of Gravitation. Nearly everyone has heard the story of how young Isaac Newton, while sitting under an apple tree one day, was struck on the head by a falling apple. This incident set Newton to thinking about falling bodies and led him at the early age of twenty-three to the discovery of the law of gravity.

It has often been said incorrectly that Newton discovered gravity. What Newton discovered was the *universal law of gravitation. Any two bodies attract each other with a force proportional to the product of their masses and inversely proportional to the square of the distance between them.* Written in algebraic symbols,

$$F \propto \frac{m_1 \, m_2}{d^2}.$$

As illustrated in Fig. 9A, F is the force of attraction, m_1 and m_2 are the two masses, and d is the distance between them. Mass m_1 pulls on m_2 with a force F to the left and m_2 pulls on m_1 with an equal force F to the right. To make an equation of this symbolism it is only necessary to replace the proportionality constant above by an equal sign and insert a constant on either side of the equality.

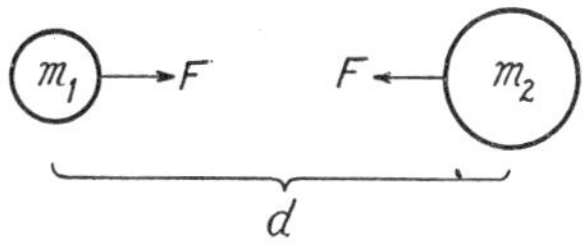

Fig. 9A—Illustrating the gravitational attraction of one body of mass m_1 for another of mass m_2.

$$F = G \frac{m_1 \, m_2}{d^2}. \tag{9a}$$

Experiment shows that if F is measured in newtons, m_1 and m_2 in kilograms, and d in meters, the "Newtonian Constant of Gravitation" G has the value

$$G = 6.66 \times 10^{-11} \frac{m^3}{\text{kg sec}^2}. \tag{9b}$$

If F is in dynes, m_1 and m_2 in grams, and d in centimeters,

$$G = 6.66 \times 10^{-8} \frac{\text{cm}^3}{\text{gm sec}^2}.$$

If F is in pounds, m_1 and m_2 in slugs, and d in feet,

$$G = 3.41 \times 10^{-8} \frac{\text{ft}^4}{\text{lb sec}^4}. \tag{9c}$$

To obtain some idea of the magnitude of gravitational forces consider the following example.

Example 1. Calculate the force of attraction between two weights of 1 lb each, held in the hands 1 ft apart.

Solution. By substitution in Eq.(9a),

$$F = 3.41 \times 10^{-8} \frac{\text{ft}^4}{\text{lb sec}^4} \cdot \frac{1 \text{ lb} \times 1 \text{ lb}}{(32 \times 32 \text{ ft}^2/\text{sec}^4) \ 1 \text{ ft}^2} = 3.33 \times 10^{-11} \text{ lb}.$$

This force is far too small to be detected by the muscle senses of the hands or arms.

9.2. The Cavendish Experiment. This is a famous experiment performed by Henry Cavendish* in the year 1797 to 1798, and is frequently

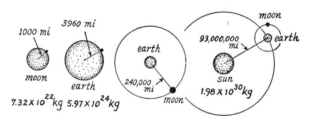

Fig. 9B—Gravitational attraction keeps the moon in its orbit around the earth, and the earth in its orbit around the sun.

referred to as "weighing the earth." The principal features of the experiment consisted in determining the attracting forces between two pairs of lead spheres by means of a torsion balance. A diagram of the apparatus is

---

* Henry Cavendish (1731-1810), English chemist and physicist, elder son of Lord Charles Cavendish, brother of the third duke of Devonshire, and Lady Anne Grey, daughter of the duke of Kent, was born at Nice on October 10, 1731. Although one of the richest men of his time through inheritance, he devoted his life to scientific work. He had little interest in society, always avoided the attention of his fellows, and never married. He was a member of the Royal Society and is best known for his experiments on gravitational attraction. He is also noted for his contributions to the chemistry of gases, and for his work on electrical condensers and the inverse square law of force between electrical charges.

shown in Fig. 9C. A rod 6 ft long was supported at its center by a long
wire P. At the ends of the rod were
two lead balls, m_1 and m_2, each 2 in.
in diameter. Two lead spheres, M_1
and M_2, each 12 in. in diameter,
were then placed on either side as
shown. Gravitational attraction between m_1 and M_1 and between m_2
and M_2 caused the rod C to turn
through a small angle and come to
rest in some position like that
shown by the solid lines.

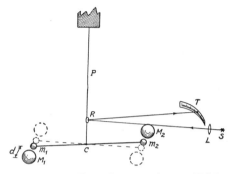

Fig. 9C—The Cavendish Experiment. Weighing the earth.

Shifting M_1 and M_2 to the opposite sides of m_1 and m_2 caused the
rod C to turn to a new position indi-
cated by the dotted lines. The angle through which the rod turned was
measured by a small telescope or by reflection of a beam of light from a small
mirror R onto a distant scale. From previous measurements of the stiffness
of the supporting wire F, and a measure of the angle turned through, the
force of attraction between the masses could be calculated.

Neglecting cross attractions, of right sphere on left ball and left sphere
on right ball, the angle between the two positions was four times as great
as the deflection of the rod due to the attraction force of one sphere on one
ball.

It will now be shown how the measured force in such an experiment
makes it possible to calculate the earth's mass. Knowing the masses of m_1
and M_1 by weighing, and the distance between them, d, from measurement,
all can be substituted in Eq.(9a) and the only
unknown quantity, G, calculated. The value
found is that given in Eqs.(9b) and (9c).

Consider now the attraction between the
earth, of unknown mass M, and a 1 gm mass
on its surface, as shown in Fig. 9D. In this instance, the force on the 1 gm mass is known.
The force is just 980 dynes for it can be calculated from Newton's Second Law, Eq.(6b),
using the measured acceleration due to gravity
$g = 980 \ cm/sec^2$. See Fig. 6E.

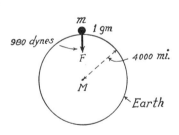

Fig. 9D—The earth exerts a
downward force of 980 dynes on
each gram of mass on its surface.

From experimental measurements and calculation the following quantities are, therefore, known.

$$m = 1 \text{ gm} \qquad G = 6.66 \times 10^{-8} \text{ cm}^3/\text{gm sec}^2$$
$$F = 980 \text{ dynes} \qquad d = 3960 \text{ mi} = 6.37 \times 10^8 \text{ cm}.$$

Substituting these values in Eq.(9a), the only unknown quantity, the mass of the earth M, can be calculated. Letting $m_1 = m$ and $m_2 = M$,

$$F = G \frac{m \times M}{d^2}.$$

Transposition and substitution of known values give

$$M = \frac{F \times d^2}{m \times G} = \frac{980 \times (6.37 \times 10^8)^2}{1 \times 6.66 \times 10^{-8}} = 5.97 \times 10^{27} \text{ gm}.$$

This is a reasonable value for the earth's mass, for if it is divided by the earth's volume, $\frac{4}{3}\pi r^3$, the average density of *5.4 gm/cm³* is obtained. The average density of the rocks found at and near the earth's surface is 2.7 gm/cm³. This means, therefore, that deep within the earth's body the average density must rise to 8 or 10 gm/cm³. Such values are entirely reasonable since most metals have just such densities.

The above experiment is assumed, therefore, to be correct in principle and to be a means for determining the mass of the earth.

Earth's mass $M = 5.97 \times 10^{27}$ gm.

9.3. Newton's Third Law of Motion.

Of Newton's three laws of motion the third is perhaps the least understood. This is probably due to the fact that it is seldom used in solving problems, and often when it is used it is incorrectly applied. The law states that *to every action force there is an equal and opposite reaction force.**

Fig. 9E — A bat at all times exerts a force on the ball equal in magnitude to the force the ball exerts on the bat.

The principle of action and reaction may be illustrated by a bat striking a ball, Fig. 9E. During impact the bat exerts a force F on the ball, and the ball exerts an equal but opposite force G on the bat. The force F being exerted on the ball gives it an acceleration to the right, while the force G being exerted on the bat gives it an acceleration to the left. The ball speeds up, during the impact and acquires a high velocity while the bat in the same time interval slows down to a lower velocity. The impulse Ft from the bat gives the ball a momentum mv. See Eq.(6j). The impulse Gt from the ball decreases the momentum of the bat from a higher value to one of lower value.

Consider the second example of a block hanging by a cord as illustrated

*Newton's Third Law, as published in Latin in his "Principia" is, Lex. III. Actioni contrariam semper et aequalem esse reactionem; sive corporum duorum actiones in se mutuo semper esse aequales et in partes contrarias dirigi.

in Fig. 9F. The weight of the block W is the force with which the earth pulls downward on the block, while the equal and opposite force X is the upward force exerted by the block on the earth.

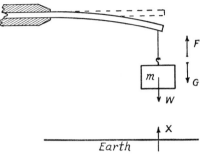

In addition to this pair of forces, the block exerts a downward force G on the cord, while the cord pulls upward with the reaction force F. Although to many people these forces may seem confusing, it should be pointed out that Newton himself had some difficulty in applying his third law to certain problems. The difficulty

Fig. 9F—Illustrating Newton's Third Law of Motion. Forces always exist in pairs.

arises from trying to apply action and reaction forces to the same body when in reality they apply to different ones. It is important to note that *the action force and the reaction force in Newton's third law of motion act on different bodies.*

Whether a body is at rest or in motion, the state of that body depends upon the forces acting on it and not upon the forces it exerts on something else. So far as the body is concerned, the latter do not determine its motion.

9.4. Isolating a Body. Forces are vector quantities and must be added by the principles of vector addition. To illustrate, the block in Fig. 9F remains at rest because two equal and opposite forces are acting upon it. To see what these forces are, the body is isolated by drawing a dotted line around it as shown in Fig. 9G. Only those forces acting on the body from outside this boundary determine its state or motion. The earth is pulling down on the block with a

Fig. 9G—Balanced forces produce equilibrium.

force W while the cord is pulling up on the block with an equal but opposite force F. By vector addition shown at the right, the resultant force must be zero. (It should be noted that F and W are not an action and reaction pair, even though they happen here to be equal.)

Suppose in Fig. 9F that the force F is increased to a value greater than W. The block will then have an unbalanced force acting and it will be accelerated upward. By vector addition, as shown in Fig. 9H, the resultant

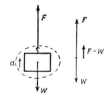

Fig. 9H—Because of a resultant force $F-W$ the body is accelerated upward.

upward force is equal to $F - W$. The acceleration can be calculated by applying Newton's Second Law, $F = ma$, the force here being $F - W$.

$$F - W = ma$$
$$\text{force} = \text{mass} \times \text{acceleration.} \tag{9d}$$

If, on the other hand, the force F is smaller than the weight W, the body will be accelerated downward and $W - F$ is the resultant force acting. Again applying Newton's Second Law,

$$W - F = ma$$
$$\text{force} = \text{mass} \times \text{acceleration.} \tag{9e}$$

In each case, the smaller force is subtracted from the larger to make the acceleration come out with a positive sign in the direction of motion.

Example 3. An elevator weighing 1000 lb is raised and lowered by a cable fastened at the top. Calculate the tension in the cable when the elevator (a) starts up with an acceleration of 2.4 ft/sec²; (b) is rising with constant velocity; (c) starts down with an acceleration of 2.4 ft/sec²; and (d) goes down with constant velocity.

Solution. (a) For acceleration upward Eq.(9d) is applied. By direct substitution,

$$F - 1000 \text{ lb} = \frac{1000 \text{ lb}}{32 \text{ ft/sec}^2} \times 2.4 \text{ ft/sec}^2$$

giving

$$F = 1000 \text{ lb} + 75 \text{ lb} = 1075 \text{ lb.}$$

(b) Moving upward with constant velocity the elevator has no acceleration. With $a = 0$, Eq.(9d) gives

$$F - W = 0 \quad \text{or} \quad F = W.$$

The tension in the cable equals the weight of the elevator, 1000 lb.

(c) For acceleration downward, Eq.(9e) is used. By direct substitution,

$$1000 \text{ lb} - F = \frac{1000 \text{ lb}}{32 \text{ ft/sec}^2} \times 2.4 \text{ ft/sec}^2$$

giving

$$F = 1000 \text{ lb} - 75 \text{ lb} = 925 \text{ lb.}$$

(d) Moving downward with constant velocity there is no acceleration, and the tension in the cable is 1000 lb.

9.5. The Atwood Machine. The Atwood Machine is a contrivance often used in the physics laboratory for determining the acceleration of gravity. The experiment involves the application of Newton's Second Law to the acceleration of a set of masses, as shown in Fig. 9I. Two equal masses are fastened to the ends of a long cord which passes over a light weight ball-bearing pulley P. At a given instant, a small mass, called a rider, is added to one side, thus setting the system moving with an acceleration a.

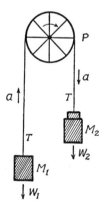

Fig. 9I—Schematic diagram of the Atwood machine.

By measuring the distances moved in *1, 2, 3, 4,* and *5* sec, the acceleration a can be calculated. Knowing the masses M_1 and M_2, the acceleration due to gravity is calculated from the formula,

$$g = \frac{M_2 + M_1}{M_2 - M_1} a. \tag{9f}$$

The first step in deriving this equation from the force equation is to find the resultant force acting on the entire moving system. On the left side there is the downward force of gravity on M_1 equal to

$$W_1 = M_1 g. \tag{9g}$$

On the right-hand side then is the downward pull of gravity on M_2 equal to

$$W_2 = M_2 g. \tag{9h}$$

Since these two forces oppose each other, the resultant force F, causing the acceleration of the system, is their difference $W_2 - W_1$.

$$F = W_2 - W_1. \tag{9i}$$

But, from Eqs.(9g) and (9h),

$$W_2 - W_1 = M_2 g - M_1 g.$$

Multiplying out,

$$W_2 - W_1 = (M_2 - M_1)g. \tag{9j}$$

Neglecting the pulley and the cord, the total moving mass is $M_2 + M_1$. Therefore, by substituting in the force equation,

$$(M_2 - M_1)g = (M_2 + M_1)a$$
$$\text{force} = \text{mass} \times \text{acceleration} \tag{9k}$$

which upon transposing becomes Eq.(9f).

To obtain a more accurate value of g from experiments with the Atwood machine, it is customary to correct for the motion of the pulley. This is done by adding what is called the *mass equivalent* of the *pulley* to the whole moving mass $M_2 + M_1$. Sometimes a correction is also made for pulley friction.

To calculate the tension in the cord passing over the pulley (see Fig. 9J), Newton's Second Law can be applied to either one of the masses M_1 or M_2 separately. First, the mass M_1 should be isolated by a dotted line as illustrated in Fig. 9H. The two forces now acting on this mass are W_1 acting downward and the tension T acting upward. Since the mass in question is moving upward with an acceleration a the tension T is greater than W_1. The resultant force is, therefore, upward and equal in magnitude to $T - W_1$. By Newton's Second Law then,

$$T - W_1 = M_1 a$$
$$\text{force} = \text{mass} \times \text{acceleration.} \tag{91}$$

Knowing W_1, M, and a the tension T can be calculated.

A similar isolation and treatment of the other mass M_2 will give the same tension T. Isolating the larger mass and noting that W_2 is greater than T, Newton's Second Law gives

$$W_2 - T = M_2 a.$$
$$\text{force} = \text{mass} \times \text{acceleration} \tag{9m}$$

The tension is assumed the same throughout the total length of the cord, the pulley acting only to change its direction.

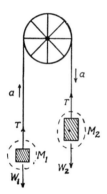

Example 4. Two masses, one of 60 gm and the other of 100 gm are fastened to opposite ends of a cord and the cord hung over a pulley. Neglecting friction, calculate (a) the acceleration of the system, and (b) the tension in the cord.

Solution. As diagrammed in Fig. 9J this problem is similar to the Atwood machine with $M_1 = 60$ *gm,* and $M_2 = 100$ *gm.* Apply Eq.(9k), and transpose.

Fig. 9J—Problem in accelerated motion.

$$a = \frac{M_2 - M_1}{M_2 + M_1} g = \frac{40 \text{ gm}}{160 \text{ gm}} 980 \frac{\text{cm}}{\text{sec}^2} = 245 \frac{\text{cm}}{\text{sec}^2}.$$

The system has an acceleration of 245 cm/sec².
To find the tension in the cord, Eq.(91) is applied to the smaller mass of 60 gm. Transpose and remember that $W = Mg$.

$$T = W_1 + M_1 a, \qquad T = 60 \text{ gm} \times 980 \frac{\text{cm}}{\text{sec}^2} + 60 \text{ gm} \times 245 \frac{\text{cm}}{\text{sec}^2} = 73{,}500 \text{ dynes.}$$

As a check apply Eq.(9m) to the larger mass. Transpose and change signs in the equation.

$$T = W_2 - M_2 a.$$

By direct substitution, we obtain, as before,

$$T = 73{,}500 \text{ dynes.}$$

9.6. The Train-and-Track Experiment.

Another illustration of Newton's Third Law is that of a train on a track, both of which, the track as well as the train, are free to move. The drive wheels push back on the track with a force B, and the track pushes forward on the wheels with an equal and opposite force F. These two form an action and reaction pair.

In Fig. 9K, the track is mounted on a large wheel with its axis of rotation vertical. With the track free to move, both forces of the pair are seen to be real, the track moves backward and the train moves forward. The track moves backward because the wheels exert a force B upon it in that direction, and the train goes forward because the track exerts a force upon it in that direction. If, when the train acquires a certain velocity, the power is shut off, the force F vanishes—so also does B—and the train and track continue to move with constant speed.

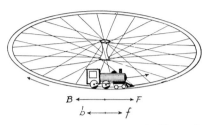

Fig. 9K—Demonstration of Newton's Third Law of Motion. The train moves forward and the track, if free to move, moves backward.

In a practical case, however, the track is not only fastened down, but there is some frictional resistance to motion. Because of this friction the track pushes forward on the wheels with a force b, and the wheels push backward on the track with an equal but opposite force f.

In order to keep a train moving with constant speed, a minimum force B great enough to overcome friction must continually be supplied to the locomotive drive wheels. The two forces acting on the train then are F and b, and these being equal and opposite have a zero resultant. There being no resultant force, there is no acceleration and the train continues to move with constant velocity.

To start the train moving, and to maintain an acceleration, F must be greater than b. Under these conditions the acceleration, by Newton's Second Law, is

$$F - b = ma$$
force = mass $\times$ acceleration.

PROBLEMS

1. Two army tanks, weighing 15 tons each, pass each other. If the distance between their centers of mass at closest approach is 14 ft what is the gravitational attraction between them in pounds?

2. A man weighs 160 lb on the earth. Calculate his weight if he were on the moon. Assume the earth's mass to be 81 times that of the moon and the respective radii to be 4000 mi and 1000 mi. (*Ans.* 31.6 lb.)

3. An elevator car weighing 1200 lb is pulled upward with an acceleration of 1.4 ft/sec. Calculate the total tension in the cables.

4. The hopper in a coal hoist has a mass of 800 kg when fully loaded. If starting from rest at the bottom of a mine shaft it is given an upward acceleration of 0.6 m/sec^2 what is the tension in the cable in newtons? (*Ans.* 8320 newtons.)

5. An elevator weighing 900 lb contains 6 persons averaging 140 lb apiece. Find the tension in the cable supporting the car if the car is (a) standing still, (b) moving upward with an acceleration of 1.5 ft/sec², and (c) moving downward with the same acceleration.

6. Two masses of 175 and 125 gm respectively are fastened to opposite ends of a string and the string hung over a pulley. Calculate (a) the acceleration of the system, and (b) the tension in the string. Neglect friction and the weight of the string and pulley. (*Ans.* (a) 163.3 cm/sec², (b) 143,000 dynes.)

7. A 15 lb weight and a 6 lb weight are fastened to opposite ends of a cord and the cord hung over a pulley. What is (a) the acceleration of the system, and (b) the tension in the cord? Neglect friction and the weight of the string and pulley.

8. If the frictional force offered to the acceleration of a 65 ton locomotive is 350 lb, what force is required to give it an acceleration of 1.5 ft/sec²? (*Ans.* 6444 lb.)

9. If the frictional force acting against the acceleration, along the runway, of a 40,000 kg transport plane is 1500 newtons what force will be required to give it an acceleration of 0.6 m/sec²?

10. A boy weighing 90 lb stands on a spring scale on the floor of an elevator. What will the scale read when (a) the elevator starts up with an acceleration of 3.2 ft/sec², (b) when it starts down with the same acceleration? (*Ans.* (a) 99 lb, (b) 81 lb.)

11. A man weighing 150 lb slides down a rope. By wrapping the rope once around his leg he maintains a downward acceleration of 2 ft/sec². What is the tension in the rope in lb?

12. An elevator car having a mass of 300 kg is descending with a speed of 5 m/sec. If the maximum load permitted on the cables is 4900 newtons, what is the shortest distance in which the car can be stopped? (*Ans.* 1.91 m.)

13. Driving along a level road at 60 mi/hr in a car weighing 3600 lb a driver suddenly applies the brakes. If the car comes to rest in 3 sec, find the average force.

14. A large box weighing 160 lb falls from a truck traveling with a speed of 45 mi/hr along the highway. If the box slides for a total distance of 120 ft what is the average force slowing it down? (*Ans.* 90.8 lb.)

15. Show that if the mass of the pulley be negligibly small, and the friction of the bearings negligibly small, etc., the tension in the cord in Fig. 9J is given by the equation $T = 2M_1M_2g/(M_1 + M_2)$.

16. Two masses of 60 gm and 50 gm, respectively, are fastened to the opposite ends of a light flexible string which passes over a pulley assumed frictionless. Neglecting the mass of the string and pulley, find (a) the acceleration, and (b) the tension in the string. (*Ans.* (a) 89.1 cm/sec². (b) 53,400 dynes.)

17. A 200 lb man stands in an elevator car. What force does the floor exert on him when the elevator (a) rises at a constant speed of 4 ft/sec, and (b) accelerates upward at 4 ft/sec².

18. A locomotive capable of exerting a force of 5 tons is connected to a train of cars. If the total weight of the train is 240 tons, and the resistance to motion amounts to 1500 lb, find the maximum possible acceleration. (*Ans.* 0.567 ft/sec².)

19. A 120 kg trunk falls from a truck traveling with a speed of 24 km/hr along the highway. If the trunk slides for a total distance of 20 m before coming to rest, what is the average force slowing it down?

20. (a) What is the least acceleration with which a man weighing 170 lb can slide down a rope that can sustain a tension of 100 lb? (b) What will his speed be after sliding 20 ft? (*Ans.* (a) 13.2 ft/sec. (b) 23 ft/sec.)

Balanced and Unbalanced Forces

Chapter 10

10.1. Conditions for Equilibrium. When one or more forces act upon a body at rest, and their resultant sum is not zero, the body will be set into motion. Under such conditions there is an *unbalanced force* acting and this force alone accounts for the motion. If, however, the vector sum of all the forces acting is zero, the body is in equilibrium and the body will either remain at rest or, if moving, maintain constant velocity. To turn this statement around is to say that *"any object remaining at rest, or moving with uniform motion, is in equilibrium and the resultant of all forces acting upon it is zero."*

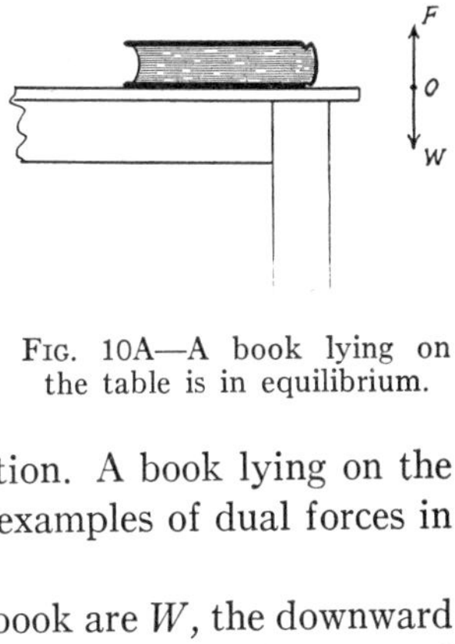

Fig. 10A—A book lying on the table is in equilibrium.

If two and only two forces act upon a body in equilibrium a little study will show that they must be equal in magnitude and opposite in direction. A book lying on the table or a lamp hanging from the ceiling are good examples of dual forces in equilibrium. See Fig. 10A.

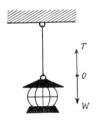

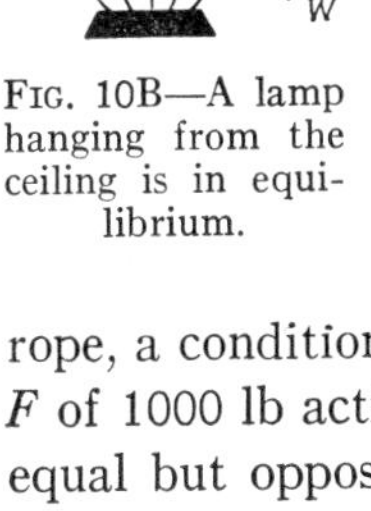

Fig. 10B—A lamp hanging from the ceiling is in equilibrium.

The two forces acting on the book are W, the downward pull of the earth, called the *weight*, and F, the upward thrust of the table. Since the book is in equilibrium, the force F is equal in magnitude to the weight W. For the lamp at the left the downward force or weight is counterbalanced by the upward tension in the cord. Here again, the forces are equal in magnitude and opposite in direction. A body moving with constant velocity is in equilibrium: since there is no acceleration, there is no unbalanced force.

In the game of tug-of-war, when two opposing teams are pulling with equal but opposite forces at the ends of a rope, a condition of equilibrium exists. As, illustrated in Fig. 10C, the force F of 1000 lb acting to pull the knot K to the right is counterbalanced by an equal but opposite force $-F$ of 1000 lb pulling it to the left. If the two forces become unequal, equilibrium will no longer exist and the knot K will move in the direction of the greater force. It should be noted in the equilibrium case that the tension in the rope is 1000 lb and not 2000 lb. This apparent paradox can be explained away by supposing that one team ties their end of the rope to a post. The other team still pulling with their 1000 lb maintains the same equilibrium conditions as before and in so doing maintains the tension of 1000 lb. One team can be looked upon as holding the rope so the other team can pull.

Fig. 10C—The tension in the rope is 1000 lb.

10.2. Three Forces in Equilibrium. When, as the result of the action of three forces, a body is in equilibrium, the *resultant* of all three forces must be zero. In other words, *to be in equilibrium, the force polygon must close.* With three forces, such a polygon would have only three sides, that is, it would be a triangle. As an illustration, consider the street light suspended from two poles as shown in Fig. 10D.

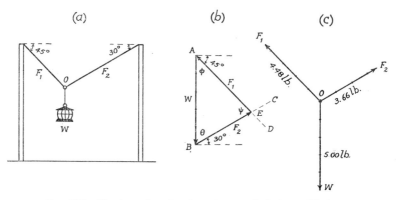

Fig. 10D—The lamp hanging from two cords is in equilibrium.

The three forces acting through the common point O are W the weight of the lamp 5 lb acting straight downward, F_1 the pull of one rope at 45° up and to the left, and F_2 the pull of the other rope at 30° up and to the right. The force polygon is shown in diagram (b), where vectorially

$$\overrightarrow{W} + \overrightarrow{F_2} + \overrightarrow{F_1} = 0.$$

In constructing this diagram, the conditions of equilibrium are imposed as a means of determining the magnitude of the forces F_1 and F_2. The graphical procedure is as follows: a vector of length 5 units is first drawn straight downward to represent W, the weight of the light. To the head of this vector at B a dotted line BC is drawn parallel to the rope exerting the force F_2. From A another dotted line AD is drawn parallel to the rope exerting the force F_1. At E, where these two lines intersect, the vectors F_1 and F_2 are terminated and arrowheads inserted in the directions shown. The solid lines AE and BE, when measured, are found to have lengths of 4.48 and 3.66 units and represent the forces $F_1 = 4.48$ lb and $F_2 = 3.66$ lb, respectively.

To solve the same problem analytically, the internal angles of the triangle ABE are first determined and then the Law of Sines applied to find the lengths of the sides AE and BE. Using the angles given in diagram (b), subtraction gives angle $\phi = 45°$, angle $\theta = 60°$, and angle $\psi = 75°$. By the Law of Sines,

$$\frac{AE}{\sin \theta} = \frac{W}{\sin \psi}, \quad \text{or} \quad AE = \frac{W \sin 60°}{\sin 75°} = \frac{5 \times 0.866}{0.966} = 4.48 \text{ lb},$$

$$\text{and} \quad \frac{BE}{\sin \phi} = \frac{W}{\sin \psi}, \quad \text{or} \quad BE = \frac{W \sin 45°}{\sin 75°} = \frac{5 \times 0.707}{0.966} = 3.66 \text{ lb}.$$

The magnitudes of the forces are therefore $F_1 = 4.48$ lb, and $F_2 = 3.66$ lb.

The method of the closed polygon applied to objects in equilibrium has many variations and applications. For example, in the problem just analyzed the tensions in the two ropes might be known quantities and the directions unknown. In other words, it might be necessary in an actual case to specify the load each rope is to support and then calculate the angles at which the ropes are to be suspended.

The graphical solution is shown in Fig. 10E, assuming forces $F_1 = 4.48$ lb, $F_2 = 3.66$ lb and $W = 5$ lb. W is first drawn vertically downward and 5 units long. With a compass of radius 4.48 units and a center at A the arc of one circle is drawn as shown by the dotted line. With a radius of 3.66 units and a center at B the arc of another circle is inscribed intersecting the first one at E.

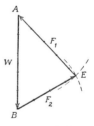

FIG. 10E—A force triangle that closes indicates equilibrium.

The point of intersection and the points A and B when connected by straight lines give the directions and magnitudes of F_1 and F_2. Knowing the lengths of all three sides of the triangle, the Law of Cosines can be applied and the angles calculated. (See Appendix II.) Calculation gives the angle at A as 45°, the angle B as 60°, and the angle E as 75°.

10.3. Resultant and Equilibrant. When, as the result of the action of three forces, a body is in equilibrium, the *resultant* of any two of the forces is always equal and opposite to the remaining force. This is but another statement of the conditions of equilibrium already treated and is in reality the reduction of a three force problem to a two force problem. Consider as an illustration the experiment shown in Fig. 10F.

A weight of 5 lb is supported by two cords at the same angles given in Fig. 10D. The spring scales in diagram (a) show the tensions in the cords, $F_1 = 4.48$ lb and $F_2 = 3.66$ lb. The downward force W in the *force diagram* (b) is the *equilibrant* of the forces F_1 and F_2. The *resultant R* of

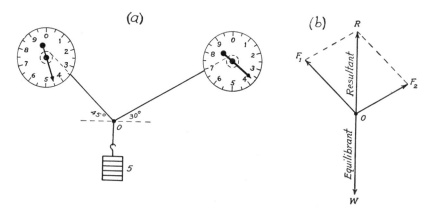

FIG. 10F—Experiment illustrating three forces in equilibrium.

the upward two forces, found by the parallelogram method, is equal and opposite to W. By another diagram similar to (b) it may be shown that the resultant of F_1 and W is a force equal and opposite to F_2, and that the resultant of F_2 and W is a force equal and opposite to F_1. The latter will be left as an exercise for the student.

10.4. Conditions for Equilibrium. *When several forces act upon a body in equilibrium, the force polygon must close.* This, the condition of equilibrium, may be expressed in terms of the x- and y-components of all forces. For a body to be in equilibrium the sum of all the x-components must equal zero, and the sum of all the y-components must equal zero. Symbolically

$$\Sigma F_x = 0 \qquad \Sigma F_y = 0. \qquad (10a)$$

The capital sigma (Σ), indicates a summation.

Example. The following four forces act upon a body, F_1 of 7 lb at 20°, F_2 of 5 lb at 130°, F_3 of 4.5 lb at 180°, and F_4 of 3 lb at 240°. Determine the direction and magnitude of a fifth force that will maintain the body in equilibrium.

First, the resultant of the four given forces will be found by the method of components. The resultant will then be reversed in direction and magnitude and added as the fifth force. By so doing, the force polygon will close, and Eq.(10a) will be satis-

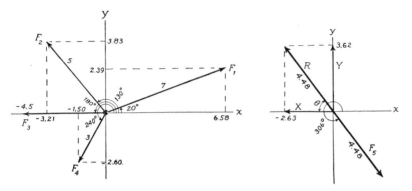

FIG. 10G—Illustrating the conditions of equilibrium by the method components.

fied. A space diagram of forces is shown at the left in Fig. 10G. Perpendiculars
dropped to the x- and y-axes give the following components.

x-components	y-components
$+ 7 \quad \cos 20°$	$+ 7 \quad \sin 20°$
$- 5 \quad \cos 50°$	$+ 5 \quad \sin 50°$
$- 4.5 \cos 0°$	$- 4.5 \sin 0°$
$- 3 \quad \cos 60°$	$- 3 \quad \sin 60°$

Substitute known values and add.

$$
\begin{array}{ll}
+ 7 \times 0.940 = + 6.58 \text{ lb} & + 7 \times 0.342 = + 2.39 \text{ lb} \\
- 5 \times 0.643 = - 3.21 & + 5 \times 0.766 = + 3.83 \\
- 4.5 \times 1 \quad = - 4.50 & - 4.5 \times 0 \quad = \quad 0 \\
- 3 \times 0.500 = - 1.50 & - 3 \times 0.866 = - 2.60 \\
\hline
X \quad = - 2.63 \text{ lb} & Y \quad = + 3.62 \text{ lb}
\end{array}
$$

These two resultant components are combined at the right in Fig. 10G.
By squaring, adding, and taking the square root, we find

$$R = \sqrt{(2.63)^2 + (3.62)^2} = 4.48 \text{ lb.}$$

The angle between R and the x-axis
is calculated from

$$\tan \theta = \frac{Y}{X} = \frac{3.62}{2.63} = 1.376.$$

From a table of tangents,

$$\theta = 54°.$$

When R is reversed, the force F_5 of
4.48 lb, with a direction angle of 306°,
becomes the equilibrant.

All five forces F_1, F_2, F_3, F_4 and F_5
are shown in Fig. 10H forming a closed
polygon. By dropping perpendiculars to

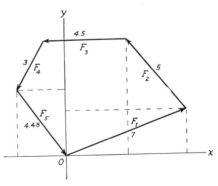

FIG. 10H—To be in equilibrium the forces acting on a body must form a closed polygon.

the x- and y-axes it is seen that the sum of the x-components must be zero, and the sum of the y-components must be zero.

By the analytical method, the summation is as follows:

x-components		*y-components*	
+ 6.58	− 3.21	+ 2.39	− 2.60
+ 2.63	− 4.50	+ 3.83	− 3.62
+ 9.21	− 1.50	0	− 6.22
	− 9.21	+ 6.22	
$\Sigma F_x = 0$		$\Sigma F_y = 0$	

The components X and Y of the resultant R have been reversed in direction to become the components of F_5.

10.5. The Inclined Plane. As an illustration of the resolution of a force into rectangular components and the principle of equilibrium consider the following problem. A boy wishes to pull a small 100 lb wagon up a 50% grade. Such a grade, as shown in Fig. 10I, is one in which for every 100 ft measured along the horizontal there is a vertical rise of 50 ft. The angle θ of such an incline is given by

$$\tan \theta = \frac{50}{100} = 0.500$$

from which $\theta = 26.5°$

To find how hard the boy must pull on the wagon the downward force W, called the weight, is resolved into two components, one a force Q paral-

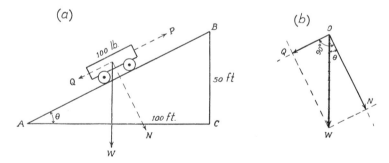

Fig. 10I—Illustrating the resolution of a force into components.

lel to the inclined plane and the other N perpendicular to it. Resolution is shown graphically in diagram (b). The component N, being perpendicular to the inclined plane, neither aids nor hinders the motion up or down. The component Q represents the force which, in the absence of a counterbalancing force, would accelerate the wagon down the incline. To pull the wagon the boy must, therefore, exert a force P equal to or greater than Q, up the plane. Once the wagon is started, a force P, equal to Q, will keep it moving with constant velocity.

To find the magnitudes of Q and N it will be noted that the triangle NOW at the right and the inclined plane at the left are similar triangles. The sides of one are perpendicular to the corresponding sides of the other, from which

$$\sin \theta = \frac{Q}{W}, \quad \text{and} \quad \cos \theta = \frac{N}{W}.$$

By trigonometry,

$$Q = W \sin \theta \qquad (10b)$$
$$N = W \cos \theta. \qquad (10c)$$

Substitute known values of W and θ.

$$Q = 100 \times 0.446 = 44.6 \text{ lb}$$
$$N = 100 \times 0.895 = 89.5 \text{ lb}.$$

An experiment illustrating the above example and its solution is shown in Fig. 10J. A car weighing 1000 lb is held in equilibrium on a 26.5° inclined plane by two cords passing over pulleys to weights of 446 lb and 895 lb. One cord runs parallel and the other perpendicular to the incline. If P is increased or decreased slightly the car will move up or down the plane, whereas if M is increased slightly the car will be lifted from the plane. The removal of the inclined plane entirely does not alter the equilibrium of the suspended mass, and the experimental arrangement is similar to that of Fig. 10F. The

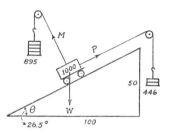

Fig. 10J—Experiment illustrating equilibrium conditions for a car on an inclined plane.

three forces acting to maintain equilibrium are P, M, and W.

10.6. Acceleration Down an Inclined Plane.

Neglecting friction, a body placed on an incline is accelerated down the plane by an unbalanced force. The active force causing the acceleration is Q, calculated in the preceding section as one of the components of the weight W.

$$Q = W \sin \theta.$$

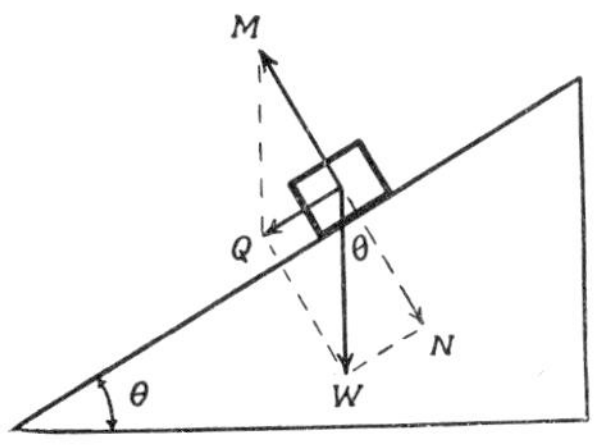

It is shown in Fig. 10K, that Q is in reality the resultant of two forces, one W the down-

Fig. 10K—A block on an inclined plane has an unbalanced force Q acting upon it

ward pull of the earth, and the other M the upward thrust of the incline. In the absence of any friction, M is equal in magnitude and opposite in direction to N, the normal component of W.

$$N = W \cos \theta \qquad (10d)$$

By Newton's Third Law of Motion, if N is taken to represent the force exerted by the block on the incline, M is the equal and opposite force of the incline on the block. The adding of M and W by the parallelogram method gives Q as a resultant. (Note that M and W are the forces acting *on the block*.)

The acceleration down the incline is given by Newton's Second Law of Motion. By the force equation, $F = ma$,

$$Q = ma, \qquad (10e)$$

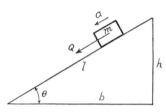

where m is the mass of the body and a is its acceleration. See Fig. 10L. Remembering that $W = mg$, substitution in Eq.(10b) gives

$$Q = mg \sin \theta, \qquad (10f)$$

which, substituted in Eq.(10e), gives

$$ma = mg \sin \theta.$$

Canceling m on both sides,

$$a = g \sin \theta. \qquad (10g)$$

Fig. 10L—A body is accelerated down an inclined plane because of the unbalanced force acting upon it.

Because the mass cancels out the acceleration is independent of mass. In other words, all bodies moving without friction down the same inclined plane should have the same acceleration. Starting from rest all the bodies should acquire the same velocity at the bottom. For an inclined plane tilted up until it is straight up and down the angle θ is increased to $90°$, $\sin \theta = 1$, and Eq.(10g) becomes $a = g$, as it should for free fall. The acceleration a then equals the acceleration due to gravity g.

Since acceleration is a vector quantity, Eq.(10g) can be derived directly from the inclined plane. Replacing W in Fig. 10I by g, component Q becomes a, and Eq.(10b) becomes Eq.(10g).

10.7. Velocity Down an Inclined Plane. To determine the velocity acquired by a body accelerated down an inclined plane standard equations for accelerated motion may be used (see Chap. 4). Assuming a body of mass m to start from rest at the top, its velocity at the bottom will be given by the equation,

$$v^2 = 2as.$$

Substituting Eq.(10g) for the acceleration a, and l the length of the inclined plane for s the distance traveled,

$$v^2 = 2 \times g \sin \theta \times l. \qquad (10h)$$

From the diagram of the incline in Fig. 10M, we obtain

$$\sin \theta = \frac{h}{l}.$$

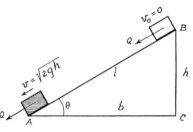

Substitution in Eq.(10h) gives

$$v^2 = 2gh,$$

or

$$v = \sqrt{2gh}. \qquad (10i)$$

FIG. 10M—The velocity acquired by a body sliding without friction down an inclined plane of length l is equal to the velocity for free fall from the same height h.

This is just the velocity acquired by a body falling freely from a height h (see Eq.(5f)). Such a result is important for it shows that the velocity acquired by a body sliding without friction down an inclined plane of any angle θ is equal in magnitude to the velocity acquired by a body falling freely from the same height h. (It should be noted that while the final velocities are the same, the accelerations and the times of descent are different.)

PROBLEMS

1. The two ends of a chain 10 ft long are fastened to hooks 6 ft apart in the ceiling. An airplane motor weighing 240 lb is suspended from the midpoint of the chain. Find the tension in the chain.

2. The ends of a rope 5 m long are fastened to hooks 3 m apart in the ceiling. A 90 kg trunk is hanging from the center of the rope. Find the tension in the rope. (*Ans.* 551.25 newtons.)

3. A farmer wishing to pull a small tree stump out of the ground, fastens one end of a 40 ft cable to the stump and the other end to the trunk of a large tree. By exerting a sideward force of 100 lb he moves the center point of the cable 18 in. Find the pull produced on the stump.

4. Two ends of a picture wire 40 in long are fastened to two screw-eyes 39 in apart on the back of the frame. If the entire picture and frame weighs 8 lb, find the tension in the wire when the picture is hung from a hook on the wall. (*Ans.* 18 lb.)

5. Two forces acting on a body are 6 lb at 20° and 8 lb at 150°. What additional single force will produce equilibrium?

6. What single force will balance the following forces: (a) 3.5 newtons at 45° and (b) 5.7 newtons at 180°. (*Ans.* 4.07 newtons at 142.7°.)

7. A force of 6 newtons has a direction angle of 30°. What two forces having direction angles of 150° and 250° will produce equilibrium?

8. A force of 450 dynes has a direction angle of 90°. What two forces having direction angles of 230° and 340° will produce equilibrium? (*Ans.* 450 dynes and 30.8 dynes.)

9. A boy weighing 80 lb sits in a swing capable of supporting a load of 140 lb. With what force would he have to pull on a horizontal rope to break the swing?

10. A boy weighing 100 lb sits in a swing. (a) With what force should he pull on a horizontal rope to keep the swing at 25° with the vertical? (b) Find the tension in the rope. (*Ans.* (a) 46.6 lb, (b) 110 lb.)

11. Four forces act on a body in equilibrium. Three of the forces are: 50 dynes at 0°, 70 dynes at 70°, and 60 dynes at 230°. Find the remaining force.

12. Four forces act on a body in equilibrium. Three of the forces are: 25 lb at 50°, 40 lb at 110°, and 30 lb at 210°. Find the remaining force. (*Ans.* 47.9 lb at 299.5°.)

13. Five forces act on a body in equilibrium. Four of the forces are; 4 newtons at 30°, 6 newtons at 70°, 5 newtons at 160°, and 7 newtons at 310°. Find (a) the x- and y-components of the remaining force, and (b) the remaining force.

14. A boy coasts down a hill on a sled. Neglecting friction, what force accelerates the boy and sled if they weigh 120 lb and the hill has a slope of 10°? (*Ans.* 20.8 lb.)

15. An automobile with a mass of 2000 kg is towed up a 4 percent grade. Neglecting friction, what force is required to keep the car moving at constant speed?

16. A loaded box-car weighs 24 tons. What force in lb is required from the engine to pull this car up a 1.8 percent grade? (*Ans.* 864 lb.)

17. A man uses a small hand truck to transport a 250 lb crate up a plank onto a station platform. If the truck weighs 70 lb, the platform is 4 ft high, and the plank is 15 ft long, what force parallel to the plank must the man exert?

18. A car on an inclined plane weighs 5500 lb when loaded with passengers. What tension is required in the cable pulling the car up if the incline has a 50 percent grade? (*Ans.* 2460 lb.)

19. A car weighing 3200 lb is coasting down a 10 percent grade. What total force applied by the brakes will keep it moving at 20 mi/hr?

20. A 5-ton truck coasts down a 3 percent grade. What total force applied by the brakes will keep it moving at a constant speed of 25 mi/hr. (*Ans.* 300 lb.)

21. A boy in a small wagon starts from rest and coasts down a hill. If the grade is 4 percent, find (a) his acceleration, and (b) his speed after traveling 300 ft. Neglect friction.

22. A toboggan sled starts from rest at the top of a slide 400 ft long. If the grade is 12 percent, find (a) the acceleration, and (b) the speed at the bottom, in mi/hr. Neglect friction. (*Ans.* (a) 3.81 ft/sec², (b) 55.2 ft/sec or 37.6 mi/hr.)

23. A car weighing 2000 lb coasts down a 4 percent grade. What total force applied by the brakes will hold the car to a downhill acceleration of 0.32 ft/sec²?

24. A train weighing 1000 tons starts down a 1.5 percent grade. What total force applied by the brakes will hold the train to a downhill acceleration of 0.20 ft/sec²? (*Ans.* 17,500 lb.)

25. A stone weighing 250 lb is attached to the upper end of a light pole which makes an angle of 45° with the horizontal. A horizontal rope attached to this same end of the pole holds it at this angle. Find (a) the pull of the rope, and (b) the compressional force in the pole.

26. A stone weighing 60 lb is suspended from one end of a light-weight horizontal rod 3 ft long, the other end of which rests against a vertical wall. The rod is supported at the stone end by a light-weight rope 5 ft long attached to the wall. Find (a) the tension in the rope, and (b) the compressional force in the rod. (*Ans.* (a) 75 lb, (b) 45 lb.)

Friction and Streamlining   Chapter 11

In the preceding chapters on mechanics, the formulas derived, the experiments described, and the problems solved, were idealized to the extent that all friction was neglected. Since friction does exist, and in some cases is not negligibly small, a quantitative treatment of friction becomes a necessity in the solving of many problems.

11.1. Pressure. It is essential in the following treatment of sliding friction to introduce the concept of *pressure* as contrasted with the meaning of *total force*. *Pressure is defined as the force per unit of area.* Written in the form of an equation,

$$\text{pressure} = \frac{\text{total force}}{\text{area}}, \qquad P = \frac{F}{A}. \qquad (11a)$$

As an illustration of the distinction between pressure and total force, consider the two aluminum metal blocks in Fig. 11A. Block (a) stands on

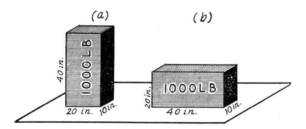

Fig. 11A—A block standing on end exerts a greater pressure than when it is lying on its side.

one end where the area is 200 sq in, while block (b) stands on one edge where the area is 400 sq in. Weighing 1000 lb, each block separately exerts the same downward force. Standing on end as in (a), the downward pressure is given by Eq.(11a) as

$$\text{pressure} = \frac{1000 \text{ lb}}{200 \text{ in}^2} = 5 \frac{\text{lb}}{\text{in}^2}.$$

This is read *5 pounds per square inch*. Standing on edge as in (b), on the other hand, the pressure is only one-half as great.

85

$$\text{pressure} = \frac{1000 \text{ lb}}{400 \text{ in}^2} = 2.5 \frac{\text{lb}}{\text{in}^2}.$$

Over each square inch in the first case there is a downward force equivalent to 5 lb while in the second case there is only 2.5 lb. The pressure in (a) is, therefore, twice as great as the pressure in (b), but the total downward force is the same.

Transposing A to the other side of Eq.(12a) gives:

$$F = P \times A. \tag{11b}$$

Total force equals pressure times area.

11.2. Friction. Whenever one body slides over another frictional forces opposing the motion are developed between them. (See Fig. 11C.) Such forces are due largely to the atomic and molecular attractive forces at the

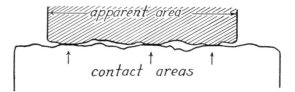

Fɪɢ. 11B—Illustrating the relatively small *contact areas* between two bodies having a much larger *apparent contact area.*

small *contact areas.* (See Fig. 11B.) Within limits the smoothness of the surfaces does not greatly effect f the force of sliding friction. If the surfaces are smooth there will be many small areas in contact while if they are rough there may be fewer but larger ones. It is well known that surfaces of the same material show greater friction than do surfaces of different materials. This is one of the reasons why machine bearings are often made of one metal like bronze while their rotating shafts are made of another like steel.

Experiments show that to start a body sliding requires a greater force than that needed to keep it moving. In other words *static friction,* or *starting friction,* is greater than *kinetic friction.* Once a body is moving, however, the force of sliding friction increases only slightly with increasing speed and then remains nearly constant over a moderate range of speeds.

Recent experiments,* particularly with metals in contact, show that when one surface is pressed against another and sliding is brought about, the enormous pressures existing at the tiny contact areas cause a kind of welding of the two materials together. With all materials in general the atoms and molecules are so close together at the contact areas that strong mutual at-

---

* Review by Frederic Palmer, American Journal of Physics, vol. 17, p. 327, 1949.

tractive forces often pull microscopic bits of material from one body to the other as they move along. To start a body moving is to break these bonds simultaneously while to keep it moving is to break them smoothly and continuously.

The general statement can be made that wherever there is motion there is friction. All forms of friction may be classified as one of three kinds— *sliding friction, rolling friction,* and *fluid friction.* Sliding and rolling friction are usually confined to solids while fluid friction applies to liquids and gases. Generally speaking, sliding friction is greater than fluid friction at low speeds while the reverse is true at high speeds.

11.3. Sliding Friction. A quantitative treatment of sliding friction will here be given as the result of a simple laboratory experiment illustrated in Fig. 11C. In diagram (a) a block of wood of mass 500 gm is shown being pulled with uniform speed across a table top by the force of a 100 gm-wt. The latter force has been arrived at by trying different loads on the hook at the right. A load greater than 100 gm will accelerate the block, while a load smaller than 100 gm will allow it to stop. Moving with constant speed the applied force F is just counterbalanced by f the force of sliding friction.

In diagram (b) a second block of mass 500 gm is added to make the sliding mass

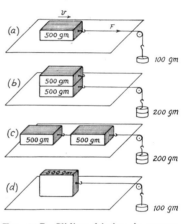

Fig. 11C—Sliding friction is proportional to the normal force pushing the surfaces together and independent of area of contact.

1000 gm. By experiment the force required to pull the two with constant velocity is now found to be a 200 gm-wt. Should a third and then a fourth block be added successively, 300 and 400 gm weights respectively will be found necessary to pull them. In other words the force of sliding friction f is directly proportional to the total downward force N.

$$f \propto N. \qquad (11c)$$

When the two blocks in diagram (b) are connected in tandem, one behind the other as in diagram (c), the force of friction is still that of a 200 gm-wt.

Again if the single block in diagram (a) is turned on edge as in diagram (d) the force of a 100 gm-wt is just enough to slide it with constant speed. These observations, along with the results of other similar experiments, may be explained largely in terms of molecular attractive forces. In general, the total contact area where molecular attraction is effective (see Fig. 11B), is small compared with the total apparent area. When a greater force is applied normal to the surfaces, the contact areas increase in size and number, and the following relations are found to hold reasonably true.

   (1) *The total contact area is proportional to the total normal force.*
   (2) *The total contact area is independent of the total apparent area.*
   (3) *The force of sliding friction is proportional to the total contact area.*
   (4) *The force of sliding friction is proportional to the total normal force.**

Introducing the Greek letter μ as a constant of proportionality, Eq.(11c) becomes

$$f = \mu N. \tag{11d}$$

μ is called the *coefficient of friction,* and is defined as the ratio

$$\mu = \frac{f}{N} . \tag{11e}$$

By knowing the value of μ for a given pair of surfaces one is able to calculate the force of friction f in terms of the normal force N. Average values of μ for a number of surfaces are given in Table 11A.

TABLE 11A. COEFFICIENTS OF SLIDING FRICTION FOR A FEW COMMON MATERIALS
(AVERAGE VALUES FOR DRY SURFACES)

Material	μ	Material	μ
Oak on Oak	0.25	Steel on Steel	0.18
Rubber on Concrete	0.70	Greased surfaces	0.05
Metals on Oak	0.55	Iron on Concrete	0.30
Metals on Elm	0.20	Leather on Metals	0.56
Hemp on Oak	0.53	Steel on Babbit	0.14

As an illustration of the general use of the coefficient of friction consider the following problem, diagrammed in Fig. 11D.

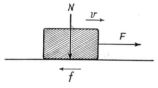

FIG. 11D—Sliding friction F is proportional to the normal force N pushing the surfaces together.

Example 1. What force is required to pull an iron box weighing 60 lb across a smooth oak floor?

Solution. From Table 11A, μ for metals on oak is 0.55. The normal force N is the weight of the box, or 60 lb. Substituting in Eq.(11d), the force of friction is found to be

$$f = 0.55 \times 60 \ \text{lb} = 33 \ \text{lb.}$$

The general observation that sliding fric-

* Curiously enough an increased normal force increases the pressure over the apparent area but not over the contact area. The proportionate increase in total contact area with increased force means that the force of friction on unit contact area is independent of apparent pressure.

tion increases only slightly at low speeds and levels off to become practically constant at higher speeds is illustrated by the following experimental values of pine on walnut wood measured by C. A. Maney.

Speed	1.88	3.87	6.21	8.54	10.00	11.5	12.81	cm/sec.
μ	0.150	0.163	0.171	0.177	0.179	0.181	0.183	

If the force F applied to a body is greater than that required to overcome friction f, the resultant force $(F - f)$ is effective in producing acceleration. As an equation of motion,

$$F - f = ma \qquad (11f)$$

resultant force = mass $\times$ acceleration.

Transposing,

$$F = f + ma$$

or,

$$F = \mu N + ma$$

11.4. Angle of Uniform Slip. One method of measuring the coefficient of sliding friction is to place a block on an inclined plane and then tilt the plane until the block slides down with constant velocity. See Fig. 11E. When this condition exists Eq.(11d) can be imposed directly upon the components of the weight W. The component F is equal in magnitude to f, the sliding friction, and the component N is the normal force pushing the two surfaces together. If θ is the angle of the incline, then

$$\mu = \frac{f}{N} = \frac{F}{N} = \frac{W \sin \theta}{W \cos \theta} = \tan \theta$$

giving

$$\mu = \tan \theta. \qquad (11g)$$

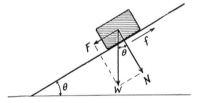

Fig. 11E—Illustrating the angle of uniform slip for a block on an inclined plane.

The coefficient of friction μ equals the tangent of the angle of uniform slip. The angle of uniform slip is defined as that angle of an incline that will keep a body sliding down it with constant velocity. At a steeper angle the force component F down the plane is greater than that required to overcome friction f and the difference between them produces an acceleration as given by Eq.(11f).

11.5. Rolling Friction. A comparison of the force required to slide a heavy box along the ground with the force required to move it on rollers shows that sliding friction is many times greater than rolling friction. It is for this reason that wheels are used on vehicles instead of runners, and that ball-bearings are employed in some machines in place of sleeve-bearings.

A comparison of the sleeve type of bearing with a ball-bearing is made in Fig. 11F. The rotating axle, as shown at the left, slides on the bottom of the sleeve at low speeds and climbs part way up the side as the speed increases. The purpose of lubricating such bearings with oils and greases is to keep the two metal surfaces from coming into direct contact. Properly lubricated the axle rides on a thin film of oil. In diagram (b) it may be seen how the axle rolls around on the balls with little or no possibility for sliding. The balls themselves roll in a groove called a "race."

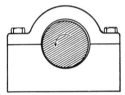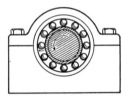

Fig. 11F—Sleeve bearing and ball-bearings illustrate the two kinds of friction, (a) sliding friction, (b) rolling friction. (Note: The clearance in the sleeve bearing is exaggerated.)

The harder a rolling wheel or ball, and the harder the surface over which it rolls, the less is the force of rolling friction. A better understanding of the origin of rolling friction is to be had by a comparison of the different kinds of wheels shown in Fig. 11G. For a hard wheel on a soft dirt road as

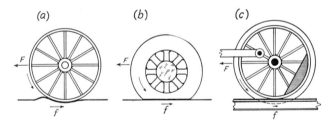

Fig. 11G—Illustrating rolling friction between soft and hard surfaces: (a) wagon wheel (b) soft automobile tire; (c) locomotive drive wheel.

shown in (a) the applied force is continually pulling the wheel over a mound developed in the ground. For a soft wheel on a hard paved road as in (b) the road is continually pushing the wheel out of shape. For a hard wheel on a hard road both wheel and road are distorted ever so little, and the force of friction is exceedingly small.

The same equations that hold for sliding friction also hold for rolling friction, the only difference being that the coefficients for rolling friction are exceedingly small.

$$f = \mu N. \tag{11h}$$

TABLE 11B. COEFFICIENTS OF ROLLING FRICTION

Cast iron on rails .... $\mu = 0.004$
Rubber tires on concrete .... $\mu = 0.030$
Ball-bearing on steel .... $\mu = 0.002$

11.6. Fluid Friction. Friction in a gas or liquid manifests itself when the fluid is made to flow around a stationary obstacle or an object is made to move through a previously stationary fluid. Such friction is involved in the propulsion of ships through the water, and automobiles, trains, and airplanes through the air. In any discussion or treatment of fluid friction it makes no difference whether the fluid is considered as moving and the object as standing still, or vice versa. It is only necessary to specify that there is a relative motion between the two

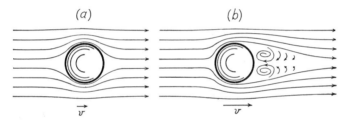

FIG. 11H—Showing the stream lines of a fluid around an obstacle; (a) low velocity showing laminar flow, and (b) high velocity showing turbulent flow.

Experiments show that at relatively low speeds the flow of fluid around an object is smooth and regular and that fluid friction is proportional to the velocity. See Fig. 11H(a).

$$f \propto v \qquad \text{or} \qquad f = Kv \tag{11i}$$

where K is a constant of proportionality.

If, initially, $v = 0$, frictional resistance to motion is zero and an applied force is entirely effective in producing acceleration. As the speed increases, however, friction increases proportionally so that less and less force is available for acceleration. Newton's Second Law, applied to motion through a fluid, therefore takes the same form as Eq.(11f) where f is given by Eq.(11i).

$$F = Kv + ma. \tag{11j}$$

The above equations hold only for "laminar flow," that is, for relatively low velocities. As the speed increases a point is reached where "turbulence" sets in and the force of friction increases rapidly and becomes proportional to the square of the velocity.

$$f \propto v^2 \qquad \text{or} \qquad f = Tv^2. \tag{11k}$$

Turbulent flow is characterized by small eddy currents that form behind the object as shown in Fig. 11H(b). Not only does the fluid have to move out and around the obstacle quickly, but considerable energy is taken up by the eddies. This, of course, results in greater loss of energy and therefore greater friction. When the velocity is increased still further the eddies, instead of forming symmetrical pairs, form alternately on one side and then the other leaving a long trail of vortex motions like those shown in Fig. 11I. These strings of whirlwinds or whirlpools are commonly referred to as

Kármán trails. The existence of such trails is illustrated by the flapping of the rope on a flagpole. The waving of the flag at the top of the pole is direct evidence of the whirlwinds that follow each other alternately along the sides. As the velocity of a streamlined body approaches the velocity of sound, friction again increases rapidly, becoming proportional to the cube of the velocity; $f \propto v^3$.

11.7. Terminal Velocity. It is well known that raindrops fall with a speed that depends upon their size and not upon the height from which they fall. Starting from rest, a particle falling in a gas or a liquid increases in velocity until the retarding force of friction becomes as great as the downward force of gravity. When this condition is reached the body is in equilibrium and falls with a constant velocity called its *terminal velocity.*

The terminal velocity for small particles like fog drops is so low that the air stream around them is one of *laminar flow.* It was Stokes who first discovered that the terminal velocity of small particles is proportional to their weight. This relation is known as *Stokes' Law.**

For increasingly larger bodies terminal velocity increases and turbulent flow sets in to eventually be the predominating part of frictional resistance. Under

Fig. 11I—Eddies set up by drawing an obstacle through still water form a *Kármán trail.*

---

* Sir George G. Stokes (1819-1903), British mathematician and physicist is well known for his fundamental contribution to hydrodynamics, diffraction, double refraction and the polarization of light. He received the Rumford Medal in 1852 and the Copley Medal in 1893, and was one time president of the Royal Society.

these conditions both the resistance to laminar flow and the resistance to turbulent flow exist, so that, equating downward forces to upward forces of friction,

$$W = Kv + Tv^2.$$

This equation applies not only to falling bodies but to airplanes in the air and ships in the water. Their speed remains constant where the resistance is just equalized by the forward thrust of the propellers.

If a parachutist delays the opening of his chute long enough, he will attain a terminal velocity of from 130 to 150 mi/hr. At such speeds wind resistance pushes upward with a total force equal to his weight with the result that he is no longer accelerated.

11.8. Streamlining. By shaping a body to the streamlines of the fluid through which it is moving, the retarding force of friction may be greatly reduced. This is particularly effective at high velocities where the conditions of turbulent flow would otherwise predominate.

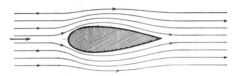

Referring to Fig. 11H(b) it may be seen that by adding a tail to an object, so that its cross-section has the form shown in Fig. 11J, the

Fig. 11J—The flow of air around a properly shaped body may be smooth and steady.

tendency to form eddy currents can be reduced and the body made to slip through the fluid with a minimum disturbance.

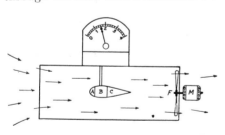

Fig. 11K—Diagram of a wind tunnel used for testing the air friction of an airfoil or streamlined body.

The experiment diagramed in Fig. 11K shows that a long pointed tail and a rounded or pointed nose are both effective in cutting down resistance. The diagrams picture a small wind tunnel through which a stream of air is drawn by a fan *F*. Objects for which wind resistance is to be measured are suspended from a support connected at the center to a spring balance. Parts of a streamlined body are tested in the order shown in Fig. 11L. Their wind resistance changes in the order indicated. Note that it is greatest for the top figure and smallest for the bottom.

The bodies of airplanes, torpedoes, and ships are streamlined to cut down resistance and hence permit higher speed with the same forward thrust of the propellers. Bombs are streamlined to enable them to acquire higher terminal velocities. Automobiles, if they are to travel at high speeds, should be streamlined to make more efficient use of gasoline.

Experiments with airplane and automobile models in wind tunnels show the importance of streamlining for speeds as low as 30 mi/hr. The findings from such tests are confirmed by full-sized planes in the air and by cars on the speedway or open road.

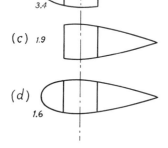

(a) 3.9

(b) 3.4

(c) 1.9

(d) 1.6

Graphs A and B in Fig. 11M give measured frictional resistance to motion of two makes of car. Car A is a model built years ago while B is a more recent streamlined model. Since cars differ considerably in weight, it is customary to compare them at different speeds by giving their resistance, $f = \mu N$, in pounds per ton of weight.

In addition to air friction, a car has solid friction due to traction between the wheels and the road. Solid friction (due to sliding and rolling parts) is approximately constant for all speeds. The resistance of lubricated bearings and low velocity air friction, on the other hand, is proportional to the velocity, while turbulent flow of the air is proportional to the square of the velocity. For car A each of these factors is shown separately by the three dotted lines at the bottom of the graph. The combined resistance of all three is summed up for car A by the equation (where v is in mi/hr),

Fig. 11L—Test bodies for the wind tunnel shown in Fig. 11K.

$$R = 10 + 0.56v + 0.026v^2.$$

It should be noted that solid friction for car B is 26 lb/ton as compared to 10 lb/ton for car A. This is to be attributed chiefly to the large balloon tires used by B as compared with the smaller harder tires used by car A. The importance of streamlining for higher speeds than 30 mi/hr is obvious from the curves. Turbulent flow as seen by the dotted curve certainly becomes the predominant factor at about 30 mi/hr.

11.9. Airplanes. The necessity for streamlining all outside structures of an airplane where high speeds must be maintained is quite clear. For land planes *solid friction* is of importance only during take-off. Once a plane is in the air, friction is almost entirely due to turbulent flow and is approximately proportional to the square of the velocity.

In Fig. 11N a streamlined plane is shown in a climb. Rising with constant velocity the conditions of equilibrium exist and all forces acting form a closed polygon. The external forces acting on an airplane may be reduced to three, *weight, thrust,* and *friction.* See Fig. 11O.

The weight W may be assumed to act vertically downward through the center of gravity of the plane. The thrust T is the result of the screw action

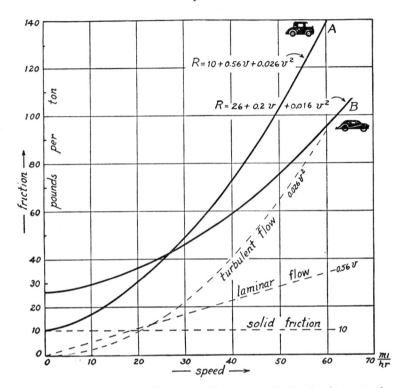

$$R = 10 + 0.56\,v + 0.026\,v^2$$

$$R = 26 + 0.2\,v + 0.016\,v^2$$

Fig. 11M—Graphs A and B show the rapid increase in frictional resistance to the motion of two cars as their velocity is increased. (Dotted curves are for car *A*.)

of the propeller through the air and acts in the direction of the propeller axis. The friction *F* is the resultant force of air friction on the plane and acts in a direction upward and back as shown in Fig. 11O(a). The angle between the plane's *attitude* and the horizontal is called the *angle* of *attack*. Note that the line of flight, the path along which the plane is flying is not quite the same as the plane's attitude.

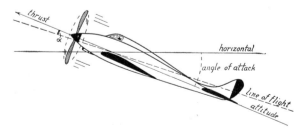

Fig. 11N—Diagram of a plane in a climb.

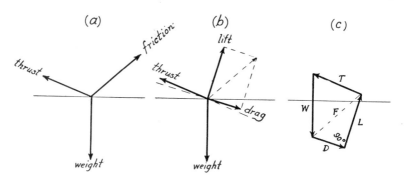

Fig. 11O—Force diagrams for airplane in a climb.

It is customary to resolve the frictional force into two components: one, a useful component perpendicular to the line of flight and called *lift*, and the other a detrimental component parallel to the line of flight called the *drag*. The conditions of equilibrium require that these combined forces form a closed polygon as shown in diagram (c). The latter polygon is often used to determine certain factors in the performance of a plane. For example, if the forward thrust and weight are known, and the line of flight determined, the force polygon may be used to find the lift *L* and the drag *D*.

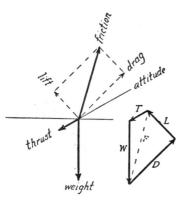

Fig. 11P—Force diagrams for airplane in a dive.

When a plane is in level flight and has constant velocity, *T* and *D* are practically horizontal, equal in magnitude, and opposite in direction, while *W* and *L* are vertical, equal in magnitude and opposite in direction. With the motor throttled down and the plane in a dive at constant velocity, equilibrium conditions exist again and the forces form a closed polygon as shown in Fig. 11P. Note again the drag component is taken parallel to the flight path and not the plane's attitude.

11.10. Supersonic Velocities. The rapid development of rockets and jet propelled planes all capable of acquiring and maintaining speeds greater than the velocity of sound has increased the importance of studying high-speed air flow around bodies of different size and shape. The flow of air around missiles moving with *supersonic velocity*, that is, a velocity greater than the velocity of sound, is characterized by the existence in the air of discontinuities known as *shock waves*.

These sudden discontinuities, clearly visible in the photograph in Fig. 11Q, are the result of sudden encounters of the air with an impenetrable body. At subsonic velocities the fluid is fore-warned and begins its outward flow in advance of the arrival of the leading edge. With supersonic velocity, however, the fluid in front of the missile is absolutely undisturbed while immediately behind it is moving sideways. The sudden impulse at the nose creates a high pressure region which traveling outward with the velocity of sound creates the conical-shaped shock wave that changes the direction of air flow.

It is customary in supersonic studies to specify the velocity of a body relative to the velocity of sound. The ratio between these two velocities is called the *Mach Number.*

$$\text{Mach Number} = \frac{\text{velocity of body}}{\text{velocity of sound}}.$$

Theory shows that the frictional force F on a missile moving with a velocity V through a fluid of density ρ may be given by

$$F = C \times S \times \tfrac{1}{2}\, \rho\, V^2$$

where C is the coefficient of friction and S is the cross-sectional area fronting the air stream. If the missile or airfoil has an angle of attack the force F is upward and back and may be resolved into *lift* and *drag* components the same as with subsonic velocities. The drag force D, for example, would then be given by

$$D = C_D \times S \times \tfrac{1}{2}\, \rho\, V^2$$

where C_D is called the *drag coefficient* of friction. For *density,* see pp. 216 and 235.

This coefficient is not a constant but depends upon the size and shape of the moving body, the smoothness of its surface, the angle of attack, and the properties of the fluid. A graph of C_D for a missile similar to the one shown in Fig. 11Q is reproduced in Fig. 11R, as being typical of most high-speed missiles.

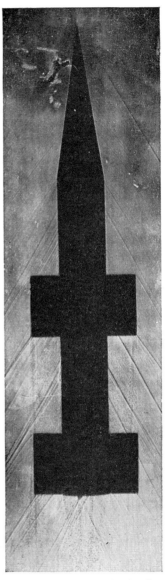

Fig. 11Q—Photograph showing the shock waves that develop around missiles moving through the air at velocities greater than sound. (Courtesy Physics Department, University of New Mexico.)

At low velocities the curve drops down because air friction is approximately proportional to V and not to V^2 as indicated in the above formula.

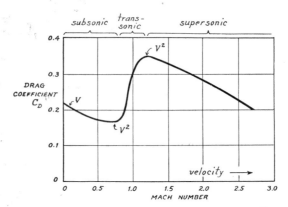

FIG. 11R—Drag coefficient for a pointed missile traveling at different velocities through the air.

At about three-fourths the velocity of sound, Mach No. 0.75, the curve becomes horizontal indicating that C_D becomes constant and the drag is proportional to V^2. The rapid rise of the curve through the transsonic region, where abrupt changes in airflow give rise to violent force reactions on the missile, indicates considerable increases in drag. Well past the velocity of sound the coefficient falls again indicating a drag increasing with somewhat less than the square of the velocity.

PROBLEMS

1. A horizontal force of 24 lb is required to pull a trunk weighing 120 lb across the floor. Find the coefficient of sliding friction.

2. A horse drawn sleigh weighing 476 lb requires a force of 12.5 lb to keep it moving over the snow at constant speed. Find the coefficient of sliding friction. (*Ans.* 0.0263.)

3. A man, driving a car weighing 3300 lb, suddenly applies the brakes, causing all rubber tires to skid. What force is exerted on the concrete pavement?

4. A metal box is to slide down an oak plank. Find the angle of uniform slip. (*Ans.* 28.8°.)

5. A car with a mass of 1200 kg is traveling at a speed of 72 km/hr. Suddenly the brakes are applied, causing all tires to skid. How far will the car travel before coming to a stop?

6. A 10 lb wooden box falls from a truck making 45 mi/hr. If the coefficient of sliding friction between wood and concrete is 0.55, how far will the box slide along the pavement in coming to rest? (*Ans.* 123.7 ft.)

7. A sleigh with steel runners and weighing 350 lb is towed along a concrete road. What horizontal force is required?

8. What force acting at an angle of 20° with the horizontal is requried to move an oak box weighing 140 lb across an oak floor? (*Ans.* 34.1 lb.)

9. The angle of uniform slip for a sled weighing 40 lb is 8°. What force is required to pull the sled up the same slope?

10. A boy weighing 80 lb on a sled weighing 20 lb finds that he can slide with uniform speed on a hill road having a 7 percent grade. How big a force will be required when he goes to pull the sled back up the same hill? Assume the coefficient of friction to be the same in both cases. (*Ans.* 2.80 lb.)

11. A 1500 kg car starts from rest at the top of a 5 percent grade and coasts for a distance of 400 m. What will be its speed at the bottom if the coefficient of rolling friction is 0.030?

12. A girl weighing 96 lb is on roller skates. Upon attaining a speed of 7.5 mi/hr she starts coasting and comes to rest after covering a distance of 128 ft. Find the coefficient of rolling friction. (*Ans.* 0.0148.)

13. A 50 lb box is tied with hemp rope. (a) Find the angle of uniform slip if the box is placed on an oak plank. (b) What force is required to pull this box up the plank when it is inclined 30° to the horizontal?

14. A truck weighing 2.5 tons starts from rest at the top of a 4 percent grade and coasts for a distance of one mile. If the coefficient of rolling friction is 0.030 find its final speed. (*Ans.* 58.1 ft/sec, or 39.7 mi/hr.)

15. If car A in Fig. 11M weighs 2800 lb, find the driving force required by the motor to maintain a speed of 40 mi/hr.

16. If car B in Fig. 11M weighs 3600 lb find the driving force required by the motor to maintain a speed of 70 mi/hr. (*Ans.* 213 lb.)

17. An airplane weighing 1600 lb is in a power climb. It maintains a constant speed when its angle of attack is 20°, and its line of flight is 16°. Assuming a lift of twice the drag calculate the forward thrust of the propeller.

18. A plane weighing 2400 lb maintains constant speed in a power climb. If the angle of attack is 12°, the line of flight is 6°, and the thrust of the jet engine is 600 lb, find (a) the lift, and (b) the drag. (*Ans.* (a) 2325 lb, (b) 346 lb.)

19. The motor of a plane weighing 3000 lb stalls while in flight and the pilot sets the plane into a glide preparatory to making a forced landing. The speed of the gliding plane is constant, the angle of attack is 18° below the horizontal, and the line of flight is 24° below the horizontal. Find (a) the lift, and (b) the drag.

20. The motor of a plane stalls while in straight and level flight and the pilot drops the nose of the ship into a glide preparatory to making a forced landing. The plane glides at a constant speed, the attitude becomes fixed at 16° below the horizontal, and the line of flight at 20° below the horizontal. If the plane weighs 3600 lb, find (a) the lift, and (b) the drag. (*Ans.* (a) 3383 lb, (b) 1231 lb.)

21. Solve Prob. 8 for angles of 0°, 5°, 10°, 15°, 20° and 25°. Plot a graph and find the angle for which the applied force is a minimum.

22. Make a graph of the variation of sliding friction with speed using the values given on page 89. Show both origins at zero. What might be concluded about μ at higher speeds?

23. A 50 kg wooden box falls from a truck traveling at a speed of 72 km/hr along the highway. If the box slides for a total distance of 50 m before coming to rest, what is the coefficient of sliding friction?

Simultaneous and
Relative Velocities   Chapter 12

SINCE velocity has magnitude and direction, it is a vector quantity, and therefore, subject to the principles of vector addition.

12.1. Velocity Is a Vector Quantity. When a body moves with two velocities simultaneously, the process of vector addition is applied to find its equivalent resultant velocity. To see what is meant by *simultaneous velocities,* and a *resultant velocity,* consider the following problem.

While an ocean liner is sailing eastward with a velocity of 12 mi/hr a man walks around the deck at the rate of 5 mi/hr. The problem is to find at all times the man's velocity with respect to the water. When he walks forward in the direction of the ship's motion, his velocity of 5 mi/hr is added to the ship's velocity of 12 mi/hr to give a resultant of 17 mi/hr eastward. As the man walks aft, however, his velocity of 5 mi/hr is subtracted from the ship's velocity of 12 mi/hr to give a resultant of 7 mi/hr eastward.

In the first case, the vectors are parallel and in the same direction and they add arithmetically, while in the second case they are oppositely directed and they subtract arithmetically.

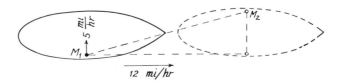

FIG. 12A—A body undergoes two simultaneous velocities.

When the man walks across the deck at right angles to the ship's motion, his resultant velocity is 13 mi/hr in a direction 22.6° North of East. To show how this answer is determined, a *space diagram* of the problem is given in Fig. 12A. The diagram at the left shows M_1 as the starting point of the man and boat, while the diagram at the right shows the position of the boat when the man reaches M_2 on the port side. The plane of the page represents the water.

The vector addition of the two velocities is shown at the left in Fig. 12B. The arrow WB is first drawn 12 units long and pointing in the direction of

the boat's motion. *BM* is next drawn up from *B*, 5 units long, and pointing
in the direction the man is walking on the boat. The triangle is then completed, the length of the side *WM* is measured from the graph and the angle
is measured with a protractor. The resultant *WM* = 13 mi/hr at 22.6° represents both in magnitude and direction, the velocity of the man with respect
to the water.

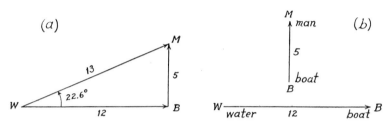

FIG. 12B—Vector addition of simultaneous velocities.

*A general procedure that can be applied to all problems involving simul-
taneous velocities is illustrated at the right in Fig. 12B. Taking the above
problem as an example, each vector is first drawn separately with its proper
magnitude and specified direction. Each is then labeled with the moving
body at the head of the arrow and the object with reference to which it is
moving at the tail. The vectors are then put together in a single diagram
with like labels together, as in diagram (a).*

12.2. Motion in a Moving Medium. The principles of vector addition
are particularly useful when applied to the motion of a body in a medium
which is itself moving. The drift of an airplane in a wind or the drift of a
boat on a moving body of water are good examples.

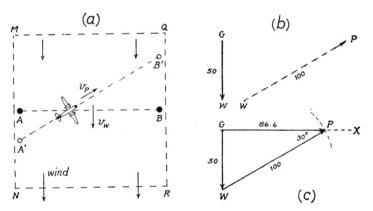

FIG. 12C—To fly a desired course the wind velocity must be taken into account.

The Airplane Problem. The pilot of a plane wishes to fly to a city directly to the east. If the plane has a cruising speed of 100 mi/hr, and a steady wind is blowing from the North with a velocity of 50 mi/hr at what angle should the pilot head his plane into the wind? See Fig. 12C(a). Because this type of problem is often solved incorrectly, its correct solution should be noted with care. The procedure to be followed is that given in italics at the end of the preceding section.

Vectors are first drawn and labeled as shown in diagram (b). With both the direction and magnitude of the wind velocity known, the first vector is drawn toward the south and 50 units long. It is then labeled with the moving body, the wind *W* at the head, and the ground *G* to which the velocity is referred, at the tail. Since only the magnitude of the airplane velocity is known, a temporary arrow is drawn 100 units long and at an arbitrary angle and then labeled with the moving body, the plane *P,* at the head and the air or wind *W* to which the velocity is referred, at the tail.

The next step is to combine the two vectors with their like labels, the wind *W,* together as follows. After drawing the vector *GW,* a horizontal line *GX* is drawn to the right. With a compass of radius 100 units and center at *W,* a short arc is drawn intersecting the horizontal line at *P.*

The vector *WP* is then completed and the length of the side *GP* measured. The vector *GP* of 86.6 pointing eastward represents the velocity of the plane *P* with respect to the ground *G* while the angle of 30°, measured from the triangle, gives the direction in which the plane must be headed.

Diagram (a) in Fig. 12C shows how the plane, heading in a direction 30° North of East, and flying through the air with a velocity of 100 mi/hr, follows the eastward land course from *A* to *B* with a velocity of 86.6 mi/hr. In the air mass (*MNRQ*) the plane flies from *A'* to *B'.*

12.3. Relative Velocity. One of the principles upon which Einstein's theory of relativity is founded is that all motions are relative. A body moving with a specified velocity with respect to one frame of reference may be moving with a different velocity when referred to another. To illustrate, suppose two seaplanes leave the same island base at the same time, one flying North-East with a speed of 200 mi/hr, the other flying East with a speed of 250 mi/hr.

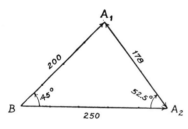

FIG. 12D—According to Einstein's theory of relativity all motions are relative.

A vector diagram of velocities is given in Fig. 12D. Vector *BA₁* represents the velocity of plane A_1 with respect to the base *B*, while vector *BA₂* represents the velocity of plane A_2 with respect to the same base. For both of these vectors, the page of the book with the fixed point *B* is the frame of reference from which the velocity of A_1 and A_2 are specified. The vector joining A_1 and A_2 represents the relative velocities of the two planes. The navigator in A_2 observes plane A_1 receding from him with a velocity of 178 mi/hr in a direction 52.5 degrees North of West, while the navigator in A_1 observes plane A_2 receding from him with a velocity of 178 mi/hr in a direction 52.5 degrees South of East.

With respect to A_2 the base B is moving West with a velocity of 250 mi/hr. With respect to A_1 the base is moving South-West with a velocity of 200 mi/hr. *All motions are relative.*

PROBLEMS

1. A motorboat capable of 10 mi/hr is headed straight across a river. If the water flows at the rate of 3 mi/hr, what will be the velocity of the boat with respect to the starting point on the bank?

2. At what angle must the boat in Prob. 1 be headed upstream in order to land on the other bank directly opposite the starting point? (*Ans.* 17.5° upstream.')

3. A man who can row a boat at 2 mi/hr wishes to cross a river 1 mile wide to a point 1 mile down the river. If the river flows with a velocity of ½ mi/hr (a) at what angle must he head the boat, and (b) how long will it take to get there?

4. A motorboat is headed straight across a river 1 mi wide. If the water flows at the rate of 2 mi/hr (a) what speed must the boat make in the water to land at a point ½ mile down the river on the opposite bank, and (b) how long will it take to get there? (*Ans.* (a) 4 mi/hr, (b) 15 min.)

5. A pilot with a plane having a cruising speed of 120 mi/hr leaves an airport and sets his course at 20° north of east. After flying for 1 hr he discovers he is 104 mi directly east of his starting point. What is the average wind velocity that blew him off his course?

6. A ship is sailing west at 20 knots, and a 15 knot wind is blowing from the north. What is the velocity of the wind with respect to the ship? What angle will the trail of smoke left by the funnels make with ship's course? (*Ans.* 25 knots at 36.8° south of east.)

7. A submarine-chaser is headed due east at 30 knots while a 25 knot wind is blowing from the northeast. (a) What is the velocity of the wind with respect to the ship? (b) What angle will a smoke screen sent up by the ship make with the ship's course?

8. To an observer on a ship sailing west at 20 knots it appears that a 20 knot wind is blowing from the southwest. Find the true wind velocity. (*Ans.* 15.31 knots at 22.5° west of north.)

9. The trail of smoke left by a ship sailing east at 20 mi/hr makes an angle of 45° south of west. When the ship's course is changed to northeast, the line of smoke becomes due south. Find the velocity of the wind. *Solve graphically.*

10. A ship sailing west at 25 mi/hr leaves a smoke trail making an angle of 45° south of east. When the ship's course is changed to southwest, the smoke trail becomes due east. Find the velocity of the wind. (*Ans.* 19.1 mi/hr at 22.5° west of south.)

11. A pilot with a plane having a crusing speed of 200 mi/hr wishes to fly from city A southwest to city B 100 mi away. Before leaving the airport the weather report for that area gives the wind velocity as 30 mi/hr from the southwest. (a) In what direction should he set his course? (b) What velocity will he make with respect to the ground? (c) How long will it take to reach his destination?

12. A pilot with a plane having a cruising speed of 200 mi/hr wishes to fly to another airport 100 mi to the north, and return. A steady wind of 30 mi/hr is blowing from the south. (a) What is his total flying time? (b) What would be his flying time if there were no wind? (c) Why are these times different? (*Ans.* (a) 1.023 hr. (b) 1 hr.)

13. A man rowing a boat upstream drops an empty bottle into the water as he passes a shore marker *A*. Continuing upstream for 15 min he turns about and rows downstream catching up with the bottle one mile downstream from *A*. Find the speed of the river.

14. A jet pilot, in a plane with a cruising speed of 480 mi/hr, sets his course due west. After flying for 30 min a ground observer reports his position as 15 mi west and 20 mi north of where he should be. Calculate the average wind velocity that blew him off his course. (*Ans.* 50 mi/hr at 36.8° west of north.)

15. A river 1 km wide flows with a speed of 4 km/hr. A man, in a boat capable of making 10 km/hr, wishes to cross the river to a point 0.5 km upstream and then to return to the starting point. In what direction should he head his boat when going over 'and when coming back?

16. A man, in a boat capable of making 15 km/hr, heads across a river in a direction making an angle of 40° with the shore. If he lands on the opposite shore ½ km upstream in 6 min, (a) what is the speed of the stream, and (b) how wide is the stream? (*Ans.* (a) 6.5 km/hr. (b) 0.96 km.)

17. In what direction should the man in Prob. 15 head his boat if he wishes to return to his starting point?

18. An automobile going 60 mi/hr overtakes and passes another that is going 55 mi/hr. Calculate the distance needed in passing if each car is 18 ft long. Assume that one car is passing the other if any part of it is opposite any part of the other. (*Ans.* 4.9 sec.)

19. A passenger train going 80 km/hr overtakes and passes a freight train traveling 50 km/hr on an adjacent track. Calculate the distance needed in passing if each train is 400 m long. Assume one train is passing the other if any part of it is opposite any part of the other.

20. The current in a river 1 km wide flows west at 6 km/hr. A motor launch leaves the north bank and crosses the river diagonally to the opposite shore 0.5 km downstream from the starting point. If the crossing requires 10 min, find (a) the speed of the boat through the water, and (b) the direction in which it is headed. (*Ans.* (a) 6.71 km/hr. (b) Upstream at 63.5° with shore.)

Projectiles   Chapter 13

13.1. Horizontal Projection. If one body falls freely from rest at the same time another is projected horizontally from the same height the two will strike the ground simultaneously. An experimental proof of this fundamental observation may be verified by an experiment of the type diagramed in Fig. 13A.

Two identical marbles M and N are supported by a rod and trough respectively in such a way that when the compressed spring S is released,

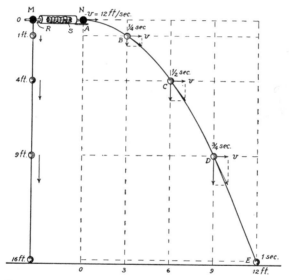

Fig. 13A—A body dropped from rest and another projected horizontally strike the ground at the same time.

the rod R springs to the right, dropping M and projecting N horizontally. Marble M falling with the acceleration of gravity g, and marble N traversing the longer path $ABCDE$ strike the ground at the same time. Repetition of the experiment with higher or lower projection velocities and from different heights ends always with the same result; both marbles hit the ground together.

The first conclusion that may be drawn from this experiment is that the downward acceleration of a projectile is the same as a freely falling body and takes place independent of its horizontal motion. Furthermore, an experimental measurement of *times* and *distances* shows that the horizontal velocity of projection continues unchanged and takes place independently of the vertical motion.

In other words, a projectile carries out two motions independently: (1) a constant horizontal velocity v; and (2) a vertically downward acceleration g.

With an initial horizontal velocity v, the horizontal distance x traveled is proportional to the time t and given by the equation

$$x = vt. \tag{13a}$$

As the marble falls at the same time with an acceleration g, the vertical distance y is proportional to the square of the time and given by the equation

$$y = \tfrac{1}{2}gt^2. \tag{13b}$$

An experimental verification of these two equations is illustrated by the numerical values given in the diagram. With an initial velocity of 12 ft/sec, marble N falls a distance of 1 ft in $\frac{1}{4}$ second and at the same time travels a horizontal distance of 3 ft. In $\frac{1}{2}$ second it falls 4 ft and travels horizontally 6 ft, etc. Since the motion obeys both formulas at the same time, the path traversed is a parabola.

As a proof, Eq.(13a) is first solved for t, then squared to give

$$t^2 = \frac{x^2}{v^2}.$$

Substitute for t^2 in Eq.(13b).

$$y = \tfrac{1}{2}g\,\frac{x^2}{v^2}, \qquad \text{or} \qquad y = \frac{g}{2v^2}x^2 \tag{13c}$$

which is the equation of a parabola with the point of projection as origin.

For the purposes of solving problems the motions of projectiles are usually determined by calculating the horizontal and vertical motions separately and combining the results by vector addition.

Example 1. A stone is thrown horizontally with a velocity of 50 ft/sec from the top of a tower 100 ft high. How long will it take to reach the ground, and at what angle and with what velocity will it strike?

Solution. The time to reach the ground is the time of free fall given by Eq.(13b). By solving for t, we obtain

$$t = \sqrt{\frac{2y}{g}} = \sqrt{\frac{2 \times 100 \text{ ft}}{32 \text{ ft/sec}^2}} = \sqrt{6.25 \text{ sec}^2} = 2.5 \text{ sec}.$$

Upon striking the ground the stone will have a horizontal velocity $v_x = 50$ ft/sec, and a vertical velocity given by Eq.(5e),

$$v_y = gt \qquad (13d)$$

$$v_y = 32 \frac{ft}{sec^2} \times 2.5 \; sec = 80 \frac{ft}{sec}.$$

Combining these two velocities vectorially as shown in Fig. 13B, gives

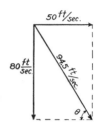

$$v = \sqrt{v_x^2 + v_y^2} = \sqrt{(50)^2 + (80)^2} = 94.5 \frac{ft}{sec}.$$

The angle θ is seen from the right triangle to be given by

$$\tan \theta = \frac{80}{50} = 1.60, \; or \; \theta = 58°.$$

Fɪɢ. 13B—Combined velocities of a projectile.

Another illustration of horizontal projection is to be found in the dropping of bombs or other loads by a low-flying plane in level flight. See Fig. 13C. Sweeping down in a dive from a greater height a bomber may level off at a low elevation and sighting on a target, release a bomb when the proper angle θ is reached. As the bomb falls with increasing speed its horizontal velocity remains constant and equal to the velocity of the plane.

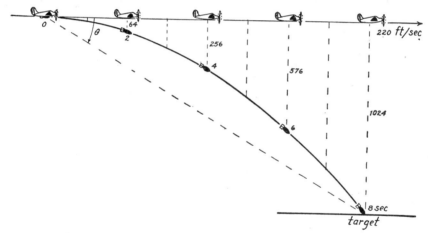

Fɪɢ. 13C—For the first few seconds after release a falling bomb remains directly beneath the plane. Later, wind resistance causes it to lag farther and farther behind.

Neglecting air friction the bomb should stay directly beneath the plane at all points along its path. To find the angle θ at which the bomb should be released, two factors must be taken into account: (1) the speed of the plane, and (2) the height above the target. From the height y the time of fall can be calculated, and from the time of fall the horizontal distance can be computed.

If x represents the horizontal distance traveled and y the vertical height, the right triangle in Fig. 13B, gives

$$\tan \theta = y/x \qquad (13e)$$

where x and y are given by Eqs.(13a) and (13b).

When bombs or other objects are dropped from great heights air friction causes them to lag somewhat behind the plane. Because the lag is negligibly small in low level bombing, and the plane is directly over the target when the bomb hits, a delayed action mechanism in the bomb has been used to avoid demolition of the plane.

To give figures on the lag due to air friction a bomb dropped from a plane making about 200 mi/hr at 6000 ft will drop back about 420 ft, having traveled horizontally some 5580 ft to the plane's 6000 ft.

13.2. Projectiles. Many missiles when projected into the air follow a parabolic path. Such is the case only for low speeds where the retarding force of air friction is negligible. For high-speed projectiles the air continually slows the motion down and the path departs from a parabola as indicated in Fig. 13D. The higher the velocity the greater is the force of air friction and the greater is the departure from a parabolic path.

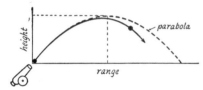

In general it is convenient to neglect air friction, calculate the theoretical path of a projectile, and then if necessary make corrections for air friction.

FIG. 13D—Projectiles tend to follow the path of a parabola. Air friction, however, slows them down, causing them to fall short of their calculated range.

As a rule the known factors concerning a given projectile are v, the initial velocity of projection, and θ the angle of departure. The latter is always measured from the horizontal, and in the case of bullets and shells is the *elevation angle* of the gun. The factors to be calculated are (1) the *time of flight*, (2) the *maximum height* reached, and (3) the *range* attained.

The time of flight of a projectile will here be defined as the time required for it to return to the same level from which it was fired. The maximum height, called the summit, is defined as the greatest vertical distance reached as measured from the horizontal projection plane, while the range is the horizontal distance from the point of projection to the point where the projectile returns again to the projection plane.

13.3. Calculation of Trajectories. To calculate the height and range of a projectile the initial velocity of projection is resolved into two components, one vertical and the other horizontal. This is illustrated in Fig. 13E. Calling v_0 the velocity of projection and θ the elevation angle, the x-

and y-components of velocity are given by the following trigonometric functions,

$$\sin \theta = \frac{v_y}{v}, \quad \text{and} \quad \cos \theta = \frac{v_x}{v}.$$

If v is transposed to the other side of each equation,

$$v_y = v \sin \theta \qquad (13f)$$
$$v_x = v \cos \theta. \qquad (13g)$$

The traversal of the actual trajectory is a combination of two motions, one the motion of a particle projected vertically upward with an initial

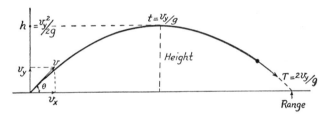

Fig. 13E—The path of a projectile showing the maximum height reached, the time of flight, and the range.

velocity v_y, the other a horizontal velocity v_x that remains constant. In other words, a particle projected vertically upward with a velocity v_y will rise to the same height and in the same time as another projected at an angle θ with a velocity v.

Since the time required to reach the highest point is equal to the time required to fall the same distance, the formula for free fall may be employed. The formula for an object falling from rest is

$$v_y = gt.$$

By transposing, and substituting from Eq.(13f), we find

$$t = \frac{v_y}{g} = \frac{v \sin \theta}{g}. \qquad (13h)$$

Because t is the time to rise, or the time to fall, the total time of flight will be $2t$. Therefore,

$$T = 2 \frac{v_y}{g}.$$

Time of flight,

$$T = \frac{2v \sin \theta}{g}. \qquad (13i)$$

To find the height h, the equation $v^2 = 2gs$ is used. See Eq.(5j). The letter s is replaced by h, and the letter v by v_y.

$$(v_y)^2 = 2gh.$$

Transposing $2g$ to the other side of this equation, and substituting:

Maximum height, $$h = \frac{(v_y)^2}{2g} = \frac{(v \sin \theta)^2}{2g}.$$ (13j)

To find the range R, the equation $s = vt$ is used. Replacing the letter s by R, v by v_x, and t by the total time of flight $T = 2v_y/g$,

$$R = v_x T = v_o \cos \theta \times \frac{2v \sin \theta}{g}$$

or

$$R = \frac{2v^2 \sin \theta \cos \theta}{g}.$$

To put this formula into another form use is made of the trigonometric relation that $2 \sin \theta \cos \theta = \sin 2\theta$. Substitution gives

Range, $$R = \frac{v^2}{g} \sin 2\theta$$ (13k)

In this form it is seen at once that for a given velocity v_o the range is a maximum when the $\sin 2\theta$ is a maximum. Since the sine has its maximum value of unity for an angle of $90°$, the angle θ above will be $45°$. Further-

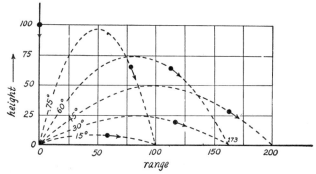

Fig. 13F—Illustrating the shape of the trajectories of objects projected at different elevation angles. The vertical and horizontal scales are for the special case where the velocity of projection is 80 ft/sec.

more, the range for any angle any number of degrees greater than $45°$ will be equal to the range for an equal number of degrees less than $45°$. This is illustrated in Fig. 13F for example by the equal ranges of 100 ft for the $15°$

and 75° projections, and the equal ranges of 173 ft for the 30° and 60° projections.

Example 5. A baseball is thrown with a velocity of 50 ft/sec at an angle of 60° with the horizontal. Calculate (a) the time of flight, (b) the maximum height, and (c) the range.

Solution. To find the time of flight, direct substitution of the given quantities in Eq.(13i) gives

$$T = \frac{2v \sin \theta}{g} = \frac{2 \times 50 \times 0.866}{32} = \frac{86.6}{32} = 2.71 \text{ sec.}$$

To find the maximum height, Eq.(13j) is used.

$$h = \frac{(v \sin \theta)^2}{2g} = \frac{(50 \times 0.866)^2}{2 \times 32} = 29.3 \text{ ft.}$$

For the range, Eq.(13k) is used.

$$R = \frac{v^2}{g} \sin 2\theta = \frac{(50)^2 \times 0.866}{32} = 67.6 \text{ ft.}$$

13.4. Monkey and Hunter Experiment. A hunter aims his gun and fires a bullet directly at a monkey in a tree. At the instant the bullet leaves

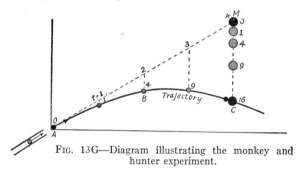

FIG. 13G—Diagram illustrating the monkey and hunter experiment.

the barrel of the gun the monkey drops. The two should collide in mid-air regardless of the speed of the bullet. If gravity could be eliminated, the bullet, as shown in Fig. 13G, would travel the straight line path *AM*, and the monkey would remain at *M*. With gravity acting, however, the bullet travels the path *ABC*, and the monkey drops from *M* to *C*. During each fraction of a second both fall the same distance from their gravity-free positions and collide at *C*. The greater the speed of the projectile the shorter will be the time and the distance *MC*.*

* The experiment may be performed by blowing a small wooden marble through a tube (about a foot long), as illustrated in Fig. 13G. Another ball representing the monkey is released at *M* by a small electromagnet. Two fine copper wires completing the electric circuit are crossed just in front of the tube at *A*. When the projectile passes this point the circuit is broken, releasing *M*. The mass *M* can be made of iron, hollow or solid, and in any shape, or it can be made of wood or any other material with a small piece of iron at the top for the magnetic attraction.

13.5. Rockets. The V-II rocket projectiles developed in Germany during World War II are capable of reaching great heights. Many of these jet propelled missiles weighing several tons each, have since been assembled and fired in the United States for test purposes. Various kinds of apparatus to measure cosmic rays, solar radiation, etc., have been mounted in the warhead, or nose, in place of the explosive charge, and the nose automatically opened for several minutes at the top of its flight path.

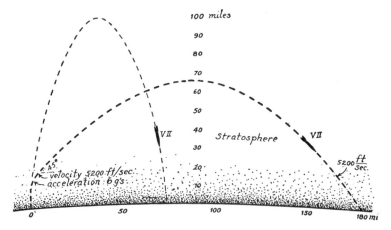

Fig. 13H—Trajectories of V II rockets developed in Germany World War II and recently used in the United States to study existing conditions high in the stratosphere.

To obtain maximum range V-II's are launched in a vertical direction as shown in Fig. 13H. As fuel is rapidly burned they rise with increasing acceleration until at a height of approximately 10 mi a gyro-control inside turns the guiding fins and hence the flight path by regular steps. At a height of about 20 mi the rocket reaches an angle of 45° just as the fuel is completely exhausted. From there on, in a highly rarefied atmosphere, the path is that of a free body in a parabolic trajectory.

Approaching the earth again some minutes later and about 150 mi away the rocket has acquired its previous high velocity of 5200 ft/sec as it enters an appreciable amount of air at 20 mi altitude. From there to impact with the ground atmospheric friction produces some deceleration but nothing compared with the acceleration of 180 ft/sec^2 attained during take-off.

Recent experiments have been performed in which rockets have risen to heights of well over 150 mi.

PROBLEMS

1. A mail plane making 180 mi/hr comes down to a 300 ft elevation where in straight and level flight it releases a mail bag to be caught in a net on the ground. What should be the horizontal distance between the plane and the net when the bag is released? Neglect air friction.

2. A supply plane making 210 mi/hr comes down to a 480 ft elevation where in straight and level flight it releases a large bundle of food to land on a ground marker. How far in advance of the marker, as measured along the ground, should the bundle be released? (*Ans.* 1687 ft.)

3. A javelin is thrown with a speed of 80 ft/sec at an elevation angle of 42°. Find (a) the maximum height, and (b) the range. (c) How much farther would the throw have gone if the elevation angle had been 45°?

4. A smooth round stone is thrown from a sling with a speed of 160 ft/sec at an elevation angle of 30°. Calculate (a) its maximum height, (b) its range, and (c) its time of flight. (*Ans.* (a) 100 ft, (b) 692.8 ft, (c) 5 sec.)

5. A shot-put is tossed for a distance of 52.0 ft. If the elevation angle of projection was 40°, how much more distance would have been obtained if it were thrown with the same speed at 45°?

6. A mortar hurls a 100 lb shell with a speed of 600 ft/sec. Neglecting friction, at what angle with the horizontal should it be aimed to hit a target on the ground 2000 yd away? (*Ans.* 16.1° or 73.9°.)

7. A smooth round stone is thrown from a sling with a speed of 49 m/sec. At what elevation angle should it be thrown to obtain a range of 245 m?

8. A baseball thrown by one player to another is in the air for 3 sec. How high did it rise? (*Ans.* 36 ft.)

9. A basketball thrown by one player to another is in the air for one second. How high did it rise?

10. Find the maximum theoretical range of a 16 in. naval gun producing a muzzle velocity of 2000 ft/sec. What is the time of flight and the height for this range? (*Ans.* 23.68 mi, 88.4 sec, and 5.92 mi.)

11. An arrow shot with a speed of 200 ft/sec reaches a maximum height of 480 ft. Calculate (a) the time of flight, (b) the elevation angle, and (c) the range.

12. Calculate the time a V-II rocket, launched at 6800 ft/sec 20 mi above the earth, spends above an altitude of 20 mi if its elevation angle at the 20 mi level is (a) 45°, and (b) 80°. Neglect friction and assume g to be constant. (*Ans.* (a) 300 sec, (b) 419 sec.)

13. A dart thrown with a speed of 160 ft/sec reaches a height of 320 ft. Calculate (a) the time of flight, (b) the angle of departure, and (c) the range.

14. A catapult hurls a stone at an elevation angle of 30° from the edge of a cliff 400 ft above the water. If the initial speed is 128 ft/sec, (a) to what height above the water does it rise, and (b) with what speed does it hit the water? (*Ans.* (a) 464 ft, (b) 205 ft/sec.)

15. An anti-aircraft gun fires at an elevation angle of 55° at an enemy plane at 12,000 ft elevation and at 40° elevation angle. Calculate the muzzle speed.

16. A stone is thrown with a speed of 40 m/sec at an elevation angle of 60°. Find (a) the position, and (b) the speed of the stone at the end of 3 sec. (*Ans.* (a) 59.8 m high and 60 m to the side, (b) 20.7 m/sec.)

Circular Motion   Chapter 14

WHEN a rigid body is set into rotation its motion is generally described with reference to the axis about which it revolves. The *axis of rotation*, as it is generally called, is sometimes fixed within the body and sometimes beyond its outermost boundary. In the case of most wheels of machinery, for example, the axes of rotation are lines through the geometrical centers perpendicular to the planes of rotation. For a stone whirled on the end of a string, however, the axis is at the opposite end of the string remote from the stone itself.

14.1. Angular Velocity. The speed with which a body rotates is called its *speed* or *frequency*. Either of these terms refers to the number of complete revolutions a body makes in unit time and is designated by the letter n.

$$n = \text{number of revolutions per second.}$$

A flywheel, for example, might be said to have a speed of 10 revolutions per second (*abbr. 10 rps*). This is equivalent to a speed or frequency of 600 revolutions per minute (*abbr. 600 rpm*), and to a speed or frequency of 36,000 revolutions per hour (*abbr. 36,000 rph*).

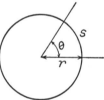

For formulating the laws of mechanics it will be found convenient to express all rotation in radians and not in degrees or revolutions. *The radian is a unit of angular measure* just as the centimeter is a unit of linear measure. It is defined as the angle subtended by the arc of a circle whose length is equal to the radius of the same circle. Referring to Fig. 14A the distance s measured along the arc is equal to the

FIG. 14A—The radian is a unit of angular measure. When the arc s equals the radius r; the angle θ equals one radian.

radius r, and the angle $\theta = 1$ *radian*.

Since the entire circumference of a circle is just 2π times the radius r there are 2π radians in one complete circle.

$$2\pi \text{ radians} = 360°.$$

Since $\pi = 3.1416$,

$$1 \text{ radian} = \frac{360°}{6.283} = 57.3°.$$

It follows from the above relations that the angle θ in radians between

114

any two points on the circumference of a circle is given by s, the length of
the arc between the two points, divided by the radius r. In words,

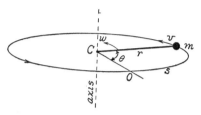

$$\text{angle in radians} = \frac{\text{arc length}}{\text{radius}}$$

or, in algebraic symbols,

$$\theta = \frac{s}{r} \qquad (14a)$$

FIG. 14B—Illustrating circular motion.

The reason for measuring angles in
radians is that it simplifies all formulas
for rotary motion. As an illustration con-
sider the speed of a stone being whirled on the end of a string as shown in
Fig. 14B. The angular velocity of the motion is defined as the angle turned
through divided by the elapsed time.

$$\text{Angular velocity} = \frac{\text{angle turned through}}{\text{time}}.$$

In algebraic symbols,

$$\omega = \theta/t \qquad (14b)$$

and is to be compared with the corresponding definition of linear velocity,

$$v = s/t. \qquad (14c)$$

Angular velocity ω corresponds to linear velocity v, and angular displacement θ corresponds to linear displacement s. With θ measured in radians
and t in seconds, the angular velocity ω has the units of radians per seconds,
(abbr. rad/sec).

As a problem suppose a stone, when it is whirled on the end of a string
50 cm long, makes 8 complete revolutions in 2 sec, and we wish to find the
angular velocity in radians per second. To employ Eq.(14b) the angle θ is
first calculated as follows. Since 1 revolution $= 2\pi$ radians, 8 revolutions
are equivalent to

$$\theta = 2\pi \times 8 = 50.2 \text{ rad.}$$

Substitution in Eq.(14b), gives

$$\omega = \frac{\theta}{t} = \frac{50.2 \text{ rad}}{2 \text{ sec}} = 25.1 \frac{\text{rad}}{\text{sec}}.$$

To find the linear speed of the stone along its curved path Eqs.(14a),
(14b) and (14c) can be used by combining them as follows. By transposing
Eq.(14a),

$$s = r\theta \qquad (14d)$$

and substituting $r\theta$ for s in Eq.(14c),

$$v = \frac{r\theta}{t} = r\frac{\theta}{t}.$$

Replace θ/t by ω (from Eq. 14b).

$$v = r\omega. \tag{14e}$$

From the problem of the stone on a string in Fig. 14B, we can now calculate the speed of the stone from the known values of r and ω. Since the angular velocity $\omega = 25.1$ rad/sec, and the length of the string is 50 cm, then in 1 sec ($t = 1$ sec) the angle turned through will be 25.1 rad, and the velocity will be

$$v = 50 \text{ cm} \times 25.1\frac{\text{rad}}{\text{sec}} = 1255\frac{\text{cm}}{\text{sec}}.$$

If it were required to find the distance traveled in 5 sec, Eq.(14c) could be transposed and used as follows:

$$s = vt = 1255\frac{\text{cm}}{\text{sec}} \times 5 \text{ sec} = 6275 \text{ cm}.$$

To find the total angle turned through in 5 sec, Eq.(14a) can be used.

$$\theta = \frac{6275 \text{ cm}}{50 \text{ cm}} = 125.5 \text{ rad}.$$

Likewise, Eq.(14b) can be used by transposition and substitution.

$$\theta = \omega t = 25.1\frac{\text{rad}}{\text{sec}} \times 5 \text{ sec} = 125.5 \text{ rad}.$$

Note that all equations are consistent with each other and that the radian as a unit has no dimensions. The radian is the ratio between two lengths and therefore has the same value in all systems of units. It is for this reason that it can be canceled out where it is not needed, or added where necessary in the above answers.

14.2. Centripetal Force. When a stone is whirling on the end of a string there is an inward force exerted by the string on the ball. This force is called the *centripetal force*. By Newton's Third Law of Motion the ball exerts an equal but opposite force on the string. This is called the *centrifugal force*. Both forces are illustrated in Fig. 14C. Since the only force acting on the ball is inward the ball is not in equilibrium but is being continually accelerated in the direction of the force, that is, toward the center.

This appears to be a physical paradox, for here is a body moving with constant speed in a circle and yet being accelerated toward the center of the circle without getting any closer to it. If the string were to break suddenly the ball would fly off on a tangent to the circle and move with constant velocity according to Newton's First Law.

To obtain a clearer picture of centripetal force and acceleration toward the center, motion in a circle as illustrated in Fig. 14D(c) is to be compared with the motion of a projectile accelerated downward by the pull of gravity as shown in Fig. 13G. Due to the earth's attraction of all bodies a projectile is continually accelerated downward away from the straight line of its original projection. In circular motion the mass is continually accelerated toward the center, always at right angles to its instantaneous velocity and away from any straight-line-tangent along which it would travel if suddenly released.

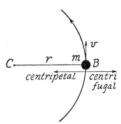

FIG. 14C—A ball or stone moving in a circle experiences a force and an acceleration toward the center.

The instantaneous velocity is shown at two points, A and B, in diagram (a) of Fig. 14D. The velocity as indicated by the vectors v, is seen to be changing in direction but not in magnitude. Diagram (b) is a velocity diagram showing v' as the change in velocity that occurs in going from A to B. Since this velocity triangle is similar to triangle ABC in diagram (a), corresponding sides are proportional to each other, and the following can be written:

$$\frac{s}{r} = \frac{v'}{v}$$

Since the velocity v' is changing and is due to an acceleration, it can, by the equation $v = at$, be replaced by at. During the time t the body moves from A to B a distance $s = vt$. For small angles θ the distance measured along the arc AB is approximately equal to the chord s so that to a close approximation s can be replaced by vt. These two substitutions made in the equation above give

$$\frac{vt}{r} = \frac{at}{v}.$$

By canceling t on both sides and transposing v, we obtain the relation

$$a = \frac{v^2}{r}. \tag{14f}$$

Thus, the *centripetal acceleration* is given by v^2/r.

As the angle θ in Fig. 14D is made smaller and smaller the arc distance s becomes more and more nearly equal to the chord, while the change in velocity v', which gives the direction of the acceleration a, becomes more nearly perpendicular to v. In the limit when θ becomes zero Eq.(14f) holds true exactly and the acceleration is perpendicular to v.

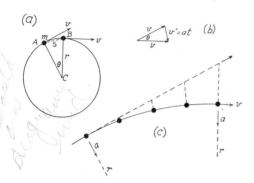

Substituting $r\omega$ for v (see Eq. (14f)) the centripetal acceleration can be expressed in terms of the angular velocity ω.

$$a = r\omega^2. \qquad (14g)$$

Fig. 14D—A body moving in a circle is continually being accelerated toward the center.

Centripetal force is defined as that constant force which acting continuously at right angles to the motion of a particle causes it to move in a circle with constant speed. Since by Newton's Second Law of Motion, $F = ma$, centripetal force is given by

$$F = m\frac{v^2}{r} \qquad (14h)$$

or in angular quantities by

$$F = mr\omega^2. \qquad (14i)$$

Example 1. A mass of 5 kg is moving in a circle of 1 m radius with an angular velocity of 2 rad/sec. Find the centripetal force.

Solution. The known quantities substituted directly in Eq.(14i) give

$$F = 5 \text{ kg} \times 1 \text{ m} \times 4\frac{\text{rad}^2}{\text{sec}^2} = 20\frac{\text{kg m}}{\text{sec}^2} = 20 \text{ newtons}.$$

Note. Radians have no dimensions and are therefore dropped out in arriving at the force in any units.

14.3. Experiments Demonstrating Centripetal Force. Many interesting experiments can be performed to illustrate centripetal force. In Fig. 14E mercury and water have been placed in a dish and the dish set rotating rapidly about a vertical axis. Since mercury is 13.6 times as heavy as an equal volume of water, the centripetal force F is 13.6 times as great as for mercury. The mercury therefore takes the outermost position in the dish.

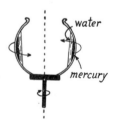

Fig. 14E—Mercury and water rotating in a dish finds the water inside the mercury.

Although the earth is often said to be spherical, it is in reality an oblate spheroid, that is, a slightly flattened sphere. Accurate measurements show that the earth's diameter is 28 mi greater through the equator than it is through the poles. The cause for this flattening is illustrated in Fig. 14F by two circular metal strips. Diagram (a) shows the strips round when at rest while (b) shows the flattening due to rapid rotation. The flattening of the earth is due to its own rotation of 2π radians every 24 hr. It is the enormous size of the earth and its lack of greater rigidity that makes it behave as though it were soft and semi-plastic.

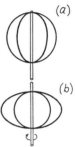

Fig. 14F—The flattening of earth is due to its rotation about the polar axis.

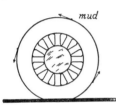

Fig. 14G—Mud or water on a fast turning wheel flies off on a tangent.

Mud or water clings to an automobile tire until the speed becomes too high and then it flies off on a tangent as shown in Fig. 14G. To remain with the tire the required centripetal force cannot exceed the force of adhesion.

Fig. 14H shows a ball rolling down a looped track. The ball will stay with the track even at the top of the loop if the required centripetal force there is equal to or greater than the downward force of gravity. This means that the speed v must be greater than a certain critical speed or the ball will fall. Such a behavior is similar to that of whirling a bucket of water in a circle up over the head and down, at arm's length without spilling it. To find the critical velocity at the top of the circle, the centripetal force mv^2/r is equated to the body's weight mg. This is the same as equating the centripetal acceleration v^2/r to the acceleration of gravity g. For any given radius r the critical speed becomes fixed by the equation,

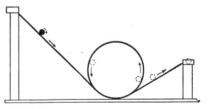

Fig. 14H—The ball will loop the loop if it starts rolling from a point high enough on the incline.

$$g = \frac{v^2}{r}.$$ (14j)

When a stone on the end of a string is whirled in a vertical circle, gravity acts downward upon it at all times. At the bottom of its path the weight must be added to the centrifugal force to obtain the tension in the string, while at the top of its path the weight must be subtracted. Whirled in a horizontal circle the stone's weight is at all times perpendicular to centripetal force and the string describes a cone. The tension in the string and its direc-

Fig. 14I—A lariat takes a circular form because each small part tries to fly off on a tangent thus getting as far from the center as possible. Centripetal force is responsible for keeping it in a circle.

tion is given by the resultant of two forces, *centrifugal* and *weight,* compounded at right angles.

The opening of the loop in a lariat as whirled and thrown by a cowboy is due to centripetal force. See Fig. 14I. Because of rotation each small section of the rope, acting as an individual mass m, tends to fly off on a tangent and thus get as far from the center of rotation as possible. The average distance from the center of all sections of the rope is a maximum when the loop takes the form of a circle rotating about an axis perpendicular to the plane of the loop.

When a small chain, as shown in Fig. 14J, is set rotating at high speed by an electric motor and then set free, it will roll along the floor as though it were a rigid metal hoop. Upon bumping into an obstacle, it will bounce into the air and upon coming down, retains its circular form as it rolls on. The rigidity of the hoop is due to the enormous centripetal force attained at high angular velocities.

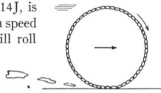

Fig. 14J—A chain turning at high speed will roll along the level as a rigid wheel.

14.4. Tension in a Rotating Loop. With a linked chain as in Fig. 14J, the centripetal force manifests itself as a tension between the links. The inward force on any one link is shown at the left in Fig. 14K as the resultant of two forces exerted upon it by the two adjacent links.

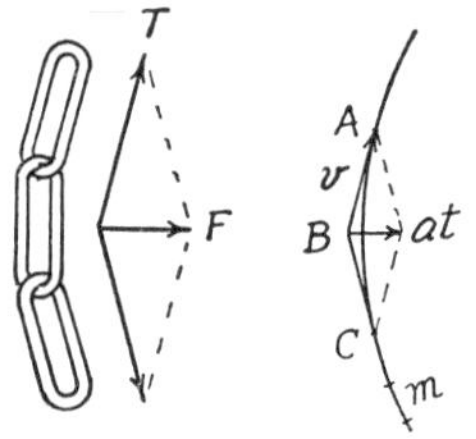

Fig. 14K—Centripetal force on a rotating chain gives rise to a tension around the loop.

To find the tension in a rotating loop, reference is made to the velocity diagram at the right. Each link or section m, moving with a velocity v, is continually changed in direction by the centripetal force. In going from C to A the direction changes from CB to BA. This change in velocity v', as has already been shown in Sec. 14.2, is equal to at. Since the force diagram at the left and the velocity diagram at the right are made up of similar triangles, corresponding sides are proportional, and

$$\frac{T}{F} = \frac{v}{at}$$

If l represents the length of the arc AC, and m the mass of each centimeter of the loop, the centripetal force F by Newton's Second Law $F = ma$ becomes $F = mla$, and

$$\frac{T}{mla} = \frac{v}{at}.$$

Since $l = vt$, a substitution of vt for l gives,

$$T = mv^2 \tag{14k}$$

The tension is proportional to m, the mass per unit of length, and to v^2, the square of the velocity. This latter means that if the angular velocity of a rotating loop is increased tenfold, the centripetal force and also the tension T increases one-hundredfold. Hence, high angular velocities give rise to very high tensions.

14.5 The Ultracentrifuge. Very high rotational speeds of 25,000 rps have been attained by specially designed tops driven by and riding on top of a jet of compressed air. See Fig. 14L. As the vertical air stream strikes the conical base of the top and is deflected out and up, the reaction forces of the air on the curved grooves in the base hold it up and at the same time drive it around with ever increasing speed. Ultra high rotational speeds of 800,000 rps have been reached by small steel balls magnetically suspended in a vacuum. At higher speeds their tensile strength is not great enough to withstand the enormous tensions set up by centripetal forces and they explode.

FIG. 14L — Small tops can be spun so fast that they literally explode because of the centrifugal reaction.

FIG. 14M—Ultracentrifuge used in medical research to speed up sedimentation processes.

It is an interesting fact that such tops, even if they are not perfectly round, are self-balancing and spin smoothly. Because of this they have been used successfully as driving units for ultra high speed centrifuging. The *ultracentrifuge* is a device whereby liquids containing microscopic particles are placed in a vessel (see Fig. 14M) and spun at very high speeds. As a result of high rotational speeds the particles sediment rapidly to the periphery. The device has been used successfully in medical researches (1) for concentrating solutions containing viruses, hormones, antibodies, and practically all proteins, (2) for purification of solutions by separating out impurities or undesirable material such as cell fragments, bacteria and coagulated substances, and (3) as a cytologic instrument for studying the effect of centrifugal displacement of the vital components of the living cell.

For a particle to sediment under the pull of gravity it must have a greater density than the solution in which it is suspended. In general, the smaller the particles, the slower they sediment. In a centrifuge, under the action of centripetal forces thousands of times greater than the force of gravity, sedimentation is speeded up tremendously.

Example 2. The drum of a centrifuge has a diameter of 8 in. Two small glass cells containing liquid are placed inside, equidistant from and on opposite sides of the center. If the drum has a speed of 1000 rps and the cells are 6 in. apart, how many times greater than the acceleration of gravity is the centripetal acceleration?

Solution. To use Eq.(14g) the angular velocity ω is first found. Since there are 2π radians in one revolution, an angular speed of 1000 rps corresponds to an angular velocity of

$$\omega = 2\pi \times 1000 = 6283 \text{ rad/sec.}$$

By Eq.(14g),

$$a = r\omega^2 = 0.25 \text{ ft} \times (6238 \text{ rad/sec})^2$$

$$a = 9.73 \times 10^6 \text{ ft/sec}^2$$

Dividing by g, ($= 32$ ft/sec^2) gives,

$$a = 304,000 \ g\text{'s.}$$

Strange as it may seem, a whirling clothes dryer works upon the principle that the clothes are pulled out of the water by centripetal force and not that the water is driven off by centrifugal force. When the centripetal force becomes too large the forces of adhesion are broken and the water continues on in a straight line. The water takes the tangent path while the clothes are pulled out of its way.

PROBLEMS

1. A 5 lb lead weight is whirled in a circle at the end of a wire 8 ft long. If the weight makes 90 rpm find (a) the angular velocity, (b) the angle turned through in 5 sec, (c) the acceleration toward the center, and (d) the centripetal force in lb. Neglect gravity.

2. A mass of 2 kg on the end of wire 250 cm long is whirled in a circle at 120 rpm. Find (a) the acceleration toward the center, and (b) the centripetal force. Neglect gravity. (*Ans.* (a) 395 m/sec, (b) 790 newtons.)

3. A merry-go-round 60 ft in diameter is rotating with an angular speed of 5 rpm. What will be (a) the speed, (b) the centripetal acceleration, and (c) the centripetal force of a person weighing 160 lb if he stands at the edge.

4. At the Worlds Fair held in Paris, France, some years ago, flowers of various kinds were planted on a huge round table. Because this table was kept turning day and night with an angular speed of 9 rpm the plants grew at an inward angle with the vertical. Calculate the angles at which these plants should grow if their distance from the center of rotation was 5 ft, 15 ft, 25 ft. Make a scale diagram showing these angles. (*Ans.* 7.9°, 22.6°, 34.6°.)

5. A Ferris Wheel 80 ft in diameter is rotating at 6 rpm. Calculate the resultant force acting on a 125 lb man riding in one of the cars when he is at (a) the top, (b) the bottom, (c) the side on a level with the hub. Do not neglect gravity.

6. A 200 gm stone is whirled at 30 rpm in a circle at the end of a cord 120 cm long. If the plane of the circle is vertical what is the tension in the string at (a) the top, and (b) the bottom of the circle? (*Ans.* (a) 0.409 newton, (b) 4.33 newtons.)

7. A weight of 2 lb is whirled at 90 rpm in a horizontal circle at the end of a string 5 ft long. Taking gravity into account find the tension in the string.

8. A 3200 lb car making 60 mi/hr rounds a curve of 1000 ft radius. What is (a) the angular speed in rad/sec, and (b) the centripetal acceleration, and (c) the centripetal force? (*Ans.* (a) 0.088 rad/sec, (b) 7.74 ft/sec, (c) 774 lb.)

9. A locomotive weighing 45 tons is traveling at 60 mi/hr. Find the centrifugal force exerted by the wheels on the rails when it is rounding a curve of 900 ft radius. Assume the road is not banked.

10. A 180 lb pilot is making 540 mi/hr when he pulls out of a dive. (a) What is the minimum radius allowed if his centripetal acceleration is not to exceed 7 times the acceleration of gravity, i.e., not to exceed 7 g's? What is the total upward force on his body when he is at the lowest point in the dive? (*Ans.* (a) 2800 ft, (b) 1440 lb.)

11. A motorcycle and rider making 75 km/hr round a curve of 100 m radius. At what angle will they lean from the vertical?

12. A man living at the equator accurately weighs himself and finds he weighs 100.00 lb. What correction must be made for the earth's rotation? (*Ans.* + 0.35 lb.)

13. A boy sits on the floor of a merry-go-round 20 ft from the center. If the coefficient of static friction is 0.5 at what angular speed will he start to slide?

Work, Energy and Power   Chapter 15

THERE is little doubt that the most important concept in all nature is energy. It is important because it represents a fundamental entity common to all forms of matter in all parts of the known physical world. Closely associated with energy is another concept *work,* a term used in civil life to describe the expenditure of one's stored up bodily energy. Because energy is most easily described in terms of work, this latter will first be treated in detail.

15.1. Work. In its simplest mechanical form *work* is defined as *the force times the distance* through which the force acts.

$$\text{work} = \text{force} \times \text{distance}.$$

Algebraically,

$$\text{work} = F \times s. \tag{15a}$$

Consider the general problem of calculating the work done in lifting a mass m to a height s above the ground. See Fig. (15A). By Newton's Second Law of Motion ($F = ma$) the force required to lift any mass m is equal to its own weight.

$$W = mg.$$

Substituting the weight mg for F in Eq. (15a),

$$\text{work done} = mg \times s. \tag{15b}$$

To give numerical values assume that a mass of 5 kg is lifted vertically a distance of 2 m. By direct substitution in Eq.(15b),

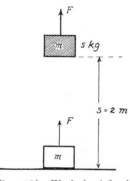

FIG. 15A—Work is defined as force × distance.

$$\text{work} = 5 \text{ kg} \times 9.8 \frac{\text{m}}{\text{sec}^2} \times 2 \text{ m} = 98 \frac{\text{kg m}^2}{\text{sec}^2}.$$

Since *force*, in *newtons*, has the units kg m/sec², the answer can also be written

work = 98 newton meters.

Work in the *mks* system is seen to have the absolute units *kg m²/sec²*, which are equal to the derived units *newton meters*. In the *cgs* system the corresponding absolute units are *gm cm²/sec²*, which are equal to the derived units *dyne centimeters*. In the English, or engineering system the units of work are *foot pounds*, abbreviated *ft lb*.

Example 1. Find the work done in lifting a weight of 5 lb to a height of 10 ft. *Solution.* By direct substitution in Eq.(15a), we obtain

work = 5 lb × 10 ft = 50 ft lb.

15.2. Ergs and Joules. In the cgs system the *dyne cm* as a unit of work is called the *erg*.

$$1 \text{ dyne cm} = 1 \text{ erg.} \tag{15c}$$

A force of 1 dyne acting through a distance of 1 cm in the same direction does 1 erg of work.

In the *mks* system of units, a force of 1 *newton* acting through a distance of 1 m in the same direction performs an amount of work equivalent to *1 joule*.

$$1 \text{ newton meter} = 1 \text{ joule.} \tag{15d}$$

Since the *newton* as a unit of force = 1 kg × 1 m/sec² = 1000 gm × 100 cm/sec² = 10^5 dynes, the *newton meter* = 10^5 dynes × 100 cm = 10^7 dyne cm. In other words,

$$1 \text{ joule} = 10^7 \text{ ergs.} \tag{15e}$$

The *joule* as a unit of work is, therefore, much larger than the *erg* and in many practical problems is to be preferred because of the smaller numbers involved in calculations.

Example 2. Calculate the work done in lifting a mass of 400 gm to a height of 250 cm. *Solution.* The known quantities are $m = 400$ gm, $s = 250$ cm, and $g = 980$ cm/sec². Substitution in Eq.(15b) gives

$$\text{work} = 400 \text{ gm} \times 980 \frac{\text{cm}}{\text{sec}^2} \times 250 \text{ cm} = 98{,}000{,}000 \frac{\text{gm cm}^2}{\text{sec}^2}.$$

$$\text{work} = 98{,}000{,}000 \text{ ergs.} \tag{15f}$$

15.3. Work Done Against Friction. In sliding a mass of 5 kg along a horizontal plane a distance of 2 m, see Fig. 15B, the work done *will not* in general be as great as that required to lift the same mass 2 m vertically.

Suppose, for example, that the coefficient of sliding friction for the block in the diagram is $\mu = 0.2$. By calculation then the force of friction is (see Eq. 11d),

$$f = \mu N = 0.2 \times 5 \ \text{kg} \times 9.8 \ \text{m/sec}^2 = 9.8 \ \text{newtons.}$$

Since a force of 9.8 newtons will slide the block, the work done, by Eq. (15b) will be,

$$\text{work} = 9.8 \ \text{newtons} \times 2 \ \text{m} = 19.6 \ \text{newton meters.}$$

This is only one-fifth as much work as that required to lift the same 5 kg mass an equal vertical distance of 2 m. See Fig. 15A. By reducing the friction between the block and plane the force F can be reduced still further. Such a reduction can be accomplished by smoothing and lubricating the sliding surfaces, or better by mounting the block on wheels. Could the friction be eliminated entirely, the work done in moving any object in a horizontal direction would be practically zero, for, once started it would continue moving with constant velocity. A vertical lift, however, requires at least an amount of work equal to the weight mg times the height s.

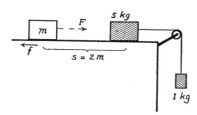

FIG. 15B—To slide a body horizontally work must be done against friction.

When a force acting on an object is applied at an angle with the direction of motion, only the component of the force in the direction of motion is effective in doing work. This is illustrated in Fig. 15C where a force of 1000

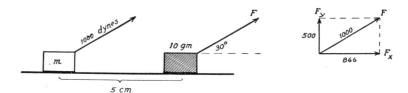

FIG. 15C—Force and distance are measured in the same direction in calculating work.

dynes applied at an angle of 30° moves a 10 gm mass a distance of 5 cm. In the right-hand diagram F is resolved into two components, F_x horizontally and F_y vertically.

By calculation or by graphical construction

$$F_x = F \cos 30° = 1000 \times 0.866 = 866 \ \text{dynes}$$
$$F_y = F \sin 30° = 1000 \times 0.500 = 500 \ \text{dynes.}$$

The vertical force of 500 dynes, being perpendicular to the direction of motion does no work since the distance moved upward is zero. Work is done only by the horizontal force F_x.

$$\text{Work} = 866 \text{ dynes} \times 5 \text{ cm} = 4330 \text{ ergs.}$$

While the vertical force does not enter directly into the calculation of work, it does help to lift the body and thereby reduce the friction between the sliding surfaces. As an illustration consider the following problem:

Example 3. A trunk having a mass of 100 kg is pulled 20 m across the floor by a rope making an angle of 35° with the horizontal. See Fig. 15D. If the coefficient of sliding friction is 0.25, find (a) the tension in the rope and (b) the work done. *Solution.* The force F is resolved into two components,

$$F_x = F \cos 35° = 0.819\ F$$
$$F_y = F \sin 35° = 0.574\ F.$$

To find the horizontal force of friction, $(f = \mu N)$ the normal force N is calculated as the resultant of two forces acting on the block; mg downward due to gravity, and F_y upward due to the pull of the rope.
Therefore,

$$N = mg - F_y$$

and the force of friction is

$$f = \mu N = 0.25\ (mg - F_y).$$

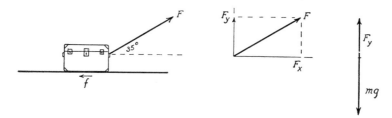

Fig. 15D—Work is done in sliding a trunk along the floor.

To overcome friction and slide the body the component F_x must be at least equal to f. Setting $f = F_x$,

$$F_x = 0.25\ (mg - F_y).$$

Substituting for F_x and F_y from the above relations, and multiplying out,

$$0.819\ F = 0.25\ mg - 0.25 \times 0.574\ F.$$

Collecting on the left, factors containing F, and substituting for m and g,

$$0.962\ F = 0.25 \times 100 \text{ kg} \times 9.8\ \frac{\text{m}}{\text{sec}^2}$$

giving (a)

$$F = 255 \text{ newtons.}$$

By Eq.(15a) the work done is $F_x \times s$,

$$\text{work} = 0.819 \times 255 \text{ newtons} \times 20 \text{ m.}$$

(b) $$\text{work} = 4177 \text{ joules.}$$

15.4. Work in the Engineering System of Units. Because it is customary in engineering design and construction to measure loads and forces in pounds it is proper to calculate work in *foot-pounds*, i.e., *force in pounds* $\times$ *distance in feet*. As an illustration consider the following problem.

Example 4. When loaded the small car of a hoist weighs 240 lb. How much work is done in lifting this load 35 ft?
Solution. By Eq.(15a),

$$\text{work} = F \times s = 240 \text{ lb} \times 35 \text{ ft} = 8400 \text{ ft lb.}$$

15.5. Potential Energy. Mechanical energy is divided into two categories, *potential energy*, and *kinetic energy*. *A body is said to have potential energy if by virtue of its position or state it is able to do work.* A car at the top of a hill or a wound clock spring is an example of an object with potential energy. The clock spring may keep a clock running for a certain length of time, and a car may, by coasting downhill, travel a great distance. Potential energy is measured by the amount of work that is available. It is therefore measured in *ergs, joules,* or *foot pounds.*

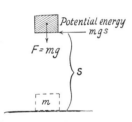

If a given mass m is raised to a specified height s, as illustrated in Fig. 15E, it then has potential energy $F \times s$ by virtue of its position above the ground level from which it has been lifted. The *work done* in lifting it has been stored up as potential energy in the block. This energy can be regained by dropping the mass back to the ground for in so

Fig. 15E—A body has potential energy by virtue of its position.

doing it can be made to perform some kind of work. By definition,

$$\text{potential energy} = F \times s \qquad (15g)$$

or, in absolute units,

$$\textbf{P.E.} = mg \times s.$$

Example 5. A mass of 5 kg is raised to a height of 2.5 m above the ground. Calculate its potential energy.
Substituting the known quantities in Eq.(15g),

$$\textbf{P.E.} = 5 \text{ kg} \times 9.8 \frac{\text{m}}{\text{sec}^2} \times 2.5 \text{ m} = 122.5 \text{ joules.}$$

If a body is lifted straight upward, carried up a staircase, or pulled up an inclined plane, the potential energy acquired is given by the *weight* $\times$ *vertical* height to which it is raised.

The meaning of positive, zero, or negative potential energy is illustrated in Fig. 15F. Located at any point above the *base plane* a body has positive potential energy, while at points below that line it has negative potential energy. To lift the mass m from A to B work is done and the mass acquires potential energy to the amount of mgs_1.

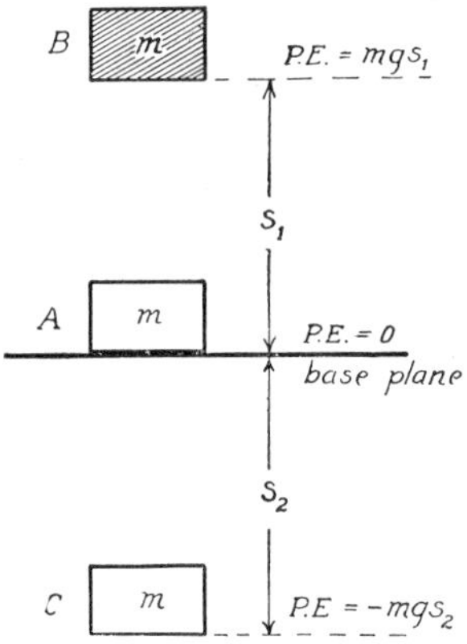

In returning from B to A the mass loses potential energy, performing *work* $= mgs_1$ on some other body. Similarly in going from A to C the body loses energy and ends up at C with mgs_2 less energy than it had at A. To raise it again to A an equivalent amount of work mgs_2 will have to be done on the body.

The choosing of a *base plane* as a zero energy level is a purely arbitrary selection. In most practical applications it is customary to select the lowest point to be reached by a body as the zero level so that all displacements from there will be positive in sign. In the engineering system of units *potential energy*, like *work*, can be expressed in foot pounds, i.e., *pounds* $\times$ *vertical distance in feet.*

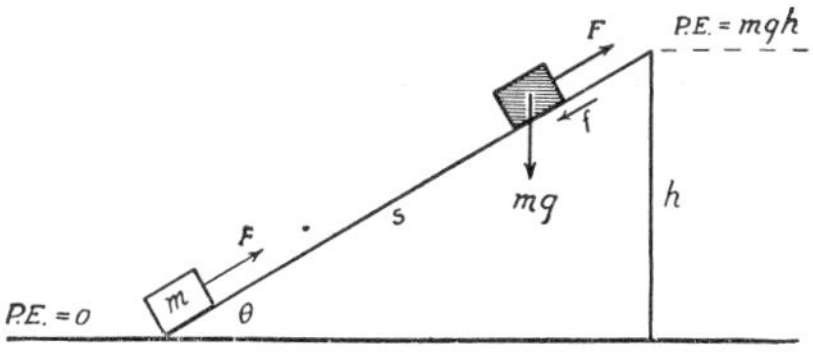

FIG. 15F — Potential energy with respect to a base plane may be plus or minus.

When a force is applied to a body to slide or roll it along the ground, the *work done* is not stored up as potential energy. Because of friction the energy is transformed into heat, and as a practical matter is considered lost for further use. If the body ends up at the same level at which it started all of the energy has gone into heat and the potential energy remains unchanged.

FIG. 15G—Part of the work done in sliding a mass up an incline goes into friction and part into potential energy.

If a body is pulled up an inclined plane, on the other hand, part of the energy goes into heat and part into potential energy. The potential energy as illustrated in Fig. 15G is given by mgh while the work done is given by $F \times s$, and the frictional energy by $f \times s$.

$$F \times s = f \times s + mgh.$$

work done = frictional energy + potential energy

15.6. Kinetic Energy. The kinetic energy of a moving body is defined as its ability to do work by virtue of its motion. A car moving along the highway has kinetic energy of translation, and a rotating wheel on a machine has kinetic energy of rotation. For a given mass m, moving in a straight line with constant velocity v, the kinetic energy is given by,

$$\text{kinetic energy} = \tfrac{1}{2}mv^2. \qquad (15h)$$

Example 6. Calculate the kinetic energy of a 20 kg mass moving with a velocity of 4 m/sec.
Solution. By direct substitution in Eq.(15h),

$$\textbf{K.E.} = \tfrac{1}{2} \times 20 \text{ kg} \times \left(4\frac{m}{\sec}\right)^2 = 160\frac{\text{kg m}^2}{\sec^2}.$$

This answer has exactly the dimensions of *work*, and *potential energy*, and can be written in the same derived units.

$$\textbf{K.E.} = 160 \text{ joules.}$$

A moving body has energy because in being brought to rest it must exert a force F on some other object, and this force acting through a distance s does work. In other words work can be done by a moving body. Conversely by applying a constant horizontal force F on a body of mass m, for a distance s, it will be given a kinetic energy $\tfrac{1}{2}mv^2$. See Fig. 15H.

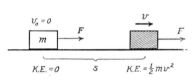

$$F \times s = \tfrac{1}{2}mv^2. \qquad (15i)$$

Fig. 15H—A body has kinetic energy by virtue of its motion.

This is known as the "work equation." In it friction is entirely neglected and the body is presumed to start from rest. To derive Eq.(15i) from previous principles, Newton's Second Law of Motion will serve as a starting point.

$$F = ma.$$

Multiplying both sides of the equation by s,

$$F \times s = mas. \qquad (15j)$$

For the product as on the right, Eq.(4h) is used. The equation $v^2 - v_0^2 = 2as$ is transformed to give

$$as = \frac{v^2 - v_0^2}{2}$$

which, substituted in Eq.(15j), gives

$$F \times s = m\frac{v^2 - v_0^2}{2}.$$

Then,

$$F \times s = \tfrac{1}{2}mv^2 - \tfrac{1}{2}mv_0^2. \tag{15k}$$

In the special case that a body starts from rest, $v_0 = 0$, the last term drops out and the equation becomes the above Eq.(15i).

Example 7. A constant horizontal force of 25 lb acts for a distance of 20 ft on a 500 lb box. If friction is neglected and the box starts from rest, what is its velocity?

Solution. The known quantities are $v_0 = 0$, $m = 500$ lb/32 ft/sec², $s = 20$ ft, and $F = 25$ lb. The special Eq.(15i) may, therefore, be applied. Transpose all but v^2 to one side of the equation.

$$v^2 = \frac{2(F \times s)}{m} = \frac{2(25 \text{ lb} \times 20 \text{ ft})}{500 \text{ lb}/32 \text{ ft/sec}^2}$$

$$v^2 = 64 \text{ ft}^2/\text{sec}^2, \quad \text{and} \quad v = 8\,\frac{\text{ft}}{\text{sec}}.$$

Note that in solving this problem the mass m must be in slugs, i.e., pounds weight divided by g in ft/sec².

15.7. Power. Power is defined as the rate of doing work, or the rate at which work is being done.

$$\text{Power} = \frac{\text{work}}{\text{time}}$$

$$P = \frac{F \times s}{t}. \tag{15m}$$

The faster a given amount of work is done the greater is the power. In other words, the smaller the time t in the above equation the greater is the fraction $F \times s/t$ and the power P.

In the metric system, with work measured in *ergs* or *joules,* power is expressed either in *ergs per second* or in *joules per second.* One joule per second is called the *watt,* a unit of power.

$$1 \text{ joule/sec} = 1 \text{ watt}. \tag{15n}$$

The *kilowatt* is another unit of power and is equal to *1000 watts.*

In the engineering system, with work measured in foot pounds, power is expressed in foot pounds per second, and in horsepower (abbr. hp).

$$1 \text{ hp} = 550 \text{ ft lb/sec}. \tag{15o}$$

Example 8. Find the power of an engine capable of lifting 200 lb to a height of 55 ft in 10 sec.

Solution. By Eq.(15m),

$$P = \frac{200 \text{ lb} \times 55 \text{ ft}}{10 \text{ sec}} = 1100\,\frac{\text{ft lb}}{\text{sec}}.$$

Dividing this answer by 550 to get horsepower,

$$\frac{1100}{550} = 2 \text{ hp.}$$

If 550 ft lb/sec is changed to the metric system (1 ft = 0.305 m, and 1 lb = 4.45 newtons).

$$1 \text{ hp} = 746 \frac{\text{joules}}{\text{sec}} = 746 \text{ watts.} \tag{15p}$$

PROBLEMS

1. (a) Calculate the work done in raising 120 lb to a height of 15 ft. (b) Find the work done in raising 250 gm a distance of 215 cm.

2. How much work in ft lbs is required to carry a 50 lb sack up two flights of stairs in an apartment house if the vertical distance between floors is 11 ft. (*Ans.* 1100 ft lbs.)

3. A horse whose mass is 500 kg climbs to a height of 1000 m. Find the potential energy in joules.

4. A boy whose mass is 50 kg climbs a mountain peak with an elevation of 300 m. Find his potential energy in newton meters as measured from sea level. (*Ans.* 1.47×10^5 newton meters.)

5. A racing car with the driver weighs 1825 lb. Find the kinetic energy in ft lbs when traveling with a speed of 100 mi/hr.

6. A boy and his bicycle weigh 140 lb. Calculate the kinetic energy in ft lbs when traveling 15 mi/hr. (*Ans.* 1059 ft lbs.)

7. An automobile weighing 3800 lb is traveling along the highway at 45 mi/hr. What force in lb applied by the brakes will stop it in 150 ft?

8. A mass of 5 kg initially at rest is given a speed of 14 m/sec by a force of 15.7 newtons. Calculate (a) the distance over which the force acts, and (b) the kinetic energy in joules. (*Ans.* (a) 31.2 m, (b) 490 joules.)

9. A car weighing 3900 lb climbs to the top of a hill 500 ft high in one minute. Neglecting friction, calculate (a) the potential energy stored up in ft lb, and (b) the power of the car in horsepower.

10. An airplane weighing 2500 lb climbs to a height of one mile in 10 min. Calculate the accomplished power in horsepower. (*Ans.* 40 hp.)

11. The hopper of a concrete hoist weighs 750 lb when half loaded. If this hopper is raised 165 ft in 6 sec, find the power required in (a) ft lb/sec, (b) horsepower, and (c) watts.

12. An elevator car with 6 passengers weighs 1400 lb. (a) Calculate the power required to raise this car 4 ft/sec. (b) If the car's weight of 600 lb is counterbalanced by weights, what power is required? (*Ans* (a) 10.2 hp, (b) 5.8 hp.)

13. A fallen tree weighing 6 tons is pulled through the forest by a tractor for a distance of 500 ft. If the tow cable makes an angle of 20° with the horizontal and the coefficient of sliding friction is 0.65, what is (a) the tension in the cable, and (b) the work done?

14. An oak box weighing 100 lb is pulled 12 ft up an oak plank inclined 30° with the horizontal. If the coefficient of friction is 0.25 find (a) the force applied parallel to the plank, (b) the work done, and (c) the potential energy at the top. (*Ans.* (a) 71.7 lb, (b) 860 ft lb, (c) 600 ft lb.)

15. A cake of ice with a mass of 20 kg slides down a plank 10 m long making an angle of 25° with the horizontal. (a) How much potential energy is lost?

16. A car weighing 3800 lb increases its speed from 15 to 45 mi/hr in 6 sec. (a) What is the change in kinetic energy, and (b) the power developed? (*Ans.* (a) 2.30 × 10⁵ ft lb, (b) 69.7 hp.)

17. A coal elevator in a mine shaft weighs 6 tons when loaded. What must be the minimum power realized by a motor that could lift this car 400 ft in one minute?

18. From what height must a 100 lb boulder fall in order to have the same amount of kinetic energy as a 5 ton truck traveling with a speed of 30 mi/hr along a level road? (*Ans.* 3025 ft.)

19. Find the power necessary to keep car A in Fig. 11M at a constant speed of 60 mi/hr along a level road. Assume the car weighs 4000 lb.

20. What power must be developed to maintain car B in Fig. 11M at a constant speed of 60 mi/hr along a level road? Assume the car to weigh 4000 lb. (*Ans.* 33.2 hp.)

21. An automobile weighing 3200 lb, and moving with a speed of 45 mi/hr, is brought to rest in 132 ft. Find (a) the time required to stop, (b) the acceleration, and (c) the power expended in the brakes.

22. How heavy a load can a 20 hp hoist lift at a steady speed of 168 ft/min without exceeding its rated output? (*Ans.* 314 lb.)

23. Find the power developed in a steam engine in which the steam exerts a force of 8000 lb on a piston and moves it forward and backward 120 times per minute through a distance of 1 ft each way.

24. Water is pumped from a river into a reservoir, a total lift of 120 m, at a rate of 10 m³/hr. What is the minimum power required? One cubic meter of water weighs 1000 kg. (*Ans.* 3.26 kw.)

25. How many cubic meters of water can be pumped in 1 hour from a river to a water tank by a 1 kw pump? Assume a lift of 25 m.

26. A diesel locomotive weighing 500 tons develops 5000 hp while hauling a 4000 ton train of cars at a constant speed of 45 mi/hr along a level track. Compute (a) the kinetic energy of the locomotive and train, and (b) the retarding force of friction. (*Ans.* (a) 6.18 × 10⁸ ft lb. (b) 41.7 tons)

27. A ski lift employs a 30 kw motor to keep the tow rope in motion. If the mass of the average person is 70 kg, and the lift carries the skiers to an elevation 200 m above the base, what is the maximum number of people that can be allowed on the lift at the same time?

28. An escalator carries persons from one floor to another 20 ft higher, and the steps move with a speed of 90 ft/min along the incline. The steps are 8 in. high and measure 18 in. from edge to edge along the incline. What size motor is needed to take care of an over-all load of 120 lb per step? (*Ans.* 4.36 hp.)

29. A funicular railway, in which the ascending car and descending car counterbalance each other, lifts ten passengers whose average mass is 70 kg a total height of 500 m in 10 min. What is the minimum power required if there are no passengers in the descending car? (*Ans.* 5.71 kw.)

30. A box slides from the top of a chute 20 ft long. The chute is inclined at an angle of 30° with the horizontal and the coefficient of sliding friction is 0.2. Find the speed of the box at the bottom of the chute. (*Ans.* 5.9 ft/sec.)

Conservation of Energy and Momentum
Chapter 16

16.1. Conservation of Energy. Most important of all the laws of nature is the law of the conservation of energy. While the law has been stated in almost as many different ways as there are books written on the subject they all have in reality the same meaning. The following three examples are typical statements: (1) *in transforming energy from one form to another, energy is always conserved,* (2) *energy is never created or destroyed, or* (3) *the sum total of all energy in the universe remains constant.*

Everyone should be aware of the fact that there are many forms of energy; for example, in addition to the two forms of *mechanical energy* already defined, there is *heat energy, electrical energy, chemical energy, light energy* and *atomic energy.* In this chapter we are concerned with the law of conservation of energy only as it applies to the two forms of mechanical energy, *potential* and *kinetic.* The law will again be encountered in connection with the other forms in the chapters on heat, electricity, and atomic structure.

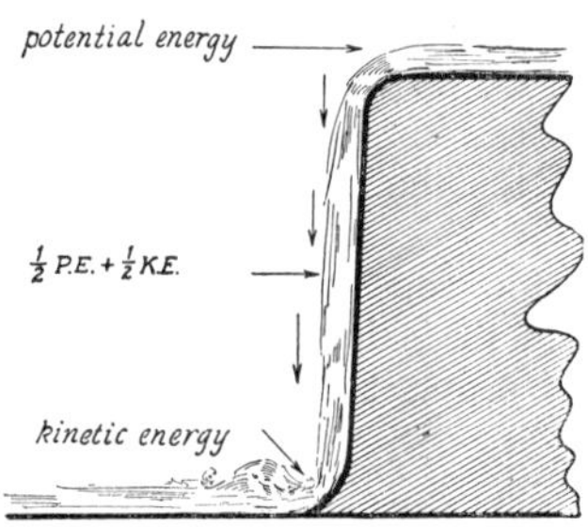

FIG. 16A—The available energy at the top of a waterfall is all potential. At the bottom it is all kinetic.

Consider the energy involved in a water fall as shown in Fig. 16A. The water at the top of the fall has potential energy by virtue of its position above the base. As it falls over and then downward with ever increasing speed, the kinetic energy $\frac{1}{2}mv^2$ increases while the potential energy decreases. At the bottom of the fall the potential energy approaches zero and the kinetic energy approaches its maximum value. At the top the energy was practically all potential while near the bottom it is mostly kinetic. Assuming the water to start from rest at the top and that no energy is lost in falling, the P.E. at the top of the falls equals the K.E. at the bottom.

$$(\text{P.E. at top}) = (\text{K.E. at bottom})$$

$$F \times s = \tfrac{1}{2}mv^2 \tag{16a}$$

or

$$mgs = \tfrac{1}{2}mv^2. \tag{16b}$$

134

Cancel m on both sides of the equation and solve for v.

$$v^2 = 2gs \qquad \text{or} \qquad v = \sqrt{2gs}. \qquad (16c)$$

This is the special Eq.(5j) derived for falling bodies in one of the preceding chapters from the laws of accelerated motion. Here the equation has been derived from the law of conservation of energy.

Example 1. A mass of 25 kg is dropped from a height of 5 m. Find the kinetic energy and velocity just as it reaches the ground.

Solution. Since the P.E. at the top is equivalent to the K.E. at the bottom,

$$\text{P.E.} = 25 \text{ kg} \times 9.8 \, \frac{\text{m}}{\text{sec}^2} \times 5 \text{ m} = 1225 \text{ joules} = \text{K.E.}$$

The velocity is found by Eq.(16c),

$$v = \sqrt{2 \times 9.8 \times 5} = 9.9 \text{ m/sec.}$$

When the falling body in the above problem is part way down, it has some P.E. and some K.E. Its total energy E is therefore of two kinds,

$$E = \tfrac{1}{2}mv^2 + mgs. \qquad (16d)$$

At the instant the body reaches the ground it is suddenly stopped and all of the energy is quickly transformed into heat. The transformation of mechanical energy into heat is often demonstrated in the physics laboratory by an experiment in which a quantity of lead-shot is dropped from a height of several feet and its temperature measured before and after falling. By raising the shot and dropping it many times, the rise in temperature amounts to several degrees.

16.2. The Inclined Plane. In Chap. 10 it was shown how a body sliding without friction down an incline of height h should acquire at the bottom a velocity $v = \sqrt{2gh}$. This same equation is readily derived from the Law of Conservation of Energy.

Starting from rest at the top of the incline a mass m has potential energy mgh and no kinetic energy. See Fig. 16B. Upon reaching the bottom the potential energy has been reduced to zero and the energy is all kinetic. By conservation the total energy is at all times constant, so that

total E at top = total E at bottom
P.E. + K.E. = P.E. + K.E. $\qquad (16e)$

$$mgh + 0 = 0 + \tfrac{1}{2}mv^2$$

from which

$$v = \sqrt{2gh}. \qquad (16f)$$

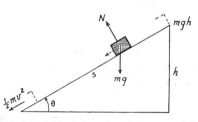

FIG. 16B—In sliding downhill, potential energy may be transformed into kinetic energy.

When sliding friction is taken into account the equation above must include an additional term. At the top of the incline the total energy is all potential and $E = mgh$. In sliding down, part of this available energy, to the amount of $f \times s$, is used up in overcoming friction and the rest goes into kinetic energy, $\frac{1}{2}mv^2$. By conservation of energy,

P.E. at top $=$ frictional energy $+$ K.E. at bottom
$$mgh = f \times s + \frac{1}{2}mv^2.$$

In applying this formula to the solving of problems, the force of friction $f = \mu N$, is found in the usual way by resolving the weight mg into components.

16.3. The Simple Pendulum. A similar energy treatment can be given for the swinging of a simple pendulum. At the extreme ends of each swing, see Fig. 16C, the bob comes momentarily to rest and the energy E is all potential and equal to mgh. At the bottom of the swing the energy E is all kinetic and equal to $\frac{1}{2}mv^2$.

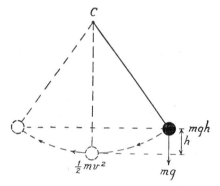

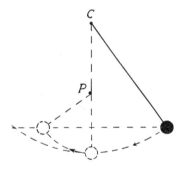

Fig. 16C—Potential energy of a pendulum changes to kinetic energy and back again.

Fig. 16D—The pendulum bob rises to the same height.

The motion of the pendulum bob is like that of a body sliding, without friction, down an inclined plane of changing angle. The kinetic energy acquired in going down one side is just sufficient to carry it up to an equal height on the other. If a pin is placed at P as shown in Fig. 16D the bob will rise to the same height h as before.

16.4. The Brachistochrone. In 1696 Jean Bernoulli addressed a letter to the mathematicians of Europe challenging them to solve within six months the following problem in mechanics. Along what path should a body move in order to descend from one point A to another point B at a lower level in the least possible time. After some months had passed Leibnitz, Jacques Bernoulli, and L'Hospital arrived at the answer. On Januray 29,

1697, Newton received from France a copy of the printed paper containing the problem and the following day sent the solution to the President of the Royal Society.

The curve of the shortest time, and now called the "Brachistochrone," is a cycloid. See Fig. 16E. The cycloid is the path traversed by a point on the rim of a wheel when it is rolled along a horizontal plane. It is interesting

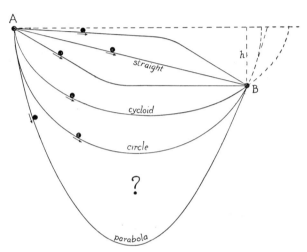

FIG. 16E—The brachistochrone. Which path should the body take to reach B in the least time?

to note that although the cycloid is the path of least time for a body starting from rest at A and sliding without friction from A to B, the velocity of arrival at B is the same for all paths. By the law of conservation of energy this final velocity is given by Eq.(16c) where s is the vertical height h between A and B.

16.5. Conservation of Momentum. When two or more bodies collide with each other, momentum is conserved. The law of conservation of momentum applies to all collision phenomena and states that the total momen-

FIG. 16F—The total momentum of two bodies before impact is equal to the total momentum after impact.

tum before impact equals the total momentum after impact. Consider as an example the "head on" encounter of two balls as shown in Fig. 16F. Before impact the mass m_1 is moving with a velocity u_1 and has a momentum m_1u_1 while m_2 is moving with a velocity u_2 and has a momentum m_2u_2. The total momentum before impact is therefore equal to the sum of the two momenta, $m_1u_1 + m_2u_2$.

By similar reasoning it is clear that after impact, m_1 and m_2, with their new velocities v_1 and v_2 have a total momentum $m_1v_1 + m_2v_2$. The law of conservation of momentum requires that

$$m_1u_1 + m_2u_2 = m_1v_1 + m_2v_2. \tag{16g}$$

momentum before impact = momentum after impact

During impact two equal but opposite forces are set up between the bodies, one the force exerted by m_1 on m_2 and the other the force exerted by m_2 on m_1. These two equal but opposite forces are an action and reaction pair explained by Newton's Third Law of Motion. Each force acts for the same short interval of time giving equal impulses Ft to both bodies. By Newton's Second Law, as expressed by the impulse equation $Ft = mv - mv_0$, equal impulses produce equal changes in momentum. One body gains as much momentum as the other loses. In other words, the total momentum remains constant.

Example 2. An ivory ball of mass 5 gm moving with a velocity of 20 cm/sec, collides with another ivory ball of mass 10 gm moving in the same direction along the same line with a velocity of 10 cm/sec. After impact the first mass is still moving in the same direction but with a velocity of only 8 cm/sec. Calculate the velocity of the second mass after impact. Apply Eq.(16g).

Solution. By direct substitution in Eq.(16g),

$$(5 \times 20) + (10 \times 10) = (5 \times 8) + (10 \times v_2)$$
$$200 = 40 + 10v_2$$
$$10v_2 = 160 \qquad v_2 = 16 \text{ cm/sec.}$$

After impact the second mass has a velocity of 16 cm/sec.

If in the above example, the total kinetic energy after impact is calculated and compared with the total kinetic energy before impact the two will not be found equal. Employing the equation K.E. $= \frac{1}{2}mv^2$,

K.E. $= \frac{1}{2}(5 \times 20^2) + \frac{1}{2}(10 \times 10^2) = 1500$ ergs, before impact
K.E. $= \frac{1}{2}(5 \times 8^2) + \frac{1}{2}(10 \times 16^2) = 1440$ ergs, after impact.

The difference in energy, to the amount of 60 ergs, has disappeared as mechanical energy and gone into heat. During impact both masses were slightly deformed in shape due to the mutually acting forces and a small amount of heat was generated internally. This heat goes to raise the temperature of the two colliding bodies. It is only by including this heat energy of 60 ergs with the mechanical energy after impact that makes it possible to retain the law of conservation of energy.

This is just another way of stating that collisions in general are not perfectly elastic. If they were perfectly elastic, conservation of mechanical energy would hold as well as conservation of momentum. Perfectly elastic collisions are known to occur between the *ultramicroscopic* atoms and molecules of a gas but not with the *macroscopic* bodies encountered in every day life. The more inelastic the colliding bodies the more energy is transformed into heat. A treatment of elasticity and its application to collision problems will be given in Chap. 24.

It is important to note from the discussion above, that *for all impact problems whether perfectly elastic or not, the law of conservation of momentum should be applied.*

16.6. Experiments. An interesting experiment illustrating conservation of momentum is shown in Fig. 16G. Two small cars of equal mass, $m_1 = m_2$, are tied together with a compressed spring between them. When the cord

FIG. 16G—Conservation of momentum holds upon release.

tie is burned with a match, releasing the spring, the two cars fly apart with equal velocities. Before the spring is released the cars are at rest and the total momentum is zero. After the spring is released the total momentum is still zero since the two velocities are oppositely directed. Momentum being a vector quantity,

$$m_1v_1 + m_2v_2 = 0. \qquad (16h)$$

With motions to the right taken as positive, v_2 is positive and v_1 negative, and the two momenta cancel.

If the experiment above is repeated with one of the cars heavily loaded as shown in diagram (b), the two fly apart as before but with unequal velocities. The lighter mass moves away with a high velocity while the heavier mass recoils with a low velocity. The product $m_1 \times v_1$, however, is equal in magnitude to the product $m_2 \times v_2$, and the sum of the two momenta are zero.

Example 3. A 60 kg shell is shot with an initial velocity of 500 m/sec, from a gun having a mass of 2000 kg. What is the initial velocity with which the gun recoils?

Solution. Applying Eq.(16h), and substituting directly the known quantities,

$$60 \text{ kg} \times 500 \text{ m/sec} + 2000 \text{ kg} \times v_2 = 0$$
$$30{,}000 \text{ kg m/sec} + 2000 \, v_2 \text{ kg} = 0$$

$$v_2 = \frac{30{,}000 \text{ kg m/sec}}{-2000 \text{ kg}} = -15 \text{ m/sec.}$$

The gun recoils with a velocity of 15 m/sec.

The law of conservation of momentum can be derived from Newton's Second Law of Motion as follows. An unbalanced force F acting on a body for a time t changes the momentum from its initial value mv_0 to a final value mv.

$$Ft = mv - mv_0. \tag{16i}$$

If to a body, or system of bodies, no external unbalanced forces are applied, $F = 0$, and the impulse $Ft = 0$.

$$0 = mv - mv_0$$

or, $$mv = mv_0.$$

Forces between individual parts of a system of bodies are internal forces and always exist in pairs.

Another interesting experiment illustrating conservation of momentum may be performed with six or seven marbles and a grooved board as shown in Fig. 16H. When one marble is rolled up to the others as shown in

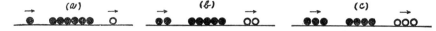

Fig. 16H—Experiment of the colliding marbles illustrating the law of conservation of momentum.

diagram (a), it will be stopped by collision with the others and the one on the extreme right-hand end will roll out with the same velocity. If two marbles are rolled up as indicated in (b), two will roll out on the other end, and if three are rolled up as in (c), three will roll out. Glass or steel marbles work best in this experiment as they are highly elastic.

When the two marbles are rolled up, why doesn't just one marble roll off on the other side with twice the velocity, thus conserving momentum? The answer to this question involves conservation of energy, for if only one came off with twice the velocity, its kinetic energy would be twice the energy available from the original two.

PROBLEMS

1. A 5 lb stone is dropped from a height of 240 ft above the ground. Find the potential energy and the kinetic energy at a point 50 ft above the ground. Neglect friction.

2. A 6 lb weight moving with a constant velocity of 30 ft/sec overtakes and bumps a 3 lb weight moving in the same direction with a constant velocity of 10 ft/sec. If after impact the 3 lb weight has a velocity of 28 ft/sec, calculate (a) the velocity of the other weight, and (b) the energy lost in the form of heat. (*Ans.* (a) 21 ft/sec, (b) 11 ft lb.)

3. A 0.2 lb bullet moving with a velocity of 2000 ft/sec passes through a 1 lb ball

of putty initially at rest. If the bullet leaves the putty at a velocity of 1400 ft/sec, what is the velocity of the ball of putty?

4. A 0.40 kg block of wood lying on a fence is hit by a rifle bullet weighing 25 gm. If the bullet enters the block with a velocity of 600 m/sec and leaves the other side with a velocity of 200 m/sec, find (a) the recoil velocity of the block, and (b) the energy lost in the form of heat. (*Ans.* (a) 25 m/sec, (b) 3875 joules.)

5. A 30 gm bullet moving with a velocity of 600 m/sec enters and becomes embedded in a block of wood weighing 3.6 kg. With what velocity will the block recoil if it were at rest before the impact?

6. An arrow having a mass of 100 gm is shot straight upward with a speed of 40 m/sec. (a) Calculate its initial kinetic energy. (b) From energy considerations calculate how high it will rise. (*Ans.* (a) 80 joules, (b) 81.6 m.)

7. A stone having a mass of 2 kg is projected straight upward with a speed of 80 m/sec. (a) Calculate its initial kinetic energy. (b) From energy considerations calculate the maximum height reached.

8. A gun weighing 500 lb fires a 4 oz shell with a muzzle velocity of 2000 ft/sec. If the gun is free to move what is its recoil velocity? (*Ans.* 1 ft/sec.)

9. An airplane weighing 6000 lb and making 360 mi/hr fires 5 rounds from a small cannon in the nose of the ship. If the bullets each weigh 1 lb and their muzzle speed is 2000 ft/sec, the plane will be slowed down to what speed?

10. A 250 gm ball is thrown upward with a speed of 25 m/sec. Upon returning to the thrower it has a speed of 20 m/sec. (a) How much energy was lost in overcoming air resistance? (b) If 60 per cent of this energy were lost on the way up how high did the ball go? (*Ans.* (a) 28.1 joules, (b) 25 m.)

11. A 1200 lb gun is mounted on wheels. It fires a 20 lb shell at an elevation angle of 45° and with a muzzle speed of 1800 ft/sec. Calculate the horizontal recoil speed.

12. A 5 kg block of wood hangs as a pendulum by a string 1 m long. When a 15 gm bullet is fired at close range into the block and becomes embedded there the block swings to a height 20 cm above its rest position. Find (a) the recoil speed of the block, and (b) the muzzle speed of the bullet. (*Ans.* (a) 198 cm/sec, (b) 660 m/sec.)

13. A 20 gm bullet, fired from a gun with a speed of 600 m/sec embeds itself in a 980 gm block of wood suspended by a 15 m long cord. (a) What is the recoil speed of the block, and (b) how high does the block rise?

14. A man weighing 160 lb while sitting in a canoe weighing 57 lb, fires a 1 oz bullet from a 3 lb gun. If the muzzle speed of the bullet is 1600 ft/sec, with what speed will the canoe recoil? (*Ans.* 0.455 ft/sec.)

15. A 10 lb box slides down an inclined plane 16 ft long and 8 ft high. With what speed will it reach the bottom (a) if the friction is neglected, and (b) if half of the energy is expended in friction?

16. A box having a mass of 25 kg starts from rest and slides down an inclined plane 8 m long and 5 m high. If its speed at the bottom is 7 m/sec, find (a) the energy loss due to friction, (b) the force of friction, and (c) the coefficient of friction. (*Ans.* (a) 612.5 joules, (b) 76.6 newtons, (c) 0.368.)

17. A 25 ton freight car moving at 10 ft/sec bumps into another of 30 tons moving 8 ft/sec in the same direction. If the cars lock together upon impact find (a) their resultant speed, and (b) the energy lost during impact.

Levers, Moments, and Center of Gravity   Chapter 17

THE great philosopher Archimedes * once said, "Give me a place to stand on and I will move the earth." In making this boast Archimedes was undoubtedly referring to the principle of the lever. It must have been common knowledge at the time of Archimedes that when some heavy object had to be lifted or a huge stone had to be loosed from the ground, a long straight pole could be used to do it.

17.1. Levers. There are in reality three classes of levers, and these are shown in their simplest form in Fig. 17A. In each illustration the pivot P

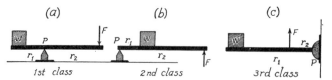

FIG. 17A—Illustrating the three classes of levers commonly used for lifting heavy objects.

is the *fulcrum,* or *axis,* about which the lever is made to turn, W is the *weight* or load to be lifted, and F is the *applied force.* The distance r_1 is called the lever arm of the load, and the distance r_2 the lever arm of the applied force.

---

* Archimedes (287-212 B.C.), Greek mathematician and inventor, was born at Syracuse in Sicily. He was the son of Pheidias, an astronomer, and was on intimate terms with, if not a relative of Hiero, king of Syracuse. Of the many stories or legends told of him and King Hiero, the one of the lever is perhaps the most famous. Having made the claim "Give me a place to stand on and I will move the earth," King Hiero summoned him for an explanation. He is said to have set one end of a lever to a ship that was just ready to be launched and King Hiero himself, upon pushing lightly upon the other end, moved the ship into the water.

Another time King Hiero, suspecting that his goldsmith had not made his crown of pure gold, as instructed, gave Archimedes the task of learning the truth without harming the crown. Just when he felt he would have to tell the king it couldn't be done, Archimedes stepped into the bath and noticed how the water ran over the edge. Springing from the bath he ran naked through the streets shouting "Eureka." To find the volume of the metal had stumped him, but now he knew that by submerging the crown in a vessel previously filled with water, the volume of the overflow water would equal the volume of metal. Knowing the actual weight of the crown and its volume, he calculated the density and found it to be less than the density of pure gold. A confession from the goldsmith confirmed the king's suspicions and Archimedes experimental observations.

The lever arm of any force is defined as the perpendicular distance between the force direction and the fulcrum. The moment of a force is defined as the product of *force times lever arm.*

$$\text{Moment} = \text{force} \times \text{lever arm.} \qquad (17a)$$

To operate a lever force F of a certain magnitude must be applied to maintain equilibrium or balance, and then the force increased ever so slightly to cause motion and lift the weight W. To maintain equilibrium the moments of both forces must counterbalance each other. In other words the moment of the force tending to produce a clockwise rotation must equal the moment of the force tending to produce a counterclockwise rotation.

Clockwise moment = counterclockwise moment.

For each of the three classes of levers in Fig. 17A,

$$W \times r_1 = F \times r_2. \qquad (17b)$$

Example 1. How great a weight can be lifted by a lever of the first class if the force applied is 150 lb? Assume the lever to be 10 ft long with the fulcrum 2 ft from the load.
Solution. Referring to Fig. 17A(a), and Eq.(17b),

$$W \times 2 = 150 \times 8$$

or
$$W = \frac{150 \times 8}{2} = 600 \text{ lb.}$$

It will be noted that the closer W is to the fulcrum P the greater will be the load that can be lifted by any given force F. This is undoubtedly what Archimedes had in mind when he said "Give me a place to stand on and I will move the earth."

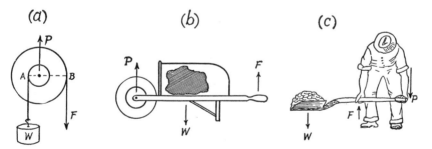

(a)   *(b)*   *(c)*

Fɪɢ. 17B—Illustrating devices in which the principle of the lever is involved.

Diagrams of three common devices are shown in Fig. 17B illustrating each of the three classes of lever. In the wheel and axle of diagram (a) the horizontal line APB represents a lever of the first class with P as a fulcrum,

AP as one lever arm, and *PB* as the other. The weight *W* is lifted by one rope wound around the axle, while the smaller force *F* is applied to another rope wrapped around the wheel. The wheel barrow in diagram (b) employs a lever of the second class with the pivot *P* at the wheel. The heavily loaded barrow is lifted to a rolling position by applying a smaller force *F* at the handles. The loaded shovel in diagram (c) illustrates a lever of the third class, the fulcrum being located in the man's left hand.

Cog wheels in a machine, a crank shaft in an engine, and pulley wheels in a block and tackle, are examples involving levers of the first class.

17.2. Center of Mass. The center of mass (abbr. *c of m*) of any given body, or system of bodies, is a point such that if any plane is passed through

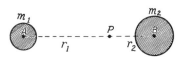

FIG. 17C—The center of mass of two bodies is located at some point on a line joining their centers of gravity.

it the mass moments on one side of the plane are equal to the mass moments on the other. Consider, for example, two spheres of mass m_1 and m_2 as shown in Fig. 17C. The *c of m P* lies on a line connecting the centers of the two bodies and in such a position that

$$m_1 r_1 = m_2 r_2. \qquad (17c)$$

Example 2. Find the *c of m* of two bodies $m_1 = 2$ gm, and $m_2 = 5$ gm, placed 14 cm apart.

Solution. Given is the distance $r_1 + r_2 = 14$ cm, from which

$$r_2 = 14 - r_1.$$

Substitute all known quantities in Eq.(17c).

$$2r_1 = 5(14 - r_1), \qquad \text{or} \qquad 2r_1 = 70 - 5r_1,$$

and

$$7r_1 = 70, \qquad \text{or } r_1 = 10.$$

Substituting this value of r_1 in Eq.(17c) gives

$$r_2 = 4 \text{ cm}.$$

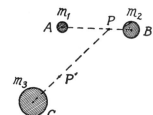

FIG. 17D—Illustrating the method for finding the center of mass of a three-body system.

The *c of m* of a three body system is found by an extension of the above principle. See Fig. 17D. To illustrate, two of the masses like *A* and *B* are first selected and their *c of m* found by use of Eq.(17c). These two bodies are then treated as though they were one body located at *P*. With one mass $(m_1 + m_2)$ located at *P* and a second mass m_3 located at *C*, Eq.(17c) is applied to find P^1 the resultant *c of m*. If a system consists of more than three bodies the above process is continued until all masses have been included.

The *c of m* of all regularly shaped bodies like those shown in Fig. 17E is at their geometrical center. A plane passed through the center of any of

   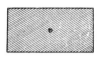

FIG. 17E—Illustrating the center of mass of regularly shaped objects.

these figures will divide the body into two equal parts. Consider, for example, a thin ring of mass M as shown in Fig. 17F(a). By drawing straight lines through the geometrical center, the total mass can be divided up into pairs of small but equal masses. Since the masses m of each pair are equidistant from the center, their *c of m* is at their midpoint P, and this is common to all pairs.

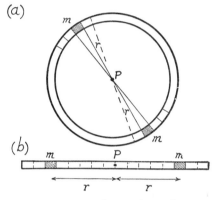

A similar process can be applied to a long thin rod or pole of equal cross section. Dividing the rod into an equal number of parts as shown in Fig. 17F(b) permits pairing off of equal parts at equal distances from the center. Since the geometrical center is the *c of m* of each pair it is also the *c of m* of the entire rod. It is now clear why the distances in Fig. 17C must be measured from the centers of the spheres; their centers give their *c of m*.

FIG. 17F—Center of mass is at the geometrical center. (a) uniform ring. (b) uniform rod.

17.3. Rotation about the Center of Mass. In Fig. 17G two masses m_1 and m_2 are shown supported at the ends of a thin rod and rotating smoothly around a pin through the *c of m*. If the pin is located at any other point, for example half way between the two masses, the experimenter will experience an unbalanced force on his hand, tending to make it "wobble."

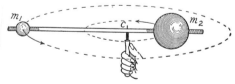

FIG. 17G—Illustrating the smooth rotation of two bodies around their center of mass.

Should the two-body system be thrown spinning into the air as shown in Fig. 17H, it will be observed to rotate about its *c of m* while the *c of m* traces out the smooth trajectory of a projectile. Rotation is smooth around this point because the centripetal forces of the two bodies are counterbalanced there. The two centripetal forces are equal in magnitude but opposite in direction. Being in opposite directions they exert no resultant force on the pivot.

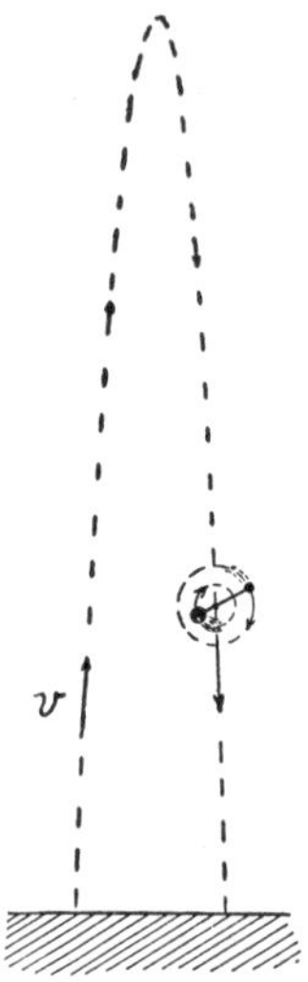

To prove this result, consider the two body system in Fig. 17C. If it is set into rotation about the *c of m*, the two centripetal forces are (see Eq.(14i)),

$$F_1 = m_1 r_1 \omega^2, \quad \text{and} \quad F_2 = m_2 r_2 \omega^2,$$

ω being the angular velocity common to both masses. Setting these forces equal to each other as required ($F_1 = F_2$), we get

$$m_1 r_1 \omega^2 = m_2 r_2 \omega^2$$

or

$$m_1 r_1 = m_2 r_2,$$

the condition for the *c of m*.

The earth and the moon serve as a good illustration of two bodies rotating freely about their *c of m*. The mass of the earth is 81 times the mass of the moon and the distance between them is approximately 240,000 mi. A calculation, as in Example 2, gives $r_2 = 2927$ mi; nearly 3000 mi from the center of the earth and 1000 mi below the earth's surface.

In a similar manner the earth and moon, considered as a single body, rotates with the sun as the second body about their *c of m*. Relatively the bodies are similar to those in Fig. 17D, with m_1 and m_2 rotating about P, and the point P and mass m_3 rotating more slowly around P^1.

FIG. 17H—A body thrown spinning into the air rotates smoothly about its center of mass while the center of mass traces out the smooth trajectory of a projectile.

17.4. Center of Gravity. The *c of m* of the two bodies in Fig. 17C is the one and only point about which the two bodies will, if pivoted, balance under the earth's gravitational pull. Furthermore a single upward force applied at C, equal in magnitude to the weight of the two bodies, will maintain equilibrium; the system will not tend to move in any direction nor will it tend to rotate.

The *c of m* is therefore a point at which all of the weight can be considered as concentrated. For this reason the *c of m* is often called the center of gravity (*abbr. c of g*).

The *c of g* of a regular or irregular shaped body of uniform or nonuniform density can be found by suspending it from one pivot point and then another as shown in Fig. 17I. With each suspension from a point P near the periphery the body will hang its *c of g* directly under that point. Lines drawn along the string supporting the plumb for each suspension will all cross at the common point, the *c of g*.

If pivoted at this point and set turning, or thrown spinning into the air, the rotation will be smooth about the *c of g*. (*Note*: Because the force of gravity decreases with altitude, the *c of g* of a body is not always at exactly the same point as the *c of m*. The lower part of a mass for example, is closer to the earth's center than the upper part and therefore has a greater weight per unit mass. For all practical purposes, however, the two terms *c of g* and *c of m* are considered synonymous.)

The principle that the *c of g* is a point at which the total weight of a body can be considered as concentrated is illustrated by the experiment in Fig. 17J. A long uniform bar is first balanced at

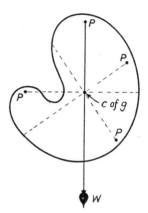

Fig. 17I—The center of gravity of any freely suspended object lies at or directly beneath the point of suspension.

its center point and then seven equal weights suspended from each side as shown in diagram (a). The *c of g* of each set of seven weights is at the

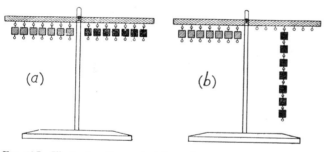

(a)　(b)

Fig. 17J—Illustrating the center of gravity with weights suspended from the two arms of a beam balance.

geometrical center, that is, at the fourth or center weight. When the other six weights are suspended from this one as in diagram (b) the bar remains in perfect balance.

PROBLEMS

1. A pole 5 m long is used as a first class lever to lift a mass of 600 kg. Where must the pivot be placed if the maximum applied force available is 750 newtons?

2. A plank 16 ft long is used as a first class lever to lift a 1200 lb load. Where must the pivot be located if the applied force is 130 lb? (*Ans.* 1.56 ft from load.)

3. A bar 2.50 m long is used as a lever of the second class to lift a mass of 50 kg. Where must the weight be suspended if the applied force is 39.2 newtons?

4. A mass of 5 kg is lifted by a lever of the third class. Where should a force of 215.6 newtons be applied if the lever is 100 cm long? (*Ans.* 22.7 cm from pivot.)

5. Two bodies 16 lb and 21 lb respectively are located 3 ft apart. Find their center of mass.

6. Two masses of 5 kg and 12 kg respectively are located 80 cm apart. Find their center of mass. (*Ans.* 56.5 cm from 5 kg.)

7. Three equal masses of 8 kg each are located at the corners of a right triangle whose sides are 3 m, 4 m, and 5 m respectively. Locate the center of mass.

8. Three masses 4 kg, 6 kg, and 8 kg are located at the corners of an equilateral triangle with sides 5 m long. Find the center of mass. (Ans. 2.42 m from 8 kg mass and 3.37 m from 4 kg mass.)

9. Two stones with masses of 2 kg and 4 kg are tied 60 cm apart at opposite ends of a wire and then thrown whirling into the air with an angular speed of 20 rad/sec. Calculate the tension in the wire.

10. Two weights, 5 lb and 8 lb respectively, are tied 3 ft apart at opposite ends of a rope and then thrown whirling into the air with an angular speed of 120 rpm. Calculate the tension in the rope. (*Ans.* 45.6 lb.)

11. A wheel and axle is used to lift a 400 lb motor. If the wheel diameter is 18 in. and the axle diameter is 2 in., what force must be applied?

12. A 250 kg stone is to be lifted by a wheel and axle. What force must be applied if the diameters of the wheel and axle are 20 cm and 6 cm respectively? (*Ans.* 735 newtons.)

13. A uniform bar *AB*, 8 m long, has a mass of 4 kg and supports three masses: 5 kg at *A*, 6 kg 2 m from *A*, and 3 kg at *B*. Find the center of mass of the system.

14. A uniform bar 3 m long has a mass of 2 kg. Find the center of mass if a 5 kg mass is fastened to one end and a 1 kg mass is fastened to the other. (*Ans.* 0.75 m from 5 kg mass.)

15. A thin hoop with a mass of 3 kg is 1 m in diameter. A mass of 2 kg is fastened to the rim at one point and a mass of 4 kg is fastened to a point diagonally opposite. Find the center of mass.

16. The center of gravity of an empty truck weighing 2600 lb is 7½ ft in front of the rear axle. The truck carries a load of 1.6 tons which is placed centrally with its center of gravity 2½ ft in front of the rear axle. Find the center of gravity. (*Ans.* 4 ft 9 in. from rear axle.)

17. The center of mass of an empty wheel barrow weighing 4 kg is located 40 cm from the center of the wheel. A load of 20 kg is centrally located in the barrow 60 cm from the center of the wheel. Find the center of mass.

18. A uniform ladder 6 m long has a mass of 20 kg. Find the center of mass if a 70 kg man is (a) 1 m from the bottom, and (b) 2 m from the top. (*Ans.* (a) 1.44 m from bottom. (b) 3.78 m from bottom.)

19. Five 2 kg spheres are equally spaced around the periphery of a semicircle. If the diameter is 2 m and the two end spheres are diametrically opposite each other, find the center of mass.

Machines   Chapter 18

ALL contrivances connected with machine installations that utilize natural sources of energy may be classified in three groups; (1) *prime movers*, (2) *machines*, and (3) *utility devices*. To the first group belong all such devices as manpower, horsepower, electric motors, water turbines, steam turbines, gas engines, diesel engines, etc. To the second group belong such mechanisms as levers, pulley wheels, gears, belts and cams, as well as combinations of them, while to the third group belong such end products as airplane and ship propellers, car and locomotive drive wheels, tractor and tank tracks, clock and watch hands, etc.

From the above definitions, therefore, a mechanical machine constitutes a device wherein mechanical energy is applied at one point and mechanical energy in a more useful form is delivered at another.

18.1. The Lever. The lever as described in detail in Sec. 17.1 is one of the simplest of all mechanical devices that may rightfully be called a machine. By applying a downward force at one end of a lever, as shown in Fig. 18A, a heavy load may be lifted at the other. The principle of the lever, given in detail in Sec. 17.1, requires that the moment on one side of the fulcrum P be equal to the moment on the other side.

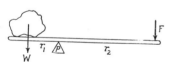

FIG. 18A—A lever of the first class.

$$W \times r_1 = F \times r_2. \qquad (18a)$$

When the two moments are exactly equal the lever is in equilibrium, that is, all parts are at rest or moving with uniform speed. If the lever is at rest then, neglecting friction, any small additional force added to F will produce the necessary lifting motion.

18.2. Mechanical Advantage. The mechanical advantage of a machine may be defined as the ratio of the *output force* delivered by the machine to the *input force* applied by the prime mover. With a simple machine like the lever, in Fig. 18B, W represents the *output force* and F represents the *input force*, and the mechanical advantage (*abbr.* M.A.) is given by

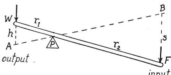

FIG. 18B—A lever is classified as a machine.

$$M.A. = W/F. \qquad (18b)$$

149

By transposing Eq.(18a), the mechanical advantage is also expressed as the ratio of the lever arms.

$$\text{M.A.} = W/F = r_2/r_1. \tag{18c}$$

Suppose for example that a man weighing 150 lb wishes to lift a heavy stone weighing 1500 lb by means of a lever. The mechanical advantage required of the lever must therefore be

$$\text{M.A.} = 1500/150 = 10.$$

Eq.(18c) shows that to obtain this mechanical advantage the lever arm r_2 must be 10 times as long as r_1. Although 1500 lb can be lifted by the application of a force only one-tenth as large, energy relations show that the operator is not getting "something for nothing." The law of conservation of energy requires that the work done by the machine be no greater than the work done on the machine. As illustrated in the diagram the work done on the machine by the operator is equal to the product of *force* $\times$ *distance*, $F \times s$, while the work done by the machine is equal to the product of *weight* $\times$ *distance*, $W \times h$.

By conservation of energy

$$W \times h = F \times s.$$
$$\text{output} \quad \text{input} \tag{18d}$$

Transposing gives

$$W/F = s/h. \tag{18e}$$

which shows that the mechanical advantage, defined as the ratio of the forces W/F, is also given by the inverse ratio of the distances, s/h. This latter is called the reduction or the magnification of the displacements.

$$\text{Magnification} = h/s. \tag{18f}$$

If s is greater than h there is a reduction in the displacement, the lever arm r_2 is greater than r_1, and the mechanical advantage, W/F, is greater than unity. If s is smaller than h there is a magnification in the displacement, the lever arm r_2 is less than r_1 and the mechanical advantage is less than unity.

Combining Eqs.(18c) and (18e), a relation between lever arms and displacements is obtained.

$$r_2/r_1 = s/h. \tag{18g}$$

This result may also be derived by referring to Fig. 18B. The two triangles PWA and PFB are similar and their corresponding sides are proportional.

18.3. Efficiency. In arriving at the above relations for the mechanical advantage, it was assumed that the lever, as a machine, operates without friction. As a practical matter such ideal conditions are desirable but never actually attained. It is customary in engineering practice to neglect friction at first by applying the above equations and then to make corrections where necessary by taking into account the efficiency of the machine.

Friction in a machine is not always a desirable feature, for by its presence energy is continually wasted in all moving parts by being transformed into heat. By the law of conservation of energy,

input work = output work + wasted energy.

The efficiency of a machine is defined as the ratio of output work to input work.

$$\text{Efficiency} = \frac{\text{output work}}{\text{input work}}. \tag{18h}$$

This ratio is always less than unity and is usually multiplied by 100 to express the efficiency in per cent.

$$\text{Per cent efficiency} = \frac{\text{output}}{\text{input}} \times 100. \tag{18i}$$

The smaller the energy lost through friction the greater is the efficiency of a machine and the nearer is the efficiency to 100%. In all cases where friction is assumed to be so small that it can be neglected, the efficiency is taken to be 100% and the mechanical advantage is given by Eqs.(18b), (18c) and (18e).

If friction is appreciably large and must be taken into account when making calculations, the mechanical advantage is still given by Eq.(18b), but not by the ratio of the lever arms r_2/r_1, or the distances moved s/h.

Example 1. A lever 10 ft long is used as shown in Fig. 18A to lift a block of concrete weighing 600 lb. If the fulcrum is located 2 ft from the stone, and the efficiency is 85%, what force must be applied at the other end?

Solution. Use Eq.(18h).

$$\text{Efficiency} = \frac{\text{output work}}{\text{input work}} = \frac{600 \text{ lb} \times h}{F \times s} = 0.85.$$

From Eq.(18g)

$$s/h = 8 \text{ ft}/2 \text{ ft} = 4.$$

Substituting this value for h/s in the above gives

$$\text{Efficiency} = \frac{600 \text{ lb}}{F \times 4} = 0.85,$$

from which

$$F = \frac{600 \text{ lb}}{3.4} = 176 \text{ lb}.$$

By neglecting friction, that is, assuming 100% efficiency, the required force would be given by Eq.(18c) as

$$F = W\,\frac{r_1}{r_2} = 600\,\text{lb} \times \frac{2\,\text{ft}}{8\,\text{ft}} = 150\,\text{lb}.$$

18.4. Wheel and Axle. The wheel and axle is a simple machine involving the principle of the lever. As shown in Fig. 18C, a heavy load W is lifted by a rope wrapped around an axle of radius r by pulling down on another rope wrapped around an attached wheel of larger radius R. By exerting the force F through a distance s the load W is lifted a distance h. Neglecting friction, the input work $F \times s$ is equal to the output work $W \times h$.

In one revolution of the wheel the force F moves down a distance s equal to the circumference of the wheel $2\pi R$, and the load W moves up a distance h equal to the circumference of the axle $2\pi r$. By conservation of energy

$$\underset{\text{output}}{W \times 2\pi r} = \underset{\text{input}}{F \times 2\pi R}. \qquad (18j)$$

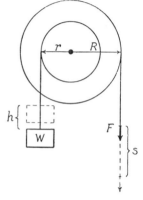

Fig. 18C—Wheel and Axle.

Transposing F to the left side of the equation and $2\pi r$ to the right, the mechanical advantage W/F is given by

$$\frac{W}{F} = \frac{2\pi R}{2\pi r} = \frac{R}{r}. \qquad (18k)$$

The similarity of this equation with Eq.(18c) shows how the two radii R and r function as do the lever arms r_2 and r_1 in Fig. 18A. Only in the absence of friction is the ratio of the forces equal to the ratio of the radii. The latter represent a theoretical mechanical advantage,

$$\text{M.A.}_{\text{theoretical}} = \frac{R}{r}. \qquad (18l)$$

If friction cannot be neglected, the efficiency will not be 100% and W/F represents the actual mechanical advantage.

$$\text{M.A.}_{\text{actual}} = \frac{W}{F}. \qquad (18m)$$

The relation between these two is given by

$$\text{M.A.}_{\text{actual}} = \text{M.A.}_{\text{theoretical}} \times \text{efficiency.} \qquad (18n)$$

Example 2. In lifting a one ton load with a wheel and axle, the operator exerts a downward force of 125 lb. The wheel is 40 in. in diameter and the axle is 2 in. in diameter. Calculate (a) the theoretical mechanical advantage, (b) the actual mechanical advantage, and (c) the efficiency of the machine.

Solution. (a) By Eq.(18l),

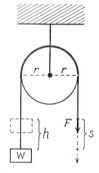

FIG. 18D—A fixed pulley.

$$\text{M.A.}_{\text{theoretical}} = R/r = 20/1 = 20.$$

(b) By Eq.(18m),

$$\text{M.A.}_{\text{actual}} = \frac{2000 \text{ lb}}{125 \text{ lb}} = 16.$$

(c) By Eq.(18n),

$$\text{efficiency} = 16/20 = 0.80, \text{ or } 80\%$$

18.5. Pulleys. The action of a pulley is the same as that of a lever having equal arms. Singly, pulleys may be used in one of two ways, either as *a fixed pulley* or as a *movable pulley.* In Fig. 18D a fixed pulley is shown being used to lift a load W by means of an applied force F. With the pivot at the center of the pulley the two forces have equal arms, each equal to the radius r. Having equal arms the forces, neglecting friction, must be equal, and the theoretical mechanical advantage is unity.

Although a mechanical advantage of unity obtained with a fixed pulley may be looked upon as no me-

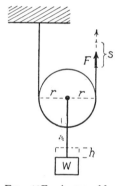

FIG. 18E—A movable pulley.

chanical advantage at all, it often happens that a downward force is more conveniently applied to lift a body than is an equal upward force.

A movable pulley, on the other hand, see Fig. 18E, has a mechanical advantage of 2. To move the load W upward a distance h, both of the supporting cords must be shortened by this same amount. To take up the slack the force F must move up a distance $s = 2h$. By energy conservation,

$$W \times h = F \times (2h)$$
$$\text{output} \qquad \text{input}$$

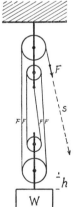

FIG. 18F—A block and a tackle.

from which the mechanical advantage $\text{M.A.}_{\text{theoretical}} = W/F = 2$.

18.6. Block and Tackle. The block and tackle is a contrivance with a large mechanical advantage, employing the use of any number of movable and fixed pulleys. One form is shown in Fig. 18F. The pulleys, it is noted, are in two blocks with two pulleys or sheaves in each block. The fixed end of the rope is attached to the lower end of the upper block and after passing around each pulley, as shown, goes to the prime mover.

In some blocks the pulleys are all of the same size and mounted side by side, while in others they are of different size and mounted one below the other as shown. Regardless of size, the function of each pulley is simply to reverse the direction of the force F so that the same tension exists throughout the supporting rope.

Neglecting friction in the pulleys and the weight of the rope, the tension in each of the four sections of rope holding up the lower block and weight W in the diagram is equal to F. For the block and weight to be in equilibrium, therefore, the total upward force $4F$ must be equal to the downward force W. This gives for the mechanical advantage,

$$\text{M.A.}_{\text{theoretical}} = W/F = 4.$$

The same result is derived from energy considerations as follows. In raising the load W a height h, each of the four ropes supporting it must be shortened by this amount, and hence the prime mover must exert the force F through a distance $s = 4h$. Since $F \times s = W \times h$, the mechanical advantage $W/F = s/h = 4$.

In general, the mechanical advantage of any block and tackle is given by the number of parallel ropes supporting the load. The load W includes the weight of the lower block.

$$\text{M.A.}_{\text{theoretical}} = \text{No. of supporting ropes.} \qquad (18o)$$

18.7. Lever Mechanism of the Inner Ear. The pre-medical student will find it of some interest to consider at this point the lever mechanism of the human ear as diagramed in Fig. 18G, and shown in a later chapter on

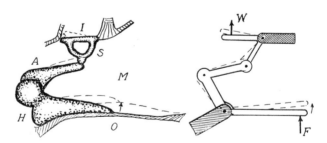

Fig. 18G—The bones of the ear act as a system of levers.

sound, Fig. 36K. The outer eardrum O and the three bones, hammer H, anvil A and stirrup S of the middle ear act as a system of levers to decrease the amplitude of the vibrations from the air. This reduction in the motion gives rise to a pressure in the inner ear I which is several times that exerted on the outer eardrum.

PROBLEMS

1. A block and tackle is used to pull tree stumps out of the ground. Each block contains three sheaves. One end of the rope is fastened to one block. (a) Which block should be fastened to the tree stump and which end to the anchor to obtain the greatest mechanical advantage? Make a diagram. (b) If a force of 100 lb is applied to the free end of the rope, and the efficiency is 50%, what force is applied to the stump?

2. In a garage a block and tackle is used to lift a 360 lb motor out of a car. If the upper and lower block each contain four sheaves and one end of the rope is fastened to the upper block, calculate (a) the theoretical mechanical advantage. If the force applied to the free end is 75 lb, calculate (b) the mechanical advantage, and (c) the efficiency. (*Ans.* (a) 8, (b) 4.8, (c) 60%.)

3. A horizontal force of 50 lb is applied to the top of an automobile tire of one of the wheels of the automobile stuck in the mud. (a) What is the effective force on the car? (b) What is the theoretical mechanical advantage?

4. A painter hoists himself up the side of a tall building by a block and tackle having two sheaves in the upper block and one in the lower block. The man and his equipment weigh 180 lb. What is the tension in the rope? (*Ans.* 45 lb.)

5. Two pulley wheels with diameters of 4 in and 14 in are mounted fast on the same shaft. Power from a motor is supplied to a belt passing around the larger pulley and a machine is belted to the smaller pulley. (a) What are the relative speeds of the two belts, and (b) what is the mechanical advantage?

6. A loaded handtruck weighing 300 lb is pushed up a plank onto a platform. If the plank is inclined at 10° to the horizontal and the applied force is 75 lb parallel to the plank, calculate (a) the theoretical mechanical advantage, (b) the actual mechanical advantage, and (c) the efficiency. (*Ans.* (a) 5.75, (b) 4.0, (c) 69.6%.)

7. A farmer raises a bucket of water weighing 45 lb from the bottom of a well. To do this he has the rope wound around a 10 in diameter wooden drum, and a crank with its handle 18 in from the center of rotation. Find (a) the theoretical mechanical advantage, and (b) the required force on the handle if the efficiency is 80%.

8. A wheel and axle have diameters of 18 in and 1.5 in respectively. Upon raising a 600 lb-load it is necessary to apply a force of 72 lb. Calculate (a) the theoretical mechanical advantage, (b) the actual mechanical advantage, and (c) the efficiency. (*Ans.* (a) 12, (b) 8.33, (c) 69.4%.)

9. A 2000-kg cable car is pulled 1 km up a 30° incline. Calculate (a) the theoretical mechanical advantage. If the tension in the cable pulling the car is 1.2×10^4 newtons, find (b) the actual mechanical advantage, and (c) the overall efficiency.

10. A 2.5-ton cable car is pulled one-half mile up a 20° incline in 15 min. Calculate (a) the theoretical mechanical advantage. (b) If the overall efficiency of the incline is 50% what is the minimum horsepower required of the motor used in pulling the car? (*Ans.* (a) 2.92, (b) 18.2 hp.)

11. An escalator carries persons from one floor to another 20 ft higher and the steps move with a speed of 60 ft/min. The steps are 8 in high and 12 in from edge to edge measured in the direction of motion. What minimum power must the driving motor have with a maximum load of 100 lb per step if the overall efficiency is 60%?

Equilibrium of
Rigid Bodies

Chapter 19

In Chap. 10 it was shown how a body acted on by any number of forces is in equilibrium if the vector sum of all the forces is zero and how each force can be resolved into x- and y-*components* and the conditions of equilibrium applied to each set of components separately. The summation of all the x-*components* of force must be zero, and the summation of all the y-*components* must be zero. Symbolically,

$$\Sigma F_x = 0, \quad \Sigma F_y = 0. \quad (19a)$$

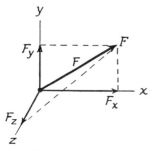

If all of the forces acting on a body lie in one plane the fulfilment of these two conditions is all that is necessary to assure translational equilibrium. If they are not all in one plane, however, a three dimensional problem is involved and each force should be resolved into three components, one along each of the three axes, x, y, and z as shown in Fig. 19A. Equilibrium in three dimensions then requires that

FIG. 19A—A single force may be resolved into three mutually perpendicular components, one along each of the three axes x, y, and z.

$$\Sigma F_x = 0 \qquad \Sigma F_y = 0 \qquad \Sigma F_z = 0. \quad (19b)$$

These equations are commonly referred to as *the 1st condition of equilibrium*. Since all of the forces in most problems are confined to one plane, the third equation can be omitted by assuming the plane of the forces to be the xy-*plane*.

19.1. Couples. When a rigid body is acted upon by a number of forces, complete equilibrium is not assured with the satisfying of the 1st condition of equilibrium alone. In Fig. 19B, for example, a body is shown acted upon by two equal but opposite forces. While Eq.(19a) is satisfied, the body is not in complete equilibrium; it is acted upon by a couple

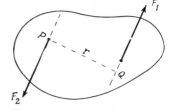

FIG. 19B—A "couple" acting on a rigid body tends to set it in rotation.

tending to set it into rotation. To prevent this turning the rigid body must be acted upon by another equal but opposite couple. In other words, to be in rotational equilibrium, couples must be balanced.

156

A couple is defined as two equal, but oppositely directed, forces not acting along the same line. The magnitude of a couple is given by the product of one of the forces and the perpendicular distance between them. From the diagram,

$$\text{couple} = F_1 \times r. \tag{19c}$$

This latter is called the moment of a couple and is to be compared with the moment of a force defined in the last chapter. A couple made up of large forces close together may have the same magnitude as a pair of small forces far apart.

A rigid body is defined as one whose various parts do not change their relative positions when forces are applied at different points. Actually no known bodies strictly satisfy this condition, but for practical purposes most solid bodies may be regarded as rigid.

19.2. Torque. When a single force acting on a body tends to produce rotation it is said to exert a *torque*. Torque is synonymous with *force-moment* and is defined as the product of force times lever arm, the lever arm being the perpendicular distance from the pivot point to the force. In Fig. 19C a body is shown acted upon by a torque. The force F is applied at the point A while the body is pivoted at the point P. The perpendicular distance r is equal to the line PQ, and the torque L is given by

$$L = F_1 \times r. \tag{19d}$$

If $F_1 = 5$ newtons, and $r = 3$ m,

$$L = 5 \text{ newtons} \times 3 \text{ m} = 15 \text{ newton m.}$$

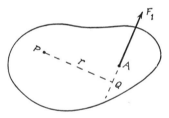

Fig. 19C—A single force acting on a rigid body pivoted at some point P exerts a torque $L = F_1 \times r$.

The dimensions *"newton m"* should not be confused with the units of *work* and *energy*. In the calculation of work, force and distance are measured in the same direction while in torque the two are measured at right angles.

Because of its similarity to the general concept of moments a torque is sometimes referred to as a force-moment. It is customary to ascribe a positive sign to all torques acting to turn a body counterclockwise and a minus sign to all torques tending to turn it clockwise.

19.3. Rotational Equilibrium. Consider the rigid body in Fig. 19D pivoted by a pin at the point P and acted upon by four forces F_1, F_2, F_3, and F_4. With lever arms of 5, 2, 5, and 8 respectively, these forces constitute torques L_1, L_2, L_3 and L_4. For this body to be in translational equilibrium the summation of all the forces, or the sums of their x- and y-*components*, must be zero. To be in rotational equilibrium the summation of all the *torques* must be zero. This latter, the 2nd condition of equilibrium, can be expressed symbolically as,

$$\Sigma L = 0. \tag{19e}$$

It will now be shown that the four forces in Fig. 19D are in translational as well as rotational equilibrium. To apply the 1st condition of equilibrium, each of the forces is resolved into x- and y-*components* and each group added separately. From the angles given in the figure,

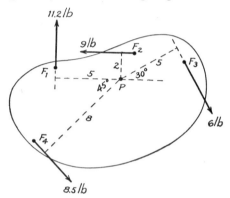

x-components

F_1,		0 lb
F_2,		-9 lb
F_3,	$6 \sin 30° =$	3 lb
F_4,	$8.5 \sin 45° =$	6 lb
	$\Sigma F_x = 0$	

y-components

	11.2 lb
	0 lb
$6 \cos 30° =$	-5.2 lb
$8.5 \cos 45° =$	-6 lb
$\Sigma F_y = 0$	

Fig. 19D—Illustrating a rigid body in equilibrium under the action of four forces.

Since $\Sigma F_x = 0$, and $\Sigma F_y = 0$, the conditions for translational equilibrium are satisfied.

Applying the 2nd condition of equilibrium,

$$
\begin{aligned}
L_1 &= 11.2 \times 5 = -56 \\
L_2 &= 9 \times 2 = +18 \\
L_3 &= 6 \times 5 = -30 \\
L_4 &= 8.5 \times 8 = +68 \\
\hline
& \Sigma L = 0
\end{aligned}
$$

Because the sum of all the torques is zero, rotational equilibrium is assured. Since the body is in complete equilibrium the pin P acting as a pivot cannot be exerting a force of any kind and can therefore be removed. After removal it can be placed at any other point in the body and equilibrium is still assured. In other words, *if all of the forces acting on a rigid body maintain complete equilibrium about one pivot point, they also are in equilibrium about any other pivot point.*

Although the body in Fig. 19C is acted upon by a single torque and is set into rotation, the pin keeps it from being moved away. In other words, the body is in translational equilibrium; the pin is exerting a force on the body equal in magnitude to F_1 and opposite in direction. Or, in other words, the force F, and the force exerted by the pin, constitute a couple.

19.4. Three Parallel Forces. As a second illustration of the equilibrium of rigid bodies, consider the experiment diagramed in Fig. 19E. A meter stick is acted upon by three horizontal forces, F_2 to the right of magnitude 300 dynes, and F_1 and F_3 to the left of magnitude 200 dynes and 100 dynes respectively. Experimentally these forces are obtained by strings that pass over pulleys to weights that can be varied until equilibrium is established. The meter stick, being made of wood, is very light and its weight will be neglected.

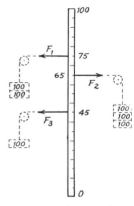

Fig. 19E—A rigid body acted upon by three parallel forces in static equilibrium.

To show that equilibrium exists, it must be shown that Eqs.(19a) and (19e) are satisfied. Applying the 1st condition of equilibrium, $\Sigma F_x = 0$ and $\Sigma F_y = 0$, it is first observed that all forces acting on the meter stick are horizontal. There being no y-components of force $\Sigma F_y = 0$, for the x-components

$$\Sigma F_x = F_2 - F_1 - F_3 = 300 - 100 - 200 = 0. \tag{19f}$$

Translational equilibrium exists since $\Sigma F_x = 0$.

To apply the 2nd condition of equilibrium, assume a pivot point to be located at the 45 cm mark. Around this point F_3 has no lever arm and cannot exert a torque. F_1 with a lever arm $75 - 45$, or 30 cm, acts counterclockwise and F_2 with a lever arm $65 - 45$, or 20 cm, acts clockwise. The torques are then summed.

$$\Sigma L = 200 \text{ dynes} \times 30 \text{ cm} - 300 \text{ dynes} \times 20 \text{ cm} \tag{19g}$$
$$= 6000 - 6000 = 0.$$

Rotational equilibrium exists since $\Sigma L = 0$.

As a check upon this result any other pivot point may be selected. For example, if force-moments are taken about the lower end of the meter stick, F_1 and F_3 act counterclockwise and F_2 acts clockwise. By summing the torques, we find

$$\Sigma L = 100 \text{ dynes} \times 45 \text{ cm} - 300 \text{ dynes} \times 65 \text{ cm} + 200 \text{ dynes} \times 75$$
$$= 4500 - 19,500 + 15,000 = 0.$$

Example 1. Two weights 9 lb and 15 lb respectively hang from opposite ends of a pole 12 ft long. What single upward force will support the pole and where should the force be applied to maintain static equilibrium? Assume the weight of the pole to be negligible. See Fig. 19F.

Solution. Applying the 1st condition of equilibrium, it is noted that there are no horizontal components of force, so that $\Sigma\,F_x = 0$ automatically. Applying Eq.(19a) to the *y-components*,

$$F_3 - 9 \text{ lb} - 15 \text{ lb} = 0$$
$$\therefore\ F_3 = 9 + 15 = 24 \text{ lb.} \tag{19h}$$

To apply the 2nd condition of equilibrium let torques first be calculated for an imaginary pivot at A. Around this point F_1 has no lever arm so that $L_1 = 0$. The other torques are $L_2 = F_2 \times 12$, and $L_3 = F_3 \times r_1$. Since their sum must be zero

$$F_3 \times r_1 - F_2 \times 12 = 0.$$

Solve for r_1.

$$r_1 = \frac{12F_2}{F_3} = \frac{12 \times 15}{24} = 7.5 \text{ ft.} \tag{19i}$$

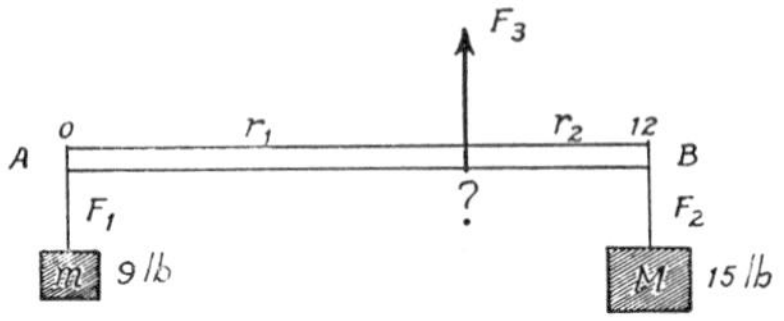

As a check upon this result, imagine the pivot to be at B. About this point F_2 has no lever arm so that $L_2 = 0$. The other torques are due to F_1 acting counterclockwise, and F_3 acting clockwise,

$$F_1 \times 12 - F_3 \times r_2 = 0$$

and

$$r_2 = \frac{9 \times 12}{24} = 4.5 \text{ ft.} \tag{19j}$$

FIG. 19F—What single upward force F_3 applied at what point will hold the 12 ft beam and weights in equilibrium?

This answer agrees with $r_1 = 7.5$ ft, found above.

To show that equilibrium exists about any point, select a pivot point along the pole 3 ft from A. Around this point there are three torques acting, L_1 and L_3 counterclockwise and L_2 clockwise.

$$\Sigma L = 9 \text{ lb} \times 3 \text{ ft} + 24 \text{ lb} \times 4.5 \text{ ft} - 15 \text{ lb} \times 9 \text{ ft} = 0$$
$$\text{or } 27 + 108 - 135 = 0.$$

Note that in solving the above example the pivot was first chosen so that one of the forces passed through it and had no lever arm. This was not necessary but it simplified the calculations by eliminating the torque produced by that force. This is an important principle to remember in solving problems for often several forces can be eliminated from the calculations by a careful selection of the pivot.

19.5. Four or More Forces. As another illustration of a rigid body in static equilibrium, consider the meter stick shown in Fig. 19G, acted upon by four parallel forces. Applying the 1st condition of equilibrium, we find that forces to the right are positive and those to the left are negative.

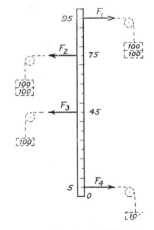

FIG. 19G—A rigid body acted upon by four parallel forces in static equilibrium.

$$\Sigma F_x = 100 - 100 + 200 - 200 = 0.$$

Neglecting the weight of the meter stick, there are no vertical forces so that $\Sigma F_y = 0$. Applying the 2nd condition of equilibrium, let torques first be calculated about the lower end.

$$\Sigma L = 100 \times 45 + 200 \times 75 - 100 \times 5 - 200 \times 95$$
$$= 4500 + 15,000 - 500 - 19,000 = 0.$$

As a check, take moments about any other point. Selecting the 75 cm mark, F_2 is eliminated and

$$\Sigma L = 100 \times 70 - 100 \times 30 - 200 \times 20$$
$$= 7000 - 3000 - 4000 = 0.$$

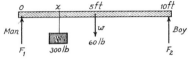

Example 2. A man and boy carry a load of 300 lb by suspending it between them from a pole resting on their shoulders. See Fig. 19H. The pole is 10 ft long and weighs 60 lb.

Fig. 19H—Problem of the boy and man carrying a load between them on a pole.

Where should the load be placed so that the man carries twice as much as the boy?

Solution. Since the weight of the pole has been specified, it must be included in the problem. As indicated by the diagram there are two upward forces on the pole, F_1 the force exerted by the man, and F_2 the force exerted by the boy. There are two downward forces acting, one is W, and the other is w, the weight of the pole, considered as acting at the pole's center of mass.

Apply the 1st condition of equilibrium.

$$\Sigma F_x = 0, \text{ since there are no } x\text{-components}$$
$$\Sigma F_y = F_1 + F_2 - 300 - 60 = 0.$$

From this latter we get,

$$F_1 + F_2 = 360 \text{ lb.}$$

Since the man is to carry twice as much as the boy, divide 360 into thirds to give $F_2 = 120$ lb, and $F_1 = 240$ lb.

Apply the 2nd condition of equilibrium, and take moments about the left end.

$$\Sigma L = F_2 \times 10 \text{ ft} - 60 \text{ lb} \times 5 \text{ ft} - 300 \text{ lb} \times x \text{ ft} = 0$$
$$120 \times 10 - 60 \times 5 - 300x = 0$$
$$x = \frac{1200 - 300}{300} = 3 \text{ ft.} \tag{19k}$$

Moments about any other point will check this result. The load must be suspended 3 ft from the man or 7 ft from the boy.

19.6. Isolating a Body. The major difficulty encountered in solving equilibrium problems is that of finding all of the forces acting and being sure that none have been omitted. As an aid in this direction it is common practice first to do what is called "isolating a body," or "freeing a body." The process is illustrated by the following example.*

* The general procedure is frequently called drawing a free body diagram.

Example 3. A uniform ladder of length l and weight 40 lb leans against a smooth wall making an angle of 60° with the floor. A nail in the floor keeps the ladder from slipping while a man weighing 160 lb climbs up. When the man is three-quarters of the way to the top what is the force exerted on the wall, what is the force exerted on the smooth floor, and what is the horizontal force on the nail?

Solution. By a smooth wall or floor is meant one that can exert only a normal force, that is, a force perpendicular to the surface. A schematic diagram of this problem is shown in Fig. 19I. By isolating the ladder as a rigid body the right hand diagram is obtained. It is observed that there are 5 forces acting, two of known magnitude and direction, and three of known direction but unknown magnitude.

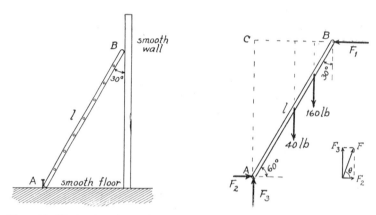

Fɪɢ. 19I—Illustrating the problem of finding the force exerted on the floor by a ladder.

Apply the first condition of equilibrium.

$$\Sigma F_x = F_2 - F_1 = 0, \text{ from which } F_1 = F_2 \tag{19l}$$

and $\quad \Sigma F_y = F_3 - 40 - 160 = 0$, from which $F_3 = 200$ lb.

Applying the second condition of equilibrium, and taking moments about A, F_2 and F_3 may be eliminated as torques. F_1 has a lever arm $l \cos \theta$ and acts counterclockwise whereas the 40 lb has a lever arm $\frac{1}{2}l \sin 30°$ and the 160 lb has a lever arm $\frac{3}{4}l \sin 30°$, both acting clockwise.

$$\Sigma L = F_1 \times l \cos 30° - 40 \times \tfrac{1}{2}l \sin 30° - 160 \times \tfrac{3}{4}l \sin 30° = 0.$$

Cancel l throughout.

$$F_1 \times 0.866 - 20 \times 0.5 - 120 \times 0.5 = 0$$

$$F_1 = \frac{10 + 60}{0.866} = 80.8 \text{ lb.} \tag{19m}$$

By Eq.(19l),

$$F_2 = 80.8 \text{ lb.} \tag{19n}$$

The magnitudes of the forces are therefore $F_1 = 80.8$ lb, $F_2 = 80.8$ lb, and $F_3 = 200$ lb.

If in this problem the floor were rough so that in the absence of a nail the latter would not slip, the floor would support both F_2 and F_3. These then are the two components of a single force F, the magnitude of which can be found from a right triangle of the small vector diagram at the lower right in the figure.

$$F = \sqrt{(80.8)^2 + (200)^2} = 215.7 \text{ lb.}$$

The direction of F is given by

$$\tan \theta = F_3/F_2 = 200/80.8 = 2.47,$$

giving $\theta = 68°$.

PROBLEMS

1. A man and a boy carry a load of 120 lb by suspending it from uniform pole carried on their shoulders. See Fig 19H. If the pole is ten feet long and weighs 20 lb and the man is to carry 2.5 times as much of the load as the boy, where should the load be suspended?

2. In a laboratory experiment a meter stick is held in equilibrium by three horizontal forces as shown in Fig. 19E. One force of 225 dynes is applied to the right at 15 cm, and the second force of 425 dynes is applied to the left at 55 cm. Where should the third force be applied to produce equilibrium and what is its magnitude? (*Ans.* 200 dynes at 100 cm.)

3. In a laboratory experiment similar to that shown in Fig. 19F a meter stick is held in equilibrium by four vertical forces. Three of the forces are 150 dynes up at 5 cm, 275 dynes up at 75 cm, and 125 dynes down at 90 cm. The meter stick weighs 100 dynes. Find the remaining force and its point of application.

4. A uniform pole 12 ft long and weighing 60 lb is suspended by two cords, one at either end. These cords are directed upward and away from the ends and make an angle of 30° with the horizontal. Find the tension in the cords. (*Ans.* 60 lb.)

5. A uniform table weighing 50 lb is 8 ft long. A weight of 30 lb is located on the table directly over the legs at one end, and a boy weighing 100 lb stands on the table 2 ft from the other end. Find the upward force at each end of the table.

6. A uniform door weighing 50 lb is 7 ft high and 3 ft wide. The hinges are located one foot from each end. Assuming the weight of the door to be carried entirely by the lower hinge, find the resultant force exerted on each door hinge. (*Ans.* 15 lb, and 52.2 lb at 16.7° from vertical.)

7. A uniform ladder 24 ft long and weighing 40 lb makes an angle of 70° with the rough floor on which it stands. The upper end rests against a smooth wall. A man weighing 160 lb stands on one step one third of the way up. Find the unknown forces. See Fig. 19I.

8. A uniform ladder 30 ft long and weighing 50 lb makes an angle of 65° with the rough floor on which it stands. The upper end rests against a smooth round horizontal bar so that the force exerted on the bar is normal to the ladder. A man weighing 180 lb stands on one step two thirds of the way up. Find the unknown forces. (*Ans.* At top $F_1 = 61.28$ lb. At bottom $F = 211.6$ lb at 74.8° with horizontal.)

9. A derrick consists of a vertical mast, or king post, 10 ft tall, and a uniform boom 6 ft long and weight 25 lb. One end of the boom is pivoted 2 ft up from the base of the king post and the far end is held up by a tie rope leading to the top of the king post. If a 50 lb load hangs from the far end of the boom and the boom is held in a horizontal position, what is (a) the tension in the tie rope, and (b) the force exerted by the boom on the king post?

10. Solve Prob. 9 if the far end of the boom is pulled up by the tie rope to where the boom makes an angle of 90° with the tie rope. *Note*—Take moments about lower end of boom first. (*Ans.* $T = 41.34$ lb, (b) 51.80 lb at 58.02°.)

11. A truck having a 12 ft wheel base weighs 2½ tons when empty. Its center of gravity is 9 ft in front of the rear wheels. Where should a 3½ ton load be placed in order that all four wheels carry the same load?

12. The center of gravity of an empty truck weighing 2 tons is 9 ft in front of the rear axle. The truck carries a load of 2 tons which is placed centrally with its center of gravity 3 ft in front of the rear axle. If the wheel base is 13 ft, find (a) the center of gravity, and (b) the load carried by each wheel. (*Ans.* (a) 6 ft in front of rear axle. (b) front wheels 1845 lb each; rear wheels 2155 lb each.)

13. When the front wheels of a loaded truck are run on a platform scales, the scale indicator reads 2450 lb; when the rear wheels are run on the scales, the indicator reads 2840 lb. If the wheel base is 14 ft, find the center of gravity.

14. One end of a 16 ft length of gas pipe weighing 50 lb rests on the ground. The pipe leans at an angle of 35° with the vertical against a smooth wall. Find all the forces acting on the pipe. (*Ans.* 5.25 lb normal to wall, and 53.0 lb at 19.3° on bottom.)

15. A crane consists of a vertical mast and a uniform boom. The latter has a mass of 100 kg and a length of 6 m. One end of the boom is pivoted at the base of the mast and the far end is held up by a tie rope leading to the top of the mast. Both boom and tie rope make an angle of 45° with the mast, and a 200 kg load hangs from the far end of the boom. Find (a) the tension in the tie rope, and (b) the force exerted by the mast on the boom.

16. Two uniform ladders, each 18 ft long and weighing 30 lb, are hinged together at the top and set up as an A-frame. The two ends of a uniform horizontal tie rod 12 ft long and weighing 10 lb are connected to points 12 ft from the apex. If the ladders stand on a smooth floor, compute (a) the tension in the tie rod, (b) the force of one ladder on the other at the hinge, and (c) the force of each ladder on the floor. (*Ans.* (a) 14.4 lb. (b) 14.4 lb. (c) 35 lb each.)

17. A uniform door 2 m high and 1 m wide is hung from two hinges, each 20 cm from the ends. If the mass of the door is 30 kg, find the magnitude of the resultant force exerted on the door by each hinge. Assume each hinge carries half the weight of the door.

18. A table 6 ft long and 30 in. high weighs 80 lb. Its center of mass is centrally located 6 in. below the table top. The table is pulled along the floor by a horizontal force applied at one end of the table top. Calculate (a) the upward force, and (b) the force of friction, on each leg if the coefficient of sliding friction is 0.40. Assume the legs to be at the extreme ends of the table. (*Ans.* (a) 1.33 lb on each rear leg, and 38.66 lb on each front leg. (b) 0.533 lb on each rear leg, and 15.47 lb on each front leg.)

Anatomical Mechanics   *Chapter 20*

In the preceding chapters it has been seen that to obtain a solution to many problems in mechanics, it is customary to neglect certain minor details like the weight of a bridge girder or the friction in a bearing in order to simplify a problem and arrive at some approximate yet practical numerical answer.

Although complicated, the **general** principles of muscle function in animals as well as in living human beings may also be simplified in much the same way by neglecting certain minor parts. As a result of such simplification the bones of the body and the muscles that move them form the compression and tension members respectively of mechanical systems already classified as levers and machines. It is, therefore, the purpose of this chapter to show in what way some of the principles of mechanics may be found in and applied to the human anatomy.

One significant fact concerning muscles and their action is that their lever arms, that is, the perpendicular distance from some joint as a fulcrum to the line of action of the muscle, is relatively short. This means that to overcome a relatively slight resistance at the extremity of some bone system a muscle must be capable of exerting far greater forces than those offering the resistance to motion. It will be seen in what follows, therefore, that the large force of a muscle exerted through a short distance moves a lesser load through a greater distance. In other words, motion is magnified while the mechanical advantage is diminished.

When one part of the body is bent toward another the action is called *flexion,* that is, bending; when the parts are straightened out the motion is called *extension.* Even though a number of muscles are involved in the flexion of a joint and another group in its extension it is often true that some one particular muscle group may be considered to be the *prime mover* for flexion and another as the prime mover for extension.

Muscles that perform a minor role in any action are called *assistors.* The function of assistor muscles is to prevent undesired actions of the prime mover such as inward and outward rotation.

20.1. Mechanics of the Foot. An elementary example of anatomical mechanics is found in an analysis of foot movement. See Fig. 20A. In the flexion and extension of the whole foot the ankle acts as a hinge or pivot about which rotation in a vertical plane takes place. The top of the *astrag-*

alus is like a ball fitting into and free to turn in the socket formed by the ends of the *fibula* and *tibia* bones of the leg. When a person attempts to rise on tiptoe, the strong muscles, the *gastro-cnemius* and *soleus* forming the calf of the leg, act as prime movers. A sufficient tightening of these muscles causes the heel to rise, and the foot to bend at *C* where the *phalanx* of the toes join the *metatarsals*.

A simple space diagram shown in Fig. 20B illustrates how rising on tiptoe involves the simplest type of lever action with a fixed pivot at *C*. The horizontal member *AC* represents the foot skeleton from *A* to *C* in Fig. 20A, and the vertical member (*BD*) the leg skeleton (*BD*) supporting the body. To calculate the tension required of the muscles and the load to be carried by the leg bones, the foot member *A* to *C* is isolated as a rigid body and all forces acting upon it taken into account.

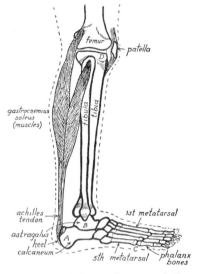

FIG. 20A—Skeleton diagram of the lower leg and foot showing the muscles and tendon used in rising on tiptoes.

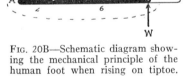

FIG. 20B—Schematic diagram showing the mechanical principle of the human foot when rising on tiptoe.

There are three forces acting on the isolated member (a) an upward force at *A* due to tension in the muscles, (b) a downward force at *B* due to the leg bones, and (c) an upward force at *C* due to the floor. As a problem let it be assumed that a person weighing 150 lb *stands on one foot* and then rises on tiptoe. Assign the dimensions of 2 in. for *AB* and 6 in. for *BC*, and calculate the tension force *T* and the compression force *P* as follows:

By taking moments about *A*, the counterclockwise torque is $W \times 8$ in. and the clockwise torque $P \times 2$ in.

Equate torques, as in conditions of equilibrium.

$$P \times 2 \text{ in.} = W \times 8 \text{ in.}$$

Substitute $W = 150$ lb and solve for *P*.

$$P = \frac{150 \text{ lb} \times 8 \text{ in.}}{2 \text{ in.}} = 600 \text{ lb.}$$

Take moments about B, and equate.

$$T \times 2 \text{ in.} = W \times 6 \text{ in.}$$

Substitute and solve for T.

$$T = \frac{150 \text{ lb} \times 6 \text{ in.}}{2 \text{ in.}} = 450 \text{ lb.}$$

As a check it is observed that the total upward force $W + T$ of 600 lb equals the total downward force P of 600 lb.

It should be pointed out that tension is produced by a contraction of the large part or "belly" of a muscle and not by the narrow section called the *tendon*.

20.2. Mechanics of the Lower Jaw. The *mandible,* or lower "jaw-bone," is a large, strong, horseshoe shaped bone, forming the lower third of the facial skeleton. See Fig. 20C. A pair of *condyles* at the ends fit into sockets one on either side of the skull just in front of the auditory canal and act as hinges about which the lower jaw pivots.

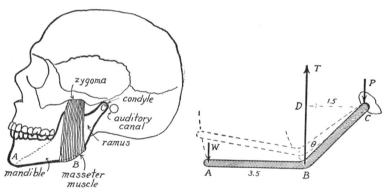

Fɪɢ. 20C—(a) Diagram of the human skull. (b) Schematic diagram showing mechanics of chewing.

The *masseter* or "chewing muscle" is one of the strongest muscles in the body. As illustrated in the figure it is located in the back part of the side of the face. Originating on the lower margin of the *zygoma* the masseter passes downward to where it terminates on the lower edge of the *ramus* of the mandible.

The action of the two masseters, one on either side of the face, is such as to lift the lower jaw and at the same time draw it slightly forward. In principle this is a lever action with a pivot at C, an upward force at B, and a load force at A introduced when chewing takes place between the teeth of the upper and lower jaws.

A schematic diagram of the lever action is shown at the right in Fig. 20C, with selected values of the dimensions given in inches. When the lever is isolated as a rigid body all of the acting forces, due to symmetry, are reduced to three, *W, T* and *P*. To calculate the magnitudes of these forces at least one of them must be known.

As a problem let it be assumed that the lower jaw, in chewing with the front teeth, is able to exert a measured force of 20 lb. To calculate the tension *T* exerted by the two masseters, the point *C* is assumed as pivot, and torques equated as follows:

$$W \times 5 \text{ in} = T \times 1.5 \text{ in.}$$

Inserting $W = 20$ lb, and solving for T,

$$T = \frac{20 \text{ lb} \times 5 \text{ in}}{1.5 \text{ in}} = 66.7 \text{ lb.}$$

Equating downward forces to upward forces,

$$P + W = T$$

from which

$$P = T - W = 66.7 - 20 = 46.7 \text{ lb.}$$

Each masseter therefore exerts one half of 66.7 lb or 33.35 lb, while the condyles each press against their sockets with a force of one-half of 46.7 lb, or 23.35 lb.

20.3. Three Non-Parallel Forces. When three non-parallel forces act upon a body in equilibrium their lines of action must intersect at a com-

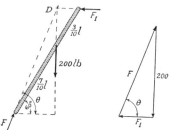

Fig. 20D—When three forces act on a rigid body in equilibrium their lines of action intersect at a common point.

mon point.* Consider as an illustration the ladder problem in Fig. 19I(b). The five forces in diagram (b) can be reduced to three by combining the 160 lb with the 40 lb into a single parallel force of 200 lb at their center

---

* To prove this principle, assume the forces do not intersect at a common point. Select a point where two of them intersect and take moments about this point. The third force then has a lever arm and therefore produces a resultant torque on the body assumed in rotational equilibrium.

of gravity. By the principle of moments applied to these two alone their center of gravity is located $3l/10$ ft from the top end. F_2 and F_3 are replaced by their resultant F.

The original five forces have therefore been reduced to three as shown in Fig. 20D, with their lines of action intersecting at D. Knowing the magnitude of the one force 200 lb, and the direction of all three, the magnitudes of F and F_1 can be calculated in either of two ways, (a) from a force diagram as shown at the right, or (b) by applying the principle of torques to the space diagram at the left.

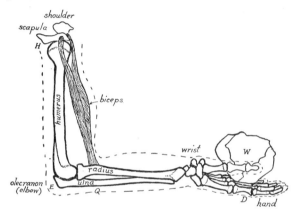

FIG. 20E—Skeleton diagram of the arm and hand showing the bicep used in lifting a load W.

20.4. The Biceps. The above procedure of solution will be applied to the muscle problem involved in the flexion of the lower arm. In Fig. 20E a skeleton of the forearm is shown in a horizontal position supporting a stone in the palm of the hand. With a pivot point at the elbow joint the forearm and hand form a compression member like the boom of a crane, while the *biceps* assuming the duty of prime mover in any flexor movement, become the tension member.

The biceps originate on the *scapula* or shoulder from where they pass downward and forward to terminate on the *radius* near the elbow.

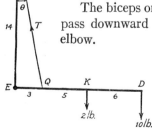

FIG. 20F—Mechanics of the forearm.

A schematic diagram of this force problem is shown in Fig. 20F; the vertical member (EH), 14 in. in length, represents the *humerus;* the horizontal member (ED), 14 in. in length, the forearm and hand; and the tension member (HQ) the biceps. A weight of 10 lb is assumed held in the hand, while the weight of the forearm and hand is taken to be 2 lb and applied at the center of mass 8 in. from the elbow.

The problem to be solved resolves itself into one of calculating (a) the upward force exerted by the biceps and (b) the downward force exerted by the humerus on the elbow. Isolation of the horizontal forearm member is shown in Fig. 20G with three forces acting upon it, F, T, and P. The force F of 12 lb is the resultant of the two weights 2 lb and 10 lb, and its point of application determined by the principle of mo-ments. S is their center of gravity, since the mo-ment on the left, 2 lb $\times$ 5 in., equals the moment on the right, 10 lb $\times$ 1 in.

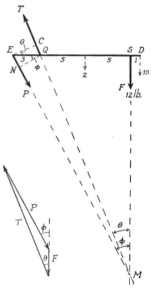

By graphical construction the line (ED) is first drawn 14 in. long. The line (SM) is next drawn vertically downward and of definite length as shown. To find the angle θ at which to draw (QM), reference is made to Fig. 20F. For the right triangle HEQ,

$$\tan \theta = \frac{3 \text{ in.}}{14 \text{ in.}} = 0.214$$

giving $\theta = 11° 54'$

Through the point Q in Fig. 20G a line is next drawn at 11° 54'. Through the point of intersec-tion at M, and E, the remaining line is drawn in to give the direction of P. Rotational equilibrium of the torques is now assured since the lines of action of all three forces have been constructed to intersect at a single point M.

Fig. 20G—Vector diagram of forces involved in lifting the forearm.

To apply equilibrium conditions it is necessary to find the length of the line (SM), and the angle ϕ. Referring to the right triangle QSM, we obtain

$$\tan \theta = \frac{(QS)}{(SM)}.$$

Transpose the equation and substitute known values.

$$(SM) = \frac{(QS)}{\tan \theta} = \frac{10}{0.214} = 46.7 \text{ in.}$$

For the right triangle ESM,

$$\tan \phi = \frac{(ES)}{(SM)} = \frac{13}{46.7} = 0.278$$

giving $\phi = 15° 33'$.

Dropping perpendiculars from E and Q two right triangles ECQ and ENQ are formed, each containing one of these same angles θ and ϕ. Take moments, or torques, about Q.

$$P \times (NQ) = F \times (QS).$$

Then

$$P = \frac{F \times (QS)}{(NQ)} = \frac{12 \times 10}{3 \cos \phi} = \frac{120}{2.89} = 41.5 \text{ lb.}$$

Take moments about E.

giving

$$T \times (EC) = F \times (ES)$$

$$T = \frac{F \times (ES)}{(EC)} = \frac{12 \times 13}{3 \cos \theta} = \frac{156}{2.93} = 53.2 \text{ lb.}$$

The force polygon shown at the lower left in Fig. 20G is drawn as a check upon the above calculated results. Closing of the triangle of forces constitutes translational equilibrium while the intersection of their lines of action in the space diagram assures rotational equilibrium.

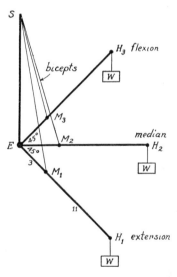

In the above problem where the forearm was assumed to be held in a horizontal position, the upward force of the biceps was found to be 53.2 lb. Should the arm be drawn upward (flexor position) the required tension decreases somewhat, whereas if it is lowered (extensor position) the tension increases. Space diagrams for all three positions are shown in Fig. 20H.

Solutions, similar to the one given above for the median position, give $T = 60.3$ lb for the extensor position 45° below the horizontal and $T = 44.9$ lb for the flexor position 45° above the horizontal.

20.5. The Quadriceps. The mechanics concerned with the extension of the lower limb involves a four-branched muscle called the *quadriceps*. One of the branches of this muscle originates above the hip on the ante-

Fig. 20H—Schematic diagram of the mechanics involved in elbow flexion and extension with a weight W held in the palm of the hand. Dimensions are in inches.

rior inferior spine of the ilium, and the other three on the front and two sides of the *femur* respectively. See Fig. 20I. All four unite around the small kneecap bone, the *patella*, and terminate as a strong tendon near the upper end of the *tibia*.

If while the body is in a sitting position the leg is extended as shown in the diagram, contraction in the quadriceps pulls the patella up over the knee joint. The action is similar to that of a pulley as indicated in the schematic diagram below. As a mechanical problem it is desired to find the tension required of the quadriceps to hold the lower part of the leg at any given angle with the horizontal, and the force exerted by the femur on the knee joint.

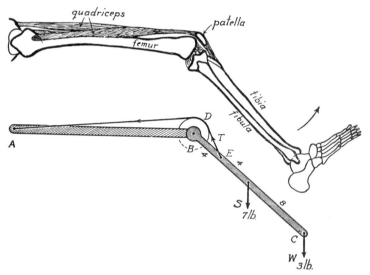

FIG. 20I—Skeleton diagram of the human leg (above) and its mechanical analogue (below).

To make these calculations it is necessary to know the weights of the foot and lower leg, their centers of gravity, and the geometry involved at the knee joint. When these are known the lower leg from B to C may be isolated and solved as a rigid body, or lever, with a pivot at B. Such solutions will be left as problems at the end of this chapter.

PROBLEMS

1. If the greatest load a 150 lb man can lift and still rise on his tiptoes with it is 250 lb, what is the corresponding muscle tension he can exert through the Achilles' tendon? Referring to Fig. 20B, assume $AB = 1.75$ in and $AC = 8.75$ in.

2. In applying the brake pedal of a truck a man exerts a force of 20 lb with the ball of his right foot. If the dimensions of his foot are $AB = 1.45$ in and $AC = 6.25$ in (see Fig. 20B) find (a) the tension in the Achilles' tendon, and (b) the compressional force on the calcaneum. (*Ans.* (a) 66.2 lb, (b) 86.2 lb.)

3. A man weighing 175 lb and carrying a 100 lb bag rises on tiptoes. Calculate (a) the downward force on the astragalus of each foot, and (b) the tension in each

Achilles' tendon if the dimensions of each foot (see Fig. 20B) are $AB = 1.45$ in and $BC = 5.7$ in.

4. A boy pedaling a bicycle weighs 120 lb. When he puts all of his weight on the ball of one foot what is the tension in the Achilles' tendon? The dimensions of his foot are $AB = 1.38$ in and $AC = 7.42$ in. (See Fig. 20B.) (*Ans.* 525.2 lb.)

5. In biting down to crack a nut with his front teeth a man exerts a force of 22 lb. Calculate the tension in the masseter muscles if the mandible has the following dimensions (see Fig. 20C), $AB = 9$ cm, $BC = 6.6$ cm and $\theta = 48°$.

6. If each masseter muscle of a man is capable of exerting a maximum force of 65 lb calculate the maximum force he can exert by his front teeth if the mandible has the following dimensions (see Fig. 20C), $AB = 3.6$ in, $BC = 2.5$ in, and $\theta = 52°$. (*Ans.* 46.0 lb.)

7. If in biting down on a hard piece of candy a boy exerts a force of 32 lb with his front teeth, find (a) the tension in each masseter, and (b) the force on each condyle. The mandible dimensions are (see Fig. 20C), $AB = 3.8$ in, $BC = 2.4$ in, and $\theta = 55°$.

8. When chewing on a piece of dried venison an Eskimo exerts a force of 12 lb with his front teeth. Find (a) the tension in each masseter, and (b) the force on each condyle. The mandible dimensions are (see Fig. 20C), $AB = 10.0$ cm, $BC = 6.0$ cm, and $\theta = 58°$. (*Ans.* (a) 17.79 lb, (b) 11.8 lb.)

9. A man holds a 7.5 kg bowling ball in the palm of his hand. If his forearm is in the median position (see Fig. 20E) what is the tension exerted by the biceps? The dimensions of his forearm are: $EQ = 10.0$ cm, $ED = 40.0$ cm, $EH = 40.0$ cm. Assume the forearm and hand to weigh 2.50 kg with the center of gravity 18.0 cm from the elbow.

10. An athlete holds a 12 lb shot-put in his hand with his forearm flexed to the median position. Calculate the force exerted by the biceps if the dimensions (see Fig. 20E) are $EQ = 2.2$ in, $ED = 16$ in, and $EH = 15$ in. Assume the forearm and hand to weigh 3.4 lb with the center of gravity 8 in from E. *Note*—take moments about the elbow. (*Ans.* 100.6 lb.)

11. Assuming the weights and dimensions given in Prob. 10 calculate the tension in the biceps for the flexion position shown schematically in Fig. 20H.

12. Assuming the weights and dimensions given in Prob. 10 calculate the tension in the biceps for the extension position shown schematically in Fig. 20H. (*Ans.* 110.5 lb.)

13. Determine the tension T exerted by the quadriceps when the leg is held in the position shown in Fig. 20I. Assume the dimensions and weights given in the figure. Angle $DEB = 30°$ and $ABC = 135°$.

14. Assuming the weights and dimensions given for the lower leg in Fig. 20I, calculate (a) the tension exerted by the quadriceps, and (b) the magnitude of the force exerted by the femur on the knee joint. Take angle $ABC = 145°$ and angle $BED = 30°$. (*Ans.* (a) 42.6 lb, (b) 33.8 lb.)

15. A strong man weighing 210 lb lifts a 400 lb weight. If his foot dimensions as shown in Fig. 20B are as follows: $AB = 2.0$ in., and $AC = 9.0$ in., find (a) the tension in the Achilles' tendons, and (b) the compressional forces sustained by the bones of the lower leg.

Kinematics and Dynamics
of Rotation
Chapter 21

WHEN a rigid body is acted upon by an unbalanced torque it is set into rotation. Free to turn about an axis, such a body increases in angular velocity acquiring, when the torque ceases to act, some final speed. See Fig. 21A.

21.1. Angular Acceleration. Just as the acceleration of a body in linear motion is defined as the rate of change of velocity, so the angular acceleration of a body in rotation is defined as the rate of change of angular velocity. By comparison these two definitions are expressed the same mathematically. See Eq.4a.

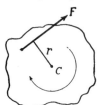

FIG. 21A—A rigid body is acted upon by a torque, F x r.

$$a = \frac{v - v_0}{t} \qquad \alpha = \frac{\omega - \omega_0}{t}. \qquad (21a)$$

linear motion   angular motion

α represents the angular acceleration and is analogous to the linear acceleration a while ω_0, the initial angular velocity, is analogous to v_0 and ω, the final angular velocity is analogous to v. If the above equations are transposed they become (see Eq. 4b)

$$v = v_0 + at \qquad\qquad \omega = \omega_0 + at. \qquad (21b)$$

linear motion   angular motion

Angular velocity ω (see Eq.15b) is defined as θ, the angle turned through, divided by t the time.

$$v = \frac{s}{t} \qquad\qquad \omega = \frac{\theta}{t}. \qquad (21c)$$

linear motion   angular motion

The following example will illustrate the meaning as well as an application of the above angular formulas.

Example 1. A flywheel starting from rest acquires, in 10 sec, a speed of 240 rpm. Find the acceleration.

Solution. Since the wheel starts from rest $\omega_0 = 0$. The final velocity in radians per second is calculated by use of Eq.(21c). Since there are 2π rad in 1 revolution

$$\omega = \frac{2\pi \times 240}{60} = 25.1 \frac{\text{rad}}{\text{sec}}.$$

Using Eq.(21a), we find that

$$a = \frac{25.1 - 0}{10} = 2.51 \frac{rad}{sec^2}.$$

It is clear from the above formulas that linear quantities s, v, and a in the linear equations have only to be replaced by the corresponding angular quantities θ, ω, and a to obtain the angular equations. This direct correspondence is the result of using the radian as a unit of angular measure and holds throughout all of the formulas in mechanics.

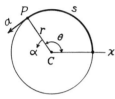

To derive a formula for the linear acceleration of a point around the periphery of an accelerated wheel, it is convenient to start with the definition of acceleration given by Eq.(21a) and substitute for the velocities v and v_0 the equality given by Eq.(14e), $v = r\omega$, and $v_0 = r\omega_0$. See Fig. 21B.

FIG. 21B—A wheel free to rotate about its center is given an angular acceleration.

$$a = \frac{v - v_0}{t} = \frac{r\omega - r\omega_0}{t} = r\left(\frac{\omega - \omega_0}{t}\right) = ra.$$

The result, $a = ra$, is to be compared with two previous formulas, Eqs. (14d) and (14e). The similarity is more conspicuous when written together.

$$s = r\theta \qquad v = r\omega \qquad a = ra. \tag{21d}$$

These interrelation equations are well worth remembering for they are found to be quite useful in the solving of many problems.

21.2. Average Angular Velocity. To calculate the total angle turned through by a rigid body undergoing constant angular acceleration, use is made of the *average angular velocity*. By analogy with linear motion (see Eq.4e) *average angular velocity is defined as one-half the sum of the initial and final angular velocities.*

Symbolically,

$$\bar{v} = \frac{v + v_0}{2} \qquad\qquad \bar{\omega} = \frac{\omega + \omega_0}{2}. \tag{21e}$$

linear motion   angular motion

Since $s = \bar{v}t$, and $\theta = \bar{\omega}t$, direct substitution gives,

$$s = \frac{v + v_0}{2} t \qquad\qquad \theta = \frac{\omega + \omega_0}{2} t. \tag{21f}$$

linear motion   angular motion

Example 2. An airplane motor while idling at 300 rpm is suddenly accelerated. At the end of 3 sec it has acquired its maximum speed of 2400 rpm. Assuming constant acceleration, find (a) the average angular velocity and (b) the total angle turned through.

Solution. We begin by changing the given speeds to radians per second.

$$\omega_o = \frac{300}{60} \times 2\pi = 31.4 \frac{rad}{sec}$$

$$\omega = \frac{2400}{60} \times 2\pi = 251.3 \frac{rad}{sec}.$$

To find (a), direct substitution in Eq.(21e) gives

$$\overline{\omega} = \frac{251.3 + 31.4}{2} = 141.4 \frac{rad}{sec}.$$

To find (b), direct substitution in Eq.(21f) gives

$$\theta = 141.4 \times 3 = 424.2 \text{ rad.}$$

21.3. Kinematics of Rotation. The term kinematics of rotation refers to a quantitative description of motion such as that given above. By combining two of the equations already studied, Eqs.(21b) and (21f), two other useful formulas may be derived.* Each of these is written here beside their analogous linear motions.

$$s = v_o t + \tfrac{1}{2}at^2 \qquad\qquad \theta = \omega_o t + \tfrac{1}{2}at^2 \qquad (21g)$$
$$v^2 = v_o^2 + 2as \qquad\qquad \omega^2 = \omega_o^2 + 2a\theta. \qquad (21h)$$
$$\text{linear motion} \qquad\qquad \text{angular motion}$$

Note here again that angular quantities θ, ω and a take the place of corresponding linear quantities s, v, and a.

Example 3. An automobile engine making 300 rpm is given an angular acceleration of 20 rad/sec² for 10 sec. Find (a) the angle turned through and (b) the total number of revolutions.

Solution. First change 300 rpm to radians per second.

$$\omega_o = \frac{300}{60} \times 2\pi = 31.4 \frac{rad}{sec}.$$

Using Eq.(21g), we obtain

$$\theta = 31.4 \frac{rad}{sec} \times 10 \text{ sec} + \tfrac{1}{2}20 \frac{rad}{sec^2} \times (10 \text{ sec})^2 = 1314 \text{ rad.}$$

$$\theta = \frac{1314}{2\pi} = 209 \text{ rev.}$$

21.4. Dynamics of Rotation. In the treatment of angular acceleration given in the preceding sections of this chapter, neither the torques causing the acceleration, nor the mass of the rotating body, entered into the

---

* The derivations of Eqs.(21g) and (21h) follow exactly the steps taken in obtaining the corresponding linear formulas, Eqs.(4h) and (4i).

calculations. When these two factors are introduced into the equations the treatment is referred to as the *dynamics of rotation.*

When a specified torque is applied to a body free to rotate about some axis, the angular acceleration produced depends not only upon the size and shape of the body but upon the distribution of the mass with respect to the axis of rotation. To see how these factors are taken into account, consider the simplest kind of example, namely, that of a small mass *m* fastened to the end of a string and set into rotation as shown in Fig. 21C.

By Newton's Second Law of Motion the acceleration *a* of the mass around the periphery of the circle should be given by

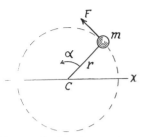

FIG. 21C—Angular acceleration depends upon torque and moment of inertia.

$$F = ma.$$

Multiply both sides of this equation by the radius of the circle *r*.

$$F \times r = ma \times r.$$

The product $F \times r$ on the left side represents the applied torque *L*. Replacing the acceleration *a* on the right by its equal, ra, from Eq.(21d), there results

$$L = mr^2a. \tag{21i}$$

Since *m* and *r* for a given body are both constants, they may be replaced by a single constant *I*, and the equation written

$$L = I\alpha \tag{21j}$$

where $I = mr^2$, and is called the *moment of inertia.* By the following comparison with the force equation,

$$F = ma \qquad\qquad L = I\alpha$$
linear motion   angular motion

the torque *L* is seen to be analogous to *F*, the angular acceleration *a* analogous to *a*, and the moment of inertia *I* analogous to *m*.

According to Eq.(21i) the angular acceleration *a* is inversely proportional to r^2. An

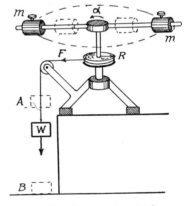

FIG. 21D—An experiment demonstrating moment of inertia.

experiment illustrating this fact is shown in Fig. 21D. Two masses *m* threaded on light horizontal arms, free to turn about a vertical axis, are acted upon by a constant torque $L = F \times R$.

When the masses are clamped at equal distances from and half way out on the arms, the angular acceleration is relatively large, and the weight W exerting the constant torque L quickly drops from A to B. When the masses m are moved to the outer ends of the arms where their distance r is doubled, the angular acceleration is reduced to $\frac{1}{4}$ and the weight W takes 2 times as long to go from A to B. By measuring the distance of each mass from the center, and the time of fall of the weight W for each part of the experiment, the product ar^2 is found to be constant.

21.5. Moment of Inertia. The moment of inertia of a body with respect to any axis is the sum of the products obtained by multiplying each elementary mass by the square of its distance from the axis. To illustrate consider the uniform ring and the thin rod as shown in Fig. 21E.

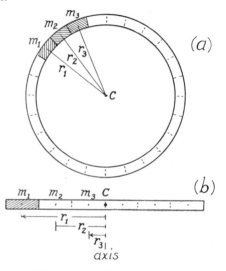

Both the ring and rod are divided into small parts as shown by the dotted lines and shaded areas, and the moment of inertia I calculated from the formula

$$I = m_1 r_1{}^2 + m_2 r_2{}^2 + m_3 r_3{}^2 + \ldots$$
$$(21k)$$

where m_1, m_2, m_3, $\ldots$ represent the masses of each small part and r_1, r_2, r_3, $\ldots$ their respective distances from the axis of rotation.

Fig. 21E—Showing the division of (a) a ring, and (b) a rod, into small masses for calculating their moments of inertia.

Since r has the same value for all masses around the ring, the subscripts on the r's can be dropped,

$$I = m_1 r^2 + m_2 r^2 + m_3 r^2 + \ldots$$

and the common factor r^2 taken out as follows:

$$I = (m_1 + m_2 + m_3 + \ldots)r^2.$$

Because the sum of all the masses $m_1 + m_2 + m_3 + \ldots$ equals M, the total mass of the ring,

$$I_{\text{ring}} = Mr^2. \tag{21l}$$

This is the same as the formula for a mass on the end of a string.

When the same procedure is applied to the rod in Fig. 21E the values of r vary from mass to mass, and the calculations, using Eq.(21k), give only an approximate value of its moment of inertia. It is not difficult to show that the larger the number of parts into which the rod is divided the more nearly will Eq.(21k) give the true moment of inertia. A derivation of the formula by which the true moment of inertia is usually calculated requires the integral calculus and gives

$$I_{\text{rod}} = \frac{1}{12}Ml^2 \tag{21m}$$

where M is the total mass of the rod and l its total length. Because the calculus method is beyond the scope of this book, this formula should be assumed to be correct. To illustrate the approximate method and compare it with this correct formula consider the following example:

Example 4. A uniform rod 12 m long and having a mass of 30 kg is pivoted to turn about an axis through its center perpendicular to its length. Calculate its moment of inertia by (a) the true formula, and (b) the approximate formula.

Solution. (a) Direct substitution in Eq.(21m) gives

$$I = \frac{1}{12} \times 30 \text{ kg} \times (12)^2 \text{ m}^2 = 360 \text{ kg m}^2$$

as the true moment of inertia.

(b) Dividing the rod into six equal parts as shown in Fig. 21E yields six masses of 5 kg each with distances 5 m, 3 m, 1 m, 1 m, 3 m, and 5 m respectively. Applying Eq.(21k), **we obtain**

$$I = 5 \times 5^2 + 5 \times 3^2 + 5 \times 1^2 + 5 \times 1^2 + 5 \times 3^2 + 5 \times 5^2 = 350 \text{ kg m}^2$$

a value nearly 3% lower than the true value.

Should the rod in part (b) have been divided into twelve equal parts the same summation process gives 357.5 kg m², a value less than 1% lower than (a). The student should confirm this last result as an exercise.

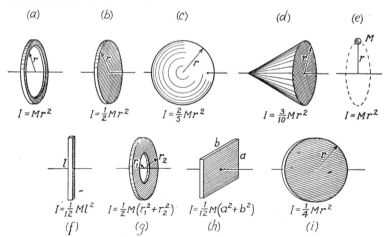

$(a) \qquad (b) \qquad (c) \qquad (d) \qquad (e)$

$I=Mr^2 \qquad I=\tfrac{1}{2}Mr^2 \qquad I=\tfrac{2}{5}Mr^2 \qquad I=\tfrac{3}{10}Mr^2 \qquad I=Mr^2$

$I=\tfrac{1}{12}Ml^2 \qquad I=\tfrac{1}{2}M(r_1^2+r_2^2) \qquad I=\tfrac{1}{12}M(a^2+b^2) \qquad I=\tfrac{1}{4}Mr^2$

$(f) \qquad\qquad (g) \qquad\qquad\qquad (h) \qquad\qquad\qquad (i)$

Fig. 21F—Formulas for the moment of inertia of certain regularly shaped bodies.

The true moments of inertia of a number of regular shaped solid bodies are given in Fig. 21F. Diagram (a) represents a thin ring or hoop or radius *r*, (b) a disk of uniform density, (c) a solid sphere with an axis through the center, etc.

Two common moments of inertia not given in the figure are:

Spherical shell, very thin—around any diameter, $I = \frac{2}{3}Mr^2$.
Uniform ring   —around any diameter, $I = \frac{1}{4}M(r_1^2 + r_2^2)$.

In the *cgs system* moment of inertia has the units of *gm cm²*, in the *mks system* as illustrated above, the units *kg m²*, and in the *fps* system the units *slug ft²* or *lb ft sec²*.

Example 5. A 120 lb flywheel, consisting of a uniform brass disk 4 ft in diameter, is mounted free to turn about an axis as shown in Fig. 21G. A constant force of 10 lb is applied to its periphery by a cord wrapped around the wheel. Calculate the angular acceleration.

Solution. By definition, the applied torque is, $L = F \times r$,

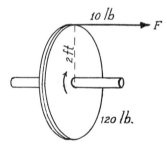

$$L = 10 \text{ lb} \times 2 \text{ ft} = 20 \text{ lb ft}.$$

The moment of inertia of a disk equals

$$I = \frac{1}{2} \cdot \frac{120 \text{ lb}}{32 \text{ ft /sec}^2} \cdot 2^2 \text{ ft}^2 = 7.5 \text{ lb ft sec}^2.$$

Substitute known values in Eq.(21j).

$$20 \text{ lb ft} = 7.5 \text{ lb ft sec}^2\alpha.$$

Solve for α, and cancel units.

Fig. 21G—A 4 ft flywheel weighing 120 lbs is acted upon by a force of 10 lb applied tangent to the periphery.

$$\alpha = 2.67 \frac{\text{rad}}{\text{sec}^2}.$$

21.6. Moment of Inertia About Any Axis.

It is to be noted in Fig. 21F that, with the exception of (e), the moments of inertia are referred to an axis through the geometrical center. For bodies of uniform density this is also the center of mass. Analysis shows that if I_o represents the moment of inertia of a body about an axis through its center of mass, the moment of inertia I about a parallel axis, at a distance h away, is

$$I = I_o + Mh^2. \tag{21n}$$

Consider for example the narrow rod in diagram (f). To find the moment of inertia about the end of the rod the axis would have to be displaced from its present position at the center to the end, a distance equal to half its length, $l/2$. Therefore,

$$I = \tfrac{1}{12}Ml^2 + M\left(\frac{l}{2}\right)^2 = \tfrac{1}{3}Ml^2.$$

The moment of inertia about the end is $\tfrac{1}{3}Ml^2$.

PROBLEMS

1. Starting from rest the large flywheel of a steam engine acquires a speed of 450 rpm in one minute. Find the angular acceleration in rad/sec².

2. An automobile engine is idling at 300 rpm. Upon acceleration it acquires a speed of 3000 rpm in 2 sec. Calculate (a) the angular acceleration, and (b) the angle turned through during the acceleration. (*Ans.* (a) 141.4 rad/sec², (b) 346 rad.)

3. An emery wheel one foot in diameter is making 3600 rpm. Find (a) the tangential velocity of a point on the rim, and (b) the distance traveled in 5 sec by a point midway between the rim and center.

4. An electric motor running at 1800 rpm has three pulley wheels on its shaft. (a) Find the linear speed of a belt when it is placed over each wheel in turn. The pulley diameters are 3 in, 6 in, and 9 in respectively. (b) If the same belt passes over a similar pulley mounted on another shaft, the 3 in to the 9 in, the 6 in to the 6 in, and the 9 in to the 3 in, what are the three possible speeds of the adjacent shaft? (*Ans.* (a) 23.56, 47.1, 70.7 ft/sec, (b) 600, 1800, and 5400 rpm.)

5. A flywheel making 1200 rpm is slowed down to 200 rpm in 10 sec by applying a brake. Find (a) the acceleration, and (b) the angular speed in rad/sec at the end of 3 sec, (c) the angle turned through in the first 3 sec.

6. Calculate the moment of inertia of an emery wheel that weighs 96 lb and has a diameter of 1 ft, (a) about its axis through the center and perpendicular to the plane of one face, and (b) about a parallel axis tangent to the rim of the wheel. (*Ans.* (a) 0.375 slug ft², (b) 1.125 slug ft².)

7. A uniform solid ball has a mass of 6 kg and a diameter of 30 cm. Calculate its moment of inertia about an axis through the center of mass, and (b) about an axis tangent to the ball.

8. A uniform door 7 ft by 3 ft weighs 30 lb. Calculate its moment of inertia about an axis perpendicular to the plane of the board and (a) through the center, and (b) through one corner. (*Ans.* (a) 4.53 slug ft², (b) 18.1 slug ft².)

9. A uniform rod 50 cm long has a mass of 1 kg and a rectangular cross-section 4 cm by 6 cm. Calculate its moment of inertia about each of three axes through its center of mass, perpendicular to (a) a 4 cm by 50 cm face, (b) a 6 cm by 50 cm face, and (c) a 4 cm by 6 cm face.

10. A uniform ring of 5 kg mass has an internal diameter of 16 cm and an external diameter of 20 cm. Find its moment of inertia about an axis perpendicular to the plane of the ring, and (a) through the center of mass, and (b) through a point 50 cm from the center of mass. (*Ans.* (a) 0.041 kg m², (b) 1.29 kg m².)

11. A uniform flywheel weighing 40 lb has a diameter of 2 ft. What force applied tangent to this wheel will give it an acceleration of 0.5 rad/sec²?

12. A cylindrical grindstone 2 ft in diameter and weighing 40 lb is mounted on the same shaft with a pulley 1 ft in diameter and weighing 8 lb. A belt passes over the pulley and exerts a continuous force of 0.5 lb. Find (a) the moment of inertia, (b) the angular acceleration, and (c) the angular speed at the end of 15 sec. Neglect the moment of inertia of the shaft and belt and assume the wheel starts from rest. (*Ans.* (a) 0.656 slug ft², (b) 0.381 rad/sec², (c) 5.71 rad/sec.)

13. A uniformly solid ball has a diameter of 10 cm and a mass of 100 gm. Supported by a string 95 cm long this ball hangs as a pendulum with its center of gravity 100 cm below the support. Calculate the moment of inertia (a) using the approximate formula in Fig. 21F(e), and (b) the more exact formula Eq.(21n).

14. Find the moment of inertia about a diameter for the ring in Prob. 10. (*Ans.* 2.05×10^{-2} kg m^2.)

15. A baton consists of a uniform rod 60 cm long, having a mass of 400 gm, with a 200 gm hollow ball of 3 cm radius soldered to one end. Find its moment of inertia about the center of mass.

16. A 20 kg flywheel of radius 0.20 m is free to turn about an axis as shown in Fig. 21F(b). A small, flat, circular disk with a mass of 4 kg and radius 5 cm is welded off-center on one side of the flywheel so that the center-to-center distance is 12 cm. Find the moment of inertia about the center of mass. (*Ans.* 0.453 kg m^2.)

17. A uniform disk has a mass of 500 gm and a diameter of 20 cm. With a string 90 cm long fastened to one edge of the disk, the system is suspended as a pendulum. Find the moment of inertia.

18. A uniform disk 16 cm in diameter has a mass of 1.2 kg. One end of a 2 kg rod 1.12 m long is welded to one edge of the disk to form a clock pendulum. Find the total moment of inertia about the top end of the rod. (*Ans.* 2.57 kg m^2.)

19. A dumbbell is composed of a uniform rod 42 cm long and 500 gm mass, and two solid spheres, one at either end, each with a diameter of 16 cm and a mass of 4000 gm. Find the moment of inertia about the center of mass.

20. The wheel of a water turbine having a moment of inertia of 250 kg m^2, and rotating at a speed of 180 rpm, is brought to rest 26 min after the gate valve is closed. Find the torque applied. (*Ans.* 3.03 newton m.)

21. A rectangular iron plate 0.5 m by 0.8 m has a mass of 120 kg. It is free to rotate about an axis as shown in Fig. 21F(h). If a torque of 100 newton m is applied to set the plate rotating, find (a) the moment of inertia of the plate, (b) the angular acceleration, and (c) the angular speed at the end of 7 sec.

22. A rope is wrapped around the grinding surface of a large cylindrical grindstone 2 ft in radius, and a 10 lb weight hangs from the rope. If the wheel is free to rotate about a horizontal axis through its center, calculate (a) its angular acceleration, and (b) the tension in the rope. Assume a moment of inertia of 2 slug ft^2 for the grindstone. (*Ans.* (a) 6.15 rad/sec. (b) 6.15 lb.)

Angular Momentum and Rotational Kinetic Energy Chapter 22

22.1. Angular Momentum. *Angular momentum* and *rotational kinetic energy* are to all rotating bodies what *linear momentum* and *kinetic energy* are to all bodies moving along a straight line. By definition the angular momentum of a rotating body is equal to the product of its moment of inertia about the axis of rotation by its angular velocity.

$$\text{Angular momentum} = I\omega. \qquad (22a)$$

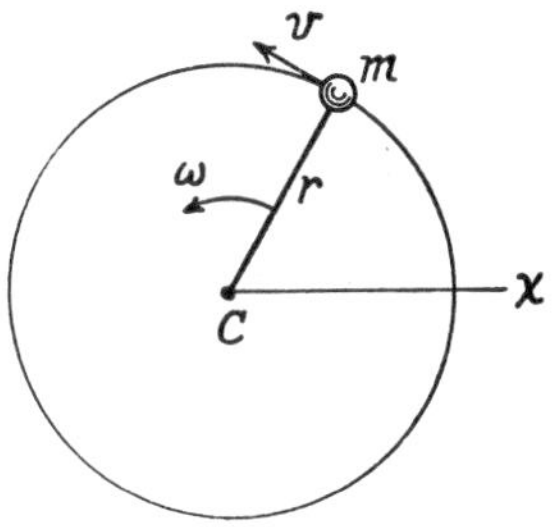

In the special case of a small mass moving in a circle, as shown in Fig. 22A, the moment of inertia equals mr^2, and

$$\text{angular momentum} = mr^2\omega. \qquad (22b)$$

If ω is replaced by its equivalent, v/r,

$$\text{angular momentum} = mvr. \qquad (22c)$$

Fig. 22A—Angular momentum of a small mass m is given by mvr, or by $m\,r^2\,w$.

The first of the above equations applies to any rotating body regardless of size or shape, while the last two apply only to bodies considered small with respect to their distance from the center of rotation. To illustrate both cases, consider the following examples.

Example 1. A 20 kg flywheel in the form of a uniform circular disk 1 m in diameter is making 120 rpm. Calculate its angular momentum.

Solution. To use Eq.(22a) the moment of inertia I and the angular velocity ω should first be calculated and expressed in the same system of units.

From the equation in Fig. 21H (b),

$$I = \tfrac{1}{2}Mr^2 = \tfrac{1}{2}20 \text{ kg} \times (0.5\text{m})^2 = 2.5 \text{ kg m}^2.$$

By Eq.(21c),

$$\omega = 2\pi \times \frac{120}{60} = 4\pi \ \frac{\text{rad}}{\text{sec}}.$$

By substituting in Eq.(22a), we obtain

$$\text{ang. mom.} = 2.5 \text{ kg m}^2 \times 4\pi \text{ rad/sec} = 31.4 \text{ kg m}^2/\text{sec}.$$

Example 2. A boy weighing 100 lb rides at the outer edge of a merry-go-round, 40 ft in diameter. Calculate his angular momentum if the merry-go-round is making 3 rpm.

Solution. Since the boy is small compared with his distance from the center of rotation, Eq.(22b) can be used. First the angular velocity ω is found by Eq.(21c).

$$\omega = \frac{3 \times 2\pi}{60} = 0.314 \frac{rad}{sec}.$$

Substitution of known values in Eq.(22b) gives

$$ang. \ mom. = \frac{100 \ lb}{32 \ ft/sec^2} \times (20 \ ft)^2 \times 0.314 \frac{rad}{sec} = 392.5 \ lb \ ft \ sec.$$

22.2. Theoretical Considerations.

To understand why angular momentum is defined as $I\omega$, return to the fundamental equation for torque given in the preceding chapter, $L = I\alpha$. If in this equation the angular accelera tion is replaced by its defining equation, $\alpha = \omega - \omega_0/t$,

$$L = I\frac{\omega - \omega_0}{t} \tag{22d}$$

Transposing t to the left side and multiplying out, an equation analogous to the impulse equation in translational motion is obtained.

$$Ft = mv - mv_0 \qquad\qquad Lt = I\omega - I\omega_0. \tag{22e}$$
$$\text{linear motion} \qquad\qquad \text{rotational motion}$$

In linear motion Ft is called the impulse and $mv - mv_0$, the change in momentum. By analogy, therefore, it is logical that Lt be called the *angular impulse* and $I\omega - I\omega_0$ the *change in angular momentum*. $I\omega_0$ is the initial angular momentum and $I\omega$ the final value.

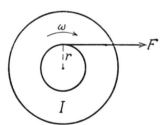

Consider the flywheel shown in Fig. 22B. Starting from rest, and acted upon by a torque $F \times r$ for a period of t seconds, the wheel acquires a final angular velocity of ω radians per second. In this special case of starting from rest, $\omega_0 = 0$, and Eq.(22e) reduces to

$$Lt = I\omega. \tag{22f}$$

FIG. 22B—An acting torque sets a wheel rotating.

Example 3. The wheel of a grindstone with a diameter of 30 cm and a mass of 5 kg has applied at its axle, 4 cm in diameter, a constant tangential force of 98 newtons. Find (a) the angular momentum acquired at the end of 10 sec, and (b) the angular velocity.

Solution. (a) Since the wheel starts from rest ($\omega_0 = 0$), Eq.(22f) can be used. To determine $I\omega$ it is most convenient to calculate its equivalent, the angular impulse Lt.

Substitution of given quantities gives

$$Lt = 98 \frac{kg \ m}{sec^2} \times 0.02 \ m \times 10 \ sec = 19.6 \frac{kg \ m^2}{sec}.$$

(b) Use Eq.(22f) and transpose.

$$\omega = \frac{Lt}{I} = \frac{19.6 \text{ kg m}^2/\text{sec}}{\frac{1}{2}5 \text{ kg} \times (0.15 \text{ m})^2} = 348 \frac{\text{rad}}{\text{sec}}.$$

22.3. Conservation of Angular Momentum.

If no external torque acts upon a body or system of bodies already in rotation the angular momentum remains constant. Setting the torque L in Eq.(22e) equal to zero, $0 = I\omega - I\omega_0$, from which

$$I\omega = I\omega_0. \tag{22g}$$

In words, the final angular momentum is always equal to the initial angular momentum.

An experiment illustrating a system of bodies in rotation is diagramed in Fig. 22C. Two equal masses m are mounted on a rod AB capable of rota-

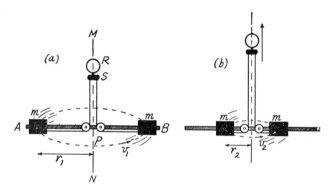

Fig. 22C—Experimental demonstration of the conservation of angular momentum.

tion about a vertical axis MN. Cords fastened to each mass and leading over pulleys at P to the ring R enable the radial distance to be changed from r_1 in (a) to r_2 in (b) by simply pulling up on the ring R. The swivel S prevents the cords from twisting.

When the system is first set rotating as in (a) with an angular velocity ω_1 the angular momentum of each mass is $I\omega_1$. On pulling up on the ring R the radius decreases to r_2 and the angular velocity ω_2 increases. Conservation of angular momentum requires that, for each mass m,

$$I\omega_1 = I\omega_2. \tag{22h}$$

In terms of speed v,

$$mv_1r_1 = mv_2r_2. \tag{22i}$$

Since the mass is not altered in value conservation of angular momentum requires that any decrease in r must be compensated for by an increase in speed. This is necessary to keep both sides of the above equation equal to each other.

Eq.(22i) shows for example that if r is reduced to half value the velocity v must double. With v doubled and the circle only half as large, the angular velocity increases four fold.

Example 4. Suppose in Fig. 22C that $m = 10$ gm, $v_1 = 20$ cm/sec, and $r_1 = 16$ cm. What will be the new speed if the radius r_1 is decreased to half value, i.e., $r_2 = 8$ cm?

Solution. By direct substitution in Eq.(22i),

$$10 \text{ gm} \times 20 \frac{\text{cm}}{\text{sec}} \times 16 \text{ cm} = 10 \text{ gm} \times v_2 \times 8 \text{ cm}$$

$$3200 \frac{\text{cm}}{\text{sec}} = 80 \, v_2$$

$$v_2 = 40 \frac{\text{cm}}{\text{sec}}.$$

An interesting experiment illustrating the same principle is diagramed in Fig. 22D. An observer stands on a turntable with weights in each hand. With arms fully extended horizontally he is first set rotating slowly. Upon drawing the hands and weights in toward the chest as shown the angular velocity is considerably increased. This experiment is best appreciated by the turning observer who feels himself speeded up by what seems to be a mysterious force.

FIG. 22D—Experiment illustrating conservation of angular momentum.

This principle is used by expert figure skaters on the ice. They start into a whirl with their arms, and perhaps one leg extended, and then upon drawing the arms and leg in, obtain a greatly increased angular velocity.

22.4. Kinetic Energy of Rotation. In a previous chapter on linear motion kinetic energy was seen to be given by $\frac{1}{2}mv^2$. By analogy the kinetic energy of a rigid body in rotation is given by $\frac{1}{2}I\omega^2$:

$$\text{KE}_{\text{trans.}} = \tfrac{1}{2} mv^2 \qquad \text{KE}_{\text{rot.}} = \tfrac{1}{2}I\omega^2. \qquad (22\text{j})$$

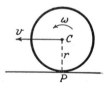

As a wheel rolls along a level road it has both kinetic energy of rotation and kinetic energy of translation. See Fig. 22E. In rotating about its geometrical center it has a moment of inertia I_o and kinetic energy $\frac{1}{2}I_o\omega^2$,

FIG. 22E—A rolling wheel has kinetic energy of rotation and kinetic energy of translation.

while the center of gravity C, moving along a straight line with velocity v has kinetic energy $\frac{1}{2}mv^2$. The total kinetic energy is, therefore,

$$KE_{total} = \tfrac{1}{2}I_o\omega^2 + \tfrac{1}{2}mv^2. \tag{22k}$$

Total K.E. = rotational K.E. + translational K.E.

22.5. Rolling Down an Inclined Plane. The velocity acquired by any smooth round body rolling down an inclined plane is not as great as that of a body sliding without friction. The reason for this is that the potential energy available at the top of the incline goes partly into rotational energy and partly into translational energy. Suppose as an illustration that a ring, a disk, or a ball starts from rest and rolls down an incline as shown in Fig. 22F.

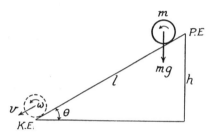

At the top the potential energy,

$$P.E. = mgh. \tag{22l}$$

FIG. 22F—A hoop rolls down an inclined plane.

At the bottom this energy, neglecting losses by friction, has been transformed into kinetic energy of rotation, $\frac{1}{2}I_o\omega^2$, and kinetic energy of translation, $\frac{1}{2}mv^2$,

$$K.E._{bottom} = \tfrac{1}{2}I_o\omega^2 + \tfrac{1}{2}mv^2.$$

By the law of conservation of energy, the total energy at the bottom, which is all kinetic, must be equal to the total energy at the top where it is all potential. Therefore,

$$mgh = \tfrac{1}{2}I_o\omega^2 + \tfrac{1}{2}mv^2. \tag{22m}$$

This is a useful equation for by it one can calculate for any round body the linear velocity acquired at the bottom of a hill. To be specific consider a thin hoop or hollow cylinder of mass m and radius r. From Fig. 21F, the moment of inertia $I = mr^2$ and the angular velocity $\omega = v/r$.

Substitution in Eq.(22m) gives

$$mgh = \tfrac{1}{2}(mr^2)\frac{v^2}{r^2} + \tfrac{1}{2}mv^2.$$

Canceling like quantities, we obtain

$$gh = \tfrac{1}{2}v^2 + \tfrac{1}{2}v^2 = v^2$$

from which

$$v = \sqrt{gh}. \tag{22n}$$

Since neither m nor r enters into this result, all rings regardless of mass or radius should acquire the same velocity. Starting together at the top of an incline two different sized rings or cylinders should, if started together, roll side by side and reach the bottom together.

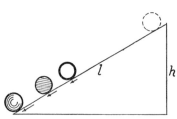

If, in the derivation above, the rolling body is assumed to be a uniform disk for which $I = \frac{1}{2}mr^2$ or a solid uniform sphere for which $I = \frac{2}{5}mr^2$, Eq.(22m) shows that

$$v = \sqrt{\tfrac{4}{3}\, gh} \qquad v = \sqrt{\tfrac{10}{7}\, gh}. \qquad (22o)$$
$$\text{for a disk} \qquad \text{for a sphere}$$

FIG. 22G—Starting together at the top of an inclined plane a solid ball reaches the bottom first, a disk second, and a ring last.

A comparison of these equations shows that while all bodies of the same kind but different size acquire the same velocity, the greatest linear velocity is acquired by a sphere. Starting together at the top of an incline a sphere will reach the bottom first, a disk second, and a ring last. See Fig. 22G.

22.6. Angular Momentum a Vector. Angular momentum, as illustrated by the rotating wheel in Fig. 22H, may be treated as a vector quantity. To obtain an angular momentum vector imagine grasping the axis of rotation with the right hand, the fingers pointing in the direction of rotation, the thumb then points in the direction of the vector. The length of the vector is given by the magnitude of $I\omega$.

Since angular momentum $I\omega$ is the result of an applied angular impulse Lt, the vector for $I\omega$ in Fig. 22H also represents Lt. In other words Lt is a vector quantity and its direction and magnitude is that of $I\omega$.

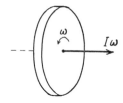

FIG. 22H—Angular momentum may be represented by a vector.

Torque is likewise a vector quantity. Its magnitude is given by $F \times r$, and its direction is given by the right-hand rule given above.

The advantage of representing angular momenta and angular impulse by vectors becomes apparent when attempting to determine the resultant motion of a body undergoing rotation about two or more axes simultaneously. The gyroscope in some of its varied forms serves as a good illustration of this.

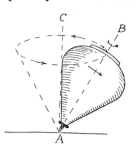

FIG. 22I—A spinning top precesses about its peg.

22.7. The Spinning Top. A common top, set spinning like the one shown in Fig. 22I, is but one of the many forms of a gyroscope. Spinning about its axis the top precesses about its peg or pivot point, the line AB describing an inverted cone about the vertical line AC. If when looking down from above, such a top is

spinning in a clockwise direction the precession is clockwise; spinning counterclockwise the precession is counterclockwise.

22.8. The Gyroscope. A fundamental study of gyroscopic precession
may be readily made by the use of a top similar to those found in toy shops,
and diagramed in Fig. 22J. The wheel W is designed to have a large moment

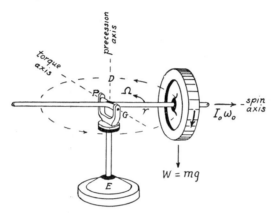

Fig. 22J—Experimental gyroscope for demonstrating
precession.

of inertia, and is often ball-bearing mounted. Free rotation in any direction
is permitted by the double pivot at the top of the stand E.

When the wheel is set spinning at high speed and released with its axis in
a horizontal position, a smooth precession takes place around the vertical
axis. The cause for this precessional motion is to be attributed to the external
force exerted by the earth's gravitational
pull downward on the wheel. Acting
through the wheel's center of gravity,
this downward force W, equal to mg, exerts a torque about a horizontal axis
through PG. This torque L, given by
$W \times r$, and acting for a time t, constitutes a torque impulse Lt and gives rise
to a corresponding angular momentum
$(I\omega)'$ about the same axis.

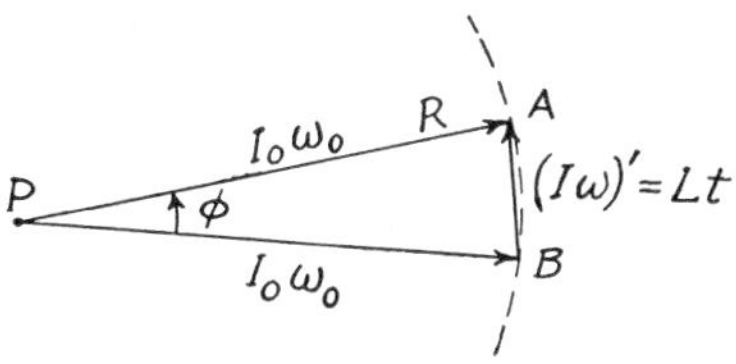

Fig. 22K—Vector diagram for precession
of a gyroscope.

$$Lt = (I\omega)' \qquad (22p)$$

The top therefore has two angular momenta, one $I_0\omega_0$ due to spin and the
other $(I\omega)'$ about a horizontal axis PG. Combining these vectorially as
shown in Fig. 22K, gives a resultant R equal in magnitude to the original
$I_0\omega_0$ and now making an angle ϕ with its direction. In other words there has
been a precession, a change in direction of the spin axis.

In the vector diagram the angular momentum $I_o\omega_o$ is changing in direction by an amount $(I\omega)'$. Since $(I\omega)'$ is increasing with time and is due to a torque L, it can, by Eq.(22p) be replaced by Lt. For small angles ϕ the distance measured along the arc AB is approximately equal to Lt so that to a close approximation we can write

$$\phi = \frac{Lt}{I_o\omega_o} \qquad (22q)$$

Because the action gives rise to a uniform precession, angle ϕ is increasing at a uniform rate and may be written

$$\phi = \Omega t \qquad (22r)$$

where Ω is the precessional angular velocity.

Combining these two equations, we obtain

$$\Omega = \frac{L}{I_o\omega_o} \qquad (22s)$$

This, the precessional angular velocity, in radians per second, is given by the torque L divided by the spin angular momentum.

By analogy, the treatment above is similar to that of circular motion given in Fig. 14D. There a mass moves in a circle at constant speed because a constant inward force is exerted upon it. Although the acceleration is toward the center, the radius remains constant while only the direction of v changes.

In precessional motion the magnitude of the angular momentum remains constant while its direction changes smoothly and continuously. And like the treatment of circular motion (see p. 116), as the angle ϕ is made smaller and smaller in Fig. 22K the arc AB becomes more and more nearly equal to the cord AB, the change in angular momentum $(I\omega)'$ becomes more nearly perpendicular to the spin axis. In the limit when ϕ becomes zero, Eq.(22s) holds exactly and the spin axis and torque axis are mutually perpendicular.

22.9. Gyroscopic Stability. If a balanced gyroscope wheel is mounted in gimbal rings as shown in Fig. 22L it will, when set spinning at high speed, exhibit a property called "gyroscopic stability."

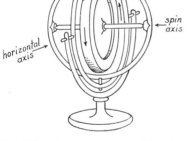

FIG. 22L—Gyroscope mounted in gimbal rings for demonstrating gyroscopic stability.

When the gyro is picked up and carried about, the base can be turned in any direction without altering the direction of the spin axis relative to the earth. In other words, the plane of the gyro wheel seems to have assumed a rigidity in space.

To change the direction of the "spin axis" a torque must be exerted upon it. It is the function of the gimbal ring mounting to allow the base support to be turned in any way without exerting any torque whatever upon the wheel.

Newton's First Law of Motion, involving the inertia of a body, has its rotational counterpart in the above experiment. A body in rotation about some fixed axis will continue to rotate about that same axis with constant speed unless it is acted upon by an unbalanced torque.

PROBLEMS

1. A uniform disk 3 ft in diameter weighs 40 lb. Calculate (a) the angular momentum, and (b) the rotational kinetic energy when it rotates as a wheel about its geometrical center making 1200 rpm.

2. A uniform solid sphere has a diameter of 20 cm and a mass of 15 kg. It rotates at 600 rpm about an axis through its center of mass. Calculate (a) its angular momentum, and (b) its rotational kinetic energy. (*Ans.* (a) 3.77 kg m²/sec, (b) 118 joules.)

3. Two small spheres weighing 1 lb each are tied to opposite ends of a string so that their centers are 4 ft apart. A slip knot is tied in the center of the string, making the spheres 18 in. apart. In this condition they are thrown whirling into the air with an angular speed of 300 rpm. While in the air the slip knot comes untied. Calculate the new angular speed in rpm.

4. A bowling ball with a diameter of 12 in. and a weight of 16 lb rolls along the floor at 20 ft/sec. Calculate its total kinetic energy. (*Ans.* 140 ft lb.)

5. A uniform hoop with an inside diameter of 0.2 m and an outside diameter of 0.24 m has a mass of 0.24 kg. If this hoop is set rolling along a level floor at 5 m/sec find (a) its moment of inertia about the geometrical center, (b) its angular speed, and (c) its total kinetic energy.

6. As a car is traveling along a road at 45 mi/hr, one of the tires comes off and rolls down the road. Calculate the kinetic energy of the tire if the inner diameter is 16 in., the outer diameter is 32 in., and it weighs 24 lb. Use equation in Fig. 21F(g). (*Ans.* 2654 ft lb.)

7. A hoop 2 ft in diameter and weighing 5 lb starts from rest and rolls 20 ft down an incline making 30° with the horizontal. Find its speed at the bottom.

8. A uniform disk with a diameter of 20 cm and a mass of 50 gm rolls 10 m down a 20° incline. Find (a) its speed at the bottom, and (b) its kinetic energy. (*Ans.* (a) 6.68 m/sec, (b) 1.68 joules.)

9. A uniform solid ball rolls 10 m down a 10° incline. Find its speed at the bottom.

10. A solid uniform ball rolls along a level plane at 20 ft/sec. (a) If it comes to a 15° incline how far up will it roll before coming to a stop? (b) How long does it remain on the incline? (*Ans.* (a) 33.8 ft, (b) 3.38 sec.)

11. A uniform disk 1 ft in diameter and 8 lb in mass starts from rest and rolls down a 10% grade. If at the bottom it has a speed of 22 ft/sec, find (a) the total kinetic energy, and (b) the distance traveled.

12. A hollow ball with a diameter of 6 cm and a mass of 50 gm rolls 20 m down a 10° incline. Find (a) its moment of inertia, (b) its kinetic energy, and (c) its final speed. (*Ans.* (a) 300 gm cm², (b) 1.70 joules, (c) 6.4 m/sec.)

13. A hollow ball starts from rest at the top of a sloping roof 6 m long. The roof makes an angle of 30° with the horizontal and the edge of the roof is 5 m above the ground. Calculate (a) the velocity of the ball upon reaching the edge of the roof, (b) the time required to reach the edge of the roof, and (c) the point where the ball strikes the ground.

14. Let the two masses m in Fig. 22C weigh 5 lb each, their initial distance from the center of rotation 2 ft, and the initial angular speed 300 rpm. If the radius is decreased to 1 ft by pulling up the swivel S, calculate (a) the initial angular momentum, (b) the final angular momentum, (c) the initial kinetic energy, (d) the final kinetic energy. (e) Where did the increased energy come from? (*Ans.* (a) 39.3 lb ft sec, (b) 39.3 lb ft sec, (c) 617 ft lb, (d) 2467 ft lb, (e) from work done in pulling the weights in.)

15. A uniform rod, having a length of 120 cm and a mass of 10 kg, can rotate about a transverse axis through its middle point. How many joules of work will be required to set it rotating at 300 rpm?

16. A flywheel, with a moment of inertia of 20 kg m², has a rotational kinetic energy of 1000 joules. What is its speed of rotation in rpm? (*Ans.* 95.5 rpm.)

17. A hoop weighing 320 lb rotates about an axis through its center at 192 rpm. If its diameter is 4 ft, find its (a) moment of inertia, (b) angular velocity, (c) angular momentum, and (d) kinetic energy.

18. A boy's hoop has a mass of 1 kg and a diameter of 1 m. It rolls along a level road at 2 m/sec. Calculate (a) the moment of inertia, (b) its angular speed, and (c) its total kinetic energy. (*Ans.* (a) 0.25 kg m², (b) 4 rad/sec, (c) 4 joules.)

19. The rotating parts of an automobile motor have a moment of inertia equivalent to that of a uniform disk 1 ft in diameter and weighing 64 lb. (a) What is its moment of inertia? (b) Find its kinetic energy when rotating at 6000 rpm.

20. Each of the four propellers on the S.S. *Normandie* has a mass of 19 tons and a moment of inertia of 60,000 slug ft². The ship makes 29 knots when the propellers are turning over at 200 rpm. Calculate (a) the angular momentum, (b) the kinetic energy of each propeller, and (c) the advance of the ship with each turn. (*Ans.* (a) 1.25×10^6 slug ft²/sec, (b) 1.31×10^7 ft lb, (c) 14.7 ft.)

The Atomic Theory of Matter

Chapter 23

IN dealing with the physical properties of matter it is convenient to divide substances into three forms or states: (1) *the solid state,* (2) *the liquid state,* and (3) *the gaseous state.* Most substances may be made to take on any one of these three forms simply by altering the temperature.

The atomic theory of matter assumes that all matter in the universe is made up of ultra-microscopic bodies called atoms and that these are at all times in a rapid state of motion. The nature of this motion and its activity depends upon the temperature and the state of the matter in question, as well as upon the kinds of atoms of which it is composed.

23.1. Kinds of Atoms. Although there are thousands of different substances known to the scientific world they all, when broken down into their smallest component parts, are found to be composed of one or more kinds of atoms. A substance which contains atoms of one kind only is called an *element,* while those containing more than one kind are called *compounds* or *mixtures.* Iron, copper, aluminum, platinum, mercury, hydrogen, and helium are examples of elements; whereas water, salt, brass, wood, and air are examples of compounds and mixtures.

The technical names and chemical abbreviations of a few of the more commonly known elements are given in Table 23A. A complete table of the nearly one hundred known elements is given in the Appendix.

TABLE 23A. SOME OF THE CHEMICAL ELEMENTS

Atomic No.	Element	Symbol	Atomic Weight	Atomic No.	Element	Symbol	Atomic Weight
1	hydrogen	H	1.0078	29	copper	Cu	63.57
2	helium	He	4.004	47	silver	Ag	107.88
3	lithium	Li	6.940	50	tin	Sn	118.70
4	beryllium	Be	9.02	78	platinum	Pt	195.23
6	carbon	C	12.01	79	gold	Au	197.2
7	nitrogen	N	14.01	80	mercury	Hg	200.61
8	oxygen	O	16.000	82	lead	Pb	207.18
10	neon	Ne	20.183	88	radium	Ra	225.95
13	aluminum	Al	26.97	92	uranium	U	238.17
26	iron	Fe	55.84	94	plutonium	Pu	239.18

With each element it is customary to associate two numbers; one is called the *atomic number,* the other the *atomic weight.* The atomic number, given at the left in the tables, specifies the position that element always occupies with respect to all the others, while the atomic weight on the right gives the average weight of one atom of that element relative to the average weight of an oxygen atom as sixteen. On this basis the lightest known element, the atoms of hydrogen, has an average weight of approximately unity.

To illustrate the minuteness of individual atoms, the actual masses in grams and approximate diameters in centimeters of the lightest element, hydrogen, and the very heavy element, plutonium, are as follows:

$$1.\ \text{hydrogen} \begin{cases} \text{mass} = 1.66 \times 10^{-24} \text{ gm} \\ \text{diameter} = 1 \times 10^{-8} \text{ cm} \end{cases}$$

$$94.\ \text{plutonium} \begin{cases} \text{mass} = 3.9 \times 10^{-22} \text{ gm} \\ \text{diameter} = 6 \times 10^{-8} \text{ cm} \end{cases}$$

The actual mass of any atom in grams can be obtained by multiplying the atomic weight of that element by the unit atomic mass 1.66×10^{-24} gm.

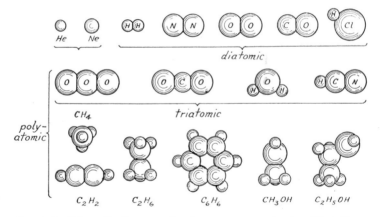

FIG. 23A—Schematic diagram of a few common molecules. First Row: Helium, neon, hydrogen, nitrogen, oxygen, carbon monoxide, hydrochloric acid. Second Row: Ozone, carbon dioxide, water, hydrocyanic acid. Third Row: Methane, acetylene, ethane, benzene, methyl alcohol, ethyl alcohol.

Although the intricate structure of each atom plays an important part in its physical and chemical behavior, we will neglect this detailed structure for the time being and think only of each atom as being a tiny sphere-like particle with a very small mass. Later in other chapters where it is pertinent to do so the structure of individual atoms will be considered in detail.

The atomic diameters of a few common elements are given in Table 23B. These are approximate values only, for as we shall see in a later chapter, atoms do not have a well defined surface boundary as indicated in Fig. 23A.

TABLE 23B. APPROXIMATE ATOMIC DIAMETERS, IN ANGSTROM UNITS
(1 ANGSTROM UNIT $= 10^{-8}$ CM)

Valence −2	−1	0	+1	+2	+3	+4
		He 1.2	Li 1.5	Be 0.7		
O 2.6	F 2.7	Ne 1.5	Na 2.0	Mg 1.6	Al 1.1	Si 0.7
S 3.4	Cl 3.6	A 2.0	K 2.7	Ca 2.1	Sc 1.6	Ti 1.2
Se 3.8	Br 3.9	Kr 2.3	Rb 3.0	Sr 2.5	Yt 2.1	Zr 1.7
Te 4.2	I 4.4	Xe 2.5	Cs 3.3	Ba 2.8	La 2.4	Cs 2.0

23.2. Molecules. One of the most important properties of atoms is their ability to act upon one another at a distance. Some atoms, when they come close together attract each other, while others exhibit a force of repulsion. When, at the close approach of two or more atoms, attraction occurs, the atoms may combine to form a molecule. Once a molecule has formed it will move about and behave as a unit particle under various physical conditions.

Molecules in general may contain almost any number of atoms. Those having but one atom are called *monatomic molecules,* those with two are called *diatomic molecules,* and those with three *triatomic molecules.* In the free state of a gas some atoms like helium, neon, and krypton, prefer to exist alone, whereas others like hydrogen, nitrogen, and oxygen, prefer to combine and move about in pairs.

Examples of monatomic molecules are helium (He), neon (Ne), and krypton (Kr); of diatomic molecules are hydrogen (H_2), nitrogen (N_2), oxygen (O_2), and carbon monoxide (CO); and of triatomic molecules are ozone (O_3), carbon dioxide (CO_2), water (H_2O), and hydro-cyanic acid (HCN). See Fig. 23A. Besides these simplest atomic aggregates there are molecules known to contain many atoms. Along with triatomic molecules they are called polyatomic molecules.

It is clear from the diagrams in Fig. 23A that the atoms of a molecule may be of the same kind or different. The question as to why some atoms cling together in pairs and others do not is a subject involving the structure of the atoms themselves. If the individual atoms of a molecule are brought much closer together than their normal separation they repel each other and are pushed apart. If they are pulled farther apart the forces become attractive, pulling them together. In other words, they act as though they were connected by springs as shown in Fig. 23B. Pushed closer together or pulled farther apart they tend to move back to some equilibrium distance. In terms of energy they occupy a position of *minimum potential energy*. To push them closer together or to separate them requires work.

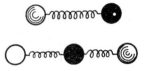

FIG. 23B—The forces between molecules act like springs.

At large distances all atomic forces become very weak so that if by some means or other the atoms of a molecule are pulled far enough apart they become completely separated as free atoms.

23.3. Molecular Weight. The molecular weight of a substance is defined as the sum of the atomic weights of the atoms which make up one molecule of that substance. A carbon dioxide molecule, for example, has two oxygen atoms of weight 16 and one carbon atom of weight 12. The molecular weight of carbon dioxide is therefore $16 + 16 + 12 = 44$. Similarly the molecular weight of nitrogen is 28, oxygen is 32, and helium is 4. To find the mass of a molecule in grams, its molecular weight should be multiplied by unit atomic mass 1.66×10^{-24} gm.

23.4. Three States of Matter. As already stated, matter may exist in three states: (1) the solid state, (2) the liquid state, and (3) the gaseous state. If a solid is heated sufficiently it can be made to melt or liquefy, and by continued heating can be boiled or vaporized. As a vapor it is in the gaseous state. If, on the other hand, a gas is cooled sufficiently it will condense and become a liquid. The continued cooling of a liquid will cause it to solidify or freeze. In the case of water, nature performs all these changes of state: ice is melted to become water, and water is vaporized to become steam; water vapor or clouds condense to become rain, and rain freezes to become ice or hail. Although it may sometimes require extreme heat or extreme cold, all substances can be transformed from any one state to another.

23.5. The Gaseous State. When a substance is in the gaseous state it is in an extremely rarefied condition. Most of the atoms are grouped together into molecules which on the average are very far apart. These molecules are not at rest but are moving about with extremely high velocities, bumping into each other and into the walls of the container. It is the bumping of many millions of molecules against the walls of the containing vessel that gives rise to what is called gas pressure.

A good example of gas pressure is to be found where air has been pumped into an automobile tire or into a toy balloon. Since there are so many more air molecules bombarding the rubber walls inside than outside, the walls are held out by greater bombardment. In addition to moving linearly, a gas molecule, made up of two or more atoms, also vibrates and rotates about its center of mass. As the temperature of the gas is raised all of these motions increase in speed, causing an increase in pressure. As the temperature is decreased the atomic motions slow down, decreasing the pressure.

Molecular motion can be illustrated by means of a mechanical model as shown in Fig. 23C. Small steel marbles are placed between two parallel glass plates and set into motion by means of vibrating metal strips around the sides. Each strip V is mounted at the end of a short strip of spring steel and is set into vibration by means of small electromagnets S. As the steel balls bump into these strips they are bounced off with high speed. On the average, the small steel marbles move considerably faster than the larger ones. This is characteristic of the different sized molecules in a mixture of two different gases like helium and neon. By increasing the vibrations of the strips the steel marbles move faster. This is analogous to the heating of a gas to a higher temperature.

23.6. The Liquid State. When a gas is continually cooled the molecular motion slows down until at a certain temperature the gas condenses into a much smaller volume and changes into a liquid. Although the molecules continue to move they no longer move as rapidly as they did in the gaseous state. Being much closer together, however, they now attract each other with sufficiently strong forces to cause them to move in closely packed swarms.

The swarming of honeybees as they fly through the air is comparable to the molecules of a gas while their subsequent collection on the branch of a tree corresponds closely to condensation into the liquid state.

23.7. Brownian Motion. Although no one has ever observed directly the random motions of molecules, it is possible to observe in a microscope the resultant recoils of larger particles under their continual bombardment. The effect was first discovered in 1827 by Robert Brown, a British botanist, who observed the irregular but life-like motions of small particles suspended in a liquid. These microscopic particles appear to be continually agitated and make a succession of quick jumps first one way and then another. The path of a single particle is illustrated in Fig. 23C(b). Such motions are called Brownian movements, after the name of their discoverer. These curious Brownian movements were first explained by Sir William Ramsey in 1879 and may be observed in either liquids or gases. The invisibly small molecules of air or water, as the case may be, move at relatively high velocities and, bombarding the larger visible particles vigorously from all sides, make them dart here and there. The larger the particles the slower their Brownian movement.

One method of observing Brownian motion in a gas is illustrated in Fig. 23D. Smoke from the tip of a match, just extinguished, is drawn into a small

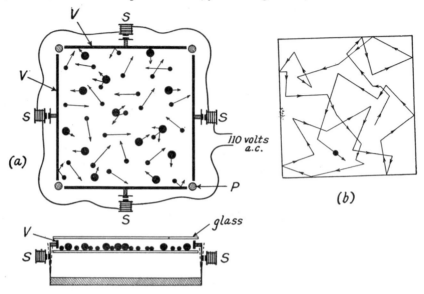

Fig. 23C—Mechanical model illustrating the random motion of molecules in a gas.

box by squeezing and releasing the rubber bulb. A strong beam of light from an arc light, entering the box through a glass lens in the side, illuminates the smoke particles, enabling them to be seen from above with a high power microscope. The tiny smoke particles appear as bright starlike points darting first one way then another.

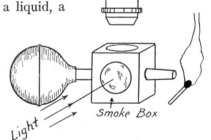

To observe Brownian movement in a liquid, a small amount of powdered gamboge (an orange-yellow gum resin) is first put into some distilled water, and one drop of this solution put on a microscope slide. By illuminating the slide with a strong light the microscopic gamboge particles will be seen dancing about as they are continually being hit by water molecules. Remembering that the gamboge particles are thousands of times heavier than the water molecules, it will

Fig. 23D—Experimental arrangement for observing the Brownian motion of smoke particles.

be realized that the latter must be moving with very high speeds to cause such visible recoils.

23.8. The Solid State. As the temperature of a liquid is lowered the molecular activity decreases. This permits the molecules to pack a little more closely together and accounts for the slight contraction of a liquid on cooling, and conversely for its expansion on heating. As they come closer and closer together the tendency of each molecule to wander through the liquid decreases. If the temperature is lowered still further a point is ultimately reached where the liquid freezes and becomes a solid.

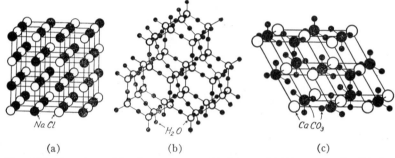

(a)   (b)   (c)

FIG. 23E—Atomic models of common crystal forms. (a) Common salt, (b) ice, and (c) calcite.

In the solid state each molecule is confined to a definite small space between neighboring molecules. This is illustrated in Fig. 23E by atomic models of ultramicroscopic crystals. The model at the left illustrates a cubic lattice, a simple type of structure in which the atoms take positions at the corners of cubes. Common table salt with its two kinds of atoms, sodium

FIG. 23F—Photographs of snow crystals exhibiting hexagonal structure.

and chlorine, always forms such a cubic lattice, the individual atoms alternating in kind in each of the three directions, Na, Cl, Na, Cl, Na, etc.

The second crystal is of the hexagonal lattice form in which the principal structure presents parallel hexagonal "holes" through the crystal. Water, in freezing to form ice, or snowflakes, takes on this form. See Fig. 23F. Note that within the atomic lattice each oxygen atom is bound by connecting links between four hydrogen atoms, while each hydrogen is linked between two oxygens. The silicon and oxygen atoms of quartz, chemically SiO_2, take on a somewhat similar structure and in the natural state also exhibit its hexagonal structure. See Fig. 23G.

FIG. 23G—Natural crystals of quartz and calcite.

The third model shows the atomic structure for a crystal of calcite. Calcite, which chemically is calcium carbonate ($CaCO_3$), is a clear transparent crystal found in nature. Because of its particular structure it has interesting optical properties that will be discussed in a later chapter on "polarized light." Note how the calcium and carbon atoms form the corners of parallelograms with each carbon atom surrounded by three oxygen atoms.

Although some elements or compounds always seem to form the same crystal pattern on solidifying, others are known to take on any one of a number of different forms. Some forms are found in nature while others have been produced in the laboratory. Diamond, one of the several known crystal forms of carbon atoms alone, is a closely packed crystal that has, until recently, defied laboratory reproduction. While some crystal types present a more open structure than others, the actual size of each atom in the models shown above has been reduced in order to reveal the positions of others behind.

Metals in general, when they cool down from the molten state, solidify into ultramicroscopic crystals that pack closely together to form a three dimensional mosaic. This is well illustrated by the electron-microscope photographs reproduced in Fig. 23H. Note the clear-cut cubic structure of pure aluminum.

Actually the atoms in most liquids begin to form localized crystal arrays before solidification takes place but, due to the rapid state of atomic vibration, each localized crystal region can move with respect to another. A liquid may therefore be looked upon as a transition state between the gas where individual molecules exist and the solid where individual atoms become part of a crystal structure and can no longer be associated with any particular molecule. The average distance between atoms in all solids, crystal or amorphous, is of the order of 2×10^{-8} cm.

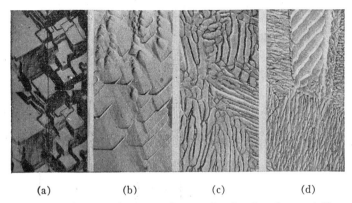

(a)   (b)   (c)   (d)

FIG. 23H—Electron microscope photographs showing the crystalline-like structure of metals (a) pure aluminum 5600x, (b) magnesium-aluminum alloy 13,000x, (c) polished steel 14000x, and (d) polished copper 14000x. *(Courtesy R. D. Heidenreich, Dow Chemical Co.)*

While each atom or molecule in a solid is confined to a definite space within the body lattice, it is in a state of motion within that space. As the temperature decreases this motion becomes slower and slower until at absolute zero, $-273°C$, all molecular motion ceases. By molecular motion is meant motion of the molecule as a whole. At absolute zero, however, the atoms of certain solids are still vibrating. This residual energy of vibration is known to be an inherent property of some solids, which cannot be utilized or taken away.

FIG. 23I—Electron microscope photo of polystyrene molecules, showing natural hexagonal packing. Diameter 5×10^{-3} cm. *Courtesy, Robley Williams.*

Properties of
Solids—Elasticity Chapter 24

IN THE following treatment of elasticity the *gram* and *kilogram* are frequently treated as units of force. Such usage is justified since the actual applied forces are directly proportional to the masses that produce them. $W \propto m$. We therefore introduce the *gram weight* and *kilogram weight* (abbr. gm-wt and kg-wt) as units of force. *One kilogram weight,* for example, *is defined as a force equivalent in magnitude to the downward pull of the earth on a one kilogram mass.* $W = mg$.

24.1. Stretching of a Spring. If a vertically mounted rod, wire, or spring is supported rigidly at its upper end and weights are added to its lower end, the amount by which it is stretched is found to be proportional to the weight applied. This is known as Hooke's law. The stretching of a spring is illustrated in Fig. 24A. Due to an added weight W the spring is

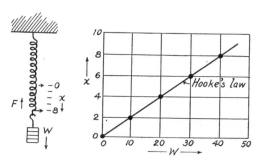

FIG. 24A—Experiment illustrating the stretching of
a spring.

stretched a distance x. If a second equal weight is added the total distance stretched will be twice that for the first one. If a third weight is added the total distance stretched will be three times that for the first one, etc. This is illustrated by the graph shown at the right in Fig. 24A. Each value of x is plotted vertically and the corresponding loads W are plotted horizontally.

More specifically, when the first 10 gram weight is added the stretch or elongation is 2 cm. With two 10 gram weights the total elongation is 4 cm, and with three weights $x = 6$ cm, etc. A continuation of this shows, as does the graph at the right in Fig. 24A, that each 10 gram weight produces an added elongation of 2 cm. To make an equation of this we write

$$W = kx \qquad (24a)$$

where k is a constant and equal in this experiment to 5. Each value of x multiplied by 5 gives the corresponding weight W. When the spring in Fig. 24A is stretched a distance x the spring itself exerts an upward force F equal but opposite in direction to W. For the spring, then,

$$F = -kx. \qquad (24b)$$

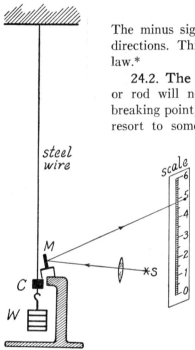

The minus sign indicates that x and F are in opposite directions. This equation is often referred to as Hooke's law.*

24.2. The Stretching of a Wire. Because a wire or rod will not stretch very far before reaching the breaking point, one must, in order to check Hooke's law, resort to some method of measuring extremely small changes in length. This is frequently done by means of a device known as the optical lever. As shown by the experiment diagramed in Fig. 24B, a beam of light is reflected from a small mirror M mounted on a small three-legged stool, two legs of which rest on a stationary platform, as shown, and the third on a small clamp C at the lower end of the wire. As the wire stretches under an added weight W the mirror tips back and the light beam is reflected up a measurable amount on the distant scale.

Fig. 24B—The stretching of a wire under tension can be measured by means of an *optical lever*.

Like the stretching of a spring described in the preceding section, the stretching of a wire obeys Hooke's law.

The amount stretched is directly proportional to the force applied and is illustrated by the straight part of the graph AB in Fig. 24C. If the weights are removed the wire will return to its original length. If weights are continually added the forces applied will

* Robert Hooke (1635-1703), English experimental physicist known principally for his contributions to the wave theory of light, universal gravitation, and atmospheric pressure. He originated many physical ideas but perfected few of them. Hooke's scientific achievements would undoubtedly have received greater acclaim had his efforts been confined to fewer subjects. He had an irritable temper, and made many virulent attacks on Newton and other men of science, claiming that work published by them was due to him.

eventually become too great, and Hooke's law will no longer hold as the elongation will increase too rapidly. This is the region BC on the graph. Carried too far in this direction, the wire will break. The point B at which

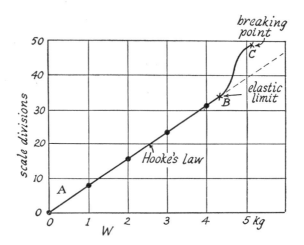

Fig. 24C—A graph of the stretching of a wire showing Hooke's law, the elastic limit, and the breaking point.

Hooke's law ceases to hold is called the *elastic limit*. If the wire is stretched beyond this point it will be permanently stretched and will not return to its original length when the weights are removed.

24.3. Stress and Strain. When a force of any magnitude is applied to a solid body, the body becomes distorted. Whether the distortion is large or small, some portion of the body is moved with respect to some neighboring portion. As a result of this displacement atomic forces of attraction set up restoring forces which resist the alteration and tend to restore the body to its original shape. The greater the applied force the greater will be the deformation necessary to set up atomic restoring forces that will bring about equilibrium.

It is common engineering practice to describe the restoring forces in a distorted body as a stress and to give to this term the quantitative definition of *force per unit area*. The actual deformation of the body produced by an applied force involves a change in geometrical form called *strain*. Strain is defined as a quantitative measure of deformation.

24.4. Hooke's Law. Hooke's law, as described above for the stretching of a spring or wire, applies equally well to other types of deformation. In general, Hooke's law states that *stress is proportional to strain*. The stress set up within an elastic body is proportional to the strain caused by the applied load.

$$\text{stress} \propto \text{strain.} \tag{24c}$$

To make an equation of this a proportionality constant K is introduced:

$$\text{stress} = K \text{ strain}$$

Transposing,

$$K = \frac{\text{stress}}{\text{strain}}. \tag{24d}$$

The constant K has a value characteristic of the material of the elastic body and is called the *modulus of elasticity*.

24.5. Young's Modulus. Consider the experiment, diagramed in Fig. 24B, where a wire or rod is clamped at one end and a load is applied at the other. Let l represent the wire's original length, A its cross-sectional area, and e the elongation produced by the applied load F. See Fig. 24D.

FIG. 24D—
Young's modulus for the stretching of a wire or rod is given by Fl/Ae.

By definition, stress is the force per unit area, and strain is the elongation per unit length.

$$\text{Stress} = F/A \quad (24e) \qquad \text{strain} = e/l. \quad (24f)$$

When these defining equations are substituted in Eq.(24d) the modulus of elasticity K is called *Young's modulus,** written as Y, and is given by

$$Y = \frac{F/A}{e/l}, \quad \text{or} \quad Y = \frac{Fl}{Ae}. \tag{24g}$$

Young's modulus Y is a very practical constant, for if its value is known for any given material, the amount of stretch produced in any size of wire or rod of that material can be calculated. Careful laboratory experiments have established such values for many common substances. (See columns two and three in Table 24A.)

Example 1. A copper wire 3 m long and 2 sq mm in cross-sectional area hangs from the ceiling. What will be its elongation if a 2 kg mass is suspended from the lower end?

* Thomas Young (1773-1829), English scientist. Born of a Quaker family, young Thomas had read the Bible twice through at the age of four and at fourteen could speak seven languages. He studied medicine in London, Edinburgh, Göttingen, and Cambridge and at twenty-eight was appointed professor of physics at the Royal Institution. Young is best known for his experiments proving the wave theory of light, but he also made valuable contributions to mechanics, medicine, and to the mechanism of sight and vision. He was one of the first to decipher successfully Egyptian hieroglyphic inscriptions.

Solution. Transpose Eq.(24g) to solve for e, and substitute known dimensions and Young's modulus for copper from Table 24A.

$$e = \frac{Fl}{AY} = \frac{2000 \text{ gm} \times 980 \text{ cm/sec}^2 \times 300 \text{ cm}}{0.02 \text{ cm}^2 \times 12.5 \times 10^{11} \text{ dynes/cm}} = 0.0235 \text{ cm}.$$

Care must be taken in solving such problems as this to express the force F in the same units as the force in the modulus.

TABLE 24A. YOUNG'S MODULUS—ELASTIC LIMIT—BREAKING POINT

Material	Young's Modulus Y		Elastic Limit E		Breaking Point P	
	Dynes/ sq cm	Lb/ sq in	Dynes/ sq cm	Lb/ sq in	Dynes/ sq cm	Lb/ sq in
Aluminum	7×10^{11}	10.2×10^6	13×10^8	19×10^3	15×10^8	22×10^3
Brass	9.02 "	13.09 "	$7 - 15$ "	$10 - 22$ "	$35 - 60$ "	$51 - 56$
Copper	12.5 "	18.0 "	$1 - 10$ "	$1.5 - 15$ "	$23 - 47$ "	$42 - 52$ "
Iron	21.0 "	30.0 "	$15 - 18$ "	$21 - 26$ "	$30 - 37$ "	$50 - 60$ "
Steel (mild)	19.2 "	27.9 "	$17 - 21$ "	$25 - 30$ "	$34 - 41$ "	$50 - 60$ "
Tendon (human)	1.6 "	2.3 "	. .	. .	$6.2 - 6.4$ "	$9.0 - 9.2$
Muscle "	0.009 "	0.013 "	. .	. .	$0.35 - 0.4$ "	$0.5 - 0.6$
Bone (tension)	22 "	32 "	. .	. .	$9 - 12$	$13 - 17$
" (Compression)	22 "	32 "	. .	. .	$3 - 10$	$4 - 23$
Nerve	0.1850 "	0.2680 "	. .	. .	1.38 "	2.00 "
Vein	0.0085 "	0.0123 "	. .	. .	0.18 "	0.26 "
Artery	0.0005 "	0.0007 "	. .	. .	0.14 "	0.20 "

Table 24A also includes values of the elastic limit E and of the breaking point P. These constants are of practical value where it is essential to know the stress required to reach the elastic limit of a material or the minimum load that would cause it to break. See Fig. 24B. The necessity for giving ranges of values for metals is due to the various work treatments applied to them in their fabrication. Some are cast, others are drawn, or rolled and some are annealed.

Example 2. Calculate for the copper wire in Example 1 the load that must be applied to reach (a) the elastic limit and (b) the breaking point. (Use minimum values listed.)

Solution. Since the values in Table 24A represent the stress that must not be exceeded, Eq.(24e) is used. Substitute the *elastic limit* E for the *stress*, and transpose.

$$F = E \times A = 1 \times 10^8 \frac{\text{dynes}}{\text{cm}^2} \times 0.02 \text{ cm}^2 = 2 \times 10^6 \text{ dynes}.$$

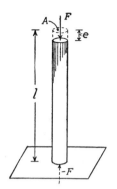

FIG. 24E—Young's modulus for the compression of a rod is given by Fl/ae.

Substitute P for the stress, and transpose.

$$F = P \times A = 23 \times 10^8 \, \frac{dynes}{cm^2} \times 0.02 \, cm^2 = 46 \times 10^6 \, dynes$$

or $\qquad\qquad F = 460 \text{ newtons.}$

24.6. Compression. When a load F is applied to the ends of a rod to compress it as shown in Fig. 24E, the decrease in length is the same in amount as the elongation it would acquire when the same load is applied as a tension. In other words, Hooke's law applies to compression, the values of Young's modulus for stretching are valid, and the above Eq.(24g) can be used for all calculations within the elastic limit.

24.7. Bending. Three ways in which a straight uniform bar may be subjected to forces causing it to bend are illustrated in Fig. 24F. The amount of bending, usually measured at the point of maximum depression, is found by experiment to obey Hooke's law; that is, *the depression is proportional to the applied load.*

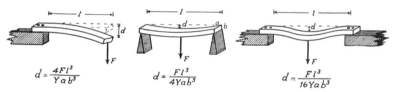

$$d = \frac{4Fl^3}{Yab^3} \qquad d = \frac{Fl^3}{4Yab^3} \qquad d = \frac{Fl^3}{16Yab^3}$$

FIG. 24F—The bending of a beam involves tension and compression at the same time.

Formulas derived from theoretical considerations are given below each of the three diagrams. The depression d is expressed in terms of the applied load, F, the length l, the breadth a and the thickness b of the bar, and Young's modulus Y. To see why Young's modulus is directly involved in bending, imagine a horizontal bar divided into thin horizontal layers. Upon bending, layers near the bottom become stretched while those near the top become compressed. Near the center is a neutral plane in which there is neither tension nor compression.

24.8. Shearing and Shear Modulus. The cutting of a piece of paper or a sheet of metal is commonly referred to as a shearing action. Technically shear is used to apply not only to such severing of material but to the action applied before severance occurs. In Fig. 24G a rivet holding two sheets of metal together is shown under the action of two opposite forces. Because these forces do not act along the same line they set up a shearing stress in the center section.

As long as the elastic limit has not been reached the amount of deformation, indicated in the right-hand diagram by the displacement s, is propor-

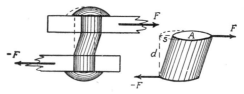

Fig. 24G—Shearing stress and strain obeys
Hooke's law.

tional to the applied force and therefore obeys Hooke's law. The stress in such action is defined as force per unit area, F/A, the area being measured parallel to the forces, while the strain is defined as the displacement per unit thickness, s/d.

$$\text{stress} = F/A \qquad\qquad \text{strain} = s/d \qquad\qquad (24h)$$

Since all forms of elasticity are defined as the ratio stress/strain, shear modulus is defined as

$$G = \frac{\text{stress}}{\text{strain}} = \frac{F/A}{s/d} = \frac{F\,d}{A\,s}. \qquad\qquad (24i)$$

Values of shear modulus for various common materials are given in Table 24B.

TABLE 24B. SHEAR MODULUS FOR A FEW COMMON MATERIALS
(average values)

Material	Shear Modulus G	
	Dynes/sq.cm	Lb/sq. in.
Aluminum	2.5×10^{11}	3.63×10^6
Brass	3.7 "	5.38 "
Copper	4.2 "	6.10 "
Iron	8.0 "	11.6 "
Steel	8.0 "	11.6 "

24.9. Torsion. A detailed knowledge of torsional stresses and strains has considerable practical application in engineering design. When a rod or bar is clamped at one end and a torque is applied at the other it is twisted as illustrated in Fig. 24H. Within the elastic limit the angular displacement θ is proportional to the applied torque L.

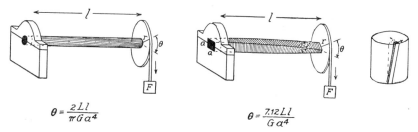

$$\theta = \frac{2Ll}{\pi G a^4}$$

$$\theta = \frac{7.12Ll}{G a^4}$$

Fig. 24H—The twisting of a rod obeys Hooke's law.

In the formulas below each diagram the angle θ is given in terms of applied torque, $L = F \times r$, the length l, the radius a or thickness a, and the shear modulus G. That a twist should involve the shear modulus is seen by the extreme right hand diagram. Each small vertical section is observed to undergo a shearing action.

Fig. 24I illustrates an application of torsional stress in the profession of *orthodontics*. Orthodontia, or dental orthopedics, is that branch of dentistry dealing principally with the straightening of teeth. In one technique it is customary to fit each tooth with a wide metal band containing an arch bracket. Each bracket has a rectangular slot into which a square arch wire is tied.

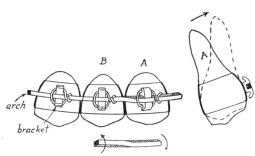

Fig. 24I—Illustrating an application of torsional stress to the straightening of teeth by the orthodontist.

To produce a rotation of tooth A as indicated at the right, a permanent twist is put into the square arch wire between that tooth and its neighbor. A torsional stress is thereby produced upon insertion of the arch wire, and over a period of several weeks the stress is gradually relieved by the turning of the tooth. The possible movement of the roots of teeth through the mandible as well as the upper jaw bone in any direction is well known to every dentist.

24.10. Impact of Elastic Bodies. When two bodies collide with each other, the law of conservation of momentum states that the total momentum before impact is equal to the total momentum after impact. This law is not sufficient, however, to determine what the individual velocities of each of the two bodies will be. Different kinds of material behave differently at impact and will move apart with different velocities. As an illustration, consider the experiment diagramed in Fig. 24J.

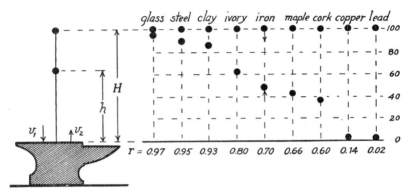

FIG. 24J—The bouncing marble experiment illustrating the resilience of different substances.

Spheres of different substances are dropped successively, all from the same height, onto the smooth top surface of a large anvil and allowed to bounce to their various heights. Contrary to one's preconceived ideas of elasticity, a glass or steel marble will bounce to a greater height than will a ball made of the best Pará or India rubber. A lead ball or marble, on the other hand, hardly bounces at all.

In this particular experiment the two bodies in collision are the marble and the anvil. Because of its very great mass the recoiling velocity of the anvil is negligibly small.

24.11. Coefficient of Restitution. The coefficient of restitution is defined as a number expressing the ratio of the velocity with which two bodies separate after collision to the velocity of their approach before collision.

$$r = \frac{\text{velocity of separation}}{\text{velocity of approach}} \qquad (24j)$$

or, as a formula,

$$r = \frac{v_2}{v_1} \qquad (24k)$$

Values of the constant r for different substances may be obtained from the above described experiment by determining the velocity v_1 of a marble just before it strikes the anvil, and the velocity v_2 just as it leaves on rebound. Rather than measure these velocities directly it is more convenient to make use of the laws of falling bodies and to calculate the velocities from other solid, note the deformation of the two balls in Fig. 24K. These are the heights to which the marbles are carried. Since $v = \sqrt{2gs}$ for falling bodies (see Eq.(16c)), $\sqrt{2gH}$ can be written for v_1 and $\sqrt{2gh}$ for v_2, to give

$$r = \frac{\sqrt{2gh}}{\sqrt{2gH}} = \sqrt{\frac{h}{H}}. \tag{241}$$

As illustrated in Fig. 24J, H is the height from which a marble falls and h is the height to which it rebounds. For a very elastic substance, like glass or steel, colliding with steel, r has a value of 0.95 or better, whereas for a very inelastic substance, like lead, colliding with steel, r is extremely small. It is seen from Eq.(241) that the smallest value r can have is zero, while the largest value is unity.

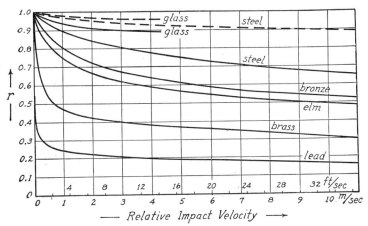

Fig. 24K—Coefficients of restitution measured for the impact of two spheres of similar material. Dotted curves at top are for small spheres dropped on thick flat plates of similar material.

Curves showing how the coefficient of restitution varies with impact velocity are given in Fig. 24K.

PROBLEMS

1. An iron wire 3 ft long and cross-sectional area 0.03 in.² is subjected to a tension of 5.1 lb. Calculate (a) its elongation, and (b) the tension required to reach the elastic limit.

2. A steel wire 16 ft long and cross-sectional area of 0.016 in.² is subjected to a tension of 60 lb. Calculate (a) its elongation, and (b) the tension required to reach the elastic limit. Assume $E = 28 \times 10^3$ lb/in.² (*Ans.* (a) 0.0258 in., (b) 448 lb.)

3. A brass wire 2.5 m long and 2.0 mm in diameter hangs from the ceiling. If a mass of 2.2 kg is suspended from the lower end, what will be (a) the elongation? Calculate the load required to reach (b) the elastic limit, and (c) the breaking point.

4. A copper wire 6 m long and diameter 1 cm hangs from the ceiling. If a mass of 40 kg hangs from the lower end find (a) the elongation. Calculate the load required to reach (b) the elastic limit, and (c) the breaking point. Assume $E = 2 \times 10^8$

dynes/cm², and $P = 25 \times 10^8$ dynes/cm². (*Ans.* (a) 0.024 cm, (b) 1.57 $\times$ 10⁸ dynes, (c) 1.96 $\times$ 10⁹ dynes.)

5. Find the elongation of a tendon 5 cm long and 0.4 cm in diameter if it is put under a tension of 1470 newtons. Assume Young's modulus to be 1.6×10^{11} dynes/cm².

6. What tension in lb would be required to break a tendon whose diameter is 0.25 in? Assume $P = 9.1 \times 10^3$ lb/in². (*Ans.* 447 lb.)

7. An artery has a length of 10 cm and a cross-sectional area of 0.30 cm². Find (a) the elongation under a tension of 40 newtons, and (b) the force required to break it.

8. A blood vein has a length of 4 cm and a cross-sectional area of 0.1 cm². Find (a) the elongation under a tension of 9.8 newtons, and (b) the force required to rupture it. (*Ans.* (a) 0.461 mm, (b) 18 newtons.)

9. Calculate the cross-sectional area of a bone that will withstand a compressional load of 5000 newtons. Assume a breaking point P of 12×10^8 dynes/cm².

10. The ends of an oak plank 2 in high by 12 in wide and 12 ft long rest on supports. Find the maximum depression if a man weighing 185 lb stands in the middle. Assume Young's modulus to be 12×10^5 lb/in². (*Ans.* 0.10 ft.)

11. The free end of a spring board at the edge of a swimming pool is 2 ft above the water. How close to the water will the board come if a 200 lb man stands on the end of the board? Assume the board to be 1 ft wide, 4.0 in thick, and 16 ft long. Young's modulus is 1.4×10^6 lb/in².

12. A two-by-six plank (2 in by 6 in) and 20 ft long is nailed in a horizontal position between two horizontal platforms 16 ft apart. Calculate the maximum depression at the center when a man weighing 160 lb walks across. $Y = 8 \times 10^5$ lb/in². (*Ans.* 0.154 ft.)

13. One end of a steel rod 2 m long and 1 cm in diameter is clamped tight while a torque of 5×10^8 dyne cm is applied at the other end. Calculate the angle through which it is twisted. Assume a shear modulus of 8×10^{11} dynes/cm².

14. An aluminum bar 1 in square and 4 ft long is subjected to a torque of 2000 lb ft. Calculate the angle through which it is twisted. (*Ans.* 2.26 rad.)

15. A golf ball when dropped from a height of 4 ft and allowed to hit a concrete pavement bounces to a height of 2.5 ft. Calculate the coefficient of restitution.

16. A glass marble is dropped from a height of 28 in onto a smooth heavy steel plate. Calculate the height to which it will bounce. (*Ans.* 26.3 in.)

17. An ivory ball weighing 8 oz and moving with a speed of 10 ft/sec collides head on with another ball of the same mass at rest. After collision the two balls have speeds of 1.5 ft/sec and 8.5 ft/sec. Find the coefficient of restitution.

18. An ivory ball with a mass of 200 gm, moving with a speed of 300 cm/sec, collides head on with another ivory ball of the same mass and size, at rest. If the coefficient of restitution is 0.65, find the velocity of each ball after collision. (*Ans.* 52.5 cm/sec and 247.5 cm/sec.)

19. A rubber ball is dropped from a height of 6 ft and allowed to bounce from a smooth concrete sidewalk. If it bounces to a height of 32 in. what is the coefficient of restitution?

20. Two ivory balls, each with a mass of 500 gm, are suspended by cords each 1 m long so that they rest in contact. If one ball is moved away until its cord makes an angle of 30° with the horizontal and is then released, find (a) its speed just before impact, and (b) the speed of each ball after impact. The coefficient of restitution of ivory on ivory is 0.65. (*Ans.* (a) 3.13 m/sec, (b) 0.60 m/sec, and 2.53 m/sec.)

21. An aluminum wire and a steel wire of equal length and cross-sections hang side by side and support a 50 lb weight. How much of the weight is supported by the aluminum wire?

Properties of Liquids   Chapter 25

PROPERTIES of solids like bending, twisting, and shearing do not exist in liquids. Liquids, however, can be put under compression and, if placed in a thoroughly cleaned vessel or container, can be subjected to very high tensions. Although these properties are of considerable interest they have not proved to be of much practical importance. There are physical properties of liquids, on the other hand, which are considered to be of general importance. These are pressure, buoyancy, surface tension, and viscosity.

25.1. Pressure. It is frequently necessary to determine the pressure at various depths within a liquid as well as the pressure on the bottom and sides of any containing vessel. The rule regarding pressure states that the

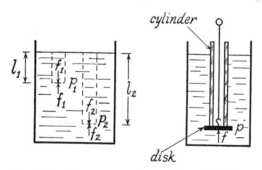

FIG. 25A—The pressure at any given depth in a liquid is equal to the weight per unit cross-section of the liquid directly above.

magnitude of the pressure at any depth is equal to the weight of a column of liquid of unit cross-section reaching from that point to the top of the liquid.

At a depth of l_1, as illustrated in Fig. 25A(a), the pressure p_1 is given by the weight of a column of liquid 1 sq cm in cross-section and l_1 centimeters in height. At a greater depth of l_2, the pressure p_2 is given by the weight of a column of liquid 1 sq cm in cross-section and l_2 centimeters in height.

This can be demonstrated with a glass cylinder and a thin light weight disk as shown at the right. With water surrounding the empty cylinder the force f, pushing up, holds the disk tight against the end. If the cylinder is

213

gradually filled with water an increasing downward force is exerted on the disk. Just as the water inside reaches the level of the water outside, the disk drops from the end of the cylinder, showing that the downward force and upward force at that point and at that instant become equal. We can conclude from this experiment that not only is the pressure at any given point in a liquid given by the weight of the liquid above it but that the pressure at one point is equal to the pressure at any other point at the same level.

Pressure in a liquid is defined as the normal force exerted by the liquid per unit area and is usually measured in *pounds per square inch, dynes per square centimeter,* or *newtons per square meter.* Because of its dimensions pressure is not a vector.

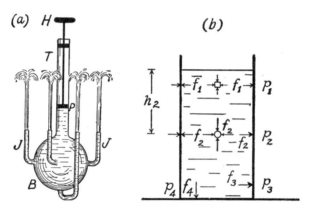

Fig. 25B—Demonstration experiments illustrating liquid pressure.

25.2. Pressure Acts in All Directions. In a liquid at rest, the force exerted by the liquid upon any surface is perpendicular to the surface. At any given point the force exerted on an element of surface is independent of the orientation of that surface. This can be illustrated in many ways. For example, in Fig. 25B(a) a hollow steel ball B, filled with water, is connected at the top by a metal tube T. By pushing down on the handle H the plunger P forces water out of the several metal tubes J leading from the sides and the bottom of the ball. Equal force in all directions is indicated by the water jets all coming to the same height as drawn.

25.3. Pressure on a Surface. Because of pressure the force f exerted by a liquid at rest is perpendicular to the wall with which the liquid is in contact. As a proof suppose the force were not perpendicular but at some angle to the surface. Such a force could be resolved into two components, one normal and the other tangent to the surface. But, the tangent component cannot exist, for if it did the wall would exert an equal and opposite force on the liquid and the liquid would move. Since the liquid is assumed to be at rest the force f must be normal to the surface.

The vessels shown in Fig. 25C are known as Pascal's vases.* Three glass vessels of different shape but the same height have screw-in metal bases that fit into the same pressure meter shown at the lower center. The three vases are inserted one after the other and filled with water to the same height h. Even though the amount of water is greatly different in each vase the pressure, as measured by the meter, is the same.

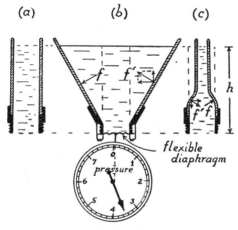

Fig. 25C—Pascal's vases.

The experimental fact that the small amount of water in vessel (c) can exert the same downward force as the large amount in vessel (b) may be considered as a verification of equal pressure. Let f represent the force of the water on unit area of the wall and f' the equal and opposite force of the wall on the water. The latter is shown resolved into vertical and horizontal components. The vertical component in (b) is upward and supplies the additional force needed to support the extra amount of water while in (c) the vertical component is downward and supplies the additional force equivalent to the missing column of water above.

25.4. Density and Specific Gravity. The density of matter whether in the solid, liquid or gaseous state, is defined in metric units as the mass per unit of volume. Algebraically,

* Blaise Pascal (1623-1662), French religious philosopher, physicist and mathematician. Noted principally for his discoveries in pure mathematics, and for his experiments with the barometer. His experiments and his treatise on the equilibrium of fluids entitle him to rank with Galileo and Stevinus as one of the founders of the science of hydrostatics and hydrodynamics.

$$\text{density} = \frac{\text{mass}}{\text{volume}} \qquad \rho = \frac{M}{V}. \qquad (25a)$$

The Greek letter ρ is commonly used to represent density. In the *cgs* system density is given in *grams per cubic centimeter*. Since the gram is defined as the mass of 1 cc of water, the density of water is 1 gm/cm³. In the *mks* system density is given in *kilograms per cubic meter*.

Example. If 25 cc of mercury have a mass of 340 gm, what is the density?
Solution. Direct substitution in Eq.(25a) gives

$$\rho = \frac{340 \text{ gm}}{25 \text{ cm}^3} = 13.6 \frac{\text{gm}}{\text{cm}^3}.$$

If the volume and density of a body are known, the mass is given by Eq.(25a) as

$$M = V \times \rho. \qquad (25b)$$

Specific gravity is another term frequently used to express the relative weights of matter. Specific gravity is defined as the ratio between the weight of a given volume of substance and the weight of an equal volume of water.

$$\text{Specific gravity} = \frac{\text{weight of a given substance}}{\text{weight of equal vol. of water}}. \qquad (25c)$$

TABLE 25A. DENSITIES AND WEIGHT-DENSITIES OF A FEW COMMON SUBSTANCES

Material		gm/cm³	lb/ft³	Material	gm/cm³	lb/ft³
Liquids				Tin	7.3	456
Alcohol	(20°C)	0.79	49.3	Zinc	7.1	446
Benzine	(0°C)	0.90	56.2			
Blood	(37°C)	1.04	65.0	Wood		
Gasoline	(0°C)	0.69	41.2	Balsa	0.11-0.13	7-8
Mercury	(20°C)	13.6	849	Cedar	0.49-0.57	30-35
Olive oil	(15°C)	0.918	57.3	Cork	0.22-0.26	14-16
Water	(0°C)	1.000	62.4	Maple	0.62-0.75	39-47
				Oak	0.60-0.90	37-56
Metals						
Aluminum		2.7	168.7	Miscellaneous		
Brass		8.5	530	Glass	2.4-2.8	150-175
Copper		8.9	556	Ice	0.91	57.2
Gold		19.3	1205	Quartz	2.65	165
Iron		7.9	493			
Lead		11.4	712			
Platinum		21.5	1342			
Silver		10.5	655			

According to this definition, the specific gravity of a substance is given by the same numerical value as the density in the *cgs* system. Being the ratio between like quantities, specific gravity has no dimensions and is therefore the same in all systems of units. For example, the specific gravity of aluminum is 2.7, which means that any solid piece of aluminum weighs 2.7 times as much as an equal volume of water.

25.5. Calculation of Pressure and Total Force. For convenience only engineers, as well as others, in this country usually employ the quantity *weight per unit volume* for the term *density*. For example the density of water is commonly said to be 62.4 lb per cubic foot. Since the pound is a unit of force it is proper to distinguish such a quantity from density as defined by Eq.(25a) by calling it weight-density.

$$\text{weight-density} = \rho g$$

where ρ is the density in *slugs*/ft^3, and g is the acceleration due to gravity, 32 ft/sec².

Since *pressure* is defined as *force per unit area* and its magnitude is given by the weight of a column of fluid above it, calculations of fluid pressure usually involve the use of the fluid density ρ. For example, to find the weight of a column of fluid we multiply the mass of the fluid by g (the weight per unit mass). Since the mass M of a fluid is given by Eq.(25b) as $V\rho$, the weight w of any volume of fluid is given by

$$w = V\rho g \tag{25d}$$

For a fluid column of unit cross-section and height h, the weight w is numerically equal to the pressure p, and the volume V is numerically equal to the height h. Therefore

$$p = h\rho g. \tag{25e}$$

This latter equation gives the pressure at any depth in a liquid of uniform density and may be used to calculate the total force acting on any wall.

Consider for example the cross-section diagram of a square bottomed tank in Fig. 25D. Over each square inch of the bottom surface of area A the pressure p is the same, and f is normal to the surface. The total downward force F on the bottom therefore is

$$F = pA. \tag{25f}$$

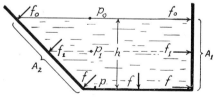

FIG. 25D—Liquid pressure is normal to the surface, and varies with the depth.

On the side walls, however, the pressure is not constant but varies with the depth. The pressure p at the bottom is twice as great as the pressure p_1 at the middle, while the pressure p_0 at the top is zero.

To calculate the total force on either side of the tank the average pressure, that is, the pressure p_1 at the center, is multiplied by the area of the surface. On the slanted wall, for example, the pressure of the depth of $\frac{1}{2}h$ is, by Eq.(25e), equal $\frac{1}{2}p$, and the total force is, therefore,

$$F = \tfrac{1}{2}pA_2.$$

If p is in newtons/m² the force F is in newtons. If p is in dynes/cm² the force F is in *dynes*, and if p is in lb/in² the force F is in lbs.

25.6. Pressure Transmission, Pascal's Principle. Any change of pressure in an enclosed fluid is transmitted undiminished to all parts of the fluid. A practical application of this principle is to be found in hydraulic systems where a force is applied on one part of the liquid and some load is moved at another. Consider as an illustration the hydraulic press illustrated in Fig. 25E.

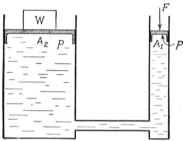

FIG. 25E—Illustrating the principles of the hydraulic press.

Two pistons, one large and one small and connected by a pipe, are filled with a liquid. When a force F is applied to the smaller piston, the increased pressure p created immediately underneath the piston of area A_1 is transmitted undiminished to the larger piston of area A_2.

Since pressure is defined as force per unit area, $p = F/A_1$ for the smaller piston while $p = W/A_2$ for the larger. Since these pressures are equal,

$$\frac{W}{A_2} = \frac{F}{A_1}, \qquad \text{from which} \qquad W = \frac{A_2}{A_1}F \qquad (25g)$$

Should the larger piston of such a press have ten times the area of the smaller, a load ten times that of the applied force may be lifted. Such a system, therefore, has a mechanical advantage equal to the ratio of the piston areas, A_2/A_1.

The hydraulic press is often used as a means of exerting large forces at the expense of a readily applied smaller one. The hydraulic brakes of most automobiles apply the same principle. A small force is applied by the brake pedal to a small piston in the master cylinder. The pressure there created is transmitted equally to larger cylinders and pistons in each of the four wheels.

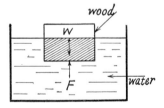

FIG. 25F—A block of wood lowered into the water sinks until the buoyant force of the water equals the weight of the block.

25.7 Archimedes' Principle. Archimedes' principle states that *a body floating or submerged in a liquid is buoyed up by a force equal to the weight of the liquid displaced.* For example, if a block of wood is floating in water, as shown in Fig. 25F, the buoyant force *F* holding the block up is equal to

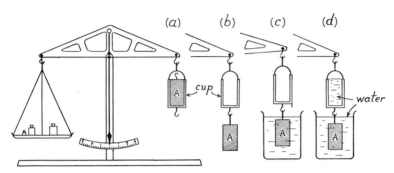

Fig. 25G—Illustrating the four steps in an experiment demonstrating
Archimedes' principle.

the weight of the water displaced (shaded area). When the block is first placed in the water it sinks until the buoyant force *F* becomes great enough to equalize the downward force, the weight of the block *W*.

An experimental demonstration of the truth of Archimedes' principle is shown in Fig. 25G. A small cylindrical cup containing a close fitting solid metal cylinder is accurately balanced by a set of weights on an equal-arm balance. No change in balance occurs when in diagram (b) the cylinder has been removed the cup and suspended from a hook underneath. In diagram (c) a beaker of water has been raised until the cylinder is com-

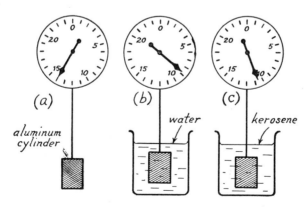

Fig. 25H—The buoyant effect of water may be used as a
means of determining the density of solids or liquids.

pletely submerged. Balance is now destroyed because of the upward buoy-ant force of the water on the cylinder.

If Archimedes' principle is correct, the buoyant force is equal to the weight of a volume of water exactly equal to the volume of the cylinder. A slow addition of water to the cup in diagram (d) shows that at the very instant the cup becomes filled, exact balance of the beam is restored. The restoring of balance confirms the principle.

25.8. Measurement of Density and Specific Gravity. One of the many ways of measuring the density of solids or liquids is by the use of Archimedes' principle. An experiment in which the density of a solid (alu-minum) and of a liquid (kerosene) may be determined is shown in Fig. 25H. A solid aluminum cylinder is weighed with spring scales (a) in air, (b) in water and (c) in kerosene.

Diagram (a) gives directly the mass of the cylinder as 1400 gm. When submerged in water the scales indicate a mass of only 880 gm. The differ-ence $1400 - 880 = 520$ gm multiplied by g is the buoyant force and there-fore the weight of the displaced fluid. But since the density of water is equal to 1 gm/cm³, 520 gm of water will have a volume of 520 cm³. Therefore 520 cm³ is the volume of the cylinder. By Eq. (25a) the density of the aluminum cylinder is

$$\rho = \frac{M}{V} = \frac{1400 \text{ gm}}{520 \text{ cm}^3} = 2.7 \frac{\text{gm}}{\text{cm}^3}.$$

Submerged in kerosene, the cylinder weighs 1040 gm-wt, indicating a buoyant force $1400 - 1040 = 360$ gm-wt. Since the cylinder displaces its volume 520 cm³ of liquid, and this liquid weighs 360 gm-wt, the density of the kerosene is

$$\rho = \frac{M}{V} = \frac{360 \text{ gm}}{520 \text{ cm}^3} = 0.69 \frac{\text{gm}}{\text{cm}^3}.$$

25.9. Hydrometers. The densities of liquids are measured by the buoyant force they exert on a floating body called an hydrometer. One form of hydrometer is employed by gas station attendants to measure the density of the acid in car storage bat-teries. The acid density in a battery is a direct measure of the amount of stored electrical energy it contains.

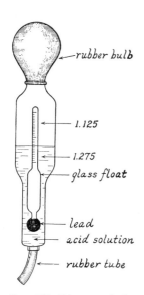

— rubber bulb

— 1.125

— 1.275

— glass float

— lead

— acid solution

— rubber tube

FIG. 25I—Diagram of the typical hydrometer used for measuring the density of the acid in a storage battery cell.

The battery hydrometer shown in Fig. 25I consists of a hollow glass tube with a weight at the bottom and a graduated stem at the top. For convenience the glass float is enclosed in a larger glass tube with a rubber bulb at the top and a short rubber tube at the bottom. The density of the battery liquid is measured by inserting the rubber tube through the vent in the top of the cell and drawing up a small sample of the solution into the main glass tube. Having a constant mass M the hydrometer tube sinks until it displaces its own weight in liquid; the more dense the liquid the higher it floats. A suitable scale on the stem is one that is calibrated directly in gm/cm³. For a fully charged battery the hydrometer will float high, the liquid level indicating 1.275 gm/cm³, whereas if it is completely discharged it will sink to a low level, indicating a density of about 1.125 gm/cm³.

Hydrometers for measuring very slight differences of density and with a high degree of accuracy have a large float and very thin stem, while those designed for greater ranges of density with less accuracy have a smaller float and thicker stem.

PROBLEMS

1. A water tank is 6 ft in diameter and 10 ft tall. Find (a) the pressure on the bottom, and (b) the total weight of water it contains when full.

2. A V-shaped trough 8 ft long and sides 2 ft wide making an angle of 60 degrees with each other is filled with water. Find the total force exerted by the water on each side. (*Ans.* 864.6 lb.)

3. A hollow iron ball 1 ft in diameter is 2 in. thick. Find its weight (a) in air, and (b) in water.

4. A hollow copper ball 20 cm outside diameter is 2 cm thick. Find its weight (a) in air, and (b) in gasoline, and express these weights in kg-wt. (*Ans.* (a) 18.19 kg-wt, (b) 15.30 kg-wt.)

5. An hydraulic press has two cylinders with diameters of 2 in. and 10 in., respectively. What is (a) the theoretical mechanical advantage, and (b) the force required on the small piston to raise a 2 ton car over the large piston?

6. Find the minimum diameter the cylinder of an hydraulic press can have if it is to lift a 2 ton car with an applied liquid pressure of 40 lb/in.² Assume 100 per cent efficiency. (*Ans.* 11.3 in.)

7. A hemispherical bowl 40 cm in diameter is filled with oil of density 0.8 gm/cm³. Find the maximum pressure exerted on the sides.

8. What pressure must a diver withstand when he is lowered 100 ft below the surface of the ocean? Assume the specific gravity of sea water to be 1.03. (*Ans.* 44.6 lb/in.²)

9. The cylinders of an hydraulic press have diameters of 3 cm and 27 cm, respectively. The large piston is 2 m above the smaller one. What load in kg-wt can be lifted if a force of 100 newtons is applied to the smaller poston and the press is filled with oil of specific gravity 0.80?

10. A cylindrical can 8 cm outside diameter and 15 cm high floats upright in the water. If a 300 gm mass is placed in the bottom of the can how high will the water line rise? (*Ans.* 5.97 cm.)

11. A raft is made of five cedar logs 1 ft in diameter and 6 ft long. Assuming the wood to have a specific gravity of 0.60, find the maximum load the raft can support. Assume the density of cedar to be 35 lb/ft³.

12. An iron casting, suspected of having a blowhole due to faulty casting practice, weighs 32.0 lb in air and 27.4 lb when submerged in water. Find the volume of the cavity. (*Ans.* 15.2 in.³)

13. A solid brass cylinder weighs 6 lb in air and 5.4 lb in a liquid. Calculate the density of the liquid. (*ans.* 53.9

14. A stone weighs 1.35 kg-wt in air, 1.10 kg-wt in water and 1.20 kg-wt in oil. Find the density of (a) the stone, and (b) the oil. (*Ans.* (a) 5.4 gm/cm³, (b) 0.60 gm/cm³.)

15. When a certain hydrometer floats in distilled water it displaces 200 cm³. If the cross-section of the narrow stem is 0.54 cm², how much lower will it sink if placed in oil of density 0.94 gm/cm³.

16. When a certain hydrometer floats in oil of density 0.95 gm/cm³ it displaces 300 cm³ of oil. How much higher will it float in water if the stem has a cross-sectional area of 1.25 cm²? (*Ans.* 12 cm.)

17. An aluminum casting is suspected of containing holes due to gas bubbles that formed when the aluminum was poured. When the casting is weighed in air it is found to have a mass of 624 gm. When weighed in water its mass appears to be 320 gm. Assuming the density of aluminum to be 2.7 gm/cm³, find the volume of the holes.

18. A solid cylinder 20 cm in diameter and 10 cm high floats in water with its top 2.2 cm above the surface. (a) What is the density of the solid, and (b) what is the mass of the solid? (*Ans.* (a) 7.80 gm/cm³, (b) 2.45 kg.)

19. A solid metal casting weighs 42 lb in air, 36 lb in water, and 38.6 lb in oil. Find (a) the weight-density of the metal, and (b) the weight-density of the oil.

20. A raft is constructed by fastening four empty oil drums to the four corners of a wooden platform. Each drum is a steel cylinder 2 ft in diameter and 3 ft high. What load can the raft support without getting the platform wet if under no load conditions the drums are only one third submerged? (*Ans.* 1568 lb.)

21. Alcohol is carefully poured over the water in a container so that the two liquids do not mix. The separation surface forms a flat horizontal plane. See Fig. 26C(a). A small, solid cylinder 4 cm in diameter and 2 cm high, having a density of 0.86 gm/cm³, is dropped into the alcohol where it sinks. How much of the cylinder lies below the separation surface?

22. A wooden cube 10 cm on a side floats in water with half of its volume above water. Find the minimum mass of iron that can be suspended from the bottom of the wood to make it sink. (*Ans.* 573 gm.)

Properties of Liquids (Continued) — Chapter 26

26.1. The Ocean Depths. Only recently has man descended to very great depths in the ocean to observe one of the most interesting regions of the earth's crust. The *bathysphere* (see Fig. 26A), a hollow but thick-walled steel sphere about $4\frac{1}{2}$ ft in diameter, descended with its two American observers Beebe * and Barton in 1931 to a depth of 1400 ft and in 1934 to a depth of 3000 ft.

Auguste Piccard, the Swiss professor who once set a balloon record into the stratosphere (see Fig. 27B), set another record in 1953 by diving into the Mediterranean, just off the coast of Italy. Accompanied by his son, Jacques, they descended in their *bathyscaphe* to a record depth of 10,300 ft. The pressure at this great depth of nearly two miles amounts to approximately 4400 lb/in.² The bathyscaphe had steel walls $3\frac{1}{2}$ in. thick, two circular portholes through which observations and photographs could be taken and, like the bathysphere, was spherical in shape.

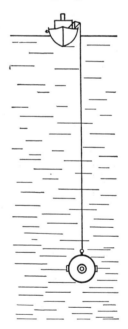

Fig. 26A—The Beebe bathysphere which in 1934 descended with its two observers to an ocean depth of 3000 ft.

At these great depths fish of many kinds were observed for the first time. How do these fish live and withstand such pressures? The answer is to be found in the fact that water circulates freely within and permeates the fish to such an extent that the pressure inside is the same as the pressure outside. The entire organism is therefore in equilibrium, for the inside forces pushing out are everywhere equal to the outside forces pushing in. If such fish are brought to the surface too suddenly, the inside pressure will not be sufficiently relieved and the fish will explode. A gradual ascent enables some of the water within to escape slowly, thus reducing the pressure inside as well as outside, and the fish can be brought to the surface alive. These fish do not live long, however, for their natural existence requires great pressures.

Example 1. Calculate the water pressure exerted on the bathyscaphe at a depth of 10,330 ft.

Solution. Table 25A gives the weight-density of water as 62.4 lb/ft³. Then, the weight of a column of water 1 ft high and 1 sq in. in cross-section is 62.4/144 = 0.433 lb. We now multiply this weight by the depth in feet to obtain

$$0.433 \times 10,330 = 4473 \text{ lb/in.}^2$$

The salt content of ocean water increases this result by a relatively small amount.

26.2. Adhesion and Cohesion. All matter is composed of atoms and molecules of one kind or another. As already stated, these ultramicroscopic particles attract each other with forces which depend upon the kinds of atoms or molecules involved and upon the distance between them. The closer two atoms or molecules are together, the greater is the attractive force between them. The attractive force between different kinds of molecules is called *adhesion,* and the attractive force between two like kinds of molecules is called *cohesion.*

Although the force of attraction between two molecules is extremely small the combined attraction of billions of molecules contained within a very small bit of matter is astonishingly great. A steel cable 1 in. in diameter, for example, will support a maximum load of 25 or more tons without breaking. This is a direct measure of the cohesive forces between hundreds of billions of atoms.

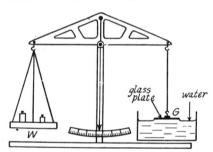

Fig. 26B—Experiment illustrating the forces of adhesion between glass and water.

The difference between adhesion and cohesion can be demonstrated by an experiment diagramed in Fig. 26B. A glass plate *G* is supported by one arm of a beam balance. The plate, after being balanced by weights on the left-hand scale pan, is brought into contact with the surface of water as shown. Additional weights are next added at *W* until the plate breaks free from the water surface. Upon examining the glass, water is found clinging to the under surface, showing that the break came between water molecules only. The adhesive forces between glass and water molecules therefore exceed the cohesive forces between water molecules. The weight added in the experiment is therefore a measure of the cohesive forces between water molecules.

If mercury is substituted for the water in the above experiment and the glass plate pulled away from the mercury surface, the added weights will

measure adhesion, the force of attraction between glass and mercury molecules. This is shown by the fact that no mercury clings to the bottom of
the glass plate. Thus the cohesion between mercury molecules is greater
than the adhesion between mercury and glass.

26.3. Surface Tension. The cohesion of molecules gives rise in liquids
to a phenomenon called surface tension. According to this aspect of molecular attraction the surface of a liquid acts at all times as though it has a
thin membrane stretched over it and that this membrane is under tension
and trying to contract. It is for this reason that fogdrops, raindrops, soap
bubbles, etc., assume a spherical shape as they fall through the air. (For
any specified volume of matter a sphere has a smaller surface area than any
other geometrical figure.)

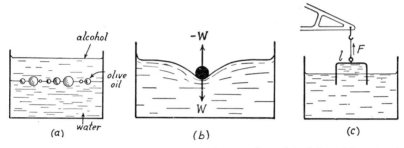

Fɪɢ. 26C—Experiments demonstrating surface tension. (a) Spheroidal state of
liquid drops. (b) Steel needle floating on water. (c) Measurement of surface
tension.

An experiment designed to illustrate the spheroidal state of a liquid drop
is shown at the left in Fig. 26C. Alcohol and water are poured carefully
into a glass vessel where they form a separation boundary, the water with
its greater density going to the bottom. Olive oil, which is not soluble in
either water or alcohol, is then dropped into the liquid. The drops quickly
take on a spherical form and, due to their intermediate density, settle slowly
to the boundary level where they remain suspended.

A second illustration of surface tension is the floating needle experiment.
A common sewing needle lowered horizontally to the surface of water in an
open dish will be found to float as shown in Fig. 26C(b). (If the needle is
first drawn through the fingers, a thin film of grease is deposited on the surface, making it easier to float. The adhesion between water and grease is
very weak.) For the needle to break through the surface, water molecules
must be pulled apart. Rather than do this the surface becomes depressed
until the upward buoyant force $-W$ is equal in magnitude to W, the
weight of the needle. See Archimedes' principle, Sec. 25.7. Surface tension
T keeps the film intact.

An interesting experiment is performed by fastening a bit of soap to the back of a small wooden boat and then placing the boat on the surface of a pond of water. As the soap goes into solution the surface tension of the water is greatly weakened in back of the boat and surface tension in front pulls the boat forward. As soon as a soap film covers the whole of the water surface the boat will stop.

A similar experiment is to scrape small bits of camphor into a dish of water. Like the boat, each tiny camphor flake is propelled rapidly around on the surface of the water. The camphor, going into solution most rapidly at the pointed end of each flake, reduces surface tension more at that point than at any other.

Surface tension in the laboratory is usually measured by an arrangement illustrated in Fig. 26C(c). A small wire frame of length l is dipped into water and then pulled slowly out. As a result of both cohesion and adhesion a thin film of water is formed in the frame. This film pulls down by a force which can be measured by suspending the frame from the arm of a beam balance. Weights are slowly added to the other scale pan, not shown (see Fig. 25G). until the film breaks. The maximum weight added without breaking the film is a direct measure of surface tension which arises from the cohesive forces of the water molecules.

Surface tension is defined as the force of contraction across a line of unit length, the line and the force being perpendicular to each other, both lying in the plane of the liquid surface. If F is the maximum force applied in the above experiment and l is the length of the wire frame, the surface tension T is given by

$$T = \frac{F}{2l}. \tag{26a}$$

The factor 2 enters because there are two surfaces to a thin film, thus making the effective length of the surface equal to $2l$.

TABLE 26A. SURFACE TENSION OF A FEW LIQUIDS

Liquid	T in dynes/cm		
	0°C	20°C	50°C
Acetone	26.3	23.7	19.9
Alcohol	24.0	22.3	19.8
Benzine	31.5	28.9	25.0
Mercury	508	480	445
Water	75.6	72.7	67.9

26.4. Capillarity. When a long glass tube is placed in a dish of water as illustrated in Fig. 26D(a), the water rises in the tube until it reaches a certain height and then stops. The finer the bore of the tube the higher the water rises.

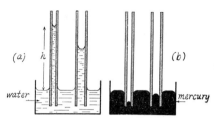

FIG. 26D—The rise of water and the depression of mercury in capillary tubes is due to adhesion and surface tension.

Water rises in capillary tubes because the adhesive forces of glass for water are greater than the cohesive forces of water. When a fine-bore tube is first placed in water the glass walls immediately above the edge of the water attract molecules to it by adhesion. These molecules in turn attract other nearby molecules, pulling them up by cohesion. This process continues, filling up the edges to form a meniscus as shown in Fig. 26E.

As the stronger attractive forces of the glass walls pull the surface film upward, the action tends to create a low pressure region in the water just under the surface. Atmospheric pressure outside then pushes the water up the tube until this reduced pressure is balanced by a column of water.

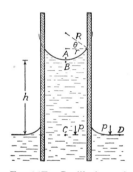

FIG. 26E—Capillarity and pressure equilibrium.

It was Laplace who first proved by a mathematical analysis that the pressure p on the concave side of a single curved surface of radius R is greater than the pressure p' on the convex side by the factor $2T/R$.

$$p - p' = 2T/R. \qquad (26b)$$

From the diagram it may be seen that $R = r/\cos\theta$.

Upon substitution for R,

$$p - p' = \frac{2T}{r}\cos\theta.$$

Within the accuracy of the weight of a column of air of height h the atmospheric pressure at A and D is the same. Since C and D are at the same level in water the pressure p at these two points is the same.

Now the pressure at C, due to the air and water columns directly above that point, is given by the pressure at A, minus the decrease in pressure between A and B, plus the pressure due to the water column of height h. See Eq.(25e). Writing each of these pressures in order, we obtain

$$p = p - \frac{2T}{r}\cos\theta + h\rho g.$$

If we cancel like terms and solve for h,

$$\frac{2T}{r} \cos \theta = h\rho g \qquad \text{or} \qquad h = \frac{2T}{r\rho g} \cos \theta \qquad (26c)$$

where, in the *cgs system*, T is the surface tension in *dynes per cm length*, r is the radius of the bore in cm, ρ is the density of the liquid in gm/cm^3, θ is the angle of contact between the water surface and the vertical glass walls in *degrees,* and g is the weight per unit mass, i.e., the acceleration due to gravity in cm/sec^2.

Eq.(26c) may also be derived from the geometry of Fig. 26F. Since the surface tension T acts at an angle θ, the component $T \cos \theta$ is the upward force per unit length of film in contact with the walls. Since the length of the film around the walls is $2\pi r$, the total upward force of surface tension is $2\pi r \times T \cos \theta$.

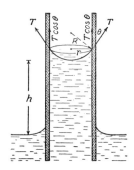

The volume of water supported in the tube is given by the product of the cross-sectional area πr^2 and the height h. Multiplying by the density ρ gives the mass in grams, and by g gives the weight in dynes, $\pi r^2 h\rho g$.

Equating the resultant upward force in dynes with the weight of the water column in dynes gives

$$2\pi r T \cos \theta = \pi r^2 h\rho g.$$

FIG. 26F—Capillarity and surface tension.

If we cancel like terms and solve for h, we obtain Eq.(26c).

Example 2. One end of a glass capillary tube with an internal diameter of 0.1 cm is placed upright with the lower end in a dish of alcohol. How high will the liquid rise in the tube if the temperature is 20°C, and the angle of contact between the surface and the walls is 20°?

Solution. Looking up the value of surface tension in Table 26A and the density of alcohol in Table 25A, and substituting directly in Eq.(26c), we obtain

$$h = \frac{2 \times 22.3}{0.05 \times 0.79 \times 980} \; 0.940 = 1.08 \text{ cm.}$$

With mercury in a glass tube, the strong cohesive forces form a surface which is convex downward as shown in Fig. 26D(b). Surface tension here tries to flatten this surface out, thus depressing the liquid to a lower level. The same formula applied to the rise of a liquid in a capillary tube may here be applied to give the depression with mercury or any other fluid which does not "wet" the tube.

26.5. The Theory of Surface Tension. The following theory of surface tension and capillarity is based upon atomic and molecular forces. Let the horizontal line in Fig. 26G represent the free surface of a liquid and the three dots at the center of the circles represent three individual atoms or molecules of the liquid. Around each molecule we imagine a sphere to be drawn of such a size that molecules inside the sphere are close enough to be attracted by the one at the center, while those outside are too far away. While such spheres of influence have no definite boundary, it is known that the attractive forces from much beyond 3 molecules away may be neglected.

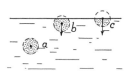

Fig. 26G—Each molecule in a liquid exerts an attractive force on all other molecules within a certain radius.

Consider molecule (a) which is well below the surface. Surrounded by equal numbers of molecules in all directions there is no resultant force act-

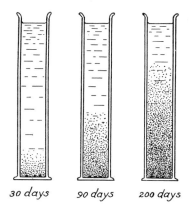

30 days   90 days   200 days

Fig. 26H—Diffusion in liquids is a slow process.

ing upon it. Molecule (b) near the surface, with more molecules in the lower half of its sphere of influence than in the upper half, experiences a small downward force. Molecule (c) in the liquid surface experiences the greatest possible downward force since all molecules inside its sphere of influence lie below it.

It is clear from these considerations that to move a molecule from the interior of the liquid to the surface and thus increase the surface area would require work to be done. An outward force would have to be exerted on the molecule for a finite distance. Therefore a minimum surface area for a given volume of water represents a minimum of potential energy. The tendency to reduce the surface to a minimum exhibits itself as a surface tension, and agrees with a well known principle in mechanics that the condition of minimum potential energy of a system is the most stable.

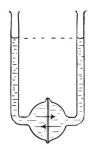

Fig. 26I—Some substances in water solution diffuse more rapidly than others through a membrane.

26.6. Diffusion. When two liquids are brought into direct contact, the molecules of each one migrate and diffuse slowly through the other. As an illustration of this spontaneous mixing, consider the experiment shown in Fig. 26H. A few crystals of copper sulfate are dropped into a vessel of pure water, whereupon they sink to the bottom and slowly begin to dissolve.

The freed copper sulfate molecules, darting first one way then the other, find their way slowly up through the water. From observations made over a period of many days, the characteristic blue coloring of the copper sulfate is found to rise higher and higher in the tube. This upward diffusion is not due to buoyancy, because copper sulfate is denser than water and according to Archimedes' principle should remain at the bottom.

A similar diffusion process also takes place when two liquids are separated only by a thin permeable membrane. In Fig. 26I we have a vessel divided into two parts by a sheet of parchment paper. When pure water is poured into one side or the other and allowed to stand for some time, diffusion through the parchment membrane takes place and eventually the water in each side comes to the same level. If common salt is next dissolved in the water on one side it too will diffuse through the membrane and eventually bring both sides to the same concentration and the same level.

Laboratory tests show that the ratio of diffusion of oxygen and carbon dioxide out of and into the blood stream through the cell walls of muscle tissue determines the rate at which the body can do work. Recent measurements indicate that no long-distance runner can be expected to exceed very much the records of Paavo Nurmi and Gunder Haagg.

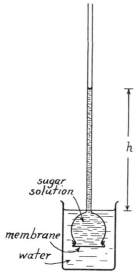

FIG. 26J—Water passes freely through the membrane but sugar does not.

The relationship between every living organism and its surroundings is to a large extent dependent upon the passage of materials through the various biological membranes separating the organism and its environment. Food as it passes from the stomach through the intestines diffuses through the blood vessels and enters the blood stream. From there it is carried to cells in all parts of the body. Through respiration, oxygen from the air we breathe enters the blood stream and, carried to all parts of the body, diffuses through cell walls. Carbon dioxide diffuses out through these same cells and into the blood stream to be eliminated by diffusion through the lungs.

26.7. Osmosis. The phenomenon of osmosis was discovered by Abbe Nollet in 1748. According to his experiments, when a pig's bladder filled with alcohol was placed in water, the bladder increased in size until finally it burst. Conversely, when the bladder was filled with water and placed in alcohol, the volume of the liquid in the bladder decreased. In both instances water had passed through the membrane while the alcohol was unable to do so. In other words a kind of one-way diffusion took place. This is called *osmosis*.

A convenient experiment that is readily performed in the laboratory is shown in Fig. 26J. A sugar solution is first poured into the bowl of a thistle tube and then a piece of parchment, skin, or cellophane tied over the end. When the bowl is lowered, membrane down, into a beaker of pure water, the liquid level in the narrow tube begins to rise. Water is able to pass through the membrane into the sugar solution but the sugar cannot pass through in the opposite direction.

Rising first at the rate of several millimeters per minute, the water level in the tube eventually slows down and stops at some maximum level. At this point a condition of equilibrium has been reached. If a correction is made for capillary and no appreciable dilution of the sugar solution has occurred, the height of the liquid h measures the osmotic pressure of the solution.

For dilute solutions of sucrose or cane sugar, osmotic pressure is found to be directly proportional to the concentration.

$$P = KC.$$

Here P represents the pressure, K a suitable proportionality constant, and C the concentration.

If C is taken as the number of grams of sugar in 100 gm of water, and P as the pressure in centimeters of mercury, K is found to have the value 53.

A correct measure of osmotic pressure can be made only if the membrane used is strictly semipermeable, that is, permits the transmission of water in either direction but no sugar molecules. While membranes can be found that are permeable to water and not to sugar, no known membrane will completely stop all substances and still allow a free exchange of water. The term exchange is used here because recent experiments using "radioactively tagged" water show that, while osmosis proceeds, water molecules actually diffuse through the membrane in both directions.

In medical terminology solutions that have the same total osmotic pressure are said to be *isotonic* with each other. A *hypertonic* solution is one with a higher osmotic pressure and a *hypotonic* solution is one with a lower osmotic pressure than that of some reference solution. Since all membranes within the human body are permeable to water, it follows that the osmotic pressure of all body fluids is held at a reasonably constant level. These fluids are therefore more or less isotonic.

PROBLEMS

1. A U-shaped wire having a length of 4.5 cm is lowered into benzine at 20°C. What force is required to break the film that forms as the wire is slowly raised? See Fig. 26C(c).

2. One end of a glass tube with an internal diameter of 0.25 mm is dipped in alcohol at 20°C. How high will the liquid rise in the tube? Assume the angle of contact $\theta = 0$. (*Ans.* 4.61 cm.)

3. One end of a glass tube with an internal diameter of 0.18 mm is dipped into water at 0°C. How high will the water rise in the tube if the angle of contact $\theta = 0$?

4. If water at 20°C rises to a height of 10 cm in a glass capillary tube what is the diameter of the bore? Assume the angle of contact $\theta = 0$. (*Ans.* 0.297 mm.)

5. If water at 50°C rises to a height of one meter in a glass tube and the angle of contact is zero what is the diameter of the bore?

6. If benzine at 20°C rises to a height of 40 cm in a glass tube what is the diameter of the bore? Assume $\theta = 0$. (*Ans.* 0.033 mm.)

7. If alcohol at 0°C rises to a height of 4.2 cm in a glass capillary tube and the angle of contact is 22° what is the diameter of the bore?

8. One end of a capillary tube is placed in mercury as shown in Fig. 26D(b). If at 20°C the mercury level inside is lowered 8 mm below the level outside what is the diameter of the tube? Assume $\theta = 50°$. (*Ans.* 1.15 mm.)

9. A glass capillary tube with a bore 1.0 mm in diameter is placed upright in a dish of mercury at 0°C. Find the depression of the mercury level. Assume the angle of contact to be 50°.

10. Twenty grams of sugar are dissolved in 250 gm of water and placed inside a thistle tube and a parchment membrane tied over the end. When lowered into a dish of water as shown in Fig. 26J, how high should the water rise in the tube? (Neglect the capillary action in the tube and assume that the sugar solution has a volume of 250 cm^3.) (*Ans.* 57.6 m.)

11. A glass tube has an internal bore 0.02 mm in diameter. How high will acetone rise in this tube if the temperature is 20°C? The density of acetone is 0.79 gm/cm^3.

12. Find the difference in air pressure between the inside and outside of a soap bubble 6 cm in diameter if the surface tension for the soap film is 12 dynes/cm. Standard atmospheric pressure is 1,013,000 dynes/cm^2. See p. 238. (*Ans.* 16 dynes/cm^2.)

13. A fog drop, as seen under a microscope wtih a micrometer eyepiece, is found to have a diameter of 0.00286 mm. Calculate the pressure inside this drop, in atmospheres, if the temperature is 20°C. Assume the air pressure outside the drop is 1 atmosphere and equal to 1,013,000 dynes/cm^2. See p. 238.

14. An air bubble just below the surface of water is 0.02 mm in diameter. If the temperature is 20°C, find the pressure inside the bubble. Assume air pressure on the surface of the water to be 1 atmosphere and equivalent to 1.013×10^6 dynes/cm^2. See p. 238. (*Ans.* 1.158×10^6 dynes/cm^2.)

15. A spherical drop of mercury has a diameter of 1 mm. Find the difference in pressure between the inside and outside if the temperature is 20°C.

16. What is the diameter of a spherical drop of water at 20°C in which the pressure inside exceeds that on the outside by 2 atmospheres. The pressure outside is equal to 1 atmosphere or 1,013,000 dynes/cm^2. (*Ans.* 0.0028 mm.)

Properties of Gases

Chapter 27

27.1. The Earth's Atmosphere. We on the earth's surface, although little conscious of the fact, are submerged in a great sea of air called the atmosphere. This air, which to the earth is the most common of all gases, is really a mixture of well-known gases: about 77% nitrogen, 21% oxygen, and 1% argon. The remaining 1% includes small quantities of such gases as carbon dioxide, hydrogen, neon, krypton, helium, ozone, and xenon.

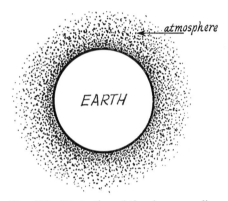

FIG. 27A—Illustration of the air surrounding the earth. The height is exaggerated to bring out the decrease in density with altitude. (If drawn to scale the earth's atmosphere would form a layer much thinner than the line shown here representing the earth's surface.)

Being most dense at sea level (see Fig. 27A), the atmosphere extends upward to a height of from fifty to several hundred miles. The apparent uncertainty as to the exact height of the atmosphere is not real, for the air gets thinner and thinner the higher one goes and finally thins out into interstellar space. Observations show that even interstellar space, which is often referred to as the most perfect vacuum, contains a small but definite amount of matter in the gaseous state: about one molecule per cubic centimeter.

Fig. 27B is a schematic cross section of the atmosphere up to a height of twenty-five miles. It will be noted on the right-hand side of the diagram that 50% of the earth's atmosphere lies below $3\frac{1}{2}$ mi, and that 99% lies below 20 mi. While this accounts for most of the atmosphere, experiments with radio waves show that the small amount of air existing at a height of several hundred miles is sufficient to reflect radio waves back to the earth.

Living as most of us do near sea level, we are constantly subjected to an enormous pressure due to the weight of the air above us. Unbelievable as it may seem, the air exerts a pressure of close to 15 lb for every square inch of surface. This, the atmospheric pressure, is given by the weight of a column of air 1 sq in in cross-section and reaching from sea level to the top of the atmosphere.

A pressure of one atmosphere is defined as the average atmospheric pressure at sea level. This is taken to be 14.7 lb/in.^{2}, or 1,013,000 dynes/cm^2.

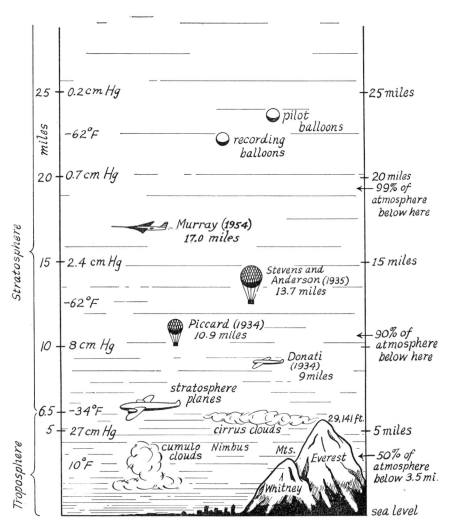

Fig. 27B—Illustrating important facts concerning the troposphere and the stratosphere and the relative heights reached by man in balloons and airplanes.

27.2. The Density of Air. That air has weight may be shown by one of the simplest of experiments. A hollow brass ball with a volume of 1 liter (1 liter = 1000 cm^3) is first weighed when it is filled with air and again when it is evacuated. See Fig. 27C. With the air removed the vessel is found

to be lighter than before by 1.29 gm. If the scales are first balanced with
the sphere evacuated and then the air allowed to enter, a mass of 1.29 gm
must be added to the opposite scale pan to restore balance. Since this is
the mass of 1000 cc of air the mass
of 1 cc will be 0.00129 gm. This is
the density of air.

If the above experiment is repeated at an elevation of 5 mi, the
air in the brass vessel will weigh
only one-third as much as at sea
level. The reason for this is that
the lower pressure at a height of 5
mi admits only one-third as much
air to an evacuated vessel.

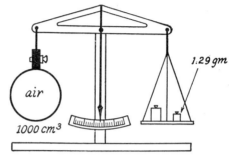

Fig. 27C—Weighing the air.

If, on the other hand, air is
pumped into the hollow sphere, the weight can be made to increase considerably, thus giving a greater than normal density. The density of a gas is
therefore standardized and defined as the mass of 1 cc of the gas measured
at standard pressure and temperature. Standard pressure is defined as a pressure of one atmosphere and standard temperature as zero degrees centigrade.
The densities of a few common gases are given in Table 27A. The reason for
specifying temperature is that gases expand with a rise in temperature. This
subject will be treated in Chap. 29 on expansion.

TABLE 27A. DENSITIES OF SIX COMMON GASES

	Air	CO_2	Helium	Hydrogen	Nitrogen	Oxygen
gm/cm³	0.00129	0.00198	0.000178	0.00009	0.00125	0.00143
lb/ft³	0.080	0.124	0.011	0.005	0.078	0.089

27.3. The Mercury Barometer. A barometer is a device for measuring the atmospheric pressure. There are in common use today two kinds of
barometers—the mercury barometer and the aneroid barometer. The mercury barometer was invented by the Italian physicist, Evangelista Torricelli,
some three hundred years ago. Torricelli's experiment is illustrated in Fig.
27D. A long glass tube is filled with mercury and the finger placed over one
end as shown in diagram (a). This tube is then inverted and with the open
end in a dish of mercury the finger is removed as in diagram (b). At the instant the finger is removed the mercury level drops in the tube to a height h

as shown. The mercury drops until the pressure due to its own weight inside the tube (at the level *P*) is equal to the atmospheric pressure outside.

At sea level the height at which the mercury column stands is about 76 cm or 30 in. This height will be the same regardless of the diameter of the tube or the length of the vacuum space at the top. Torricelli's experiment shows that a column of air 1 sq. cm in cross section and reaching to the top of the atmosphere is equal in weight to a column of mercury of the same cross section and 76 cm high.

It was the French philosopher and mathematician, Blaise Pascal, who first showed that when a mercury barometer is taken to a high elevation like the top of a mountain, the height of the mercury column drops considerably. It drops because there is less air above that point and hence a lesser downward pressure on the free mercury surface.

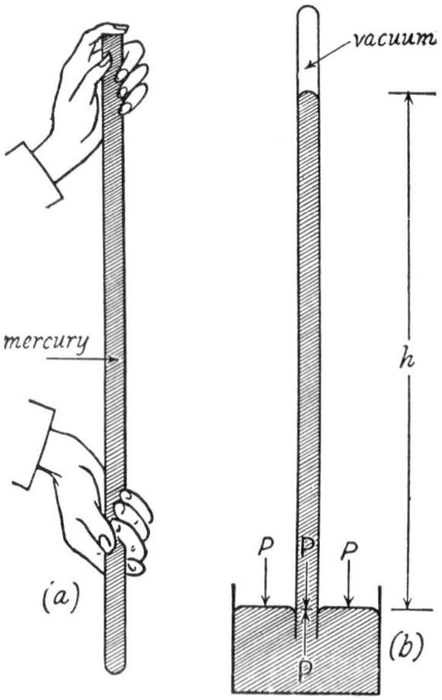

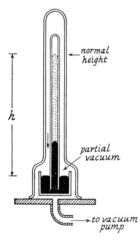

FIG. 27D—Torricelli's experiment. The making of a mercury barometer.

Fig. 27E is a diagram of an experiment demonstrating that it is the atmosphere outside of a barometer pushing down on the exposed mercury surface which supports the mercury column inside and not the vacuum in the space above drawing it up. An entire barometer is placed in a tall cylinder and the air removed by means of a vacuum pump. As the air slowly leaves, the mercury column drops steadily. When the cylinder is well evacuated the level of the mercury inside the tube is the same as the level in the small reservoir outside. A return of the air forces the mercury back into the tube and up to its original height *h*.

The height of the mercury in a barometer measures directly the atmospheric pressure. Instead of specifying the pressure in lb/in.² or in dynes/cm², it is customary to give the height of the mercury column in inches or centimeters. The pressure so expressed in centimeters of Hg (the

FIG 27E—Experimental arrangement demonstrating that atmospheric pressure supports the column of mercury in a barometer tube. When the air is removed the mercury column drops from its normal height.

chemical symbol for mercury is Hg) is given at each 5 mi interval at the left in Fig. 27B.

If a barometer were made to employ water in place of mercury the barometer tube would have to be at least 13.6 times as high, or 1034 cm. This is equivalent to about 34 ft. Such an instrument would be too cumbersome to be of much practical value.

27.4. The Aneroid Barometer. The desirability of a small portable pressure measuring instrument has led to the development of the aneroid barometer. This device is frequently used as an altimeter and barom-

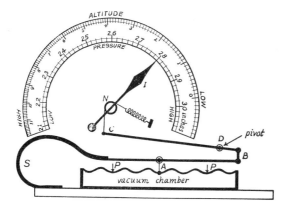

Fig. 27F—Schematic diagram and cross-section of an aneroid barometer.

eter combined. A cross-section diagram of such an instrument is shown in Fig. 27F and photographs are reproduced in Fig. 27G(a). A small flat metal box, evacuated and with a flexible top, is attached at A to a multiplying system of levers. The end of the lever system is connected to a small cable C which is wrapped around a spindle N carrying a pointer I. If the atmospheric pressure P increases, the flexible boxtop is pushed down at A. This lowers the end of the lever system at B, and with a pivot at D raises the point C. The cable winds up on the spindle N, turning the pointer I to the right to a scale reading of higher pressure. The scale of the aneroid is calibrated by a standard mercury barometer so the pressure is always given in centimeters or inches of mercury.

Since the atmospheric pressure decreases as one goes to higher altitudes, a barometer is often used to determine elevation. As a matter of fact, aneroid barometers are freqently made with an altitude scale attached. Such instruments, called *altimeters,* are to be found on the instrument panel of every airplane and dirigible. Some of these instruments are small enough to be carried in the pocket like a watch, and others are so sensitive they will indicate a change in elevation of 1 ft. The altitude scale usually has its zero mark near the sea-level pressure as shown in Fig. 27F.

Atmospheric pressure not only varies with altitude but also with time. Although these time variations are small and do not follow any regular law, they can be and are used by the weather bureau as an aid to predicting weather conditions. If at any place the exact height of a barometer is measured carefully throughout the day and the season, slight changes will be observed. When the barometric pressure begins to fall, it is a good sign of changing weather. If the pressure continues to fall, rain usually follows. As the storm passes, the barometer rises again. So, by keeping close watch of changing barometric pressure in the vicinity of an observer, the weather for that locality can be forecast.

27.5. Standard Atmospheric Pressure. Standard atmospheric pressure is defined as the pressure equivalent to a column of mercury 76 cm high when the temperature is 0°C. This is equivalent to 29.92 in. of mercury at 32°F. To calculate the equivalent pressure in dynes per square centimeter, multiply by the density of mercury and the acceleration of gravity.

$$76 \times 13.6 \times 980 = 1.013 \times 10^6$$
$$1 \text{ atmosphere} = 1.013 \times 10^6 \text{ dynes/cm}^2. \qquad (27a)$$

It is common practice in meteorology to measure atmospheric pressure in bars and millibars.

$$1 \text{ bar} = 1,000,000 \text{ dynes/cm}^2 \qquad 1 \text{ millibar} = 1000 \text{ dynes/cm}^2.$$

On this basis,

$$1 \text{ atmosphere} = 1.013 \text{ bars} = 1013 \text{ millibars}. \qquad (27b)$$

The United States Weather Bureau obtains daily records of the barometric pressure from hundreds of places over the country. These records are obtained automatically at each station by means of a specially designed aneroid like the one shown in Fig. 27G(b). A pen or stylus from the barom-

 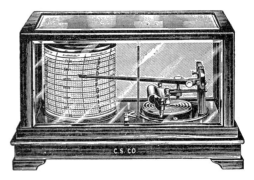

Fɪɢ. 27G—(a) Aneroid barometer used for measuring atmospheric pressure. (b) Self-recording aneroid barometer, or barograph. (*Courtesy Central Scientific Co.*)

eter itself moves up and down on a slowly rotating drum, thus recording the pressure at every instant. These records are then compiled by the United States Weather Bureau and maps are published daily of the equal pressure areas over the country. One such map is shown in Fig. 27H, the irregular lines representing points of equal pressure. It is standard practice now to give the pressure in millibars (see Eq. 27b).

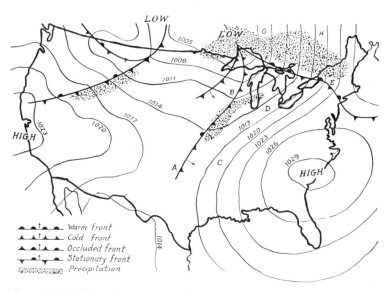

FIG. 27H—U. S. weather map for Dec. 9, 1946, showing barometric pressures, warm and cold air fronts and precipitation areas.

LOW areas, indicating stormy weather, move slowly and continuously across the country, sometimes growing in intensity and at other times breaking up and disappearing. Particularly noticeable in the diagram is the *HIGH* pressure region on the Atlantic sea coast and the pronounced *LOW* pressure region just North-West of the Great Lakes. Like the arms of a great windmill the cold and warm air masses around every pronounced *LOW*, rotate in a counterclockwise direction. As cold air fronts like *AB* sweep down from the polar regions and advance upon warm air masses like *CD*, they push the warm air ahead of them and up over a slowly moving or stationary cool front like *EF*. There at *EFGH* the warm air above the cold is cooled below its saturation temperature and the precipitation of snow or rain takes place. The slipping of some warm air up over the advancing cold front *AB* causes some precipitation there as shown.

27.6. Experiments Illustrating Atmospheric Pressure. Normal atmospheric pressure of 15 lb/sq. in. does not ordinarily impress a person as being very great. Taken over a considerable area, however, such a pressure gives rise to a tremendous force. Consider the evacuated bulb of an incandescent lamp 3 in in diameter. A sphere of this diameter has an area of about 28 in², and hence a total of 28 × 15 or 420 lb is exerted inward upon its walls. The thin glass walls can withstand this because the force is

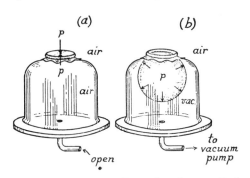

(a) *(b)*

Fig. 27I—Experiments illustrating the magnitude of atmospheric pressure.

distributed uniformly over the whole surface. If it were all applied at one small point the bulb would surely break. A spherical or cylindrical vessel can have thin walls and yet stand enormous pressures, whereas a vessel with flat sides may not. It is for this reason that all large vessels used for storing liquids or gases have curved walls instead of flat ones.

An experiment illustrating atmospheric pressure is diagramed in Fig. 27I. In diagram (a) a thin sheet of rubber is first tied over the top end of a jar. When this is done the air pressure inside is the same as that outside. If now the inside force, upward on the rubber, is removed by means of a vacuum pump, the outside force pushes the rubber down inside as shown in diagram (b).

The principles of breathing in the human body are demonstrated in Fig. 27J. Muscular contraction in pulling down on the *diaphragm* creates a low pressure around the lungs and atmospheric pressure pushes air into the lungs. Retraction of the diaphragm raises the pressure and compresses the lungs, forcing air and carbon dioxide out.

Two additional experiments are illustrated in Fig. 27K. The first diagram represents an inverted cylinder and piston. By pumping out the air from the cylinder chamber, the atmospheric pressure lifts the piston and accompanying heavy weights

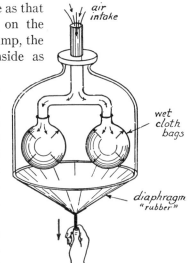

Fig. 27J—Experimental demonstration of the principles of breathing by the human body.

W. With a circular piston only 5 in in diameter a total weight of 295 lb can be lifted. The second diagram represents the drinking of water from a glass by means of a straw. The water is not drawn up through the straw; it

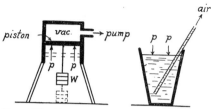

is pushed up from the outside. Suction at the top end of the straw removes the air, and hence the pressure at that point, and the atmospheric pressure at the liquid surface in the glass pushes the water up the straw and into the mouth. This is similar in its action to a siphon.

FIG. 27K—Experiments illustrating the pres- ence of atmospheric pressure and its action in all directions.

27.7. The Magdeburg Hemispheres. In the year 1654 Otto von Guericke * performed before the Emperor Ferdinand III, at Regensburg, the celebrated experiment of the "Magdeburg hemispheres." Two copper hemispheres, about 22 in. in diameter, were placed together to form a sphere as shown in Fig. 27L. A ring of leather soaked in oil and wax was set between them to make an airtight joint. When the sphere was evacuated two teams, consisting of eight horses each, were unable to pull the hemispheres apart. This is not to be wondered at for the force required to pull them apart is easily calculated and amounts to nearly three tons.

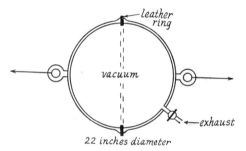

FIG. 27L—The Magdeburg hemisphere designed by Otto von Guericke.

27.8. Measurement of Gas Pressure. There are many kinds of gauges used for measuring gas pressure. One of the simplest instruments used in fixed installations is the manometer. As shown in Fig. 27M these devices are U-shaped glass tubes containing mercury, alcohol, water or other liquids.

In the open-tube manometer at the left, atmospheric pressure p_0 acts downward on the exposed liquid surface at B. The pressure at the level A in the right-hand column is therefore p_0 plus the pressure due to the liquid column of height h. Since this must be equal to the pressure at the same level A in the left-hand column

$$p = p_0 + h\rho g. \tag{27c}$$

This is the pressure p exerted by the enclosed gas on the liquid surface

* Otto von Guericke (1602-1686), German philosopher, lawyer, physicist, and magistrate. Incited by the discoveries of Galileo, Pascal, and Torricelli, he produced the first vacuum and made the first air pump. From researches in astronomy he predicted the periodic return of comets.

and the container walls. If p and p_0 are in dynes/cm², h is in centimeters, ρ is the density of the liquid in the manometer in gm/cm³, and g is the acceleration of gravity in cm/sec².

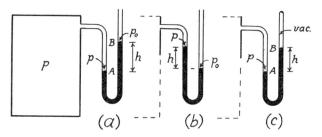

Fig. 27M—Diagrams of open and closed manometer tubes as used in measuring gas pressure.

If the liquid in the manometer is mercury, it is customary to specify p, p_0 and h in centimeters of mercury.

$$p = p_0 + h \tag{27d}$$

A similar reasoning applied to the open manometer tube of diagram (b) shows that the absolute pressure p inside the vessel (indicated by dotted lines) is less than atmospheric pressure by an amount equal to the mercury column h,

$$p = p_0 - h \tag{27e}$$

The closed-tube manometer shown at the right is frequently used where pressures of only a fraction of one atmosphere are to be measured. The right hand side of the U-tube is closed at the top and evacuated. With the atmospheric pressure thus eliminated, the gas pressure to be measured is given by the mercury column h.

$$p = h \tag{27f}$$

27.9. Absolute Pressure. When an automobile tire goes flat from a puncture, the small amount of air remaining in the tire is at atmospheric pressure the same as the air outside. This is roughly 15 lb/in². If the tire is repaired and pumped up to a pressure of 30 lb/in.², as read on a standard air pressure gauge, the absolute pressure of the enclosed gas is 30 + 15 or 45 lb/in². In other words, a pressure gauge gives the difference between atmospheric pressure outside and the air pressure inside.

In the manometer tubes of Fig. 27M, the mercury column h is the gauge pressure, and to this is added the atmospheric pressure p_0 to get the absolute pressure. In the closed-tube diagram (c) h measures directly the absolute pressure. Bourdon gauges are usually adjusted to a zero reading when disconnected so that atmospheric pressure must be added to their reading to obtain the absolute pressure.

27.10. Kinetic Theory of Gases. According to the kinetic theory of matter the pressure exerted by a gas upon the walls of the containing vessel is due to the continual bombardment of the walls by the rapidly moving gas molecules. If the temperature of the gas is raised the molecules move faster and the pressure rises, whereas if it is lowered they move slower and the pressure decreases. The absolute temperature of a gas is proportional to the average kinetic energy of translation of the molecules.

The more gas that is pumped into a vessel of constant volume, the more molecules there are to bombard the walls per second and the greater is the resultant pressure. At any given instant of time some molecules are moving in one direction and some in another; some are traveling fast, some slow, and a few are momentarily at rest.

In any reasonably large volume of gas there are many molecules (about 10^{24} molecules/cu ft at normal atmospheric pressure and room temperature) and according to the mathematical laws of probability some average speed can be determined which if possessed by all the molecules, would correspond to the same temperature and would give rise to the same wall pressure. Denoting this average speed by $\bar{v}$, we will now derive a formula for the pressure.

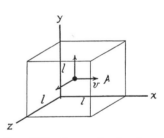

Consider a cubical vessel whose volume, as shown in Fig. 27N, is l^3. Because the total number of molecules present, N, is very large the calculations are simplified by assuming that one-third are moving in the x-direction, one-third in the y-direction and one-third in the z-direction.

Fig. 27N—Gas molecules in a closed compartment create pressure by virtue of their impact against the walls.

Select now the one-third that are moving in the x-direction. Each molecule as it approaches the right-hand wall of the vessel is moving with a velocity $\bar{v}$ and after collision it rebounds with a velocity $-\bar{v}$. There has been a change in velocity of $2\bar{v}$. Since the impulse Ft exerted on the wall is given by the change in momentum, we may write

$$Ft = 2m\bar{v}. \qquad (27g)$$

Bouncing back and forth between opposite walls of the vessel, each molecule will make many impacts on the same wall in unit time. Now, t is the average time required for the molecule to make the round trip, $2l$, from the right-hand wall to the left-hand wall and back. Therefore

$$t = 2l/\bar{v}$$

Since the impulse, Ft, is given by the change of momentum, we may write

$$F \times 2l/\bar{v} = 2m\bar{v} \qquad \text{or} \qquad F = m\bar{v}^2/l.$$

For $\frac{1}{3}N$ molecules then the force will be $N/3$ times that for one molecule, or

$$F = \frac{Nm\bar{v}^2}{3l}.$$

Since pressure is the force per unit area, and the area of the wall is l^2

$$p = \frac{F}{l^2} = \frac{Nm\bar{v}^2}{3l^3}. \qquad (27h)$$

Since the number of molecules N multiplied by the mass of a single molecule gives the total mass of the gas, and l^3 gives its volume, the density ρ is given by

$$\rho = \frac{Nm}{l^3}.$$

By substituting ρ for Nm/l^3 in Eq.(27h), we obtain for the pressure

$$p = \tfrac{1}{3}\rho\bar{v}^2. \qquad (27i)$$

The average velocity of molecules in a gas of density ρ, under an absolute pressure p, is given by rearranging the terms.

$$\bar{v} = \sqrt{3p/\rho}. \qquad (27j)$$

Example. Calculate the average velocity of hydrogen molecules in a gas at normal atmospheric pressure and room temperatures.

Solution. From the gas densities in Table 27A and the value for standard atmospheric pressure,

$$\bar{v} = \sqrt{\frac{3 \times 1,013,000 \text{ dynes/cm}^2}{0.000090 \text{ gm/cm}^3}} = 184,000 \frac{\text{cm}}{\text{sec}}.$$

This is considerably faster than a rifle bullet or the shells from the largest guns.

The formula above shows that the greater the density of a gas the lower is the average speed of its molecules. For a gas like oxygen, with sixteen times the density of hydrogen, the molecules will be moving with only one-quarter the average speed of the hydrogen molecules. This is well illustrated by the mechanical model shown in Fig. 23C, representing the case of a mixture of two gases of different density.

PROBLEMS

1. A spherical balloon 50 ft in diameter is filled with hydrogen. If the balloon-bag, basket and all necessary gear weigh 800 lb, what is the maximum load it can carry when taking off at sea level?

2. A large balloon 20 m in diameter is filled with helium at standard temperature and pressure. If the ballon-bag, basket, and all necessary gear have a mass of 550 kg, what is the maximum load it can carry when taking off at sea level? (*Ans.* 4100 kg-wt.)

3. A hollow glass sphere 20 cm in diameter is evacuated. Calculate the total inward force on the outside surface under standard atmospheric pressure.

4. A circular screen of a television tube is 20 in. in diameter. With the tube thoroughly evacuated and with standard atmospheric pressure outside, what is the total inward force on the screen? Assume the screen to be flat. (*Ans.* 4618 lb.)

5. Magdeburg hemispheres with an internal diameter of 10 cm are put together and thoroughly evacuated. What minimum force will pull them apart at (a) sea level, and (b) 3.5 mi elevation where the atmospheric pressure is 50% that at sea level?

6. Magdeburg hemispheres 0.5 m in diameter are thoroughly evacuated. Calculate the minimum force required to pull them apart (a) at sea level, and (b) at an altitude of 19 mi. (*Ans.* (a) 1.99×10^4 newtons, (b) 1.99×10^2 newtons.)

7. If a barometer contains water in place of mercury, how high will the water column be (a) at sea level, and (b) at an altitude of 3.5 mi?

8. A brass cylinder 4 cm in diameter and 10 cm high is being weighed on an accurate beam balance. What is the mass equivalent of the buoyant force of the air on the cylinder? (*Ans.* 0.162 gm.)

9. Calculate the average velocity of helium atoms in a gas at normal atmospheric pressure and 0°C.

10. Find the average velocity of the oxygen molecules in the air at normal temperature and pressure. (*Ans.* 461 m/sec.)

11. A large spherical balloon 40 ft in diameter is filled with hydrogen at a pressure of 1 atmosphere. If the balloon, bag, basket, and all necessary equipment weigh 450 lb, find the maximum load the balloon can carry when taking off at sea level.

12. One Magdeburg hemisphere 2 ft in diameter has a thick glass plate placed over the opening and then evacuated. Calculate the total inward force on the glass plate. (*Ans.* 6780 lb.)

13. A cylindrical pipe 12 in. in diameter has flat brass plates clamped on the ends. If the pipe is thoroughly evacuated, find the total inward force exerted by the outside air on each plate.

14. If a cylindrical tin can 8 cm in diameter and 10 cm tall were thoroughly evacuated, what would be the force on each end? (*Ans.* 510 newtons.)

15. Compute the average velocity of the nitrogen molecules in the air at normal temperature and pressure.

Fluids in Motion   Chapter 28

THE term fluid applies to any substance capable of flowing and includes gases as well as liquids. Since all fluids have mass, Newton's Second Law of Motion implies that unbalanced forces are required to set them in motion. As a matter of practical interest we will consider the various means by which such forces are obtained, how they are applied to fluids, and what factors control the resultant motion. In these discussions the student would do well to keep in mind the fact that liquids are practically incompressible.

28.1. Velocity Through an Orifice. Many city water supply systems store water in reservoirs on some hilltop or in a nearby water tower and from these run the water through pipes into the houses, stores and factories in and around the city. Such an arrangement is called a "gravity system."

When a hole is opened in the side of a vessel containing a liquid the velocity of flow through the orifice increases with depth. Here the unbalanced force setting the liquid in motion is gravity acting through the liquid as pressure. We have already seen how the pressure at any given depth is given by $p = h\rho g$ and is the same in all directions. At a depth h_1 (see Fig. 28A), the liquid exerts a pressure p_1 against the walls and the walls exert an equal and opposite pressure against the liquid.

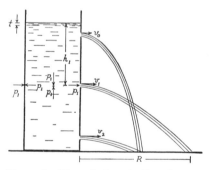

FIG. 28A—The velocity of efflux through a hole in the side of a vessel of water increases with depth.

The instant an opening is made in the side of the vessel the wall pressure **is destroyed at that** point and the liquid pressure inside pushes the liquid directly in front of the hole, giving it an acceleration outward and normal to the plane of the opening. To find the velocity of escape consider the potential energy of the liquid body in the vessel when the hole is first opened and then a short time later when a small amount of liquid has escaped, dropping the surface level a distance t.

As far as energy is concerned the change is the same as though the top layer of water had been lowered a distance h_1 and its potential energy mgh_1 converted into kinetic energy $\frac{1}{2}mv_1^2$ in the emergent stream. By conservation of energy,

$$mgh_1 = \tfrac{1}{2}mv_1^2. \tag{28a}$$

Since m is the same on both sides it may be canceled, giving

$$v = \sqrt{2gh_1} \tag{28b}$$

the same as the law of falling bodies. In other words, the velocity of efflux at any depth h is equivalent to the velocity acquired by free fall from the same height. This relation, first discovered by Torricelli * is known as Torricelli's theorem.

It is interesting to note that the parabolic path followed by an emerging stream of liquid is such that the greatest horizontal range R (see diagram) is obtained from an orifice midway between any base level and the top surface of the liquid and that holes equidistant above and below this point have lesser but equal ranges. The proof of this will be left as a problem for the student.

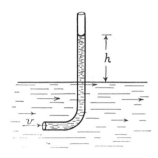

FIG. 28B—A pitot tube is often used to measure the velocity of water in a stream.

28.2. Measuring the Velocity of a Stream.

One method of measuring the velocity of water in a trough or river bed is to use an L-shaped tube called a "pitot tube." See Fig. 28B. If the water were at rest it would rise in the vertical arm to the height of the surface outside.

The pressure exerted by the moving stream, however, raises it to a height h above the surface. This, it may be recognized, is Torricelli's theorem in reverse, the height h measuring the velocity of the moving stream through Eq.(28a). we obtain

$$h = \frac{v^2}{2g}. \tag{28c}$$

The right-hand term $v^2/2g$ is called the *velocity head* of the moving stream.

The simplest method of measuring the velocity of a jet of water is to turn it straight upward and from the height of rise calculate the velocity from the law of falling bodies, Eq.(28b).

28.3. Flow Through a Pipe.
One of the factors determining the flow of water, oil, or gas through a pipe, or the flow of blood through the arteries and veins of the body is the resistance to flow offered by the confining walls. Consider the experiment shown in Fig. 28C in which water from a vertical tank at the left is made to flow through a horizontal glass tube at the bottom. The pressure at five equally spaced points along the tube is measured

* Evangelista Torricelli (1608-1647). An Italian physicist and mathematician and disciple of Galileo. He is most noted for his scientific articles on fluid motion, on the theory of projectiles, and on geometrical optics.

by vertical standpipes, and the velocity of flow is controlled by the valve at the right. By means of a "water supply" and "over-flow" pipe the water level in the tank is maintained at a constant level, thus assuring a constant pressure and hence a steady flow.

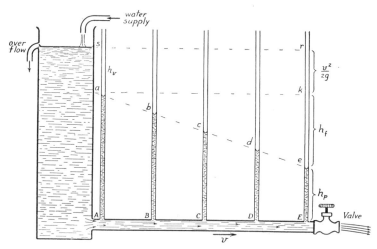

Fig. 28C—Flow of water through a pipe showing the velocity head h_v, friction head h_f, and the pressure head h_p.

With the valve closed the water "seeking its own level" soon brings all standpipes to the same level sr. Their heights thereby indicate equal pressures at all points along the pipe A to E. When the valve is partially opened and a steady flow is attained, the water in each pipe drops to different levels similar to those shown. The more the valve is opened, the more rapid is the flow and the steeper is the straight line $abcde$.

Since at all times the heights of columns aA, bB, cC, dD, and eE measure the pressures at the points A, B, C, D, and E respectively, the straight line ae indicates a smooth and uniform drop in pressure all along the pipe from A to E. Such a drop in pressure, designated h_f in the figure, is due to *fluid friction* in the pipe and is called the *friction head*. By measuring the friction head for different rates of flow a comparison of the results will show that h_f is exactly proportional to the velocity v. This may be expressed as an equation

$$h_t = Kv \qquad (28d)$$

where K is the proportionality constant.

The pronounced drop in level from s in the tank to a in the first standpipe measures the drop in pressure at A where the water is practically at rest in the tank and is then speeded up to a velocity v upon entering the pipe. Just as in Torricelli's theorem the drop in potential energy from s to a is converted into kinetic energy in the stream, and by Eqs.(28b or (28c),

$$h_\mathrm{v} = v^2/2g. \tag{28e}$$

Here h_v equals sa and is the *velocity-head*.

The final pressure at the point E where the water is being drawn from the pipe is directly measured by the height of the liquid column Ee, and is called the *pressure head* h_p. Thus with a total pressure h available at the tank there is first a velocity-head drop of h_v, and then a friction-head drop h_f, giving as the final pressure $h_\mathrm{p} = h - h_\mathrm{v} - h_\mathrm{f}$. For all points along a uniform pipe the velocity head is constant while the friction head increases proportionally with the distance from the source.

The above equations also apply to the flow of gas through a pipe provided that the pressure is relatively small. If the pressure is large the formulas must be modified to allow for the compressibility of the gas.

28.4. Viscosity of Liquids. If a thick syrup or heavy oil is subjected to pressure and made to flow through a pipe, the rate of flow will not be as great as when gasoline or water is sent through the same pipe under the same total pressure. This difference in rate of flow is due to an internal fluid resistance called viscosity. In some ways viscosity resembles the friction between solids and in other respects it is quite different.

Consider the slow steady flow of water over the sandy bed of a river or stream. See Fig. 28D. Flow measurements show that the speed is a maximum at the top surface and decreases with depth, becoming approximately zero at the bottom.

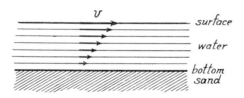

FIG. 28D—The water in a river flows fastest at the top surface.

If we imagine the water divided into thin layers as indicated, it will be seen that the motion is such that the layers are sliding over one another. Because of the interlocking forces between molecules, the sandy river bed tends to keep the bottom layer from moving at all, the bottom layer in turn tends to hold back the second layer, this second layer tends to hold back the third, etc. Since the division into layers is an arbitrary one we see that all the way up through the liquid there must be frictional forces tending to resist relative motion. The greater the resistance to motion, the greater is the viscosity.

To obtain a quantitative measure of viscosity consider Fig. 28E. The distribution of speed causes any section of the liquid that is cubical in shape at one instant to become rhomboidal a short time later. Let h be the height of the cube shown, v the speed by which the upper face of area A exceeds that of the lower face, and F the force parallel to A causing the shear. Viscosity is now defined as the ratio of *shearing stress to rate of shear.*

Shearing stress is given by the force per unit area, F/A, and the rate of shear by v/h.

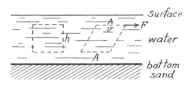

$$\eta = \frac{F/A}{v/h} = \frac{Fh}{Av} \qquad (28f)$$

Fig. 28E—Flowing water may be described as a continuous shearing motion.

where η is called the coefficient of viscosity and is similar to the expression for the shear modulus of solids. Values of the coefficient of viscosity for a few common liquids and gases are given in Table 28A.

TABLE 28A. VISCOSITY OF A FEW COMMON SUBSTANCES IN DYNE-SECONDS
PER SQUARE CENTIMETER

Liquids	η	Gases	η
Alcohol	0.012	Air	1.9×10^{-4}
Blood	0.023	Helium	1.7×10^{-4}
Glycerine	8.300	Hydrogen	0.9×10^{-4}
Olive oil	0.840	Oxygen	2.0×10^{-4}
Water 0°C	0.010	Nitrogen	1.8×10^{-4}
" 100°C	0.003		

A simple demonstration of the effect of viscosity on the flow of a liquid around an obstacle is given in Fig. 28F. Two identical weights are dropped simultaneously, one into water and one into glycerine. In water the weight settles quickly but in glycerine the descent is very slow.

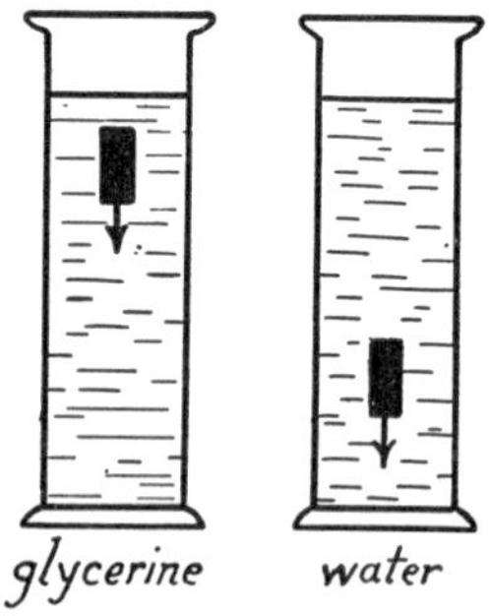

A demonstration of the viscosity of gases is illustrated in Fig. 28G. A cardboard disk suspended at its center by a thread is placed close to but not touching a wooden disk. When the latter is set into rapid rotation the cardboard disk begins to rotate in the same direction and gradually picks up speed.

glycerine   *water*

Fig. 28F—The rate at which a weight settles in a fluid is a measure of viscosity.

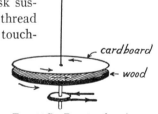

Fig. 28G—Due to the viscosity of the air the cardboard disk is carried around by the rotating disk below.

28.5. Measurement of Viscosity. The most common method used for measuring the coefficient of viscosity of liquids is to measure the rate of flow through a tube of relatively small bore. See Fig. 28H. Friction between the neighboring sections of the liquid and the tube walls tends to hold the liquid back.

If we imagine the liquid divided into concentric cylinders, then each cylinder will be sliding lengthwise through the other, the velocity of flow being greatest at the center and decreasing with the distance from the center to become zero at the tube walls. The motion is similar to the sliding of the tube sections of a small pocket telescope.

Let L be the length of a pipe of internal radius r, and let p be the pressure on the liquid forced through it as shown in Fig. 28H. It may be shown that the volume of liquid flowing through in a time t is given by

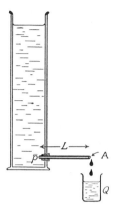

$$Q = \frac{p\pi r^4}{8L\eta}\, t. \tag{28g}$$

This formula, known as Poiseuille's law, is in good agreement with experiment, provided the tube used has a bore small enough to keep the velocity low. Under similar circumstances this law holds for the flow of gases and may be used to find η.

28.6. Blood Circulation in the Human Body. It has been estimated that the circulation of blood through the human body involves a vessel system containing several thousand arteries and veins and well over one billion capillaries. Any attempt to analyze the mechanical principles involved in circulation, therefore, must of necessity simplify the problem in one way or another. While this has been done successfully by numerous research studies, only the most elementary considerations can be presented here.

A schematic diagram of the circulation is given in Fig. 28I, and shows a combination of series and parallel paths between the *left ventricle* where the blood leaves the heart and the *right atrium* where it enters again. The heart pulsating is a force pump containing two chambers, the right and left ventricles, joined into a single unit and pumping in synchronism. During the compression stroke of the heart, called *systole,* the blood in the *right ventricle* is forced out through the valve above into the lungs while the blood in the left ventricle is forced into the *aorta.* During the filling stroke, called *diastole,* blood from the veins and right atrium enters the right ventricle while blood from the lungs enters the left atrium and left ventricle.

The entrance and exit valves of the right and left ventricles consist of two or three flaps or leaves attached to the edge of each opening and meeting at the center. These cusps are free to move apart when the flow is in one direction, but are forced together closing the opening when the flow attempts to reverse.

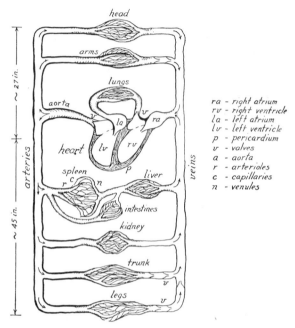

Fig. 28I—Schematic diagram of blood circulation, showing the series and parallel circuits between the large systemic arteries and the large veins.

Upon leaving the largest artery, the aorta, the blood enters the main arteries leading to all parts of the body. After branching into smaller *arterioles,* and then into the numerous small capillaries, the blood emerges into the many small venous branches, the *venules,* and finally into the large veins where it is returned to the heart.

While passing through the capillaries of the lungs the red corpuscles in the blood stream take in oxygen by diffusion, while upon passing through the capillaries in other parts of the body, they give it up and acquire carbon dioxide by diffusion through the cell walls. The tubular capillaries in man are about 8 microns in diameter and the red blood cells average 7.5 microns (1 micron $= 10^{-4}$ cm).

During systole the maximum pressure reached in the aorta (called *systolic pressure*) is about 120 mm while during diastole the pressure (called *diastolic pressure*) drops to about 80 mm. Both of these extreme pressures vary considerably with the health and age of the individual.

In considering variations in blood pressure throughout the entire circulation system, it should be kept in mind that all vessels are semi-elastic tubes instead of rigid pipes. The two principal functions of this elasticity are (1) to smooth out the pulsating outflow from the heart into a more steady flow through the arteries and capillaries and (2) to allow contraction by muscles thus diverting blood through some channels in preference to others when conditions require it.

As the blood is forced out of the heart, the aortic wall expands under the pressure and part of the energy of the ejected blood is stored momentarily as potential energy in the distended wall. This distension travels along the aortic wall and arteries as a kind of transverse wave. As the wave passes by, the stored potential energy is returned to the blood, thereby smoothing out the flow.

A patient's blood pressure is generally measured at the same horizontal level as the heart by means of a thin-walled rubber tube wrapped around the upper arm. As air is pumped in, the expansion of the tube squeezes the arm until the *brachial artery* is collapsed. The pressure of the air in the tube is then measured with an attached U-tube mercury manometer or a Bourdon gauge (see Fig. 27M). When the air pressure in the tube is slowly reduced by means of an escape valve, a point will be reached (about 110 to 120 mm) where small pressure pulses due to the heart action may be observed on the gauge. The gauge reading is then taken to be the systolic blood pressure.

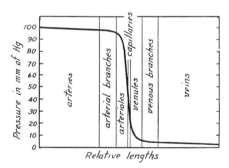

Fig. 28J—Blood pressure curve for the average human body in a prone-position. (Lengths of capillaries greatly exaggerated.)

The effect of gravity on venous pressure in different parts of the body differs markedly between *prone, sitting* and *standing positions*. Pressure in the arteries varies too but not to so great a degree, for muscular action partially compensates for hydrostatic pressure differences. Laboratory experiments on blood pressure measured with the body in the prone position have resulted in the pressure curve shown in Fig. 28J. The very small pressure drop through the arteries and veins as compared with the long drop through the capillaries is readily understood from the relative diameters, as may be seen from the following tabulated data.

	Number	Diameter, mm	Length, cm
Aorta and large arteries	40	3-10	40-20
Arterial branches	2400	0.6-1.0	1-10
Arterioles	40,000,000	0.02	0.2
Capillaries	1,200,000,000	0.008	0.1
Venules	80,000,000	0.03	0.2
Venous branches	24,000	1.5-2.4	1-10
Vena cava and large veins	40	6-12	40-20

Note the enormous cross-section of a large vein or artery as compared with a capillary. A detailed analysis of the above curve and the tables shows that *viscosity* and *Poiseuille's law* (see Sec. 28.5) account for the pressure changes and that *velocity head* is relatively small. Maximum flow velocity in the aorta may reach as high as 40 cm/sec.

When the body is upright, the variations in blood pressure with height above or below the heart level are quite appreciable. First of all the pressure developed by the heart must be sufficient to pump blood to the top of the head overcoming gravity as well as friction. Gravity alone is sufficient to return the blood through the veins. The vessels leading to the lower extremities and back again are like an inverted siphon.

The pressure gained in the arteries leading to the feet is transmitted through the capillaries to the veins where it is used to raise the blood again to the heart level.

Example. What minimum pressure is required to force blood from the heart to the top of the head if the vertical distance is 27 in.? Assume the density of blood to be 1.04 gm/cm^3, and neglect friction.

Solution. The pressure will be equivalent to the weight of a column of liquid 27 in. in height. Changing inches to centimeters gives

$$27 \times 2.54 \times 1.04 = 71.3 \text{ gm/cm}^2.$$

Dividing by the density of mercury will convert this to an equivalent mercury column.

$$\frac{71.3}{13.6} = 5.24 \text{ cm} = 52.4 \text{ mm}.$$

The following observation will demonstrate the wide variation in blood pressure with elevation above or below the heart. With the hand held palm down at waist level, observe the bulging of the veins on the back of the hand. Now slowly raise the hand higher and higher and notice carefully the height at which the bulges disappear. At this height the pressure in the veins has become zero at the hand level and, due to gravity, the blood flows downward through the arm to the heart.

28.7. Bernoulli's Principle. When a river runs through broad open country, the water runs slowly, but when it comes to a narrow rocky gorge its velocity increases many fold. Similarly when a gas or liquid flowing through a pipe comes to a narrow constricted section, the velocity increases as it enters the constriction and decreases again as it leaves the other end. This is illustrated by an experiment diagramed in Fig. 28K.

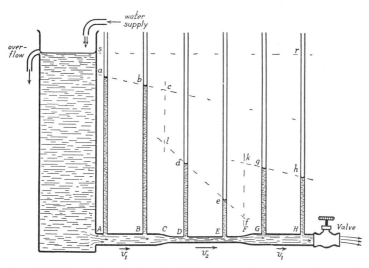

FIG. 28K—Where the velocity of a fluid increases the pressure drops, and where the velocity of a fluid decreases the pressure rises.

The arrangement is the same as in Fig. 28C except that the horizontal flow pipe contains a short section *DE* having only half the cross-sectional area as elsewhere. When the valve is opened and a condition of steady flow exists, the water in the standpipes will have dropped from *sr* to new levels like *a*, *b*, *d*, etc., as shown. It is to be noted that as the water enters the constriction at *C* the velocity of flow increases and the pressure drops from *c* to *l*. Farther along where it leaves the narrow tube at *F*, the velocity decreases and the pressure rises from *f* to *k*.

This illustrates Bernoulli's principle which may be stated as follows: "where the velocity of a fluid is high the pressure is low, and where the velocity of a fluid is low the pressure is high." The drops in pressure from *a* to *b*, *d* to *e*, and *g* to *h* represent friction heads for the pipe sections *AB*, *DE*, and *GH* respectively. The drop from *s* to *a* gives directly the velocity head $v_1^2/2g$ for the pipe sections *AB* and *GH*, and to this must be added the drop from *c* to *l* to obtain the velocity head $v_2^2/2g$ for the narrow pipe section *DE*. The simplest of laboratory measurements confirm the result that narrowing the tube to half the cross-section doubles the velocity and quadruples the velocity head.

28.8. Experiments Illustrating Bernoulli's Principle. Bernoulli's principle is often referred to as a physical paradox and is the basis of many interesting phenomena. Nine experiments involving this principle are diagramed in Fig. 28L. In the first illustration (a) a blast of air from a nozzle is blown between two sheets of cardboard suspended `about 3 in. apart by cords. Instead of being blown apart, as one might expect, they come together. The reason for this action is that between the two sheets where the velocity of the air is high the pressure p_2 is low. On the two outside surfaces where the air is not moving the pressure p_1 (atmospheric pressure) is high and pushes the two sheets together.

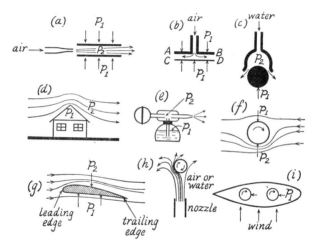

Fig. 28L—Experiments illustrating Bernoulli's principle.

In the second diagram (b) air is blown through a hole in the center of a disk AB as shown. When a piece of paper CD is placed close to the opening it is not blown away but is drawn toward the disk. Where the velocity of air between the disk and paper is high the pressure is low, and the higher pressure p_1 on the underside of the paper pushes it up against the disk.

A similar experiment is illustrated in (c) with water as the moving fluid and an inverted cup and ball in place of the disk and paper. The ball is made of wood or metal and almost fits into the cup. The fast moving stream of water passing over the top surface of the ball produces a low pressure region p_2 and the atmospheric pressure below pushes the ball up.

One often hears it said that, during a certain wind storm, tornado, or hurricane. the roofs of one or more houses were blown off without otherwise damaging the house. This is not as freakish an accident as one might think, for there is a simple explanation. A high wind blowing over the roof, as shown in Fig. 28L(d), creates a low pressure p_2 on top, and the atmospheric pressure p_1 inside where the wind is not blowing lifts the roof off.

The fifth diagram (e) represents a common form of perfume atomizer. Squeezing the bulb sends a stream of air through the central tube, creating a low pressure p_2 inside. Atmospheric pressure p_1 on the liquid surface pushes liquid up the stem to be blown out the right-hand tube with the air stream.

Most of the baseballs thrown by a pitcher are curves, some up or down and others in or out, i.e., to right or left. This is an art, accomplished by throwing the ball so that it spins rapidly about some particular axis. To produce a downward curve, i.e., a *drop ball,* the ball is given a top spin as shown in diagram (f). Here instead of having the ball moving to the right we can imagine the ball standing still, but spinning, and the air to be moving from right to left. At the top surface where the wind and ball are moving in opposite directions the air is slowed down by friction, giving rise to a high pressure region. On the underside the surface moving with the wind keeps the velocity high, thus creating a low pressure region. The resultant downward force thus causes the ball to drop faster than usual.

The same principle has been applied to the historical *Flettner rotor ship* which instead of using sails, employed two tall, rotating cylinders, motor driven. As shown by the top view diagram (i) a wind from broadside the ship produces a forward force. Such a ship, carrying a cargo, crossed the Atlantic twice not many years ago. Although the trips were successful, the uncertainty of a strong wind makes shipping with such boats unreliable.

If a small "ping-pong" ball is placed in a vertical stream of air or water it will rise to a given height above the nozzle and stay at that level, spinning and bobbing around without falling. If the ball goes to one side as illustrated in diagram (h) the fluid going by on the left side causes the ball to spin as shown. The velocity being high on the left means a low pressure. The higher pressure on the right where the velocity is low pushes the ball back into the stream.

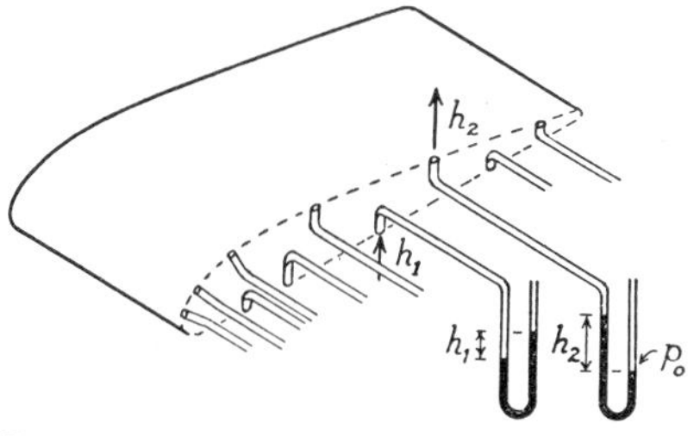

28.9. The Lift of an Airplane Wing.

The major part of the lift of an airplane wing is due to the top surface. This discovery has been made in laboratory wind tunnels by setting up sections of air foils in fast moving currents of air and measuring the pressure at various regions of the surface with

Fig. 28M—Experimental arrangement of mercury manometers, showing how the air pressure can be measured at various points over the surface of an airfoil.

pressure gauges. Fig. 28M shows how this can be done with mercury manometers connected by long tubes to small openings on the top and bottom surfaces.

When the air is still all manometer tubes show equal heights in their two arms and normal atmospheric pressure p_o exists at all points inside the hollow wing as well as outside. When the air stream is set in motion manometers connected to the top surface show a drop from atmospheric pressure while those connected below show a rise. Since atmospheric pressure on the outside surfaces was previously counterbalanced at all points by the atmospheric pressure inside the hollow wing, the manometer readings h_1 and h_2 give directly the resultant pressures on the two wing coverings.

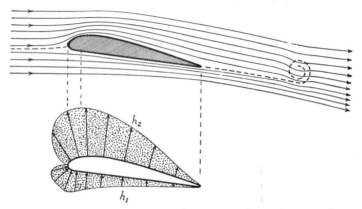

Fig. 28N—Diagram showing the air stream and pressure around an airplane wing. Angle of attack 10°.

A graphical representation of the manometer pressures is shown below in Fig. 28N. Note the very large effect of the upper surface as compared with the lower surface, particularly near the leading edge.

PROBLEMS

1. A pipe enters a water tank at a point 20 ft below the surface of the contained water. What is the water pressure in this pipe?

2. A cylindrical tank 80 ft high and full of water develops a hole in its side 16 ft below the top. How far from the base of the tank will the emerging water strike the ground? (*Ans.* 64 ft.)

3. At what speed will benzine emerge from a hole in the side of a tank if the hole is 10 m below the liquid surface?

4. At what speed will the velocity head of a stream of water be equal to 10 cm of mercury? (*Ans.* 5.16 m/sec.)

5. If when a "pitot tube" is immersed in a stream of water the velocity head is 0.50 m, what is the speed of the water?

6. The following measurements were made for the experiment shown in Fig. 28C. Distance $sa = 10$ cm, $sA = 40$ cm and $eE = 5$ cm. The internal diameter of the tube is 0.8 cm. Find (a) the velocity of flow through the tube, (b) the friction head between A and E, and (c) the quantity of water delivered in 1 min. (*Ans.* (a) 140 cm/sec, (b) 25 cm, (c) 421 cm³.)

7. Glycerine in a tall cylinder is made to flow through a horizontal capillary tube 60 cm below the surface as shown in Fig. 28H. If the tube measures 12 cm long and 0.8 mm internal diameter, how much glycerine will flow through in 1 min? Assume the density of glycerine to be 0.90 gm/cm³.

8. Olive oil is contained in a viscosity apparatus as shown in Fig. 28H. The capillary tube is 10 cm long, 0.2 cm inside diameter and is located 50 cm below the liquid surface. How much olive oil will flow through in 20 sec? The density of olive oil is 0.918 gm/cm³. (*Ans.* 4.20 cm³.)

9. A lubricating oil for cars is placed in a viscosity apparatus as shown in Fig. 28H. The capillary tube used is located 100 cm below the top surface, is 20 cm long, and has an internal diameter of 0.20 cm. If the oil density is 0.85 gm/cm³ and 65 cm³ flows through in 5.0 min, find the viscosity.

10. Assuming the blood in a large artery to have a velocity of 25 cm/sec what pressure drop is attributed to velocity head? (*Ans.* 0.23 mm of Hg.)

11. Assuming the aorta to be a rigid pipe 0.9 cm in diameter how much blood would be pumped through the heart with each pulse? Assume a pulse rate of 65 per minute and a velocity of flow through the aorta of 35 cm/sec.

12. Water flowing with a velocity of 1 m/sec in a 3 cm diameter pipe enters a short section having a diameter of only 1 cm and then a section having a diameter of 5 cm. Calculate (a) the velocity in the last two pipes and (b) the velocity head in all three. (*Ans.* (a) 9 m/sec, and 36 cm/sec, (b) 5.1 cm, 413 cm, 0.66 cm.)

13. Water flowing in a 4 in. pipe at the rate of 1.4 ft/sec comes to a small $\frac{1}{2}$ in. pipe, and then a 2 in. pipe. Find (a) the velocity in the last two pipes, and (b) the velocity head in all three pipes.

14. A water tank is located on a platform 48 ft above the ground. If the water is 16 ft deep at the time that a hole develops in the side of the tank very close to the bottom, how far away from the platform and tank will the escaping stream of water strike the ground? (*Ans.* 55.4 ft.)

15. In a laboratory experiment performed with apparatus like that shown in Fig. 28K, the following measurements were made: $sA = 150$ cm, and $sa = 5$ cm. The diameter of the middle section DE of the horizontal tube equals 1 cm, and the diameter of the end sections AB and GH equal 2 cm. Find the speed of the water in (a) AB, and (b) DE. (c) What is the pressure drop cl in cm of water?

16. A pressure gauge on a pipe leading from the bottom of a water tank indicates a pressure of 40 lb/in.² When a valve in the pipe is opened to let water flow out, the gauge pressure drops to 36 lb/in.² Find the speed of the water in the pipe. (*Ans.* 24.3 ft/sec.)

17. Glycerine is placed in a viscosity measuring apparatus like that shown in Fig. 28H. The capillary tube is 5 cm long, 0.2 cm in diameter, and is located 100 cm below the liquid surface. How much glycerine will flow through in 10 min? The density of glycerine is 1.26 gm/cm³.

Temperature and Expansion   Chapter 29

TEMPERATURE is only relative, and like time, is difficult to define in terms of the simplest concepts. The word temperature means intensity of heat and may be defined as a number on a scale. To be more technical, the absolute temperature of a body is proportional to the average kinetic energy of the molecules of which the body is composed.

29.1. Thermometers. The first authentic record of a thermometer dates back to the time of Galileo. Galileo's thermometer, as illustrated in Fig. 29A, consists of a narrow glass tube with an opening at one end and a bulb at the other. The open end of the tube is filled with colored water and inverted in a dish of water. When the temperature of the surrounding air rises, the air within the bulb expands, forcing the water down the tube. If the bulb is cooled, the air inside contracts, drawing the water up. (To be exact, atmospheric pressure outside pushes the water up.) A scale attached to the narrow tube can be calibrated to any temperature scale, low temperatures at the top and high temperatures at the bottom.

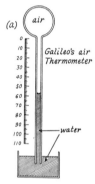

FIG. 29A—Air on heating expands and pushes the water down in the tube. On cooling the air contracts and the water rises.

Of the many forms of temperature measuring devices, the mercury thermometer is the most common. A mercury thermometer, as shown in Fig. 29B, consists of a narrow glass tube (called a capillary), the bottom end being sealed to a small bulb and the top end being closed. The bulb and part of the capillary are filled with mercury, and the remaining section is evacuated. When the temperature rises, the mercury and the glass bulb both expand. The mercury, however, expands more than the glass, forcing a small part of the mercury up the narrow capillary. A scale is engraved on the glass to read temperature.

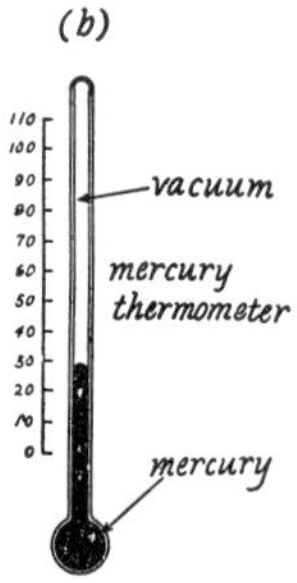

FIG. 29B—On heating a thermometer the mercury expands more than the glass tube and the mercury level rises.

29.2. Temperature Scales. There are in general use today four different temperature scales. These are the Fahrenheit, Rankine, Centigrade, and Kelvin or Absolute. Each scale is shown by a diagram in Fig. 29C. The thermometers are all identically made but each has a differ-

260

ent scale. In the United States the Fahrenheit scale is commonly used in civil life, and the Rankine scale is used by engineers. The Centigrade and Kelvin scales are used in all countries for scientific measurements.

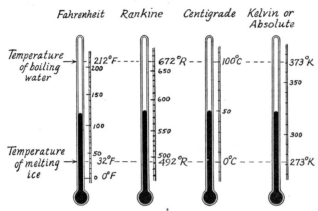

FIG. 29C—Mercury thermometers illustrating the four common temperature scales.

All manufactured thermometers are calibrated to one of these four scales. To calibrate a thermometer, the bulb is first placed in a mixture of ice and water and the height of the mercury column marked on the side of the stem. It is next placed in steam just above boiling water and again marked. These two marks then determine the end points for whatever scale is to be used.

Between the temperatures of melting ice and boiling water there are 180° on the Fahrenheit and Rankine scales, as compared with 100° on the Centigrade and Kelvin scales. The ratio of these numbers is 9:5. This comparison shows that a temperature rise of 9°F, or 9°R, is equivalent to a rise of only 5°C, or 5°K.

The lowest temperature ever reached is approximately −273.16°C, or −459.69°F. For theoretical reasons, which will be given later, this is the lowest temperature that can ever be attained. The Kelvin and Rankine scales start with the lowest possible temperature as *absolute zero*. On the basis of the Centigrade and Fahrenheit scale divisions, this locates the freezing point of water, to the nearest whole number, at 273°K or 492°R, and the boiling point at 373°K or 672°R.

It is frequently necessary to change temperature readings from one temperature scale to another. Rather than develop formulas for such changes it is more convenient to work out the simple mathematical steps by the inspection of a diagram like Fig. 29C.

29.3. Electrical Thermometers. If very low or very high temperatures are to be measured, other than mercury thermometers must be employed. At temperatures below −39°C mercury freezes and becomes a solid, and at high temperatures glass melts and becomes a liquid. For both of these temperature extremes electrical thermometers are commonly used. These instruments operate upon the principle that the resistance a wire offers to a flow of electric current through it changes with temperature. The higher the temperature the greater is the resistance.

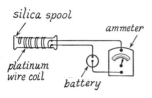

silica spool

ammeter

platinum wire coil

battery

FIG. 29D—Electrical resistance thermometer showing connections between the platinum wire coil, the battery, and the ammeter.

A diagram of an electrical thermometer is shown in Fig. 29D. A fine piece of platinum wire is wound around a small spool made of silica. The ends of this wire are connected to a battery and an ammeter. The purpose of the battery is to supply the electric current and the ammeter is to determine its exact value. When the temperature of a hot body like a furnace is to be measured, the spool of platinum wire is placed inside the furnace and the battery and ammeter outside. A rise in temperature causes the resistance of the platinum wire to increase, and the current, therefore, to decrease. When the platinum wire reaches the temperature of the furnace its resistance reaches a constant value and the ammeter pointer indicates a steady current. In many cases the ammeter scale is calibrated to give the temperature directly in degrees.

Another form of electrical thermometer, called a *thermocouple,* is illustrated in Fig. 29E(a). This temperature recording device is based upon a principle, discovered in 1821 by Seebeck, known as the *thermo-electric effect.* Two pieces of wire, one copper and one iron, are joined together at the ends to form a complete loop. When one junction is heated and the other kept cool an electric current flows around the loop in the direction indicated by the arrows. The greater the difference in temperature between the two junctions the greater is the electric current.

Diagram (b) in Fig. 29E represents a thermocouple connected by wires to an ammeter. If the junction of the thermocouple is first placed in melting

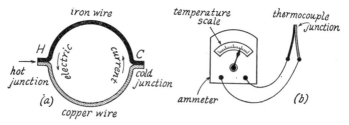

iron wire   *temperature scale*   *thermocouple junction*

H   *C*

hot junction   *electric current*   *cold junction*

(a)   *ammeter*   *(b)*

copper wire

FIG. 29E—Illustrating the thermoelectric effect and its use as a thermocouple for measuring temperature.

ice and then in boiling water, the two scale readings of the ammeter can be marked 0°C and 100°C at the appropriate points. This calibrates the instrument, making of it a direct reading thermometer.

Thermocouples are not always made of copper and iron as shown in Fig. 29E. Any two different metals when brought into contact will exhibit a thermo-electric effect. Some combinations of two metals, however, produce larger currents than others. For very high temperature measurements platinum and platinum-iridium alloys are used, owing to their very high melting point temperatures. See Table 30B.

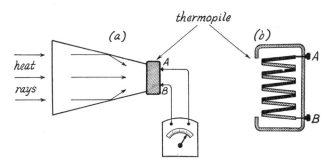

Fig. 29F—Cross-section of a thermopile for measuring heat radiation from hot bodies.

A set of thermocouples, when connected together as shown in Fig. 29F, form what is commonly called a *thermopile*. Small rods of two different metals are joined alternately as shown in diagram (b). One set of junctions is usually protected by placing them at the back of a small box container and the other set is exposed to heat rays through the opposite side which is left open. A funnel or horn-shaped reflector mounted over the open side will collect more heat rays from a distant hot object and thereby increase the electric current. Thermocouples containing several hundred elements can be made so sensitive that they will detect the heat of a candle flame several hundred feet away.

29.4. Thermal Expansion of Solids. In general, when an object is heated, whether it be a solid, liquid, or gas, it expands. There are but a few known exceptions to this. The expansion of a solid with a rise in temperature can be demonstrated by heating a long wire and measuring its over-all elongation. One experimental arrangement for demonstrating this is shown in Fig. 29G. An iron wire about 2 m in length is fastened to a hook A at one end and to a weight W at the other. Between these two points the wire passes over three pulleys B, C, and D. The wire is heated by connecting it to a battery and sending an electric current through it from end to end.

As the wire is heated and lengthens, the weight slowly falls, thus

turning the pulleys as well as the pointer *P*. When the current is turned off
by opening the switch, the wire cools and at the same time contracts to its
original length. In the well-equipped laboratory accurate measurements of
the rise in temperature and the lengthening of a solid rod are readily made.

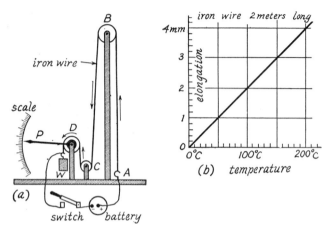

Fɪɢ. 29G—Experiment illustrating the expansion (elongation) of a wire due to a rise in temperature.

The graph at the right in Fig. 29G illustrates the straight-line relation between the rise in temperature and the elongation. By the elongation is
meant the increase in length and not the total length of the wire. For an
iron wire 2 m long, a rise in temperature of 50°C produces an elongation
of 1 mm, 100°C produces an elongation of 2 mm, 150°C an elongation of
3 mm, etc. The straight line means, therefore, that the elongation is
directly proportional to the rise in temperature.

There are many instances in engineering where the expansion of solids
is an important factor in design and construction. Particularly is this true
in the construction of suspension bridges and railroads. When the steel
rails of the early railroads were first put in place, small gaps were left at
every union. The reason for this is that in summer, when the temperature
rises, the rails expand and close these gaps. If the gaps are not large enough
in cold weather, the track may buckle up in summer and cause serious accidents. In winter when the rails contract and the gaps are wider, they become noisy to travel as the car wheels roll over them.

Not all substances expand by the same amount when heated through
the same difference in temperature. This is illustrated by the linear coefficients of thermal expansion of a few common substances given in Table
29A.

TABLE 29A. LINEAR COEFFICIENTS OF THERMAL EXPANSION (CENTIGRADE)

Material	α per °C	Material	α per °C
Aluminum	25×10^{-6}	Iron	11×10^{-6}
Brass	18×10^{-6}	Platinum	9×10^{-6}
Copper	17×10^{-6}	Silver	18×10^{-6}
Glass (soda)	17×10^{-6}	Quartz	0.4×10^{-6}
" (pyrex)	3×10^{-6}	Pine wood (along grain) ...	5×10^{-6}
Gold	14×10^{-6}	" " (across grain) ..	30×10^{-6}

The linear coefficient of thermal expansion α is defined as the change in length per unit length of a substance per 1° rise in temperature. Once this constant is known, the linear expansion for any sized object made of that same material can be calculated for any rise in temperature by the following formula:

$$\text{elongation} = \alpha \times \text{length} \times \text{rise in temperature}$$

$$e = \alpha L(t_2 - t_1). \tag{29a}$$

In this equation t_1 is the original temperature of the body, t_2 the final temperature to which it is raised, and L its original length.*

Example. A pyrex glass rod is ground and polished to a length of 10 cm when the room temperature is 20°C. If this same rod is heated to a temperature of 420°C, how much does it elongate?

Solution. From the above equation we write

$$e = 3 \times 10^{-6} \times 10 \times (420 - 20)$$
$$= 3 \times 10^{-6} \times 10 \times 400 = 0.012 \text{ cm}.$$

The rod thus lengthens by only 0.012 cm to give an over-all length of 10.012 cm. It should be noted that had the length of the rod been given as 10 in. the elongation would have been 0.012 in. In other words, e and L are always in the same units, so that the coefficients of thermal expansion are valid in the metric as well as the English system. The coefficients given in Table 29A, however, are for the centigrade temperature scale only. Should the known temperature be Fahrenheit or Rankine, the change in temperature should be converted to the Centigrade scale.

29.5. Differential Expansion. In the previous section it was stated that all substances do not expand alike. Some metals like brass and aluminum expand twice as much as others, like iron and platinum. See Table

---

* It is customary in formulas to use the letter t for temperature on either the Centigrade or Fahrenheit scale. When absolute temperature must be used, however, the capital letter T is used.

29A. This difference in expansion is demonstrated by the heating of a bi-metallic strip as shown in Fig. 29H. Two thin strips of different metal are placed side by side and welded together over their entire length. When heated, one metal expands more than the other, causing the strip to bend. The hotter it becomes the more it bends. When it cools down to its original temperature the strip becomes straight again, and if cooled still further it bends in the opposite direction.

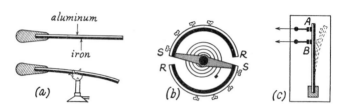

FIG. 29H—Different substances expand by different amounts (a) Bi-metallic strip, (b) balance wheel of a watch, (c) a thermostat.

Differential expansion as shown by this experiment finds many practical applications in industry. Bi-metallic strips are used, for example, in the making of balance wheels for fine watches and in thermostats for refrigerators, hot water heaters, and car radiators. When on a hot day the spokes of the balance of a watch expand, they shift the weight of the rim farther from the center, causing the balance wheel to oscillate more slowly. By making the rim of the wheel of two bi-metallic strips this can be compensated for as shown in Fig. 29H(b). With a rise in temperature the ends of the spokes S move out and the free ends R of the bi-metallic strips bend in closer to the axis of rotation. One expansion compensates the other, keeping the watch running at the same rate.

Thermostats are so commonly employed in electrical devices today that their explanation will be given here. An electrical thermostat is an automatic electric switch which closes when the temperature reaches one desired temperature and opens when it reaches another. One type of switch is shown in Fig. 29H(c). If the temperature is low the bi-metallic strip is straight and makes electrical contact between the points A and B. This operates an electrical device which, for argument's sake, might open a gas valve of a furnace in the basement of a house. When the air in the house rises to the desired temperature the bi-metallic strip has bent far enough away to break the electrical contact at A and B thus turning off the furnace. As the air cools the strip straightens out and makes contact, again turning on the furnace.

29.6. Area and Volume Expansion. When the temperature of a wire is raised it not only lengthens but the diameter and cross-sectional area increase as well. A disk, when heated, increases in radius and area, while a sphere or cube increases in volume. In isotropic substances like copper, linear expansion takes place equally in all directions. In non-isotropic substances like wood, expansion at right angles to the grain is quite different from expansion parallel to the grain. See Table 29A. To find the increased area or volume of such materials the linear expansion formula, Eq.(29a), must be applied to each direction separately. The same procedure can be applied to isotropic substances but more rapid calculations can be made by the following formulas.

For area expansion of isotropic media

$$a = 2\alpha A (t_2 - t_1) \tag{29b}$$

where A is the original area of the surface, a is the increase in area due to expansion, α is the linear coefficient of expansion, and $t_2 - t_1$ is the rise in temperature.

For volume expansion of isotropic media,

$$v = 3\alpha V (t_2 - t_1) \tag{29c}$$

where V is the original volume of the solid, v is the increase in volume, and the remaining symbols are the same as before.

The cavity in a hollow ball or container expands as though it were a solid block of the same material. For example, a platinum cup with a volume of 1000 cm³ at 0°C will, when raised to 100°C, have the following increase in volume:

$$v = 3 \times 9 \times 10^{-6} \times 1000 \times (100 - 0) = 2.7 \text{ cm}^3.$$

Its new volume will be 1002.7 cm³.

The following question will be left as a problem for the student. If the temperature of a copper washer, i.e., a copper disk with a hole in the center, is raised, will the hole in the center become larger or smaller?

29.7. Thermal Expansion of Liquids. Accurate measurements of the expansion of liquids with a rise in temperature are made difficult by the simultaneous expansion of the containing vessel. This difficulty can be overcome, however, and one finds that most liquids, like solids, expand by an amount which is proportional to the rise in temperature. This is illustrated by the straight-line graphs for alcohol and mercury in Fig. 29I(a).

A straight-line graph here means that with each degree rise in temperature the increase in volume due to expansion is exactly the same. If 1 cc of mercury at 0°C is heated to a temperature of 1°C its volume will be 1.00018 cm³, or an increase of 0.00018 cm³. At 10° the increase will be ten times this amount, or 0.0018 cm³. Thus for each degree rise the increase is the

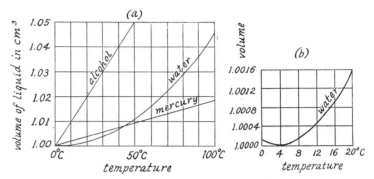

Fig. 29I—Volume-temperature graphs of the thermal expansion of liquids.

same and equal to 0.00018. This number is called the volume coefficient of thermal expansion of mercury. For alcohol the coefficient is 0.0011 per degree centigrade.

TABLE 29B. VOLUME COEFFICIENTS OF EXPANSION FOR FOUR COMMON LIQUIDS

Liquid	per °C	per °F
Alcohol	11.0×10^{-4}	6.6×10^{-4}
Glycerine	5.3×10^{-4}	2.9×10^{-4}
Mercury	1.8×10^{-4}	1.0×10^{-4}
Turpentine	10.5×10^{-4}	5.8×10^{-4}

The volume expansion of liquids like mercury or alcohol is given by a formula of exactly the same form as the one for solids. See Eq.(11a).

$$v = \beta V (t_2 - t_1) \qquad (29d)$$

where v is the change in volume, β the volume coefficient of thermal expansion, V the original volume, and $t_2 - t_1$ is the difference in temperature.

29.8. Anomalous Expansion of Water. Over a large range in temperature, liquids do not expand linearly. Actually their graphs curve slightly upward, indicating a more rapid rise at higher temperatures. The extent of the departure from a straight-line graph differs considerably with liquids. At 100°C, for example, alcohol expands about 20% more for each degree rise than it does at 0°C. Mercury, on the other hand, varies by less than one hundredth of 1% and may be assumed accurately linear between these two temperatures.

Starting at its freezing temperature of 0°C, and being slowly heated, water contracts until it reaches a temperature of 4°C and then expands. At 4°C where it reaches its minimum volume it has its maximum density. It might be considered fortunate that water expands on being cooled from 4°C to 0°C. If this were not the case and it contracted the way most liquids do, ice would form at the bottom of lakes instead of at the top.

When a pond of water cools toward the freezing point, the surface water next to the cold air cools first. Having cooled and contracted it has a greater density than the water below and it sinks. This process continues until all the water reaches 4°C. Now, as the surface water cools below 4°C it expands, and, becoming less dense, floats. The water on the surface therefore reaches 0°C first and freezes. In freezing, the water expands still more to become ice. Ice floats on water because its density is less than that of water. When 1 cc of water at 4°C is cooled down to 0°C and frozen, it expands about 9%. Its new volume as a solid at 0°C is 1.09 cm³.

QUESTIONS

1. Name and diagram the four temperature scales.
2. Diagram and explain the principle of the thermocouple.
3. Give an example of, and explain, differential expansion.
4. Explain why the top surface of a pan of water freezes first.
5. Explain how to calibrate a new thermometer so that it reads temperature on the centigrade scale.

PROBLEMS

1. If a Centigrade thermometer indicates a temperature of 35°C, what would a Fahrenheit thermometer read in the same room?

2. What temperature on the Centigrade scale and the Rankine scale is equivalent to the following: (a) 50°F, (b) 77°F, (c) 95°F, (d) 85°F, and (e) −40°F. (*Ans.* (a) 10°C, 510°R, (b) 25°C, 537°R, (c) 35°C, 555°R, (d) 29.4°C, 545°R, (e) −40°C, 420°R.)

3. A standard gauge block, made of silver, is exactly 5.000 cm long at 20°C. Calculate its length when the temperature is 30°C.

4. A pine wood meter stick is exactly 100 cm long when the temperature is 32°F. Find its exact length when the temperature is 77°F. (*Ans.* 100.0125 cm.)

5. A standard platinum meter bar at the Bureau of Standards is exactly calibrated at 27°C. Find the distance between the end marks when the temperature is 37°C.

6. The iron rails used in building railroads are 60 ft in length. If at the time they are nailed into place the temperature is 95°F, how large will the gaps between rails be when the temperature drops to −22°F? (*Ans.* 0.51 in.)

7. The Eiffel Tower in Paris is 984 ft high and is made of iron. Calculate its change in height when the temperature changes from 0°C to 40°C.

8. A spherical fabricated tank made of iron is 1 m in diameter when the temperature is 50°C. Find its change in volume when the temperature drops to 0°C. (*Ans.* 864 cm³.)

9. A cylindrical tank made of sheet iron has a volume of 1000 gallons when the temperature is 32°F. Find its change in volume when the temperature rises to 113°F.

10. A storage tank made of sheet iron holds 1000 gallons of alcohol when the tem-

perature is −10°C. How much alcohol will spill out if the temperature is raised to 40°C. (*Ans.* 53.4 gal.)

11. A storage tank made of sheet brass holds 500 gallons of turpentine when the temperature is −22°F. How much turpentine will spill out when the temperature is raised to 95°F?

12. A gold disk at 20°C has a diameter of 10 cm and a hole cut in the center that is 5 cm in diameter. Calculate the diameter of the hole when the temperature is raised to 50°C. (*Ans.* 5.0021 cm.)

13. A pine board is cut and carefully planed so that it is exactly 20 cm wide and 2 m long when the temperature is 68°F. Calculate the increase in area when the temperature is raised to 158°F.

14. A copper wire 1 m long hangs from the ceiling. To the lower end is fastened an aluminum wire 2 m long, and to the lower end of the aluminum wire a small weight. How far will the weight descend if the temperature is raised from 10°C to 60°C? (*Ans.* 0.335 cm.)

15. A gold strip is made into a ring whose inside diameter is 20 mm at 20°C. Find the inside diameter when the temperature is raised to 70°C.

16. The iron rim of a wagon wheel has an internal diameter of 1.5 m when the temperature is 120°C. What is its internal diameter when the temperature is lowered to 20°C? (*Ans.* 149.835 cm.)

17. A soda glass flask with a volume of 1 liter is full of mercury at 15°C. How many cubic centimeters will flow out when the temperature is raised to 45°C?

18. At a temperature of 25°C, a solid brass sphere has a diameter of 4.00 cm and a brass ring has an inside diameter of 3.95 cm. To what temperature should the ring be heated so that the sphere will just pass through the ring? (*Ans.* 719°C.)

19. Find the coefficient of thermal expansion of a 30 ft metal rod if its length increases by 0.1% when the temperature rises 60°C.

20. A steel tape measure 100 ft long is standardized to be used at 73°F. What will be its increase in length at 100°F? The linear coefficient of thermal expansion for steel is 5×10^{-6} per °F. (*Ans.* 0.162 in.)

21. A spool contains 1000 m of copper wire at 30°C. How much will this wire be shortened when the temperature drops to 0°C?

Heat Capacity and Change of State

Chapter 30

ACCORDING to the kinetic theory of matter the individual atoms of which all substances are made are in a state of rapid motion. As a body is heated to a higher temperature this atomic motion increases and the body expands. As a body cools the atomic motions decrease and the body shrinks. That heat is a form of energy and is due to the kinetic energy of molecular motion was first proposed by Count Rumford the latter part of the 18th century.*

It is not always clear to the beginning student that temperature and quantity of heat are different entities. The difference between the two can be illustrated by the heating of two pans of water. More gas must be burned to heat a large pan of water than a small pan. Although both are started at the same temperature and both are raised to the same boiling point, 100°C, the larger pan has required more thermal energy, called heat.

30.1. The Calorie. The difference between temperature and quantity of heat is well illustrated by the following experiment. See Fig. 30A. Five marbles, all of the same size but made of different materials, are heated in boiling water to a temperature of 100°C. At a given instant they are all

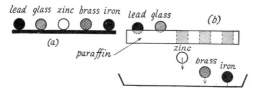

FIG. 30A—Experiment illustrating the different heat capacities of different substances.

* Benjamin Thompson was born in Rumford, New Hampshire, in 1753. He spent most of his adult life in Germany, where, amongst other things, he managed an artillery factory. From his observations about the heat developed in boring cannon, he was able to show that heat is not a pervading fluid, but a form of internal energy of the atoms or molecules forming the substance. His own expression was that heat was a mode of motion of these particles. For these and other services, the Emperor chose to appoint him to the German nobility, and Thompson chose the name of his birthplace, Rumford, as his title.

placed on a sheet of paraffin about 0.5 cm thick and permitted to melt their way through. The iron and brass marbles are observed to drop through first, but the lead and glass marbles never do. This illustrates the fact that the heat content of the iron and brass, even though raised to the same temperature as the others, is considerably greater than the heat content of the glass and lead.

In order to determine the exact heat capacity of a substance, we must first define the *calorie* and the *British thermal unit*. *The amount of heat required to raise the temperature of 1 gm of water 1°C is called the calorie* (abbr. cal). *The quantity of heat required to raise the temperature of 1 lb of water 1°F is called the British thermal unit* (abbr. Btu). The ratio between these two units is readily computed and found to be

$$1 \text{ Btu} = 252 \text{ cal.} \tag{30a}$$

Once the calorie or the Btu is defined the amount of heat required to raise any amount of water from one temperature to another may be calculated by simply multiplying the mass of water by the temperature rise. For example, to raise 25 gm of water from 10°C to 50°C requires $25 \times 40 = 1000$ cal, or to raise 6 lb of water from 32°F to 60°F requires $6 \times 28 = 168$ Btu.

While 1 cal of heat will raise 1 gm of water 1°C, a different number of calories will be required to raise the temperature of 1 gm of some other substance 1°C. For example, to raise 1 gm of iron 1°C requires only one-tenth of a calorie, while to raise 1 gm of lead 1°C requires only one-thirtieth of a calorie. In other words, the thermal capacities of equal masses of different materials have different values.

The thermal capacity of a substance is defined as the number of calories required to raise 1 gm of that substance through 1°C, or *the amount of heat to raise 1 lb 1°F*. The ratio between the thermal capacity of a substance and the thermal capacity of water is called *specific heat*. Numerically specific heat has the same value as thermal capacity; being a ratio, however, it is like *specific gravity* and has no units.

The specific heats or thermal capacities of a few common substances are given in the following table.

TABLE 30A. SPECIFIC HEATS

	c		c		c
Aluminum	0.220	Gold	0.031	Lead	0.031
Brass	0.092	Glycerine	0.60	Mercury	0.033
Copper	0.093	Ice	0.50	Silver	0.056
Glass	0.160	Iron	0.105	Zinc	0.092

To illustrate the use of this table, consider the calculation of the heat content of the marbles used in the above experiment. The measured mass of each marble is given in the second row of the following tabulation and the corresponding thermal capacity in the next row. The product of these two quantities gives the values shown in the third row; they represent the amount of heat required to raise that marble 1°C. Since all marbles were raised from room temperature 20°C to the boiling point of water, 100°C, the values in the third row have been multiplied by the rise in temperature 80°C to obtain the total heat values in the last row.

TABULATED RESULTS OF THE MARBLE EXPERIMENT

	Lead	Glass	Zinc	Brass	Iron
Mass in grams	45	10	24	30	28
Thermal capacity, cal/gm deg.	0.031	0.160	0.092	0.092	0.105
Heat to raise 1°C, cal.	1.39	1.60	2.20	2.76	2.94
Heat to raise 80°C, cal.	111	128	176	221	235

These numbers clearly indicate that in the experiment above, iron and brass should melt through the paraffin first: they have available within them the largest amounts of stored thermal energy, 235 and 221 calories, respectively.

The definition of thermal capacity and the calculation of total heat content may be summarized by a generally useful formula of the following form,

$$H = m \times c \times (t_2 - t_1). \tag{30b}$$

H represents the total amount of heat in calories or Btu, m the mass of the body to which it is added, c is the thermal capacity, and $t_2 - t_1$ is the rise in temperature.

30.2. Calorimetry. Calorimetry is a term applied to an experimental process by which quantities of heat are measured. The process involves the weighing of certain objects and the measuring of their temperatures, followed by calculations using the total heat capacity formula Eq.(30b).

To illustrate the procedure and principles used, consider the following experiment in which the specific heat of iron (taken here to be an unknown) can be determined. The apparatus diagramed in Fig. 30B shows a cylindrical steam jacket containing a thermometer and a small iron block I suspended by a string. At the right is a double-walled calorimeter containing a thermometer and a measured quantity of water at close to room temperature. The purpose of the steam jacket is to heat the iron to a relatively high temperature that can be measured.

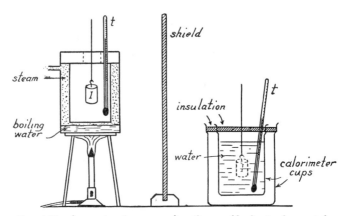

FIG. 30B—Apparatus for measuring the specific heat of a metal.

When the thermometer in the steam jacket indicates a steady reading near 100°C the iron block is quickly lifted out and lowered into the water of the calorimeter (shown dotted). The iron gives up heat in cooling and the water gains heat. The steady rise in temperature as noted by the thermometer soon stops, thereby indicating that both the iron and water have reached the same temperature.

The following data which were taken in such an experiment will be used to demonstrate the calculation of specific heat.

Mass of iron block .... 458 gm
Mass of copper calorimeter cup .... 362 gm
Mass of water in cup .... 500 gm
Initial temperature of iron .... 98.6°C
Initial temperature of water .... 18.4°C
Final temperature of mixture .... 25.0°C

Since the heat lost by the iron is given up to the water and inner calorimeter cup we start by writing down, by conservation of energy,

$$\text{heat lost} = \text{heat gained.} \qquad (30c)$$

We note that the heated iron is the only body that loses heat and that the thermal capacity formula, Eq.(30b), gives for the left-hand side,

$$\text{heat lost,} \qquad H = 458 \text{ gm} \times c \times (98.6 - 25.0) \text{ deg.}$$

where c is the unknown quantity to be determined.

$$H = 33{,}700 \times c \text{ gm deg.}$$

To find the right-hand side of the equation it will be noted that in addition to the water the inner calorimeter cup also gains heat. It is assumed that the outer cup, which in a good calorimeter is well insulated from the inner cup, neither gains nor loses heat during the experiment.

For the water and inner cup respectively, Eq.(30b) gives

$$\text{heat gained} \quad H = 500 \text{ gm} \times 1 \frac{\text{cal}}{\text{gm deg.}} (25.0 - 18.4) \text{ deg.}$$

$$+ 362 \text{ gm} \times 0.093 \frac{\text{cal}}{\text{gm deg.}} (25.0 - 18.4) \text{ deg.}$$

By taking out the common factor, we obtain

$$H = (500 + 33.7)(25.0 - 18.4) \text{ cal,}$$

from which

$$H = 533.7 \times 6.6 \text{ cal} = 3522 \text{ cal.}$$

If we substitute these values of H for heat lost and heat gained in Eq.(30c),

$$33,700 \, c \text{ gm deg} = 3522 \text{ cal.}$$

Solving for the unknown c, we obtain

$$c = \frac{3522 \text{ cal}}{33,700 \text{ gm deg}} = 0.105 \frac{\text{cal}}{\text{gm deg}}$$

a value of the thermal capacity or specific heat in agreement with the value generally given in accepted tables.

In obtaining this result it has been necessary to know the thermal capacity of the inner calorimeter cup. The mass of the cup multiplied by the thermal capacity of copper gives what is called the *water equivalent* of the cup ($m \times c = 33.7$). The term water equivalent signifies that as far as the experiment is concerned, the cup absorbs an amount of heat equivalent to 33.7 gm of water.

The thermometer too has a water equivalent and should rightly be included, but due to its relatively small mass the heat it absorbs may be neglected without appreciably affecting the calculated result.

30.3. Change of State. The continuous addition of heat to a solid or liquid mass will eventually bring about a change of state. The general behavior of many substances can be illustrated by a detailed description of the changes that occur with the most common of all liquids, water. If a block of ice at a temperature of $-50°C$ is placed in a pan and put on a stove to heat, its temperature will rise slowly until it reaches $0°C$.

At $0°C$ the temperature stops rising and the ice begins to melt. More and more ice is melted as heat is continually added and not until it has all turned

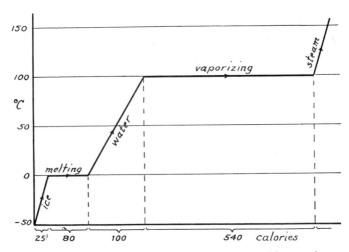

FIG. 30C—Heat-temperature graph for one gram of ice starting at
—50°C., illustrating the latent heat of fusion and vaporization.

to water does the temperature begin to rise. As the water becomes hotter and
hotter it eventually reaches a temperature of 100°C where vigorous boiling
sets in. Here again the temperature stops rising and, as heat is added,
more and more water is boiled away to become steam. Finally when all has
become steam at 100°C the temperature begins to rise once more.

All of these changes of temperature and changes of state are shown by a
graph in Fig. 30C. The horizontal sections represent changes of state without change in temperature, while the slanted sections on either side represent changes in temperature without abrupt changes in state.

30.4. Melting Point. The melting point is defined as the temperature
at which a substance under normal atmospheric pressure changes from the
solid to the liquid state, or vice versa. Every substance has its own melting
point, which for water is at 0°C. As shown by a few common substances
listed in Table 30B, some substances melt at very low temperatures while
others require extremely high temperatures.

Recent studies of the atomic structure of certain liquids show that at
temperatures approaching the freezing point, the lattice formation assumed
by the individual atoms is essentially that of the solid state, whereas others
show no such resemblance or similarity right up to the freezing temperature.

30.5. Boiling Point. The boiling point is defined as the temperature at
which a substance, under normal atmospheric pressure, changes from the
liquid to the vapor state, or vice versa. These temperatures too are listed
in Table 30B. A knowledge of melting and boiling points is of considerable
practical importance. Solid carbon dioxide, liquid air, liquid hydrogen and

liquid helium are used as refrigerants for cooling, whereas metals like tungsten and platinum are used in furnaces designed for the heating of bodies to very high temperatures.

30.6. Latent Heat of Fusion. We have seen above that when ice is melting, heat is continually added with no resultant rise in temperature. To melt 1 gm of ice requires 80 calories, and to melt 1 lb requires 143 Btu. Similar heat determinations for other solids show that they too require a definite amount of heat to melt them without a rise in temperature. To melt 1 gm of gold requires 16 cal, 1 gm of silver 21 cal, etc. These values, the so-called *latent heat of fusion,* are tabulated for a number of elements in Table 30B.

Latent heat of fusion is defined as the quantity of heat necessary to change 1 gm of solid to 1 gm of liquid with no change in temperature.

The reverse of fusion is *solidification,* a process in which heat is liberated by the substance. The amount of heat liberated by matter on solidification is equal to the amount of heat taken in on fusion; pure water on freezing gives up 80 cal/gm, gold 16 cal/gm, silver 21 cal/gm, etc. Letting L represent the latent heat of fusion and m the mass of a given substance to be

TABLE 30B. MELTING POINT, LATENT HEAT OF FUSION, BOILING POINT, AND HEAT OF VAPORIZATION OF SOME COMMON SUBSTANCES

Substance	Melting Point °C	Heat of Fusion cal/gm	Boiling Point °C	Heat of Vaporization cal/gm
Air	−212	5.5	−191	51
Aluminum	658	77	1800	..
Copper	1080	42	2310	..
Gold	1063	16	2500	..
Helium	−271	..	−268	6
Hydrogen	−259	14	−252	108
Iron	1530	6	2450	..
Lead	327	5.9	1525	..
Mercury	−39	2.8	357	65
Nitrogen	−210	6.1	−195	48
Oxygen	−219	3.3	−184	51
Platinum	1760	27	3910	..
Silicon	1420	..	3500	..
Silver	962	21	1955	..
Sulfur Dioxide	73	24	−10	95
Tin	232	14	2270	..
Tungsten	3400	..	5830	..
Water	0	80	100	540

fused or solidified, the quantity of heat required or liberated as the case may be is given by

$$H = mL_f. \qquad (30d)$$

If m is the mass in grams, then L_f should be in cal/gm and H will be in calories. If m is in pounds, then L_f should be in Btu/lb, and H will be in Btu.

30.7. Heat of Vaporization. When water is being boiled, heat is continually being added without a rise in temperature. This added heat is not retained by the liquid but is carried off by the vapor through the boiling process. To vaporize 1 gm of boiling water requires 540 calories, and to vaporize 1 lb requires 970 Btu. These values, the so-called *heat of vaporization,* are tabulated along with others for a number of substances in Table 30B. (For the metals with very high melting points the heat of vaporization has never been measured.)

The same Eq.(30d) used for calculating heat quantities during fusion may be used to determine heat quantities during vaporization. If we let L_v be the heat of vaporization and m the mass of substance to be vaporized, the quantity of heat H required is given by

$$H = mL_v. \qquad (30e)$$

This is also the amount of heat liberated by the same amount of vapor when it condenses to the liquid state.

Since heat is a form of energy and its addition to a body raises the average kinetic energy of the molecules, the absolute temperature increases proportionately. During fusion and vaporization, however, heat is added without a temperature change. During change of state the heat energy goes into potential energy of the molecules, exerting forces through collision which push the molecules farther apart against their attractive forces.

Example. Calculate the amount of heat required to change 50 gm of ice at $-20°C$ to steam at $140°C$.

Solution. To heat the ice from $-20°C$ to the melting point at $0°C$, use Eq.(30b) and the thermal capacity of ice from Table 30A.

$$H_1 = mc(t_2 - t_1) = 50 \times 0.50 \times 20 = 500 \text{ cal.}$$

To melt the ice to water at $0°C$ use Eq.(30d) and the heat of fusion from Table 30B.

$$H_2 = mL_f = 50 \times 80 = 4000 \text{ cal.}$$

To heat the water from $0°C$ to the boiling point at $100°C$ use Eq.(30b) and the thermal capacity of water.

$$H_3 = mc(t_2 - t_1) = 50 \times 1 \times 100 = 5000 \text{ cal.}$$

To vaporize the water to steam at $100°C$ use Eq.(30e) and the heat of vaporization of water.

$$H_4 = 50 \times 540 = 27{,}000 \text{ cal.}$$

To heat the steam from 100°C to steam at the desired temperature 140°C, use Eq.(30b) and the thermal capacity of steam.

$$H_5 = mc(t_2 - t_1) = 50 \times 0.5 \times 40 = 1000 \text{ cal.}$$

By adding all of these, we obtain the total required heat.

$$H = 500 + 4000 + 5000 + 27,000 + 1000 = 37,500 \text{ cal.}$$

30.8. Heat of Combustion. When gas, wood, or coal, is burned, heat is liberated. The amount of heat given off per unit mass of completely burned fuel is called its *heat of combustion*. The following table gives the heats of combustion of several commonly used fuels.

Coal	6,600 cal/gm	12,000 Btu/lb
Coke	6,100 cal/gm	11,000 Btu/lb
Gasoline	11,600 cal/gm	21,000 Btu/lb
Wood	2,500 cal/gm	4,500 Btu/lb
Natural gas	13,700 cal/liter	1,500 Btu/ft³
Methane	9,100 cal/liter	1,000 Btu/ft³

To measure the heat of combustion of gas a continuous flow calorimeter like that shown in Fig. 30D is often used. Gas under constant pressure from the gas mains is passed through a meter and then burned in a Bunsen burner. The hot gases of combustion rise up the center cavity of the double-walled

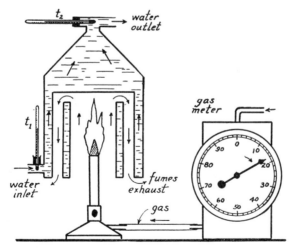

FIG. 30D—Continuous flow calorimeter as used to measure the heat of combustion of natural gas.

vessel and down through a number of exhaust pipes. Water under constant pressure from the water mains is thus heated as it flows through at a constant rate. By measuring the rate of flow of gas to the burner, the rate of flow of water through the apparatus, and the rise in temperature, the amount of heat generated per minute can be calculated.

In a test experiment the following data were taken.

Water flowing through in 1 min . . . . . 8.32 lb
Gas burned per minute . . . . 0.071 cu ft
Entrance temperature of water . . . . . . 65.5°F
Exit temperature of water . . . . 78.0°F

The total heat generated in 1 min is given by the amount of water flowing through, 8.32 lb/min, multiplied by the rise in temperature,

$$8.32(78.0 - 65.5) = 104 \text{ Btu/min.}$$

Dividing by the gas consumed in the same time gives

$$\frac{104 \text{ Btu/min}}{0.071 \text{ ft}^3/\text{min}} = 1465 \frac{\text{Btu}}{\text{ft}^3} \cdot$$

The heat of combustion of liquid fuels can be measured in exactly the same way. For solids like coal, however, a bomb calorimeter similar to that described in the following section is frequently used.

30.9. Food and Its Heat Value. The food we eat, when oxidized in

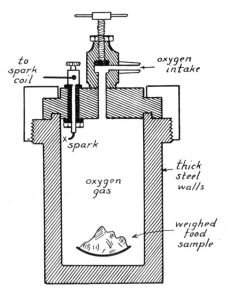

Fig. 30E—Cross-section of a bomb-calorim-
eter as used to measure the heat of combustion of foodstuffs.

the body, furnishes heat energy needed for growth, exercise and the average maintenance of a healthy body. By knowing the heat of combustion of the various foods we eat it is possible to calculate the energy made available to the body for possible storage.

The total available heat content of food is measured by means of a "bomb calorimeter." Such a device is a thick-walled steel container of the kind shown in cross-section in Fig. 30E. Food to be burned is placed in a metal dish at the bottom. After the heavy steel cap is screwed in place, oxygen under considerable pressure is pumped in through the valve provided at the top. The bomb is then immersed in water in a standard calorimeter cup and the contents of the bomb ignited by means of an electric spark. Complete oxidation of all the food takes place quickly and the resultant rise in temperature of the water is measured. If we know the temperature before and after combustion and the weight measurements of water, calorimeter, etc., the total heat liberated can be calculated as outlined in Sec. 30.2.

The following table gives average fuel values of typically common foods.

TABLE 30C. HEAT CONTENT OF AVERAGE SERVINGS OF FOOD

Food	K-Cal	Btu
Baked beans, 3 oz.	300	1200
Bread, 1 slice	100	400
Butter, ½ oz.	100	400
Cake, 3 oz.	250	1000
Cream, 1 oz.	75	300
Egg, one	80	320
Meat, 3 oz.	300	1200
Pie, ⅙th	250	1000
Potatoes, one medium size	100	400
Sugar, 3 large cubes	100	400

K-cal is an abbreviation for the kilo-calorie, or large calorie, a unit of heat equal to 1000 calories.

$$1 \text{ kilo-calorie} = 1000 \text{ calories.}$$

PROBLEMS

1. Find the number of calories of heat required to raise the temperature of 2 kg of lead from 20°C to 100°C.

2. Calculate the amount of heat required to raise 0.40 kg of gold from 65°F to 155°F. (*Ans.* 620 cal.)

3. Lead shot weighing 800 gm at 100°C is dropped into a brass calorimeter cup containing 350 gm of water. If the cup has a mass of 280 gm and the water is initially at 15°C, what will be the final temperature?

4. A 2 kg block of iron at 100°C is dropped into 750 gm of water contained in a 325 gm copper calorimeter cup. If the initial temperature of the water is 12°C what will be its final temperature? (*Ans.* 30.7°C.)

5. A cylinder of metal having a mass of 450 gm at 150°C is dropped into 200 gm of water at 15°C. If the water is contained in a brass calorimeter weighing 200 gm, and the temperature rises to 38°C, what is the thermal capacity of the metal?

6. A metal cylinder weighing 10 lb at 212°F is dropped into 4 lb of water at 50°F. If the water is contained in a copper calorimeter cup weighing 1.5 lb and the temperature rises 95°F, what is the thermal capacity of the metal? (*Ans.* 0.159 Btu/lb °F.)

7. Calculate the heat required to change 50 gm of ice at − 5°C to water at 30°C.

8. Find the heat necessary to change 5 kg of water at 30°C to steam at 100°C. (*Ans.* 3.05×10^6 cal.)

9. How much heat is required to melt 5 lb of lead at 327°C?

10. How much heat will vaporize 4 kg of mercury at 357°C? (*Ans.* 2.6×10^5 cal.)

11. How much coal must be burned to raise the temperature of 500 lb of water from 41°F to the boiling point? If the price of coal is $20 per ton, find the cost.

12. A small crucible containing 300 gm of gold is heated to the temperature of a small furnace and then the gold dropped into 1 kg of water at 10°C. If the final temperature comes to 20°C, find the temperature of the furnace. Neglect heat losses to any container. (*Ans.* 1095°C.)

13. A 0.75 kg block of metal at 100°C is dropped into a 50 gm copper calorimeter cup containing 0.56 kg of water at 20°C. If the final temperature reached is 30°C, find the specific heat of the metal. Identify the metal from Table 30A.

14. A 2 kg block of metal at 100°C is dropped into a cavity in a large block of ice at 0°C. If 268 gm of ice are melted, find the specific heat of the metal. Identify the metal by referring to Table 30A. (*Ans.* 0.107; iron.)

15. How many kilograms of coal must be burned to heat a bathtub full of water from 0°C to 30°C if the water has a mass of 150 kg? Assume the heater efficiency to be 60%. Find the cost if the price of coal is 2 cents/kg.

16. Let 800 gm of lead at 90°C, and 300 gm of copper at 100°C, be dropped into a 100 gm copper calorimeter cup containing 500 gm of water at 15°C. Find the resultant temperature. (*Ans.* 22.5°C.)

Heat Transfer and the Atmosphere

Chapter 31

THERE are numerous methods by which heat may be transmitted from one place to another. Some of these methods are slow and round about while others are very fast and straight to the point. A careful study of all known methods has led to the realization that there are but three general types of heat transfer. These are *conduction, convection,* and *radiation.* Conduction is a slow process by which heat is transmitted through a substance by molecular activity. Convection is a more rapid process involving the motion of heated matter itself from one place to another. Radiation of heat from one place to another takes place in the same manner and with the same speed as light, 186,000 mi/sec.

31.1. Conduction. Not all bodies are good conductors of heat. Metals like copper and silver are much better for this purpose than are other substances like wood, glass, paper, and water. The ability of a given substance to conduct heat is called its *thermal conductivity.*

The relative conductivities of different substances can be illustrated by an experiment performed as follows: Similar rods of six different metals, copper, aluminum, brass, tin, german silver and lead, are coated with a special yellow paint and arranged as shown in Fig. 31A. The ends of the rods, mounted in rubber corks, project through holes in a metal tube where their lower ends are heated to 100°C by steam passing through the tube. As the heat travels slowly up each rod the yellow paint turns to red.

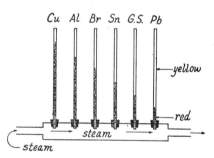

FIG. 31A—Experiment illustrating the relative heat conductivities of six different metals: copper, aluminum, brass, tin, German silver, and lead.

After 5 or 10 min running, the height to which the paint has turned color is approximately as shown by the stippled areas in the figure. Of these six metals, copper is observed to be the best conductor and lead the poorest.

In order to heat an object it is customary to bring it into contact with some other body at a higher temperature. A pan of water, for example, is

283

generally heated by placing it over an open flame. The combustion of natural gas first sets the gas molecules into a rapid state of motion. These molecules striking the bottom of the pan set the molecules of the metal into rapid vibration. They in turn strike other metal molecules, thus transferring the motion through to the other side. This is called heat conduction. The metal molecules set the first layer of water molecules moving and they in turn set others moving. Thus molecular motion, called heat, has been given to the body of water.

Laboratory experiments show that the amount of heat flowing through a rod is proportional to the time, the cross-sectional area, and the difference in temperature between the ends, and is inversely proportional to the length.

Using appropriate symbols for each of these factors and inserting a proportionality constant, the following equation is set up:

$$H = k \frac{A(t_2 - t_1)}{L} T. \qquad (31a)$$

H is the amount of heat flowing through the body of length L and cross section A, k is the thermal conductivity, T is the time interval of flow, t_2 is the temperature of the hot end, and t_1 is the temperature of the cold end. It is quite clear to almost everyone that if the temperature difference $t_2 - t_1$, or the area A is increased (see Fig. 31B) the amount of heat passing through is increased. It is not as obvious, however, that an increase in the length L causes a decrease in heat flow, or that a decrease in length produces an increase. This latter will be illustrated by two experiments.

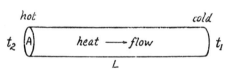

Fig. 31B—Illustrating the various measurable factors involved in the flow of heat through a body by conduction.

Although paper is a poor conductor, the flow of heat through it can be made very great by increasing A, the cross-sectional area, and decreasing L, the distance it has to flow. Diagram (a) in Fig. 31C, illustrates thermal conductivity by the boiling of water in a paper cup. Although the gas flame plays directly against the surface of the paper the cup will not burn. The reason for this is that the heat from the lower surface of the paper is conducted through to the water fast enough to keep the temperature of the paper from rising too high. If the paper is thick the lower surface will burn. Strange as it may seem, the thinner the paper, the less is the chance of burning.

In diagram (b) of Fig. 31C, a thin piece of paper is wrapped once around a rod made half of wood and half of copper. When the flame is brought up as shown the paper burns only where it is in contact with the wood and not at all where it is in contact with the copper. Copper, being a good conductor, carries the heat into the interior of the metal and away from the metal surface. Since wood is a poor conductor it cannot conduct the heat

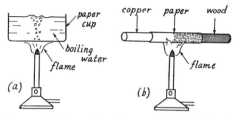

FIG. 31C—Illustrating the conduction of heat through paper.

away from the surface fast enough and the paper heats up and soon burns.

The thermal conductivities of a few common substances are given in Table 31A.

TABLE 31A. THERMAL CONDUCTIVITIES, k, in cal cm/sec cm^2 C°

Substance	k	Substance	k
Silver	0.97	Mercury	0.02
Copper	0.92	Tile	0.002
Aluminum	0.50	Glass	0.0025
Brass	0.26	Water	0.0014
Iron	0.16	Wood	0.0005
Lead	0.08	Paper	0.0003
German Silver	0.08	Felt	0.00004

The number k is the quantity of heat in calories that in 1 sec will pass through a 1 cc cube when two opposite faces are maintained at 1°C difference in temperature. Knowing the value of k for a given substance, it is possible to calculate, by means of Eq.(31a), the amount of heat flowing through any sized object made of that same substance.

Example. One end of an aluminum rod 40 cm long and 5 cm^2 in cross section is maintained at a temperature of 100°C and the other end at 20°C. Find the amount of heat that will flow through the rod in 2 min.

Solution. Substitution in Eq.(31a) gives

$$H = 0.50 \frac{5(100 - 20)}{40} 120 = 600 \text{ cal.} \qquad (31b)$$

31.2. Convection. Why is it that a poor conductor of heat like water can be heated so quickly when it is placed in a pan over a hot fire? It is due to the second method of heat transfer known as *convection*. Water on the bottom of a pan is heated first. Because of a rise in temperature it expands. Being lighter than the cold water above, it then rises to the top, permitting cold water to come to the bottom from the sides. This action sets up a flow of water called a *convection current*. See Fig. 31D. Convection currents thus keep the water stirred up as it heats.

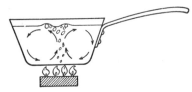

FIG. 31D—Convection currents in a pan of water being heated over a stove burner.

Convection currents set up by the heating of a vessel of water are illustrated in Fig. 31E(a). A glass tube in the shape of a letter O is filled with water and then heated at one of the lower corners as indicated. A drop of ink admitted at the top opening will mix with the water and quickly flow around the tube in a counterclockwise direction. This circulation is the basis of the hot water heating systems used in some houses. As illustrated in diagram (b), hot water from a supply tank in a lower room or basement rises and flows through several radiators only to return, somewhat cooled, to the tank again where it is reheated.

Similar to this in its action is the hot air heating system used in some houses. Air heated in a furnace in the basement rises through an outlet in or near the floor as shown in Fig. 31F. Rising up one side of the room this air travels across the ceiling, down

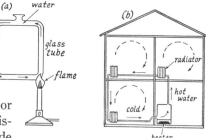

FIG. 31E—Illustrations of heat convection by the circulation of water in a pipe and air in a room.

the other side and across the floor to return to the furnace by another opening.

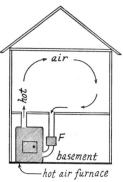

FIG. 31F—Convection air currents set up by heating.

Convection currents in the atmosphere are quite noticeable and account for the wind. Along the sea coast cool air from over the ocean comes as a sea breeze due to convection. The sun's rays are absorbed more readily by the land than they are by water and the warmed air over the land rises while cooler air from the ocean comes in to take its place.

At night the land cools quickly by radiation back toward the cold sky and soon the air over the water is the warmer, and rising causes a reversal in air movement. The wind blows from the land to the sea. These air currents are readily observed by smoke from a fire built on the seashore. During the day the smoke blows inland and at night it blows seaward.

Pilots are well aware of rising air currents over certain local areas of ground. Solar radiation being absorbed more completely by a newly plowed field, for example, will warm the air sufficiently to cause convection. Flying into such an upward draft of air the plane receives a sudden lift. During certain seasons these updrafts of warm air are cooled by the air layers above and water vapor is condensed to form clouds.

31.3. Radiation. When the sun comes over the horizon in the early morning the heat can be felt as soon as the sun becomes visible. This heat, called *radiation*, travels with the speed of light, 186,000 mi/sec. In fact, heat waves, like visible light, are electromagnetic waves and have all the general properties known to visible light. The essential difference between the two is that heat waves, sometimes called *infrared rays*, are not visible to the human eye.

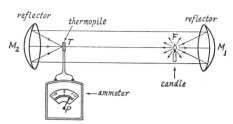

Fig. 31G—Reflection of heat rays by concave mirrors.

A demonstration of the reflection of infrared rays is diagramed in Fig. 31G. A candle flame acting as a source at F emits light and heat rays in all directions. Of these rays only the ones traveling toward the concave mirror M_1 are reflected into a parallel beam. Arriving at the second concave mirror M_2, these rays are again reflected, being brought together to a focus on the exposed junctions of a thermopile T. As the junctions of the thermopile warm up an electric current is produced, causing the ammeter pointer P to move to the right. When the candle is removed the pointer returns to zero.

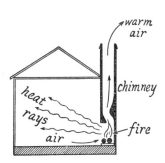

Fig. 31H—A fireplace heats a room by radiation from the flame, the coals, and the stove walls. Convection currents set up a draft and carry warm air and smoke out the chimney.

A practical example of heat radiation is to be found in every home where a fireplace is used as a means of heating. Contrary to most beliefs, the heat entering a room from a fireplace is practically all in the form of infrared rays originating in the flames, the coals, and the stone or brick walls. The air that is heated within the fireplace does not enter the room but is carried up the chimney as a convection current. See Fig. 31H. This rising current of air draws fresh air into the the room and into the fire, thus supplying fresh oxygen to the burning wood or coal.

A Dewar-flask or "thermos bottle" is an example of a practical device in which the conduction, convection, and radiation of heat are reduced as much as possible. As shown by the cross-section diagram in Fig. 31I, a thermos bottle consists of a double-walled glass vessel silvered on the inside. The purpose of the silvering is to reflect all radiant heat attempting to enter or leave the vessel. The space between the walls is highly evacuated to prevent convection, and the glass, being a poor conductor, minimizes conduction through the walls of the neck. With the exception of the vacuum space between walls, a calorimeter of the type commonly used in laboratories is similar to a Dewar-flask.

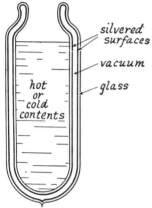

Fig. 31 I—The Dewar-flask, or "thermos bottle" minimizes conduction by using glass, convection by evacuating, and radiation by silvering.

A new type of heating system for public buildings and private dwellings has recently been developed. Known to engineers as *panel heating,* this system heats the walls of the rooms by hot air or water pipes that run through them. Even though the windows are open on the coldest days, radiant heat keeps the occupants warm.

31.4. Newton's Law of Cooling. The rate at which a hot body cools to the temperature of its surroundings is given by an empirical formula first discovered by Sir Isaac Newton. The law states that the rate at which heat is lost by a body to its surroundings is proportional to the difference in temperature between them. Symbolically,

$$H = c(t_2 - t_1) \qquad (31c)$$

where H is the heat lost per unit time, t_2 the temperature of the hot body,

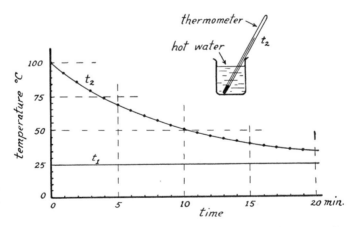

Fig. 31J—Cooling curve for a cup of water. Illustrating Newton's law of cooling.

t_1 the temperature of the surroundings, and c a proportionality constant. The law holds quite accurately for temperature differences small compared with the absolute temperature, and includes losses due to both convection and radiation. A graph showing the cooling of a cup of hot water is given in Fig. 31J. The data were taken by heating a cup of water to the boiling point and observing its temperature at the end of every minute with a mercury thermometer.

31.5. Prevost's Law of Heat Exchange. Laboratory experiments have been performed which show that all bodies whether they are hot or cold, radiate heat. The words "hot" and "cold" are only relative terms, since even ice radiates heat. The greater the absolute temperature of a body the greater is the rate at which it radiates, and ice at 0°C is 273° above absolute zero.

If a cold block of metal is brought into a warm room, it radiates heat to the walls of the room and the walls of the room radiate heat to the block. Because the walls are at a higher temperature they give more heat per second to the block than the block gives up in return. Due to this unequal exchange of heat, the temperature of the cold block rises until it comes to the same temperature as the room, at which time it radiates and absorbs at exactly the same rate. The principle that a body at the temperature of its surroundings is radiating and receiving heat at equal rates is known as *Prevost's law of exchanges.*

When a person stands near a fireplace he feels warm because his body receives more heat from the fire than it emits. If he stands next to a cold window he feels chilly because he radiates more heat than he absorbs. The side of his body facing the window gets noticeably colder than the other.

An interesting experiment in heat exchange may be performed with the two metallic reflectors shown in Fig. 31G. When the candle flame that produced the deflection shown in the diagram is replaced by an ice cube, the pointer deflects to the left of zero. It is not correct to explain this by saying that ice radiates cold to the thermopile. Actually the ice radiates heat, which is reflected from M_1 to M_2 and to the left face of the thermopile. The thermopile at the same time radiates heat, which is reflected from M_2 to M_1 and to the ice cube; there is, therefore, an exchange of heat radiation, but the thermopile, being at the higher of the two temperatures, radiates more per second than it receives from the ice in the same time. The temperature of the thermopile drops because of its own radiation.

31.6. Maintenance of Constant Body Temperature. It is well known that the human body maintains an almost constant temperature of 98.6°F irrespective of its surroundings. By combustion (metabolism) the body, at rest, generates on the average 2,500,000 calories per day, and, by conduction, convection, radiation, and the evaporation of water from the skin and lungs, emits the same amount of heat.

In winter when the surrounding temperatures are relatively low, excessive heat losses are prevented by heavier wearing apparel, while in summer months when the surroundings are close to body temperature, insufficient heat losses are increased by wearing lighter weight clothes and by increasing the exposed surface area. Blankets and clothing are warmer because they and the air they entrap between their fibers are poor conductors of heat. Furthermore, the entrapped air between the clothes and the body and between the fibers prevents loss of heat by convection.

The radiation of heat from the body depends upon the temperature of the surface and the temperature of the surrounding air. The body does have some control over surface temperature by regulating, through reflex action, the flow of blood in the vessels near the surface. When the skin temperature is 90°F there is a temperature rise of as much as 5°F in the first inch of flesh below the surface. When heavy clothing is worn the inside surface rises to almost body temperature and by Prevost's law of exchanges, some of the lost radiation is regained by the body.

In hot weather and as a result of manual labor, the sweat glands of the skin open and there is an increased evaporation of moisture that results in cooling. A considerable amount of water and salt too are given up by the body in this process and its oral replacement should follow without delay.

31.7. Emission and Absorption. The rate at which a body radiates or absorbs heat depends not only upon the absolute temperature but upon the nature of the exposed surfaces as well. Objects that are good emitters of heat are also good absorbers of the same kind of radiation. This is known as *Kirchhoff's Law of Radiation.* A body whose surface is blackened is an excellent emitter as well as an excellent absorber. If the same body is chromium plated it becomes a poor emitter and a poor absorber.

If the outside surface of the cup in Fig. 31J were painted a dull black the rate of cooling would be more rapid than if it were chromium plated. The highly polished surface, as in the Dewar-flask, would help by reflection to keep radiant heat from crossing the boundary.

Black clothes should not be worn on a hot day since black is a good absorber of the sun's radiant heat. While black is also a good emitter, the external temperature is higher than the body temperature and the exchange rate is therefore such as to heat the body. White clothes are worn in hot climates because white is a good reflector and therefore a poor absorber.

31.8. Black Body Radiation. The relation between the radiant heat *E* emitted by a body and its temperature was first made through the extensive laboratory experiments of Josef Stefan. The same law was later derived from theoretical considerations by Ludwig Boltzmann, and is now known as the *Stefan-Boltzmann law.**

$$E = kT^4.$$

Here E represents the energy radiated per second by a body at an absolute temperature T, and k is a proportionality constant. The law applies only to so-called "black bodies," a black body being defined as one which absorbs all of the radiant heat that falls upon it. Such a perfect absorber would also be a perfect emitter.

If E represents the heat in calories radiated per second per square centimeter of a black body, then $k = 1.36 \times 10^{-12}$. If E is measured in ergs/cm^2 sec, then $k = 5.7 \times 10^{-5}$.

The best laboratory approach to a black body is a hole in a blackened box. Practically all heat entering such a hole would be absorbed inside. Black velvet cloth or a surface painted dull with lampblack will absorb about 97% of the radiant heat falling on it, and may for many purposes be considered a black body. Polished metal surfaces, however, are far from black bodies; they absorb only about 6% of the incident energy and reflect the remainder. Most other substances have absorption ratios between these two extremes.

31.9. Radiant Heat from the Sun. Instruments designed to measure solar radiation are called pyroheliometers. See Fig. 31K. A beam of sunlight of known cross-sectional area is allowed to fall upon the blackened

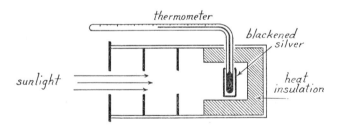

FIG. 31K—Abbot's pyroheliometer for measuring the heat radiated by the sun.

surface of a silver disk where it is absorbed. A drill hole in the metal disk admits the narrow bulb of a sensitive mercury thermometer, the latter being bent and threaded through a hole in the heat insulated box as shown in the

* Ludwig Boltzmann (1844-1906), Austrian theoretical physicist, was educated at Linz and Vienna. At 23 he was appointed assistant at the physical institute in Vienna. Later he became professor at Graz, then at Munich and finally back at Vienna. His first publication was on the second law of thermodynamics, and was followed by numerous papers on molecular motion, on viscosity and diffusion of gases, on Maxwell's electromagnetic theory, on Hertz's electrical experiments and on Stefan's law for black body radiation.

diagram. Knowing the heat capacity of the metal and its rise in temperature, the total number of calories per minute can be calculated.

Measurements of this kind by various observers are in remarkable agreement with each other and give a value of 1.938 cal/sq.cm/min. This number, called *the solar constant*, is defined as the average amount of energy falling in 1 min on 1 sq. cm of surface placed at right angles to the sun's rays. Multiplying the solar constant by the area of a sphere 93 million mi in radius, we obtain the figure 9×10^{25} cal/sec as the total heat radiated by the sun.

An appreciation of these figures can be had by the following comparison. If all the energy radiated by the sun could be used to heat the oceans of the earth, the temperature would rise from the freezing point to the boiling point in less than 2 sec. Where all this heat comes from within the sun has long been a puzzle to astronomer and physicist alike. A satisfactory answer to the problem has recently been found and will be given in Chap. 75.

31.10. The Seasons. The reason for the earth's polar ice caps and warm equator, as well as the difference in temperature between winter and summer, is to be attributed to the different angles at which the sun's rays arrive at the earth's surface. When it is summer in the northern hemisphere the sun's rays strike the earth's surface from the direction shown in Fig. 31L. It will be noted that a given bundle of rays near the poles is spread over a much larger area C to D and E to F, than an equal bundle of rays near the equator A to B.

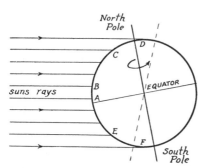

FIG. 31L—Solar radiation is spread over a bigger area at the earth's poles than it is at the equator.

With the arrival of less heat per unit area the resulting temperature will be lowest near the poles and highest near the equator. As the earth moves slowly in its orbit around the sun, the South pole is in darkness for many months and it is winter in the southern hemisphere; the north pole is in the light and it is summer. Six months later, when the orientation of the sun's rays with respect to the earth is like that shown by the dotted axis in the diagram, the conditions and seasons are reversed.

Not all of the solar radiation coming toward the earth gets through the atmosphere to be absorbed by the surface. While a small per cent is absorbed by the atmosphere on the clearest of days, the presence of fog and clouds in regions away from the equator and toward the polar caps often absorbs 30% to 40% and reflects a similar amount back into space. Under such conditions only a small amount of heat may get to the ground.

On clear cold nights the temperature at the earth's surface drops rapidly because of direct heat radiation into space. An intervening cloud blanket, however, will prevent this and the resultant surface temperature will remain considerably higher.

31.11. Convection Currents of Air Around the Earth. The earth's atmosphere is not a stationary body of air but one that is continually moving. A "wind pattern" showing the average air currents around the earth is given in Fig. 31M. Warm air masses at the equator rise because of convection and colder air from both

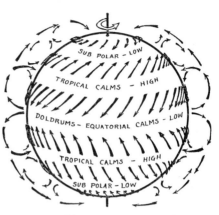

Fig. 31M—Air current pattern for the earth, due to convection and earth's rotation.

sides rushes in to take its place. The rising currents divide high up in the atmosphere and return to the earth at other regions north and south.

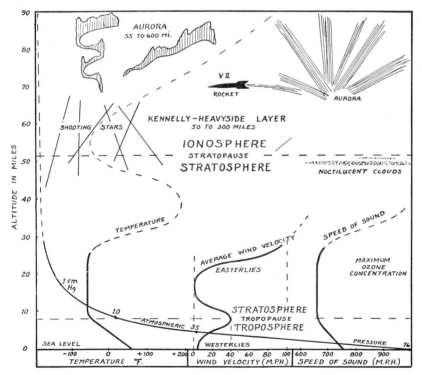

Fig. 31N—Diagrams and graphs for the earth's atmosphere.

This circulation of air is altered by the earth's rotation from east to west about its polar axis. The air masses that move north and south from the regions of tropical calms move to a region of lower or higher ground speeds with the result that the air gets ahead of the earth's rotation or behind respectively. This gives rise to the diagonal movements of the trade winds as shown. Where the air currents rise at the equator the average barometric pressure is less than in the regions of tropical calms where the currents are down.

The absorption of the sun's rays by the earth and its lower atmosphere causes the temperature at sea level to be greater than the temperature at higher altitudes. Normally the temperature decreases steadily with height until as shown in Fig. 31N, an altitude is reached beyond which the temperature remains constant at −67°F. This altitude, which is about 5 mi at the poles and 10 mi at the equator, is the upper limit of the so-called *troposphere*. This layer contains about 80% of the atmospheric mass.

PROBLEMS

1. A brass rod is 6 cm long and 1 cm in diameter. How much heat will flow through this rod in 5 min if one end is maintained at −40°C and the other end at +40°C?

2. One end of an aluminum rod 15 cm long and cross-sectional area 5 cm² is maintained at 20°C and the other end at 210°C. How much heat will flow through the rod in 1 hr? (*Ans.* 114,000 cal.)

3. A large leaded window contains 25 panes of glass, each one of which is 20 cm by 30 cm and 0.5 cm thick. If the snow outside maintains the outer surface at 0°C, and the heat of the room maintains the inner surface at 12°C, how much heat will be conducted through the glass in one hr?

4. The bottom of a copper boiler is 1 mm thick and has a cross-sectional area of 400 cm². If the upper surface is maintained at 80°C and gas flames keep the under surface at 100°C how much heat will flow through in 5 min? (*Ans.* 2.21×10^7 cal.)

5. A small copper ball 4 cm in diameter is coated with lampblack and heated to a temperature of 827°C. How much heat is radiated from this sphere in 1 min?

6. A horseshoe removed from the forge is set aside to cool. During the first minute its temperature drops from 660°C to 580°C. If the room temperature is 20°C, what will be the approximate temperature of the horseshoe at the end of 5 min? (*Ans.* 348°C.)

7. The rear wall of a brick fireplace has an effective open area of 1 m². Find the number of calories radiated per minute if this area is maintained at 127°C. Assume the surface to be a blackbody.

8. The wooden handle on a frying pan is 2.5 cm in diameter and 12 cm long. If the pan temperature is 160°C and the free end of the handle is kept at 40°C, how much heat will flow through in 1 min? (*Ans.* 1.47 cal.)

9. In cold climates where the temperature falls below freezing, the touching of an iron railing with the bare hand tends to make the fingers stick to the metal. This does not happen so readily with a wooden railing. Explain.

Change of State and Refrigeration
Chapter 32

32.1. Expansion and Contraction on Fusion. When molten metal of one kind or another is poured into a mold for casting, the metal may contract or expand on solidifying and then, on cooling down to room temperature, contract or expand according to its coefficient of thermal expansion. Cast iron, for example, is a substance which, on solidifying, expands slightly but then, on cooling down to room temperature, contracts about 1% of its length. It is therefore well suited to casting since slight expansion on solidifying aids in the reproduction of every detail in the mold. To allow for shrinkage in cooling, however, an increase of ⅛ in per ft must be introduced in the wood pattern used in making the mold.

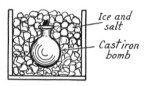

Fig. 32A—When the water inside the bomb freezes, the expansion bursts the cast-iron walls.

An experiment illustrating the enormous expansion forces of freezing water is diagramed in Fig. 32A. A small cast iron bomb, about 2 in. in diameter and ⅛ in. thick is completely filled with water at a temperature close to 0°C. After the threaded iron plug is screwed in tight the bomb is packed in a freezing mixture of cracked ice and salt. After some minutes the water freezes as it explodes the bomb with a dull thud.

32.2. Effect of Pressure on Freezing. The freezing point of a liquid is affected only slightly by the pressure to which it is usually subjected. *For liquids that contract on freezing an increase of pressure raises the freezing point. For liquids that expand upon freezing, an increase of pressure lowers the freezing point.* These statements are consistent with molecular structure and activity since increased pressure should tend to prevent expansion and consequently hold off solidification until a lower temperature is reached.

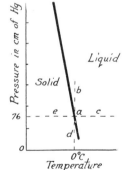

Fig. 32B—Pressure-temperature curve for water at the freezing point.

A curve showing the behavior of water is given in Fig. 32B. The slope of the curve is greatly exaggerated; it should be more nearly vertical. Extending upward and slightly to the left an enormous pressure of 110 atmospheres is required to lower the melting point but 1°C. To better understand the meaning of the graph, consider the conditions represented by the point *a* near the bottom. Here at 0°C and 76 cm of Hg, water and ice can exist together without change. To raise the temperature at this same pressure (point *c*) heat would have to be added, first to melt the ice, and second to raise the temperature of the water.

To lower the temperature at this same pressure (point *e*) heat would first have to be given up by the water to freeze it, and then additional heat given up to lower the temperature of the ice. To raise the pressure without a change in temperature (point *b*) heat would have to be added to melt the ice, whereas, to lower the pressure without a change in temperature (point *d*) heat would have to be given up to freeze the water.

In the diagram, therefore, the region to the right of the line represents all possible temperatures and pressures for the existence of the *liquid state*, while the region to the left represents all possible conditions for the existence of the *solid state*. The line itself gives the pressure and temperature conditions under which the liquid and solid can exist together in equilibrium.

32.3. Regelation. If two small blocks of ice are held in opposite hands and two of their relatively flat surfaces pressed tightly together, they will upon release be stuck together. The explanation is that where contact is made between the blocks, high pressure at localized spots lowers the melting point sufficiently to melt the ice. In order to melt, the ice must acquire heat (80 cal/gm) and this it gets by conduction from the nearby ice. The water then flows to one side and, returning the heat it had taken away from the nearby ice, freezes, sealing the blocks together. This is a process called

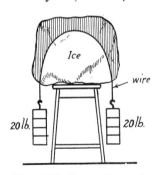

regelation. The same process explains why snow when squeezed in the hands, sticks together to form well packed snowballs.

Glaciers are well known to seemingly "flow" around hard jutting rocks as they move slowly down a rocky ravine. The ice melts under the pressure it receives from a rock on one side and the water flowing down and around to the open gap on the other side freezes again to go on as if the rock were never there.

A simple laboratory experiment demonstrating this principle is shown in Fig. 32C. A small wire with heavy weights attached is hung over a block of ice and allowed to remain for some time.

Fig. 32C—Ice melts under pressure allowing the wire to work its way through.

Slowly the wire is observed to melt its way through the ice. On completion of the cut the block of ice is still in one piece, the gap made by the wire having frozen shut. The high pressure under the wire melts the ice, and the water flows around to the other side where it freezes again.

32.4. Cooling by Evaporation. When water is left in an open dish it slowly exaporates, i.e., it goes spontaneously into the gaseous state. Evaporation therefore is a free expansion, and expansion is always accompanied by cooling. This phenomenon of cooling by evaporation, which is so important from the standpoint of its many commercial applications, is explained by the kinetic theory of matter.

Due to the random motions of the molecules of a liquid, some molecules obtain, momentarily, a very high velocity. If a molecule at the surface is given a high velocity in an upward direction it may escape into the air above. Some of these escaped molecules soon find their way back into the liquid by chance collisions with air molecules from above the surface but many of them do not. See Fig. 32D. The sporadic escape of molecules

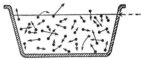

Fig. 32D—Evaporation of water from an open dish is due to the rapid motion of the water molecules and their occasional escape into the air space above.

may be speeded up by blowing air across the surface. The air carries the newly escaped molecules away before they have a chance to return to the liquid.

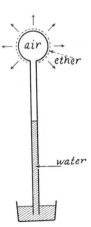

Fig. 32E—Experiment demonstrating the cooling effect produced by the evaporation of ether.

By virtue of the high speed of the molecules escaping from a liquid surface, considerably more than the average kinetic energy is carried away with them. A lowering of the average kinetic energy of the remaining liquid molecules means a lowering of the temperature. The more rapid the evaporation, therefore, the faster will be the cooling. This is strikingly demonstrated by pouring a small amount of ether or alcohol on the finger. Either of these liquids, and particularly ether, evaporates very rapidly, cooling the surface of the finger quickly. Ether is often used in this way by surgeons, in place of an anesthetic, to freeze local spots of the body before beginning a minor operation.

Cooling by evaporation can be demonstrated to a large group by pouring a small quantity of ether over the bulb of an air thermometer as shown in Fig. 32E. Due to the cooling of the glass bulb the air inside contracts, drawing more water up into the stem of the thermometer.

32.5. Humidity. When water molecules escape by evaporation from the free surface of a liquid they mix with the air molecules above. If the space above the liquid surface is enclosed, as shown in Fig. 32F, this mixture cannot escape. Under these circumstances the water will continue to evaporate until the air above becomes saturated

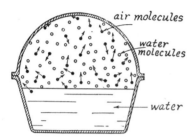

FIG. 32F—Illustrating the saturation of air with water vapor.

with water vapor, that is, until it can hold no more. When this condition is reached, as many free water molecules will be returning to the liquid every second as there are water molecules escaping.

The maximum amount of water the air can hold in the vapor state depends upon the temperature and very little upon the air pressure. This is illustrated by the values given in Table 32A. The temperature of the air is given in one column and the maximum amount of water that can exist in the vapor state in a cubic meter of air is given in the other.

TABLE 32A. MASS OF WATER VAPOR IN ONE CUBIC METER OF SATURATED AIR

Temperature	Water Vapor	Temperature	Water Vapor
0°C or 32°F	4.8 gm	20°C or 68°F	17.1 gm
5°C " 41°F	6.8 gm	25°C " 77°F	22.8 gm
10°C " 50°F	9.3 gm	30°C " 86°F	30.0 gm
15°C " 59°F	12.7 gm	35°C " 95°F	39.2 gm

It is clearly seen from the table that the hotter the air the greater is the amount of water it can hold in the vapor state.

The atmosphere which we might term free air is not always saturated with water vapor. If it contains very little or no water vapor we say the air is dry; if it contains a great deal we say it is damp.

The quantity of water vapor present in 1 cu m of air is called the *absolute humidity*. It is, therefore, a measure of the dampness of the air. It is measured by the number of grams of water vapor present in 1 cu m of air. For example, the absolute humidity might be said to be 14 gm/cu m.

It is customary in speaking of the dampness of air, not to specify the absolute humidity but the *relative humidity*. The relative humidity is defined as the ratio of the quantity of water vapor actually present in any volume of air to the quantity required to saturate the same volume of air at the same temperature. To illustrate this, suppose the air at the present time contains 5.7 gm/cu m of water vapor and the temperature is 25°C. If the air were saturated at this temperature (see Table 32A) it would contain 22.8 gm/cu m. Therefore the

$$\text{relative humidity} = 5.7/22.8 = 0.25.$$

It is customary to express such answers in per cent and say that the relative humidity in this case is 25%.

If air which is saturated with water vapor is cooled to a lower temperature, some of the water vapor may condense to the liquid state. These are the conditions under which rain and fogdrops are formed. The reason for this condensation is that at the lower temperature and equilibrium conditions less water can exist in the vapor state and still saturate the air. If the air cools without the formation of rain or fog the air takes on an unstable state in which it is supersaturated.

32.6. The Dew Point. When the temperature of a glass of water is slowly cooled a temperature is reached where water condenses on the outside. The temperature at which this occurs is called the *dew point,* and signifies that the air has become saturated with water vapor. Any measurement of the dew-point temperature therefore offers a means of determining the relative humidity.

Suppose, for example, the following experiment is performed in a room whose temperature is 35°C. A polished metal cup containing water and a thermometer is slowly cooled by adding cracked ice. The first appearance of moisture on the outside is noted to occur at 20°C. Referring to Table 32A, the saturated density for 20°C is 17.1 gm/m³, and for 35°C is 39.2 gm/m³. The first of these gives the actual amount of water vapor present in the room and the latter gives the amount the air in the room could hold when saturated. The absolute humidity is therefore 17.1 gm/m³, and the

relative humidity $= 17.1/39.2 \times 100 = 43.6\%$. (32a)

Meteorologists often determine relative humidity from the dew point by means of a *sling-psychrometer*. Such a device consists as shown in Fig. 32G, of two identical mercury thermometers mounted on a base with a convenient handle for whirling. One bulb is exposed to the air and is called the *dry bulb* while the other, with a water-soaked cloth tied to it, is called the *wet bulb*. When the psychrometer is whirled in the air for several minutes, being stopped occasionally to observe the temperature readings, the wet bulb will be observed to drop to some value and remain there during any subsequent whirling.

The lowest obtainable wet-bulb temperature is not the dew point even though whirling causes evaporation, and evaporation produces cooling. By applying a correction from well known tables the dew point can be determined from the wet and dry bulb readings. Eq. 32a is then applied to the densities read from Table 32A.

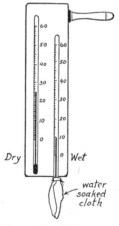

Fig. 32G—Sling-psychrometer with wet- and dry-bulb thermometers for determining the dew point and relative humidity.

32.7. Vapor Pressure. The presence of water vapor in the air increases atmospheric pressure. To explain why it does so, consider again Fig. 32F. As more and more water evaporates into the space above, the pressure due to the bombardment of the walls by the water molecules becomes greater and greater, reaching a maximum at saturation. The water molecules exert pressure and the air molecules exert pressure, each independent of the other.

Vapor pressure is usually expressed in centimeters of mercury and at saturation is referred to as the saturated vapor pressure. Values of saturated vapor pressure are given in Table 32B for every five degrees between 0°C and 100°C, and at ten-degree intervals to 160°C.

As an illustration of the meaning of Table 32B, assume that we have dry air at normal atmospheric pressure of 76 cm of Hg and room temperature of 25°C, and we then proceed to saturate it with water vapor. From the table the saturated vapor pressure at 25°C is found to be 2.37 cm of Hg. Adding these two, the total gas pressure becomes 76 + 2.37 or 78.37 cm of Hg. The 76 cm represents the *partial pressure* of the air and 2.37 represents the *partial pressure* of the water vapor.

TABLE 32B. SATURATED VAPOR PRESSURE OF WATER

Temp., ° C	Pressure cm Hg.	Temp., ° C	Pressure cm Hg.	Temp., ° C	Pressure cm Hg.
0	0.458	45	7.19	90	52.58
5	0.654	50	9.25	95	63.39
10	0.921	55	11.80	100	76.00
15	1.28	60	14.94	110	107.4
20	1.75	65	18.75	120	148.9
25	2.37	70	23.37	130	202.6
30	3.18	75	28.91	140	271.1
35	4.22	80	35.51	150	357.0
40	5.53	85	43.36	160	463.6

This relation between partial pressures and total pressure was first discovered by the English chemist and physicist, John Dalton, and is known as *Dalton's Law.* *The total pressure exerted by a mixture of two or more gases that do not chemically combine is equal to the sum of the pressures which the several gases would exert separately if each were permitted to occupy the entire space alone at the same temperature.* In other words, each gas in a mixture exerts its own pressure independent of the pressure exerted by the other gases.

32.8. Boiling. The boiling of a liquid is but a state of rapid evaporation. As the temperature of water is raised, the rate of evaporation increases until at the boiling temperature it reaches a maximum. Beyond this temperature water can exist only in the vapor state.

When water boils at normal atmospheric pressure evaporation takes place throughout the liquid as well as at the surface. Evidence of this is seen in the bubbles of saturated vapor that form near the bottom of a vessel and increase in size as they rise to the surface. The bubbles are able to form because the saturated vapor pressure at 100°C (see Table 32B) is 76 cm of Hg and equal to the external pressure of the atmosphere. Boiling cannot occur unless the saturated vapor pressure is equal to or slightly greater than the pressure exerted on the liquid.

32.9. Geysers. One of the great wonders of the western world is the spontaneous eruption almost hourly of the mammoth geyser "Old Faithful" in Yellowstone National Park. The following explanation of geyser activity was first given by Bunsen in 1847, and is based upon the above explanation of boiling.

Water from nearby streams seeps into the vertical shaft or hole where, due to volcanic heat below, it is gradually heated to the boiling point. See Fig. 32H. Because the water is heated from below, and convection currents are shut off by the narrowness of the shaft, a temperature considerably higher than 100°C must be reached before the water at the bottom can boil. Since atmospheric pressure exists at the surface, the water there will boil at 100°C. Far down the shaft however, the added pressure of nearly 70 ft of water requires a temperature of 130°C to produce boiling. Because the water is heated from below, this high temperature is reached near the bottom and boiling begins there before it does at the top. When a sufficiently high temperature is reached, the vapor pressure

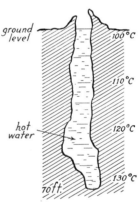

Fig. 32H—Diagram illustrating the principles of a geyser like "Old Faithful" in Yellowstone National Park.

deep down exceeds the pressure due to the air and water column above and the rise of numerous bubbles, by pushing out the column of hot water above, starts an eruption. Nearing the surface the vapor pressure of the superheated water is so high that the remaining water is pushed out with great force.

32.10. Boiling at Low Temperatures. Just as water can be made to boil at temperatures higher than 100°C by increasing the pressure, so can it be made to boil at temperatures below 100°C by reducing atmospheric pressure. Because of the practical importance of this basic fact, a detailed explanation should be given. Fig. 32I is a graph of the saturated vapor pressures of water given in Table 32B. This curve represents conditions under which water and saturated water vapor can exist together in equilibrium.

Since boiling at the surface of water takes place when the saturated vapor pressure becomes equal to the atmospheric pressure, it follows that by lowering atmospheric pressure a lower vapor pressure can bring about the conditions for boiling. The curved line in the graph is therefore a boiling point curve; all pressures and temperatures to the right represent the vapor state, all points to the left the liquid state.

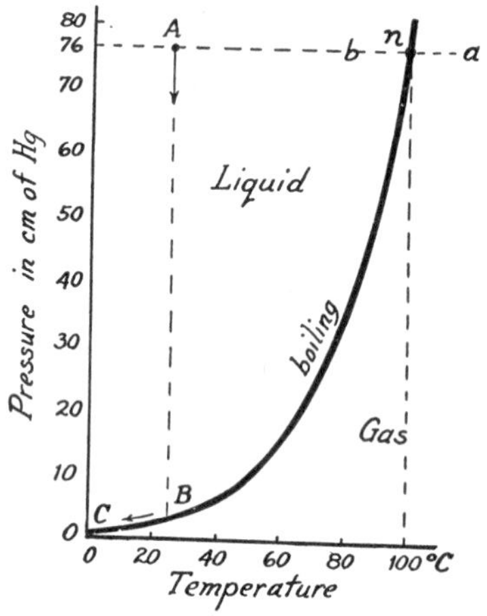

Consider, for example, water at the normal boiling point of 100°C and 76 cm of Hg. To raise its temperature without raising the pressure, point a, heat must be added to vaporize the water and the resultant steam. To lower its temperature (point b) heat must be given up to liquefy the steam and additional heat to lower the temperature of all the water.

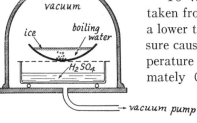

FIG. 32I—Boiling point curve for water at pressures below 76 cm of Hg.

To go one step farther, suppose water at room temperature, 25°C, is placed in a vacuum jar as shown in Fig. 32J and the pressure is slowly reduced by means of a vacuum pump. Starting at the point A on the graph, the pressure decreases until it reaches B, about 2.37 cm of Hg, where bubbles form and the water begins to boil.

To vaporize water requires heat and this is taken from the remaining water, thus cooling it to a lower temperature. Continued reduction in pressure causes continued boiling and lowering of temperature until finally the freezing point at approximately 0°C is reached. Continued evaporation cools the surface of the water until ice forms over the surface of the boiling water. Here then is a condition in which water boils and freezes at the same time and at 0°C. (The small dish of sulfuric acid, H_2SO_4, placed in the vacuum chamber absorbs water vapor, thus aiding the pumps in keeping the pressure sufficiently low.)

FIG. 32J—The boiling point of a liquid like water is lowered by lowering the atmospheric pressure. Water in a vacuum will boil and freeze at the same time.

Although water under normal atmospheric pressure at sea level boils at 100°C, water at higher altitudes boils at lower temperatures. Evidence of this fact is well known to those who like to camp in the higher mountains. There, at reduced atmospheric pressure, it takes longer than usual to cook all kinds of foods. The boiling points given in Table 32C show specific values for different elevations.

TABLE 32C. ATMOSPHERIC PRESSURE AND BOILING POINT OF WATER AT VARIOUS HEIGHTS ABOVE SEA LEVEL

Atmospheric Pressure		Altitude	Boiling Point	Atmospheric Pressure		Altitude	Boiling Point
cm	lb/in²	ft	° C	cm	lb/in²	ft	° C
76	14.7	Sea Level	100	42.4	8.2	15,000	84.4
70.2	13.6	2,000	97.8	35.0	6.7	20,000	79.6
65.6	12.7	4,000	96.0	22.5	4.4	30,000	69.2
61.0	11.8	6,000	94.0	14.1	2.7	40,000	58.8
56.8	11.0	8,000	92.1	8.75	1.7	50,000	48.9
52.2	10.1	10,000	89.8	0.82	0.16	100,000	9.8

Flying at high altitudes the water in water-cooled engines boils at lower temperatures. At a height of 6 mi, gasoline boils at the normal temperature of −65°C. At 12 mi elevation, blood boils at the body temperature of 98.6°F (37°C).

32.11. Sublimation. Under certain conditions many substances will go from the solid to the vapor state without passing through the liquid phase. A good illustration of this is the heating of iodine crystals or the evaporation of so-called "dry ice." Iodine crystals, when placed in a test tube at room temperature and pressure, and slowly heated, pass directly into iodine vapor. This is called sublimation.

Dry ice, which chemically is carbon dioxide, CO_2, is normally at a temperature of −78.5°C and, when standing in the open air, evaporates directly without liquefying. The visible fumes rising from it are water vapor from the surrounding air condensed by the cold CO_2 gases that leave.

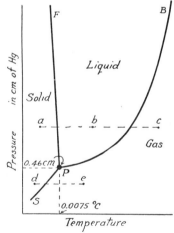

FIG. 32K—Triple point graph for water.

Ice over the ponds and lakes in cold climates sublimes slowly at the surface. By enclosing the space above ice at below 0°C, the saturated vapor pressure can be measured just as it is for water as shown in Fig. 32F.

The result of such measurements is represented by the sublimation curve *PS* in the "triple point" graph in Fig. 32K. The curve *PF* is the freezing point curve of Fig. 32B and *PB* is the boiling point curve of Fig. 32I. Every point along *PF* represents the conditions of equilibrium for ice and water and every point along *PB* represents the conditions of equilibrium for water and water vapor. The experimental fact that these curves intersect at one common point, the so-called *triple point*, means that at that pressure and temperature all three states, *solid, liquid,* and *gas,* can exist in equilibrium. These were the conditions attained in the experiment in Fig. 32J.

32.12. Refrigeration. A refrigerator in the home or corner grocery store is now a commonplace. It is not the purpose here to describe any particular commercial refrigerator but to present the physical principles underlying the operation of a typical machine. It is probably safe to say that nearly all refrigerators are based upon the principle that the rapid evaporation of a liquid or the expansion of a gas produces cooling. The most common fluids used in the machines today are liquid ammonia (NH_3), sulfur dioxide (SO_2), and methyl chloride (CH_3Cl).

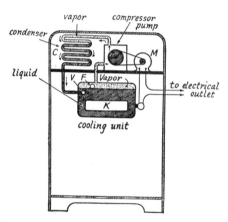

Fig. 32L—Schematic diagram of the working parts of a common electrically operated refrigerator.

A schematic diagram of an electrically operated refrigerator is shown in Fig. 32L. The three principal parts of this machine are (1) the cooling unit, (2) the compressor, and (3) the condenser. The cooling unit *K* and the condenser coils are partly filled with one of the above mentioned liquids, and the remaining parts with vapor. By means of an electric motor and pump the vapor is removed from the top of the cooling unit and pumped into the hollow coiled pipes of the condenser. The low pressure in the cooling unit causes the liquid to boil, resulting in the cooling of the entire unit by evaporation. In pumping more and more vapor into the condenser, the compression heats the vapor considerably above room temperature. Before and after the motor stops running, the heated vapor cools and condenses into a liquid by transferring heat into the room.

When the liquid in the cooling unit falls to a certain low level the float *F* opens a valve *V*, letting in liquid from the condenser. Being cold, the cooling unit absorbs heat from the refrigerator and warms up. When the temperature rises to a certain value the thermostat makes electrical contact (see Fig. 11G(c)) and starts the motor. The pump then lowers the pressure which in turn causes evaporation and cooling. At the moment the temperature of the cooling unit and thermostat drops to the desired value the thermostat opens the electric circuit, stopping the motor and pump.

PROBLEMS

1. If the air contains 14.5 gm of water vapor per cubic meter of air when the temperature is 86°F, what is the relative humidity?
2. If the air contains 12.0 gm of water vapor per cubic meter of air when the temperature is 28°C, what is the relative humidity? (*Ans.* 44%.)
3. Plot a temperature vs water-vapor graph for standard air. Use the centigrade values given in Table 32A, and extrapolate the curve to 40°C.
4. The dew point is found to be 50°F when the room temperature is 74°F. What is the relative humidity? (*Ans.* 44.5%.)
5. A sling-psychrometer is whirled until the dew point is found from the wet-bulb and conversion tables to be 8°C. Calculate the relative humidity if the dry-bulb temperature is 30°C.
6. At what temperature will water boil at an altitude of 12,000 ft? (*Ans.* 87.6°C.)
7. At what altitude will water boil at 95°C?
8. If air at a temperature of 30°C has a relative humidity of 75%, how much water vapor will be condensed per cubic meter of air if the temperature is lowered to 10°C? (*Ans.* 13.2 gm.)
9. If the relative humidity is 38% and the temperature is 75°F, what is the absolute humidity?
10. If the absolute humidity is 8 gm/m³ and the temperature is 87°F, what is the relative humidity? (*Ans.* 25.7%.)
11. Plot a temperature vs water-vapor graph for saturated air. Use the Fahrenheit scale for temperatures as given in Table 32A, and extrapolate the curve to 104°F.
12. Plot a graph of the boiling point of water vs altitude in meters. Cover the range 0 to 30,000 m.
13. An air conditioning system in a building delivers 2000 m³/hr of air. When the air is 25°C and the relative humidity is 90%, the system removes 7.6 kg of water per hr without changing the temperature. Find the final (a) relative humidity, and (b) absolute humidity.
14. If, at a temperature of 77°F, the relative humidity is 62% how much water per cubic meter will be condensed if the temperature goes down to freezing, that is, 32°F? (*Ans.* 9.33 gm.)
15. If the relative humidity is 42% when the temperature is 41°F, what will it be if the temperature rises to 68°F?
16. At what temperature will water boil at the bottom of a geyser 110 ft deep? (*Ans.* 146°C.)
17. At what temperature will water boil 20 m below the surface of the water in a geyser?
18. At what depth in a geyser will water begin to boil at 162°C? (*Ans.* 52.7 m.)

Heat Energy
and Gas Laws

Chapter 33

Frequent reference has been made to the fact that heat is a form of energy. To add heat to a body is to increase the motion of the molecules. Having mass and velocity, each molecule has kinetic energy, $\frac{1}{2}mv^2$. The absolute temperature of a body is proportional to the average translational kinetic energy of the molecules. The total energy in a body on the other hand is a measure of the total heat content and is given by the sum of kinetic and potential energies.

33.1. Thermodynamics. Thermodynamics is that branch of physics dealing with the conversion of mechanical energy into thermal energy, and the reverse process, heat into work. There are numerous ways of carrying out either of these transformations. By rubbing the palms of the hands together, for example, heat is produced; by rubbing two sticks of wood together a fire may be started. If a weight falls freely from some height, heat is developed when the weight strikes the ground. The bearings of a car motor or the wheels of a freight car, if not lubricated, will get hot and either "burn out" or lock together, as in a "hot box." These are all examples of mechanical energy being transformed into heat.

The reverse process of transforming heat into mechanical energy is illustrated by present-day steam, diesel, gasoline, and jet propulsion engines. In all of these engines fuel is burned to produce heat and by expanding gases the heat is turned into mechanical energy. Jet propulsion is not a new idea. A simple device based upon the principle of jet propulsion is to be found in the writings of some of the ancient philosophers of Archimedes' time.

33.2. The First Law of Thermodynamics. The first law of thermodynamics is frequently referred to as *the mechanical equivalent of heat*. It is to the painstaking work of Joule (1843)* that we attribute this fundamental verification of the universal law of conservation of energy. With his apparatus he was able to show that when a moving body is brought to rest the energy which disappears is directly proportional to the amount of heat produced. In his most famous experiment he set water into motion in a

* James Prescott Joule (1818-89), English physicist, was born on December 24, 1818, near Manchester. Although he owned a large brewery he devoted his life to scientific research. At the age of 22 he discovered the law giving the relation between electrical energy and heat, and a short time later the law known as the first law of thermodynamics.

306

bucket by means of rotating paddles and then brought the water to rest by stationary paddles. He was able to show that if all of the work used in churning the water goes into producing heat, then the same amount of work will always produce the same amount of heat regardless of the method used to carry out the transformation. In other words, the calorie, which is a unit of heat energy, is equivalent to a definite number of ergs of mechanical energy.

The number of energy units which upon conversion gives one heat unit is called the mechanical equivalent of heat. By experiment

$$1 \text{ cal} = 41,800,000 \text{ ergs}$$

and
$$1 \text{ Btu} = 778 \text{ ft lb} \tag{33a}$$

As an equation,

$$\frac{\text{Work}}{\text{Heat}} = \text{mech. equiv. of heat.} \qquad \frac{W}{H} = J. \tag{33b}$$

Because of the fundamental importance of this relation many experimenters have devoted considerable time and effort to obtain a more accurate value of the constant J. In 1879 the famous American physicist Rowland, using an improved form of Joule's apparatus, obtained the value $J = 4.179 \times 10^7$ ergs/cal. Since that time simpler experiments have been devised that make use of a method first employed by Joule, namely, that of heating by electric currents. Such an experiment will be described in a later chapter.

In honor of Joule and his most important discovery, it is customary to express the mechanical equivalent of heat as

$$1 \text{ cal} = 4.18 \text{ joules}$$

where 1 joule $= 10^7$ ergs, as defined in Eq.(15e).

33.3. Experiments on Mechanical Equivalent of Heat. There are numerous ways of transforming mechanical energy into heat. By rubbing the palms of the hands together, for example, heat is produced by friction. Again, if a weight is dropped from any height, heat is developed when it strikes the ground. A 1 lb weight dropped $3\frac{1}{2}$ ft will, on stopping, produce 1 cal.

One simple laboratory method of measuring the mechanical equivalent of heat is to place a measured amount of lead shot (about 100 gm) in a tube about 5 cm in diameter and 100 cm long. After reading the temperature of the shot with a thermometer, the tube is turned end for end about 200 times, stopping

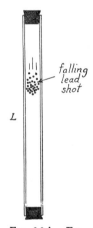

falling lead shot

L

Fig. 33 A—Experiment for determining the mechanical equivalent of heat.

each time in a vertical position to allow the shot to fall the full 100 cm and strike the bottom. See Fig. 33A. The temperature of the shot is then measured again. From the known mass of shot, m, its specific heat s, and the rise in temperature, $t_2 - t_1$, the total *heat gained* can be calculated, $H = mc(t_2 - t_1)$. From the mass of the shot m, the acceleration due to gravity g, the number of tube inversions n, and the length of the tube l, the input energy is calculated. Since *work done* equals *force times distance*, $W = mg \times nl$. Substituting in Eq.(33b),

$$J = \frac{W}{H} = \frac{mg\ nl}{mc(t_2 - t_1)} = \frac{g\,n\,l}{s(t_2 - t_1)}. \qquad (33c)$$

The canceling of m is to be expected since, for example, the dropping of twice the amount of shot will produce twice as much heat, but this will be divided between twice the amount of lead.

Consider as a problem the calculation of the mechanical equivalent of heat from the following data taken in such a laboratory experiment.

Initial temperature of lead shot .... 23.4°C
Final temperature of lead shot .... 24.9°C
Length of tube .... 104 cm
Number of falls 200

By substituting these values in Eq.(33c), and the specific heat of lead from Table 30A, we obtain

$$J = \frac{980 \times 200 \times 104}{0.031(24.9 - 23.4)} = 4.38\ \frac{\text{joules}}{\text{cal}}.$$

The difference between any experimental result and its accepted value, divided by the accepted value, and multiplied by one hundred gives the percentage error.

$$\text{Per cent error} = \frac{4.38 - 4.18}{4.18} \times 100 = 4.8\%.$$

While the type of experiment just described is not capable of high accuracy, it does illustrate the relation between mechanical energy and heat. The inaccuracies are due chiefly to the method of temperature measurement and to the absorption of heat by the tube and tube ends. The latter may be reduced by using materials having a low thermal conductivity.

The transformation of potential energy into heat usually occurs by first changing it into kinetic energy. In the above experiment, for example, the lead shot acquired a velocity in falling and its kinetic energy $\frac{1}{2}mv^2$ was changed into heat at the bottom. Due to the impact the molecules of the colliding bodies were given additional kinetic energy.

Example. A 1 kg hammer moving with a velocity of 50 m/sec strikes a 200 gm iron rod lying on the ground. If half of the energy goes into heating the iron rod, what will be its rise in temperature?

Solution.

KE of hammer $= \frac{1}{2}mv^2 = \frac{1}{2} \times 1000$ gm $\times$ (5000 cm/sec)$^2 = 12.5 \times 10^9$ ergs.

From Eq.(33c), the heat produced will be

$$H = \frac{W}{J} = \frac{12.5 \times 10^9}{4.18 \times 10^7} = 299 \text{ cal.}$$

Since one-half goes to heat 200 gm of iron of specific heat 0.105

$$149.5 \text{ cal} = 200 \times 0.105 \ (t_2 - t_1).$$

Solving for the rise in temperature $(t_2 - t_1)$ gives

$$t_2 - t_1 = \frac{149.5}{200 \times 0.105} = 7.1°C.$$

33.4. Boyle's * Law. This is a law dealing with the compression and expansion of a gas at constant temperature. It states that the pressure of a given quantity of gas varies inversely as its volume. In algebraic symbols p is proportional to $1/V$, or as an equation $p = \text{const.} \times 1/V$. Transposing V to the other side of the equality,

$$pV = \text{constant.} \qquad (33d)$$

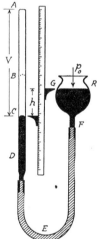

This is Boyle's law. A laboratory experiment frequently performed to check the above relation is shown in Fig. 33B. A quantity of air is trapped by a column of mercury in a straight uniform tube AD. By raising the mercury reservoir the gas pressure increases and the volume of air decreases. By lowering the reservoir the pressure falls and the gas expands.

For each set position of the reservoir the volume V is read directly from the scale and pointer (shown at C) and the pressure is determined by measuring the difference in mercury level h. If the level F lies above C the total gas pressure p is equal to atmospheric pressure p_o, as read from a barometer, plus the height h. If F lies below C the height h is subtracted from p_o.

FIG. 33B—Apparatus for studying Boyle's law for gases.

* Robert Boyle (1627-91). English natural philosopher and fourteenth child of Richard Boyle, the great earl of Cork. Fourteen years of age found him in Italy studying the paradoxes of the famous star gazer, Galileo. Besides enunciating the law now known by his name, he discovered how sound is propagated through the air, investigated the refractive powers of crystals, and proposed the corpuscular theory of chemical compounds and mixtures. He had a profound interest in theology and spent much time and money "for proving the Christian religion against all others."

Care must always be taken when changing the reservoir to each new position to allow several minutes for the gas to come to room temperature.

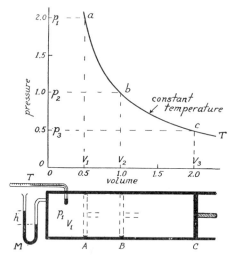

The necessity for doing this is that upon compression the gas gets warmer and on expansion it cools. Multiplying each of the measured gas pressures p by their corresponding volumes V will give a series of products, which, within the limits of experimental error, are constant.

A similar experiment illustrating Boyle's law is diagramed in Fig. 33C. A metal cylinder is fitted with a movable piston C, a mercury U-tube manometer M, and a bent thermometer T. For various positions of the piston, A, B, C, etc., the pressure is determined from the manometer height h and the volume by the position of the piston along the cylinder.

Fig. 33C—Compression and expansion of a gas at constant temperature obeys Boyle's law, $p\,v =$ constant.

With each setting, adequate time is allowed for the gas to come to the same temperature T as noted by the thermometer.

The graph drawn above gives the conditions for a range of pressures and volumes of the gas and is referred to as an *isothermal* curve. Following Eq. (33d), such a curve is recognized as an equilateral hyperbola, and is a graphical representation of Boyle's law.

If a second set of pressures and volumes are measured bringing the temperature each time to some new value T_1, Boyle's law will again be found to hold true and the graph for such changes will be another equilateral hyperbola. A third set of readings for a third temperature will give a third curve, etc. A family of iso-thermal curves is given in Fig. 33D, all drawn for the same gas sample.

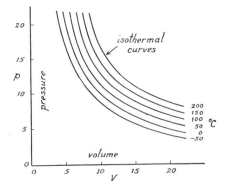

Fig. 33D—Isothermal curves for a gas like oxygen, nitrogen, or air. Each curve conforms to Boyle's law.

33.5. Deviation's from Boyle's Law. While Boyle's law is sufficiently accurate for many purposes it is not quite correct for large ranges of pressure and volume. Extensive tests carried out by Amagat have shown that when the pressure of air is carried to many atmospheres the product pV diminishes gradually until at 78 atmospheres its value is 98% of its value at 1 atmosphere. At still greater pressures the product pV increases again until at 3000 atmospheres its value is 4.2 times the original value.

Similar deviations from Boyle's law are observed with other gases. It was Van der Waals who, assuming gas pressure to be due to molecular motions, derived from mathematical considerations a law that agrees much better with Amagat's experiments. His formula is

$$\left(p + \frac{a}{V^2} \right)\left(V - b \right) = \text{constant} \tag{33e}$$

where a and b are constants to be determined experimentally for each different gas.

The terms a/V^2 and $-b$ are correction terms for the pressure and volume respectively, and under ordinary conditions are extremely small. The function of the term a/V^2 is to correct for the attractive forces between molecules when at very high pressures they are very close together. Although small, these Van der Waals forces, as they are called, add to the external pressure.

The subtraction of b from the volume V takes account of the very small volume occupied by the molecules themselves. Although negligibly small at normal temperatures and pressures, the volumes of the molecules themselves become, at high pressures, an appreciable fraction of the space to which the gas is confined.

When for any specified range of temperatures and pressures the correcting terms a/V^2 and b can be neglected, and Boyle's law holds with sufficiently high precision, $pV = \text{constant}$, a gas is referred to as *an ideal gas*. Strictly speaking, however, an ideal gas does not exist for it would be one in which the molecules were geometrical points having no volume, and their intermolecular forces would be zero.

33.6. The General Gas Law. If a gas is expanded or compressed, without permitting heat to flow in or out, Boyle's law will no longer hold even approximately. Under these conditions there occurs what is called an *adiabatic* change. An experiment illustrating an *adiabatic expansion* or *compression* is shown in Fig. 33E, along with a pressure volume graph of the results above.

A heat insulated cylinder and movable piston is arranged with a mercury manometer and a sensitive thermometer. The gas pressure is determined from the manometer height h and atmospheric pressure p_0, the volume V from the position of the piston, and the gas temperature T from the thermometer. For position A the pressure is represented by p_1, the volume by V_1

and the temperature by T_1. Moving the piston to position B is an adiabatic expansion in which the pressure and temperature drops to p_2 and T_2 respectively and the volume increases to V_2.

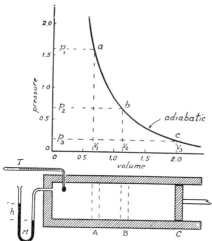

A further expansion brings the piston to the point C and the curve on the graph to the point c.

Such an *adiabatic process* as this conforms to a law known as the *general gas law*. According to this law *the pressure of any given quantity of gas is proportional to the absolute temperature and inversely proportional to the volume*. As an equation

$$\frac{pV}{T} = \text{constant}. \qquad (33f)$$

FIG. 33E—Adiabatic compression and expansion of gas.

For the three points a, b, and c in the diagram, this means

$$\frac{p_1 V_1}{T_1} = \frac{p_2 V_2}{T_2} = \frac{p_3 V_3}{T_3}. \qquad (33g)$$

Practical use of the general gas law is illustrated by the following:

Example. A balloon in a partially filled condition contains 1000 ft³ of helium gas at ground level where the pressure is 14.7 lb/in² and the temperature is 27°C. Calculate the gas volume when this balloon rises into the stratosphere to a height of 10 mi where the pressure drops to 1.5 lb/in² and the temperature to −55°C.

Solution. The above values may be substituted directly in the general gas law as expressed by Eq.(33g),

$$\frac{p_2 V_2}{T_2} = \frac{p_1 V_1}{T_1}, \qquad \frac{14.7 \text{ lb/in}^2 \times 1000 \text{ ft}^3}{(273 + 27) \text{ °Abs.}} = \frac{1.5 \text{ lb/in}^2 \times V_2}{(273 - 55) \text{ °Abs.}}.$$

Cancel like units on opposite sides and solve for V_2.

$$V_2 = \frac{14.7 \times 218 \times 1000 \text{ ft}^3}{1.5 \times 300} = 6780 \text{ ft}^3.$$

To prove the general gas law by experiment we return to the family of isothermal curves in Fig. 33D. For each of these curves alone Boyle's law holds, $pV = $ constant, yet the constant for each different curve has a different value. When these constants are plotted against temperature as shown in Fig. 33F, the points all lie on a straight line. When extrapolated back to zero, the straight line intercepts the temperature axis at −273°C. This is the absolute zero at which practically all molecular motion ceases and the pressure of a gas becomes zero.

If −273°C is the zero point on an absolute temperature scale, the straight line signifies that pV for a perfect gas is proportional to the absolute temperature T; $pV \propto T$. Inserting a proportionality constant

$$pV = RT \qquad \text{(33h)}$$

where R is a constant, the value of which depends upon the quantity of gas chosen.

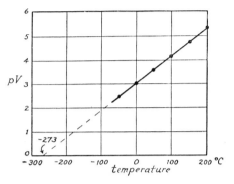

Fig. 33F—Graph for the expansion of a gas showing extrapolation to find absolute zero of temperature.

33.7. Special Cases. Although the general gas law permits all three variables, *pressure, volume,* and *temperature* to change, there are special cases in which one is held constant. Boyle's law is a special case in which the temperature remains constant. If in Eq.(33g) the temperatures are all equal, $T_1 = T_2 = T_3$, the denominators all cancel giving

Boyle's law $\qquad p_1V_1 = p_2V_2 = p_3V_3.$ $\qquad$ (33i)

If on the other hand the pressure of a gas is held constant, then $p_1 = p_2 = p_3$, and the special cases known as Charles' Law I results.

Charles' Law I. $\qquad \dfrac{V_1}{T_1} = \dfrac{V_2}{T_2} = \dfrac{V_3}{T_3}.$ $\qquad$ (33j)

Charles' Law I may be stated: the pressure of a gas remaining constant, any change in volume is accompanied by a proportional change in temperature.

Similarly, if the volume of a gas remains constant, any change in pressure is accompanied by a corresponding change in absolute temperature.

Charles' Law II. $\qquad \dfrac{p_1}{T_1} = \dfrac{p_2}{T_2} = \dfrac{p_3}{T_3}.$ $\qquad$ (33k)

PROBLEMS

1. A heavy box having a mass of 200 kg is pulled along the floor for 15 meters. If the coefficient of sliding friction is 0.40, how much heat is developed?

2. A horizontal force of 35 lb is required to pull a heavy trunk along the floor. How much heat is developed for each 100 ft it slides? (*Ans.* 4.50 Btu.)

3. The water drops 80 m in a large waterfall. Assuming the available energy all goes into heat, find the temperature difference between the water at the bottom and the water at the top.

4. A 16-lb lead shotput is dropped from a tower 100 ft high. Assuming half the energy goes into heating the lead, find the rise in temperature. (*Ans.* 2.07°F.)

5. A 50-gm steel bullet having a velocity of 800 m/sec is shot into the ground. Find its rise in temperature if half of the energy goes into the bullet.

6. A train weighing 600 tons and traveling 60 mi/hr is brought to a stop by applying the brakes. Find the heat developed. (*Ans.* 186,600 Btu.)

7. A boy weighing 100 lb, riding a bicycle weighing 40 lb, is making 15 mi/hr. When the brakes are applied to come to a stop, how much heat is developed?

8. A 5 kg mortar shell fails to explode when it hits the ground traveling with a speed of 200 m/sec. How much heat is developed? (*Ans.* 2.39×10^4 cal.)

9. A gas tank contains helium gas at a gauge pressure of 450 lb/in² when the temperature is 15°C. Calculate the gauge pressure when the temperature goes up to 35°C. (Note a gauge reads the difference in pressure between the air outside and the gas inside.)

10. A tank with a piston like that in Fig. 33C contains 5×10^6 cm³ of nitrogen gas at 40° C. If the pressure on the piston is held constant, what will be its volume when the temperature is lowered to 10°C? (*Ans.* 4.52×10^6 cm³.)

11. An automobile tire has a gauge pressure of 28 lb/in² when the temperature is 59°F. After running at high speed on a hot pavement the temperature rises to 140°F. Find the gauge pressure at this temperature assuming the volume has not changed.

12. A deep sea diver exhales air at a depth of 30 m where the temperature is 10°C. If the bubbles formed have a diameter of 2 cm, what will be their diameter at the surface where the temperature is 20°C? (*Ans.* 3.21 cm.)

13. A tank of compressed oxygen has a volume of 3.5 ft³, and its gauge indicates a pressure of 400 lb/in². If the valve is opened until the gauge pressure reading is down to 300 lb/in², how many cubic ft of oxygen measured at normal pressure of 15 lb/in² has escaped? Assume constant temperature.

14. A rubber balloon 3 ft in diameter is inflated with hydrogen gas at 30°C at sea level and 2 lb/in² gauge pressure. Find the diameter of the balloon at an altitude of 30,000 ft where the gauge pressure is again 2 lb/in², the atmospheric pressure is 4.4 lb/in², and the temperature is −35°C. (Assume standard pressure = 14.7 lb/in².) (*Ans.* 3.81 ft.)

15. If a gas has a volume of 3 m³ at a gauge pressure of 76 cm of mercury and a temperature of 50°F, what volume will it occupy when the gauge pressure is doubled and the temperature is raised to 212°F?

16. A liter (1000 cm³) of oxygen gas at normal atmospheric pressure is compressed to a volume of 250 cm³. Find the resulting absolute pressure if the compression is isothermal. (*Ans.* 4 atm, or 304 cm of Hg.)

17. How deep must a pond be in order that air bubbles formed at the bottom will have double the diameter upon reaching the surface? Assume constant temperature.

18. Steel cylinders having a volume of 1.2 ft³ contain helium at a pressure of 900 lb/in². How many full cylinders will be required to fill a balloon 40 ft in diameter to a pressure of 15 lb/in²? Assume constant temperature. (*Ans.* 46.)

19. A metal cylinder with a volume of 2 ft³ contains oxygen gas at a temperature of 27°C and a gauge pressure of 510 lb/in². If 40 ft³ of oxygen at standard atmospheric pressure and at 27°C are removed, what pressure will the gauge indicate?

Heat Engines   Chapter 34

In general heat engines are classified under one of the three following headings: (1) *steam engines,* (2) *internal combustion engines,* and (3) *jet propulsion engines.* While the first engines ever made were probably based upon jet propulsion using steam, reciprocating steam engines and turbines were the first to be developed. These were followed by gasoline and diesel engines and in recent years by the jet propulsion engines used principally in airplanes and rockets.

In this chapter we will not be concerned so much with the detailed mechanical parts of all kinds of engines, but rather with the fundamental principles involved in their transformation of heat into energy and with their general over-all efficiency in the process. To begin with, however, some of the mechanical details of at least one typical heat engine should be given.

34.1. The Gasoline Engine. Since the operation of most heat engines is based upon the same thermodynamic principles, an internal combustion engine will be explained as a typical example of all. A cross-section diagram of one of the six or more cylinders of the gasoline engine with overhead valves is given in Fig. 34A. As the crankshaft H of such a motor turns clockwise as shown, each piston moves up and down in its cylinder while the cam shaft turns the small valve cams K_1 and K_2 at half speed.

When the piston shown is at the top of its stroke (a) and it starts down, cam K_1 opens the intake valve V_1 and gasoline vapor mixed with air from the carburetor enters. The falling of the piston reduces the pressure and atmospheric pressure outside forces air and gasoline vapor in. Upon reaching (b) the cylinder is full of explosive gasoline mixture and the intake valve closes. The rising piston now compresses the gas, raising its temperature.

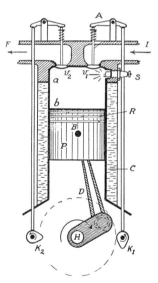

Fig. 34A—One cylinder of a gasoline engine of the type used in automobiles.

This time when the piston reaches the top and starts down, an electric spark at the tip of the spark plug ignites the already hot vapor and the resulting explosion drives the piston down with great force. At the bottom

315

of the stroke the cam K_2 opens the exhaust valve V_2 and the rising piston drives the waste fumes out. At the top of this stroke the closing of the exhaust valve is followed immediately by the opening of the intake valve and the above process is repeated.

With this type of engine the piston moves up and down twice for each explosive impulse. The several cylinders of the motor, however, are so connected to the crankshaft that they fire one after the other. In an eight-cylinder engine, for example, two cylinders are at the top when two others are on their way down, two are at the bottom and two more on their way up.

The cylinders then fire one-quarter of a turn apart so that in two complete revolutions each cylinder has fired once. With impulses coming at regular intervals one quarter of a cycle apart, the driving action is so nearly continuous that a smooth development of power from the crankshaft to the wheels results.

For the average automobile in high gear five turns of the engine produce one turn of the wheels. At 60 mi/hr when most cars develop their maximum power and the wheels are making about 10 rps, an eight-cylinder motor is turning at 50 rps and firing 200 times/sec.

34.2. Isothermal and Adiabatic Processes. An *isothermal process* (see Sec. 33.4) is one in which the pressure and volume of a gas is altered without a change in temperature, while an *adiabatic process* is one (see Sec. 33.6) in which the pressure and volume are altered without an exchange of heat. Such processes are graphically illustrated in Fig. 34B.

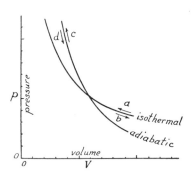

FIG. 34B—Curves showing (a) isothermal compression, (b) isothermal expansion, (c) adiabatic compression, and (d) adiabatic expansion.

Referring to Fig. 33C for an experimental arrangement and to Fig. 34B for a graphical description, an isothermal compression requires that an external force be applied to the piston and that work be done in moving it through some distance. Since a compression produces heat, a constant temperature can be maintained only by the liberation of heat. An isothermal compression, direction (a) in Fig. 34B, is therefore one in which mechanical energy is supplied and heat energy is liberated. On expansion, direction (b), the reverse changes take place; work is done by the gas in pushing the piston outward and heat must be added to prevent cooling.

When an adiabatic compression takes place, direction (c), mechanical work is done on the gas and the heat produced raises the temperature. On adiabatic expansion, work is delivered by the gas, resulting in a lowering of its temperature.

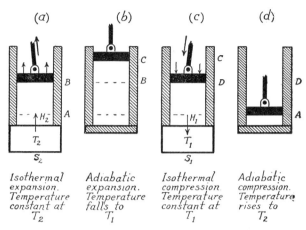

(a) Isothermal expansion. Temperature constant at T_2

(b) Adiabatic expansion. Temperature falls to T_1

(c) Isothermal compression. Temperature constant at T_1

(d) Adiabatic compression. Temperature rises to T_2

FIG. 34C—Diagram showing four stages in the operation of Carnot's ideal heat engine.

34.3. Carnot's Cycle. The thermodynamic principles of heat engines were first explained by S. Carnot in 1824. He described, as will be done here, a perfect heat engine in which four ideal heat processes take place in cyclic procession. He described what is shown schematically in Fig. 34C, a frictionless one cylinder engine having perfectly non-conducting walls and a base that is a perfect heat conductor. The box S_2 represents a source of heat capable of delivering any amount of heat at a high temperature T_2 and the box S_1 is a sink into which energy can be exhausted at a lower temperature T_1.

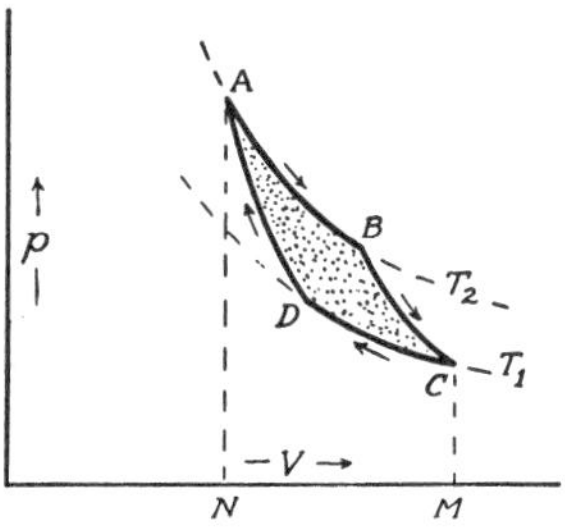

The four diagrams (a), (b), (c), and (d) show four separate stages in one complete cycle of Carnot's engine. The four corresponding pressure-volume changes are shown graphically in Fig. 34D. Starting with diagram (a), an isothermal expansion is carried out in which an amount of heat H_2 at a temperature T_2 flows into the gas, pushing the piston up from position A to position B. This corresponds in Fig. 34D to a graph-point traversing the curve A to B. At this moment the heat supply is replaced by a perfect heat insulator, diagram (b), and the second half of the expansion stroke takes place. This is an adiabatic change in which no heat flows in or out, work is done by the gas in pushing the piston from B to C, and the gas cools to a temperature T_1.

FIG. 34D—Graphical representation of Carnot's cycle for an ideal heat engine.

The cylinder is now shifted to T_1 where in diagram (c) an isothermal compression begins. As the piston in the one diagram, and the graph point in the other, moves from C to D an amount of heat H_1 flows out of the gas. Shifting finally to the insulated plate, diagram (d), the last part of the stroke is carried out as an adiabatic compression D to A, with a corresponding rise in the gas temperature to T_2.

During the complete cycle an amount of heat H_2 is taken in by the gas at the high temperature T_2 and an amount H_1 is exhausted from it at the lower temperature T_1. External work was done during the complete expansion A to C and some of it was given back upon compression from C to A. Although proof will not be given here, it can be shown that the external work done during expansion is given by the area $ABCMN$ in Fig. 34D and that the energy given back to the gas during compression is represented by the area $ADCMN$. The difference between these two, the area $ABCD$ is therefore the net work performed by the gas. Heat has been supplied and work has been done.

34.4. The Efficiency of Heat Engines. The efficiency of any heat engine is defined as the ratio of the external work done by the engine to the total heat input. Expressing the output work in heat units,

$$\text{Efficiency} = \frac{H_2 - H_1}{H_2}. \tag{34a}$$

Carnot proved that no heat engine could be more efficient than this formula indicates and that the same result can be expressed in terms of the two absolute temperatures between which the engine works.

$$\text{Efficiency} = \frac{T_2 - T_1}{T_2}. \tag{34b}$$

In practical cases the efficiency of heat engines is relatively low and never attains Carnot's efficiency. Nearly all heat engines, steam, gasoline, diesel, etc., have efficiencies in the range 10 to 20%. Some, however, reach as high as 34%. A good steam locomotive averages 10% efficiency while a steam turbine may go as high at 25%. An automobile engine in the best tuned up condition will give about 25% efficiency and a diesel engine about 34%. As yet jet propelled planes have relatively low efficiencies, about 10%, but they are rapidly being improved. The following figures for a gasoline engine of 21% efficiency will indicate where all of the consumed energy goes; 21% into work done, 36% into cooling water and radiation, 35% out the exhaust, and 8% into friction.

Example. A steam engine takes heat into its cylinders from the steam boilers at a temperature of 200°C and a pressure of 225 lb/in.^{2} and exhausts it at a temperature of 100°C and a pressure of 15 lb/in². Calculate the maximum efficiency as given by Carnot's formula.

Solution. The specified temperatures correspond to the absolute temperatures of 473°K and 373°K. Substitute these values in Eq.(34b).

$$\text{Efficiency} = \frac{473 - 373}{473} = 0.21.$$

Multiplying by 100 gives 21% efficiency.

While steam and internal combustion engines do not operate under the ideal circumstances described by Carnot, their maximum possible efficiency is, in principle, given by Eq.(34b). Furthermore, a pressure-volume indicator diagram may be, and is, frequently used to study the operating conditions of various kinds of engines in order to determine what experimental factors may improve their running efficiency. Such indicator diagrams as shown in Fig. 34E are made from actual measurements on machines while running.

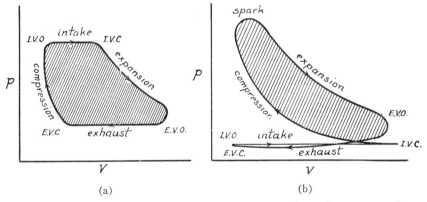

Fig. 34E—Pressure-volume indicator diagrams for (a) reciprocating steam engine, (b) internal combustion engine.

The effect produced by premature or delayed opening and closing of valves shows up as reduced curve areas. The larger the area of a curve the greater is its efficiency. The time of the *Opening* and *Closing* of the *Intake* and *Exhaust* valves is indicated in the diagrams by IVO, IVC, EVO, and EVC.

34.5. The Human Body as a Heat Engine. The human body may be considered as a heat engine in which food and oxygen are taken in as fuel, external work is done by muscular activity, and heat and carbon dioxide are exhausted as the principal waste products. The medical term applied to such transformations in the body is *metabolism.*

While the process of metabolism is chiefly one of chemistry, the principal result is the production of heat and mechanical work. From experimental heat measurements with human beings confined for hours in specially designed calorimeters (see Fig. 34F) the discovery has been made that quantitative measures of the oxygen inhaled and carbon dioxide exhaled are directly proportional to the heat production and metabolism. For example, one liter of oxygen gas will oxidize sufficient carbohydrate, protein, or fat in the body tissues to produce 4800 cal.

Fig. 34F—The human body is, in principle, a heat engine.

During rest periods in which a subject lies motionless in a warm comfortable environment, a steady rate of heat production takes place. While this rate, called *basal metabolism,* varies with height, weight, age, sex, and state of health, certain normal rates have been set up by medical clinics so that by measuring the basal metabolism of an individual the value may be used as an aid in diagnosing certain ailments.

When a person is standing and working, energy over and above the basal metabolism rate is being transformed through muscular activity into mechanical work. Basal metabolism is therefore comparable to the idling of a car motor where a certain amount of fuel is consumed in keeping the motor running. The body at work is like the running of an automobile along a level road or up a hill.

Experiments performed to test the human body as regards the conservation of energy have been made by numerous investigators over a period of many years. For example, in 1895 Atwater and Benedict constructed a large heat-insulated box for a calorimeter. In this box a man could sleep, eat his meals, and at times ride a stationary bicycle. The energy given him as food is calculated from known heats of combustion. The heat given off by his body is removed for measurement by a stream of water flowing through a copper pipe on the ceiling, while work done when pedaling the bicycle is measured by a copper disk and electro-magnet in the place of the rear wheel.

The results of these experiments, carried out with twenty different subjects over a period of several months, are given in the following tabulations. The first table clearly demonstrates the conformity of the human body to the law of conservation of energy.

	Input per Day in kilo-calories	Output per Day in kilo-calories	Diff. %
Resting	2262	2268	0.3
Working	4175	4163	0.3

The second table shows the average distribution of heat energy as it is dissipated by the body during the rest period and during average working hours.

Heat Losses by	During Rest %	During Work %
Conduction, convection and radiation	78	45
Evaporation	22	44
External work	0	11

The following are average values determined under ideal working conditions and they represent the highest efficiency that can be expected of the human body.

Energy required per hour of rest .... 100 K-cal
Energy required per hour of work .... 250 K-cal
Actual work done (in heat units) .... 45 K-cal

The difference between the first two numbers, 150 K-cal, is the energy supplied to do work. The net efficiency is, therefore,

$$\frac{45}{150} \times 100 = 30\%$$

while the over-all efficiency is

$$\frac{45}{250} \times 100 = 18\%.$$

The power developed by the average man under ideal conditions is shown in the following table.

Kind of Work	Time Interval	Power Developed, hp
Mountain climbing (moderate)	Many hours	0.11
Mountain climbing (severe)	1 hr	0.19
Steep mountain climbing	4 min	0.143
Climbing a treadmill	30 sec	0.65
Running upstairs	30 sec	0.93

34.6. The Turbo Jet. This engine, used extensively in high-speed aircraft, is shown schematically in Fig. 34G. Air needed for combustion enters the nose of the *shroud* where it is compressed by a fan-like centrifugal *com-*

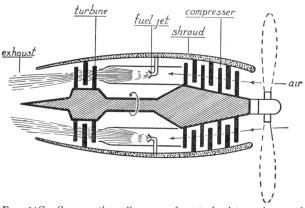

Fig. 34G—Cross-section diagram of a turbo-jet engine used principally in aircraft (propeller optional). Top speed probably 600 mi/hr.

pressor. This air along with the fuel to be burned is injected into a *combustion chamber* and there the mixture ignited. The rapidly expanding gases drive a fan-like *turbine* wheel and at the same time create a forward thrust on the walls by exhausting through the rear as shown.

While the principal function of the turbine is to drive the compressor and small auxiliary equipment like fuel pumps, generators, etc., some aircraft installations employ a propeller to assist *take-off*. At high speeds such propellers are stopped and "feathered" by a suitable clutch mechanism and all forward thrust comes from the exhaust jet.

34.7. The Ram-Jet. With perhaps the exception of the rocket the ram-jet exceeds all other engines in simplicity. See Fig. 34H. When flying through the air at high speed, air enters the funnel shaped nose where oxy-

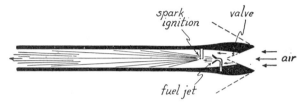

Fig. 34H—Diagram of a ram-jet. Top speed probably 1000 mi/hr.

gen mixed with fuel from the jets supports a more or less continuous combustion. The expanding gases exert a forward thrust on the ram walls as they exhaust through the rear as shown. Such a ram-jet is hardly more than a streamlined hollow tube, yet it develops an enormous thrust when moving at high speed.

One modification of the ram-jet, developed originally in Germany for the V-I "buzz bombs," employs a valve mechanism and spark-plug ignition system (show dotted in the figures). Incoming air forces a leaf-valve open and after mixing with the fuel is ignited by a properly timed spark. The explosion drives the valve closed and the ram forward as the expanding and cooling gases exhaust through the end of the long pipe. When the rear pressure is again lowered, the valve opens and the above process is repeated. Resonating like a reed organ pipe, with a node at the center and a loop at each end, the pulse-jet sounds forth with a *very loud roar*.

34.8. The Rocket. The rocket of today owes so much of its early development to the American experimenter, Goddard. Rockets are classified as engines of very low efficiency but are definitely capable of enormous power and high speeds. While the turbo-jet and the ram-jet engines require large quantities of air for their proper operation and are thereby confined to aircraft operating at relatively low altitudes, the rocket carries its own

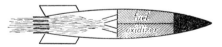

Fig. 34I—Rocket ship for inter-planetary travel; top speed almost unlimited.

oxygen supply as well as *fuel* and is capable of operating beyond the earth's atmosphere. See Fig. 34I.

Because *fuel* and *oxidizer* must both be carried along, rocket ships are, as yet, quite limited in range. The *JATO* units developed in the United

States for assisting *take-off* of planes, and the V-II rocket bomb developed in Germany near the close of World War II are illustrations of rocket power. See Fig. 13H.

Like that of all heat engines, the efficiency of the turbo-jet, ram-jet and rocket depends upon the operating temperatures T_1 and T_2 in Eq.(34b). The high temperature T_2 is limited in large measure by the melting point of the engine parts and a great deal of effort has been expended in the search for materials that will maintain the required mechanical strength at higher temperatures.

The forward *thrust F* derived from all such jet propulsion devices is given by the *impulse equation*. See Eq.(8h).

$$Ft = m(V - v_j) \qquad \text{or} \qquad F = \frac{m}{t}(V - v_j)$$

where m/t is the mass of gas per second leaving with a velocity v_j, and V is the velocity of the engine. V and v_j are measured with respect to the ground.

PROBLEMS

1. A coal burning locomotive supplies steam to its cylinders at 608°F and exhausts this steam into the surrounding air at 410°F. Find the theoretical efficiency.

2. An oil burning steam turbine takes in steam at 350°C and exhausts it into the surrounding air at 188°C. Find its theoretical efficiency. (*Ans.* 26.0%.)

3. While in flight the effective high temperature of the flaming gas in a jet fighter engine reaches 1100°F. If its efficiency is 25% what is the effective exhaust temperature?

4. Each of the four jet engines in a transport plane operate between a high temperature of 1182°F and an exhaust temperature of 800°F. Find their efficiency. (*Ans.* 23.3%.)

5. A boy weighing 120 lb climbs a 6000 ft mountain peak in 5 hrs and 20 min. During this time his body uses up 1320 K-cal. (a) What power is developed, and (b) what is his net efficiency if the energy required per hour of rest is 120 K-cal?

6. A bricklayer averages 80,000 ft-lb of work per hr of work. Working for a 6 hr day his body uses up 1800 K-cal of energy. Find his net efficiency if on resting his body averages 105 K-cal per hr. (*Ans.* 13.3%.)

7. During a 24 hr day of rest a man consumes 2600 K-cal, and during a 24 hr day when he works he consumes 4000 K-cal. Find the total work done in ft-lb if his net efficiency during an 8 hr shift is 20% and during the remainder of the time is zero. What power did he develop during working hours?

8. A jet fighter plane making 600 mi/hr exhausts gas from the tail pipe at a speed of 2000 ft/sec, thereby producing a forward thrust of 5 tons. Calculate the rate at which gas mass is exhausted. (*Ans.* 286 lb/sec.)

Vibrations and Waves   *Chapter 35*

35.1. Simple Harmonic Motion. Any motion, simple or complex, which repeats itself in equal intervals of time is called *periodic motion*. There are many examples in everyday life which give rise to a special kind of periodic motion called *simple periodic motion*. The swinging of the clock pendulum, the turning of the balance wheel of a watch, or the vibration of a tuning fork, are good examples of such motions. The term simple periodic motion applies to these because each can be described in terms of one of the simplest known types of periodic motion—namely, *uniform circular motion*.

Simple harmonic motion is defined as the projection on any diameter of a point moving in a circle with uniform speed. This is illustrated in Fig. 35A. The point p moves around the circle of ra-

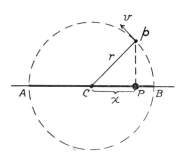

dius r with uniform speed v. If at every instant a perpendicular is drawn from p to the diameter AB, the intercept P will move with simple harmonic motion. Moving back and forth along the straight line from A to B the velocity v_x is continually changing. At the center point C it has its greatest velocity, while at A and B it is momentarily at rest. Starting from either end of its path the velocity increases until it reaches C; from there it slows down again, coming to rest at the opposite end of its path.

Fig. 35A—Diagram illustrating simple harmonic motion along a straight line.

The *displacement* of a simple harmonic motion is defined as the distance from the center C to the point P. As shown in Fig. 35A, the displacement x varies in magnitude from zero at C up to r, the radius of the *circle of reference*, at A or B.

The *amplitude* r is defined as the maximum value of the *displacement* x, and the *period* is defined as the time required to make one complete vibration.

If a vibration starts at A it is not completed until the point moves across to B and back again to A. If it starts from C and moves to B and back to C, only half a vibration has been completed. The amplitude r is usually measured in centimeters and the period T in seconds.

The frequency of a harmonic motion is defined as the number of complete vibrations per second. For example, if a particular vibrating object completes one vibration in one-half second (the period $T = 1/2$ sec), then it will make two complete vibrations in 1 sec (the frequency $n = 2$ vib/sec). If again a body completes one vibration in one-tenth of a second, $T = 1/10$ sec, it will make ten vibrations in 1 sec, $n = 10$ vib/sec. In other words, n and T are reciprocals of each other.

$$\text{Period} = \frac{1}{\text{frequency}} \quad \text{or} \quad \text{frequency} = \frac{1}{\text{period}}. \quad (35a)$$

In algebraic symbolism,

$$T = \frac{1}{n} \qquad\qquad n = \frac{1}{T}. \quad (35b)$$

35.2. Vibrating Strips. If a strip of wood or metal is clamped tightly at one end, as shown in Fig. 35B, it may be set into a natural state of vibra-

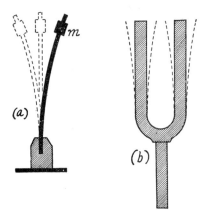

tion. Pulled to one side and then released, the free end of the strip will move back and forth with simple harmonic motion. If the mass m clamped to the free end is increased the frequency of vibration will decrease; whereas, if the strip is made stiffer either by increasing its thickness or decreasing its length, the frequency will increase.

Shown in diagram (b) is a tuning fork as used by musicians to determine pitch. Striking one prong of a fork against some object sets both prongs vibrating simultaneously in opposite directions. The thinner the prongs of the fork the lower is the frequency of vibration; the shorter the prongs of the fork the higher is the frequency of vibration.

Fig. 35B—Illustrating the variations of (a) a strip clamped at one end and weighted near the other, and (b) the prongs of a tuning fork.

Besides being used as standards of pitch by musicians, tuning forks are used for scientific purposes. As scientific instruments they perform one very useful function of marking off short but equal intervals of time. A common fork used for this purpose has a frequency of one thousand, $n = 1000$ vib/sec, and is frequently kept vibrating by means of an electrical circuit similar to that of a doorbell.

35.3. Sources of Waves. The motion of any material object may be considered as a source of waves. A board striking the water, the snap of a finger, or a bowed violin string are examples of this.

Suppose that the far end of a rope is fastened to a post, as shown in

Fig. 35C, and that the other end (a), which is held in the hand, is given a sudden flip up and down. The disturbance sent out along the rope travels down the rope to the post, as shown, and is then reflected back again toward the hand. This kind of wave is called a single *wave pulse*. If instead of a sudden pulse the hand is moved up and down with simple harmonic motion, a *train of waves,* like that shown in diagram (b), travels down the rope.

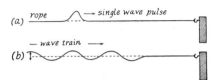

Fig. 35C—Examples of transverse waves sent out along a rope.

When the prongs of a tuning fork are made to vibrate they set the surrounding air into periodic motions. Each prong periodically strikes the air molecules next to it and these molecules in turn strike others, thus transmitting the disturbance outward. Traveling outward in all directions, such periodic disturbances constitute sound waves.

35.4. Transverse Waves. Transverse waves are those in which each particle vibrates along a line perpendicular to the direction of propagation. Along any one line of travel all particles are vibrating in one plane only. Such waves are illustrated in Fig. 35D by means of a wave machine designed

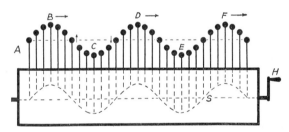

Fig. 35D—Diagram of a wave machine for demonstrating transverse waves.

for this purpose. As the handle *H* is turned one way or the other the small round balls at the top move up and down with simple harmonic motion. As they move up and down, each along its own line, the wave form *ABCDEF* will move to the right or to the left. Light is an example of transverse wave motion.

35.5. Longitudinal Waves. Longitudinal waves are those in which the vibrations of the particles are along straight lines parallel to the direction of propagation. This type of wave is illustrated in Fig. 35E by another wave machine. As the handle is turned each small ball moves horizontally and in the plane of the page with simple harmonic motion. In so doing the regions of rarefaction *B* and *D* and the regions of condensation *A, C,* and *E* move to the right, always keeping their same relative distances.

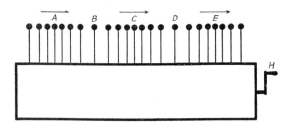

Fig. 35E—Diagram of a wave-machine for demonstrating longitudinal waves.

Sound waves in air are examples of longitudinal waves. Each air molecule vibrates back and forth about some equilibrium position as the wave train passes by.

35.6. Water Waves. The motion of the surface of water as a wave passes by is a combination of both transverse and longitudinal waves. The water molecules move back and forth and at the same time up and down,

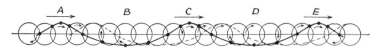

Fig. 35F—Water-waves. Each water molecule moves in a circle or an ellipse as the waves pass by. This is a combination of longitudinal and transverse wave motion.

i.e., in circles or ellipses. As illustrated by the diagram in Fig. 35F, each molecule moves in a circle in a vertical plane to form moving crests at *A, C,* and *E* and troughs at *B* and *D*. A small cork placed on the surface of water and observed from the side will exhibit this circular motion. When a person is swimming in a rough sea, and the crest of a wave approaches, he is first carried upward and forward in the direction the wave is traveling; after the crest has passed he falls and then is carried backward.

35.7. Standing Waves. Nearly all sounds emanating from musical instruments are the result of standing waves. Standing waves may be produced in any substance whether it is a solid, liquid, or gas, by two wave trains of the same frequency traveling in the same medium in opposite directions. One of the ways in which this is done is illustrated in Fig. 35G. One end of a rope is fastened to a post and the other end, held taut, is moved up and down with simple harmonic motion. As the waves reach the fixed end of the rope they are reflected back to meet succeeding waves just coming up. If the waves have just the right frequency the rope will sustain both wave trains by dividing into sections as shown. The points L_1 to L_5, where the rope has

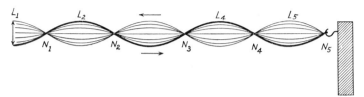

FIG. 35G—Standing waves produced by reflecting a train of transverse waves from the fixed end of a rope.

a maximum up and down motion, are called *anti-nodes,* and the points of no motion halfway between are called *nodes.* The heavy line represents the rope at one instant and the other lines represent it at other instants. The entire wave section between two consecutive nodes is called a *loop.*

Standing waves with longitudinal vibrations may be demonstrated with a long flexible spring as shown in Fig. 35H(a). The right-hand end of the spring is fixed and the left-hand end is moved back and forth with simple

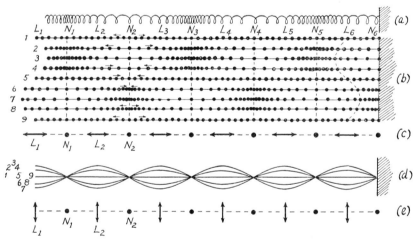

FIG. 35H—Illustrating standing waves as they are produced with (a) the longitudinal waves of a spring, (b) the longitudinal waves of sound in the air, and (d) the transverse waves of a rope. (c) and (e) indicate the direction of vibration at the antinodes.

harmonic motion. If the impressed vibration has the proper frequency the waves traveling to the right in meeting the reflected waves traveling to the left set up *nodes* and *anti-nodes.* The nodes N correspond to points where there is no motion, and the anti-nodes L to points where the motion is a maximum. The dots in diagram (b) show the relative positions and motions of each individual coil of the spring at nine different times during one complete vibration. The dots at the nodes remain fixed at all times while those at the anti-nodes move back and forth as shown by the arrows in diagram (c). At one instant (3), compressions are formed at the odd-numbered nodes N_1, N_3 and N_5 and rarefactions at the even-numbered nodes N_2, N_4 and N_6. Half a vibration later, (7), they change, the nodes of compression become nodes of rarefaction, and vice versa.

A direct comparison of standing transverse and standing longitudinal waves is given by diagrams (b), (c), (d) and (e) in Fig. 35H. The numbers

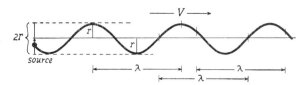

Fig. 35I—Illustrating the wave length λ as the distance between corresponding points on two consecutive waves, and the amplitude r as the maximum displacement.

(1), (2), (3), etc., indicate the corresponding states in the vibrations of each. Diagram (c) indicates the amplitudes of the longitudinal motions at the anti-nodes of the spring, and diagram (e) the transverse motions at the anti-nodes of the rope.

It should be explained that the dots in diagram (b) also represent the motions of air molecules when sound waves are reflected from a flat wall, back on themselves, to produce standing waves. As we shall see in the next chapter, these are like the sustained vibrations of the air in an organ pipe, a flute, or some other musical wind instrument.

While sound waves in air are longitudinal vibrations it is customary, for convenience only, to draw them as transverse waves. It is for this reason that the comparisons in Fig. 35H are made here. In the following two chapters, therefore, sound waves will usually be drawn as though they were transverse.

35.8. Wavelength. When a vibrating object sends out waves through a homogeneous medium the waves travel with constant velocity. If the source vibrates with simple harmonic motion and waves are transverse, they have the general appearance of the waves shown in Fig. 35I. The *wavelength* is defined as the distance between two similar points of any two consecutive waves, and is represented by the Greek letter lambda, λ. The distance between two consecutive wave crests, for example, is equal to one wave length.

The amplitude of a wave is defined as the maximum value of the displacement. This is illustrated by r in Fig. 35I, the amplitude of the waves being proportional to the amplitude of the source. The frequency of a train of waves is defined as the number of waves passing any given point per second. This is equal to the frequency of the source and is usually designated by n. It is customary to express frequency in *vibrations per second* or in *cycles per second*.

From the definitions of velocity, frequency, and wavelength, the following very simple relation exists between them:

$$V = n\lambda. \tag{35c}$$

The length of one wave, λ, times the number of waves per second, n, equals the total distance traveled in 1 sec, V.

Since the period is defined as the time required for one wave to pass by a given point, the relation between frequency and period given for vibrating sources in Eq.(35b) also applies to waves.

Example. If a train of waves moving along a rope has a velocity of 100 ft/sec and a wavelength of 20 ft, what is the frequency and period of the source?

Solution. By inserting these values in the proper places of Eq.(35c), we obtain

$$100 \text{ ft/sec} = n \times 20 \text{ ft} \qquad \text{or} \qquad n = 100/20 = 5 \text{ vib/sec.}$$

By Eq.(35b),

$$T = 1/5 = 0.2 \text{ sec.}$$

The frequency is 5 vib/sec, and the period is 0.2 sec.

35.9. Theory of Simple Harmonic Motion.

It is intended here to derive a general formula for the period of vibrating bodies executing simple harmonic motion. Referring to Sec. 35.1, the period T is defined as the time required to make one complete vibration. Referring to Fig. 35J, the point p, moving with a speed v, will travel once around the circle of reference, a distance $2\pi r$, in a time T. Applying the relation that *time equals distance divided by velocity*, we get

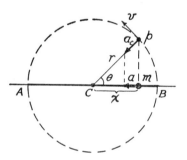

FIG. 35J—In any simple harmonic motion the acceleration is always toward the central equilibrium position.

$$T = \frac{2\pi r}{v}. \tag{35d}$$

The centripetal acceleration of p toward the center C is $a_c = v^2/r$, and its component a along the x axis is $a = \frac{v^2}{r} \cos \theta$. Since $\cos \theta = x/r$, the acceleration

$$a = \frac{v^2}{r} \cos \theta \qquad\qquad a = \frac{v^2}{r} \cdot \frac{x}{r} \qquad\qquad a = \frac{v^2}{r^2} x.$$

By transposing and taking the square root, we obtain

$$\frac{r^2}{v^2} = \frac{x}{a} \qquad \text{or} \qquad \frac{r}{v} = \sqrt{\frac{x}{a}}.$$

Substituting in Eq.(35d) gives

$$T = 2\pi \sqrt{\frac{x}{a}}. \tag{35e}$$

This is a useful equation because it gives the period of vibration in terms of the displacement x and the corresponding acceleration. Note that the acceleration a is always opposite in direction to the displacement x, and is always directed toward the center.

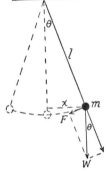

35.10. The Simple Pendulum. If a simple pendulum, as shown in Fig. 35K, is set swinging in an arc which is not too big, its period T is given by the following formula,

$$T = 2\pi \sqrt{\frac{l}{g}}. \tag{35f}$$

T is the time of one complete vibration, l is the length of the pendulum, and g is the acceleration due to gravity. If the angle of swing is much greater than 5° the period will be slightly increased.

Fig. 35K—A pendulum bob executes simple harmonic motion along a curved path.

The statement can now be made that the bob of a simple pendulum moves along its arc with *simple periodic motion.* At the ends of its swing the velocity is momentarily zero and at the center is a maximum. The driving force which starts the bob at one end of its path and accelerates it until it reaches the center and then decelerates it, bringing it to rest at the other end, is the component F_1 of the force of gravity W. The component F_2 is the tension in the cord supporting the mass m.

The fact that the mass of a pendulum bob does not appear in Eq.(35f) signifies that pendulums of equal length but different mass should have the same period T. Started together, and with small amplitudes (see Fig. 35L), simple pendulums of different mass will swing in synchronism.

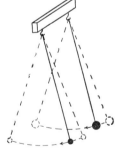

The effect of the acceleration of gravity g on the period is illustrated in Fig. 35M. If the pull of gravity could be increased the period of all pendulums would decrease, that is, they would swing faster. If

Fig. 35L—Two simple pendulums of the same length but different mass have the same period of vibration.

gravity could be decreased the periods would be greater, that is, they would swing more slowly. In the diagram the pull of gravity is imitated by means of an electro-magnet. When the magnet is turned on it pulls down on the iron bob and makes it swing more quickly.

The effect of the length l on the period is shown in Fig. 35N. Two pendulums of lengths l, and $4l$ are shown at the same instant a short time after having started simultaneously at their respective origins S. While the pendulum l has made one complete swing, the pendulum of length $4l$ has made but half a swing. This shows that to double the time of swing the length must be made four times as large. This is in agreement with Eq.(35f) in which the length occurs under the square root sign.

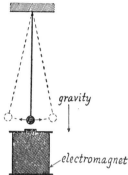

FIG. 35M—An increase in gravitational attraction like the downward pull of the magnet will shorten the period of a simple pendulum.

A derivation of Eq.(35f)

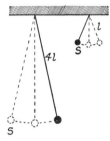

FIG. 35N—To double the period of a simple pendulum the length must increase fourfold.

can be obtained from Fig. 35K as follows. The downward pull of gravity on the bob of mass m is W, and this has been resolved into two components, one parallel to the support l and the other F perpendicular to it. Because of equal angles θ in the two right triangles and the theorem that corresponding sides of similar triangles are proportional, we may write

$$\frac{F}{W} = \frac{x}{l}.$$

Since the force F accelerates the mass m in the direction of motion, and the weight W is equal to mg, substituting in the above proportionality gives

$$\frac{ma}{mg} = \frac{x}{l} \quad \text{or} \quad \frac{x}{a} = \frac{l}{g}.$$

Substituting l/g for x/a in Eq.(35e) gives

$$T = 2\pi\sqrt{l/g}.$$

35.11. Vibrating Spring. Any elastic body may be set into a state of vibration by first distorting it in some way and then releasing it. This is demonstrated by a weight on the end of a spring as shown in Fig. 35O. In diagram (a) the spring S and mass m hang in a state of equilibrium. At (b) a force F has been applied to stretch the spring, displacing the mass a distance a. After being released the mass m moves up and down with simple harmonic motion. In diagram (c) the spring is shown compressed with m at

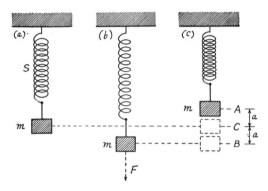

Fɪɢ. 350—A mass on the end of a spring executes simple harmonic motion.

its highest point. The amplitude a of the vibration is determined by the original distance to which the spring is stretched, and the period T is given by the algebraic equation:

$$T = 2\pi\sqrt{m/k} \qquad (35\text{g})$$

where m is the mass of the vibrating body and k a number expressing the stiffness of the spring. See Sec. 24.1. The constant k is the force in dynes required to stretch the spring 1 cm. This formula shows that, if m is made larger, the period is increased and that when a stiffer spring is used (k being in the denominator), the period is decreased.

Obeying Hooke's law (see Sec. 24.1), the stretch of a spring is given by the relation

$$F = kx$$

where F is the applied force, x the displacement, and k the same as above. Since a force of magnitude F acts to accelerate the mass m, $F = ma$, gives

$$ma = kx \qquad \text{or} \qquad x/a = m/k.$$

Substituting m/k for x/a in Eq.(35e) gives Eq.(35g).

PROBLEMS

1. A train of waves moves along a cable with a speed of 30 ft/sec. Find the frequency and period of the source if their wavelength is 3 in.

2. A vibrating source with a frequency of 22 vib/sec sends waves along a rope

with a velocity of 6 m/sec. Find (a) the period of the source, and (b) the wavelength of the waves. (*Ans.* (a) 0.0454 sec, (b) 27.3 cm.)

3. A pendulum bob has a length of 50 cm. Find its period and frequency.

4. A simple pendulum is to have a period of $\frac{1}{4}$ sec. How long should it be if $g = 32.00$ ft/sec^2? (*Ans.* 0.608 in.)

5. A clock pendulum swings with a period of 1 sec where $g = 32.26$ ft/sec^2. How many sec will it lose in 24 hrs if it is taken to a high mountain where $g = 32.10$ ft/sec^2?

6. A clock pendulum made of aluminum has a length of 100 cm when the temperature is 20°C. How many sec will this clock lose in 24 hrs if the temperature is maintained at 30°C? See Eq.(29a). (*Ans.* 11 sec.)

7. When a 5 lb weight is fastened to the lower end of a spring as shown in Fig. 35O, it stretches the spring a distance of 3 in. If the suspended weight is then set vibrating, what will be its frequency?

8. A mass of 250 gm is to be suspended from a spring as shown in Fig. 35O. If the mass is set vibrating and the frequency is found to be 20 vib/sec, what is the value of the spring constant k? (*Ans.* 3.95×10^6 dynes/cm.)

9. When a mass of 100 gm is suspended from a spring as shown in Fig. 35O, it stretches the spring a distance of 5 cm. If the 100 gm mass is now replaced by one of 30 gm, and then set vibrating up and down what will be the frequency?

10. When a 50 lb weight is suspended from a spring as shown in Fig. 35O, the spring stretches 6 in. After the 50 lb weight is removed a boy jumps up and hangs on to the lower end. If in doing so he is set vibrating with a period of 1 sec, how much does he weigh? (*Ans.* 81 lb.)

11. The velocity of radio waves is 3×10^8 m/sec. What is the wavelength from a station broadcasting on a frequency of 550 kilocycles/sec?

12. A radio station broadcasts on a wavelength of 30 meters. What is the frequency in megacycles/sec if the velocity of radio waves is 3×10^{10} cm/sec? (*Ans.* 10.)

13. The amplitude of a particle executing simple harmonic motion is 20 cm; the period is 0.5 sec. Calculate (a) the maximum acceleration of the particle, and (b) its maximum velocity.

14. The maximum velocity of a particle moving with simple harmonic motion is 20 cm/sec. If its period of vibration is 1 sec, what is (a) the amplitude, and (b) the maximum acceleration? (*Ans.* (a) 3.18 cm, (b) 125.8 cm/sec^2.)

15. A small mass moves with simple harmonic motion. If it has an amplitude of 1 cm and a period of 0.01 sec, find (a) its maximum speed, and (b) its maximum acceleration.

16. A tiny pendulum 1 mm long is made of a quartz fiber and a quartz bead. Calculate (a) its period, and (b) its frequency. (*Ans.* (a) 0.0653 sec. (b) 15.3 vib/sec.)

17. A simple pendulum, generally called a Foucault pendulum, is 30 m long and hangs from the dome of a cathedral. From such an arrangement, the effect of the earth's rotation can be observed. Find the period of the pendulum.

18. A mass of 50 gm, fastened to the end of a light-weight spring and set vibrating up and down, is found to have a frequency of 2 vib/sec. Calculate the frequency when the mass is reduced to 5 gm. (*Ans.* 6.32 vib/sec.)

Sound, Its Transmission and Detection Chapter 36

36.1. Sound Transmission. The transmission of sound from one place to the other, from source to receiver, requires a material medium through which to travel. This is to be contrasted with light which travels best through a vacuum.

That sound is transmitted by air, or any other gas, may be demonstrated by placing a small bell in an evacuated jar. This is illustrated in Fig. 36A.

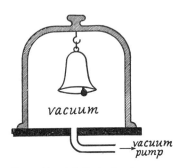

vacuum

vacuum
pump

FIG. 36A—A bell ringing in a vacuum cannot be heard.

As the air is slowly removed from the jar the ringing of the bell grows fainter and fainter until, when a good vacuum is obtained, no sound can be heard. As soon as the air is admitted, however, the ringing becomes clearly audible again. The vibrating bell strikes air molecules, knocking them away from the metal surface. These fast moving molecules strike the adjacent air molecules and they in turn strike others. Upon reaching the side of the jar, the glass walls are periodically bombarded by the molecules and set vibrating. The walls in turn set the outside air vibrating. Arriving at the observer's ear, the disturbance strikes the eardrum, setting it into motion. Without air to transmit the vibrations from the bell to the inside surface of the glass jar, no sound could ever leave the jar.

It should be made clear at this point that sound waves are longitudinal vibrations. The moving balls on the wave machine in Fig. 35E represent the molecular motions superposed upon the random thermal-motions of the air molecules.

The transmission of sound by liquids may be illustrated by an experiment shown in Fig. 36B(a). A tuning fork with a disk attached to its base is set vibrating and then touched to the surface of a dish of water. The vibrations of the fork and disk travel through the water to the bottom of the dish and to the table top. The table top itself is set into vibration with the same frequency as the fork, thus acting like a *sounding board* to make the sound louder.

The transmission of sound by solids is illustrated in diagram (b). A vibrating tuning fork is brought into contact with the end of a long wooden rod. The longitudinal vibrations travel down the length of the rod, setting the hollow wooden box at the other end vibrating. Sound is clearly heard coming from the box.

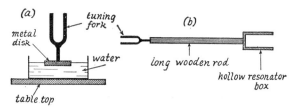

Fig. 36B—Experiments demonstrating the transmission of sound by (a) liquids, like water; and (b) solids, like wood.

36.2. Velocity of Sound. Although light and sound both travel with a finite velocity, the velocity of light is so great in comparison that an instantaneous flash may be regarded as taking no time to travel many miles. When we see the light of a distant lightning flash and hear the thunder later, we know that the difference in time is due to the relatively low velocity of sound. Knowing that sound requires 5 sec to travel 1 mi, the distance of a passing thunderstorm can be noted by the second hand of a watch. Similarly, when a distant train starts up and we watch for the first puff of smoke as it starts out, the arrival of the accompanying sound is not heard until an appreciable time afterward.

The earliest successful attempts to measure the velocity of sound in air were made in 1640 by Marin Mersenne, a French physicist, and in 1656 by Giovanni Borelli and Vincenzo Viviani, Italian physicists. Since that time many experimenters have improved upon these earliest measurements by using various different methods and devices. The most recent and probably the most accurate measurements are those made in 1934 by Miller.* With coast defense guns as a source of sound and a set of receivers located at certain distances apart, very accurate velocity determinations were made. The results gave a velocity of 331 m/sec at a temperature of 0°C. This is equivalent to 1087 ft/sec.

As a general rule, sound travels faster in solids and liquids than it does

* Dayton C. Miller (1866-1940), American physicist, noted for his experiments on the quality of musical sounds, and on the ether drift. He collected and had in his possession the largest collection of flutes in the world. These instruments he turned over to the Smithsonian Institute in Washington, D.C., where they are now on exhibit. A member of the National Academy of Sciences, and one-time president of the American Physical Society, he has been awarded the Elliott Cresson Medal and the Cleveland Distinguished Service Medal.

in gases. This is illustrated by the measured velocities for a few common substances given in Table 36A.

TABLE 36A. VELOCITY OF SOUND IN DIFFERENT SUBSTANCES

Substance	Velocity in $\dfrac{m}{sec}$	Velocity in $\dfrac{ft}{sec}$
Air (at 0°C)	331	1,087
Hydrogen	1,269	4,165
Water	1,435	4,708
Alcohol	1,213	3,890
Iron	5,130	16,820
Glass	5,000	16,410

It is well known that the temperature has a small but measurable effect upon the velocity of sound. For each degree centigrade rise in temperature the velocity in air increases by 61 cm/sec, or its equivalent of 2 ft/sec. Written as an equation,

$$V = V_0 + 0.61t,$$

where V_0 is the velocity in meters per second at 0°C, and t is the temperature in °C. For each degree on the Fahrenheit scale the velocity increases by 1.1 ft/sec. This is an approximate relation which holds near 32°F.

A velocity of 1087 ft/sec is equivalent to 740 mi/hr. High in the stratosphere where the daytime temperature reaches 200°F (see Fig. 31N) the velocity of sound increases 185 ft/sec. There the velocity of 1272 ft/sec is equivalent to 867 mi/hr.

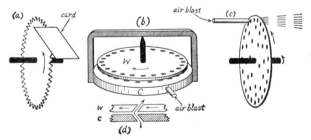

FIG. 36C—Sound demonstrations illustrating the relation between pitch and frequency.

36.3. Pitch. The pitch of a musical note refers to its position on a musical scale, and is determined by the frequency of the sound impulses sent out by the vibrating source. The dependence of pitch upon frequency can be demonstrated in many ways. Diagram (a) of Fig. 36C represents a toothed wheel (called Savart's wheel) rotating at high speed. A small card held against the teeth is set into vibration, giving out a musical note. As the wheel slows down the vibration frequency of the card decreases and the note lowers in pitch.

Diagram (b) is a siren similar to those commonly used as factory whistles. The energy as well as the sound is derived from compressed air which is blown through small holes in the hollow container *C*. The air issuing from these jets passes through similar holes in a rotating disk *W*. With the holes drilled at an angle as shown in detail (d) the air blasts from the stationary holes below exert a force on one side of the holes in *W*, causing the disk to turn. As the disk turns each blast of air is momentarily cut off until another hole arrives just above it. The intermittent pulses of air issuing from the disk give rise to a musical note.

Diagram (c) in Fig. 36C represents a siren in which a single blast of air is interrupted by a rotating disk containing several rings of holes. Detailed experiments with many trained and untrained observers alike show that pitch and frequency are not identical.

Pitch is a *subjective* measurement and is therefore a sensory magnitude depending upon the individual, while frequency is a *physical* measurement of the number of vibrations per second. As the intensity of a pure tone of 300 vib/sec is increased, for example, it appears to most observers to change in quality and at the same time to decrease slightly in pitch. Conversely, at a high frequency, an increase in the intensity seems to increase the pitch.

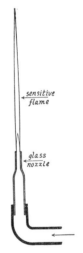

36.4. Detection of Sound. By far the most important instrument by which sound is detected is the ear. This hearing mechanism, which is sensitive to very faint as well as loud sounds and to very high as well as low frequencies, is treated in detail in Sec. 36.8.

Various electrical devices commonly called microphones have been invented for detecting sound waves and transforming them into varying electric currents. These currents may then be amplified, transmitted long or short distances, and then reconverted into sound. Sometimes they are fed into an oscilloscope for a study of wave motion, a "cutting head" for recording, a light source for sound recording on film, or an electromagnet for recording on wire or tape. Some of these devices are considered in detail in later chapters.

Sound may also be detected by a rather interesting but impractical device known as the sensitive flame. This detector, as illustrated in Fig. 36D, consists of a tall, thin gas flame produced

FIG. 36D—Diagram of a gas flame sensitive to high-pitched sound waves. As the waves pass the tip of the nozzle the flame dips down.

by gas issuing from a small nozzle. As sound waves pass by the tip of the nozzle, the gas stream is disturbed and the flame becomes unstable and drops in height. This action is particularly noticeable with high-pitched sounds like those from a blowing whistle, or those from a jingling bunch of keys.

36.5. Reflection of Sound. The reflection of sound waves may be demonstrated in various ways. One arrangement is shown in Fig. 36E in which a Galton whistle sounding a high-pitched note acts as a source of sound and a sensitive flame as the receiver. A solid screen between the two casts a "sound shadow" thus permitting only the reflected waves from the wall of the room to reach it.

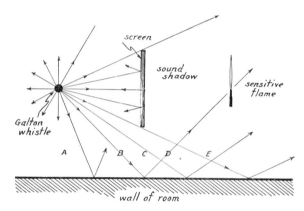

Fig. 36E—Experiment demonstrating the reflection of sound waves from the wall of a room.

When the whistle, blown by compressed air, is sounded continuously, the flame will remain unstable. If, under these conditions, the experimenter walks beside the wall through the sound path the flame will be quite unstable when he reaches *A, C,* or *E,* but will burn smoothly when he intercepts the beam at *B* or *D.*

Sound shadows of the kind shown in this experiment are characteristic of high-pitched notes only and demonstrate that short waves tend to travel in straight lines. The longer waves of low-pitched sounds, however, tend to bend around corners. This latter effect, known as diffraction, is quite noticeable where a carillon of large bells is being played. On walking around the corner of a nearby building the sharp cutoff in the intensity of the high-pitched bells is quite marked, while the low-pitched bells continue in good strength. It should be pointed out that high-pitched notes also show diffraction but to a lesser degree. The phenomenon is due to the wave nature of sound and will be explained in principle in the case of light waves in another chapter.

36.6. Refraction of Sound Waves. The bending of sound waves in layers of air at different temperatures is called refraction. The phenomenon can be observed in various ways and is due to the greater velocity of sound in warm air than the velocity in cold (see Sec. 36.2).

A good illustration is found in the frequent observation while boating on a lake or river of being able to hear the music from a quite distant radio or phonograph at night but not in the daytime. The reason for this is shown in Fig. 36F. At night the air near the water is colder than it is higher up and the higher velocity in the warmer air bends the waves back down. During the day the air close to the water is warmer and the waves bend up away from the water as shown.

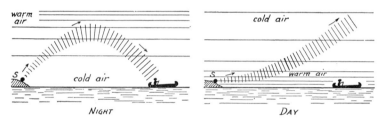

FIG. 36F—The higher velocity of sound waves in warm air causes sound waves to be refracted down at night and up in the daytime.

Recent experiments of this kind have been performed with the very loud sounds from big guns. Sound waves refracted back from high up in the stratosphere indicate with some degree of certainty the existence of very warm layers of air at altitudes of 25 to 40 mi (see Fig. 31N). Refraction in such cases as this is similar to reflection from a mirror surface since the waves travel in more or less straight lines going up and back but bend over when they enter, more or less abruptly, a warmer layer.

36.7. Intensity of Sound. There are three fundamental characteristics of all sounds: (1) *intensity*, (2) *pitch*, and (3) *tone quality*. The intensity of sound is characterized by its loudness and is measured scientifically by the amount of energy in a given volume of the space through which the sound is traveling. In other words, sound waves constitute a flow of energy through matter. This may be demonstrated by an experiment, arranged as shown in Fig. 36G. A vibrating tuning fork is placed near one opening of a

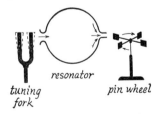

FIG. 36G—A pinwheel may be set rotating by sound waves from a tuning fork, demonstrating that sound waves transport energy.

Helmholtz* resonator and a very lightly constructed pinwheel is placed near the other. Air pulses from the vibrating prongs of the fork traveling through the resonator come out reinforced at the other opening and strike the vanes of the pinwheel. When the fork is removed the pinwheel stops rotating. *Loudness is a subjective measurement of sound power and is therefore a sensory magnitude. Intensity, on the other hand, is an objective measurement of the sound power being delivered.*

One method of specifying the intensity of a sound is to state the amount of energy flowing through unit area per second. Since the rate of flow of energy in most common sounds is extremely small, the ordinary unit of power, the *watt*, is too large to be practical. Consequently a unit one million times smaller, the *microwatt*, is used. One microwatt equals 10^{-6} watt. *Sound intensity is defined as the power flowing through unit area taken normal to the direction of the waves* (see Fig. 36H). One microwatt is equivalent to 10^{-6} joules/sec, or 10 ergs/sec.

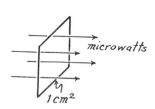

Fig. 36H—Sound intensity is measured in microwatts flowing through 1 cm² of area.

A common method of specifying intensity is to compare the power in a given sound with the power in another. *When the power in one sound is ten times that in another, the ratio of intensity is said to be 1 bel.* The *bel* is so called in honor of Alexander Graham Bell, the inventor of the electric telephone. According to this definition, an intensity scale in bels is a logarithmic scale of power.

$$B_{\text{bels}} = \log_{10} E/E_o, \tag{36a}$$

where E is the intensity, or power, of one sound and E_o that of another. The following tabulation will illustrate this equation.

Relative power,	E/E_o =	1	10	100	1000	10,000
Relative intensity, in bels	B_{bels} =	0	1	2	3	4

The numbers in the lower row are just the logarithms of those directly above. According to these figures a sound with 1000 times the power of another is 3 bels louder.

Because the *bel* represents large differences in intensity, a smaller unit, the *decibel* (abbr. db), has been introduced and used by telephone and radio engineers, as well as by physicians (ear specialists). According to this

* Hermann Helmholtz (1821-1894), noted German physicist, who during his lifetime made outstanding contributions to the subjects of light, sound, and electricity. Probably his greatest contribution was his explanation of tone quality in musical notes. He demonstrated that quality depends upon the number and intensity of the overtones or harmonics present in the musical tone.

smaller unit, the bel is divided into ten equal ratios by the following equation.

$$b_{db} = 10 \log_{10} E/E_o. \tag{36b}$$

The following tabulation will illustrate

Relative power, $E/E_o =$ 1.00 1.26 1.58 2.00 2.51 3.16 3.98 5.01 6.31 7.94 10.0
Relative intensity,
in decibels $b_{db} =$ 0 1 2 3 4 5 6 7 8 9 10

Each power ratio in the upper row is 26% greater than the preceding value. Because such a change is just detectable by the human ear, the decibel is considered a practical unit. The sounds from several common sources are compared in different units, as follows.

	Intensity in microwatts/cm^2	Sound level in bels	Sound level in decibels
Threshold of hearing	10^{-10}	0	0
Rustling leaves	10^{-8}	2	20
Talking (at 3 ft)	10^{-6}	4	40
Noisy office or store	10^{-4}	6	60
Subway car	1	10	100
Threshold of feeling	100	12	120

An audiogram for the normal human ear is given in Fig. 36I. The lower curve gives the faintest sounds that can be heard and the upper curve the loudest that can be heard without pain. It will be noted that the ear is most

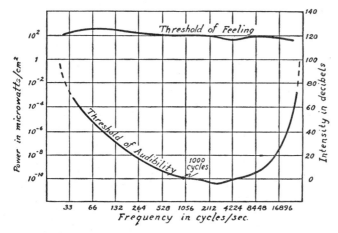

FIG. 36I—Audiogram of the average human being showing the threshold of hearing for different frequencies of sound.

sensitive to frequencies between 2000 and 4000 cycles and that the sensitivity diminishes rapidly at higher and lower frequencies.

As a practical matter, sound experts have adopted as a zero level of sound intensity, $E_o = 10^{-10}$ microwatts/cm^2 at a frequency of 1000 cycles. This is the limit of audibility of the average human being for a thousand cycle note.

To see how intensity affects the frequency limits of audibility, consider the horizontal line at 20 db. At this intensity level, with a flow of energy 100 times that necessary to hear the faintest thousand cycle note, frequencies below about 200 and above 15,000 cannot be heard. At 40 db with a flow of energy 10,000 times the threshold of audibility at 1000 cycles the lowest frequency to be heard is about 100 cycles/sec, whereas the upper limit may be as high as 20,000 cycles/sec.

Theory indicates and experiments prove that *the intensity of sound is inversely proportional to the square of the distance from the source.* As an equation, $E = E_o/d^2$, where E_o is the intensity at unit distance, $d = 1$, and E is the intensity at any distance d. This is called *the inverse square law.*

The amplitude of the sound waves at the threshold of audibility at 1000 cycles has been determined and found to be about 1×10^{-8} cm. This is about the diameter of a hydrogen atom and gives some idea of the enormous sensitivity of the human ear. When a sound becomes so loud that it is painful to the ear the amplitude is of the order of one or two millimeters.

36.8. The Human Ear. The ear is by far the most important and most universal receiver of sound. It has an enormous range of frequency and sensitivity, and can distinguish between musical tones whose frequencies differ by less than 1%. In addition to this it can analyze some sounds into their component notes and concentrate on these notes one at a time.

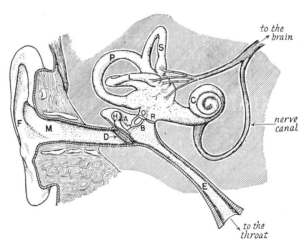

FIG. 36J—Cross-section of the human ear.

The process of hearing has long been a subject for discussion by men in many branches of science. Although most of the experts agree on the general structure and the mechanical motions within the ear, there still exist several controversies regarding the functions of certain parts. The entire hearing mechanism is divided into three parts: the *outer ear,* the *middle ear,* and the *inner ear* (see Fig. 36J).

The outer ear consists of the pinna *F,* used to collect the sound waves from the outside, and the ear canal *M* to carry the waves to the eardrum *D.* The middle ear contains three small bones *H, A,* and *B,* called the *hammer* (malleus), *anvil* (incus), and *stirrup* (stapes) respectively, and is connected to the nasopharynx and thus to the outside air by means of a small canal, the *Eustachian tube E.* The function of the three bones is to transmit the vibrations of the eardrum to the *oval window* of the inner ear. The inner ear itself consists of two essential parts: the *cochlea C,* and the semicircular canals *P, L,* and *S.* In the cochlea are found the nerve endings which are stimulated by sound vibrations and give rise to the sense of hearing, and in the semicircular canals are the nerve endings which give rise to a sense of balance.

The entire inner ear is contained within the cavity of a solid bony structure and is sometimes referred to as the *bony labyrinth.* This labyrinth is entirely filled with a watery liquid through which the sound vibrations from

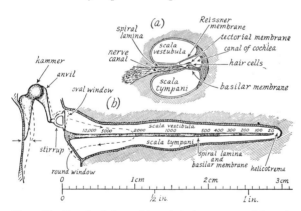

Fig. 36K—Detail of the cochlea of the human ear; (a) typical cross-section and (b) straightened cochlea illustrating the various regions of the spiral lamina sensitive to sounds of various frequencies.

the outside are transmitted to the sensitive membranes of the cochlea. The cochlea consists of two and one-half turns of a spiral cavity shaped like a snail shell and divided lengthwise into three parts by what are called the *spiral lamina* and *Reissner's membrane.* Cross-sections of the cochlea are shown in Fig. 36K. Diagram (a) represents a section directly across one turn of the spiral, and diagram (b) a lengthwise cross-section as it would appear if the cochlea could be straightened out.

Throughout the total length of the basilar membrane, which is just a little over 3 cm in length, there are about 30,000 nerve endings. This amounts to 1000 nerves per millimeter length which must pass through the bony spiral lamina and into the cochlear nerve canal leading to the brain. The work of many experimentalists shows that the nerve endings nearest the oval window, where the sound vibrations enter the *scala vestibula*, respond to the notes of highest pitch, whereas those at the farther end respond to those of lowest pitch. The various regions sympathetic to the entire frequency scale is shown in the diagram.

The eardrum and the bones of the middle ear act as a lever mechanism to decrease the amplitude of the vibrations from the air, a very light medium, to the liquid, a much more dense medium. This reduction in the motion gives rise to a pressure on the stirrup which is from 30 to 50 times that exerted on the eardrum. As the stirrup tips in and out with a low frequency, the entire liquid column from the oval window down the *scala vestibula* to the *helicotrema,* and back along the *scala tympani* to the round window, is set into vibration. Since liquids are practically noncompressible, the round window moves out when the oval window and stirrup move in, and vice versa.

When a higher frequency like 2000 vib/sec is sounded, the vibrations in the liquid, set up by the motion of the stirrup at the oval window, travel the path shown by the dotted line in Fig. 36K, diagram (b). As the waves travel through the thin Reissner membrane and across the edge of the spiral lamina, there is a relative motion set up between the *basilar membrane* and the *tectorial membrane,* which causes the local hair cells to stimulate the nerve endings at their base. Somewhere in this stimulation and motion, part of the energy is transformed into electrical impulses which travel along the cochlear nerve canal to the brain.

36.9. Resonance, or Sympathetic Vibrations. If two violin strings are tuned to the same frequency and one is set vibrating, the other stationed some distance away will soon pick up the vibrations and give out the same note. This is a case of *resonance,* a phenomenon which occurs only if two objects have the same natural frequency of vibration.

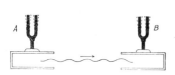

Fig. 36L—Tuning forks mounted on resonator boxes for demonstrating resonance.

An experimental demonstration of resonance is illustrated in Fig. 36L. Two tuning forks with exactly the same pitch are mounted on separate hollow boxes as shown. Fork *A* is first set vibrating for a moment and then stopped by touching the prongs with the fingers. Fork *B* will then be found vibrating. Taking into account the hollow boxes, whose purpose it is to act as sounding boards and intensify the sound, the explanation is quite simple. Each sound pulse emerging from the box with each vibration of fork *A* passes into the other box, pushing out the sides at just the right time to make the prongs of fork *B* move in the same direction as with the previous pulse.

36.10. Beat Notes. When two notes of slightly different pitch are sounded together, beats are heard. This phenomenon is used in organ pipes to produce the familiar vibrato effect. Two pipes tuned to slightly different frequencies are used for every note.

The phenomenon of beats may be demonstrated by two tuning forks mounted as shown in Fig. 36L. One fork is made slightly out of tune with the other by looping rubber bands *tightly* around the prongs. If the two forks are sounded directly the intensity of loudness of the sound rises and falls periodically. This is illustrated by means of vibration graphs as shown in Fig. 36M. The upper curve represents the sound vibrations arriving at the ear from one fork and the second curve the vibrations from the other. Both waves arriving at the ear are first in phase, i.e., in step with each other, then out of phase, then in phase, then out of phase, etc.

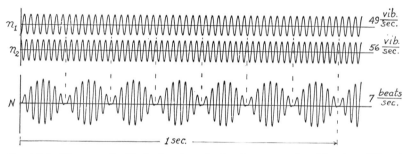

Fig. 36M—Wave graphs illustrating how *beat notes* are produced by two different frequencies.

The resultant action of these two waves on the eardrum is represented by the third line. When the waves are in phase the resultant has a large amplitude equal to the sum of the amplitudes of the two. When they are out of phase the amplitude becomes zero. The number of beats per second, *N*, is determined by the difference between n_2 and n_1, the respective frequencies of the two sources producing the sound.

$$\text{Beat frequency } N = n_2 - n_1. \qquad (36c)$$

When the beat frequency lies between about 1 and 6 vibrations per second the ear perceives an intertone half-way between the two sounded but periodically waxing and waning in intensity. As the beat frequency increases the smooth rise and fall gives way to a succession of pulses, then to a sensation of roughness, and finally to two clearly perceived tones.

36.11. The Doppler Effect. Nearly everyone has at some time, perhaps without realizing it, observed the *Doppler Effect*. The sounding horn of a car passing at high speed on the highway exhibits the phenomenon. The pitch of the horn, as the car goes by, drops as much as two whole notes on the musical scale. A similar observation can be made by listening to the roar of the motor of a racing car as it approaches and recedes from an observer at the race track. The motor seems to slow down as it passes by. Again, the pitch of the whistle on a fast moving train sounds higher as the train approaches the observer than it does after the train has passed by.

This change in pitch is due to the relative motions of the source of sound and the observer. To see how this produces the effect, consider the following example. A train at rest in blowing its whistle sends out waves traveling with the same velocity in all directions. To all stationary observers, no matter in what direction they are located, the true pitch of the whistle is heard, since just as many waves arrive at the ear per second as there are waves leaving the whistle. If, on the other hand, the train is moving as shown in Fig. 36N, the whistle is moving away from the waves traveling to the rear and toward the waves traveling forward. The result is that the waves behind are considerably drawn out while those in front are crowded together. With each new wave sent out by the source, the train is farther from the preceding wave sent out to the rear and nearer to the one sent out ahead. Since the velocity of sound is the same in all directions an observer at O_1 therefore hears more waves per second and an observer at O_2 hears fewer.

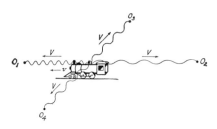

Fig. 36N—The Doppler effect. The pitch of a whistle on a fast moving train sounds higher to an observer in front of the train, lower to an observer in back, and normal to observers off at the sides.

To an observer O_3 or O_4, at right angles and at some little distance from the moving source, the pitch remains unchanged. For these side positions the source is neither approaching nor receding from the observer; so that approximately the same number of waves are received per second as there are waves leaving the source.

The general relations for the Doppler effect are given by the following single equation:

$$\frac{n_o}{V - v_o} = \frac{n_s}{V - v_s} \tag{36d}$$

where n_s is the frequency of the source, n_o is the frequency heard by the observer, V is the velocity of sound, v_s the velocity of the source, and v_o the velocity of the observer. *The velocity of sound V at the observer is positive, and its direction is taken as the positive direction for all velocities.* Either v_o or v_s is positive if it is directed along the positive direction, and negative if it is oppositely directed.

Case 1. If source and observer are approaching each other, v_s is $+$, and v_o is $-$.

Case 2. If source and observer are moving in the same direction, v_s and v_o are both $+$.

Case 3. The observer is at rest and the source is approaching at a velocity $v_s = 2V$. Here $v_o = 0$ and v_s is $+$. This is an interesting case since n_o is the negative of n_s. The observer hears the sound backward, as if played backward on a tape recorder, and it is heard after the source has passed him.*

PROBLEMS

1. Calculate the velocity of sound in air when the temperature is 30°C.

2. Determine the velocity of sound in air at an altitude of 12 mi where the temperature is −62°F. See Fig. 27B. (*Ans.* 984 ft/sec.)

3. Find the velocity of sound in mi/hr for air at 77°F.

4. If one sound is 30 db louder than the other, what are their relative energies? (*Ans.* 1000:1.)

5. If one sound is 15 db louder than another, what are the relative energies?

6. Three feet in front of a radio loud-speaker the sound level is 40 db. Calculate the intensity at a distance of 15 ft. (*Ans.* 26.0 db.)

7. The noise from a racing car motor is 60 db at a distance of 10 ft. What is the noise level at 200 ft?

8. At a distance of 4 m from a jet plane the noise level on open throttle is 90 db. What is the noise level when the plane flies overhead at an altitude of 2000 m? (*Ans.* 36 db.)

9. At one mile the sound level of a fire siren is 20 db. What is the intensity at a distance of only 10 ft?

10. Two tuning forks have frequencies of 164 and 592 vib/sec respectively. Find the beat frequency. (*Ans.* 428.)

11. The horn of a car is blown as the car approaches an intersection at 60 mi/hr. If the frequency heard by an observer standing at the intersection is 200 vib/sec, what is the frequency of the horn? Assume a temperature of 25°C.

12. The siren of a ranger station along the highway is sounded with a frequency of 600 vib/sec. What frequency is heard by motorists traveling 60 mi/hr along the highway if they are (a) approaching, and (b) receding from the station? Assume a temperature of 30°C. (*Ans.* (a) 646 vib/sec, (b) 554 vib/sec.)

13. To one standing in front of a flight of steps, a sharp clap of the hands will produce a sound wave that is reflected back to the observer from each step. If the step treads are 14 in. deep, what frequency is heard by the observer? Assume a temperature of 68°F.

* For other details of this treatment, see **American Journal of Physics, vol. 23, 37, 1954.**

Sources of Musical Sounds   Chapter 37

37.1. Stringed Instruments. There are two principal reasons why stringed instruments of different kinds do not sound alike as regards *tone quality*—first, the design of the instrument, and second, the method by which the strings are set into vibration. The violin and cello are bowed with long strands of tightly stretched horsehair, the harp and guitar are plucked with the fingers or picks, and the piano is hammered with light felt mallets.

FIG. 37A—Single string vibrating with its fundamental frequency.

Under very special conditions a string may be made to vibrate with nodes at either end as shown in Fig. 37A. In this state of motion the string gives rise to its lowest possible note, and it is said to be vibrating with its *fundamental frequency*.

Every musician knows that a thick heavy string has a lower natural pitch than a thin one, that a short strong string has a higher pitch than a long one, and that the tighter a string is stretched the higher is its pitch. The *G* string of a violin, for example, is thicker and heavier than the high-pitched *E* string, and the *bass* strings of the piano are longer and heavier than the strings of the *treble*.

37.2. Harmonics and Overtones. When a professional violinist plays "in harmonics" he touches the strings lightly at various points and sets each

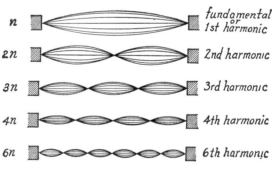

FIG. 37B—Vibration modes for strings of musical instruments.

one vibrating in two or more segments as shown in Fig. 37B. If a string is touched at the center, a node is formed at that point and the vibration frequency, as shown by Eq.(37c), becomes double that of the fundamental. If the string is touched lightly at a point one-third the distance from the end, it will vibrate in three sections and have a frequency three times that of the fundamental.

In the elementary theory of string instruments it is assumed that each string is thin, uniform, and highly flexible, and that it vibrates with small amplitude between unyielding supports. For such an ideal string the above vibration modes have frequencies exactly equal to whole number multiples of the fundamental frequency n, and are called *harmonics*. To show how closely a real string meets these ideal conditions the measured frequencies of a piano string whose fundamental frequency is 32.70 vib/sec are given in the following table.*

Mode Number	1	2	3	4	5	6	7	8
Meas. Freq.	32.70	65.52	98.39	131.4	164.7	198.4	232.4	266.8
Harmonic Freq.	32.70	65.40	98.10	130.8	163.5	196.2	228.9	261.6
Ratio	1.000	2.003	3.008	4.018	5.038	6.066	7.106	8.159

It is not difficult to set a string vibrating with its fundamental and several of its higher modes at the same time. This is accomplished by plucking or bowing the string vigorously. As an illustration a diagram of an ideal string vibrating with two normal modes at the same time is shown in Fig. 37C. As the string vibrates in two loops with a frequency $2n$, it also moves up and down as a single loop with the fundamental frequency n.

The sound wave sent out by such a vibrating string, see Fig. 38E(c), is composed of two frequencies, the fundamental or first harmonic of frequency n, diagram (a), and the second harmonic or first partial with the frequency $2n$, diagram (b).

Fig. 37C—String vibrating with its fundamental and first partial simultaneously.

An interesting experiment with a vibrating string is diagramed in Fig. 37D. Light from an arc lamp is focused on the central section of a stretched steel string, which, except for a small vertical slot, is masked by a screen. An image of the slot and the string section seen through it is focused by a second lens, after reflection from a rotating mirror, on a screen. As the string vibrates up and down only a blurred image of the short section of string is seen, but when the mirror is rotated the wire section draws out a clearly visible curve W.

* See R. W. Young, *American Journal of Physics,* vol. 20, p. 177, 1952.

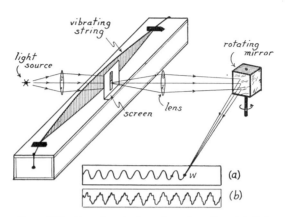

FIG. 37D—Experiment for observing the detailed
vibrations of stretched string.

If the string is plucked gently near the center a smooth wave form (a) is
drawn out on the screen, but if it is plucked hard near the end to produce a
harsh sounding note the wave form is more complex as shown in (b). In the
first case the string is vibrating only with its fundamental mode, while in the
second case various overtones, or partials, are also present.

As a string vibrates with *transverse waves* it strikes air molecules all
around it sending periodic impulses through the air as *longitudinal waves*.

37.3. The Theory of Vibrating Strings. A string set into vibration
with nodes and loops is but an example of standing waves (see Fig. 35H).
A disturbance produced at one end, as in the plucking or bowing of a string,
sends a wave or train of waves along the string to be reflected back and forth
from end to end. When traveling in one direction the wave is on top and,
upon reflection, it flips to the under side. Being always on top when moving
to the right and on the bottom when moving to the left gives rise to a flip-
ping up and down of the string.

Since the fundamental frequency of vibration is equal to the number of
times per second the wave arrives at the same end, the pitch will depend
upon the velocity of the waves and the distance they have to travel.

The velocity of transverse waves along a rope or string under tension is
given by Eq.(14k). Transposing gives

$$V = \sqrt{F/m}, \qquad (37a)$$

where F is the tension and m is the mass per unit length of string. When
standing waves are produced the distance L between any two consecutive
nodes is just equal to half a wavelength, $\frac{1}{2}\lambda$. Accordingly,

$$\lambda = 2L. \qquad (37b)$$

To obtain an equation for the fundamental frequency of a vibrating string, the general wave equation $V = n\lambda$ (see Eq.(35c)) is used. If we transpose and then substitute the above values for V and λ, we obtain

$$n = \frac{1}{2L}\sqrt{F/m}. \tag{37c}$$

Accurate measurements with vibrating strings and musical instruments confirm this equation.

Example. A piano string that sounds three octaves below middle C is 110 cm long. Calculate the tension on the string when, in proper tune, its frequency is 33 vib/sec. Assume the mass of the string to be 160 gm.

Solution. The *mass per unit length* of string is $m = 160$ gm/110 cm $= 1.45$ gm/cm. Transposing $2L$ to the left side of Eq.(37c), squaring both sides, and transposing m, the frequency equation becomes $F = 4n^2L^2m$. By direct substitution,

$$F = 4 \times (33)^2 \times (110)^2 \times 1.45 = 76,400,000 \text{ dynes.}$$

Dividing by 980 changes dynes to gm-wt; and then dividing by 454 changes gm-wt to lb. The result is

$$F = 172 \text{ lb.}$$

The vibration of a string brought about by bowing is associated with friction. Because starting friction is greater than sliding friction, the resinous bow periodically engages the string, pushing or pulling it to one side. During one-half the vibration the string clings to the bow and is carried along by it. When the tension becomes too great and exceeds starting friction, the string slips back to the opposite side of its vibration. There it stops and upon reversal in direction is grabbed again by the bow.

37.4. Wind Instruments. Musical instruments often classified as "wind instruments" are usually divided into two subclasses, "wood winds" and "brasses." Under the heading of wood winds we find such instruments as the *flute, piccolo, clarinet, bass clarinet, saxophone, bassoon,* and *contra bassoon,* and under the brasses such instruments as the *French horn, cornet, trumpet, tenor trombone, bass trombone,* and *tuba* (or *bombardon*).

The fundamental principles involved in the vibration of an air column are demonstrated by means of an experiment shown in Fig. 37E. A vibrating tuning fork acting as a source of sound waves is held over the open end of a long hollow tube containing water. Traveling down the tube with the velocity of sound in air, each train of sound waves is reflected from the water surface back toward the

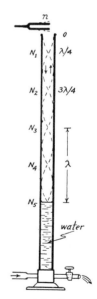

Fig. 3 7 E—S o u n d waves from tuning fork set up standing waves in air column adjusted to proper length.

top. If the water is raised or lowered to the proper level, standing waves will be set up and the air column will resonate to the frequency of the tuning fork.

The first resonance occurs at N_1 when the water level is but a short distance from the top. The second resonance occurs at N_2, three times the distance of N_1 below the top, and the third N_3 at five times the distance, etc. The reason for these odd fractions is that only a *node* can form at the closed end of the pipe, i.e., at the water surface, and an *anti-node* at the open end.

Standing waves in air are longitudinal in character and they are difficult to represent in any drawing (see Fig. 35I). For convenience only it is quite customary to indicate the positions of nodes and loops as if they were transverse standing waves (dotted lines in the diagram). If the frequency of the tuning fork used in the above experiment is known, the velocity of sound in air can be calculated. The distance between consecutive nodes is equal to $\lambda/2$, so that λ is equal to the length of 2 segments $N_3 - N_1$, $N_4 - N_2$, or $N_5 - N_3$ as shown in the diagram. In an actual experiment when the temperature is 27°C, and a tuning fork sounding 512 vib/sec, the nodes are 13.37 in apart. Substitution of these values in the general wave equation, Eq.(35c) gives

$$V = n\lambda = 512 \times 26.74 = 13690 \text{ in/sec.}$$

Dividing by 12 gives $V = 1141$ ft/sec.

37.5. Vibrating Air Columns. The various modes in which air columns may vibrate in open or closed pipes are shown in Fig. 37F. Starting at the left, a pipe open at both ends may vibrate with (1) a single node at the middle and an anti-node at both ends, (2) two nodes and three anti-nodes, or (3) with three nodes and four anti-nodes, etc. On the other hand, a pipe

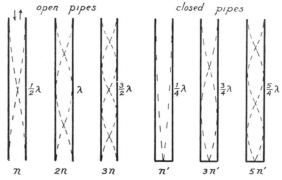

Fig. 37F—Air columns in open and closed pipes have definite frequencies of vibration.

closed at one end and open at the other may vibrate with (1) one node and one anti-node, (2) two nodes and two anti-nodes, or (3) three nodes and three anti-nodes, etc. *In all vibrating air columns an anti-node always forms at an open end and a node at a closed end.*

The various possible frequencies to which a pipe may resonate are definite and fixed in value and depend only upon the length of the pipe and the velocity of sound in air. If, for example, the pipes in Fig. 37F are all 2 ft long and the velocity of sound in air is 1120 ft/sec, Eq.(35c), $V = n\lambda$, shows that they will vibrate with the following respective frequencies,

n	$2n$	$3n$	n'	$3n'$	$5n'$
280	560	840	140	420	700

With an open pipe the lowest possible vibration frequency is called the *fundamental* and the others with whole numbered multiples of the fundamental frequency, $2n$, $3n$, $4n$, etc., are called *harmonics*. With closed pipes the lowest frequency is again the fundamental and the others with odd integral multiples, $3n'$, $5n'$, $7n'$, etc., are harmonics. All these vibration modes are referred to as natural modes and their corresponding frequencies as natural frequencies. *The fundamental is also called the first harmonic.*

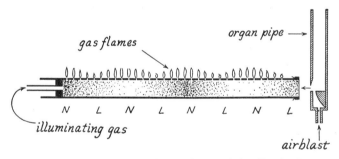

Fig. 37G—Standing waves in a long tube containing illuminating gas.

The existence of standing waves in a resonating air column may be demonstrated by a long hollow tube filled with illuminating gas as shown in Fig. 37G. Entering through an adjustable plunger at the left the gas escapes through tiny holes spaced at regular intervals in a row along the top. Sound waves from an organ pipe enter the gas column by setting into vibration a thin paper sheet stretched over the right-hand end. When resonance is attained by sliding the plunger to the correct position, the small gas flames will appear as shown. Where the nodes occur in the vibrating gas column the air molecules are not moving (see Fig. 35H(b)) ; at these points the pressure is high and the flames are tallest. Halfway between are the anti-nodes —regions where the molecules vibrate back and forth with large amplitudes, and the flames are low. Bernoulli's principle is chiefly responsible for the pressure differences (see Sec. 28.7), for where the velocity of the molecules is high the pressure is low, and where the velocity is low the pressure is high.

In many of the wind instruments of the orchestra the vibrating air columns are not entirely uniform and the far open end is considerably flared. Because of this non-uniformity the nodes are not equally spaced nor are the possible frequencies exactly harmonics of the fundamental. As an example of how nearly the various normal modes come to being harmonics of a fundamental the following measured frequencies of the *open notes* of a B♭ cornet are given in the table below: ($n = 116.7$ vib/sec.)

Mode Number	2	3	4	5	6	8
Meas. Freq.	233.4	349.8	467.5	587.7	706.2	948.6
Harmonic Freq.	233.4	350.1	466.8	583.5	700.2	933.6
Ratio	2.000	2.998	4.007	5.037	6.058	8.130

Open notes are those for which all valves are open and the entire air column is vibrating.

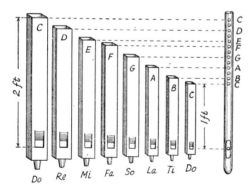

FIG. 37H—Organ pipes arranged in a musical scale. The longer the pipe the lower is its fundamental frequency and pitch. The vibrating air column of the flute is terminated at various points by openings along the tube.

37.6. Theory of Vibrating Air Columns.

The various notes produced by most wind instruments are brought about by varying the length of the vibrating air column. This is illustrated by the organ pipes in Fig. 37H. The longer the pipe the lower the fundamental frequency or pitch of the note. In a regular concert organ the pipes vary in length from about 6 in for the highest note to almost 16 ft for the lowest. For the middle octave of the musical scale the open-ended pipes vary from 2 ft for middle C to 1 ft for C^1 one octave higher. In the wood winds, like the flute, the length of the column is varied by openings in the side of the instrument; and in many of the brasses, like the trumpet, by means of valves. A valve is a piston which on being pressed down, throws in an additional length of tube.

Since a vibrating air column is a condition of standing waves, the frequency of vibration will depend upon two factors, the length of the pipe and the velocity of waves through it. The velocity of longitudinal waves in a gas is given by Newton's formula as modified by Laplace,

$$V = \sqrt{K \frac{p}{\rho}} \qquad (37d)$$

where K is a number representing the compressibility of a gas, p is the gas pressure in dynes/cm^2, and ρ its density in gm/cm^3. For monatomic gases $K = 1.67$, diatomic gases $K = 1.40$, triatomic gases $K = 1.33$.

For all standing waves the distance L between any two consecutive nodes, that is, the length of one segment, is just equal to half a wave length, $\lambda/2$. Accordingly,

$$\lambda = 2L.$$

By substituting this relation and the velocity above in the general wave equation, Eq.(35c), we get the general formula,

$$n = \frac{V}{\lambda} = \frac{1}{2L}\sqrt{K \frac{p}{\rho}}. \qquad (37e)$$

Measurements with resonating pipes confirm this relation.

The effect of the density of a gas on the pitch of a note may be demonstrated by a very interesting experiment with the human voice. Voice sounds originate in the vibrations of the vocal chords in the larynx (see Fig. 37I). This source of vibration, which determines the fundamental pitch of the speaking or singing voice, is controlled by muscular tension on the chords. The quality of the voice is determined by the size and shape of the throat, mouth and nasal cavities.

If a gas lighter than air is breathed into the lungs, the above equation shows that the voice

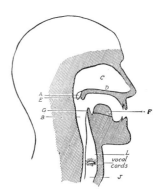

FIG. 37I—Cross-section diagram showing the vocal chords in the larynx. *A*. Soft palate; *B*. pharynx; *C*. nasal cavity; *D*. hard palate; *F*. tongue; *G*. epiglottis; *J*. windpipe.

quality should change. The demonstration can be best and safely performed by exhaling completely and then filling the lungs with helium gas (hydrogen is unsafe). Upon speaking, the experimeter will be observed to have a very peculiar, high pitched voice, which must be heard to be appreciated. The peculiarities arise from the fact that the fundamental pitch, due to the vocal-chord frequency, remains practically normal, while the harmonics from the resonating mouth, throat, and nasal cavities are raised by about two and one-half octaves.

37.7. Edge Tones. Although the pitch of the note sounded by any wind instrument is determined by the vibration of an air column according to principles of resonance, the method by which the air is set into vibration varies widely among instruments. In instruments like the saxophone, clarinet, oboe and bassoon, air is blown against a thin strip of wood called a reed, setting it into vibration. In most of the brasses the musician's lips are made to vibrate with certain required frequencies, while in certain wood winds, like the flute and piccolo and in organs and whistles, air is blown across the sharp edge of an opening near one end of the instrument, setting the air into vibration. A brief discussion of these source vibrations is therefore important here.

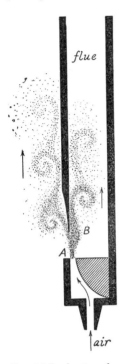

When wind or a blast of air encounters a small obstacle, little whirlwinds are formed in the air stream behind the obstacle. This is illustrated by the cross section of a flue organ pipe in Fig. 37J. Whether the obstacle is long, or a small round object, the whirlwinds are formed alternately on the two sides as shown (see Fig. 11I). The air stream at *B* waves back and forth, sending a pulse of air first up one side and then the other. Although the wind blows through the opening *A* as a continuous stream, the separate whirlwinds going up each side of the obstacle become periodic shocks to the surrounding air. Coming at perfectly regular intervals these pulses give rise to a musical note often described as "edge tones."

Fig. 37 J—A steady stream of air blown across the lip of an organ pipe sets up whirlwinds along both sides of the partition.

The number of whirlwinds formed per second, and therefore the pitch of the edge tone, increases with the wind velocity. When the wind howls through the trees the pitch of the note rises and falls, its frequency at any time denoting the velocity of the wind. For a given wind velocity smaller objects give rise to higher pitched notes than large objects. A fine stretched wire or rubber band, when placed in an open window or in the wind, will be set into vibration and give out a musical note. Each whirlwind shock to the air reacts on the obstacle (the wire or rubber band), pushing it first to one side and then the other. These are the pushes that cause the rope of a flagpole to flap periodically in the breeze, while the waving of the flag at the top of a pole shows the whirlwinds that follow each other along each side.

The air column in an organ pipe, flute, or piccolo, has its own natural frequency of vibration which may or may not coincide with the frequency of an edge tone. If it does coincide, resonance will occur, the air column will vibrate with a large amplitude, and the returning pulses of air down the tube with each vibration will force the air stream out at just the right moment, thus aiding in building up the natural frequency of the pipe. If the edge tone has a frequency different from the fundamental of the string, or air column, vibrations will be set up but not as intensely as before. If the frequency of the edge tone of an organ pipe, for example, comes close to double that of the fundamental, and this can be obtained by a stronger blast of air, the pipe will resonate to double its fundamental frequency and give out a strong note one octave higher.

By blowing more sharply against the opening in a piccolo or flute the entire scale of notes can be raised one octave above normal playing range of the instrument. In all instruments like those mentioned above where air is blown across the sharp edge of an opening to make it sing, as in the organ pipe of Fig. 37J, an anti-node is formed at that end. Whether an anti-node or node forms at the other end depends upon whether it is open or closed, respectively.

37.8. Percussion Instruments. Vibrating Rods. If a number of small sticks are dropped upon the floor, the sound that is heard is described as a noise. If one stick alone is dropped one would also describe the sound as a noise, unless, of course, a set of sticks of varying lengths are arranged in order of length and each one dropped in its order. If this is done, one notices that each stick gives rise to a rather definite musical note and that the set of sticks could be cut to the proper length to form a musical scale. The use of vibrating rods in a musical instrument is found in the *xylophone,* the *marimba,* and the *triangle.* Standing waves in a rod, like those in a stretched string, may be any one of three different kinds—transverse, longitudinal, and torsional. Only the first two of these modes of vibration will be treated here.

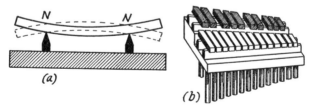

Fig. 37K—The bars of the marimba or xylophone vibrate transversely with nodes near each end.

Transverse waves in a rod are usually set up by supporting the rod at points near each end and striking it a blow at or near the center. As illustrated in Fig. 37K(a), the center and ends of the rod move up and down, forming nodes at the two supports. Like a stretched string of a musical instrument, the shorter the rod the higher is its pitch, and the longer and heavier the rod the lower is its frequency of vibration and pitch.

The xylophone is a musical instrument based upon the *transverse vibrations* of wooden rods of different lengths. Mounted as shown in Fig. 37K(b), the longer rods produce the low notes and the shorter ones the higher notes. The marimba is essentially a xylophone with a long straight hollow tube suspended vertically under each rod. Each tube is cut to such a length that the enclosed air column will resonate to the sound waves sent out by the rod directly above. Each resonator tube, being open at both ends, forms a node at its center.

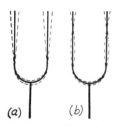

(a)   (b)

Fig. 37L—Vibration nodes of a tuning fork show (a) fundamental, (b) first overtone.

The tuning fork depends for its pitch upon the transverse vibrations of a bar. Sounding its fundamental as shown in Fig. 37L, an anti-node forms at both ends. Due to the bend in the center the two nodes are closer together than in a straight bar, and the anti-node at the center transmits forceful vibrations of small amplitude through the shaft to any surface on which it is rested.

37.9. Vibrating Plates. Although the drum or the cymbals should hardly be called musical instruments, they are classified as such and made use of in nearly all large orchestras and bands. The noise given out by a vibrating drumhead or cymbal plate is in general due to the high intensity of certain characteristic overtones. These overtones in turn are due to the very complicated modes of vibration of the source.

Cymbals consist of two thin metal disks with handles at the centers. Upon being struck together their edges are set into vibration with a clang. A drumhead, on the other hand, is a stretched membrane of leather held tight at the periphery, and is set into vibration by being struck a blow at or near the center.

To illustrate the complexity of the vibrations of a circular plate, two typical sand patterns are shown in Fig. 37M. The sand pattern method of studying the motions of plates was invented in the eighteenth century by *Chladni*, a German physicist. A thin circular metal plate is clamped at the center C and sand is sprinkled over the top surface. Then, while touching the rim of the plate at two points N_1 and N_2, a cello bow is drawn down over the edge at a point L. Nodes are formed at the stationary points N_1 and N_2 and anti-nodes in the regions of L_1 and L_2. The grains of sand bounce away from the loops and into the nodes, the regions of no motion. At one instant the regions marked with a ($+$) sign all move up, while the regions marked with a (—) sign all move down. Half a vibration later the + regions are moving down and the — regions up. Such diagrams are called *Chladni's sand figures*.

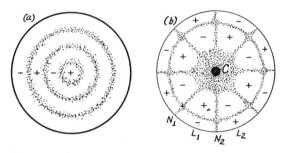

Fig. 37M—Chladni's sand figures showing the nodes and loops of (a) vibrating drumhead (clamped at the edge), and (b) a vibrating cymbal plate (clamped at the center).

With cymbal plates held tightly at the center by means of handles a node is always formed there, and anti-nodes are always formed at the periphery. With a drumhead, on the other hand, the periphery is always a node and the center is sometimes but not always an anti-node.

37.10. Bells. In some respects a bell is like a cymbal plate, for when it is struck a blow by the clapper, the rim in particular is set vibrating with nodes and loops distributed in a symmetrical pattern over the whole surface. The vibration of the rim is illustrated by a diagram in Fig. 37N (a) and by

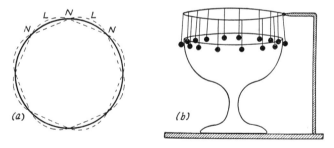

Fig. 37N—Experiment illustrating how the rim of a bell or glass vibrates with nodes and loops.

an experiment in diagram (b). Small cork balls are suspended by threads around and just touching the outside rim of a large glass bowl. A violin bow drawn across the edge of the bowl will set the rim into vibration with nodes at some points and loops at others. The nodes are always even in number just as they are in cymbal plates and drumheads, and alternate loops move in while the others move out.

Strictly speaking, a bell is not a very musical instrument. This is due to the very complex vibrations of the bell surface giving rise to so many loud overtones. Some of these overtones harmonize with the fundamental while others do not.

1. A violin string 35 cm long has a mass of 0.05 gm/cm length. Find the tension in newtons if the frequency of vibration is 660 vib/sec.

2. A piano string 20 cm long has a frequency of 1056 vib/sec, and a mass of 0.08 gm/cm length. Find the tension in newtons. (*Ans.* 1430.)

3. Find the mass per unit length of a violin string 35 cm long if under a tension of 500 newtons it has a vibration frequency of 440 vib/sec.

4. Find the frequency of (a) the fundamental, and (b) the 5th harmonic of a 12 ft organ pipe, closed at one end and open at the other. Assume a temperature of 77°F. (*Ans.* (a) 23.7 vib/sec, (b) 118.5 vib/sec.)

5. What is the shortest length of pipe, open at both ends, that will resonate to a tuning fork of frequency 440 vib/sec? Assume a temperature of 68°F.

6. An organ pipe with one end closed has a fundamental frequency of 440 vib/sec when the temperature is 77°F. Find its frequency when the temperature drops to 32°F. (*Ans.* 421 vib/sec.)

7. Calculate the velocity of sound in nitrogen at normal atmospheric pressure and 0°C. Assume the density of nitrogen under these standard conditions is 1.25×10^{-3} gm/cm^3.

8. A tuning fork of frequency 256 vib/sec is used in the experiment shown in Fig. 37E. Find the distance between consecutive nodes if the temperature is 68°F. (*Ans.* 2.20 ft.)

9. An organ pipe 50 cm long, with both ends open, is used to produce the sound waves in the experiment shown in Fig. 37G. If the velocity of sound in air is 1100 ft/sec, and in the illuminating gas used is 1400 ft/sec, what is the distance between consecutive points where the flames are a maximum?

10. Calculate the velocity of sound in carbon dioxide if at 0°C and 76 cm Hg pressure the density is 1.98×10^{-3} gm/cm^3. (*Ans.* 261 m/sec.)

11. A steel wire 1 m long has a total mass of 20 gm. If this wire is fastened at both ends and then put under a tension of 200 newtons, what is the theoretical frequency of its third harmonic?

12. A string 1 m long has a mass of 0.080 kg. Find the speed with which waves will travel along this string if it is put under a tension of 10 newtons. (*Ans.* 111.8 m/sec.)

13. An organ pipe filled with air at 0°C has a fundamental frequency of 220 vib/sec. What would be its fundamental frequency if the air was replaced by carbon dioxide? The speed of sound in CO_2 is 261 m/sec.

14. A whistle has a fundamental frequency of 4140 vib/sec at a temperature of 0°C. If anti-nodes are formed at both ends, find the length of the air column. (*Ans.* 4 cm.)

The Science of the Musical Scale

Chapter 38

FROM the scientific point of view the musical scale is based upon the relative frequencies of different sound waves. The frequencies of the various notes are so chosen that they produce the greatest amount of *harmony*. Two or more notes are said to be *harmonious* or *concordant* if they are pleasing to the ear. If they are not pleasant to hear they are *discordant*.

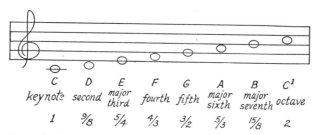

	C	D	E	F	G	A	B	C¹
	keynote	second	major third	fourth	fifth	major sixth	major seventh	octave
	1	9/8	5/4	4/3	3/2	5/3	15/8	2

FIG. 38A—Diagram giving the names, and fractional ratios of the frequencies, of the different tone intervals on the diatonic musical scale.

The general form of the musical scale is illustrated by the *notes, letters, intervals,* and *scale ratios* given in Fig. 38A. The numbers indicate frequency ratios. Whatever frequency is selected for the keynote C, the frequency of the octave C^1 will be twice as great, the frequency of the fifth, G, will be three-halves as great, the fourth F will be four-thirds as great, etc. These fractions are important because they have the same values in all octaves of the musical scale.

The musical pitch of an orchestral scale is usually determined by specifying the frequency of the A string of the first violin, although sometimes it is given by the middle C on the piano. In the history of modern music the standard of pitch has varied so widely and changed so frequently that no set pitch can universally be called standard.* For many scientific purposes the A string of the violin is tuned to a frequency of 440 vib/sec, whereas in a few

* For a brief historical discussion of normal standards of pitch the student is referred to the book, "The Science of Musical Sounds," by D. C. Miller. For other treatments of the science of music see "Sound," by Capstick, "Science and Music," by James Jeans, "Sound and Music," by J. A. Zahn, and "Hearing," by Stevens and Davis.

cases the slightly different scale of 256 vib/sec is used for the keynote, some-times called middle C.

38.1. The Diatonic Scale. The diatonic musical scale, first introduced by Zarlino in 1558, is based entirely on harmonious tone intervals. The middle octave of the scale is given in Fig. 38B assuming as a standard of pitch $A = 440$ vib/sec. The *frequencies* of all the notes are given in the fourth row. These numbers represent the actual frequencies of the vibrating source producing the note as well as the frequencies of the waves that travel through the air and reach the ear.

	major tone	*minor tone*	*semitone*	*major tone*	*minor tone*	*major tone*	*semitone*	*majortone*
scale notes	C	D	E	F	G	A	B	C^1
vocal notes	Do	Re	Mi	Fa	So	La	Ti	Do
ratio numbers	24	27	30	32	36	40	45	48
frequencies	264	297	330	352	396	440	495	528
scale ratios	1	9/8	5/4	4/3	3/2	5/3	15/8	2
tone ratios	8:9	9:10	15:16	8:9	9:10	8:9	15:16	8:9

Fɪɢ. 38B—The diatonic musical scale illustrated by the middle octave with C as the tonic and $A = 440$ as the standard pitch.

Of equal importance are the *ratio numbers* in the third row. These are the smallest whole numbers that are proportional to both the *scale ratios* and to the actual *frequencies*. They are readily used to calculate the frequencies for all octaves of the scale. If the ratio numbers in row three are multiplied by 11 they give the actual frequencies in the fourth row. If these same ratio numbers are multiplied by 22 they will give the frequencies of the first octave above, while multiplied by 5.5 they will give the first octave below the middle.

C_2	D_2	E_2	F_2	G_2	A_2	B_2	C_1	D_1	E_1	F_1	G_1	A_1	B_1	C
66	74	82	88	99	110	124	132	148	165	176	198	220	248	264

C	D	E	F	G	A	B	C^1	D^1	E^1	F^1	G^1	A^1	B^1	C^2
264	297	330	352	396	440	495	528	594	660	704	792	880	990	1056

The various octaves above the middle are labeled with numerical super-scripts as shown here, while the octaves below the middle are designated by subscripts.

Each of the *tone ratios* given at the bottom of the table in Fig. 38B represents the ratio between the frequencies of two consecutive notes. The fraction representing the frequency ratio designates what is called an *interval*. Throughout the scale it will be noted that between successive notes there are but three different intervals—*major tones* with a frequency ratio 9/8, *minor tones* with a ratio 10/9, and *diatonic semitones* with a ratio 16/15. The semitone, it will be noted, is a little larger than half of either a major or minor tone.

A better understanding and appreciation of the diatonic scale is to be had by a study of other intervals and their frequency ratios. Of interest to every composer of music are the following intervals:

perfect consonances	octave	2:1	C^1C,	D^2D,	E^1E
	fifth	3:2	GC	BE	D^1G
	fourth	4:3	FC	AE	C^1G
imperfect consonances	major third	5:4	EC	AF	BG
	minor third	6:5	GE	C^1A	
	major sixth	5:3	AC	BD	E^1G
	minor sixth	8:5	C^1E	F^1A	
dissonant intervals	second	9:8	DC		
	major seventh	15:8	BC		
	minor seventh	16:9	C^1D		

A study of these tone intervals clearly indicates that harmony* is associated with the simplicity of the ratios between frequencies. The smaller the whole numbers expressing the ratio of any two notes the more *harmonious* or *consonant* is the musical effect. The larger the whole numbers, the more *discordant*, or *dissonant*, is the effect.

According to this notion the *octave*, with a frequency ratio 2:1, is the most harmonious of all intervals. This becomes evident when it is recalled how natural it is for male and female voices to sing one octave apart. A bass or baritone voice, in accompanying a melody sung by a soprano voice, will naturally sing one octave lower.

The next perfect consonant, *the fifth*, has a frequency ratio of 3:2. Musicians call the fifth note above the keynote the *dominant*, and the fifth note below, the *sub-dominant*. When C is the keynote, G is the dominant and F_1 is the sub-dominant. Next in the order of consonance comes the perfect *fourth* as a musical interval with its frequency ratio of 4:3.

---

* The essential difference between *melody* and *harmony* is quite generally recognized by everyone. Melody consists of a succession of notes and conveys the idea of motion that should go on and on, while harmony consists of the simultaneous and often sustained sounding of several notes like a chord, followed by other similar combinations of notes. The latter seems to stand still, each chord of notes being more or less complete in itself.

In the *diatonic scale* of Fig. 38B it will be seen that a fifth (like *CG*) added to a fourth (like *GC*[1]) is one octave. To add two tone intervals their frequency ratios are multiplied. For example, a fifth plus a fourth is written $3/2 \times 4/3 = 2$, or $2:1$, an exact octave. Similarly a fourth (like *CF*) subtracted from a fifth (like *CG*) always gives a major tone. To subtract one interval from another the frequency ratios are divided. For example, a fifth minus a fourth is written $3/2 \div 4/3 = 9/8$, an exact major tone.

38.2. Chords. The simultaneous sounding of two or more notes, each of which forms a *concordant* interval with the others, constitutes a chord. An added restriction is that the highest and lowest notes be not more than one octave apart. Two notes sounded together constitute a *dyad*, three notes a *triad*, and four notes a *tetrad*. The *octave, fifth,* and *fourth,* considered in detail in the previous section, are examples of *harmonious dyads*.

Musicians generally agree that there are six harmonious triads, and these are listed as follows:

Harmonic Triads or Chords			*Frequency Ratio*	*Example*
Major third followed by	minor third		4:5:6	*C E G*
Fourth "	"	major third	3:4:5	*C F A*
Minor third "	"	major third	5:6, 4:5	*E G B*
Minor third "	"	fourth	5:6, 3:4	*E G C*[1]
Major third "	"	fourth	4:5, 3:4	*C E A*
Fourth "	"	minor third	3:4, 5:6	*E A C*[1]

The first chord in the tabulation above is generally called a perfect major chord, and the second a perfect minor chord. It is quite common practice to add the octave to each of these triads to form the tetrads *CEGC*[1] and *CFAC*[1].

38.3. The Chromatic Scale. Contrary to the belief of many, the sharp of one note and the flat of the next higher major or minor tone are not of the same pitch. The reason for this false impression is that on the piano the

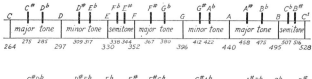

Fig. 38C—Scale diagrams showing the diatonic and chromatic scale above and the equal tempered scale below.

black keys represent a compromise. The piano is not tuned to the diatonic scale but to an *equal tempered scale.* Experiments with eminent musicians, and particularly violinists, have shown that they play in what is called *pure intonation,* that is, to a *chromatic scale* and not according to *equal tempera-ment,* as will be described in the next section.

On the chromatic scale of the musician the ratio between the frequency of one note and the frequency of its sharp or flat is 25:24. This interval, the smallest usually used in music, is just the difference between a diatonic semi-tone and a minor tone, i.e., $15/16 \div 9/10 = 25/24$. The actual fre-quencies of the various sharps and flats for the middle octave of the chro-matic scale, based upon $A = 440$, are shown in Fig. 38 C. $C^\sharp$, for example, has a frequency of 275, whereas $D^\flat$ is 285. This is a difference of 10 vib/sec, an interval easily recognized at this pitch by most everyone.

38.4. The Equal Tempered Scale. The white keys of the piano are not tuned to the exact frequency ratios of the diatonic scale; they are tuned to an *equal tempered scale.* Each octave is divided into twelve equal ratio intervals as illustrated in Fig. 38C. The *whole tone* and *half tone* intervals shown represent the white keys of the piano, as indicated in Fig. 38D, and the sharps and flats represent the black keys. Including the black keys, all twelve tone intervals in every octave are exactly the same. The frequency of any note in the equal tempered scale turns out to be 6% higher than the one pre-ceding it. More accurately, the frequency of any one note multiplied by 1.05946 gives the frequency of the note one-half tone higher. For example, $A = 440$ multiplied by 1.05946 gives $A^\sharp$ or $B^\flat$ as 466.1 vib/sec. Similarly, 466.1×1.05946 gives 493.9.

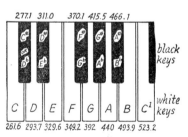

Fɪɢ. 38D—The equal tempered scale of the piano illustrating the frequen-cies of the middle octave based upon $A = 440$ as the standard pitch.

The reason for tuning the piano to an equal tempered scale is to enable the pianist to play in any key and yet stay within a given pitch range. In so doing, any given composition can be played within the range of a given person's voice. In other words, any single note can be taken as the tonic of the musical scale.

Although the notes of the piano are not quite as harmonious as if they were tuned to a diatonic scale, they are not far out of tune. This can be seen by a comparison of the actual frequencies of the notes of the two scales in Fig. 38C.

38.5. Quality of Musical Notes. Although two musical notes have the same pitch and intensity, they may differ widely in tone quality. Tone qual-ity is determined by the number and intensity of the harmonics present. This is illustrated by a detailed examination of either the vibrating source or of the sound waves emerging from the source. There are numerous experimental methods by which this is accomplished.

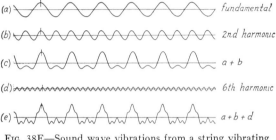

FIG. 38E—Sound wave vibrations from a string vibrating with its fundamental and the second and sixth harmonics.

A relatively convenient and simple demonstration is given in Fig. 37D where the vibrating source of sound is a stretched piano string. If the string is made to vibrate with its fundamental alone, its own motion or that of the emitted sound waves have the form shown in diagram (a) of Fig. 38E. If it vibrates in two segments or six segments (see Fig. 37B), the wave forms will be like those in diagrams (b) and (d) respectively. Should the string be set vibrating with its fundamental and second harmonic simultaneously, Fig. 37C, the wave form will appear something like diagram (c). If, in addition to the fundamental, a string vibrates with the second and sixth harmonics, the wave will look like diagram (e). This is like diagram (c) with the sixth harmonic added to it.

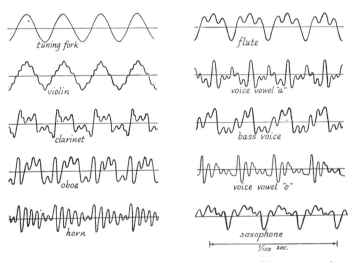

FIG. 38F—Wave forms of sound from different musical instruments singing the same note.

It is difficult to make a string vibrate with its fundamental alone. As a rule there are many harmonics present. Some of these harmonics harmonize with the fundamental and some do not. Those which harmonize are called *concordant overtones*, and those which do not are called *discordant overtones*. If middle $C = 264$ is sounded with its next seven harmonics, they will have 2, 3, 4, 5, 6, 7, and 8 times 264 vib/sec. These on the diatonic scale will correspond to notes C^1, G^1, C^2, E^2, G^2, X and C^3. All of these except X, the seventh harmonic, belong to some harmonic triad. This very overtone is discordant and should be suppressed. In a piano this is accomplished by striking the string one-seventh of its length from one end, thus preventing a node at that point.

The ten different wave forms in Fig. 38F represent the sound vibrations coming from different musical instruments all singing the note $A = 440$ vib/sec. Observe that each wave form is repeated four times in the same time interval but that the overtones, the small "wiggles" in the curves, are different in every case.

When complicated sound vibrations enter the ear, they are analyzed into their component frequencies. One set of nerve endings responds to the fundamental frequency while other sets respond to the various overtones. The fundamental frequency generally has most of the energy and therefore the greatest amplitude, while the overtones with their higher frequencies have relatively small amplitudes.

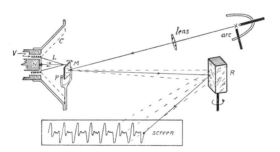

Fig. 38G—Radio loud speaker attachment and apparatus for observing the wave forms of musical sounds.

An excellent experiment for demonstrating the wave forms of musical sounds is diagramed in Fig. 38G. A small mirror M is connected to the voice coil V of a radio loud-speaker by three small aluminum wires L. As the voice coil vibrates, moving the paper cone C back and forth to produce sound, the tiny mirror M tips back and forth around the pivot P. As the voice coil and cone move out to the right the mirror tips forward, and when the voice coil and cone move to the left, the mirror tips back.

Light from an arc lamp and lens is reflected as a narrow beam from the vibrating mirror M to a rotating mirror R and then to a screen as shown. The beam from M to R moves up and down with the exact motion of mirror M, and the rotation of R sweeps the beam across the screen, thus tracing out the vibrations as shown. Each of the four mirrors on R sweeps out a wave across the screen. If the sound is a sustained note the successive wave forms are alike and may be made to overlap, whereas if the notes are continually changing, each wave form is different. Persistence of vision enables the observer to see a long wave instead of a moving point. (With distances of several feet between mirrors and screen, wave amplitudes of at least 1 ft are readily obtained on a large screen or on the walls of a room.)

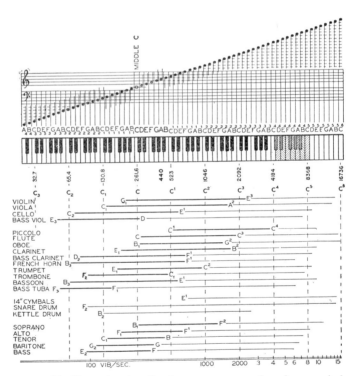

Fig. 38H—Chart showing the frequency range of various musical instruments.

38.6. The Ranges of Musical Instruments. A chart showing the ranges of various musical instruments and singing voices is given in Fig. 38H. The male speaking voice has an average fundamental frequency of about 150 vib/sec with a singing range of about six notes up and six down, whereas the average female voice has a frequency of about 230 vib/sec with approximately the same singing range. The *quality,* or *timbre,* depends almost entirely on two sets of overtones. Good quality singing voices emphasize two sets of overtones or partials, one around 500 cycles and the other around 2400 to 3200 cycles. The lower frequency seems to be the natural frequency of the *pharynx* (see Fig. 37I) and the higher frequencies to other throat, mouth, and nasal cavities.

38.7. Aural Harmonics. Research experiments show that when a pure note of one frequency is sounded with medium intensity one and only one region of nerve endings in the basilar membrane is stimulated to audibility. See Fig. 36K. As the intensity is continuously raised, however, successive *harmonics* appear at successively higher levels thereby stimulating other nerve endings at regular intervals along the basilar membrane. See Fig. 38I.

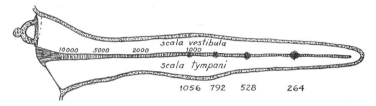

Fig. 38I—Cross-section of the cochlea of the ear showing the nerve centers stimulated by the sounding of a loud pure tone C = 264 vib/sec.

The origin of these harmonics, with their frequencies of 2, 3, 4, etc., times the frequency of the source, is attributed largely to what is called the *non-linear* response of the middle and inner ear to large amplitudes.* Although each harmonic is from 10 to 30 db lower in intensity than its predecessor its apparent loudness may be relatively high, particularly if it comes in a frequency range of high aural sensitivity. See Fig. 36I.

38.8. Aural Combination Tones. When two pure tones are sounded simultaneously the basilar membrane may respond not only to the two frequencies and their respective harmonics but to their *sum-* and *difference-tones* as well. For example, if U and L represent the frequencies of the upper and lower notes respectively, *summation-tones* with frequencies given by ($pU + qL$) and *difference-tones* given by ($pU - qL$) can be heard. Here p and q are whole numbers and pU and qL correspond to the harmonics of U and L.

$$N = pU \pm qL \qquad (38a)$$

On the average, the relative loudness of combination-tones as well as harmonics is given by the order number $N = p + q - 1$. The smaller the value of N the louder the tone.

* See "Hearing," by Stevens and Davis. Pub., Wiley and Sons. Chap. 7.

38.9. A Physical Basis for Harmony. It would appear from present knowledge that harmony, as sung by vocalists and played by musicians may be traced directly to the regularity of the stimulus pattern set up on the basilar membrane. In general it can be said that *the more nearly the ratios of the primary frequencies sounded are to small whole numbers the more consonant is the interval, the more harmonious is the combination, and the more regular is the stimulated pattern on the basilar membrane.*

As an illustration consider the sounding of two pure tones $C = 264$ vib/sec and $G = 396$ vib/sec. Together this harmonious dyad, with a frequency ratio 2 :3 constitutes a *perfect fifth.* Sounded separately or together the wave forms reaching the ear are similar to those shown in Fig. 38J. As heard by

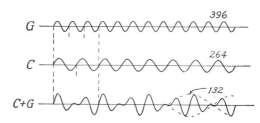

Fig. 38J—Sound wave vibrations for the musical notes of a perfect fifth. Two notes are sounded but quite a number may be heard.

the ear however, there will in general be the two fundamentals as well as their harmonics and combination tones given by

Harmonics, $U, 2U, 3U, 4U, \ldots, L, 2L, 3L, 4L, \ldots$
Summation-tones, $U+L, 2U+L, 3U+L, U+2L, U+3L, 2U+2L, \ldots,$
Difference-tones, $U-L, 2U-L, 3U-L, U-2L, U-3L, 2U-2L, \ldots,$

The stimulated nerve endings in the ear present a regularly spaced pattern like that shown in diagrams (a), (b), and (c) in Fig. 38K. When a

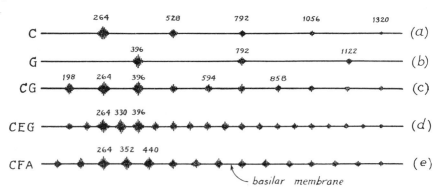

Fig. 38K—Stimulus patterns of the basilar membrane for certain harmonious tones.

discordant dyad like $C = 264$ and $D = 297$ is sounded no such regular pattern as this is established.

What has just been said of an harmonic dyad like the perfect fifth can also be said of a chord. If for example $E = 330$ vib/sec is added to C and G discussed above to form a perfect major chord CEG, some of the many combination-tones produced strengthen those already set up by C and G (diagram c) while the rest stimulate new regions half-way between them. Thus a regular stimulation pattern is produced as shown in diagram (d) with a spacing of 66 vib/sec. Similarly when a *perfect fourth* like C and F are sounded, and then A is added to make the *perfect minor chord CFA*, the regular two-note pattern with an 88 vib/sec spacing retains the same spacing when A is added but the combination tones already there are strengthened thereby adding richness to the sound. Adding the octave $C = 528$ vib/sec to either of these chords to form tetrads goes to further strengthen many combination tones already present.

PROBLEMS

1. Calculate the frequencies of the second, third, and fourth octaves above the middle octave of the diatonic musical scale based on $A = 440$ vib/sec.

2. Calculate the frequencies of the third octave below the middle octave of the diatonic musical scale based upon $A = 440$ vib/sec.

3. Calculate the frequencies of $D\sharp$ and $D\flat$ based upon the diatonic musical scale with $A = 440$ vib/sec.

4. Calculate the frequencies of $A\flat$ and $G\sharp$ based upon the diatonic musical scale with $A = 430$ vib/sec. (*Ans.* 412.8, 403.1 vib/sec.)

5. Make a list of the first eight harmonics of the fundamental 396 vib/sec. Where possible denote the scale note to which each harmonic corresponds in the diatonic scale based on $A = 440$.

6. Solve Prob. 5 for the fundamental frequency of 440 vib/sec. (*Ans. A, A^1, E^2, A^2, X, E^3, X, A^3.*)

7. Two pure tones are sounded separately and then together, $E = 330$, and $B = 495$. Make separate lists of the following: (a) the first three aural harmonics of E, (b) the first three aural harmonics of B, (c) the summation tones for (a) and (b) together, and (d) the difference tones for (a) and (b) together.

8. Find answers to parts (a), (b), (c) and (d) of Prob. 7, if the two notes sounded are $A = 440$ vib/sec, and $E = 330$ vib/sec.

9. Calculate the frequencies of the notes forming the middle octave of an equal tempered scale based upon $A = 460$ vib/sec.

10. What three notes on the diatonic scale form an harmonic triad with G as the lower frequency, if the two intervals consist of a major third followed by a minor third? (*Ans. G B D^1.*)

11. What three notes on the diatonic scale form an harmonic triad with G as the lower frequency if the two intervals consist of a fourth followed by a major third?

Illumination and Photometry

Chapter 39

LIGHT and its various phenomena present some of the most interesting studies in the whole realm of physics. They are interesting because the results of many experiments are revealed through the sense of vision as color phenomena. Equally important and every bit as interesting is the historical development and discovery of the various principles, concepts, and properties of light which give rise to these phenomena.

An awakening appreciation of the value of good lighting during recent years has led to a considerable amount of experimentation and publicity, and the demand for better office, factory, and house lighting. Careful research has shown that for good internal lighting numerous factors are involved. In addition to the many varieties and sizes of light sources, the finish of desk and table tops, the color and surface finish of ceilings, walls, and floors, and the painting of machines and fixtures are of primary importance.

To begin the study of light and illumination it is well that we start with the methods by which quantities of light are measured.

39.1. Candle Power. Candle power refers to the *luminous intensity* of any light source and is a term commonly employed to specify the total light output of a lamp. The *standard candle,* or *international candle* as it is frequently called, is the luminous intensity of the flame of a certain make of candle, the constituents of which were at one time specified by international agreement. Many years ago this form of standard was found to be unsatisfactory and it has since been replaced by the light emitted by an incandescent platinum metal surface. Platinum metal, at its freezing temperature of 2033° K., has a luminance of 60 candles/cm² of projected area.

Ordinary tungsten filament light bulbs used in general house lighting give a little more than one candle power per watt of electrical power used. A 60-watt lamp, for example, has a luminous intensity I of about 66 candle power, and a 100-watt lamp a luminous intensity of about 127 candle power, etc. (see Table 39A). Luminescent tubes, on the other hand, have considerably higher efficiency and yield about 4 candle power per watt. The construction and electrical operation of all kinds of light sources are treated in detail in Chap. 62.

39.2. The Rectilinear Propagation of Light. The rectilinear propagation of light is another way of saying that "light travels in straight lines." The fact that objects may be made to cast fairly sharp shadows is an experimental demonstration of this principle. Another illustration is the image formation of an object produced by light passing through a small opening, as diagramed in Fig. 39A. In this figure the object is an ordinary incan-

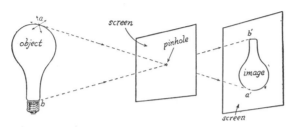

FIG. 39A—Illustrating the principle that light travels in straight lines.

descent light bulb. In order to see how an image is formed, consider the rays of light emanating from a single point *a* near the top of the bulb. Of the many rays of light radiating in all directions, the ray which travels in the direction of the hole passes through to the point *a′* near the bottom of the image screen. Similarly, a ray leaving *b* near the bottom of the bulb and passing through the hole will arrive at *b′* near the top of the image screen. Thus it may be seen that an inverted image is formed.

If the image screen is moved closer to the pinhole screen the image will be proportionately smaller, whereas if it is moved farther away the image will be proportionately larger. The same thing happens when either the object or the pinhole is moved. Excellent photographs can be made with this arrangement by making a pinhole in one end of a small box and placing a photographic film or plate at the other. Such an arrangement is called a pinhole camera. For good sharp photographs the hole must be very small, as its size determines the amount of blurring produced. The photograph shown in Fig. 39B was taken with such a camera. Note the undistorted perspective lines of the building.

FIG. 39B—Photograph taken with a pinhole camera.

39.3. The Inverse Square Law. One direct consequence of the rectilinear propagation of light is the inverse square law. This law applies to the illumination of a surface due to the luminous intensity of a point source of light. While no source of light is actually confined to a point, many are so small in comparison with the distances to illuminated areas that they may be regarded as point sources.

The illumination of a surface is called *illuminance* and is defined as the amount of light falling on a unit area. If a screen is placed one foot from a point source of one candle power, the illuminance will be one foot-candle. One foot from a 50 candle-power source the illuminance will be 50 ft-candles, etc.

When the top surface of a table is illuminated by a single light directly above it and then the light raised to twice the height, the illuminance on the surface will only be one-fourth as great. If it is raised to three times the first height the illuminance will only be one-ninth as great, etc. In other words, *illuminance is proportional to the luminous intensity of the light source and is inversely proportional to the square of the distance.* This, the inverse square law, is illustrated in Fig. 39C(a) by the three shaded patches

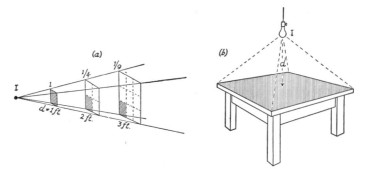

Fɪɢ 39C—Illustrating the inverse square law as it applies to light and illumination.

of equal area. If the letter I represents the luminous intensity of a light source in candles and d the distance to the illuminated surface in feet, the illuminance E in foot-candles will be given by

$$E = \frac{I}{d^2}. \tag{39a}$$

To illustrate this equation, consider the following example.

Example. The illuminance on the road directly under a street light suspended 25 ft above the ground is 1.2 ft-candles. Calculate the candle power of the lamp.

Solution. Transposing Eq.(39a) and substituting the known values, $E = 1.2$ ft-candles, and $d = 25$ ft, gives

$$I = Ed^2 = 1.2 \times (25)^2 = 750 \text{ candle power.}$$

39.4. Photometry. The word photometry is applied to the experimental process by which the intensities of two light sources are compared and measured.

One of the earliest methods for accomplishing this is due to Count Rumford and is known as the *shadow photometer*. His experimental arrangement consists simply of casting two shadows of the same rod as shown in Fig. 39D.

The distances between screen and lamps are varied until the illumination of the two shadows appears equal.

A plan diagram of such an arrangement will show that the shadow cast by lamp I_1 is illuminated only by lamp I_2, while the shadow cast by I_2 is illuminated only by lamp I_1. By the inverse square law, Eq.(39a),

$$E_1 = \frac{I_1}{d_1{}^2} \qquad E_2 = \frac{I_2}{d_2{}^2}.$$

When the illuminated shadow areas are equally bright, E_1 is equal to E_2 and the two equations above become equal to each other. Equating the right-hand sides,

$$\frac{I_1}{d_1{}^2} = \frac{I_2}{d_2{}^2}, \quad \text{or} \quad \frac{I_1}{I_2} = \frac{d_1{}^2}{d_2{}^2}. \tag{39b}$$

In words, the relative intensities of the two lamps are directly proportional to the square of their relative distances from the screen.

If the candle power of one of the lamps is known, its value, along with the measured distances d_1 and d_2, may be substituted in either of these equations and the candle power of the unknown lamp calculated.

While photometer screens of many kinds and descriptions have been invented, one of the simplest is shown at the center in Fig. 39E. Two blocks of paraffin with a layer of tin-foil between them are held together as a unit. When such a photometer is moved back and forth along a

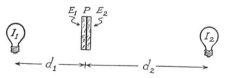

straight line joining the two lamps, a position is easily located where the edges of both blocks appear equally bright. Light from each lamp entering the paraffin block facing it is scattered throughout that particular block only. Being side by side and touching each other, the blocks can be easily matched. When a matched position is located the measured distances d_1 and

d_2 are substituted in Eq.(39b) as before and the candle power of the unknown lamp calculated.

Example. A lamp of 150 candle power (cp) is placed 10 ft from a lamp of unknown candle power. If a photometer screen placed between the lamps is equally illuminated when 3 ft from the unknown lamp, what is the unknown lamp's intensity?

Solution. Making use of Eq.(39b), and calling I the candle power of the unknown lamp, the known quantities in the formula are $I_2 = 150$ cp, $d_2 = 7$ ft, and $d_1 = 3$ ft. Upon substitution

$$\frac{I_1}{150} = \frac{3^2}{7^2} \quad \text{giving} \quad I_1 = 150\frac{9}{49} = 27.5 \text{ cp.} \tag{39c}$$

39.5. Foot-Candle Meter. Many different kinds of direct reading instruments for measuring the illuminance on a surface have been devised and manufactured. Most of these employ a *photoelectric cell* of one kind or another, and are classified as *Illuminometers*. One such instrument using a special kind of photoelectric cell requiring no batteries is shown in Fig. 39F.

Light falling on the photocell in the upper half of the instrument gives rise to an electric current, which in turn activates a highly sensitive ammeter and pointer shown in the lower half. If the scale under the pointer is calibrated in foot-candles as in the photograph, the instrument is called a *foot-candle meter*, but if it is calibrated with an arbitrary number scale it may be labeled an *exposure meter* of the kind used by photographers. The useful range of such in-

Fig. 39F—Weston type of Foot-Candle meter. *(Courtesy of Weston Instruments Co.).*

struments can be greatly extended by placing a screen with holes of a known size over the sensitive photocell area.

When using a foot-candle meter to measure the illuminance on a desk top, the face of the photocell should first be placed parallel to the surface. Turned at an angle the amount of light intercepted by the sensitive area may be quite different. The change in illuminance produced by a change in the direction of the incident light is shown diagrammatically in Fig. 39G. A maxi-

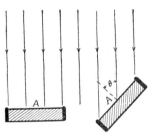

Fig. 39G—Illumination is usually measured normal to the incident light rays.

mum amount of light is intercepted by a given plane area A when it is perpendicular to the incident light rays as shown at the left. Turned at an angle θ, the effective area is smaller and given by $A \cos \theta$. If, therefore, the inverse square law, as given in Eq.(39a), is to be applied to general problems, the factor $\cos \theta$ should be included.

$$E = \frac{I}{d^2} \cos \theta. \qquad (39d)$$

Example. The top of a drafting table, inclined at an angle of 30° with the horizontal, is illuminated by a single 250-cp lamp suspended 4 ft directly above the center Calculate the illuminance on the table top directly beneath the lamp.

Solution. The given quantities in this problem are $I = 250$ cp, $d = 4$ ft, and $\theta = 30°$. By direct substitution in Eq.(39d), we obtain

$$E = \frac{250}{16} 0.866 = 13.5 \text{ ft-candles}$$

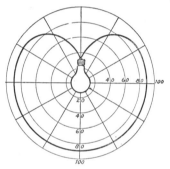

FIG. 39H—Polar graph of light emitted by ordinary 60-watt tungsten filament bulb.

39.6. The Lumen. Light sources in general do not radiate the same in all directions. When, for example, a tungsten filament lamp is photometered, the calculated candle power will vary considerably with the direction. The radial graph for a 60-watt lamp given in Fig. 39H shows how in the direction of the lamp base the radiation falls practically to zero.

Because of such variations it has become common practice among illuminating engineers to describe light sources and the visible light they emit in terms of power. Traveling as it does in straight lines, light constitutes a flow of energy radially outward from the source. The flow of light energy is called the light *flux* and is measured in *lumens*.

The lumen is defined as the amount of visible light flux which falling normally on one square foot of area will produce an illuminance of one foot-candle. On this basis it can readily be shown that a one candle-power source radiating equally in all directions would give out 4π lumens of light (see Fig. 39I). Imagine a hollow sphere of one foot radius surrounding a point source of one candle power. Being one foot away at all points, $d = 1$ ft, the surface illuminance is one foot-candle, while the total area of the surface is

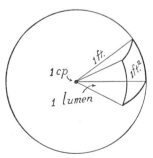

FIG. 39I—Unit light flux is called the lumen.

$4\pi r^2$, or 4π ft². The foot-candle therefore refers to the illuminance of a surface and is independent of the area illuminated, whereas the lumen refers to the amount of visible light radiating outward from a source.

It is customary with light manufacturers to measure the light output of a lamp in all directions and to specify its total output in lumens. When the total output in lumens is known, the average candle power, more commonly called the mean candle power, is obtained by dividing by 4π. For comparison purposes the outputs of several gas-filled tungsten filament lamps are given in Table 39A.

TABLE 39A. EFFICIENCY OF GAS-FILLED TUNGSTEN FILAMENT LIGHT BULBS

Input Power in Watts	Output in Candle Power	Output in Lumens	Efficiency lumens/watt
25	20.7	260	10.4
50	55.0	695	13.9
100	125	1,580	15.8
200	290	3,640	18.2
500	800	10,050	20.1
1000	1640	20,700	20.7

39.7. Luminance (or Brightness). Whether a body is self-luminous or just a reflector of the light that falls upon it, luminance refers to the light the surface gives off in the direction of an observer. Suppose as an experiment that a number of different kinds of surfaces like rough and polished metal, cotton fabric, black, grey and white paint, wood, etc., are equally illuminated from above as shown in Fig. 39J. Due to different amounts of reflection and absorption some of these surfaces will appear to be brighter than others. Furthermore, as the angle of observation is altered, the brightness of some will change markedly while others will remain practically constant. *Brightness is a subjective measurement of the visible light coming from a surface and is therefore a sensory magnitude.* Luminance, on the other hand, is an objective measurement of the luminous power coming from a surface. An increase in the luminance results in an increase in brightness.

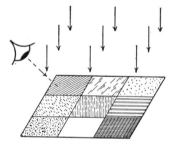

FIG. 39J—Although equally illuminated the brightness of different surfaces may be widely different.

When light falls on any surface, some of it is absorbed and the remainder is reflected or re-emitted. In general it can be said that black surfaces absorb practically all light falling upon them, whereas white, or polished metal surfaces, reflect nearly all the light. Other bodies lie between these two extremes. If a body has a *diffuse surface,* that is, rough like sandpaper, so that

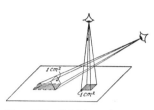

it reflects normally incident light equally in all directions, the surface will appear equally bright from all angles. If the surface is smooth, however, reflection in a preferred direction takes place and the body appears brighter in that direction.

Luminance is measured in *foot-lamberts* or in candles (c) per square centimeter of area. To illustrate; a surface that diffuses light equally in all directions without absorbing any is called a perfect diffuser. When the illuminance on such a surface is one foot-candle, the surface has a luminance of one foot-lambert. 1 c/ft^2 = 3.14 ft lamberts.

Fig. 39K—Brightness is measured normal to the direction of observation.

Examples of luminance, as measured in the metric system, are given in the following table for a number of common surfaces and fields of view.

Clear blue sky	1	c/cm^2	Full moon	3 c/cm^2
Desert sand	1.5	c/cm^2	Snow in sunlight	3 c/cm^2
Fluorescent lamp	2	c/cm^2	Sun	50,000 c/cm^2
Frosted mazda lamp	5	c/cm^2	Tungsten filament	2,500 c/cm^2

All of these appear to have almost equal brightness in all directions.

Eyestrain may result from continued observation of one or more small light sources with high luminance, or from an extended area of lower luminance. When looking for some time at brightly illuminated pavement, desert sands, snow, or the blue sky, dark goggles should be worn to reduce the amount of light entering the eye.

Although safety limits vary widely between individuals, some eye specialists recommend that the eyes should not be subjected to a luminance of more than 2 c/cm^2. For years tungsten lamps were made with clear bulbs, thereby exposing to direct vision a filament luminance of about 2500 c/cm^2. With the introduction of frosted bulbs the diffuse glass surface reduced the value to about 5 c/cm^2. Still further reduction is accomplished by surrounding one or more such bulbs with large translucent glass fixtures. Additional diffusing areas are not necessary with fluorescent lamps since their emitting area, the glass walls of the tube, are sufficiently large to reduce the luminance to about 1 c/cm^2.

It should be pointed out that *the apparent brightness of any extended area is independent of the distance to the observer.* As an observer moves away from a surface the light reaching his eye from each relatively small area decreases with the square of the distance. At the same time the surface area subtended by the same solid angle at the eye increases as the square of the distance, thus keeping the light received per unit solid angle the same.

39.8. Recommended Illumination. One important factor concerned with the maintenance of good health involves good seeing conditions brought about by proper illumination. Experiments on the speed with which people see show that it gains rapidly at first, with increasing illuminance, and then begins leveling off with an illuminance of about 25 ft-candles. This is borne out by numerous checks on the output of factory pieceworkers of all kinds.

Carefully conducted researches in schools, hospitals, office buildings, etc., have also been made to determine proper lighting needed for the most efficient execution of various duties. The results of statistical studies by illuminating engineers, physicians, dentists, etc., under controlled conditions have led to the following values.

	Foot-candles
Hospital operating rooms	1000
Dental clinic	250
Fine needle work	50-100
Book-keeping, auditing, drafting	20-50
Offices, class rooms, laboratories	10-30
Library reading rooms	10-25
Factories	10-50

These are minimum values only and higher levels of illumination are often desirable and recommended.

39.9 Illumination Requirements for Surgical Operations. The hospital operating table is one place where very high illumination by well diffused light is extremely desirable. Surgeons, of necessity, frequently operate near the limits of their knowledge and skill, and always, in order to reduce the surgical shock, at the greatest possible speed. The more quickly and surely they see, the less they have to depend upon the sense of touch. This increases their confidence, their speed and safety factor, by reducing their tension and rapid fatigue build-up.

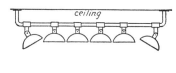
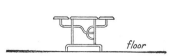

Fɪɢ. 39L—Operating tables in hospitals should be well illuminated.

In major operations involving deep penetration of the body, the edges of the incision and the surgeon's hands block off considerable light so that of the light that reaches the plane of the incision only about one-quarter diffuses inside the wound. Because of the high absorption by cut flesh, only about 10% of this light reflects back from surfaces. This means that forty times as much light as comes from the wound toward the surgeon's eyes must be sent to the wound. Setting 25 ft-lamberts as the minimum amount of light that must come from a wound, the incident light should be of the order of 25 × 40 or 1000 ft-candles. In other words, to produce a luminance of 25 ft-lamberts requires an illuminance of 1000 ft-candles. Additional requirements are (1) the light must come from many directions to eliminate shadows of any kind, (2) approximately daylight color is desirable in order that *veins, arteries,* or *yellow bile ducts* can be distinguished one from the other, and (3) heat radiation from the very strong light sources must be filtered out to reduce the annoying heat sensation on the back of the surgeon's neck and hands.

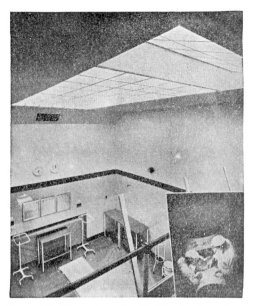

Fɪɢ. 39M—Illustrating scientific illumination of an Operating Theatre, compared to the spot-lighting technique with its resulting dark "surround." (*Courtesy of the Holophane Co. Illumination Service*).

39.10. Fechner's Law. The visual response of the human eye to light of various intensities has been studied by many trained researchers. Recent investigations show remarkable similarities between the eyes response to wide ranges of light intensity and the ears response to wide ranges of sound intensity. Fechner's law, which for sound is given by Eq.(36b), may be extended to light as follows: *The sensation of brightness is proportional to the logarithm of the intensity.*

While the sensation of brightness and loudness do not follow logarithmic relations exactly, Fechner's law is so attractively simple that it has become firmly established in the subject of audition and acoustics. The proposal to extend the law to optics is, therefore, equally attractive and justified.*

According to Fechner's law, the difference in brightness between two light levels is given by the logarithm of the ratio of the two intensities. The unit brightness difference, here called the *decilam,* in honor of the English physicist John H. Lambert (abbr. dm) is analogous to the sound unit *decibel* (abbr. db).

* S. S. Stevens, *Physics Today,* vol. 8, p. 12, Oct. 1955.

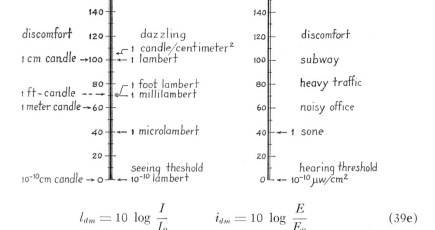

$$l_{dm} = 10 \, \log \frac{I}{I_0} \qquad\qquad i_{dm} = 10 \, \log \frac{E}{E_0} \qquad\qquad (39e)$$

where I, I_0, E, and E_0 represent any luminance or illuminance intensities. A zero level of intensity is arbitrary, and is here chosen as $I_0 = 10^{-10}$ lambert *for luminance measurements,* and $E_0 = 10^{-10}$ centimeter candles *for illuminance measurements.* Like the analogous reference for sound measurements of 10^{-10} microwatt/cm², this reference of 10^{-10} lambert is slightly below the normal absolute threshold for the most sensitive region of the dark adapted eye. *The lambert as a unit of luminance is defined as* $1/\pi$ *candle/cm². The centimeter candle is defined as the illuminance produced on a screen 1 cm from a 1 candle power source.*

Illustrations of the relative magnitudes of different light units and sources in common use today are shown in Fig. 30N. 1 ft-candle = 70.32 decilams.

Example. A light source close to and above a table top produces an illuminance of 100 ft-candles. If the source is raised and the illuminance drops to 8 ft-candles what is the decrease in brightness?

Solution. Here we can substitute directly in Eq.(39e) and obtain

$$i_{dm} = 10 \, \log \frac{E}{E_0} = 10 \, \log \frac{100}{8} = 10 \, \log 12.5 = 10 \times 1.097$$

Hence the brightness drops by 10.97 decilams.

PROBLEMS

1. A 50 watt tungsten filament lamp has an efficiency of 1.10 candles/watt. How far above a table top should this lamp be placed to produce an illuminance of 5 ft-candles?

2. A 100-cp source is located 2.5 ft above a table top. What additional lamp at the same point will bring the illuminance up to 20 ft-candles? (*Ans.* 25-cp.)

3. A 100-cp lamp is located 10 ft from a lamp of unknown candle power. If a photometer screen placed between the lamps is equally illuminated when 4 ft from the unknown lamp, what is its candle power?

4. A 60-cp lamp is located 150 cm from an unknown lamp. If a photometer screen placed between the lamps is equally illuminated when it is 60 cm from the unknown lamp, what is its luminous intensity? (*Ans.* 26.6 cp.)

5. Two lamps $I_1 = 50$ cp and $I_2 = 150$ cp, respectively, are located 10 ft apart. (a) At what two positions along a straight line through the lamps will equal illuminance be produced? (b) What will be the illuminance from each lamp position?

6. Two lamps $A = 20$ cp and $B = 30$ cp, respectively, are located 6 ft apart. (a) At what two positions along a line through the lamps will equal illumination be produced? (b) What will be the illuminance from each lamp in each position? (*Ans.* (a) 2.7 ft and 26.7 ft from A, (b) 2.7 ft-candles and 0.028 ft-candles.)

7. How many 1000 watt tungsten filament lamps located 5 ft above an operating table are required to produce an illuminance of 500 ft-candles? Assume an efficiency of 1.25 candles/watt.

8. Two 100-watt tungsten filament lamps are located 4 ft above a table top. How many additional lamps of the same size, located 6 ft above the same table will bring the total illuminance to 36 ft-candles? Assume an efficiency of 1.25 candles/watt. (*Ans.* 6 lamps.)

9. A chandelier at the center of the ceiling in a theatre is located 25 ft above the floor. How many 60-watt tungsten filament lamps must it contain to produce an illuminance of 5 ft-candles on the floor? Assume an efficiency of 1.1 candles/watt.

10. A table is illuminated by two 60-watt lamps spaced 6 ft apart and 4 ft above at top. Calculate the illuminance in ft-candles on the top (a) at a point directly under one lamp, and (b) at a point half way between them. Assume an efficiency of 1.1 c/watt. (*Ans.* (a) 4.82 ft-c, (b) 4.22 ft-c.)

11. A book lying on a table is illuminated by three 60-watt lamps placed in a line, spaced 4 ft apart, and 3 ft above the top. Calculate the illuminance in ft-candles on the book if it lies directly under one of the end lamps. Assume efficiency of 1.1 c/watt.

12. Solve problem 11 if the book lies directly under the center lamp. (*Ans.* 11.6 ft-c.)

13. A fluorescent lamp tube is 3 cm in diameter and 60 cm long. Calculate its candle power if it has a luminance of 2 c/cm².

14. A 40-watt fluorescent lamp tube is 2 ft long and 1 in. in diameter. If it has a total candle power of 167, what is its surface luminance? (*Ans.* 0.69 c/cm².)

15. Calculate the mean candle power of a 100 watt tungsten filament lamp if its output is found to be 1620 lumens.

16. A light source 2 ft above a table top produces an illuminance of 80 ft-candles. If the source is raised to a height of 12 ft find (a) the illuminance, and (b) the decrease in brightness in decilams.

17. A 100 cp light source is placed 1 m from a diffuse white wall. The source is moved to a distance of 6 m. Find (a) the original illuminance, (b) the original luminance of the wall, (c) the final illuminance, (d) the final luminance, and (e) the decrease in brightness in decilams.

18. Find the absolute brightness level of the illuminance in problem 16.

Properties of Light   Chapter 40

ALL of the various known properties of light are conveniently described in terms of the experiments by which they were discovered and the many and varied experiments by which they are now commonly demonstrated. Numerous as they are, these experiments may be grouped together and classified under one of the three following heads: (1) *geometrical optics*, (2) *physical optics*, and (3) *quantum optics*. Each of these may be subdivided as follows:

Geometrical Optics	Physical Optics	Quantum Optics
rectilinear propagation	*diffraction*	*photo-electric effect*
finite velocity	*interference*	*Compton effect*
reflection	*polarization*	*atomic excitation*
refraction	*double refraction*	*pair production*

The first group, geometrical optics, is treated in the preceding chapter, this chapter, and the following chapter, and deals with those optical phenomena that are most easily described with straight lines and plane geometry. The second group, physical optics, dealing with the wave nature of light, is treated in Chaps. 46 and 47, whereas the third group, dealing with the quantum aspects of light, is treated in Chaps. 64, 68, and 69.

40.1. Galileo's Experiment on the Velocity of Light. History tells us that Galileo once tried to measure the velocity of light but without success. Galileo stationed himself on one hilltop with one lamp and an assistant on another hilltop with a similar lamp. Galileo would first uncover his lamp for an instant, sending a short flash of light to the assistant. As soon as the assistant saw this light he uncovered his own lamp, sending a flash back to Galileo, who noted the total time elapsed. After numerous repetitions of this experiment at greater and greater distances between observers Galileo came to the conclusion that they could not uncover their lamps fast enough and that light probably travels with an infinite speed. Knowing as we do now that light travels with the amazing speed of 186,000 mi/sec, it is easy to see why Galileo's experiment failed.

40.2. Fizeau's Experiment. The first terrestrial method of measuring the velocity of light was devised by Fizeau in 1849. His experimental arrangement is shown in Fig. 40A. Light from an intense source S was reflected from a semitransparent mirror G and then brought to a focus at the point O by means of a lens L_1. After being made into a parallel beam by a second lens L_2, the light traveled a distance of 5.39 mi to a hilltop, where a mirror M and lens L_3 reflected the light back again. Returning by the same path, some of the light passed through the mirror G and entered the eye of the observer at E.

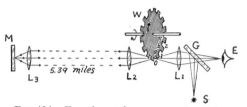

FIG. 40A—Experimental arrangement used by Fizeau in determining the velocity of light.

The purpose of the rotating toothed wheel was to chop the light beam into short flashes and to measure the time it takes each of these signals to travel over to the far mirror and back. With the wheel at rest and in such a position that the light passes through an opening between 2 teeth at O, the observer at E will see an image of the light source S. If the wheel is now set rotating with slowly increasing speed, a condition will soon be reached in which the light passing through 0 will return just in time to be stopped by a, that passing through opening 1 will return just in time to be stopped by b, etc. Under these conditions the image will be completely eclipsed from the observer. By further increasing the speed, the light will reappear, increasing in intensity until a maximum is reached. This will occur when the flashes set out through the openings $0, 1, 2, 3$, etc., return just in time to get through the openings $1, 2, 3, 4$, etc., respectively. With a wheel containing 720 teeth, Fizeau observed this maximum at a speed of 25 rps. The time required for the light to travel over and back can therefore be calculated as 1/25 times 1/720, or 1/18,000th of a second. This, from the measured distance over and back of 10.78 mi, gives a velocity of 194,000 mi/sec, or 313,000 km/sec.

40.3. Michelson's Measurements of the Velocity of Light. In the years that followed these earliest experiments, several investigators improved upon Fizeau's apparatus and methods of observation and obtained more accurate values for the velocity of light. Of these, Michelson's * contributions

* Albert A. Michelson (1852-1931). Distinguished American physicist, celebrated for the invention and development of the interferometer, an optical instrument, now named in his honor, and its use in establishing the length of the standard meter in terms of the wavelength of light, in the ether drift experiments (see Chap. on Relativity), in determining the rigidity of the earth, in the measurement of the distances of and diameters of giant stars, and ior the measurement of the velocity of light. He was the first American scientist to have been awarded the Nobel Prize (1907).

and improvements stand out above the rest. Replacing the toothed wheel by a small eight-sided mirror and increasing the light path to some 44 mi, Michelson in 1926 obtained a value of 299,796 km/sec.

Believing that a still more accurate value could be obtained by measuring the velocity of light in a vacuum, Michelson, with the help of Pease and Pearson, constructed a vacuum tube 1 mi long. The form of the apparatus used is shown diagrammatically in Fig. 40B. Light from a carbon arc is

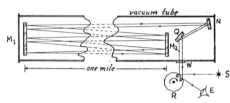

reflected from *a*, one of the 32 faces of a rotating mirror *R*, into the vacuum pipe through a window *W*. After reflection from the mirrors *Q* and *N* the light travels back and forth from one end of the tube to the other by reflection from the large flat mirrors M_1 and M_2. Returning after the tenth traversal to *N* and *Q*, the light

Fig. 40B—Diagrams of the two ends of the 1 mile long vacuum tube used by Michelson, Pease, and Pearson in measuring the velocity of light in a vacuum.

leaves through the same window *W* to strike *b*, an adjacent face of *R*, from where it is reflected to the observer at *E*.

Driven as an air turbine by a steady blast of air, the mirror *R* is rotated faster and faster until a condition is reached where the light reflected from each face at the position *a* will return just in time to be reflected to the observer by the same mirror face when it reaches the position *b*. The exact speed required to do this was found by a stroboscopic * comparison of the rotating mirror with a standard electrically driven tuning fork to be 582 rps.

With the passing of Michelson in 1931, the experiments were completed three years later by Pease and Pearson. From 2885 individual measurements, these observers obtained the following average value for the velocity of light, $c = 299,774$ km/sec. This is lower than any of the values previously obtained but is undoubtedly the most nearly correct.

An extensive and critical study of the values of the velocity of light measured by all observers has been made by Birge.† He concludes that the most probable value at the present time is as follows:

$$c = 299,790 \text{ km/sec}, \tag{40a}$$

or
$$c = 186,280 \text{ mi/sec}.$$

* For an explanation of the stroboscopic effect, see Sec. 1.8.

† Raymond T. Birge (1887-   ), American physicist. Noted for his valuable contributions to the analysis of band spectra as a method of determining the structure of diatomic molecules; for his discovery, with A. S. King, of the carbon isotope 13; and for computations of the best probable values of the general physical constants. He was appointed chairman of the Department of Physics at the University of California in 1933 and elected to the National Academy of Sciences in 1932.

For practical purposes where calculations are to be made, the velocity of light in air or in a vacuum may be assumed to be 300,000 km/sec, or 3×10^{10} cm/sec. One is justified in using this round-number value since it differs from the more accurate value in Eq.(40a) by less than one-tenth of 1%.

40.4. The Velocity of Light in Stationary Matter. In 1850 Foucault completed and published the results of an experiment in which he had measured the velocity of light in water. This was a crucial experiment for it settled a long existing controversy concerning the nature of light. According to Newton and his followers, light was believed to be made up of small particles or corpuscles emanating from a source. Huygens, on the other hand, regarded light as being composed of waves, similar in nature perhaps to water waves or sound waves. Now, Newton's corpuscular theory required light to travel faster in a dense medium like water than it did in a less dense medium like air, whereas Huygens' wave theory required it to travel slower. By sending light back and forth through a long tube of water, Foucault found its velocity to be less than that in air. This was a strong confirmation of Huygens' wave theory.

Years later Michelson also measured the velocity of light in water and found a value of 225,000 km/sec. This is just three-quarters the velocity in a vacuum. In common glass the velocity is still lower, being about two-thirds the velocity in vacuo, or 200,000 km/sec. In air the velocity is very little less than the velocity in a vacuum, differing only by about 70 km/sec at sea level and less at higher altitudes where the air is less dense. For most practical cases this difference can be neglected, and the velocity in air said to be the same as in a vacuum.

40.5. The Refractive Index. The ratio between the velocity of light in a vacuum and the velocity in a medium is called the *refractive index,* or the *index of refraction* of the medium.

$$\frac{\text{Velocity of light in vacuo}}{\text{Velocity of light in a medium}} = \text{refractive index.}$$

Symbolically,

$$\frac{c}{v} = \mu. \tag{40b}$$

The Greek letter μ (mu) is frequently used to represent this ratio. Substituting the velocities given in the preceding section, the following refractive indices may be calculated:

$$\text{for water, } \mu = 1.33 \tag{40c}$$
$$\text{'' glass, } \mu = 1.5 \tag{40d}$$
$$\text{'' air, } \mu = 1.00. \tag{40e}$$

Very exact measurements of the refractive index of air give a value 1.00029.

40.6. The Law of Reflection. Experiment shows that whenever a ray of light is reflected from a plane surface the nature of the reflected light can be described in terms of a number of simple and well-defined laws. The simplest of these is the one known as the law of re-

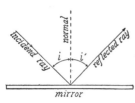

flection. According to this law, the angle at which a ray of light strikes the reflecting surface is exactly equal to the angle the reflected ray makes with the same surface. Instead of measuring the angle of incidence and the angle of reflection from the mirror surface, however, it is customary to measure both

Fig. 40C—Illustrating the law of reflection from a plane surface.

from a line perpendicular to the plane of the mirror. This line as shown in Fig. 40C is called the *normal*. As the angle i increases the angle i' increases by exactly the same amount so that, for all angles of incidence,

$$\text{angle } i = \text{angle } i'. \tag{40f}$$

A second part of this law stipulates that the reflected ray lies in the plane of incidence, the plane of incidence being defined as the plane containing the incident ray and the normal. In other words, *the incident ray, the normal and the reflected ray all lie in the same plane.*

In speaking of a mirror surface one does not necessarily mean a silvered plate of glass; a mirror is any surface smooth enough to produce regular reflection as it has just been described.

40.7. Image in a Plane Mirror. The image of one's self seen in a mirror is formed by rays of light traveling in straight lines which are reflected according to the law of reflection. All objects seen in a plane mirror are images formed by reflection. This can be demonstrated by the experiment shown in Fig. 40D. A lighted candle O is placed on the table near a plate of glass MN. With the candle itself hidden in the box H the observer at E sees only the reflected image at I. If a glass of water is placed at B this image appears as a real candle burning under water.

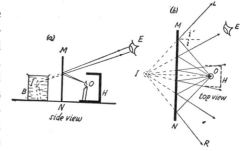

Fig. 40D—An experiment illustrating reflection from a mirror or plate of glass. Light from the candle flame at O appears to come from I.

As shown in the top view, all rays of light leaving the source O are reflected according to the law of reflection. To an observer anywhere between

L and R on the right side of the mirror, all light appears to come from the same point I. This image point is just as far behind the mirror as the object O is in front of it, and the two lie on the same perpendicular to the mirror.

The image one sees in a plane mirror is not a real image but a virtual image. A virtual image is one from which rays seem to radiate but actually do not. In the figure the rays do not come from I', they come from O and by reflection reach the observer.

This experiment illustrates a trick commonly used to make ghost-like figures appear to move about a room or stage. Light from real persons or objects, located below or above the stage, is reflected from a large sheet of plate glass at the front of the stage. With proper drapes and a darkened room the illusion is very effective.

40.8. Multiple Reflections. When light is reflected from two plane mirrors a number of virtual images may be seen. If the two mirrors are parallel to each other, as illustrated by MN in Fig. 40E(a), the images all lie on a straight line, a line which passes through the object perpendicular to both mirrors. The images M_1, M_2, N_1, N_2, etc., of both mirrors are all equally spaced and the images *1*, *2*, *3*, of the object are symmetrically located on each side of them. The solid lines representing real rays show that images numbered *2* appear after

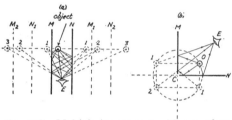

Fig. 40E—Multiple images seen with two plane mirrors.

two reflections, once from each mirror, and that images numbered *3* appear after three reflections, once from one mirror and twice from the other. The number of images visible is limited by the intensity of the light and the reflecting power of the mirrors.

When two mirrors are placed at an angle with each other the object and all of its images lie on a circle whose center is at the intersection of the two mirrors and whose plane is perpendicular to both mirrors. In Fig. 40E(b) the two mirrors are shown at 90° with each other. The two images numbered *1* appear after one reflection and are the same distances behind their respective mirrors as the object is in front. Image *2* appears after two reflections. If the mirrors are placed at an angle of 60°, five virtual images may be seen, in addition to the object, making six in all. If the angle is 45°, seven virtual images may be seen, in addition to the object, making eight in all. Drawings of these are left as exercises for the student.

If one looks at his own face in a plane mirror the image observed is technically described as *perverted*. The image is the same as though the face were reproduced as a rubber mask and the mask turned inside out and viewed from the new front. The right ear of the subject becomes the left ear of the image and vice versa.

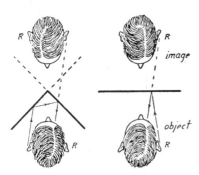

FIG. 40F—One's own image seen in 90° mirrors is normal; that seen in a plane mirror is perverted.

To see one's face as others see it, two front silvered mirrors should be placed 90° apart and touching each other along one edge as shown in Fig. 40F. The observer's right ear will then be seen, because of two reflections, as the right ear of his image, etc. This experiment must be performed to be appreciated since many people's faces are, unknowingly, slightly unsymmetrical. Seen in 90° mirrors all such irregularities are reversed and therefore appear double in magnitude and are very noticeable.

PROBLEMS

1. Find the velocity of light in gasoline if the refractive index is 1.425. Assume the velocity of light in a vacuum to be 186,300 mi/sec.

2. Find the velocity of light in carbon bisulfide if the refractive index is 1.670. Assume the velocity of light in a vacuum to be 186,300 mi/sec. (*Ans.* 11.16 $\times$ 10^4 mi/sec.)

3. At the earth's closest approach to the sun it is 91 $\times$ 10^6 mi away. Find the time it takes the sunlight to reach the earth.

4. Sirius the "dog star" is about 4 light years away, that is, it takes 4 years for the light to reach the earth. Calculate its distance in miles. (*Ans.* 2.35 $\times$ 10^{13} mi.)

5. If the distance to one of the nearest stars is 2.46 $\times$ 10^{13} mi, how many years does it take its light to reach the earth?

6. If Fizeau's velocity of light experiment (see Fig. 40A) were performed with a distant mirror 15 mi away, and a wheel having 90 teeth, how fast would the wheel have to turn for each pulse of light returning through the first succeeding opening to be seen? Assume the velocity of light to be 186,300 mi/sec. (*Ans.* 69 rps.)

7. Make a diagram showing two mirrors with their edges together and forming an angle of 45° with each other. Place an object between them and locate all images.

8. A room with six equal walls, each 4 ft long, has the shape of a hexagon. A lamp is located in one corner 1 ft from each of two walls. Make a diagram and show the positions of all images formed by one reflection only.

9. A box two feet wide and 3 feet long has mirrors on the inside walls. A lamp is located in one corner 6 in from each of the two walls. Make a diagram and show the positions of all images formed by single and double reflections only.

10. Find the distance from the object to the farthest image due to only one reflection for the box in problem 9. (*Ans.* 5 ft.)

11. What must be the length of a mirror in order for a man to see a full view of himself in it?

Refraction   Chapter 41

WHEN light falls upon the smooth surface of a transparent substance like water or glass, part of it is reflected according to the law of reflection and the rest is refracted into the medium (see Fig. 41A). This bending is due to the change in the velocity of the light upon entering the second medium. The direction of the refracted ray, like the incident and reflected rays, is always measured by the angle it makes with the normal.

The angle of refraction, *r*, is found by experiment to depend upon two factors: (1) *the angle of incidence i*, and (2) *the index of refraction μ*. As defined in Sec. 40.5., *the index of refraction is the ratio of the velocity of light in vacuo to the velocity of light in the medium.*

FIG. 41A—Reflection and refraction of light at the boundary of a glass surface.

To determine the angle of refraction from these two factors we perform the following graphical construction (see Fig. 41B). A parallel beam of light of width *PQ* is incident at an angle *i* on the surface of water. From the point *A* where the beam first strikes the surface, a line is drawn perpendicular to the beam intersecting *QC* at *B*.

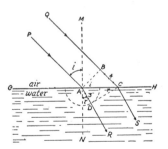

FIG. 41B—Illustrating the graphical method of determining the angle of refraction.

Assuming a refractive index of $\mu = 1.33$ for water, the line *BC* is divided into four equal parts. With a radius of three of these units and a center at *A*, the arc of a circle is scribed as shown. From the point *C* a tangent is drawn intersecting the arc at *D*. The refracted ray *ADR* is then drawn in and the other edge of the ray *CS* drawn parallel to it.

The law of refraction may now be stated in terms of the lines *BC* and *AD* as follows:

$$\frac{BC}{AD} = \mu. \tag{41a}$$

It was the Dutch astronomer and mathematician, Willebrord Snell, who first discovered from experiment that the ratio of these two lines for a given substance is the same for all angles of incidence. In other words, μ is a constant. The relation as given by Eq.(41a) is therefore called Snell's law.* The reason for the constancy of this ratio is that, while the light travels from B to C in air, it travels the corresponding lesser distance AD in water. The ratio $4/3 = 1.33 = \mu$. For common glass with a refractive index, $\mu = 1.5$, the same two lines should be divided into 3 and 2 parts, respectively.

41.1. Snell's Law of Refraction. It is customary, in treating the refraction of light, to express Snell's law in trigonometric terms. Referring to Fig. 41B, triangles ABC and ACD are right triangles. Since line PA is $\perp$ to AB and line MA is $\perp$ to AC, angle $i = $ angle BAC. By similar relations too angle $r = $ angle ACD. From triangles ABC, and ACD,

$$BC = AC \sin i, \qquad \text{and} \qquad AD = AC \sin r.$$

Substituting for BC and AD in Eq.(41a) gives

$$\frac{BC}{AD} = \frac{AC \sin i}{AC \sin r} = \frac{\sin i}{\sin r} = \mu \qquad \text{or} \qquad \mu = \frac{\sin i}{\sin r}. \tag{41b}$$

This latter is the most useful form of Snell's law. For any given transparent substance, the ratio of the sine of the angle of incidence to the sine of the angle of refraction is the same for all angles of incidence and is equal to the refraction index, μ. Since μ is the ratio of the velocities of light in the two media (see Sec. 40.6), Snell's law may also be written

$$\frac{\sin i}{\sin r} = \frac{V_1}{V_2} = \mu \tag{41c}$$

where V_1 represents the velocity in the first medium and V_2 the velocity in the second medium.

Example. Light, in air, is incident at an angle of $45°$ on the surface of a glass plate for which the refractive index is 1.52. Through what angle is the light deviated upon refraction at the top surface?

Solution. First find the angle of refraction r by use of Eq.(41b). By transposing and substituting the given quantities, we obtain

$$\sin r = \frac{\sin i}{\mu} = \frac{\sin 45°}{1.52} = \frac{0.707}{1.52} = 0.465.$$

If we look up 0.465 in a table of natural sines, we find that angle $r = 27.7°$. Since the deviation of the light is the difference between angle i and angle r ($45° - 27.7°$),

$$\text{deviation} = 17.3°.$$

* Willebrord Snell (1591-1626), Dutch astronomer and mathematician, was born at Leyden in 1591. At the age of twenty-two he succeeded his father as professor of mathematics at the University of Leyden. In 1617 he determined the size of the earth from measurements of its curvature between Alkmaar and Bergen-op-Zoom. In 1621 he discovered the law of refraction which now carries his name.

41.2. Displacement in a Parallel Plate. One very useful principle concerning the behavior of light is *the reversibility of light rays.* If, in any of the experiments or illustrations already described, the light rays could be reversed in direction, they would be found to retrace their paths exactly.

If a beam of light, on being refracted into a denser medium like glass, is bent toward the normal, light passing through and out of this denser medium into the air should be bent away from the normal. This can be demonstrated by sending light through a plane-parallel plate of glass as

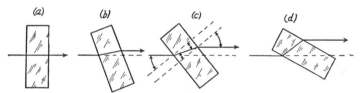

Fig. 41C—Illustrating the lateral displacement of a beam of light passing through a parallel plate of glass.

illustrated in Fig. 41C. In (c) the light is incident on the first surface at an angle i and is refracted at an angle r. This internal ray is now incident on the second surface at the same angle r and is refracted into the air at the same angle i. The light thus emerges in a direction parallel to the original beam but displaced from it laterally.

This lateral displacement is zero for normal incidence as in (a) and increases with the angle i as shown in figures (b), (c) and (d), respectively. If the parallel plate is very thin, as in the case of an ordinary windowpane, the displacement is quite small and for most practical purposes can be neglected.

41.3. Deviation in a Prism. When light passes through a prism it is refracted at both surfaces and comes out in a different direction from that at which it entered. As shown by the three prisms in Fig. 41D the light is always bent away from the refracting edge A. The larger the angle of the prism the larger is the angle of deviation D. Upon entering the prism at the first surface, see diagram (c), the light is bent toward the normal. Emerging into the air from the second surface, the light is bent away from the normal.

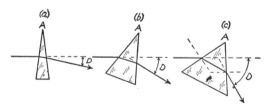

Fig. 41D—Illustrating the bending of a beam of light passing through glass prisms of the same glass but having different angles.

In verifying these results by experiment, light of only one color should be used since white light will be spread out into a spectrum of colors. Light of one color only, is readily obtained by inserting a piece of red or green colored glass into a beam of white light.

41.4. Minimum Deviation. If, during the time a beam of light is refracted by a prism, the prism is rotated continuously in one direction about

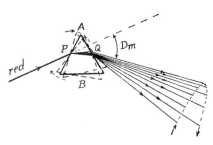

an axis parallel to the refracting edge A, the angle of deviation will be observed to decrease, reach a minimum, and then increase again as shown in Fig. 41E. The smallest deviation angle is called the angle of minimum deviation, and occurs at that particular angle of incidence where the refracted ray inside the prism makes equal angles with the prism faces P and Q.

FIG. 41E—Light refracted by a prism has a minimum angle of deviation D_m.

To derive a formula from which the angle of minimum deviation D_m can be calculated, reference is made to Fig. 41F. To start with, $i = i'$, and $r = r'$. To prove these angles equal, assume i does not equal i' when minimum deviation occurs. Reversing the direction of the light rays will give the same angle of minimum deviation, yet the incident angle is now different from what it was before. This would mean that there are two different angles of incidence capable of giving minimum deviation. Since by experiment there is only one, the two angles, i and i' must be equal.

By geometrical construction,

$$\angle i = \angle i' \qquad \angle r = \angle r'$$
$$\text{and} \qquad \angle x = \angle x'.$$

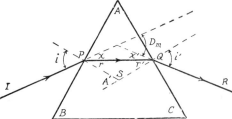

Since two of the angles in the four-sided figure $APSQ$ are right angles, the sum of the other two angles, $A + S = 180°$. Furthermore, for a straight angle, $A' + S = 180°$. Therefore,

FIG. 41F—Geometrical relations for minimum deviation in a prism.

$$\angle A = \angle A'.$$

In the isosceles triangle PQS, the exterior angle A' equals the sum of the interior angles, $r + r'$. Similarly, the exterior angle D_m equals the sum of the interior angles $x + x'$.

Consequently,

$$A = 2r \qquad D_m = 2x \qquad \text{and} \qquad i = r + x.$$

If we solve these three equations for angle i and angle r,

$$r = \tfrac{1}{2}A \qquad i = \tfrac{1}{2}A + \tfrac{1}{2}D_m \qquad \text{or} \qquad i = \tfrac{1}{2}(A + D_m).$$

Since, by Snell's law, $\mu = \sin i / \sin r$,

$$\mu = \frac{\sin \tfrac{1}{2}(A + D_m)}{\sin \tfrac{1}{2}A}. \tag{41d}$$

This is the formula we set out to derive.

When, in the manufacture of optical glass, the refractive index of a given melt must be determined, a small prism is made from a sample of the glass and angles A and D determined experimentally. The measured values are then substituted in Eq.(41d), and μ is calculated. Almost without exception the light used for such measurements is the yellow light from a sodium lamp (see Fig. 60D).

Example. Glass of known refractive index $\mu = 1.52$ is ground and polished into a prism having a refracting angle $A = 60°$. Calculate the angle of minimum deviation.

Solution. Since D_m is the unknown quantity, Eq.(41d) is transposed and the known values A and μ substituted as follows:

$$\sin \tfrac{1}{2}(A + D) = \mu \sin \tfrac{1}{2}A = 1.52 \sin \tfrac{1}{2}60° = 1.52 \times 0.50$$

$$\sin \tfrac{1}{2}(A + D) = 0.760.$$

Looking up the angle whose sine is 0.760, we find

$$\tfrac{1}{2}(A + D) = 49.5°$$

which, on substituting $A = 60°$,

$$A + D = 99° \qquad \text{or} \qquad D = 99 - 60 = 39°.$$

41.5. Critical Angle of Refraction. When light passes from a medium, such as air, into a more dense medium, like glass or water, the angle of refraction is always less than the angle of incidence. As a result of this decrease in angle there exists a range of angles for which no refracted light is possible. To see what this range of angles is, consider the diagram in Fig. 41G, where for several angles of incidence the corresponding angles of refraction are shown. It is to be noted that in the limiting case where the incident rays approach the angle of 90°, i.e., where they graze along the surface, the refracted rays approach a certain angle c, beyond which no refracted light is possible. In any me-

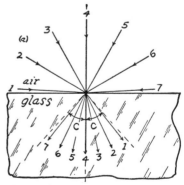

Fig. 41G—Illustrating the critical angle of refraction.

dium this limiting angle, called *the critical angle,* depends for its value upon the index of refraction.

To calculate the critical angle of refraction, it is noted that the angle of incidence $i = 90°$ and angle r = angle c. Since $\sin 90° = 1$, Snell's law becomes

$$\mu = \frac{1}{\sin c} \qquad \text{or} \qquad \sin c = \frac{1}{\mu}. \qquad (41e)$$

For the most common of crown glass $\mu = 1.515$, substitution in this formula gives $c = 41.3°$. For water of index $\mu = 1.33$ it gives $c = 49°$. It should be noted in particular that the critical angle is measured from the normal and not from the refracting surface.

41.6. Total Reflection. Another experiment illustrating the reversibility of light rays is shown in diagram (a) in Fig. 41H. A beam of light is refracted at an angle r into a tank of water. From there it is reflected from a silvered mirror at the bottom of the tank, illustrating the law of reflection

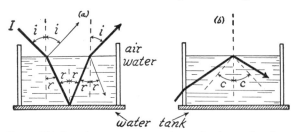

FIG. 41H—Experiment demonstrating reflection, refraction, and total reflection at the surface boundary between air and water.

in a medium other than air. The reflected ray arriving at the upper surface at the same angle r is refracted into the air at the incident angle i. At each refraction at the air-water boundary a small amount of the incident light is reflected as indicated by the fine-lined arrows.

When a beam of light within a medium like water or glass approaches the surface at an angle greater than the critical angle, all of the light is reflected back into the medium. In other words, a water-to-air or glass-to-air surface acts under these conditions like a perfect reflector. This phenomenon is called *total internal reflection.* Since no light can be refracted into the water at such an angle (see Fig. 41G), none inside the water and at large angles of incidence can be refracted out. The experiment is illustrated with a tank of water as shown in diagram (b) in Fig. 41H. If light is sent into the water through a glass plate in one end, the light approaches the upper surface at an angle greater than c, there to be totally reflected back into the water as shown.

An interesting demonstration can be performed with a clear glass or plastic rod bent into almost any form as shown in Fig. 41I. Light, on entering one end, reflects from wall to wall by total reflection, causing it to follow the rod to the end and emerge as a divergent beam. Various instruments used by physicians and surgeons employ this principle for internal body observations.

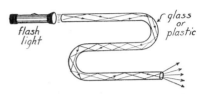

FIG. 41I—Light follows a bent rod by total reflection.

Another demonstration consists of placing a lighted tungsten lamp in the bottom of a pitcher of water and pouring the water slowly into a larger vessel. The light follows the stream of water and produces an interesting display of light where it splashes into the other vessel. (Care should be taken to avoid electrical shock from this experiment.)

Total reflection is also employed in optical instruments such as telescopes, microscopes, prism binoculars, spectroscopes, etc. The optical parts employing this principle are known as *total reflection prisms*. Such prisms are usually made of common glass with one angle a right angle and the other two 45° angles. As illustrated in Fig. 41J there are three ways in which these prisms may be used. Incident normally upon the first surface, as in (a), the light enters the prism without deviation. Arriving at the second surface at an angle of 45°, just 3° greater than the critical angle, the light is totally

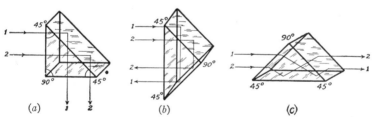

FIG. 41J—(a) Total reflection prism, (b) porro prism, and (c) dove prism.

reflected according to the law of reflection. Having thus been deviated through 90°, the light passes normally through the third surface without further deviation. The prism has therefore acted like a plane mirror with its reflecting surface at *AB*.

In diagram (b) the light enters normally near one end of the long-diagonal face of the prism. Arriving at the second surface at 45°, total reflection takes place exactly as in (a). A second reflection occurs at the third surface, sending the light out near the bottom of, and normal to, the first surface. The light has thus been reversed in direction. Used in this way, the prism performs the function of two prisms each used as in (a).

In diagram (c) the light enters the first prism face at an angle. After refraction the light is totally reflected from the second face and then re-fracted out of the third surface to be parallel to the original beam. Used in this way the prism is called an *erecting prism.* The incident ray, *l,* which is on top reverses its position and emerges from the prism at the bottom.

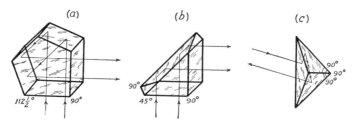

FIG. 41K—Special prisms (a) pentaprism, (b) roof-prism, and (c) triple prism.

Three special prisms of considerable interest are shown in Fig. 41K. The first, called a *penta-prism,* is commonly used in range finders, whereas the second is a *roof-prism* and is used in various optical instruments for erecting images that would otherwise be inverted. The third, called a *triple prism,* is like the corner of a cube with three mutually perpendicular faces and has the unusual property of returning every beam of light that enters it back in the exact direction from which it came. Although the same results can be obtained with mirrors in all cases, prisms have the principal advantage that they are rigid and the reflecting faces cannot be put out of alignment with each other by jarring. The back faces of the penta-prism must be silvered.

41.7. Reflecting Power. Thus far in the treatment of reflection and refraction little has been said concerning the relative intensities of the re-

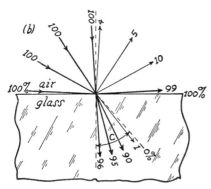

FIG. 41L—Showing the relative intensities of the reflected and refracted rays for different angles of incidence.

fracted rays for different angles of incidence. At and near normal incidence on glass (see Fig. 41L), the reflected light contains only 4% of the incident light and the refracted light contains the remainder or 96%. As the angle of incidence increases the intensity of the reflected beam increases, slowly at first and then more rapidly, approaching 100% at 90°. At the same time the refracted ray decreases in intensity and vanishes as the angle of refraction reaches the critical angle.

Although formulas for the reflecting power of all kinds of substances have been derived, they are generally quite complicated. For non-metallic substances at normal incidence, however, the relations are considerably simplified.

$$\text{Reflecting power} = \frac{(\mu - 1)^2}{(\mu + 1)^2}. \tag{41f}$$

This formula also holds for internal reflection where the incident light is in the medium of index μ and comes to an air or vacuum boundary. To express reflecting power in per cent, multiply Eq.(41f) by 100. Polished metal surfaces in general have a high reflecting power at all angles of incidence. Silver and aluminum, for example, have a reflecting power of 90% or better at normal incidence and for this reason are commonly used on glass mirrors.

PROBLEMS

1. Light is incident at 50° on the surface of a clear crystal whose refractive index is 1.25. Construct a refraction diagram similar to Fig. 41B and determine the angle of refraction. Check your result by calculation.

2. A glass cube 2 in on a side has a refractive index of 1.620. A ray of light incident on one side at 45° passes through the cube and out the opposite side. What is the lateral displacement? (*Ans.* 0.728 in.)

3. A rectangular aquarium with glass sides and filled with water is 1 ft thick. Find the lateral displacement of a beam of light incident on one of the sides at 30°. Neglect the glass thickness.

4. A 60° plastic prism has a refractive index of 1.414. Calculate (a) the angle of minimum deviation, and (b) the angle of incidence that gives minimum deviation (*Ans.* (a) 30°, (b) 45°.)

5. A dense flint glass prism of index 1.67 has a refraction angle of 50°. Calculate the angle of minimum deviation.

6. A 60° prism exhibits an angle of minimum deviation of 43°. Calculate the refractive index. (*Ans.* 1.56.)

7. A 50° prism exhibits an angle of minimum deviation of 34°. Calculate the refractive index.

8. Find the critical angle of refraction for a dense flint glass of index 1.68. (Ans. 36.5°.)

9. Calculate the critical angle of refraction for plastic of index 1.48.

10. If the critical angle of a certain glass is 30°, what is its refractive index? (*Ans.* 2.00.)

11. The critical angle of a crystalline substance is measured to be 35.5°. What is its refractive index?

12. Calculate the reflecting power for diamond at normal incidence if its refractive index is 2.42. (*Ans.* 17.2%.)

13. Green light is incident at 50° on one face of a 60° glass prism. Find the total deviation of the light if the refractive index is 1.50.

14. Yellow light is incident at an angle of 55° on one face of a 60° prism. Find the total deviation of the light if the refractive index is 1.50. (*Ans.* 37.75°.)

Dispersion   Chapter 42

42.1. Dispersion. It was known to the ancients that sunlight, on passing through transparent crystals and jewels of various kinds, would produce brilliant colors of light. The early philosophers, attempting to explain the phenomenon, attributed the origin of the colors to the crystal itself. It was Newton who first demonstrated with prisms that the colors were already present in the white sunlight and that the function of the prism was to separate the colors by refracting them in different directions. This is shown diagrammatically in Fig. 42A.

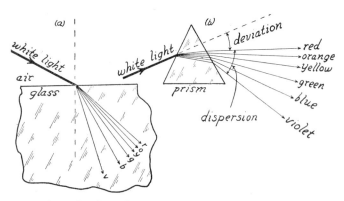

Fig. 42A—Refraction of white sunlight into its spectrum of pure colors.

We have already seen how light of one color is refracted at the boundary of a medium like glass or water and how it is deviated by a prism. It may be seen in the diagram how, *with white light, each color is refracted by a different amount* to produce its own angle of deviation. *Red light is refracted least and violet light is refracted most.* The angular spread of all the colors produced by sending white light through a prism is called the *dispersion* and the band of color so produced is called *a spectrum.*

If white light is sent through a group of similar prisms made of different substances each prism will be found to have a different dispersion. This can be demonstrated for solids by *flint* and *crown glass prisms,* and for liquids by *kerosene, carbon dioxide,* and *water.* It will be noted that the two glass prisms in Fig. 42B, one of flint glass and the other of crown glass, produce

402

quite different dispersions. The liquid prisms, produced by filling thin-walled glass troughs with liquid, also disperse light by different amounts.

Since different colors are refracted by different amounts, the index of refraction is different for each color. In a vacuum all colors travel with the same speed, 186,300 mi/sec, but in a transparent medium, like glass or water, they travel considerably slower and at different speeds. Among the spectrum

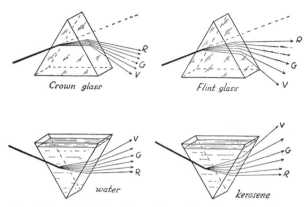

FIG. 42B—Illustrating the relative dispersions of solid as well as liquid prisms.

colors, red travels the fastest and violet the slowest, with the speeds of all other colors somewhere in between. In air there is very little dispersion and in a vacuum there is absolutely none. This latter statement is proved by the fact that when the dark star of an eclipsing binary passes in front of its brighter companion, all colors disappear and reappear simultaneously. If one color were to travel slightly faster than another, the dip in stellar intensity for that color would have plenty of time in its many years of travel to the earth to get ahead.

TABLE 42A. REFRACTIVE INDEX FOR SEVERAL TRANSPARENT SOLIDS

Substance Color wave length λ $\times 10^{-8}$ cm	Violet 4100	Blue 4700	Green 5300	Yellow 5900	Orange 6100	Red 6700
Crown glass	1.5380	1.5310	1.5260	1.5225	1.5216	1.5200
Light flint	1.6040	1.5960	1.5910	1.5875	1.5867	1.5850
Dense flint	1.6980	1.6836	1.6738	1.6670	1.6650	1.6620
Quartz	1.5570	1.5510	1.5468	1.5438	1.5432	1.5420
Diamond	2.4580	2.4439	2.4260	2.4172	2.4150	2.4100
Ice	1.3170	1.3136	1.3110	1.3087	1.3080	1.3060

The refractive indices for a number of transparent solids are given in Table 42A. It will be noted that, although the values for any one substance do not vary greatly between colors, the values for blue and violet are the largest and those for orange and red are the smallest. Note the relatively high values for diamond and the relatively low values for ice.

In the physics laboratory the index of refraction is determined with a prism and usually one having an angle of 60°. The prism is placed on a spectrometer where the spectrum of white light is observed in a small telescope and the angle of minimum deviation is measured for each color separately. As the prism is slowly turned, the spectrum widens or narrows continuously and each color goes through its own angle of minimum deviation just as the rays of that same color make equal angles with the two prism faces.

42.2. Prism Combinations. While substances that produce large deviations also produce large dispersions, the two properties are by no means proportional to each other. If a flint glass prism, for example, produces twice the dispersion of a crown glass prism, it is not true that the deviation of each color by the flint prism is twice that of the crown glass prism. Useful devices illustrating this fact can be demonstrated by combining two prisms in opposition as shown in Fig. 42C.

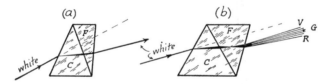

FIG. 42C—Prism combinations. (a) achromatic prism giving deviation without dispersion. (b) direct vision prism giving dispersion without deviation.

For the achromatic combination in (a) the angles of both prisms are so selected that each prism alone will produce the same total dispersion. Since flint glass has the higher dispersive power the flint prism will have a smaller angle as shown. Placed in opposition the crown glass spreads the colors out and the flint prism bends them back parallel to each other again. Since the deviation produced by the two prisms is not the same, light will emerge as white light but in a different direction from that in which it first entered.

For the direct vision combination in (b) the angles of the prisms are so selected that each prism alone will produce the same deviation for green light. For two such matched prisms the flint prism will produce the greatest dispersion. Combined in opposition, the green light comes out on the far side, parallel to the incident white light on the left and the other spectrum colors on either side as shown.

42.3. The Rainbow. The rainbow is nature's most spectacular display of the spectrum of white light. The required conditions for the appearance of the phenomenon are that the sun be shining in one part of the sky and the rain be falling in the opposite part of the sky. Turning one's back to the sun, the bright primary bow and sometimes the fainter secondary bow, with colors reversed, are seen as the arcs of circles. From a high vantage point or an airplane these bows may form complete circles whose common center lies in the direction of the observer's shadow.

The elementary theory of the rainbow was first given by Antonius de Demini in the year 1611 and later developed more exactly by Descartes. The general characteristics of the *primary* and *secondary bows* are satisfactorily accounted for by considering only the reflection and refraction of light by spherical raindrops. To understand how the phenomenon arises we first confine our attention to an individual raindrop as shown in Fig. 42D. In diagram (a) a ray of sunlight is shown entering a single raindrop at a point *A* near the top. At this point some of the light is reflected (not shown), and the remainder is refracted into the liquid sphere. At this first refraction the light is dispersed into its spectrum colors, violet being deviated the most and red the least.

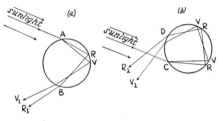

Fig. 42D—Diagrams showing the dispersion of sunlight by individual raindrops in the production of the primary and secondary rainbows.

Arriving at the opposite side of the drop, each color is partly refracted out into the air (not shown) and partly reflected back into the liquid. Reaching the surface at the lower boundary each color is again reflected (not shown), and refracted. This second refraction is quite similar to that of a prism (see Fig. 42A) where refraction at the second surface increases the dispersion already produced at the first. This is the path of the light in thousands of drops giving rise to the bright primary rainbow.

In diagram (b) of Fig. 42D, a ray of sunlight, coming from the same direction as in diagram (a), is shown entering a single raindrop at a point *C* near the bottom. After one refraction and two internal reflections the light is again refracted and dispersed, this time in a direction not greatly different from that in diagram (a). This is the path of the light in thousands of drops giving rise to the fainter secondary rainbow.

Of all the sun's rays falling on one face of each individual drop, only a small part of them are responsible for the main features of both rainbows. The reasons for excluding the other will be explained in later paragraphs.

Assuming for the present that the two rays shown are the only rays to be considered, let us see why the bows appear as they do in the sky.

As shown in Fig. 42E, the primary bow appears inside the secondary bow and arises from sunlight entering the tops of drops properly located. Those in a region R_1 refract red light toward the observer's eye at O, and the violet

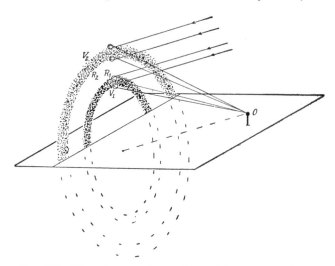

Fig. 42E—The primary and secondary rainbows as seen by an observer at O.

and other colors over his head. Drops in the region of V_1 refract violet light to the observer's eye at O, and the red and other colors toward his feet. In other words, the light seen from any one drop is but one color, all drops giving this color lying on the arc of a circle. The reason they lie on the arc of a circle is that the angle between the incident sunlight and the refracted light of any one color is of necessity the same for each drop. In the primary bow this angle is 42° for the red light and 40° for the violet.

The secondary bow is formed by similar reasoning and appears at higher angles of elevation, and with the colors reversed. The angles subtended by the secondary bow are 50° for the red and 54° for the violet.

42.4. The Theory of the Rainbow. The complete theory of the rainbow was first proposed by Thomas Young, and later worked out in detail by Potter, and Airy. To understand why the particular rays shown in Fig. 42D are responsible for the rainbow, and that other rays which certainly enter the drop can be neglected, see Fig. 42F. Here, in the parallel beam of sunlight entering a single drop, our attention is confined to the rays of only one color. By this simplification the phenomenon of dispersion is dispensed with and we consider only the reflection and refraction of red light.

As each of the parallel red rays *A, B, C,* etc., from the sun enter the drop they are deviated according to the law of refraction. At the opposite side of the drop, in the region *d* to *u″*, these rays are partly reflected to the lower left boundary at *a′, b′, c′,* etc., where, by refraction, they pass out into the air in the direction of *A′, B′, C′,* etc., respectively, and partly refracted in the direction of *a″, b″, c″,* etc., respectively.

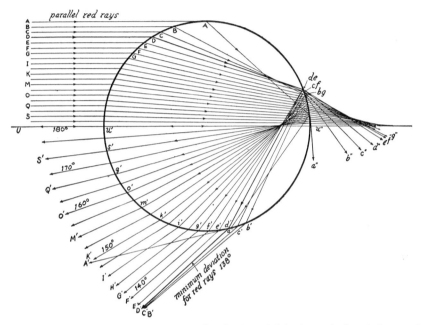

F<small>IG</small>. 42F—Illustrating the refraction and reflection of light by a single raindrop and the minimum deviation of certain rays that produce the primary rainbow.

From the diagram it will be noted that a ray like *A* entering at the very edge of the drop is deviated through an angle close to 180°, that is, it emerges in almost the opposite direction to that in which it entered. The same is true of a ray like *Q* nearer the center of the drop. Ray *U* is exactly reversed in direction and therefore deviated exactly 180°. Ray *D*, on the other hand, is seen to be deviated least of all and is therefore referred to as the ray at minimum deviation. In going from *A* to *U* with the incident light, the emergent light is deviated less and less until it reaches a minimum for *D′* and then increases again, reaching 180° with the axial ray *UU′*. The net result of this behavior is seen to be a slight crowding together of a considerable number of nearly parallel rays at minimum deviation where the light emerges as an intense and nearly parallel beam *B′* to *G′*.

It should be noted that raindrops are spheres and not circles as represented in the figures and that the refracted rays emerge as cones of light. Rotating Fig. 42F about the axial ray UU' the emerging rays A', B', C', etc., are confined to a cone bounded at the edges by the rays that have suffered the least deviation. In the direction of D', the edge of the cone, the radiation is very intense, and inside the cone the rays are divergent and the radiation feeble. Outside the cone there is no light. Thus the selected ray A of the incident light in Fig. 42D(a) is the ray D in Fig. 42F.

Similar diagrams for other colors lead to angles of minimum deviation and cones of light whose angles decrease in the order of the spectral colors red, orange, yellow, green, blue, and violet. An experimental demonstration of this can be made by sending a beam of parallel light from a carbon arc through a round glass bulb filled with water. The refracted cones of light falling on a screen in back of the arc source forms a complete primary rainbow. Outside this primary bow, and with colors reversed, is the fainter secondary bow.

To understand the secondary rainbow, additional rays must be added to Fig. 42F. Internally reflected rays from the points a', b', c', etc., are drawn up to where they again strike the surface of the drop and there are refracted out into the air. Out of these rays a given set of rays, like those for the primary bow, will have a preferred direction in which the light is most intense. When the figure is rotated about the axial line UU', the rays form a secondary cone of light, the inner edge of which is sharply defined.

It is interesting to point out that no light emerges in the region between the primary and secondary cones of light. This agrees with the observations that the region between the two rainbows is quite dark, whereas outside the secondary bow and inside the primary bow a considerable amount of light is visible.

Theoretically three, four, and five reflections within raindrops should give rise to other rainbows. The third and fourth bows are located between the observer and the sun and, because the direct sunlight is so bright compared with the faint bows, the phenomenon has probably never been observed. The fifth bow, however, occurs in the same part of the sky as the primary and secondary bows, and would be seen except for the faintness of the light.

42.5. Coronas, and Lunar Bows. On occasions when the primary and secondary rainbows are particularly bright, a third bow just inside the primary and a fourth bow just outside the secondary bow may be seen. These are called supernumerary bows, and are due to peculiar interference effects of light. This interference occurs between pairs of rays which are parallel to each other on emergence, but which have traveled different paths within the drop. Such pairs of rays, for example, are D' and E', C' and F', B' and G', and A' and Q'. The two rays in each of these pairs are just those that cross each other at the reflecting surface d to u'' and are therefore symmetrical with the corresponding incident pairs of rays.

Lunar bows may be seen under favorable conditions. When the full moon appears in one part of the sky and rain is falling in another part of the sky, an observer with his back to the moon may observe a barely visible rainbow. As a rule only the brighter colors, red and yellow, are visible.

At times when the sun or moon shines through a thin veil of fog we observe a circular colored bow with the sun or moon at the geometrical center. Such a corona, as it is technically called, is due to the diffraction of light around the tiny fog particles. Popularly called a ring around the sun or a ring around the moon, a corona appears close to the luminary with red on the outside and should not be confused with the larger rings or halos with red on the inside.

42.6. Halos. Halos are commonly observed as faint rainbow-like rings around the sun or moon and are due to tiny ice crystals floating in the upper stratosphere. Such crystals are hexagonal in shape and, acting like prisms, refract and disperse white light into a spectrum. Two halos are frequently observed, the brighter one making an angle of 22° with the luminary and the fainter one an angle of 46°. Both exhibit confused spectrum colors with a decided red tint on the inside.

Crystals, like prisms, have an angle of minimum deviation for each color of light and, because they are oriented at random in space, millions of them appear to each observer to concentrate the light in a circle with the luminary at the center. As shown in Fig. 42G, the angle of minimum deviation for light entering and leav-

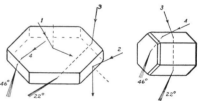

Fig. 42G—Typical forms of ice crystals showing reflected and refracted rays of sunlight giving rise to halos and "mock suns."

ing different faces of either plate-like or rod-like crystals is 22° and 46°. The 22° angle arises from rays like (3) where the two refracting surfaces are alternate faces that make an angle of 60° with each other. The 46° angle arises from rays like (4) where the two refracting surfaces make an angle of 90°. (The refractive index of ice for red light is 1.3060.)

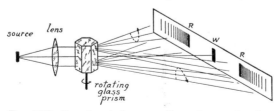

Fig. 42H—Experiment demonstrating colors produced at minimum deviation by a single rotating prism.

A demonstration of such color effects can be produced as shown in Fig. 42H by means of a hexagonal or octagonal glass prism rotated rapidly about its axis in a strong beam of white light. Dispersed light refracted by alternate faces sweeps in from either side of the screen, slows down and stops at minimum deviation, and then retreats again. The blurred patches of light on the screen are brightest at the minimum deviation angles R.

42.7. "Mock Suns," or "Sundogs." Another natural phenomenon of great interest, and one which is quite spectacular, is the formation of "mock suns" or "sundogs." Although the phenomenon is most commonly seen in the polar regions, it is occasionally observed at low latitudes and at a time of day when the sun is not far from the horizon (see Fig. 42I).

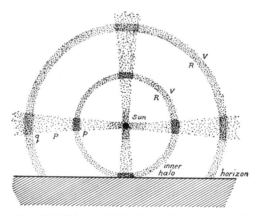

FIG. 42I—Halos and "mock suns" or "sundogs" as seen frequently in polar regions and occasionally at lower latitudes. *P,* parhelic circle; *p,* mock suns or parhelia; *q,* paranthelia.

This display too is caused by myriads of tiny ice crystals in the upper atmosphere, reflecting and refracting the light according to the well-established laws of optics. As shown in Fig. 42I, there are, in addition to the two rainbow-like halos at 22° and 46°, four radial streaks of white light, two vertical and two horizontal. Where these streaks of white light cross the halos, the colors appear intensified and form what are called *mock suns* or *sundogs.*

The explanation of the halos is the same as explained above while the white streaks are due to reflection from all crystal faces. The plate-like crystals, falling freely under gravity, flutter slowly downward like leaves from a tree. Wobbling slightly about a horizontal plane, they present vertical and horizontal faces from which light is reflected. At positions close in line between the sun and observer, the light reflected toward the observer is incident at a grazing angle where the reflecting power for all transparent solids is high.

42.8. Mirages and Flying Saucers. When walking across the desert sands or driving along a straight and level highway on a hot day, the sand or the dark asphalt in the distance seems to be covered with water. The water, of course, is just a reflected image of the sky, and a distant object above the horizon will appear upside down below the horizon. The air in contact with the ground has been heated to a high temperature and, because its refractive index is lowered due to expansion, light rays are reflected as if from a plane mirror.

Oftentimes at night when the air at the ground is cooler than the air above, the bending of light rays will occur in the opposite direction, and distant objects, like a row of bright city street lights, can be seen against the sky. This and similar phenomena, explain most of the "flying saucer" observations,* first observed centuries ago and reported so frequently in the last decade.

PROBLEMS

1. White light is incident at 85° on one face of a diamond. Calculate the dispersion produced by one surface, that is, the angle between the red and violet rays.†

2. White light is incident at 75° on the surface of quartz. Calculate the dispersion produced by one surface, that is, the angle between the red and violet rays.† (*Ans.* 26′ or 0.45°.)

3. White light is incident at 20° on one face of a quartz prism having a refractive angle of 45°. Find the dispersion produced between the red and violet rays.†

4. White light is incident at 40° on one face of a dense flint glass prism having a refractive angle of 50°. Find the dispersion produced between emergent red and violet rays. For refractive indices see Table 42A. (*Ans.* 2°43′ or 2.72°.)

5. A six sided prism is rotated in a beam of white light like that shown in Fig. 42H. If the prism is made of crown glass of index 1.62, what will be the angle between the two minimum deviation positions *RR*?

6. A ten sided prism is rotated in a beam of white light like that shown in Fig. 42H. If the prism is made of quartz with a red index of 1.5420, what will be the total angle between the two minimum deviation positions *RR*? (*Ans.* 41.9°.)

7. Solve Problem 6 if the prism is twelve sided.

8. A parallel beam of green light is incident on a spherical raindrop as shown in Fig. 42F. Calculate the angle of deviation for a ray like *F*, at a distance three fourths of the way up from the center line toward the edge. Assume the refractive index to be 1.3333. (*Ans.* 140°16′ or 140.27°.)

9. Solve problem 8 for the ray *K*, at a distance half way up from the center line toward the edge.

* See "Flying Saucers," by D. H. Menzel, Harvard University Press.
† Use four place trigonometry tables.

Lenses and Mirrors
Chapter 43

43.1. Lenses. The primary function of a lens is to form images of real objects. Although most lenses are made of common glass, a few special lenses are made of other transparent materials like *quartz* and *fluorite*. To understand the principles upon which a lens functions, imagine a set of several matched prisms and blocks of glass arranged in the order shown in Fig. 43A. In the first arrangement the prisms are made so as to refract the incoming parallel light rays and to converge them to a focus at F. In the second arrangement the parallel rays are made to diverge as if they had come from a

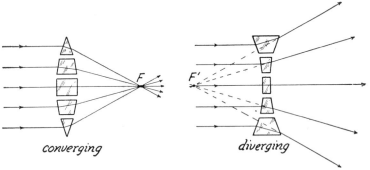

Fig. 43A—Diagram of the refraction of light by sets of prisms, matched to represent (a) a converging lens, and (b) a diverging lens.

common point F'. In each system the greatest deviation occurs at the outermost prisms, for they have the greatest angle between the two refracting surfaces. No deviation occurs for the central rays, for at that point the glass faces are parallel to each other.

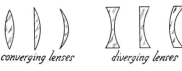

converging lenses   *diverging lenses*

Fig. 43B—Cross-section of standard forms of common lenses.

A real lens is not made of prisms, as indicated in Fig. 43A, but of a solid piece of glass with surfaces ground to the form of a sphere. Cross sections of several standard forms are shown in Fig. 43B. The first three lenses, which are thicker in the center, are called *converging* or *positive lenses,* while the last three, which are thinner in the center, are called *diverging* or *negative lenses.* Special names attached to each of the six lens types shown are (1) *double convex,* (2) *plano-convex,* (3) *convex miniscus,* (4) *double concave,* (5) *plano-concave,* and (6) *concave miniscus.*

412

There are two good reasons why lenses have spherical surfaces; first, with this shape they form reasonably good images; and second, a spherical form is by far the most practical shape to which smooth polished surfaces can be ground.

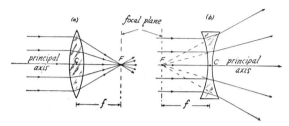

Fig. 43C—Converging and diverging lenses showing the principal axis, principal focus *F*, and focal length.

Diagrams showing the refraction of light by converging and diverging lenses are given in Fig. 43C. The principal axis in each case is a straight line passing through the center of a lens perpendicular to the two faces at the points of intersection. The principal focus *F* lies on the principal axis and is defined for a converging lens as the point where parallel light rays are brought together, and for a negative lens as a point from which parallel light rays appear to originate. *By symmetry every lens has two principal foci, one on each side of the lens and at the same distance from the center of the lens.* The distance from the focal point to the lens is called the focal length.

$$CF = \text{focal length} = f.$$

A plane perpendicular to the principal axis which passes through either principal focus is called the *focal plane*. Parallel light rays entering the lens from any other direction than shown in the diagrams will come to a focus at some point on the focal plane. This point is readily located by remembering that a ray through the lens center does not change in direction.

The greater the curvature of the two surfaces of a lens, the shorter is its focal length. The reason for this, as can be seen from the diagrams, is that the greater the curvature the greater is the deviation of the light rays passing through near the edges of the lens.

One important principle concerning lenses is the reversibility of light rays. If a point source of light is placed at *F* in Fig. 43C(a), the rays of light which strike the lens will be refracted into a parallel beam of light moving to the left. Similarly, in Fig. 43C(b) if light rays are converging toward the focal point *F'* they will be refracted by the lens into a parallel beam.

43.2. Image Formation. When an object is placed on one side of a converging lens beyond the principal focus, a real image will be formed on the opposite side of the lens. This is illustrated in Fig. 43D. If the object is

moved closer to the focal point the image will be formed farther away from
the lens and will be bigger, that is, magnified. As the object is moved farther
away from the lens the image is formed closer to the focal point and is
smaller in size.

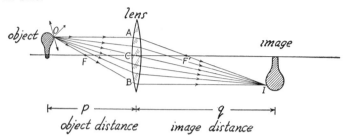

FIG. 43D—Ray diagram illustrating the formation of a real image by
means of a single converging lens.

In general there are two ways of accurately determining the position of
an image: one is by graphical construction and the other is by use of the lens
formula.

$$\frac{1}{p} + \frac{1}{q} = \frac{1}{f},$$ (43a)

where *p is the object distance, q the image distance,* and *f the focal length.*

The graphical method is illustrated in Fig. 43E. Consider the light
emitted by some one particular point like *O* in the object. Of the rays going
out from this point in all directions the ray *OA* traveling parallel to the

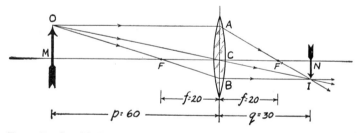

FIG. 43E—Graphical determination of the size and position of the image
formed by a converging lens.

principal axis will be refracted to pass through the focal point *F* (see Fig.
43C(a)). The ray *OC* arriving at the center of the lens where the faces are
parallel will pass straight through, meeting the other ray at some point *I*.
These two rays locate the tip of the image at *I*. All other rays from the
point *O* which strike the lens will be brought to a focus at this same point.
To check this note that the ray *OF*, which passes from *O* through the left-

hand focal point, by the principle of the reversibility of light rays, will be refracted parallel to the principal axis, crossing the other ray at I, as shown.

The use of the lens formula can be illustrated by the following example. Let an object be placed 60 cm in front of a lens of focal length 20 cm. If we solve Eq.(43a) for q, we obtain the expression:

$$q = \frac{pf}{p - f} \qquad (43b)$$

Then substituting the known quantities, we obtain

$$q = \frac{60 \times 20}{60 - 20} = 30 \text{ cm}.$$

The image is formed 30 cm from the lens or 10 cm from F.

The size of the image can be calculated from the following simple relation:

$$\frac{\text{size of image}}{\text{size of object}} = \frac{\text{image distance}}{\text{object distance}}.$$

This is the image formula,

$$\frac{I}{O} = -\frac{q}{p}, \qquad (43c)$$

in which the ratio I/O is called the *magnification*. If we substitute known values of O, p, and q from the above problem, as an example, we obtain

$$m = \frac{I}{O} = -\frac{30}{60} \qquad I = -\tfrac{1}{2}O.$$

The answer shows that the image is half the size of the object and that the magnification is $\tfrac{1}{2}$. The minus sign means the image is inverted.

If a centimeter rule is used to construct this problem graphically, the resultant diagram will be similar to Fig. 43E. Each line is drawn in its proper position and size and when the image is located by rays (1), (2), and (3) its position and size are measured by the same scale. Drawn carefully, the graphical results will agree in every detail with those calculated by the above formulas.

43.3. Virtual Images. The images formed by the lenses in Figs. 43D and 43E are *real*. *Real images* are defined as those which can be formed on a screen and are characterized by the fact that rays of light are actually brought together to a focus there. *Virtual images* are not real, they cannot be formed on a screen, and the rays from different points on the object do not pass through corresponding points in the image. Virtual images may be observed with a converging lens by placing an object close to the lens and inside the focal point, or by a diverging lens with the object at any point. These two examples are illustrated in Fig. 43F.

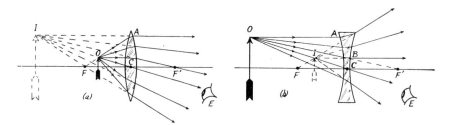

Fɪɢ. 43F—Illustrating the formation of virtual images (a) with a converging lens and (b) with a diverging lens.

In the first case the lens is used as a magnifier, or reading glass. Rays of light radiating from the point of the object at *O* are refracted in the proper direction but are not sufficiently deviated to come to a focus. To the observer's eye at *E* these rays appear to be coming from a point *I* back of the lens. This is a *virtual image, right side up and magnified.* To find this image graphically we observe that the ray *FOA* must be refracted parallel to the principal axis. The ray *OC* through the center of the lens goes on undeviated. These two refracted rays extended backward intersect at *I*. If the lens formula Eq.(43b) is used to find the image in such a case the image distance *q* will come out as a negative quantity, showing it is a virtual image on the same side of the lens as the object.

In the case of a negative lens the image is always virtual, closer to the lens, and smaller in size than the object. As shown in Fig. 43F(b), light rays diverging from the object point *O* are made more divergent by the lens. To the observer's eye at *E* these rays appear to be coming from the point *I* back of but close to the lens. To find this image we observe that the ray *OA* parallel to the principal axis must be refracted in such a direction that it appears to come from *F*. The ray *OC* through the center goes on undeviated. Since these two directions intersect at *I* the image is formed there.

In applying the lens formula to a diverging lens the focal length *f* is always *negative* in sign. To illustrate this, consider the following example.

Example. An object is placed 30 cm in front of a diverging lens of focal length of 15 cm. Locate the image position.

Solution. Direct substitution in Eq.(43b) gives

$$q = \frac{30 \times (-15)}{30 - (-15)} \quad \text{or} \quad q = \frac{-450}{45}.$$

From which

$$q = -10 \text{ cm.}$$

The image is found at 10 cm from the lens, the negative sign indicating it is virtual and therefore on the same side of the lens as the object.

A convenient sign convention for all lens problems solved with Eq.(43b) is the following: for any object on the left side of a lens the object distance is positive, and for any image on the right side the image distance is positive. An object on the right side of the lens is negative, and an image on the left side is negative.

43.4. Conjugate Foci. Since the lens equation, Eq.(43a), is symmetrical in p and q, it follows that a real image and the object from which it was formed may be interchanged. For example, in Figs. 43D and 43E if the object is located at I, the image would be located at O. The distances p and q are called *conjugate distances*, O and I *conjugate points*, and the intersections of the optic axis with the object and image planes *conjugate foci*.

In demonstrating conjugate distances with a lens and screen the object and image can be interchanged in position, or, the lens can be moved. If, for example, an object distance $p = 30$ cm and an image distance $q = 50$ cm, the lens may be moved to a new position $p = 50$ cm and the image will be formed at $q = 30$ cm. In other words, for a fixed distance between object and image screen, there are two lens positions of good image formation (see

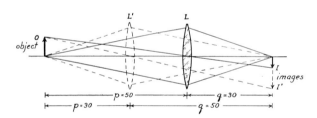

Fɪɢ. 43G—Illustrating conjugate foci for a single converging lens.

Fig. 43G). Because of the image object relation, Eq.(43c), the two images will differ in size, the one being smaller than the object by the ratio 3/5 as shown by the solid arrow, and the other larger by the ratio 5/3 as shown by the dotted arrow.

43.5. The Lens Maker's Formula. To grind and polish a lens to some predetermined focal length, the refractive index of the glass should be known. Usually the refractive index is specified for the particular wavelength of yellow light emitted by a sodium lamp. With the index known, the radii of curvature of the two spherical surfaces can be calculated from the equation:

$$\frac{1}{f} = (\mu - 1)\left(\frac{1}{r_1} - \frac{1}{r_2}\right). \tag{43d}$$

The sign convention for r_1 and r_2 is based upon the following rules:

(*1*) *Light rays entering and passing through a lens are always drawn from left to right;*

(*2*) *When such a ray encounters a convex surface, the radius r is positive;*

(*3*) *When a light ray encounters a concave surface, the radius r is negative.*

To illustrate the use of the lens maker's formula, consider the following example.

Example. A plano-convex lens having a focal length of 50 cm is to be made of glass of refractive index 1.52. Calculate the radius of curvature of the grinding and polishing tools that must be used to make this lens.

Solution. Since a plano-convex lens has one flat surface, the radius of curvature for that surface is infinite, and r_1 in Eq.(43d) is replaced by ∞. r_2 is the unknown. Direct substitution of all known quantities in the formula gives

$$\frac{1}{50} = (1.52 - 1)\left(\frac{1}{\infty} - \frac{1}{r_2}\right). \tag{43e}$$

Transpose and solve for r_2.

$$\frac{1}{50} = (0.52)\left(0 - \frac{1}{r_2}\right), \qquad \frac{1}{50} = -\frac{0.52}{r_2},$$

giving
$$r_2 = 50 \times 0.52 = -26.0 \text{ cm.}$$

43.6. Defects of the Image. Although a simple converging lens may be made to form a relatively clear image of almost any object, there is present in every image a number of common defects tending to blur it. These defects are known as *spherical aberration, chromatic aberration, curvature of field, astigmatism, distortion,* and *coma.* Although some of these *aberrations,* as they are called, can be partly or almost entirely corrected by one means or another, they cannot all be eliminated entirely. These corrections are refinements that are usually considered in the design of lenses and are of some importance in the understanding of the principal action of a lens. We will be content to consider briefly the first three defects mentioned above—namely, spherical aberration, chromatic aberration, and curvature of field.

43.7. Spherical Aberration. Spherical aberration is an undesirable defect in the focusing properties of single glass lenses and is attributed to the fact that spherical surfaces are not exactly the correct surfaces to which a lens should be ground and polished. The reason they are not correct is shown for a double convex lens in Fig. 43H. Rays of light parallel to the principal axis and passing through the outer parts of the lens are not brought to exactly the same focus as those rays passing through the central portion. The result is that nowhere can a sharply defined image of a distant object be formed on a screen.

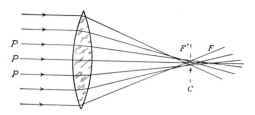

Fig. 43H—Illustrating spherical aberration of a lens. *P*,
paraxial rays; *C*, circle of least confusion.

When a screen is placed between *F* and *F'* and a blurred image is obtained it is not difficult to find a position where the least blurring occurs. This point, *C* in the diagram, is called the *circle of least confusion*.

There are various ways in which spherical aberration in a lens may be reduced. Some of these are easily carried out while others require expert lens design.

(1) The easiest way to reduce spherical aberration is to place a circular diaphragm in front of the lens and allow only the central bundle of rays to pass through. Such a procedure reduces the size of the circle of least confusion and thereby produces sharper images. This is one of the functions of the *iris diaphragm* in the lens cell of a camera. The smaller the effective diameter of a lens the more sharply defined is its image focusing properties. Reduced aperture, however, reduces the light gathering power and for some purposes is not desirable.

Rays passing through or near the center of a lens, and at the same time making relatively small angles with the principal axis, are called *paraxial rays*. It is for such rays only that reasonably sharp focus is obtained and the equations used in the preceding sections apply.

(2) Because peripheral rays are deviated through too great an angle (see Fig. 43H), any method that will bring about lesser deviation from the outer edges of a lens will result in better focusing. The principle of minimum deviation offers one such method for by carefully selecting the radii of curvature for the two lens faces the peripheral rays can be brought to much more nearly the same focal point as the paraxial rays (see Fig. 43I). In diagram (a) parallel rays entering normal to the flat surface of a plano-convex lens are refracted at the second surface only, the outer rays being deviated through too great an angle. In (b) the outer rays, because they enter one face and leave the other at nearly the same angle, are near minimum deviation and cross the axis farther out. If, for any given object distance and image distance, the radii of curvature r_1 and r_2 are so chosen that *the peripheral rays pass through the lens at minimum deviation*, the lens will have a minimum of spherical aberration.

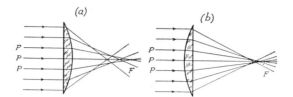

FIG. 43I—Spherical aberration for parallel rays is different on the two sides of a plane-convex lens. *P*, paraxial
rays.

(3) To correct for spherical aberration the two lens surfaces are sometimes ground and polished to other than a spherical form. Such a process,
called *aspherizing*, is not only tedious and difficult, but any lens so made is
good for only one pair of object and image distances.

(4) A fourth method of correcting spherical abberration is to combine a
positive crown glass lens with a negative flint glass lens. Although both
lenses have spherical surfaces, the curvatures of the two can be so chosen that
the errors of one practically cancel those of the other.

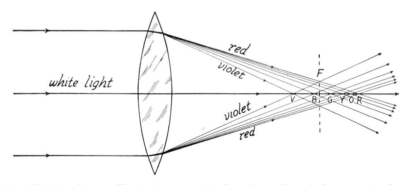

FIG. 43J—Ray diagram illustrating chromatic aberration with a single converging lens.

43.8. Chromatic Aberration. When white light passes through a lens
close to the edge it is dispersed in much the same way that it is when passing through a large angle prism (see Fig. 43J). The violet light, being deviated the most, comes to a focus nearer the lens than the red. The ray
passing through the center of the lens and along the principal axis is not
dispersed. For white light a single lens, therefore, cannot possibly form a
sharply defined image.

To correct a lens for chromatic aberration, use is made of the principle
of the achromatic prism (see Fig. 42C(a)). Two prisms, one of crown glass,
the other of flint glass, are so chosen that when placed in opposition they
produce deviation without dispersion.

A similar combination can be constructed of flint and crown glass lenses, as illustrated in Fig. 43K, whereby the dispersion in one lens is compensated for by the opposite dispersion in the other and yet the light is deviated to bring all colors to a common focus. Such a combination is called an *achromatic lens.* All first-class optical instruments use achromatic lenses. By the proper selection of surface curvatures spherical aberration as well as chromatic aberration can be minimized with two lenses.

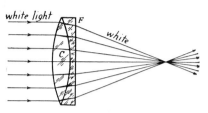

Fig. 43K—Achromatic lens combination.

The two exposed surfaces are chosen to give approximately minimum deviation and the two inner surfaces adjusted to correct chromatic aberration.

When two *thin lenses* are placed in contact the combination behaves as a single lens with a focal length of its own. If f_1 and f_2 represent the focal lengths of the two lenses respectively, the equivalent focal length f of the combination is given by

$$\frac{1}{f} = \frac{1}{f_1} + \frac{1}{f_2} . \tag{43f}$$

Example. An achromatic lens is composed of two lenses: a converging crown glass lens with a focal length of 8 in and a diverging flint glass lens with a focal length of 12 in. Find the equivalent focal length.

Solution. The two focal lengths given are $f_1 = +8$ in, and $f_2 = -12$ in. Substitution in Eq.(43f) gives

$$\frac{1}{f} = \frac{1}{8} - \frac{1}{12} \qquad \frac{1}{f} = \frac{3}{24} - \frac{2}{24} \qquad \frac{1}{f} = \frac{1}{24},$$

from which $f = 24$ in.

43.9. Concave Mirrors. The concave mirror is an optical device which, like a glass lens, may by pure reflection form images on a screen. Such mirrors are often used in optical instruments in place of a lens. There are several very good reasons for this, one of them being that the concave mirror does not exhibit chromatic aberration, and another that there is but one curved surface to prepare and polish instead of two or more.

Schematic diagrams, showing how a beam of parallel light is reflected by a spherical mirror, are shown in Fig. 43L. Each ray striking the mirror obeys the law of reflection, namely, that the angle of incidence i equals the angle of reflection i'. The point F where the rays in the first diagram cross the principal axis is called the principal focus and the distance A to F is called the *focal length f.* In the second diagram the rays, after reflection, diverge as if they came from a common point F.

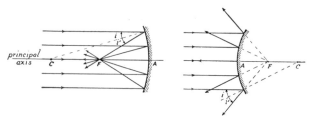

Fig. 43L—Concave and convex mirrors showing the focal points *F* and centers of curvature *C*.

The geometry of the reflection from a concave or convex mirror is such that the focal length *AF* is always equal to one-half the radius of curvature *r*, where $r = AC$, and *C* is the center of curvature. As an equation,

$$AF = \tfrac{1}{2}AC \qquad \text{or} \qquad f = -\frac{r}{2}. \qquad (43g)$$

Furthermore the lens formula, Eq.(43a) holds for mirrors as well as for lenses, *p*, *q*, and *f* having the same meaning as before.

$$\frac{1}{p} + \frac{1}{q} = \frac{1}{f}. \qquad (43h)$$

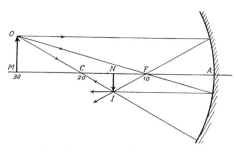

Fig. 43M—Showing graphical construction for locating the image formed by a concave mirror.

As an illustration of the image forming properties of a concave spherical mirror, consider the graphical construction in Fig. 43M. An object *O* is located 30 cm from a concave mirror of radius $r = -20$ cm, center at *C*. By Eq.(43g) *F* must be halfway between *A* and *C*, giving $f = +10$ cm.

A light ray from *O* parallel to the principal axis is reflected, by definition of the focal point, through *F*. By the reversibility of light rays, another ray from *O* passing through *F* is reflected parallel to the principal axis. Where these two rays cross at *I* the image is formed. A third ray from *O* through the center of curvature *C* strikes the mirror normally and is reflected back on itself where it passes through *I*. Any two of these three rays is sufficient to locate the image. The third ray is then a check upon the other two.

To solve this mirror arrangement as a problem, Eq.(43h) can be applied directly. Given are the quantities, $p = 30$ cm, $f = +10$ cm. By substitution

$$\frac{1}{30}+\frac{1}{q}=\frac{1}{10} \qquad \frac{1}{q}=\frac{1}{10}-\frac{1}{30} \qquad \frac{1}{q}=\frac{3}{30}-\frac{1}{30},$$

from which

$$\frac{1}{q}=\frac{2}{30} \qquad \text{and} \qquad q=\frac{30}{2}=15 \text{ cm.}$$

An interesting experiment can be performed with a large concave mirror under the conditions illustrated in Fig. 43N(a). A flower hanging upside down in a box and placed just below the center of curvature will form a real and erect image at O directly above. An observer to the left cannot see

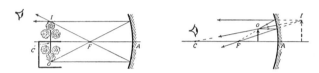

Fig. 43N—Showing rays by which images are located.

the flower directly but can see the real image. So real is this image that it cannot be distinguished from a real object; the rays of light as shown in the diagram diverge from I the same as they would if the object were located there.

In (b) an object is placed inside the focal point and the rays after reflection diverge as if they had come from the point I. To the eye of an observer at E a virtual image is seen magnified and right side up at I. As a problem let the object distance $p = 10$ cm, the focal length $f = +20$ cm. Substitution of these in Eq.(43h) gives

$$\frac{1}{10}+\frac{1}{q}=\frac{1}{20} \qquad \frac{1}{q}=\frac{1}{20}-\frac{1}{10} \qquad \frac{1}{q}=\frac{1}{20}-\frac{2}{20},$$

from which

$$\frac{1}{q}=-\frac{1}{20} \qquad \text{or} \qquad q=-20 \text{ cm.}$$

The image is located 20 cm from the mirror, the minus sign indicating that it is virtual and on the opposite side of the mirror from the object.

No matter where a real object is located in front of a convex mirror, the image is virtual and cannot be formed on a screen. When in using Eq.(43h) the focal length of a convex mirror is known, its value is substituted with a minus sign.

Although spherical mirrors do not produce chromatic aberration, they do exhibit other aberrations common to lenses. In Fig. 43O the focusing property of a large aperture mirror is compared with that of a parabolic mirror. Like a spherical lens, a spherical mirror deviates the outer rays to a shorter focus than those near the center. The parabola, on the other hand, brings all rays to focus at one point. A small source of light located at the focal point of a parabolic reflector becomes a parallel beam after reflection, a principle used in spotlights, searchlights, and automobile headlights.

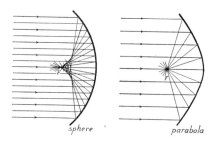

FIG. 43O—Diagrams showing the caustic curve obtained with a spherical mirror and the point focus with a paraboloidal mirror.

Spherical aberration for a spherical mirror is reduced by reducing the aperture or, what is the same thing, by keeping the focal length large compared with the reflector diameter.

PROBLEMS

1. An object 5 cm high is located 12 cm in front of a converging lens of focal length +8 cm. Find (a) the position, and (b) the size of the image by the lens formula and by the graphical method.

2. An object 3 in high is located 20 in in front of a converging lens of focal length +12 in. Find (a) the position, and (b) the size of the image by the lens formula and by the graphical method. (*Ans.* (a) 30 in, (b) −4.5 in.)

3. A converging lens has a focal length of +12 in. Find the position and size of the image if an object 3 in. high is located in front of the lens at a distance of (a) 60 in, (b) 30 in, (c) 18 in, (d) 12 in, (e) 8 in, (f) 4 in.

4. A converging lens has a focal length of +16 cm. Find the position and size of the image if an object 4 cm high is located in front of the lens at a distance of (a) 80 cm, (b) 32 cm, (c) 20 cm, (d) 16 cm, and (e) 8 cm. (*Ans.* (a) 20 cm, −1 cm, (b) 32 cm, −4 cm, (c) 80 cm, −16 cm, (d) ∞, ∞, (e) −16 cm, +8 cm.)

5. An object 2 ft high is located 10 ft in front of a diverging lens whose focal length is −6 ft. Find the position and size of the image.

6. An object 10 cm high is located 50 cm in front of a diverging lens of focal length −20 cm. Find the size and position of the image. (*Ans.* +2.86 cm, −14.28 cm.)

7. Solve problem 4 if the lens is diverging.

8. Solve problem 3 if the lens is diverging. (*Ans.* (a) −10, +0.5, (b) −8.57, +0.857, (c) −7.2, + 1.2, (d) −6.0, +1.5, (e) −4.8, +1.6, (f) −3.0, +2.25 in.)

9. An object 3 cm high is located 15 cm in front of a concave mirror $r = -12$ cm. Find graphically and by formula the (a) position, and (b) size of the image.

10. An object 6 in high is located on the axis and 12 in from a concave mirror of radius $r = -20$ in. Find graphically and by formula (a) the position, and (b) the size of the image. (*Ans.* (a) 60 in, (b) −30 in.)

11. Solve problem 10 if the mirror is convex with $r = +20$ in.

12. Solve problem 9 if the mirror is convex with $r = +12$ cm. (*Ans.* (a) -4.29 cm, (b) $+0.857$ cm.)

13. A double convex lens of index 1.50 has the following radii: $r_1 = +20$ cm, and $r_2 = -12$ cm. Find its focal length.

14. A double convex lens of index 1.60 has the following radii: $r_1 = +5$ cm, and $r_2 = -20$ cm. Calculate its focal length. (*Ans.* $+6.67$ cm.)

15. A concave miniscus lens with radii $r_1 = -24$ cm and $r_2 = -6$ cm. Find its focal length if the refractive index is 1.58.

16. A concave miniscus lens with radii $r_1 = -30$ in and $r_2 = -5$ in, has an index 1.62. Find its focal length. (*Ans.* $+9.68$ in.)

17. Where should an object be placed in front of a lens of $+20$ cm focal length if the image to be formed is twice the size of the object and (a) real, and (b) virtual?

18. Where should an object be placed in front of a lens of focal length $+12$ in if the image to be formed is three times the size of the object and is real and inverted? (*Ans.* 16 in.)

19. The radii of the two surfaces of a double convex lens are measured as 10 cm and 30 cm respectively. If its focal length is measured to be $+28$ cm, what is the refractive index of the glass?

20. The radii of a concave miniscus lens are measured as -20 cm and -5 cm. If its focal length is measured to be $+9.0$ cm, what is the refractive index of the glass? (*Ans.* 1.741.)

21. A plano-concave flint glass lens with an index 1.65, and an equi-convex crown glass lens with an index 1.53 are placed in contact to make an achromatic lens. If all curved surfaces have radii of 50 cm, find the equivalent focal length.

22. An equi-convex crown glass lens with an index 1.63 and a plano-concave flint glass lens with an index 1.52 are placed in contact to make an achromatic telescope objective lens. If all curved surfaces have radii of 40 cm, find the equivalent focal length. (*Ans.* 54.0 cm.)

23. A growing flower is planted 9 ft from a wall. Where should a lens be placed to form a real image on the wall if its focal length is $+2$ ft?

24. A lens with a focal length of $+30$ cm is used to form a real image on a screen 150 cm from an object. How far from the object should the lens be placed? (*Ans.* 41.5 cm or 108.5 cm.)

25. An object 5 cm high is located 60 cm in front of a converging lens of focal length $+15$ cm. A diverging lens of focal length -60 cm is located 5 cm beyond the first lens. (a) Where is the final image located, and (b) what is its size and nature?

26. An object 2 cm high is located on the axis 40 cm in front of a lens of focal length $+20$ cm. A second lens of focal length $+30$ cm is located 10 cm beyond the first lens. (a) Where is the final image located, and (b) what is its size and nature? (*Ans.* Real, inverted, 1 cm high and at 15 cm from second lens.)

27. Sunlight falls on a divergent lens with a focal length of 20 cm. If a converging lens with a focal length of 20 cm is located 5 cm beyond this lens, where should a screen be placed to receive the sun's image?

28. Three lenses with focal lengths of $+20$ cm, -20 cm, and $+20$ cm, respectively, are spaced in line with their centers 2 cm apart. If the sunlight enters the first lens along its axis, where will the final image of the sun be located? (*Ans.* 18 cm from the third lens.)

Optical Instruments   Chapter 44

44.1. The Camera. Since the photographic camera employs but a single lens unit it may be considered as one of the simplest of all optical instruments. As illustrated by the roll-film camera in Fig. 44A, a converging lens forms a *real* and *inverted image* on the film. If the object is far away the light rays approaching the lens are nearly parallel and the image is formed at the focal plane. If the object is close up the image will be formed beyond

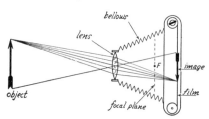

FIG. 44A—Diagram of the image formation by a camera.

the focal plane as shown in the diagram. To permit distant landscapes or "close ups" to be taken with the same camera, a bellows is used, allowing the lens distance to be varied at will. Motion of the lens to the proper image distance is called *focusing*.

Only a simple converging lens is used in the cheapest of cameras, which means that all of the common defects of images are present to give rise to a slightly blurred or diffuse image. In more expensive cameras, however, the most objectionable defects are fairly well corrected by a compound lens made of several individual lenses. As a rule, a good camera lens will contain from three to five lens elements and will partially correct for *chromatic aberration, spherical aberration, astigmatism,* and *curvature of field.*

The purpose of an iris diaphragm is to decrease the effective aperture of a lens and hence increase its *f*-number. Such practice is desirable in photographing still objects because the smaller the lens opening, the sharper will be the focus of near and far as well as central and peripheral objects. *The f-number of a lens is equal to its focal length divided by its diameter.*

44.2. The Eye. Some aspects of this most remarkable optical instrument, the human eye, have been presented in Chap. I. There it was pointed out that a single eye is in principle an exceptionally fine camera with an elaborate lens system on one side and a sensitive screen or photographic film called the *retina* on the other.

When light from a distant object passes through the lens system of the eye it is refracted and brought to a focus on the retina. There a real but inverted image of the object is formed. It is a most amazing fact that, while

426

all retinal images are inverted, as shown in Fig. 44B, they are interpreted as being erect.

Accommodation is the ability to focus the eyes on near and far objects. In a camera the focusing of a picture on the photographic film or plate is accomplished by moving the lens toward or away from the film. In the human eye, however, *focusing is brought about by changing the shape of the crystalline lens.* This is accomplished by a rather complicated system of ligaments and muscles. Due to a tension which exists in the lens capsule (see Fig. 1B), the crystalline lens, if completely free, would tend to become spherical in shape.

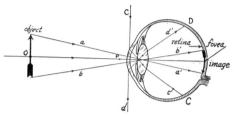

FIG. 44B—The human eye is similar to a camera. All retinal images are inverted.

The edge of the lens is surrounded by the *ciliary muscle* which, by contracting, causes the lens to bulge out. This reduces the focal length of the lens, bringing nearby objects to focus on the retina. When the ciliary muscle relaxes, the suspensory ligaments, being under tension, pull at the edges of the lens, thus tending to flatten it. Under these conditions the focal length increases, bringing distant objects to focus on the retina. This is the accommodation process.

The normal eye is most relaxed when it is focused for parallel light, i.e., for objects far away. To study the detail of an object, however, the object should be brought close to the eye. The reason for this is that the closer the object is to the eye the larger is the image formed on the retina. A distance of about 10 in. is found to be the distance of most distinct vision. Prolonged observation at distances of 10 in. or less will result in a considerable amount of fatigue and eyestrain.

44.3. Eye Correction with Spectacle Lenses. As the average person grows older the crystalline lens of the eye tends to harden and the muscles that control it to grow weaker, thus making accommodation more and more

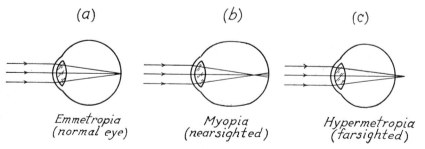

FIG. 44C—Common eye conditions accompanying old age. Presbyopia.

difficult. The existence of these conditions is referred to as *presbyopia*. The speed of the hardening varies between individuals. If the length of the eyeball is such that parallel incident rays converge to a point in front of the retina (see Fig. 44C(b)), the person is nearsighted and is said by the eye specialist to have *myopia*. If parallel incident rays converge to a point back of the retina, as in diagram (c), the person is farsighted and is said to have *hypermetropia*.

To correct these defects a diverging spectacle lens of the proper focal length is placed in front of the myopic eye and a converging lens of the proper focal length in front of the hypermetropic eye. The function of such lenses is shown in Fig. 44D. For the nearsighted eye, rays from a nearby

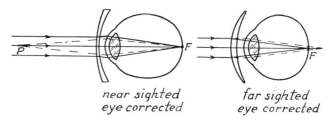

near sighted
eye corrected

far sighted
eye corrected

Fig. 44D—Nearsighted and farsighted eyes can be corrected by the proper selection of spectacle lenses.

object at some point *P* will, in the absence of spectacles, come to focus on the fovea *F*. Insertion of the proper diverging lens will now diverge parallel rays as if they came from *P* and thus bring a distant object to focus at *F*. For the farsighted eye a converging lens adds some convergence to the incoming rays before they meet the eye lens and thus enable distant objects to be seen in good focus. To see close at hand this same eye requires the use of a converging lens of still greater power. In other words this person should wear bi-focals, lenses whose upper and lower halves have different focal lengths.

It is customary in optometry and opthalmology to express the focal length of any lens in *diopters* and to speak of the power of a lens in such terms. *The power of a lens in diopters is given by the reciprocal of the focal length in meters.*

$$\frac{1 \text{ meter}}{\text{focal length in meters}} = \text{diopters} \qquad \frac{1}{f} = P. \qquad (44a)$$

A lens with a focal length of $+50$ cm, for example, has a power of $+2$ diopters (D), $P = +2D$, whereas one of $+20$ cm focal length has a power of $+5D$, $P = +5D$, etc. Converging lenses have a plus power while diverging lenses have a minus power. Spectacle lenses are made to the nearest quarter of a diopter, thereby reducing the number of grinding and polishing tools required in the optical shops. Furthermore, the sides next to the eyes are always concave to permit free movement of the eyelashes and yet keep the lens as close to the eye as possible as they turn one way and then another.

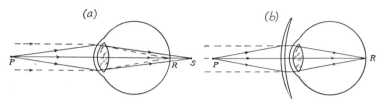

FIG. 44E—The normal eye, having lost accommodation because of age, sees distant objects in good focus. To see nearby objects in focus requires spectacle lenses.

When, with age, practically all accommodation has been lost, even the normal eye, functioning as shown in (a) of Fig. 44C, will require a lens of about $+3D$ to obtain good vision of objects at a normal reading distance. As illustrated by the dotted lines in Fig. 44E(a) parallel rays entering the unaided eye are brought to a good focus on the retina R. For an object close by, however, the power of the eye lens is not great enough and the rays converge toward a point S beyond the retina. With an object P located $33\frac{1}{3}$ cm away and a $+3$ D lens in front of the eye, diagram (b), parallel rays enter the eye from the lens and these are brought to a good focus on the retina R.

The principal advantage of the diopter system of measuring lens action is that, when two or more thin lenses are placed in contact, their combined power is just the sum of their separate powers. From Eq.(43f), and the use of Eq.(44a) for power

$$\frac{1}{f} = \frac{1}{f_1} + \frac{1}{f_2} \qquad \text{or} \qquad P = P_1 + P_2. \qquad \text{(44b)}$$

The power P of a combination of two thin lenses is equal to the sum of the powers of the two separately. As an illustration, two lenses of $+2\frac{1}{4}$ D and $+3\frac{1}{2}$ D respectively give, in combination, a power of $+5\frac{3}{4}$ D, and two lenses of $+3\frac{1}{2}$ D and $-2\frac{1}{4}$ D respectively give a power of $+1\frac{1}{4}$ D.

Example. A person with hypermetropia (see Fig. 44C) requires a $+1\frac{1}{4}$ D spectacle lens to see objects clearly at a great distance (see Fig. 44E(b)). What power spectacles will this person require to see objects at 20 in. (or 50 cm)?

Solution. Since lens powers are additive a lens can be added to the one already present, and of such a power that it will take the rays from any point on an object 50 cm away and make them parallel. A lens of focal length 50 cm will do just this, and by Eq.(44a) corresponds to a power of $+2$ D. Combining a $+2$ D lens with the $+1\frac{1}{4}$ D already required gives an equivalent power of $3\frac{1}{4}$ D. Therefore spectacle lenses with a power of $+3\frac{1}{4}$ D should be worn.

It frequently happens that the cornea acquires a greater curvature in one plane than in another. Such irregularities are called *astigmatism*. Whether accommodation by the crystalline lens has been lost or not, such eyes require astigmatic spectacle lenses, that is, lenses that have more curvature in one direction than at right angles. The surfaces of such lenses are not spherical and are a little more difficult to grind and polish.

44.4. The Telescope. History informs us that the first telescope was probably constructed in Holland in 1608 by an obscure spectacle lens grinder, Hans Lippershey. A few months later Galileo, upon hearing that objects at a distance may be made to appear close at hand by means of two lenses, designed and made with his own hands the first authentic telescope. The elements of this telescope are still in existence and may be seen on exhibit in Florence, Italy.

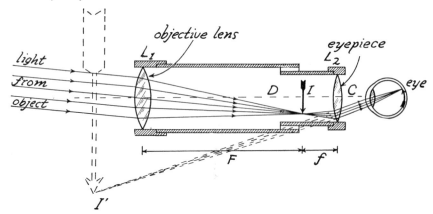

FIG. 44F—Illustrating the paths of light rays in a simple astronomical telescope.

Astronomical telescopes today are practically the same in principle as they were in the earliest days of their development. A diagram of a small telescope is shown in Fig. 44F. Light rays from a single point of a far distant object are shown entering the objective lens as a parallel beam. These rays are brought to a focus and form a point image at *I*. In a similar manner, parallel sets of rays from other points of the same object (not shown) will form point images in the focal plane of the objective. Assuming that the distant object is an arrow pointing upward, the image, as shown in the diagram by a black arrow, is *real* and *inverted*.

The function of the second lens in a telescope is to magnify the image formed by the objective. For this purpose a converging lens of short focus, called the *eyepiece*, is usually used. If the eyepiece is moved to a position where the image *I* is just inside its focal plane, a magnified image *I'* will be seen by the eye. For normal observation, the image *I* and the focal planes of both lenses are in conjunction, and the light emerging from the eyepiece is parallel. The image I' under these conditions appears to be far off to the left of L_1, "at infinity," and is of approximately the same angular size as shown in the diagram. Actually, of course, the final image is the one formed on the retina by rays which appear to have come from I'.

The magnifying power of a telescope is defined as the ratio between the angle subtended at the eye by the final image I' and the angle subtended at the eye by the object itself. In other words, it is the number of times larger an object appears to be when viewed with the telescope. When plane geometry is applied to a simple light-ray diagram of a telescope it is found that the magnifying power is equal to the ratio of the focal lengths of the two lenses.

$$\text{Magnifying power} = -\frac{F}{f}, \qquad (44c)$$

where F is the focal length of the objective, and f is the focal length of the eyepiece.

As an illustration, suppose the objective lens of a small telescope has a focal length of one yard and that it is used with an eyepiece having a focal length of 1 in.; the magnifying power would be 36/1 or 36. Distant objects viewed through this telescope would appear to be 36 times as tall and 36 times as wide as when viewed with the unaided eye. If an eyepiece with a focal length of only half an inch is used with the same objective the magnification will be twice as great, or 72.

This would seem to indicate that the magnification of a telescope can be increased indefinitely, but this is not the case. There are a number of factors which set a practical upper limit, the chief one of which for small telescopes is the diameter of the objective lens.

If a telescope is to be used for astronomical purposes only, an inverted image is of no consequence to the observer, but if it is to be used to observe objects on the earth the magnified images should be right side up. Instruments which give erect images are called *terrestrial telescopes*. To right the inverted image in a telescope, any one of several methods may be employed; one is to use a third lens, and another is to insert an erecting

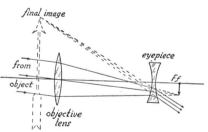

Fig. 44G—Lens and ray diagram of an opera glass, or Galilean telescope.

prism of the type shown in Fig. 41I(c) just in front of the eyepiece in place of the converging lens. A third method is the arrangement devised by Galileo in his first telescopes, and now commonly used in *field* and *opera glasses* (see Fig. 44G).

44.5. Prism Binoculars. Prism binoculars are in reality a pair of twin telescopes mounted side by side, one for each of the two eyes. The objective lenses in front and the eyepieces at the rear are converging lenses as in the astronomical telescope but each pair of total reflecting prisms (see Fig. 44H), inverts the rays to give erect images. The doubling back of the light rays has the advantage of enabling long focus objective lenses to be used in short tubes, thus giving higher magnification. In addition to good achromatic lenses and accurately ground prisms, there are three features that go to make up good binoculars: these are (1) *magnification,* (2) *field of view,* and (3) *light gathering power.*

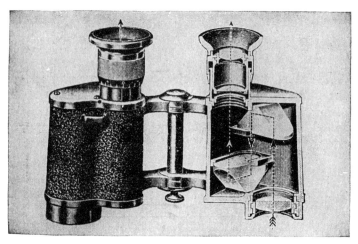

Fig. 44H—Diagram of prism binoculars showing the lenses and total reflecting prisms. *(Courtesy of the Central Scientific Co.)*

For hand-held use, binoculars with a 6, 7, or 8 power magnification are most generally useful. Glasses with powers above 8 are desirable but require a tripod mount to hold them steady. For powers less than 4, lens aberrations usually offset the magnification and the average person can usually see better with the unaided eyes.

The field of view is determined principally by the eyepiece aperture and should be as large as is practical. For 7 power binoculars a 6° field taken in by the objective is considered large since in the eyepiece the same field is spread over an angle of 7 x 6 or 42°.

The diameter of each objective lens determines the light gathering power, and is important at night only when there is so little light available.

Binoculars with the specification 6 x 30 have a magnification of 6 and objective lenses with an effective diameter of 30 mm. The specification 7 x 50 means a magnification of 7 and objective lenses 50 mm in diameter. Although glasses with the latter specifications are excellent day or night, they are considerably larger and more cumbersome than daytime glasses specified as 6 x 30's or 8 x 30's. For general civilian use these latter two types are by far the most useful.

44.6. The Reflection Telescope. Nearly all of the very large astronomical telescopes in the world today employ concave mirrors instead of lenses. There are several advantages to this: first, a concave mirror does not exhibit chromatic aberration, thereby requiring but one piece of glass and one surface to be ground; and second, greater stability of the telescope is attained by having the large and heaviest optical part at the bottom of the instrument.

A diagram of the great 100-in. reflecting telescope of the Mt. Wilson Observatory is shown in Fig. 44I. Parallel light rays entering the telescope tube are brought to a focus at F. Instead of viewing or photographing images at this point a small mirror m reflects the convergent rays to a focus at F'. Here, out of the path of the incoming light the star images can be observed

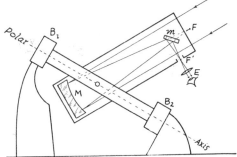

FIG. 44I—Diagram of the 100 in. reflecting telescope of the Mt. Wilson Observatory.

and photographed. While the small mirror m casts a shadow on the objective mirror M the shadow area is relatively small so that only a small per cent of the light is lost.

The new 200-in telescope now in operation on Palomar Mountain in Southern California (see Fig. 44J) is of the same optical design. The objective mirror is a little over 16 ft in diameter and has a hole 40 in in diameter through its center. This hole cuts out only 4% of the mirror's total area. For various kinds of observations photographic instruments and cameras of one kind or another are located in an observing booth 40 in in diameter and located at the focal plane, F, in Fig. 44I. On other occasions a 40-in convex mirror is placed at m and the light reflected back down the telescope tube through the hole in the big objective where it is brought to a focus below the telescope.

44.7. The Microscope. The simplest of microscopes is just a single converging lens of short focus used as a magnifier as shown in Fig. 43F(a). Since the shortest focal length lenses produce the greatest magnification, it is

THE TWO HVNDRED INCH
TELESCOPE · LOOKING NORT

R·W·Por
193

FIG. 44J—Drawing of the 200-in. telescope on Mt. Palomar in Southern California. (*Drawing by Porter*

not surprising that small glass beads in the form of perfect spheres were the first really successful microscopes. Lenses of this description were used by the famous Dutch microscopist, Van Leeuwenhoek, when in 1674 he discovered and gave an accurate account of the red corpuscles in blood.

The compound microscope, which now exceeds by far the magnifying power of a simple microscope, was invented by Galileo in 1610. Like a tele-

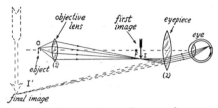

FIG. 44K—Lens and ray diagram of a compound microscope.

scope, these instruments consist of an optical train of two lenses, one called the objective and the other the eyepiece. The objective of the microscope differs from the telescope, however, in that, instead of having a long focus, it has a short focus and it is placed close to the object as shown in Fig. 44K. This lens forms a real and magnified image at a point I just in front of the eyepiece. Being another short focus lens the eyepiece is used as a simple microscope or magnifying glass to produce a magnified virtual image at I'.

Early forms of the compound microscope displayed so much chromatic aberration that only low magnifying powers were attained. High-powered microscopes of today overcome this and other defects by using an objective containing as many as eight or ten lenses and an eyepiece containing two or more. Under suitable illumination, magnifying powers of a little more than 2000 diameters are commonly attained. Although this is not an upper limit to the magnification for optical microscopes of the future, we know from the wave nature of light that the ultimate limit is not many times that which has already been attained. This is not a pessimistic attitude but a scientific truth based upon our present knowledge of the atomic structure of matter itself.

The electron microscope, capable of magnifications 50 to 100 times that of the best optical microscope, is described in Sec. 65.9.

44.8. The Kellner-Schmidt Optical System. The Kellner*-Schmidt optical system combines a concave spherical mirror with an aspheric lens as shown in Fig. 44L. The purpose of the lens is to refract incoming parallel rays in such a direction that after reflection from the spherical mirror they all come to focus at the same axial point F. Since the lens is located at the mirror's center of curvature, parallel rays entering the system at large angles with the principal axis are brought to a relatively good focus at F'. The focal surface of such a system is a spherical surface with its center at C.

Such an optical system has several remarkable and useful properties.

---

* American Patent No. 969785; published 1910.

First as a camera, with a small film at the center or a large film curved to fit the focal surface, it has a very high speed and covers a wide angle of 45° or more. In photographer's terminology, the system has an *f-number* of 0.5. Be-

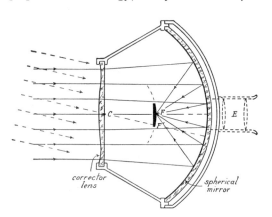

Fig. 44L—Kellner-Schmidt optical system (speed f/0.5).

cause of their large light gathering power Kellner-Schmidt systems are used by astronomers to obtain photographs of faint stars. They are used for similar reasons in television receivers to project the images from an oscilloscope tube onto a relatively large screen. In this case the convex oscilloscope screen is placed in the focal plane *FF'* so that light from the bright image screen is reflected by the mirror, through the corrector lens to the observing screen.

If a convex silvered mirror is located at *FF'*, rays from any distant source will on entering the system form a point image on *FF'* and after reflection emerge again as a parallel bundle in the exact direction of the source. Used in this fashion the device is referred to as an *auto-collimator*, and is similar in its action to a *triple prism* as shown in Fig. 41K (c). If this small convex mirror is coated with fluorescent paint ultraviolet light from a distant invisible ultraviolet light source will form a bright spot at some point on *FF'* and visible light emitted from this spot will emerge only in the direction of the source. Should an opening be made in the center of the large concave mirror, and an eyepiece be inserted to view the fluorescent screen in the focal plane, ultraviolet light sources can be seen as visible sources. As such, the device becomes a wide angled ultraviolet telescope.

44.9. Endoscopes. Endoscopes are long narrow telescopes used by physicians and surgeons, and are designed to be inserted through a body opening into a cavity for the purpose of visually examining the cavity walls. A majority of such instruments are manufactured for specific purposes and listed under the titles, *bronchoscopes, cystoscopes, gastroscopes* and *laryngoscopes*. All of these make use of the same principles and differ from each other chiefly in their length and diameter, and in their arrangement and number of mirrors, prisms, lenses, and miniature light bulbs.

The far end section of many endoscopes is usually removable and has interchangeable optical and surgical attachments that can be manipulated from the outside. Often times a sheath is first introduced into the body opening and then the telescope inserted. A cross-section diagram is shown in Fig. 44M as a typical example of a cystoscope.

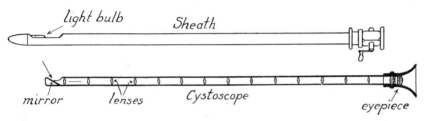

Fig. 44M—Diagram of a cystoscope and sheath showing the principal optical parts.

Since the outside diameter of a cystoscope must be kept small the telescope tube (usually about 6 mm in diameter) contains a long train of some thirty small, accurately spaced, lenses. The image formed by the objective end is passed on from one set of lenses to the next without magnification until it reaches the eyepiece. There a two- or three-fold magnified image may be seen. In some cases the eyepiece is replaced by a special camera thereby permitting photographs of the cavity walls to be made.

PROBLEMS

1. The lens of a camera has an aperture of 4.0 cm and a focal length of $+11.2$ cm. What is its *f-number?*

2. A portrait camera lens has an aperture of 2.2 in and an *f*-number of 4.5. What is its focal length? (*Ans.* $+9.9$ in.)

3. A camera lens has a focal length of $+8$ in. Calculate image distances for the following object distances: (a) infinity, (b) 20 ft, (c) 10 ft, (d) 5 ft, (e) 3 ft, (f) 2 ft. Make a scale 4 in long showing $\frac{1}{4}$ and $\frac{1}{2}$ in divisions and put marks on it at the calculated image distances but labeled with the corresponding object distances.

4. A telephoto lens has a 20 cm focal length. Calculate image distances for the following object distances: (a) infinity, (b) 10 m, (c) 5 m, (d) 3 m, (e) 2 m, (f) 1 m. Make a millimeter scale 5 cm long, mark it with lines at the proper image distances, and label them with the corresponding object distances. (*Ans.* 20.0, 20.41, 20.83, 21.43, 22.22, 25.00 cm.)

5. A nearsighted person sees objects clearly at a distance of 20 cm. Having lost his accommodation, what power spectacle lenses will enable him to see distant objects clearly?

6. A middle-aged man with *presbyopia* sees distant objects clearly. Calculate to the nearest quarter diopter the power of the spectacle lenses that will enable him to see objects (a) 6 ft away, and (b) to read a book at 16 in. (*Ans.* (a) +0.5 D, (b) +2.5 D.)

7. A woman with *hypermetropia* requires +1.25 D spectacle lenses to see clearly at a distance. What power spectacle lenses will she require to read a book at 18 in.?

8. The objective lens of an astronomical telescope has a focal length of +8 ft while the eyepiece has a focal length of +2 in. What is its magnifying power? (*Ans.* 48.)

9. The eyepiece of a 12 power astronomical telescope has a focal length of +0.75 in. What is the focal length of the objective?

10. An astronomical telescope objective has a focal length of +60 cm. What focal length eyepiece will give it a magnification of −15? (*Ans.* +4 cm.)

11. To an observer on the earth the moon subtends an angle of approximately 0.5 degrees. If a telescope objective lens with a focal length of +20 ft is used to photograph the moon, what will be the diameter of the image formed at the focal plane of the lens?

12. A pair of binoculars have the designation 6 × 32. If the eyepieces have a focal length of 1 in., (a) what are the diameters, and (b) the focal lengths of the objectives? (*Ans.* (a) 32 mm, (b) 15.24 cm.)

13. A pair of Navy-type binoculars have the designation 11 × 60. If the eyepieces have a focal length of 2.5 cm, (a) what are the diameters, and (b) the focal lengths of the objective lenses?

14. The objective lenses of a pair of 7 × 50 binoculars have a focal length of 21 cm. The eyepieces have an effective diameter of 2.5 cm. Find (a) the focal length of the eyepieces, and (b) the effective field seen by the instrument in any one position. (*Ans.* (a) 3.0 cm, (b) 6.8°.)

15. A person with *presbyopia* finds he must hold the telephone book at a distance of 60 cm from his eyes in order to see the print clearly. What power lenses should he have in order to see clearly when the book is 25 cm from his eyes?

16. The objective and eyepiece of a telescope have focal lengths of 48 cm and 2 cm, respectively. The objective lens has a diameter of 5.0 cm. Calculate (a) the magnifying power, and (b) the size and position of the image of the objective lens formed by the eyepiece. (*Ans.* (a) −24, (b) 0.208 cm in diameter, 2.08 cm beyond the eyepiece.)

17. A Kellner-Schmidt optical system is used as an astronomical telescope. The mirror has a 2 m radius of curvature, the corrector lens a diameter of 50 cm, and the circular focal surface a diameter of 20 cm. Find (a) the *f*-number of the system, and (b) the angular field it can photograph in one picture.

18. A small lens with a focal length of 2 cm is to be used as the eyepiece of an inexpensive reflecting telescope. To what radius of curvature should the objective mirror be ground if the instrument is to have a magnifying power of −45? (*Ans.* 180 cm concave.)

The Science of Color   Chapter 45

COLOR vision is perhaps the most valued gift of nature. While color is for the most part a physiological phenomenon, its origin is considered by some to belong to the realm of physics. There is on the one hand the theory of *color mixing* and on the other the theory of *color vision*. The first of these theories deals with the action of matter on light before it reaches the eye, and the second with the visual functions of the eye. The science of color mixing has been made possible through the discovery that all colors can be completely analyzed by spreading them out into a prismatic spectrum. The science of color vision, on the other hand, involving the optics of the eye as well as the physiological functions of the entire vision mechanism, is not completely understood. Both of these subjects will be treated in this chapter on the science of color.

45.1. Effect of Illumination on Color. To see a body in its true color, that body must be illuminated by light of the same color. If a red rose, as an illustration, is placed in the different colors of a prismatic spectrum it will appear a brilliant red in red light and grey or black in all the others.

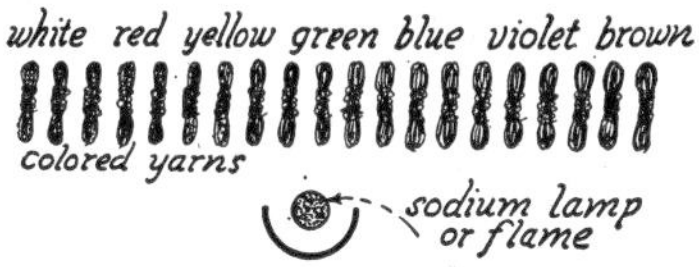

FIG. 45A—Experiment with colored skeins of yarn showing that to see an object in its true surface color it must be illuminated by the proper light.

Another experiment is illustrated in Fig. 45A where yellow light from a sodium arc lamp is shown illuminating a row of colored skeins of yarn. When the lamp is turned on only the yellow yarn appears with its true color; the white yarn is yellow and the others are black or grey. If the same set of colored yarns is illuminated with red light only the red yarn will appear in its true color; the white yarn will now be red and the others will be grey or black. In other words, unless the source emits the proper colors the body cannot be seen in its true color. Sunlight will show each yarn in its true color, for sunlight contains all colors of the spectrum.

45.2. Surface Color. The above experiments demonstrate what is called *surface color*. When sunlight falls on a red rose, red yarn, red paint, or red glass, all of the colors except red are absorbed and do not get through or out again. The red, as it passes through, is reflected and refracted by the fine grains of pigment and comes out in all directions as shown in Fig. 45B(a).

Not all of the other colors are completely absorbed, for a small amount

439

of each color is reflected from the first surface the white light strikes. This may be illustrated by a polished sheet of red glass as shown in diagram (b). Although the glass appears red from both sides a small amount of white light is reflected from the top surface, obeying the law of reflection. Some of the red, on the other hand, is reflected and refracted in the usual way at each surface as shown.

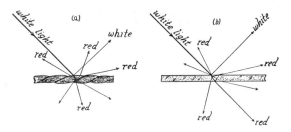

Fig. 45B—Illustrating surface color. Red yarn and red glass appear red on all sides. The other colors, orange, yellow, green, blue, and violet, present in white light are absorbed within the body.

The three aspects of surface color are *hue,* lightness or *brightness,* and *saturation.* Hue refers to the *name* of a color, brightness to the relative *magnitude* of the sensory response, and saturation to the color *strength.* Hue is qualitative and is the most distinctive aspect of color, for without hue there is no color. Hue cannot be defined but only exemplified: red, yellow, green, blue, violet, purple, and various intermediaries between these are hues. *Brightness* is a subjective intensity and may exist alone, as in white light. White is devoid of hue and hence is devoid of color. Hue cannot exist alone for if we have hue it has a certain brightness and saturation. Illustrations of these three concepts are shown below in Fig. 45H.

Colors which do not contain any trace of white light are said to be *saturated.* The more white they contain the less saturated they become. Pink is not a saturated color since it is a mixture of red and white. This may be demonstrated by mixing a small amount of red pigment with white paint, or, what is still more striking, by pulverizing a piece of red glass. As the glass is ground finer and finer the amount of white light reflected is increased by the increasing surface area, until the powder becomes almost white. Although the red light is still present, the white light by comparison is much stronger. A similar effect is produced by transparent substances like crystals and window glass; when powdered they become white. *The smaller the amount of white light mixed in with a color, the greater is the saturation.*

45.3. Metallic Color. Some substances appear to be one color by reflected light and a different color by transmitted light. This is particularly true of metals and of certain aniline dyes. Gold, for example, is always yellow-orange by reflected light but, if thin enough, is blue-green by transmitted light. This is illustrated in Fig. 45C.

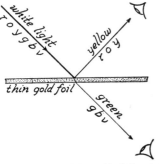

FIG. 45C—A thin gold foil appears yellow-orange by reflected light and blue-green by transmitted light.

White light, composed of the spectrum colors red, orange, yellow, green, blue, and violet, is incident on the thin film of gold. Although all of these colors are partially reflected and partially transmitted, the predominant colors in the transmitted light are green, blue, and violet, while those in the reflected light are red, orange, and yellow. To the eye the mixture of reflected colors appears yellow, and the mixture of transmitted colors appears green.

Graphs of the reflecting power of copper, silver, and gold are reproduced in Fig. 45D. Copper, it will be noted, reflects about 80% of all red light incident upon it and only 40% of the violet. Curiously enough, all metals are good absorbers of colors they best reflect; so that white light incident on a thin copper foil is partly robbed of red, orange, and yellow by having some of each of these colors reflected and some absorbed. Since smaller amounts of the green, blue, and violet are reflected and absorbed, these colors will predominate in the transmitted light, giving it, like gold, a blue-green or cyan appearance. If the metal is too thick it becomes opaque to all colors. In a rough way the curves in Fig. 45D represent the absorption of light by metals as well as the reflecting power. Silver, like so many other metals, is a good reflector of all colors and therefore is nearly white.

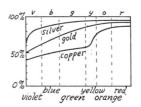

FIG. 45D—Graphs showing the reflecting power of metals for different colors o the spectrum.

45.4. Mixing Spectrum Colors. Over a period of many years different color charts and color theories have been proposed, some of them good and some of them bad. Because the most successful theories have, of necessity, been detailed and complicated, some simplification of their concepts and an explanation of their common principles will be given here.

As a starting point consider the experiment shown in Fig. 45E in which a narrow beam of white light from a carbon arc and lens falls on a glass prism and is spread out into a complete spectrum. With the prism located near the center of curvature of a large concave mirror all colors after reflection are brought to a focus on a translucent glass rod where, combined again, they produce white. A large white card is next held in front of the mirror to act as a screen to control the colors that are permitted to mix at the rod. By screening off violet, blue and green, for example, the remaining colors, red, orange and yellow, come together and the rod appears orange.

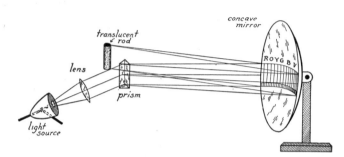

Fig. 45E—Experimental arrangements for mixing pure spectrum colors to form all primary colors. (*After Wallace Brode.*)

We now proceed to divide the spectrum up into three equal parts as shown at the lower left in Fig. 45F and to call these parts the *additive primaries*. When red and orange are allowed to mix, the rod appears a bright red; when yellow and green are mixed the rod appears bright green, and when blue and violet are mixed it appears blue-violet. As colors these additive primaries, red, green and blue, appear like the three large circular areas at the upper left in Fig. 45F.

The next step is to mix two *primary colors* two at a time and to observe their resultant color mixture. When primary red and primary green mix at the glass rod they produce yellow, red and blue produce magenta, and green and blue produce cyan, a light blue-green. These, the so-called *subtractive primaries* are shown by the three large circles at the upper right in Fig. 45F, and the overlapping areas at the upper left. The pure spectrum colors that go to make up each subtractive primary are shown at the lower right.

45.5. The Color Triangle. The color triangle, as illustrated in Fig. 45G, is a triangular arrangement of the additive and subtractive primaries with white at the center. Red, green, and blue are located at the corners while magenta, yellow, and cyan are located at the sides. The order of the colors is such that the sum of any two additive primaries at the corners gives the subtractive primary between them on the sides, and the sum of all three gives white at the center.

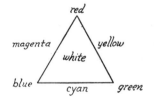

Colors opposite each other on the color triangle are *complementary. Two colors are said to be*

Fig. 45G—Diagram of the color triangle, with the additive primaries at the corners and the subtractive primaries at the sides.

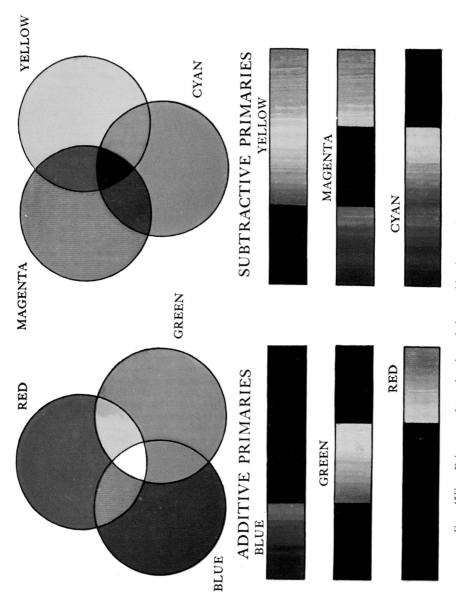

YELLOW

CYAN

MAGENTA

RED

GREEN

BLUE

SUBTRACTIVE PRIMARIES

YELLOW

MAGENTA

CYAN

ADDITIVE PRIMARIES

BLUE

GREEN

RED

Fig. 45F — Primary colors showing their combinations and component spectral colors.

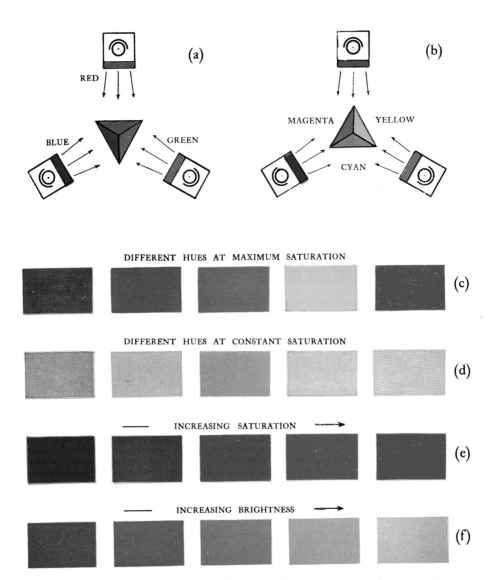

FIG. 45H—(a) Additive primaries. (b) equal mixing of primary pairs, (c) Different hues at their maximum saturation values, (d) Different hues at constant saturation and equal brightness, (e) The same hue at constant brightness but increasing saturation, (f) The same hue at constant saturation but increasing brightness.

complementary if when added together they produce white. Magenta and green are complementary, for when added together, as can be seen from their spectral distributions in Fig. 45F, they contain all of the spectrum colors of white light. Similarly red and cyan, as well as yellow and blue, are complementary.

45.6. Additive Method of Color Mixing. The mixing of colored lights described in the two proceding sections is called the additive method of color mixing and differs greatly from the subtractive method to be described in the following section. An interesting experiment for demonstrating the additive method is shown in Fig. 45H. Three boxes containing white lights are arranged to illuminate separately the three sides of a white pyramid. A matched set of glass filters, one for each of the additive primary hues, red, green, and blue, respectively, are placed in front of each box opening, thereby illuminating the pyramid faces as shown in the left-hand diagram.

Upon rotating the pyramid slowly a point is reached, as shown in the right-hand diagram, where pairs of lights mix in equal amounts on each of the three faces. These mixtures are the subtractive primaries, magenta, yellow, and cyan. As the pyramid turns from position (a) to position (b), all variations of two colors are seen on the pyramid faces. Television in full color is produced by the additive method of color mixing and is described in Chap. 66.

45.7. Subtractive Method of Color Mixing. This is the method most familiar to everyone, the method used in the mixing of pigments to produce various colored paints. For this purpose the subtractive primaries, *magenta, yellow,* and *cyan,* often referred to by artists as *red, yellow* and *blue,* are the most useful. The mixing in equal amounts of any two subtractive primaries will produce the additive primary lying between them on the color triangle. When cyan and yellow paints are mixed the result is green.

At first it seems strange that yellow and cyan, neither one of which has the appearance of an additive primary, should produce green when mixed together. A spectrum analysis of these two colors, as shown at the lower right in Fig. 45F, shows that green and yellow are spectrum colors common to both.

Mixing by the subtractive method is demonstrated with prisms and filters in Fig. 45I. To see what happens to each spectral hue in each filter the white light is first spread out into its complete spectrum. To illustrate, the yellow filter alone in diagram (h) absorbs blue and violet, and the cyan filter alone in (f) absorbs red and orange. When both are inserted as in diagram (d) only green and yellow are transmitted. To the eye this mixture appears bright green. The other two pairs of filters in diagrams (e) and (i) give the other two primaries red and blue.

To carry these experimental demonstrations to the mixing of paint, each little grain of pigment is like a piece of colored glass (see Fig. 45J). Assuming the oil in which the yellow pigment is imbedded to be transparent, white light entering the paint is reflected and refracted as shown. Wherever blue or violet rays pass through pigment grains they are absorbed. After many reflections and refractions the red, orange, yellow, and green can still escape. Together these four colors (see Fig. 45F) appear as yellow.

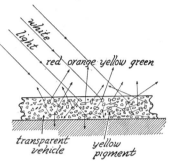

FIG. 45J—Illustration of the absorption of blue and violet light by yellow paint and the emission of red, orange, yellow, and green.

When yellow and cyan pigments are mixed together as illustrated by the detailed diagram in Fig. 45K, only green and yellow light is transmitted by both pigments.

The essential difference between the additive method and subtractive method of color mixing is just that suggested by the name; in the additive method the resultant color is just the *sum* of the two constituents used to produce it, and in the subtractive method it is just the *difference* between the two. Addition always produces a brighter color and subtraction produces a darker color. Just as the additive mixing of red, green, and blue produces white, so the subtractive mixing of magenta, yellow, and cyan produces black. Similarly, two complementary colors, when mixed additively, produce white, and when mixed subtractively produce black.

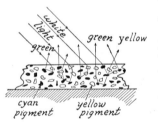

FIG. 45K—When cyan and yellow paints are mixed together green and yellow are the only pure spectral colors transmitted by both pigments.

45.8. Color Vision. When radiant energy at different wave lengths of the spectrum fall upon the retina of the normal human being, the visual sensations vary as shown at the top in Fig. 45L. The maximum which occurs in the green, at $\lambda = 5550$A, is assigned the arbitrary value of 1000. On either side of this maximum the response falls off smoothly toward the violet at one end and the red at the other.

The *standard luminosity curve* is experimentally determined by matching the brightness of one color against that of another for each part of the spectrum and then measuring the relative amounts of energy in each of the two color fields. In comparing green and red, for example, much less intensity is required to give green light a brightness apparently equal to that of a red light. The solid curve is therefore a plot of *photometric energy magnitudes* and not relative brightness.

Brightness is a *sensory magnitude* in light just as loudness is a sensory

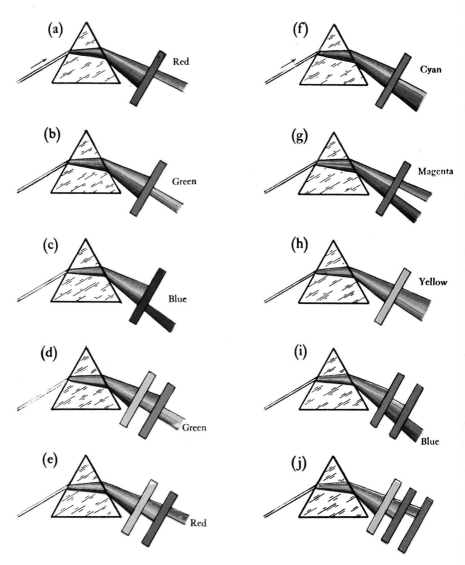

Fig. 45I—Diagram illustrating the absorption of spectral colors by colored filters and the subtractive method of color mixing.

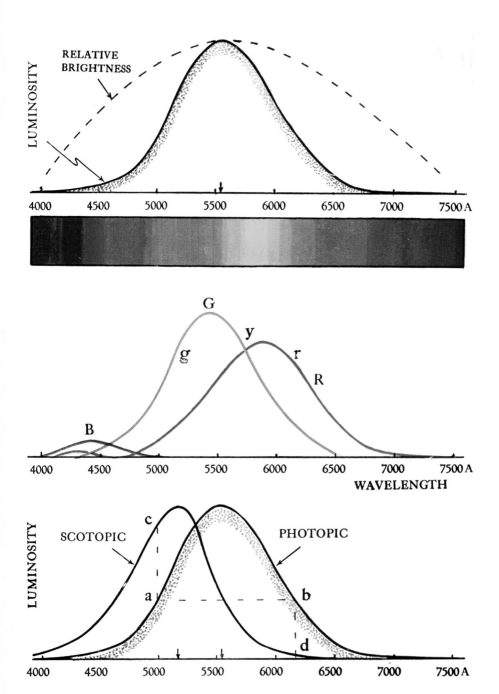

Fig. 45L—(a) Standard luminosity and relative brightness curves for the visible spectrum, (b) Tri-stimulus curves for the red, green, and blue sensitive cones of the retina, (c) Photopic and scotopic curves comparing cone vision by day with rod vision by night.

magnitude in sound. Both vary over a wide range of values as the logarithm of the energy (see Eq.(36a)). To double the brightness of a surface its emission must increase many fold. A plot of the logarithms of the luminosity gives the *relative brightness* curve for an equal energy spectrum. In other words, the dotted curve represents the relative brightness of the colors of a constant energy spectrum and clearly indicates the rather abrupt cutoff at either end.

During the past century many attempts to formulate a scientific theory of color vision have been made. While some of these theories have met with considerable success, none of them have been able to explain every known phenomenon. The most successful theory was first advanced by the English scientist, Thomas Young, and later improved by the German scientist, von Helmholtz. According to the Young-Helmholtz theory the tiny cones in the retina of the eye (see Fig. 1B) are of three kinds. One set of cones produces the visual sensation of red, the second set gives the sensation of green, and the third set the sensation of blue. A set of sensation graphs for each of these color-sensitive cones is given by the center curves in Fig. 45L. The R-curve shows that to stimulate the red-response cones any wave length from spectral violet to red is satisfactory, but wave length 6000A will produce the maximum response. Similarly the B- and G-cones are seen to be stimulated by a whole range of different wave lengths.

When pure spectrum yellow enters the eye, as represented by y in the diagram, both the R- and G-cones respond equally and the sensation is yellow. If pure spectral red and pure spectral green are permitted to enter the eye (like r and g in the diagram) both the R- and G-cones again respond equally and the sensation produced is yellow. Because of the stimulus equality the brain is unable to tell the difference from the y-stimulus and the mixture has neither *redness* nor *greenness*. It is therefore possible to obtain a yellow hue with no spectral yellow present. A similar behavior occurs near wave length 5000A where the B- and G-cones are stimulated equally to produce a *cyan hue*.

If the eye is subjected to faint light of wave length 4500A the visual sensation is *blue,* but when the intensity is raised the hue turns to violet or purple indicating a noticeable stimulation of the R-cones. This is the evidence for the small "bump" in the R-curve in Fig. 45L. White is produced by the presence of all wave lengths in equal amounts but it can also be produced by as few as three wave lengths only.

By the additive process of three primary responses, red, green, and blue, all of the thousands of recognized hues can be produced. The power of the eye and the brain to synthesize colors is to be compared with the reverse process by which the ear and brain are able to analyze musical tones into components.

45.9. Color Deficiency, and Color Blindness. About 8% of males and 1% of females are color deficient or color blind, that is, do not have normal color vision. Although there are many forms and degrees of this defect, the two most common types are called *protanopia* and *deuteranopia*.* Numerous tests and experiments indicate that protanopia is due to the absence of R-cones in the retina (see Fig. 45L(b)), whereas deuteranopia arises where-ever the G-cones have the same spectral response as the normal R-cones.

The true *protanope* is characterized by his observation that the long wave length end of the spectrum is green and stops at about 6800A instead of the normal 7600A. While able to match colors reasonably well the number of hues seen by this individual is only a small fraction of those seen by the normal. With only two primary colors, blue and green, at his disposal he sees only those hues produced by their mixture in all possible proportions.

To the *deuteranope* the spectrum is not shortened at the ends but since the G- and R-cones are equally stimulated with all longer wave lengths he sees only yellow from about 5700A on. With only red and blue primaries, only hues described by the normal as yellow, blue or white are produced. Although various methods have been devised for detecting color deficiencies the most sensitive and accurate determinations are made with an optical instrument known as the *anomaloscope*.

Color vision with but two primaries as in protanopia and deuteranopia is called *dichromacy*, whereas vision with only a partial deficiency of one of the three cone types is called *anomalous trichromacy*. In the *anomalous trichromat* there is a reduction in the brightness of either red, green, or less commonly blue, but the number of possible hues is greater than with the *dichromat* and in many cases approaches the *normal* who is a *trichromat*.

45.10. Photopic and Scotopic Vision. In a well-lighted room or in bright sunlight the peak sensitivity of the eye is in the yellow-green part of the visible spectrum. When the light is extremely faint, however, the maximum shifts to the blue green region and practically all color discrimination disappears. Two brightness sensitivity curves, one for high level illumination and the other for very low illumination are shown in Fig. 45L. Although the peaks are drawn to the same height, the vertical scales for the two are different. The P curve is actually thousands of times higher than the S curve.

Under daytime illumination, normal vision is acquired by what is called *photopic vision,* a condition whereby the color sensitive cones in the retina of the eye are responsible for visual sensations. On dark nights, however,

---

* Both these forms of *dichromacy* are hereditary, recessive and sex-linked. Theoretically one woman in seven is a genetic carrier who does not herself exhibit color deficiency but transmits it *through* half of her daughters and *to* half of her sons. If one of these dichromatic males marries a normal woman, all of their children will be normal but the daughters will all be carriers.

when the illumination is very low, the highly sensitive rods account for what little vision is attained and we have what is called *scotopic vision. Photopic vision is cone vision, scotopic vision is rod vision.* The normal eye contains about 7 million cones and 130 million rods.

An interesting demonstration may be performed with an ordinary projection lantern, a slide that is half red and half blue, and an iris diaphragm located in front of the projection lens. The red and blue glass of the slide should be matched for equal brightness under normal projection on a white screen. As the iris diaphragm is narrowed down the red field will appear to fade more rapidly than the blue and finally to disappear altogether. The persistence of the blue is more strikingly observed by directing the eyes to one side of the two colored fields. If the original matching of red and blue corresponds to equal brightness points like (a) and (b) in Fig. 45L, the reduced illumination corresponds to the unequal brightness points (c) and (d). This observed phenomenon is called the Purkinje effect.

45.11. Color Photography. Out of the scientific research laboratories of the world there has come in recent years a number of processes by which photographs in full color can be faithfully reproduced. For example there are the "Lumiere" process developed in France, the "Agfa" process developed in Germany, and the "Kodachrome" and "Technicolor" processes developed in the United States.

Many of the full color pictures printed in the magazines of today are reproduced from photographs that were originally taken with a somewhat complicated three-color process. The rapid growth of this industry of color photography justifies a brief description here of the most recent and successful processes.

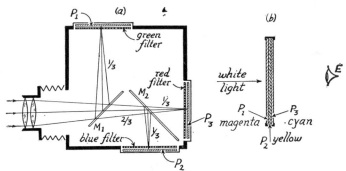

Fig. 45M—(a) Camera arrangement for taking three-color photographs. (b) Superposition of three colored films to produce the final photograph.

For "still pictures" a special box camera having one lens and three separate film holders is often used (see Fig. 45M). Instead of taking but one picture at a time, as in the ordinary camera, three pictures are taken simultaneously. This is accomplished by the use of two lightly silvered mirrors. The first mirror M_1 reflects one-third of the light to one photographic film at P_1, the second mirror M_2 reflects half of the remaining light to a film at P_2, and the remainder travels straight through to a film at P_3. Before reaching each photographic film the light is made to pass through glass plates, colored to transmit only the *primary colors, red, green and blue* (see Fig. 45F). Light from a red object, for example, will pass through the red filter but not through the green and blue filters.

After a picture is taken, the films are developed as "black and white" negatives as shown by the contrast illustrations in Fig. 45N. Instead of printing these on white paper as in the ordinary photographic processing, they are either put through a reversing process whereby white is made black and black is made white, or they are printed on three separate films, P_1, P_2, and P_3, and called *positives*. These positive films which are "white and black" are next bleached out and dyed colors complementary to the filters used in taking the cor-

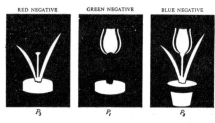

FIG. 45N—Drawing of three separation negatives obtained as the first step in color photography.

responding negatives. As shown at the top of Fig. 45O, film P_1 is dyed magenta, P_2 is dyed yellow, and P_3 is dyed cyan. *Where a color was bright in the original scene the positive is now transparent, and where there was no light it is now colored with the dye.*

The three colored films are next superimposed as shown at the right in Fig. 45M, and when they are viewed with white light the result will appear as at the left center in Fig. 45O. Where the red tulip petals are located in the original scene the positive P_1 is magenta, P_2 is yellow, and P_3 is transparent. Of all the colors in white light only red and orange will be transmitted at this point for only red and orange get through the magenta-yellow combination. Where the original background was white, light was transmitted by all three filters in the camera and each of the colored positives is transparent. Where the scene contained black, no light reached any of the negatives and the positives are all colored. When superimposed no light can get through all three. Thus, by the subtractive method of color mixing a colored photograph exhibiting all the natural colors is obtained. Even pastel shades of pink, blue, and green are quite faithfully rendered.

45.12. Colored Motion Pictures. The "Technicolor" process used in the motion picture industry is quite similar to the "still picture" process just described above. With each snap of the camera, twenty-four times per

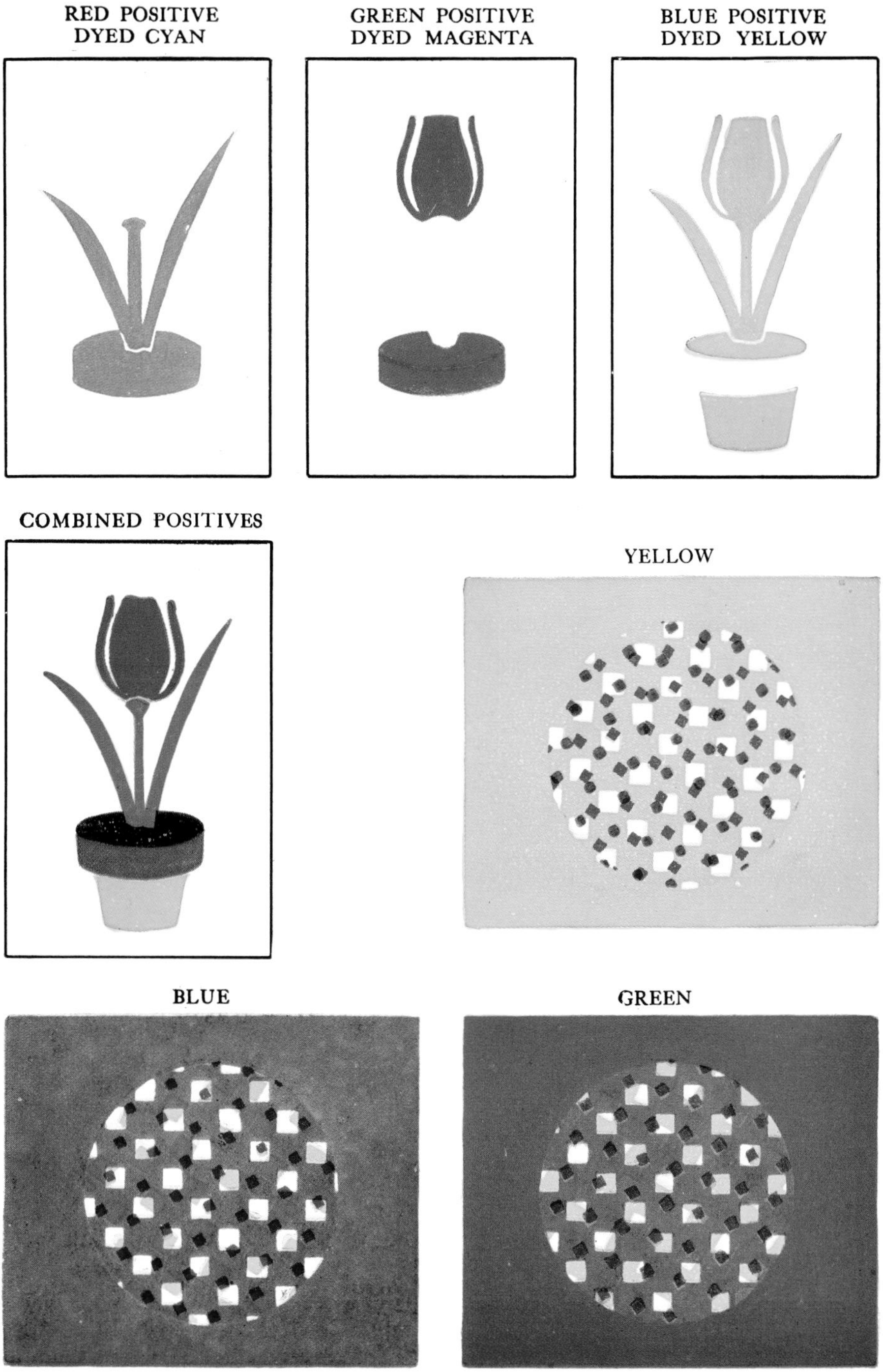

RED POSITIVE
DYED CYAN

GREEN POSITIVE
DYED MAGENTA

BLUE POSITIVE
DYED YELLOW

COMBINED POSITIVES

YELLOW

BLUE

GREEN

FIG. 450 — Illustrating the processes of color photography and color printing.

second, a picture for each of the three colors is taken simultaneously through colored filters.

A detail of the optical system of the *Technicolor* camera is shown in Fig. 45P. A semitransparent mirror *M* divides the light into two nearly equal beams. The one image is formed on a green sensitive panchromatic film after passing through a green filter, and the other image, after passing through a

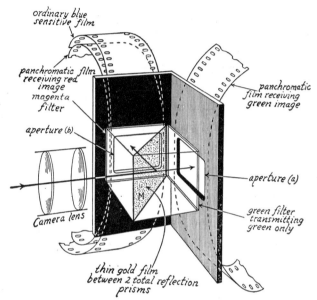

FIG. 45P—Detail diagram of the optical parts of a "Techni-color" moving picture camera.

magenta filter, is formed on two films with their sensitive surfaces in contact. The first of the two films is sensitive only to blue and violet and the rear film is sensitive to red. When all three strips of film are developed they become the color separation negatives as in the still picture process described above.

45.13. The Kodachrome Process. In the "Kodachrome" process, developed by the "Eastman Kodak Company," three sensitive photographic emulsions and one layer of dyed gelatine are laid down on one celluloid film. A cross-section diagram of a section of film is shown, greatly magnified, in Fig. 45Q. The top emulsion is sensitive to blue and violet only. The second emulsion is sensitive to green, blue, and violet, but the yellow filter absorbs the blue and violet; hence, only green images affect this emulsion. The third emulsion is sensitive to red, blue, and violet, but, since the yellow filter absorbs the blue and violet, only the red images develop up there.

Suppose blue, green, and red light enters the film in the three regions *B, G,* and *R* as indicated in Fig. 45Q. Then, upon regular development, the silver bromide in these regions is reduced to pure silver and hence is black at these points. The film is then exposed to red light from the back, thus affecting the regions *b*. The film is now developed in a special bath containing a coupler which forms in the lowest layer a cyan (blue-green) dye with

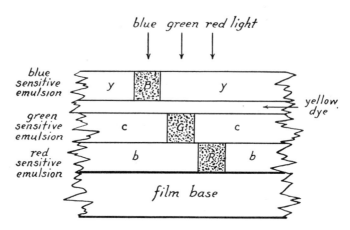

Fig. 45Q—Cross-section diagram of kodachrome film showing layers of emulsion and colored dye.

the oxidized developer. This means that as the regions *b* become black, cyan dye is deposited there. The film is next exposed from the top to blue light, thus affecting the regions *y*, which, upon development with the proper coupler, forms a yellow dye. Yellow dye is thus deposited with the black silver grains in *y*. The film is then exposed from the top to green light, which makes the areas *c* developable, and these are developed with a coupler in the developer which forms a magenta dye in these areas. All the silver is then oxidized and converted into silver bromide, which is removed by a fixing bath. This operation also bleaches the yellow dye in the interlayer. The film is fixed, washed, and dried. This leaves regions *B, G,* and *R* clear; *y,* *yellow; c, magenta;* and *b, cyan* (blue-green). White light upon passing through the entire film at the clear section *B* will have the green absorbed in *c* and the red absorbed in *b* with blue only getting through as desired. White light upon entering the film directly above the clear spot *G* will have the blue and violet absorbed by the first film and the red absorbed by the lower film, with only the green getting through as desired. White light entering the film above *R* will have the blue and the green absorbed by the two upper layers, allowing only the red to pass.

45.14. Color Printing. If the average color picture in a book or magazine is examined with a microscope it will be found, as shown in the lower part of Fig. 45O, to be made up of thousands of tiny colored dots. In the illustration the background of the three squares is the resultant color effect of three sets of dots shown magnified 20-fold in the corresponding circles. Viewed from a distance of 20 to 30 ft the circles of large dots blend with their own background.

A careful examination of the dot patterns will show that three separate screens, one for each of the primary colors, is used. With their rows 60° apart with respect to each other, these screens print rectangular patterns of dots one on top of the other. The amount of each color is regulated by the size of the dots and, because each color is printed separately, the overlapping of dots is quite random. As illustrated in the upper right hand square, yellow is produced by large yellow dots covering almost the entire field, the small red and cyan dots contributing only a slight darkening effect.

Green, as shown in the lower right-hand circle, is produced by large yellow and cyan dots with negligibly small magenta dots. Where the yellow and cyan overlap, green is produced by subtractive color mixing. White light to be reflected from the white paper underneath must go through both yellow and cyan so that only spectrum green and yellow emerge as explained in Sec.45.7. Where the dots do not overlap additive color mixing takes place. The yellow dots reflect spectrum red, orange, yellow and green, while cyan dots reflect yellow, green, blue, and violet. Because both reflect spectrum yellow and green, and all remaining spectrum colors are present, the net effect is white light with a preponderance of green and yellow. Hence green is produced by both the additive and subtractive processes. The darkening that results from overlapping areas can be brightened by white areas so that any desired effect is produced by increasing or decreasing the dot size. In some processes black dots are added to darken some color fields and left out where brighter hues are desired.

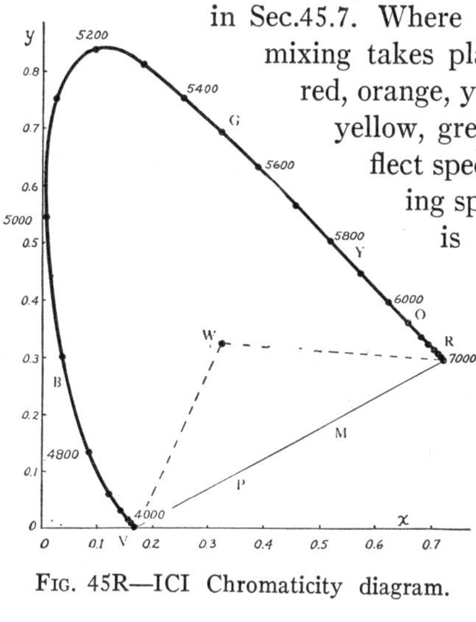

Fig. 45R—ICI Chromaticity diagram.

45.15. The ICI Chromaticity Diagram. Well-planned steps toward a quantitative measurement of color were taken by the International Commission on Illumination in 1931. At that time three additive primaries, red, green, and blue, were adopted in which the visible spectrum was divided into three overlapping spectral response curves somewhat similar to those in Fig. 45L. Although a treatment of this standard ICI system * must be left for more advanced studies it should be mentioned here that any given color sample can be measured with a spectroscope in terms of the three adopted primaries and the results of the measurements expressed by two numbers. These two numbers can then be plotted on a graph.

When the pure spectrum colors ROYGBV are matched against a mixture of the standard primaries, a smooth curve as shown in Fig. 45R is obtained. With white at the center, the complete gamut of all possible color mixtures lie within the enclosed area *RGBVW* with the purples *P* and magentas *M* confined to the region *RWV* between the two ends of the spectrum.

PROBLEMS

1. The following pairs of colors are mixed additively. What is their resultant color? (a) red and green, (b) red and blue, (c) blue and green, (d) blue and yellow, (e) red and cyan.

2. The following pairs of colors are mixed subtractively. What is their resultant color? (a) yellow and cyan, (b) magenta and cyan, (c) magenta and yellow, (d) magenta and green, (e) red and cyan. (*Ans.* (a) green, (b) blue, (c) red, (d) black, (e) black.)

3. Make charts showing the various parts of the pure spectrum colors belonging to each of the additive and subtractive primaries.

4. Diagram the color triangle from memory.

5. Draw scotopic and photopic curves for day and night vision and briefly explain the Purkinje effect.

6. Yellow and cyan are mixed (a) additively, and (b) subtractively. What are the resultant colors in each case? (*Ans.* (a) greenish white, (b) green.)

7. (a) What color added to red will give white? (b) What color subtracted from red will give black?

8. If Kodachrome film is used in photographing a green object, what color is each of the three color sensitive emulsions at this area in the final processed film? (*Ans.* The blue sensitive emulsion is yellow, the green sensitive emulsion is clear, and the red sensitive emulsion is cyan.)

9. If Kodachrome film is used in photographing a red rose, what color is each of the three sensitive emulsions at this area in the final processed film?

10. What colors are complementary to each of the following: (a) red, (b) yellow, (c) green, (d) cyan, (e) blue, (f) magenta, (g) white, and (h) black. (*Ans.* (a) cyan, (b) blue, (c) magenta, (d) red, (e) yellow, (f) green, (g) black, (h) white.)

* For a treatment of the ICI color system see "Principles of Physics," Chap. 13, by F. W. Sears, pub. by Addison-Wesley Press.

Diffraction and Interference   Chapter 46

46.1. Shadows. When light passes close to the edge of any object, it is bent in its path and travels on in a new direction. This bending of light around corners is called *diffraction*. In the preceding chapters light has been

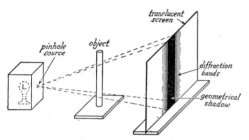

assumed to travel in straight lines and to obey the laws of reflection and refraction. Furthermore, according to the rectilinear propagation of light, it is customary to assume that an object will cast a sharp and well-defined shadow. A close examination of every shadow, however, shows that the edges are not sharp, but blurred and diffused.

FIG. 46A—The shadow cast by the light from a small source is not sharp at the edges but exhibits a banded structure.

If one is careful to choose a small source of light, such as the light emanating from a pinhole in a screen, the shadow of an object cast on a distant screen is bounded at the edges by narrow bands or fringes of light. To observe these effects the following sim-

FIG. 46B—Photographs of the shadows cast by small objects. The narrow bands are due to the diffraction of light.

ple experiment may be performed in a darkened room. A box containing a light bulb and a pinhole is placed on one side of the room and a ground glass observing screen or photographic film is placed on the other. The objects whose shadows are to be observed are then placed about half way between the source and the screen as shown in Fig. 46A. This is the arrangement used in obtaining the original photographs reproduced in Figs. 46B and 46C. The latter is an enlarged photograph of the light diffracted by a small circular opening.

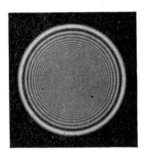

Fig. 46C—Diffraction of light by a small circular opening. (*Original photograph by Hufford.*)

46.2. Huygens' Principle. The phenomenon of diffraction was explained in the time of Newton by assuming that light is composed of small particles or corpuscles obeying the ordinary laws of mechanical motion. And so it was that Newton and his followers held for many years to the idea that a source of light is a source of high-speed particles radiated in all directions.

Although such a viewpoint was believed for many years, it was later abandoned in favor of a wave theory of light, according to which a beam of light is made up of many waves of extremely short wave lengths. By adopting the wave hypothesis a complete and adequate account of *reflection, refraction, diffraction, interference,* and *polarization* phenomena was finally formulated on a mathematical basis by Augustin Fresnel, a French physicist, at the beginning of the nineteenth century. The wave theory of light was first proposed by the English physicist, Robert Hooke, in 1665, and improved twenty years later by the Dutch scientist and mathematician, Christian Huygens.*

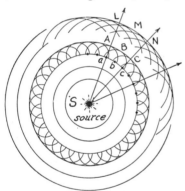

Fig. 46D—Diagram of waves spreading out from a point source. The secondary wavelets and new wave fronts illustrate Huygen's principle.

Everyone has at some time or other dropped a stone in a still pond of water and watched the waves spread slowly outward in ever-widening concentric circles.

* Christian Huygens (1629-1695), famous Dutch physicist and contemporary of Isaac Newton. Born at The Hague in 1629, young Christian got his first ideas about waves and their propagation by watching the ripples on the canals about his home. Although his chief title-deed to immortality is his development of the wave theory of light, he made many and valuable contributions to mathematics and astronomy. He improved upon the method of grinding telescope lenses and discovered the Orion nebula, part of which is now known by his name. He was elected to the Royal Society of London in 1663, and delivered before that august body the first clear statement of the laws governing the collision of elastic bodies. He died a confirmed bachelor at The Hague in 1695.

In the analogous case of a point source of light, the spreading waves form concentric spheres moving outward with the extremely high velocity of 186,300 mi/sec. This is represented diagrammatically in Fig. 46D. Each circle represents the crest of a wave so that the distance between consecutive circles is one wave length.

According to Huygens' principle every point on any wave front may be regarded as a new point source of waves. Regarding each of any number of points like *a, b, c,* etc., as point sources like *S,* secondary wavelets spread out simultaneously as shown. The envelope of these an instant later is the new wave front *A, B, C,* etc., and still later the wave front *L, M, N,* etc. Although Huygens' principle at first hand might seem to be a useless play with circles, it has quite general application to many optical phenomena.

46.3. Reflection and Refraction of Waves. A diagram illustrating the application of Huygens' secondary wavelets to reflection is shown in Fig. 46E. A parallel beam of light of width *KM* is incident at an arbitrary angle on the polished surface of a piece of glass. As indicated by the wavy lines

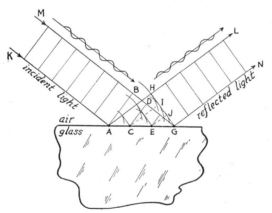

Fig. 46E—Illustrating the applications of Huygens' principle of secondary wavelets to reflection.

at the side of each beam the crests of the waves are represented by equidistant lines perpendicular to the direction of motion.

At the instant one end of a crest strikes the surface at A the opposite end is at *B.* While this upper edge travels from *B* to *G* the lower side is reflected and travels an equal distant *AH.* Each of the points *A, C, E,* and *G* acting as new point sources, sends out a secondary wavelet, at the instant a wave arrives there, to form the new wave front *HG.* If from other points between *A* and *G* on the mirror, secondary wavelets are drawn, they will all fall tangent to the reflected wave fronts, traveling off in the direction shown.

The geometry of the diagram shows that the angle of incidence equals the angle of reflection.

A similar diagram illustrating refraction is given in Fig. 46F. The same points A, C, E and G, acting as point sources of light for the reflected light, also send out secondary wavelets into the medium. Since the velocity of light is less in the medium than in air the waves are shorter, i.e., the wavelets are crowded together. If we assume a refractive index of 1.5, the wavelets and new wave fronts in the glass will be only two-thirds as far apart as they are in the air. Their new directions are found by setting a compass at the points A, C, E, and G and drawing arcs of circles two-thirds as far apart as the waves in air. The lines AR and GS, drawn through

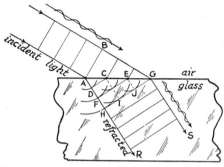

Fig. 46F—Illustrating the application of Huygens' principle of secondary wavelets to refraction.

the points of tangency, are perpendicular to the new wave fronts DC, FE, and HG.

When the beam is refracted from the lower face of the glass plate in Fig. 46F, the secondary wavelets emerge from the lower boundary into the air again. In this instance the distance between waves and wavelets returns to that for the incident light. The direction of the refracted beam, which is left as an exercise for the student, will be found to be parallel to the incident beam.

The action of a converging lens on light waves is illustrated in Fig. 46G. If a point source of light is placed at the focal point, as in diagram (a), the

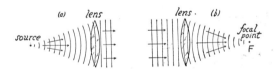

Fig. 46G—Illustrating the behavior of light waves as they pass through a converging lens.

expanding waves pass through the lens and come out as plane waves, i.e., as parallel light. In diagram (b) incident plane waves are shown emerging from the lens as contracting waves which come to a focus at F. The change brought about by the lens can be explained by the fact that light travels faster in air than it does in glass.

46.4. Diffraction at a Single Small Opening.

A direct experimental demonstration of Huygens' principle is illustrated in Fig. 46H. Plane waves

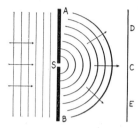

FIG. 46H—Diagram of the diffraction of waves at a small opening. Huygens' principle.

approaching a barrier *AB* from the left are reflected or absorbed at every point except at *S* where they are allowed to pass on through. When the experiment is carried out with water waves, one can see the waves spreading out in all directions as if *S* were a point source.

If *AB* is an opaque screen and *S* is a pinhole small in comparison to the wave length of light, the light waves will spread out in hemispheres with *S* at their center. If *S* is a long narrow slit (perpendicular to the page), the waves spread out with cylindrical wave fronts. Cross sections of all these cases are represented by the semicircles, the light traveling in the direction of the arrows.

46.5. Young's Double-Slit Experiment.

The crucial test between Newton's corpuscular theory of light and Huygens' wave theory came in 1801 when Thomas Young performed his now famous interference experiment. This is represented schematically in Fig. 46I. Sunlight from a pinhole *S* was allowed to fall on a distant screen containing two pinholes, S_1 and S_2. The two sets of spherical waves emerging from the two holes interfered with each other in such a way as to form a symmetrical pattern of bands on another screen *MN*. This experiment is now regarded as the first definite proof that light is a wave motion.

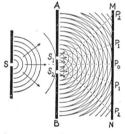

FIG. 46I—Diagram of Young's double-slit experiment illustrating the interference of light waves.

For convenience it is now customary to repeat Young's experiment with narrow slits in place of pinholes. If *S*, S_1 and S_2 in Fig. 46I represent the cross

FIG. 46J —Interference fringes produced by a double-slit as in Young's experiment.

sections of three narrow slits, the light falling on the farther screen *MN* has the appearance of equidistant bands or fringes as shown by the photograph in Fig. 46J. The bright fringes correspond to the points P_o, P_1, P_2, etc., and the dark fringes to the points halfway between.

As the waves travel outward from each slit S_1 and S_2, they cross each other only at points which lie along the dotted lines shown in the diagram. These represent the points where the crests of two waves come together and produce a maximum brightness. About halfway between these dotted lines lie other points where the crest of one wave and the trough of another cancel each other and produce darkness. This is called *interference*. Where the bright fringes are formed there is *constructive interference* and where the dark fringes appear there is *destructive interference*.

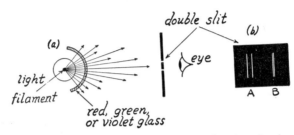

FIG. 46K—(a) Experimental arrangement for observing interference fringes by Young's double-slit experiment. (b) Detail of double-slit showing two pairs of slits.

One of the simplest methods of demonstrating interference fringes is illustrated in Fig. 46K(a). The best source of light for this purpose is a light bulb of clear glass with a vertical, single wire filament. Double slits for each observer can be made from small pieces of photographic plate about 1 in. square. Two sets of slits, as shown in diagram (b), are made in the photographic emulsion by drawing the point of a penknife across the plate. Holding one pair of slits close to one eye as shown in diagram (a) and looking at the source, a number of closely spaced colored fringes will be seen.

46.6. Measuring the Wave Length of Light. A formula for the wave length of light can be derived from the geometry of Young's double-slit experiment as shown in Fig. 46L.

Let P be the position of any bright fringe on the screen, and x its distance from the central fringe at P_0. P_0 is located on the perpendicular bisector of the double slit S_1 and S_2. A straight line from each slit to the point P is drawn in and with a compass of radius S_1P the arc of a circle S_1M is scribed. By this construc-

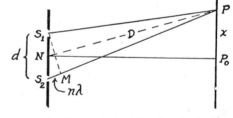

FIG. 46L—Geometrical relation for the double-slit experiment.

tion line MP is made equal to S_1P and the short line S_2M becomes the extra distance light must travel from the lower slit. To produce a bright fringe at P the interval S_2M must be equal to one whole wave length, two whole wave lengths, three whole wave lengths, etc., for only then will the waves from S_1 and S_2 arrive at P in phase. Therefore, S_2M must be equal to $n\lambda$, where n is a whole number, $n = 0, 1, 2, 3, 4$, etc., and λ is the wave length of the light.

Since the distance d between slit centers is extremely small compared with the distance D to the screen, line S_1M may be considered straight and at right angles to all three lines S_1P, NP, and S_2P. With corresponding sides mutually perpendicular to each other, triangles S_1S_2M and NPP_0 are similar to each other. From the well-known theorem that corresponding sides of similar triangles are proportional,

$$\frac{n\lambda}{d} = \frac{x}{D} \quad \text{or} \quad \lambda = \frac{xd}{nD}. \tag{46a}$$

If we let x_1 be the distance from the central fringe to the first one on either side, then $n = 1$, and the equation becomes

$$\lambda = x_1 \frac{d}{D}. \tag{46b}$$

Because the fringes are evenly spaced x_1 represents the spacing all along the pattern. By measuring the three distances d, x, and D, the wave length of light can be calculated. Repeated experiments, carefully performed, give the following results.

Red,	$\lambda = 0.000066$ cm	Green,	$\lambda = 0.000054$ cm
Orange,	$\lambda = 0.000061$ cm	Blue,	$\lambda = 0.000046$ cm
Yellow,	$\lambda = 0.000058$ cm	Violet,	$\lambda = 0.000042$ cm

As illustrated by waves in Fig. 46M, red light has the longest waves.

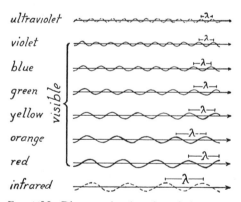

Fig. 46M—Diagram showing the relative wave
lengths of light.

A scale of wave lengths showing the range over which each of the visible colors extends is shown in Fig. 45L. The above wave lengths measured by the double-slit experiment are therefore average values since each color corresponds to a range of different wave lengths.

46.7. The Diffraction Grating. The diffraction grating is an optical device widely used in place of a prism for studying the spectrum and measuring the wave lengths of light. Gratings are made by ruling fine grooves with a diamond point either on a glass plate to produce a transmission grating or on a polished metal mirror to produce a reflecting grating. As illustrated in Fig. 46N the rulings are all parallel, and equally spaced. The best gratings are several inches in width and contain from 5000 to 30,000 lines/in.

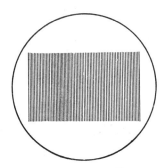

Fig. 46N—Schematic diagram of the grooves or rulings on a diffraction grating.

The transmission grating and its effect on light is idealized by the cross-section diagrams in Fig. 46O. The heavy black lines represent the lines which permit no light to get through and the open intervals between them represent the undisturbed parts of the glass which transmit the light and act like parallel slits as in Young's double-slit experiment. In diagram (a) parallel light is shown arriving at the grating surface as a succession of plane waves. The light then passing through the openings

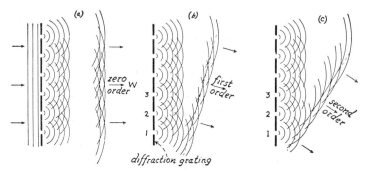

Fig. 46O—Diagrams showing the formation of wave fronts forming the various orders of interference observed with a diffraction grating.

spreads out as Huygens' wavelets, and forms new wave fronts parallel to the grating face. These wave fronts, parallel to the original waves, constitute a beam of light W traveling on in the same direction as the original beam.

These are not the only wave fronts, however, for other beams of parallel light are to be found traveling away from the grating in other directions. Two other such wave fronts are illustrated in diagrams (b) and (c). In (b), a dotted line is drawn tangent to the seventh wave from opening *1*, the eighth wave from opening *2*, the ninth wave from opening *3*, etc., to form what is called a wave front of the first order of interference. In (c), a line is drawn tangent to the fourth wave from opening *1,* the sixth wave from opening *2,* the eighth wave from opening *3,* etc., to form what is called a wave front of the second order of interference. Similarly, by taking every third

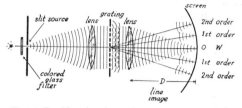

wave or every fourth wave from consecutive slits, other parallel wave fronts corresponding to the third or fourth orders are found moving off at greater angles. By symmetry all of the orders found on one side of the zeroth order are also found at the same angle on the other side.

FIG. 46P—Showing how the wave fronts of the various orders of interference are brought to a focus by the same lens.

Experimentally there are two methods of observing the various orders of interference from a small diffraction grating; one is to place the grating directly in front of the eye as illustrated by the double slit in Fig. 46K, and the other is to place it in the parallel beam of light between two lenses as shown in Fig. 46P. In the latter case the second lens is shown converging the various wave fronts of the different orders to a focus on a distant screen. If the source is a slit as shown at the left, and a colored glass filter is used to let through any one color of light, like violet,

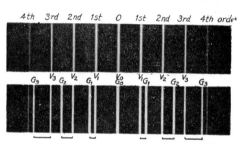

FIG. 46Q—Photographs of the different orders of interference of violet and green light obtained with a diffraction grating as shown in Fig. 46P.

the light falling on the screen will appear as shown in the top photograph in Fig. 46Q. Each vertical line is an image of the slit source and is violet in color.

If the three diagrams in Fig. 46O are redrawn for light of a longer wave length, i.e., a greater distance between waves, the central beam of light *W* would travel on in the same direction as before, but the various *orders of interference* would be diffracted out at greater angles. Should green light of one wave length be used in Fig. 46P, the slit images formed on the screen would be farther apart than for violet light, as illustrated by the images marked *G* in Fig. 46Q(b). This lower photograph was taken with both violet and green light from a mercury arc passing through the grating. These line images are called spectrum lines.

It will be noted that the separation of the spectrum lines *V* and *G* in the *third order* is three times as great as in the *first order.* In other words, any two spectrum lines are separated by an amount which is proportional to the order of interference.

If white light is sent through a grating, all of the different wave lengths, corresponding to the different colors, form their own characteristic wave fronts and produce a complete and continuous spectrum in each order of

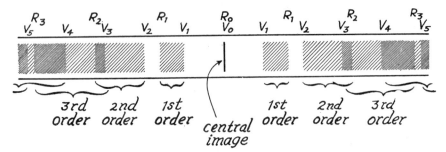

3rd   2nd   1st   1st   2nd   3rd
order   order   order   central   order   order   order
                         image

Fig. 46R—Diagram of the first several orders of the continuous spectrum as displayed by a diffraction grating.

interference. This is illustrated by a diagram in Fig. 46R. Since the zeroth order for all colors comes to the same point, the central image is white. Because the width of each spectrum is proportional to the order, the higher orders overlap one another more and more. The violet of the third order, V_3 for example, falls on the red of second order, R_2. It is for this reason that only the first and second orders of the spectrum from any grating are the ones generally used in practice.

The general appearance of a spectrum, produced by a diffraction grating spectrograph, can be seen in the photographs reproduced in Chap. 62. Diagrams of reflection grating spectrographs are given in Figs. 61F and 61G.

46.8. Mathematical Theory of the Diffraction Grating. The theory of the diffraction grating is similar to that of the double slit and is shown in its simplest form in Fig. 46S. These diagrams derive their construction from Fig. 46O. The wave fronts for the first order emerge at such an angle θ that the difference in path between the rays from any two consecutive rulings like A and B is just one wave length. Since any tangent drawn to any circle is always perpendicular to the radius drawn through the point of contact, triangle ABD is a right triangle, and $\sin \theta = \lambda/d$. Transposing

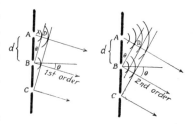

$$\lambda = d \sin \theta, \qquad (46c)$$

where λ is the wave length of the light, d is

Fig. 46S—Geometry for the wave theory of the diffraction grating.

the grating spacing and θ is the angle the emergent light of the first order makes with the grating normal.

By similar reasoning, and diagrams like the one shown for the second order, it will be seen that the second, third, fourth, etc., order spectra are formed at such angles θ that the difference in path between consecutive slits is 2λ, 3λ, 4λ, etc. In general, the side AD of the right triangle ABD must be equal to $n\lambda$, where $n = 1, 2, 3, 4$, etc., and $sin\ \theta = n\lambda/d$. If we transpose as before, we obtain the general formula

$$n\lambda = d \sin \theta. \qquad (46d)$$

In this general grating formula n is the spectrum order.

Example. Red light of one particular wave length falls normally on a grating having 4000 lines per cm. If the second order spectrum makes an angle of 36° with the grating normal what is the wave length of the light?

Solution. Since the grating has 4000 lines per cm the spacing between lines is 1/4000, or $d = 0.00025$ cm. The other given quantities are $\theta = 36°$ and $n = 2$. Substituting in Eq.(46d), and solving for λ,

$$\lambda = \frac{0.00025 \times \sin 36°}{2} = \frac{0.00025 \times 0.588}{2} = 0.0000735 \text{ cm.}$$

PROBLEMS

1. Red light of wavelength 6×10^{-5} cm is used in observing the interference fringes produced by a double slit. If the centers of the two slit openings are 0.5 mm apart and the distance to the observing screen is 2 m, what is the fringe spacing?

2. Green light of wavelength 5×10^{-5} cm falls on a double slit and 2 m away on a white screen interference fringes are formed 5 mm apart. Calculate the double slit separation. (*Ans.* 0.20 mm.)

3. Monochromatic light falls upon a double slit. The distance between the slit centers is 1.1 mm and the distance between consecutive fringes on a screen 5 m away is 0.3 cm. What is the wavelength and the color of the light?

4. A beam of parallel light, $\lambda = 10^{-5}$ cm falls normally on a grating and the fourth order is diffracted at an angle of 30° with the grating normal. How many lines per cm are on the grating? (*Ans.* 2500.)

5. Parallel blue light of wavelength 4.6×10^{-5} cm falls normally on one side of a diffraction grating having 5000 lines per cm. Calculate the angle between the first order spectrum on opposite sides of the grating normal.

6. A diffraction grating with 8000 lines per cm is used with two lenses, each of 3 m focal length, as shown in Fig. 46P. Find the width of the first order spectrum of white light as it is formed on the screen. Assume $\lambda = 4 \times 10^{-5}$ cm and $\lambda = 7 \times 10^{-5}$ cm for the shortest and longest wavelengths and a curved screen of radius 300 cm. (*Ans.* 81 cm.)

7. A grating having 2000 lines per cm is set up with 1 m focal length lenses as shown in Fig. 46P. What fourth order wavelength will be diffracted at the same angle as the third order of $\lambda = 60 \times 10^{-5}$ cm?

The Polarization of Light   Chapter 47

THE experiments described in the preceding chapter illustrating the *diffraction* and *interference* of light are generally regarded as proof that *light is a wave motion*. Although such experiments enable the experimentalist to measure accurately the wave lengths of light, they give no information of the kinds of waves involved. The reason for this is that all types of waves, under the proper conditions, will exhibit diffraction and interference. The desired information in the case of light waves is found in another group of phenomena known as *polarized light*. Some of the phenomena, which will be described in this chapter, are considered to be a proof that *light is a transverse wave motion* in contrast with the longitudinal wave motion in sound.

In the case of longitudinal waves the vibrations are always parallel to the direction of propagation, so that in a plane at right angles to the direction of travel there is no motion and hence there is perfect symmetry. If light is a transverse wave motion, the vibrations of a beam of light are all at right angles to the direction of propagation and there may or may not be perfect symmetry around the direction of travel. If perfect symmetry does not exist for a beam of light the beam is said to be *polarized*.

The experimental methods by which light may be polarized are classified under one of the following heads: (1) *reflection*, (2) *double refraction*, (3) *selective absorption*, and (4) *scattering*.

47.1. Plane-Polarized Light. A better understanding of the experiments to be described in this chapter can best be attained by first presenting the graphical methods of representing transverse waves. We assume at the outset that each light wave is a transverse wave whose vibrations are along straight lines at right angles to the direction of propagation (see Fig. 35D). Furthermore, we assume that a beam of ordinary light consists of millions of such waves, each with its own plane of vibration, and that there are waves vibrating in all planes with equal probability. Looking at such a beam end-on as in Fig. 47A, there should be just as many waves vibrating in one plane as there are vibrating in any other. This then can be referred to as perfect symmetry.

FIG. 47A—End-on view of a beam of unpolarized light illustrating schematically the equal probability of all planes of vibration.

If, by some means or other, all the waves in a beam of light are made to vibrate in planes parallel to each other, the light is said to be plane-polarized.

Diagrams illustrating such light are shown in Fig. 47B. The top diagram (a) represents plane-polarized light waves traveling to the right and vibrating in a vertical plane, while the second diagram (b) represents a ray of plane-polarized light vibrating in a horizontal plane. The dotted line indicating waves in diagram (a) is usually omitted.

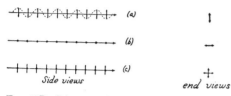

FIG. 47B—Diagrams illustrating plane polarized rays of light.

It can be shown that a beam of ordinary unpolarized light, vibrating in all planes, may be regarded as being made up of two kinds of vibrations only, half of the waves vibrating in a vertical plane as in diagram (a) and the other half vibrating perpendicular to it as in diagram (b). The reason for this is that waves not vibrating in either of these two planes can be resolved into two components, one component vibrating in a vertical plane and the other vibrating in a horizontal plane. Although these two components may not be equal to each other, the similarly resolved components from all waves will average out to be equal. Diagram (c) is regarded therefore as being equivalent to ordinary unpolarized light.

47.2. Polarization by Reflection.

When ordinary unpolarized light is incident at an angle of about 57° on the polished surface of a plate of glass the reflected light is plane-polarized. This fact was first discovered by Etienne Malus, a French physicist, in 1808. The experiment usually performed to demonstrate his discovery is illustrated in Fig. 47C.

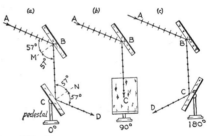

FIG. 47C—Common experiment performed to demonstrate the polarization of light by reflection from a smooth glass surface.

A beam of unpolarized light *AB* is incident at an angle of 57° on the first glass surface at *B*. This light is again reflected at the same angle by a second glass plate *C* placed parallel to the first, as in diagram (a). If now the lower plate is rotated about the line *BC* by slowly turning the pedestal on which it is mounted, the intensity of the reflected beam *CD* is found to decrease slowly and vanish completely at an angle of 90°. With further rotation the reflected beam *CD* appears again, reaching a maximum at an angle of 180° as shown in diagram (c). Continued rotation causes the intensity to decrease to zero again at 270°, and to reappear and reach a maximum at 360°, the starting point as in diagram (a). During this one complete rotation the angle of incidence on the lower plate, as well as the upper, has re-mained at 57°.

If the angle of incidence on either the upper or lower plate is not 57°, the beam CD will go through maxima and minima every 90° as before, but the minima will not go to zero. In other words, there will always be a reflected beam CD.

A complete mathematical theory of the polarization of light by reflection was first given by Fresnel * in 1820. The remarkable confirmation of this theory, in every detail, by experimental observations on the behavior of light and measurements establishes Fresnel as the greatest contributor to the whole field of optics.

The explanation of the above experiment is made clearer by a detailed study of what happens to ordinary light reflected at the polarizing angle of 57° from glass. As illustrated in Fig. 47D, 8% of the light is reflected as plane-polarized light vibrating in the plane at right angles to the plane of incidence, and the other 92% is refracted as partially plane-polarized light, 42% vibrating perpendicular to the plane of incidence and 50% vibrating parallel to the plane of incidence. The plane of incidence is defined as the plane passing through the incident ray and the ray normal NN. In nearly all diagrams the plane of the page is the plane of incidence.

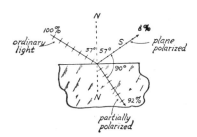

Fig. 47D—Light reflected from glass at an angle of 57° is plane polarized, while the refracted light is only partially plane polarized.

If in Fig. 47D the angle of incidence is changed to some other value than 57° the reflected beam will not be plane-polarized but will contain a certain amount of light vibrating parallel to the plane of incidence. In general, the light reflected from a transparent medium like glass or water is only partially plane-polarized and only at a certain angle, called the *polarizing angle,* is it plane-polarized. It was Sir David Brewster, a Scottish physicist, who first discovered that *at the polarizing angle the reflected and refracted rays are 90° apart.* This is now known as *Brewster's law.* The polarizing angle for water is 53°, for at this angle the reflected and refracted rays make an angle of 90° with each other.

*Augustin Fresnel (1788-1827), French physicist. Although starting his career as a civil engineer Fresnel became interested in optics at the age of 26. His mathematical development of the wave theory of light and its complete validation of experiment have marked this man as an outstanding genius of the nineteenth century. His true scientific attitude is illustrated by a statement from one of his memoirs, "All the compliments that I have received from Arago, Laplace, and Biot never gave me so much pleasure as the discovery of a theoretic truth, or the confirmation of a calculation by experiment."

Because these two rays make 90° with each other the angle of incidence i and the angle of refraction r are complements of each other and sin r in *Snells law* (sin i/sin $r = \mu$) can be replaced by cos i, giving

$$\frac{\sin i}{\cos i} = \mu \qquad \text{or} \qquad \tan i = \mu. \qquad (47a)$$

This formula is useful in calculating the angle of polarization. For example, with water, $\mu = 1.33$, angle $i = 53°$; whereas for glass with $\mu = 1.52$, angle $i = 57°$.

Returning to the experiment demonstrated in Fig. 47C, we observe that the reflected light from the first mirror is plane-polarized as shown, and that the refracted light goes into the glass plate where it is absorbed by the black paint on the back face. The second mirror acts as a testing device or analyzer for polarized light. A certain fraction of the incident waves is reflected when the vibrations are perpendicular to the plane of incidence, and all are refracted (to be absorbed) when the vibrations are parallel to the plane of incidence.

47.3. Double Refraction. The double refraction of light by Iceland spar (calcite) was first observed by a Swedish physician, Erasmus Bartholinus, in 1669, and later studied in detail by Huygens and Newton. Nearly all crystalline substances are now known to exhibit the phenomenon. The following are but a few samples of crystals which show the effect: *calcite, quartz, mica, sugar, topaz, selenite, aragonite,* and *ice.* Calcite and quartz are of particular importance because they are used extensively in the manufacture of special optical instruments.

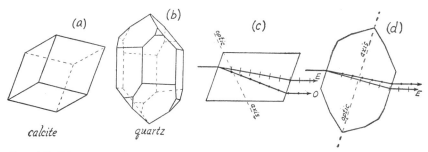

Fig. 47E—Diagrams and cross sections of calcite and quartz crystals showing double refraction and polarization.

Calcite as found in nature always has the characteristic shape shown in Fig. 47E(a), whereas quartz has many different forms, the most complicated of which is illustrated in diagram (b). (For photographs of crystals, see Fig. 23G). Each face of every calcite crystal is a parallelogram whose angles are 78° and 102°. Chemically, calcite is a hydrated calcium carbonate, $CaCO_3$, and quartz is silicon dioxide, SiO_2.

Not only is light doubly refracted by calcite and quartz, but both rays are found to be plane-polarized. One ray, called the *ordinary ray*, is polarized with its vibrations in one plane, and the other ray, called the *extraordinary ray*, is polarized with its vibrations in a plane at right angles to the first. This polarization is illustrated in diagrams (c) and (d) by *dots* and *lines* and can be proved by a glass plate rotated as plate *C* in Fig. 47C, or with some other analyzing device like a *Nicol prism* or a *polarizing film*. These latter devices will be described in the next two sections.

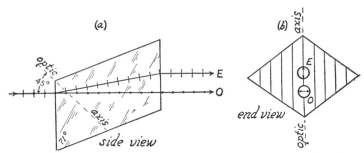

Fig. 47F—Double refraction in calcite. At normal incidence the *O* ray travels straight through and the *E* ray is refracted to one side.

Since the two opposite faces of a calcite crystal are always parallel to each other, the two refracted rays always emerge parallel to the incident light and are therefore parallel to each other. If the incident light falls perpendicularly upon the surface of the crystal, as in Fig. 47F, the extraordinary ray will be refracted away from the normal and come out parallel to, but displaced from, the incident beam, and the ordinary ray will pass straight through without deviation.

In general, the *O* ray obeys the ordinary laws of refraction, and in this way the crystal acts like glass or water, whereas the *E* ray obeys no such simple law and behaves quite abnormally.

In other words, the *O* ray travels with the same velocity regardless of its direction through the crystal, whereas the velocity of the *E* ray is different in different directions. This is the origin of the designations ordinary and extraordinary.

One important property of calcite and quartz is that there is one and only one direction through either crystal in which there is no double refraction. This particular direction, called the *optic axis*, is shown by the dashed lines in Fig. 47E. The optic axis, it should be noted, is not a single line through a crystal but a direction.

A plane passing through the crystal parallel to the optic axis and perpendicular to one face of the crystal is called a *principal section*. The plane of the page in Fig. 47F(a) is but one of any number of principal sections which, from the end view in diagram (b), appears as a vertical line. A useful rule always to be remembered is that the vibrations of the O ray are always perpendicular to the optic axis.

47.4. The Nicol Prism. The Nicol prism is an optical device made from a calcite crystal and used in many optical instruments for producing and analyzing polarized light. Such a prism, as illustrated in Fig. 47G, is made by cutting a crystal along a diagonal and cementing it back together again with a special cement called *Canada balsam*. Canada balsam is used because it is a clear transparent substance whose reflective index is midway between that of the calcite for the O and E *rays*.

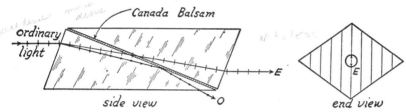

FIG. 47G—Cross section and end view of a Nicol prism showing the elimination of the O ray by total reflection.

Optically the Canada balsam is more dense than calcite for the E ray and less dense for the O ray. There exists, therefore, a critical angle of refraction ιor the one O ray (see Sec. 41.6), but not for the E ray. After both rays are refracted at the first crystal surface the O ray is *totally reflected* by the first

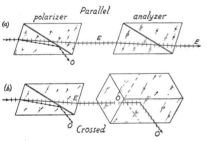

FIG. 47H—Two Nicol prisms mounted as polarizer and analyzer. (a) Parallel Nicols. (b) Crossed Nicols.

Canada balsam surface, as illustrated in the diagram, while the E ray passes on through to emerge parallel to the incident light. Starting with ordinary unpolarized light a Nicol prism thus transmits plane polarized light only.

If two Nicols are lined up one behind the other as in Fig. 47H, they form an optical system frequently used in specially constructed microscopes for studying the optical properties of other crystals. The first Nicol which is used to produce plane-polarized light is called the *polarizer* and the second which is used to test the light is called the *analyzer*.

In the parallel position, diagram (a), the polarized light from the polarizer passes on through the analyzer. Upon rotating the analyzer through 90° as in diagram (b) no light is transmitted. For the same reason that the *O* vibrations in the original beam were totally reflected in the polarizer, the *E* vibrations are totally reflected as *O* vibrations in the analyzer.

Rotated another 90°, the light again gets through the analyzer just as in the parallel position in diagram (a). Still another 90° finds the Nicols crossed again with no light passing through.

47.5. Polarization by Selective Absorption. When ordinary light enters a crystal of tourmaline, double refraction takes place in much the same way that it does in calcite, but with this difference: one ray, the so-called *O* ray, is entirely absorbed by the crystal, while the other ray, the *E* ray, passes on through. This phenomenon is called selective absorption because the crystal absorbs light waves vibrating in one plane and not those vibrating in the other.

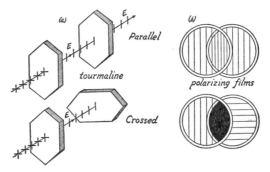

Fig. 47I—Diagrams illustrating the polarization of light by (a) tourmaline crystals, and (b) polarizing films.

Tourmaline crystals are therefore like Nicol prisms, for they take in ordinary light, dispose of the *O* vibrations, and transmit plane-polarized light as illustrated in Fig. 47I(a). When two such crystals are lined up parallel with one behind the other, the plane-polarized light from the first crystal passes through the second with little loss in intensity. If either crystal is turned at 90° to the other, i.e., in the *cross position*, the light is completely absorbed and none passes through.

The behavior of tourmaline and similar optical substances is due to the molecular structure of the crystal. To draw an analogy, the regularly spaced molecules of a single crystal are like the regularly spaced trees in an orchard or grove. If one tries to run between the rows of trees carrying a very long pole held at right angles to the direction of motion the pole must be held in a vertical position. If it is held in the horizontal plane the runner will be stopped.

The reason tourmaline is not used in optical instruments in place of Nicol prisms is that the crystals are yellow in color and do not transmit white light.

A more satisfactory substance for this purpose which does transmit white light is a relatively new manufactured material known as "Polaroid." This material is made in the form of very thin films, which have the general appearance of the more common substance "Cellophane," and is made from small needle-shaped crystals of an organic compound *iodosulphate of quinine*. Lined up parallel to each other and embedded in a *nitrocellulose mastic*, these crystals act like tourmaline by absorbing one component of polarization and transmitting the other. Two such films mounted separately in rings between thin glass plates are shown schematically in Fig. 47I. In the crossed position no light can pass through both films, whereas in the parallel position white light vibrating in the plane indicated by the parallel lines is transmitted. Polarizing films of this kind are finding many practical applications, particularly wherever glaring light is not desired. The glaring light reflected at an angle from a table top, a book, a window pane, the water, or the road ahead when driving a car, is polarized and can be partly eliminated by polarizing films.

47.6. Dispersion by a Calcite Prism. In Fig. 47J a prism is shown cut from a calcite crystal with the optic axis parallel to the refracting edge *A*. The optic axis, being perpendicular to the page, is represented by dots. (For the direction of the optic axis in calcite see Fig. 47E.)

When white light is incident on one side of this prism, two completely separated spectra emerge from the other side. Not only is each spectrum complete in all its colors from red to violet but the light in each is plane-polarized. This can be demonstrated with an analyzing device like a Nicol prism, or polarizing film. By inserting the analyzer anywhere in the light beam and rotating it, one spectrum disappears first and then 90° from it the other fades and disappears while the other returns to full intensity.

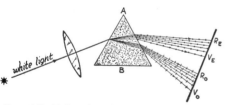

FIG. 47J—Refraction of white light by a prism cut from a calcite crystal.

The vibrations of all colors in the lower spectrum in Fig. 47J are perpendicular to the optic axis and are *O* vibrations. The upper spectrum with all vibrations parallel to the optic axis consists of *E* vibrations. If a prism were cut so that the refracted light as it travels through the crystal is parallel to the optic axis only one spectrum is produced.

47.7. Scattering and the Blue Sky. The blue of the sky and the red of the sunset are due to a phenomenon called scattering. When sunlight passes through the earth's atmosphere much of the light is "picked" up by the air molecules and given out again in some other direction. The effect is quite similar to the action of water waves on floating objects. If, for example, the ripples from a stone dropped in a still pond of water encounter a small cork floating on the surface, the cork is set bobbing up and down with the frequency of the passing waves.

Light is pictured as acting in the same way on air molecules and fine dust particles. Once set into vibration by a light wave a molecule or particle can send out the absorbed light again, sometimes in the same direction but generally in almost any other direction. This is illustrated schematically in Fig. 47K. In diagram (a) waves of light are shown being scattered at random in all directions.

(a)

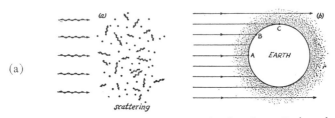

Fig. 47K—Schematic diagrams showing the scattering of light by the air molecules of the earth's atmosphere.

Experiments show, in agreement with the theory of scattering, that the shortest waves are scattered more readily than longer waves. To be more specific, the scattering is inversely proportional to the fourth power of the wave length.

$$\text{Scattering} \propto \frac{1}{\lambda^4}. \tag{47b}$$

According to this law the short waves of violet light are scattered ten times as readily as the longer waves of red light. The other colors are scattered by intermediate amounts. Thus when sunlight enters the earth's atmosphere, *violet* and *blue light* are scattered the most, followed by *green, yellow, orange,* and *red,* in the order named. For every ten violet waves ($\lambda = 0.00004$ cm) scattered from a beam there is only one red wave ($\lambda = 0.00007$ cm).

At noon on a clear day when the sun is directly overhead, as illustrated by an observer at A in diagram (b), the whole sky appears as *light blue.* This is the composite color of the mixture of colors scattered most effectively by the air molecules. As illustrated by the spectral color distribution in Fig. 45F, light blue of the color triangle is obtained by the added mixture of *violet, blue, green,* and *yellow.*

47.8. The Red Sunset. The occasional observation of an orange-red sunset is attributed to the *scattering of light* by fine dust and smoke particles near the earth's surface. This is illustrated in Fig. 47L. To an observer at *A* it is noonday and the direct sunlight from overhead, seen only by looking directly at the sun itself, travels through a relatively short dust path. As a result, very little violet and blue are scattered away and the sun appears white.

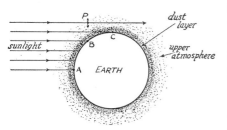

Fig. 47L—The scattering of light by a layer of dust near the earth's surface causes the sun to turn yellow, then orange, and finally red at sunset.

As sunset approaches, however, the direct sunlight has to travel through an ever-increasing dust path. The result is that an hour or so before sundown, when the observer is at *B*, practically all of the blue and violet have been scattered out and, owing to the remaining colors, red, orange, yellow, and a little green, the sun appears yellow. At sunset, when the observer is at *C*, the direct rays must travel through so many miles of dust particles that all but red are completely scattered out and the sun appears red. At this same time the sky overhead is still light blue. If the dust blanket is too dense, even the red will be scattered appreciably from the direct sunlight and the deepening red sun will become lost from view before it reaches the horizon.

An excellent demonstration of scattering by fine particles is illustrated in Fig. 47M. A parallel beam of white light from a carbon arc and lens L_1 is sent through a water trough with glass sides. After passing through an iris diaphragm at the other end a second lens L_2 forms an image of the cir-

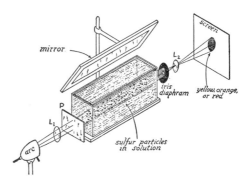

Fig. 47M—The sunset experiment. Demonstration of the scattering and polarization of light by small particles.

cular opening on the screen. To produce the fine particles for scattering, about 40 gm of photographic fixing powder (hyposulfite of soda) are first dissolved in about 2 gallons of water. Next, about 1 to 2 cm³ of concentrated sulphuric acid are added and the two thoroughly mixed in the trough.*

---

* The correct amount of acid to produce the best results is determined by trial. The first visible precipitate should appear after 2 or 3 min.

As the microscopic sulfur particles begin to form, scattered blue light will outline the parallel beam through the trough. A little later, when more particles have formed, the entire body of water will appear light blue, due principally to multiple scattering. Light scattered out of the central beam of light is scattered again and again before emerging from the trough. At first the transmitted light which falls on the screen appears white. Later, as more scattering takes out the shorter wave lengths, this image representing the sun turns yellow, then orange, and finally red.

47.9. Polarization by Scattering. If the blue of the sky is observed through a Nicol prism or a piece of polaroid, the light is found to be partially plane-polarized. This polarization can also be seen in the scattering experiment described above. Observed through a polaroid film the beam in the tank appears bright at one orientation of the polaroid and disappears with a 90° rotation.

PROBLEMS

1. Calculate the polarizing angle for blue light incident on crown glass. See Table 42A for index.

2. The polarizing angle for green light incident on a clear transparent material is 67.6°. Calculate the refractive index and identify the material from Table 42A. (*Ans.* $\mu = 2.427$, diamond.)

3. The polarizing angle for yellow light incident on a clear transparent solid is 57.8°. Calculate the refractive index and identify the material.

4. Find the polarizing angle for a clear plastic with a refractive index of 1.455 for yellow light. (*Ans.* 55.5°.)

5. The polarizing angle of a piece of glass, for green light, is 60°. Find the angle of minimum deviation for a 60° prism made of the same glass.

6. If the polarizing angle of a piece of clear plastic is 55°, find the angle of minimum deviation for a 70° prism made of the same plastic. (*Ans.* 40.0°.)

7. If the critical angle of a clear crystal for green light is 24.4°, calculate the polarizing angle.

8. The critical angle for violet light incident on a piece of glass is 36°. (a) Identify this glass in Table 42A, and (b) calculate its corresponding polarizing angle. (*Ans.* (a) dense flint, (b) 59.5°.)

9. Zinc sulfide deposited on a glass surface is a clear transparent material having a refractive index of 2.50. Calculate the polarizing angle for this medium.

10. A 60° calcite prism is cut with its faces parallel to the optic axis. Calculate the angle of minimum deviation for yellow light for each of the two polarized rays. The refractive index for calcite for the O ray is 1.658, and for the E ray, 1.486. (*Ans.* 52° and 36°.)

11. Find the polarizing angle for the boundary separating water of index 1.33 from glass of index 1.52. Assume the incident ray to be in water.

12. Find the amount of light, relative to yellow light, scattered by each of the following wave lengths of light: ultraviolet light 2.0×10^{-5} cm, violet light 4.0×10^{-5} cm, yellow light 5.8×10^{-5} cm, red light 7.0×10^{-5} cm, and infrared light 10×10^{-5} cm. (*Ans.* 77, 4.8, 1.0, 0.51, and 0.12 times, respectively.)

Electricity at Rest   Chapter 48

48.1. Electrification by Friction. It is impossible to say when electricity was first discovered. Records show that as early as 600 B.C. the attractive properties of amber were known. Thales of Miletus (640-546 B.C.), one of the "seven wise men" of ancient Greece, is credited with having observed the attraction of amber, when previously rubbed, for small fibrous materials and bits of straw. Amber was used by these people even as it is now, for ornamental purposes. Just as the precious metals had their names of gold and silver, so amber had its name "electron."

Although the electrification of amber by friction was handed down from one writer to another, nothing new about the phenomenon was discovered for more than two thousand years. It was not until the beginning of the seventeenth century that Sir William Gilbert* announced the discovery that many substances can be electrified by friction. Gilbert named this effect "electric" after the word "electron." It is now a well-established fact that all bodies when rubbed together become electrified and that amber is just one of a number of substances which show the effect most strongly.

48.2. Electrostatic Attraction. The word electrostatic means electricity at rest, and the word attraction refers to the force exerted by one body upon another at a distance. To demonstrate electrostatic attraction one often uses a rubber or amber rod and rubs it with a piece of flannel or fur. This electrifies the rod so that when it is held close over some small bits of paper they jump up to the rod and hold fast. *wood, H₂O*

The attraction of an electrified rubber rod for wood is illustrated in Fig. 48A. A small arrow cut from a piece of dry wood is mounted so that it is free to turn as shown. When the electrified rubber rod is brought near to

---

* Sir William Gilbert (1540-1603), court physician to Queen Elizabeth and a noted philosopher and experimental physicist. In 1600 he published a book on magnetism, "De Magnete." This book was full of valuable facts and experiments on electricity and magnetism, and among other things contained many criticisms of his contemporaries, predecessors and the early philosophers. In his preface he wrote: "Why should I submit this new philosophy to the judgment of men who have taken oaths to follow the opinions of others, to the most senseless corrupters of the arts, to lettered clowns, grammatists, sophists, spouters, and the wrong-headed rabble. To you alone true philosophers, ingenious minds, who not only in books but in things themselves look for knowledge, have I dedicated these foundations of magnetic science." So strongly does he advocate here, and carry out, himself, the experimental method that he is to be classed as a scientist with his contemporary Galileo, "the father of modern physics."

the pointed end of the arrow it attracts the wood, turning the arrow until it points toward the rod. Brought near the opposite end, the wood is again attracted, turning the arrow to point away from the rubber rod.

An ordinary hard rubber comb when drawn through the hair becomes charged with electricity and will attract light objects in the same way. So great are the electrical charges produced on a comb sometimes that tiny

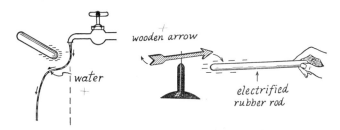

wooden arrow

water

electrified rubber rod

Fig. 48A—A rubber rod, electrified by rubbing against a piece of fur, attracts wood as shown by the turning of the arrow, and water by the bending of the stream.

sparks can be seen to jump between the comb and hair. This is particularly noticeable in a darkened room. These sparks are the cause for the crackling noise so often heard when hair is being combed.

A spectacular effect is produced by bringing a charged rubber rod close to one side of a smoothly running stream of water from a faucet. As shown at the right of Fig. 48A, the stream is diverted to one side and even into the horizontal before it falls again.

An ordinary sheet of writing paper placed on the panel of a door or other similar flat surface and rubbed will hold fast and remain there for some little time without falling down.

48.3. Electricity + and —. When two different substances are rubbed together and then separated, both are found to be electrified, one with one kind of electricity and the other with another. To illustrate this, one end of a rubber rod is charged by rubbing with fur and then suspended in a small wire stirrup as shown in Fig. 48B. When the electrified end of a similarly charged rod is brought close by, as shown in diagram (a), the suspended rod turns away, showing repulsion. If the fur is brought close by in place of the rubber, the suspended rod is attracted and turns toward the fur. When a glass rod, previously rubbed with silk, is brought close by, as in diagram (b), there is attraction, and when the silk is brought up there is repulsion.

Since the fur, as well as the glass, attracts the electrified rubber rod, they each have the same kind of electrification: they are said to be *positively charged*. By similar notation the rubber and silk by their actions are said to be *negatively charged.* Positive charges are designated by a (+) sign and negative charges by a (−) sign.

Not only do the above experiments indicate the existence of two kinds of electrification but also demonstrate a rule concerning the action of one kind on another. Diagram (a), illustrating a negatively charged rubber rod repelling a similar rod, shows that two negative charges repel each other. Dia-

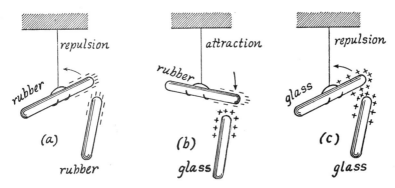

Fig. 48B—Like charges of electricity repel each other and unlike charges attract.

gram (b) shows that positive and negatives charges attract each other, and diagram (c) that two positive charges repel each other. The general law can therefore be stated that *like charges repel and unlike charges attract.*

48.4. Theory of Electrification. Historically there have been two outstanding theories of electrification: the one-fluid theory of Benjamin Franklin* and the two-fluid theory of Charles Du Fay. According to the two-fluid theory all objects contain equal amounts of two fluids. When two different substances are rubbed together, one kind of fluid (positive) is spread over one object and the other kind of fluid (negative) over the other.

According to the one-fluid theory of Franklin all bodies contain a certain specified amount of an "electric fire" or fluid to keep them in an uncharged or neutral state. When two objects are rubbed together one accumulates an excess of fluid and becomes positively charged while the other loses fluid and becomes negatively charged. To Franklin we owe the terms "plus" and "minus," "positive" and "negative" electricity.

Both of these theories are in part correct, for now we know the mecha-

_____

* Benjamin Franklin (1706-1790). From printer's apprentice as a youth he became a man of unusual powers, not only in politics and diplomacy but also in scientific research. His most famous scientific achievement was the discovery of the electrical nature of lightning. This he did by flying a kite into the clouds on a stormy day and noting the electrical sparks at the ground end of the kite string (a copper wire). Among his many practical applications of scientific discoveries he invented the lightning rod and made the first pair of bifocal eyeglasses.

nism by which bodies become electrified by friction. The modern theory is based upon the principle already put forward—that all substances are made of atoms and molecules. Each atom contains a nucleus having a known amount of positive charge (see Fig. 48C). This positive charge is due to the presence in the nucleus of a certain number of *protons*. All protons are alike and have the same mass and positive charge. Around every atomic nucleus there are a number of negatively charged particles called *electrons*.

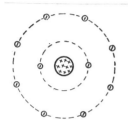

FIG. 48C—Schematic diagram of a neon atom showing its nucleus at the center with ten positively charged particles (called protons) surrounded on the outside by ten negatively charged particles (called electrons).

Normally each atom of a substance is electrically neutral; in other words, it has equal amounts of negative and positive charge. Since each electron has the same amount of charge as every other electron and the same amount as every proton but of opposite sign, there are just as many protons in every nucleus as there are electrons around the outside. While protons are much smaller than electrons in size, they contain the bulk of the mass of every atom. One proton, for example, weighs nearly two thousand times as much as an electron. The electrons therefore are light particles or objects around a small but relatively heavy nucleus.

Individual atoms or large groups of atoms and molecules have an *affinity,* an *attraction,* for additional electrons over and above the exact number which will just neutralize the positive charges of the nuclei. This attraction of the atoms for more than a sufficient number of electrons varies considerably from atom to atom and substance to substance. When, therefore, two different substances are brought into contact, the substance with greater electron affinity seizes nearby electrons from the other and thus acquires a net negative charge. Such is the case, for example, with rubber and amber when rubbed with fur. Having a strong affinity for electrons, both of these solids become strongly negative, whereas the fur becomes deficient of electrons and thereby positively charged.

48.5. The Electroscope. An electroscope is an instrument for measuring the electrical potential of a charged body. A thin strip of gold leaf is fastened to the side of a long narrow rod of metal and mounted in a metal and glass box (see Fig. 48D). The gold-leaf support, which will here be called the "stem," is insulated with amber from the box. When the metal knob N is touched by a charged rubber rod, some of the charge flows onto and distributes itself over the gold leaf and support. Since like charges repel each other, the gold leaf is pushed out as shown in the diagram. When the source of charge is taken away the electroscope retains its acquired charge, which, distributing itself more or less uniformly over the stem, causes the leaf, as shown in diagram (b), to stand out at a somewhat smaller angle. The more charge given the electroscope, the higher the gold leaf is repelled.

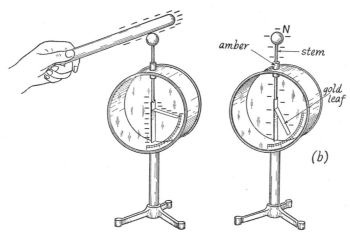

FIG. 48D—Diagrams of an electroscope showing how such an instrument may be given a negative charge.

If an electroscope is first charged negatively as shown in Fig. 48D(b) and then a negatively charged body is brought close to but not touching the knob, as shown in Fig. 48E(a), the gold leaf will rise as indicated. The reason is that the electrons are repelled away from the knob to the far end

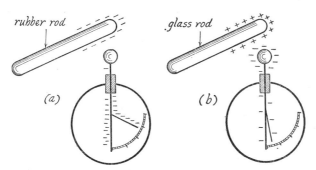

FIG. 48E—Brought near a negatively charged electroscope, (a) a negatively charged body causes the gold leaf to rise, and (b) a positively charged body causes the gold leaf to fall.

of the stem, causing the gold leaf to rise still higher. As long as the two bodies do not touch each other and allow more negatives to go to the electroscope, the gold leaf will fall back to its original angle when the negatively charged rod is taken away.

If a positively charged body is brought up as shown in Fig. 48E(b), negatives from the stem and gold leaf are attracted to the knob, causing the gold leaf to fall. *Thus with a negatively charged electroscope, a positive charge brought nearby causes the gold leaf to drop, and a negatively charged body causes it to rise.* If the electroscope is positively charged the reverse action will take place, a positive charge causes it to rise and a negative causes it to fall.

48.6. Conductors and Insulators. Not all substances are good conductors of electricity. As a general rule, metals are good conductors whereas nonmetals are poor conductors. The poorest of conductors are commonly called *insulators,* or *non-conductors.* Several examples of conductors and non-conductors are listed in Table 48A.

TABLE 48A. EXAMPLES OF SUBSTANCES THAT ARE GOOD ELECTRICAL CONDUCTORS AND OTHERS THAT ARE NON-CONDUCTORS OR INSULATORS

Conductors		Non-conductors	
Silver	Nickel	Glass	Sulfur
Aluminum	Platinum	Amber	Porcelain
Copper	Iron	Rubber	Paper
Gold	Mercury	Mica	Silk

The property of electrical conduction is illustrated by an experiment in Fig. 48F. One end of a long thin copper wire is connected to an electroscope and the other end to a small brass knob mounted on a glass pedestal. When

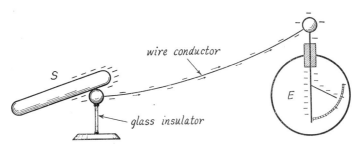

FIG. 48F—Experiment illustrating an electric current as the flow of electrons along a wire conductor.

a charged rubber rod is touched to the knob as shown, the gold leaf of the distant electroscope rises immediately. Electrons have been conducted along the wire. If a positively charged rod contacts the knob, electrons flow away from the electroscope, leaving the gold leaf with a positive charge.

If the copper wire in the above experiment is replaced by a non-conductor, like a silk thread, the electroscope cannot be charged by the rod contacting the distant knob. Poor conductors, such as glass and amber, are used to support metal parts of electrical apparatus for the purpose of insulating them from unnecessary losses of electricity. An electroscope, for example, will retain its electric charge well if the gold leaf and stem are insulated from the electroscope case with amber as shown in Fig. 48D.

The difference between a conductor and an insulator, or dielectric, is that in a conductor there are free electrons, whereas in an insulator all the electrons are tightly bound to their respective atoms. In an uncharged body there are an equal number of positive and negative charges. In metals a few of the electrons are free to move from atom to atom; so that when a negatively charged rod is brought to the end of a conductor it repels nearby free electrons in the conductor, causing them to move. They in turn repel free electrons in front of them, thus giving rise to a flow of electrons all along the conductor. Hence in Fig. 48F it is not necessarily the electrons from the charged rubber rod that actually reach the electroscope leaf, but rather the electrons from the end of the wire where it touches the electroscope knob.

There are a large number of substances that are neither good conductors of electricity nor good insulators. These substances are called *semi-conductors*. In them electrons are capable of being moved only with some difficulty, i.e., with considerable force.

48.7. The Law of Electrostatic Force. It has already been demonstrated that like charges repel and unlike charges attract. Nothing which has thus far been said, however, has indicated just how strong the repulsion or attraction might be, nor how it depends on the magnitude of the charges and the distance between them.

The first quantitative measurements of the force between two charged bodies was made by Coulomb, a French scientist and engineer, in 1780. He proved experimentally that *the force acting between two charges is directly proportional to the product of the two charges and inversely proportional to the square of the distance between them.* Symbolically this law is usually written as an algebraic equation,

$$F = k \frac{QQ'}{d^2} \tag{48a}$$

where F is the force, Q and Q' are the charges, and d is the distance between them (see Fig. 48G). The constant of proportionality, k, has a value which depends upon the units of charge chosen.

In the electrostatic system of units, force is measured in *dynes*, distance in *centimeters*, and *unit charge* is chosen so that $k = 1$. Coulomb's law with $k = 1$ then defines unit charge called the *electrostatic unit* or the *statcou-*

lomb. One electrostatic unit or, *one statcoulomb, is defined as that charge which when placed one centimeter from an equivalent charge exerts upon it a force of one dyne.*

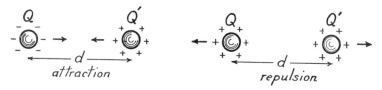

Fɪɢ. 48G—Coulomb's law. Two like charges repel each other, or two unlike charges attract each other, with a force proportional to the product of their charges and inversely proportional to the square of the distance between them.

In the *mks* system, force is given in *newtons*, distance in *meters*, charge in *coulombs*, and $k = 9 \times 10^9$. It is customary to define the coulomb in terms of electric currents. (See Sec. 49.3.) *One coulomb is that quantity of electric charge which flowing by any point in a wire in one second produces a current of one ampere.* Experimental measurements give as the best probable value *1* coulomb $= 2.9979 \times 10^9$ statcoulombs. For most practical uses we will assume

$$1 \text{ coulomb} = 3 \times 10^9 \text{ statcoulombs.}$$

Experiments described in later chapters show that electrons are all alike and that each carries a charge $e = 4.8022 \times 10^{-10}$ electrostatic units, (4.8022×10^{-10} statcoulombs) or

$$e = 1.6019 \times 10^{-19} \text{ coulomb.} \tag{48b}$$

This means that when a body has a unit negative charge of one coulomb it has an excess of 6.24×10^{18} electrons and that a body charged positively with one coulomb has a deficiency of 6.24×10^{18} electrons.

$$1 \text{ coulomb} = 6.24 \times 10^{18} \text{ electrons} \tag{48c}$$

Since the unit of charge in the *mks* system is measured in terms of electric currents the numerical value of k in Eq.(48a) must be determined experimentally. The best value to date is $k = 8.9878 \times 10^9$. For most practical problems the approximation $k = 9 \times 10^9$ will be used.

$$k = 9 \times 10^9 \frac{\text{newton-meter}^2}{\text{coulomb}^2} \tag{48d}$$

To simplify some of the equations that are derived from Coulomb's law it is convenient to introduce a new constant ϵ_0 in place of k,

$$k = \frac{1}{4\pi\epsilon_0} \tag{48e}$$

and write Coulomb's law

$$F = \frac{1}{4\pi\epsilon_0} \cdot \frac{QQ'}{d^2} \qquad (48f)$$

Using the numerical value of k from Eq.(48d) it follows that

$$\epsilon_0 = \frac{1}{4\pi \times 9 \times 10^9} = 8.85 \times 10^{-12} \frac{\text{coulomb}^2}{\text{newton-meter}^2} \qquad (48g)$$

This is the so-called rationalized *mks* system.*

Problem. A charge of $+25 \times 10^{-9}$ coulombs is located 6 cm from a charge of -72×10^{-9} coulombs. Calculate the force between them.

Solution. The given quantities are $Q = 25 \times 10^{-9}$ coulombs and $Q' = -72 \times 10^{-9}$ coulombs, $d = 0.06$ m. Substitution in Eq.(48a) gives

$$F = 9 \times 10^9 \frac{\text{newton-m}^2}{\text{coulomb}^2} \cdot \frac{(25 \times 10^{-9})(-72 \times 10^{-9}) \text{ coulomb}^2}{(0.06)^2 \text{ m}^2} \cdot$$

$$F = -4.50 \times 10^{-3} \text{ newton.}$$

The minus sign indicates attraction.

48.8. Attraction of Neutral Bodies. An interesting demonstration of electrostatic attraction is shown in Fig. 48H. A tiny ball cut from the pithy core of a corn cob is coated with tin foil or metallic paint and suspended by a silk thread. When a charged rod is brought near by as in (a), the pith ball is attracted to the rod and upon contact bounces away. As the rod is now moved toward the ball it avoids the rod and keeps as far away as possible.

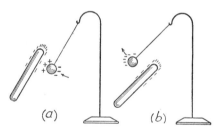

Fig. 48H—(a) A metallic coated pith ball is attracted by a charged rod. (b) After contact the pith ball is repelled.

To explain this result, assume the rod negatively charged in the position shown in (a). Free electrons on the sphere are repelled to the opposite side, leaving an equal number of positives on the near side unneutralized. Attraction now takes place because the positive charges are closest and the attractive force acting on them is greater than the repelling force on the negatives. When contact is made, negatives on the rod neutralize all the positives and the ball moves away with its negative charges by mutual repulsion.

48.9. Charging by Induction. To charge a body by induction is to give

---

* Some books define $\mathcal{E}_0$ by the equation $\mathcal{E}_0 = 1/k$ instead of $1/4\pi k$. Coulomb's law then becomes $F = QQ'/\mathcal{E}_0 d^2$, where $\mathcal{E}_0 = 1.11 \times 10^{-10}$. This is the so-called nonrationalized *mks* system. One must be careful in reading other texts to determine which system is being used.

it a charge without touching it. One method of inducing a charge is illustrated in Fig. 48I. Two metal spheres A and B, insulated by glass standards, are touching each other when a charged rubber rod is brought close to one of them. If sphere B is now moved away and then the rod removed from the

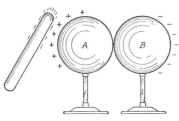

vicinity, both spheres are found to be charged, sphere A positively and sphere B negatively.

The explanation is similar to that of the pith ball in the preceding section, the close proximity of the charged rod repels free electrons from sphere A to the far side of sphere B leaving unneutralized positives behind. Separated under these conditions, both spheres are left with their respective

Fig. 48I—Experiment showing how bodies may be charged by induction.

charges. This is called *charging by induction.*

48.10. Faraday Ice-Pail Experiment. The distribution of charge over a metallic conductor can in part be demonstrated by an experiment first performed by Michael Faraday in 1810. This demonstration, known as *Faraday's ice-pail experiment,* involves a small metal ball, a hollow metal container like a tin pail, and an electroscope, as shown in Fig. 48J.

If the ball is charged from another source and then lowered into the pail, the leaf of the electroscope rises. Upon moving the ball around inside the pail and even touching the inside surface with it, no change in the potential is shown by the electroscope leaf. After the ball has been removed, the inner surface of the pail and the ball are found to be completely free of charge.

To explain what happens, let the ball be charged negatively and lowered to the position shown. Free electrons in the metal pail are repelled to the outer surface and to the connecting

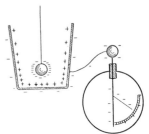

Fig. 48J—Diagram illustrating Faraday's ice-pail experiment.

electroscope, leaving positives on the inside unneutralized. When the ball touches the pail all negatives leave the ball and neutralize an equal number of positives. The fact that the electroscope leaf remains fixed when the ball is removed shows (1) that there is no redistribution of the negative charges on the outer pail surface, and (2) that the number of induced positives is equal to the number of negatives on the ball.

When static charges are acquired by a non-conductor like hard rubber, glass or amber, they remain where they were first located. When a conductor like copper, silver, or gold acquires a charge, however, the charge quickly spreads over the entire surface. With a metallic sphere, whether solid or hollow, the charge spreads uniformly over the surface as shown in Fig. 48 K. On other shaped conductors the charge distributes itself according to surface curvature, concentrating more at points and less where the walls are more nearly straight.

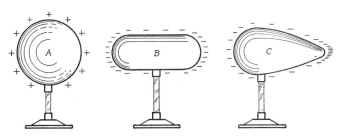

FIG. 48K—Charge density on conductors is greatest in regions of greatest curvature.

PROBLEMS

1. A positive charge of 5×10^{-8} coulomb is located 5 cm from a negative charge of 10×10^{-8} coulomb. Calculate the force in newtons exerted by either charge upon the other.

2. A charge of -5×10^{-7} coulomb is located 20 cm from another charge of -5×10^{-7} coulomb. Calculate the force in newtons exerted by one charge upon the other. (*Ans.* 0.056 newtons.)

3. Two charges of -9×10^{-7} coulomb each are located 6 cm apart. What is the repelling force on each in newtons?

4. Two unlike charges of 20×10^{-8} coulomb are each located 30 cm apart. What is the attracting force on each in dynes? (*Ans.* 400 dynes.)

5. Two equal charges are located 12 cm apart and repel each other with a force of 0.36 newtons. Find the magnitude of each charge in (a) electrostatic units, and (b) coulombs.

6. Two small metal spheres 24 cm apart, and having equal negative charges, repel each other with a force of 1×10^{-3} newton. Find the total charge on the two bodies in coulombs. (*Ans.* 8×10^{-8} coulomb.)

7. Three equal charges of $+8 \times 10^{-6}$ coulomb each are located at the corners of an equilateral triangle whose sides are 16 cm long. Calculate the resultant force on each charge.

8. Three equal charges of $+4 \times 10^{-8}$ coulomb are each located at the corners of a right triangle whose sides are 5 cm, 12 cm, and 13 cm respectively. Find the force exerted on the charge located at the 90° angle. (*Ans.* 5.8×10^{-3} newton at 10°.)

9. Four equal charges of $+6 \times 10^{-6}$ coulomb each are located at the corners of the square 4 cm on each side. Calculate the magnitude of the force on each charge and show its direction on a diagram drawn to scale.

10. Two positive charges, $+4 \times 10^{-7}$ coulomb each, are located at diagonally opposite corners of a square 3 cm on a side. Two negative charges -4×10^{-7} coulomb each are located at the other corners respectively. Calculate the resultant force on each charge and show this resultant on a diagram drawn to scale. (*Ans.* 1.46 newtons diagonally inward on each.)

Electricity in Motion   Chapter 49

WHEN an electric charge is at rest it is spoken of as *static electricity,* but when it is in motion it is referred to as an *electric current.* In most cases, an electric current is described as a flow of electric charge along a conductor. Such is the case, for example, in the experiment of charging an electroscope from a distant point by means of a long copper wire and a charged rubber rod (see Fig. 48F). This experiment is explained by stating that electrons already in the wire are pushed along toward the electroscope by the repulsion of electrons from behind. No sooner does this current start, however, than the negative charge of the rod is dissipated and the current stops flowing.

To make an electric current flow continuously along a wire, a continuous supply of electrons must be available at one end and a continuous supply of positive charges at the other (see Fig. 49A). This is like the flow of water through a pipe; to obtain a continuous flow a continuous supply of water must be provided at one end and an opening for its escape into some receptacle at the other. The continuous supply of positive charge at the one end of a wire offers a means of escape for the electrons. If this is not provided for, electrons will accumulate at the end of the wire and their repulsion back along the wire will stop the current flow.

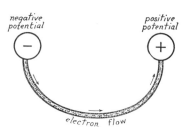

FIG. 49A—Two terminals at different potentials and connected by a conductor give rise to an electric current.

There are two general methods by which a continuous supply of electrical charge is obtained: one is by means of *a battery,* and the other is by means of *an electric generator.* The battery is a device by which chemical energy is transformed into electrical energy and the generator is a device by which mechanical energy is transformed into electrical energy.

49.1. Batteries. Batteries as continuous sources of electrical energy are the result of a long series of experiments which started with the discoveries of Alessandro Volta* more than one hundred years ago. Today battery cells

* Alessandro Volta (1745-1827), Italian scientist, and for more than twenty years professor of physics at Pavia. Traveling considerably throughout Europe he became acquainted with many celebrities. In 1801 he was awarded the Copley medal of the Royal Society of London, and then was called to Paris and awarded a medal by Napoleon. In 1815 the emperor of Austria made him director of the philosophical faculty of the University of Padua. A statue now stands in his memory at Como, his birthplace.

are manufactured in two common forms: (1) *dry cells* as used in flashlights, portable radios, etc., and (2) *wet cells,* as used in automobiles, airplanes, boats, etc.

Each cell of every battery has two terminals: one negative, the other positive. The difference of potential between the terminals of every dry cell, regardless of size, is approximately 1.5 volts, whereas the difference of potential between the terminals of a lead storage cell is approximately 2 volts. The concept of potential, and potential difference will be taken up in detail in the next chapter. The larger the cell, the greater is the amount of energy stored within it. When the available energy in dry cells becomes exhausted they are thrown away and new ones are secured, but when storage batteries become exhausted they are recharged.

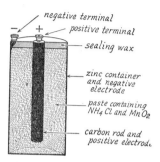

FIG. 49B—Cross-section diagram of a dry cell or "flashlight" battery, showing the essential elements.

The difference of potential between the terminals of any dry or wet cell depends in principle upon the particular chemicals used in its construction, whereas the total charge capacity depends upon the quantity of chemicals present.

The negative terminal of a dry cell is the zinc metal container in which

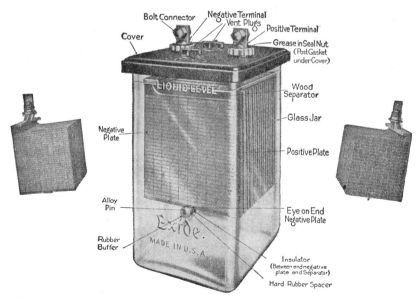

FIG. 49C—Photographs of the elements of a storage battery cell. (*Courtesy of the Electric Storage Battery Co.*)

all chemical ingredients are sealed, whereas the positive terminal is a round carbon rod, the end of which protrudes through the surface at one end (see Fig. 49B). The positive electrode of a storage cell, shown at the right in Fig. 49C, is a set of lead grills filled with porous lead dioxide (PbO_2) and fastened together with a single terminal at the top right-hand corner. The negative electrode, shown at the left, consists of a set of parallel grills filled with spongy lead (Pb). When these two sets of plates are put together with glass or wood separators and the entire ensemble immersed in *dilute sulphuric acid,* as in the center figure, chemical activity between the lead and acid gives rise to electric charges. The details of this process belong to that branch of science called physical chemistry and will not be treated here.

49.2. Battery Cells in Series and Parallel. The storage battery in the average automobile contains three wet cells *connected in series.* By series connections is mean that the ($+$) terminal of one cell is connected to the ($-$) terminal of another, etc., as illustrated in Fig. 49D. Two dry cells are also connected in series in diagram (b) and two others in parallel in diagram (c).

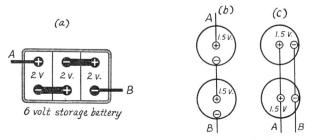

Fig. 49D—Diagrams of battery cells connected in series and parallel. (a) A storage battery of three cells connected in series. (b) Two dry cells connected in series. (c) Two dry cells connected in parallel.

The purpose of connecting two or more cells in series is to obtain a higher potential difference than that available with one cell alone. The potential difference between the end terminals A and B of any battery is just the sum of those for the individual cells. The three cells of a storage battery, for example, give $2 + 2 + 2$ or 6 volts and the two dry cells in diagram (b) give $1.5 + 1.5$, or 3 volts. One hundred dry cells in series would give 100×1.5 or 150 volts, while fifteen wet cells in series would give 15×2 or 30 volts.

When battery cells are connected in parallel, the potential difference of the combination is not raised above that of any one of the cells alone. Such connections are seldom made and only then if the cells are of the same kind and voltage. As shown in diagram (c) the potential difference between A and B is 1.5 volts. Occasionally it happens that the voltage of a cell is high enough for the purpose for which it is to be used but it cannot supply a large enough current. Connecting several small cells in parallel, or using a single but large cell, will overcome this difficulty.

49.3. Electric Currents. When the two ends of a wire are connected to the terminals of a battery as illustrated in Fig. 49A, electrons from the negative terminal flow through the wire to the positive terminal. This electric current continues to flow as long as the wire remains connected, and the battery is able to supply negative charges at the one electrode and positive at the other. The free electrons in the wire near the (+) terminal are attracted by the (+) charge, those near the (−) terminal are repelled by the negative charge, and those distributed all along the wire are pushed along by other electrons coming up from behind. This is why the potential difference between two battery terminals, which may be thought of as a kind of driving force behind the electrons, is sometimes called the *electromotive force* (abbr. *e.m.f.*).

Electric current is measured in units called *amperes*. *The ampere,* named in honor of the French physicist Ampère,* *is defined as the flow of one coulomb per second.* In other words, one coulomb flowing past any given point in a wire in one second constitutes a current of one ampere (amp). If twice this quantity passes by in one second the current is 2 amp. Thus electric current is analogous to the rate of flow of water through a pipe.

$$\text{Current} = \frac{\text{quantity of charge}}{\text{time}},$$

$$1 \text{ ampere} = \frac{1 \text{ coulomb}}{1 \text{ second}}, \qquad I = \frac{Q}{t}. \qquad (49a)$$

Remembering that one coulomb = 6.24×10^{18} electrons (see Sec. 48.7), a current of one ampere means a flow of 6.24×10^{18} electrons per second past any given point.

This enormous number does not mean that the electrons are moving with high speed through a conductor. Actually the number of moving charges is so large that their average velocity is but a small fraction of a millimeter per second. When we picture a solid conductor as a crystal lattice, similar to that shown in Fig. 23E, the electrons are thought of as moving through the intervening spaces. This movement is not completely free, however, but is influenced by the repulsion and attraction of like and unlike charges.

Many years ago, before it was known which of the electric charges (+)

---

* André M. Ampère (1775-1836), French physicist and mathematician. Ampère began his career as professor of physics and chemistry at Bourg at the early age of 26 and later established the relation between electricity and magnetism, and helped to develop the subject he called electrodynamics. His only son, Jean J. Ampère, also became famous as a philologist, lecturer, and historian.

or (—) moved through a wire there seemed to be some evidence that it was the positive charge and not the negative. This notion became so thoroughly entrenched in the minds of those interested in electrical phenomena that in later years, when it was discovered that the electrons move in solid conductors and not the positives, it became difficult to change.

The convention that electric currents flow from plus to minus is still to be found in many books and is used by some electrical engineers in designing electrical machines and appliances. The rapid growth and the importance of radio engineering and electronics, however, is bringing about a change in this practice and we shall hereafter in this text speak of current as one of electron flow from (—) to (+), and call it *electron current*.

49.4. Resistance. Every material object offers some resistance to the flow of an electron current through it. Good conductors like the metals, copper, silver, and aluminum, offer very little resistance, while non-conductors such as glass, wood, and paper offer a very high resistance.

The unit by which resistance is measured is called the *ohm*, in honor of the German physicist G. S. Ohm.* The standard international ohm is defined as the resistance offered to a steady electric current by a column of mercury 1 sq mm in cross section and 106.3 cm long at a temperature of 0°C. An iron wire of these dimensions has a resistance of about one-tenth of an ohm. In the *mks* system the unit of resistance is the *volt per ampere*. *One volt per ampere is called one ohm.*

There are several factors that determine the electric resistance of any wire: (1) the material of which it is composed, (2) the size of the wire, and (3) its temperature. If the length of a wire is doubled its resistance is likewise doubled; if the cross-sectional area is doubled the resistance is halved. In more general terms, the resistance of a wire is proportional to its length and inversely proportional to its cross-sectional area. Symbolically,

$$R = \rho \frac{L}{A}, \qquad\qquad (49b)$$

where R is the resistance, L the length, A the cross-sectional area, and ρ the resistivity of the material in question. Resistivity is defined as the resistance of a wire 1 m long and 1 m² in cross-section. Values of this constant are

---

* George Simon Ohm (1787-1854), German physicist, was born at Erlavgen and educated at the university there. After teaching mathematics in Cologne for sixteen years, and in Nuremberg for sixteen more, he became professor of experimental physics in the high school at Munich. His writings were numerous and but for one exception were not of the first order. This single exception consists of a pamphlet on electric currents, the most important part of which is summarized in what is now called "Ohm's law." For this work he was awarded the Copley Medal of the Royal Society of London in 1841 and made a foreign member of the society one year later.

given for several common metals in Table 49A. The smaller the constant ρ, the better is the substance as a conductor.

TABLE 49A. RESISTIVITY OF METALS, ρ, IN OHM METERS

Aluminum	$\rho = 3.2 \times 10^{-8}$	Mercury	$\rho = 94.1 \times 10^{-8}$
Bismuth	$\rho = 119 \times 10^{-8}$	Silver	$\rho = 1.05 \times 10^{-8}$
Copper	$\rho = 1.72 \times 10^{-8}$	Tungsten	$\rho = 5.5 \times 10^{-8}$
Iron	$\rho = 15 \times 10^{-8}$	Platinum	$\rho = 11 \times 10^{-8}$

To find the resistance of any sized wire made of one of these metals, the value of ρ is inserted in Eq.(49b) along with the length and cross-sectional area, and the value of R is calculated. To illustrate the method, consider the following:

Example. Find the resistance of a copper wire 1 sq. mm in cross-section and 300 m long.

Solution. If we use Eq.(49b) and remember that there are 1000 mm in 1 m, we find that

$$R = 1.72 \times 10^{-8} \frac{300 \text{ m}}{1 \times 10^{-6} \text{ m}^2} = 5.16 \text{ ohms.} \tag{49c}$$

The greater the resistivity of a wire the poorer it is as an electrical conductor. Because of this a term called the *conductivity* is sometimes used to specify the current carrying ability of a material and is defined as the reciprocal of the resistivity. $\sigma = 1/\rho$.

49.5. Ohm's Law. This is the well known and fundamental law in electricity which makes it possible to determine the current flowing through a circuit when the resistance of the circuit and the potential difference applied to it are known. What Ohm discovered was that the ratio of the potential difference between the ends of a metallic conductor and the current flowing through the metallic conductor is a constant. The proportionality constant is the electrical *resistance*.

$$\text{resistance} = \frac{\text{potential difference}}{\text{current}}.$$

Symbolically, Ohm's law is often written,

$$R = \frac{V}{I}, \qquad \text{or} \qquad 1 \text{ ohm} = \frac{1 \text{ volt}}{1 \text{ ampere}}. \tag{49d}$$

The law is of great importance because of its very general application to so many electrical phenomena. One of its simplest applications is illustrated in Fig. 49E. A dry cell is directly connected by wires to a small light bulb. The battery maintains a potential difference of 1.5 volts across the lamp. If the electron current flowing through the circuit is 0.5 ampere, the resistance of the circuit is

$$R = \frac{1.5 \text{ volts}}{0.5 \text{ amp.}} = 3 \text{ ohms.}$$

Although the resistance as found here is assumed to be the resistance of the light bulb, it really includes the resistance of the connecting wires, as well as the resistance of the battery. See Sec. 49.8.

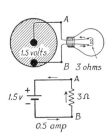

In practice one usually uses wires of sufficiently low resistance that they can be neglected in most calculations. If they are not small, they cannot be neglected and must be added in as part of the R in Ohm's law.

Although *electromotive force* and *potential difference* are both measured in *volts* there is a real distinction between them. *Electromotive force is defined as the work per unit charge done by the battery or generator on the charges in moving them around the circuit. Potential difference between two points is defined as the work per unit charge done by the charges in moving from the one point to the other.*

Fig. 49E—Two different diagrams of the same electrical circuit consisting of one dry cell and one small light bulb.

If any two of the three quantities, *resistance, current,* and *potential difference* are known for a circuit, the third can always be determined by substituting in Ohm's law. In other words, any one of the three factors may be the unknown, and Ohm's law may be written in any one of three ways:

$$I = \frac{V}{R} \qquad R = \frac{V}{I} \qquad V = IR. \tag{49e}$$

49.6. Resistors in Series and Parallel. When several electrical devices are connected together in series the resistance R of the combination is equal to the sum of the resistances of the individuals. Symbolically,

$$R = R_1 + R_2 + R_3 + R_4 + \text{etc.} \tag{49f}$$

This, *the law of series resistances,* is illustrated by an application of Ohm's law to the complete electric circuit in Fig. 49F(a). Three resistors $R_1 = 5$ ohms, $R_2 = 1$ ohm, and $R_3 = 3$ ohms are connected in series with a battery of nine storage cells. The sum of the resistances given $R = 5 + 1 + 3 = 9$ ohms, and the emf of the battery $V = 9 \times 2 = 18$ volts. Applying Ohm's law (Eq.49d), the electron current flowing through the circuit is

$$I = 18/9 = 2 \text{ amp.}$$

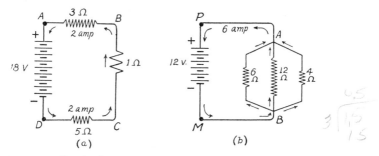

F<small>IG</small>. 49F—Circuit diagrams for (a) three resistors in series, and (b) three resistors in parallel.

This means that the same electron current flows through the high resistance as well as the low. Like water flowing through pipes of different sizes connected one after the other, just as much water passes through one pipe per second of time as through any other, and none can accumulate at any point.

When several resistors are connected together in parallel the reciprocal of the resistance of the combination is given by the sum of the reciprocals of the individual resistors.

$$\frac{1}{R} = \frac{1}{R_1} + \frac{1}{R_2} + \frac{1}{R_3} + \ldots \text{ etc.} \qquad (49\text{g})$$

This, *the law of parallel resistances,* is illustrated by the complete circuit diagram in Fig. 49F(b).

Three resistors $R_1 = 6$ ohms, $R_2 = 12$ ohms, and $R_3 = 4$ ohms are connected in parallel to a battery of six storage cells giving a total emf across PM of 12 volts. To find the electron current supplied by the battery the equivalent resistance R of R_1, R_2 and R_3 is first determined.

Substitute known values in Eq.(49g).

$$\frac{1}{R} = \frac{1}{6} + \frac{1}{12} + \frac{1}{4}.$$

Express each fraction in terms of a common denominator.

$$\frac{1}{R} = \frac{2}{12} + \frac{1}{12} + \frac{3}{12} = \frac{6}{12}.$$

Invert both sides of the equation.

$$\frac{R}{1} = \frac{12}{6} \quad \text{or} \quad R = 2 \text{ ohms.}$$

Now applying Ohm's law, $I = V/R$,

$$I = \frac{12}{2} = 6 \text{ amp.}$$

Thus 6 amp flow from the $(-)$ terminal at M along the wire to the junction at B where it divides into three parts. Coming together again at junction A the total electron current of 6 amp flows to the terminal P.

To determine just how the electron current divides, that is, how much flows through one resistor and how much through the other, Ohm's law may be applied to each resistor separately.

For R_1,	$I_1 = 12/6 \ = 2$ amp,
for R_2,	$I_2 = 12/12 = 1$ amp,
and for R_3,	$I_3 = 12/4 \ = 3$ amp.

If these are the correct currents, their sum must check with the total electron current calculated first: $I = 2 + 1 + 3 = 6$ amp, the same as before.

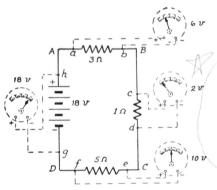

FIG. 49G—Series resistances showing drop in potential as measured by a voltmeter.

At B in Fig. 49F(b) the current divides, 2 amperes going through R_1, 1 ampere going through R_2 and 3 amperes going through R_3.

This problem illustrates one of Kirchhoff's two laws for electric currents, namely, *in any closed network of electrical conductors carrying electric currents the sum of the currents flowing into any branch point is equal to the sum of the currents flowing out.* A branch point is a point in a network at which three or more conductors are joined.

Kirchhoff's second law states that the algebraic sum of the emf's in any closed loop of a network equals the algebraic sum of the potential drops around the loop.

49.7 Drop in Potential, or IR Drop.

When an electron current flows through a closed circuit there is a potential drop all along the line from the $+$ terminal of the battery to the $-$. Consider, for example, the series circuit in Fig. 49F where the electron current I through the entire system was found by Ohm's law to be 2 amp. If, while the current is flowing, a voltmeter is connected across any

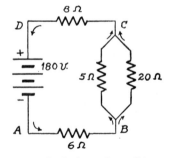

FIG. 49H—Series and parallel resistances in the same circuit.

one of the resistors (see Fig. 49I), the instrument pointer will indicate the voltage shown beside each dotted figure. In each case this reading, representing the potential difference between the two points where the voltmeter is connected, is referred to by electrical engineers as the *IR* drop.

The *IR* drop across any part of a circuit is given by the electron current through that part multiplied by the resistance. Between the points *a* and *b* the electron current is 2 amp, and the resistance is 3 ohms. The product *IR* or 6 volts is in agreement with the reading of the voltmeter. Similarly the *IR* drop from *c* to *d* is 2 amp $\times$ 1 ohm, or 2 volts, and the drop from *e* to *f* is 2 amp $\times$ 5 ohms, or 10 volts.

The *IR* drop from *a* to *d*, i.e., across the two resistors of 3 ohms + 1 ohm, is 2 amp $\times$ 4 ohms, or 8 volts, while from *a* to *f*, i.e., across all three resistors 3 ohms + 1 ohm + 5 ohms, the drop is 2 amp $\times$ 9 ohms or 18 volts. This latter is equivalent to the emf supplied by the battery and to the reading of the voltmeter when connected to the two points shown.

Starting at *A* and going clockwise around the circuit the potential drops 6 volts in crossing to *B*, two volts more in crossing to *C*, and ten volts more in crossing to *D*. In crossing the battery from *D* to *A* the potential rises 18 volts.

Example. A battery supplies a potential difference of 180 volts to the ends of a circuit containing four resistors of 5, 6, 8, and 20 ohms as shown in Fig. 49H. Calculate (a) the equivalent resistance of the 5 and 20 ohm parallel combination, (b) the electron current supplied by the battery, and (c) the electron current through each resistor.

Solution. (a) Apply the law of parallel resistances, Eq.(49g).

$$\frac{1}{R} = \frac{1}{5} + \frac{1}{20} = \frac{4}{20} + \frac{1}{20} = \frac{5}{20},$$

from which, by inverting, we obtain

$$R = 20/5 = 4 \text{ ohms.}$$

(b) Since the parallel combination of 5 and 20 ohms is equivalent to 4 ohms, and it is in series with the other two of 6 and 8 ohms, respectively, the three are added by the law of series resistance, Eq.(49f),

$$R = 6 + 4 + 8 = 18 \text{ ohms.}$$

Apply Ohm's law, Eq.(49d).

$$I = \frac{V}{R} = \frac{180 \text{ volts}}{18 \text{ ohms}} = 10 \text{ amp.}$$

(c) The electron current of 10 amp flows through the 6-ohm resistor and divides at the parallel circuit. Combining again at *C* the total electron current flows through the 8-ohm resistor. To find how the current divides in the parallel circuit the *IR* drop across that circuit is found.

$$IR = 10 \text{ amp} \times 4 \text{ ohms} = 40 \text{ volts}.$$

This value of 40 volts is the potential difference between B and C. If we apply Ohm's law to each of the two resistors separately, we obtain

$$I = \frac{40 \text{ volts}}{5 \text{ ohms}} = 8 \text{ amp} \quad \text{and} \quad I = \frac{40 \text{ volts}}{20 \text{ ohms}} = 2 \text{ amp}.$$

Hence 8 amp flows through the 5-ohm resistor and 2 amp through the 20-ohm resistor. Note that these currents are in inverse proportion to their resistances.

49.8. Internal Resistance.

If a voltmeter is connected to the terminals of a battery when it is supplying an electron current to some circuit, and again when the circuit is open and there is no current flowing, the two readings will not be the same. On *open circuit* the voltmeter reading will be a maximum and will indicate the electromotive force of the battery. When the circuit is closed and an electron current I flows around the circuit, the internal resistance of the battery gives rise to an IR drop.

To illustrate the principles involved consider a battery of cells (see Fig. 49I) for which a voltmeter on *open circuit* shows an electromotive force of

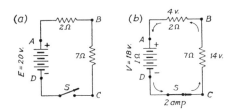

20 volts. When the switch S is closed as in diagram (b) the circuit resistance is a series combination of two external resistors of 2 ohms and 7 ohms respectively, and one internal battery resistor of 1 ohm. The combined resistance of the circuit is therefore $R = 2 + 7 + 1 = 10$ ohms.

In applying Ohm's law we now use the electromotive force of the battery and write

Fig. 49I—Illustrating the difference of potential across a battery on (a) open circuit, and (b) closed circuit.

$$I = \frac{E}{R} = \frac{20 \text{ volts}}{10 \text{ ohms}} = 2 \text{ amp}.$$

With an electron current of 2 amperes through the entire circuit, the IR drops across each of the two external resistors are 4 volts and 14 volts respectively, and the drop across the battery resistance is 2 volts. The sum of these must be equal to 20 volts, the emf of the battery. With a battery emf of 20 volts and an internal IR drop of 2 volts on closed circuit, the terminal voltage, that is the potential difference between A and D, will be 18 volts.

Note that the electron current flows through the battery as well as the external circuit. The battery here is analogous to a water pump which supplies the energy to maintain a continuous stream of water flowing around a pipe circuit and back through the pump.

49.9. The Wheatstone Bridge. An accurate method commonly employed for measuring resistance is known as the Wheatstone Bridge. As shown in Fig. 49J this device consists of an electrical network of four resistors R_1, R_2, R_3 and X, a galvanometer G and a battery V. By sliding the contact D along the straight resistance wire AB a point is located where the galvanometer current is zero. Under these conditions the electron

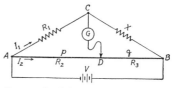

Fig. 49J—Slide-wire Wheatstone Bridge.

current I_1 must go on through X, the current I_2 must go on through R_3 and points C and D must be at the same potential. From the latter it is seen that the potential difference across R_1 must be the same as that across R_2, and the difference across X must be the same as that across R_3. Hence we can write

$$I_1R_1 = I_2R_2 \qquad \text{and} \qquad I_1X = I_2R_3.$$

Dividing the second equation by the first gives

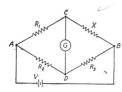

Fig. 49K—Wheatstone Bridge.

$$\frac{I_1X}{I_1R_1} = \frac{I_2R_3}{I_2R_2} \qquad \text{or} \qquad X = R_1\frac{R_3}{R_2} \tag{49h}$$

Since the resistors R_2 and R_3 are proportional to the wire lengths p and q, their ratio q/p can be substituted for R_3/R_2. Knowing the value of R_1 and measuring the lengths of p and q the unknown resistance X can be calculated. In some arrangements the slide-wire AB is done away with, and three adjustable resistance boxes are used for R_1, R_2 and R_3 as shown in Fig. 49K.

49.10. The Potential Divider. A potential divider is an electrical circuit constructed around a variable resistor or rheostat with one sliding contact. Connected to a battery as shown schematically in Fig. 49L, its purpose is to supply any desired potential difference from zero up to the full voltage of the battery.

Suppose, as an illustration, that a battery supplies 20 volts to the extreme ends of a resistance wire AB and a voltmeter V is connected to one end A and sliding contact C. When the slider C is at A the voltmeter will read zero but as it moves down toward B the reading will steadily rise. One-quarter of the way along the voltmeter will read 5 volts, half-way along 10 volts, three-quarters of the way 15 volts, and finally at B it will

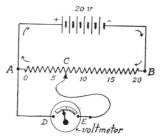

Fig. 49L—Potential divider circuit for obtaining variable voltage.

read 20 volts. As a general rule the potential difference is directly proportional to the length of the resistance wire between A and C.

As a sample calculation let the total resistance A to B in Fig. 49L be 100 ohms. By Ohm's law the current through AB will be

$$I = \frac{20 \text{ volts}}{100 \text{ ohms}} = 0.2 \text{ amp.}$$

Let C be located three-quarters of the way along toward B so that the resistance A to C is $100 \times \frac{3}{4}$, or 75 ohms. The IR drop across this portion is, therefore,

$$IR = 0.2 \times 75 = 15 \text{ volts,}$$

as read by the voltmeter.

PROBLEMS

1. An electric light bulb connected to a house lighting circuit of 110 volts draws a current of 0.25 amp. (a) Calculate the number of coulombs per second flowing through the wire. (b) How many electrons per second pass by any given point in the wire?

2. A wire 1 mm in diameter and 1 km long is made of copper. What is its total resistance? (*Ans.* 21.9 ohms.)

3. The heater wire in a small stove is made of iron ribbon wire, 0.01 cm by 0.05 cm in cross-section and 2 m long. Calculate its resistance.

4. A fine platinum wire 0.1 mm in diameter and 50 cm long is used as the sensitive element in an electrical resistance thermometer. Find the resistance. (*Ans.* 7 ohms.)

5. A battery of 2 dry cells in series is used in a flashlight having a bulb with a resistance of 25 ohms. Find the electron current when the light is turned on.

6. A storage battery of 6 cells is used in a truck. Each headlight bulb has a resistance of 2.5 ohms. Find the current supplied to each bulb. (*Ans.* 4.8 amp.)

7. Three resistors $R_1 = 7$ ohms, $R_2 = 12$ ohms, and $R_3 = 8$ ohms, are connected in series, and then to a battery of 10 dry cells. Calculate the electron current flowing.

8. Three resistors $R_1 = 8$ ohms, $R_2 = 10$ ohms, and $R_3 = 40$ ohms are connected in parallel. Find the equivalent resistance. (*Ans.* 4 ohms.)

9. Three resistors of 3, 6, and 9 ohms respectively are connected in parallel. Calculate the equivalent resistance of the combination.

10. Two resistors $R_1 = 5$ ohms, and $R_2 = 20$ ohms are connected in parallel and then to a battery whose terminal voltage is 40 volts. Calculate (a) the equivalent resistance of the two parallel resistors, (b) the electron current supplied by the battery, and (c) the electron current flowing through R_1 and R_2 separately. (*Ans.* (a) 4 ohms, (b) 10 amps, (c) 8 amps, and 2 amps.)

11. Three resistors of 10, 20, and 30 ohms respectively are connected in series and then to a battery with a terminal voltage of 120 volts. Calculate (a) the electron current through the circuit, and (b) the drop in potential across each resistance.

12. Two resistors $R_1 = 10$ ohms and $R_2 = 14$ ohms are connected in series to a battery whose voltage on open circuit is 50 volts. If the internal resistance of the battery is 1 ohm, find (a) the resistance of the circuit, (b) the electron current in the circuit, (c) the drop in potential across R_1 and R_2 and (d) the voltage across the battery. (*Ans.* (a) 25 ohms, (b) 2 amps, (c) 20 v and 28 v, (d) 48 v.)

13. Two resistors of 20 and 80 ohms respectively are connected in parallel and the combination connected to a 70 volt battery whose internal resistance is 1.5 ohms. Find (a) the resistance of the external circuit, (b) the electron current supplied by the battery, (c) the electron current through the external resistance, and (d) the voltage across the battery.

14. Two resistors $R_1 = 12$ ohms and $R_2 = 24$ ohms are connected in parallel. The combination is connected in series to a third resistor $R_3 = 6$ ohms, and a 120 volt battery with an internal resistance of 1 ohm. Find (a) the current through the battery, (b) the drop in potential across the parallel circuit, (c) the current through each resistor, and (d) the voltage across the battery. (*Ans.* (a) 8 amps, (b) 64 v, (c) 5.33, 2.66, and 8 amps, (d) 112 v.)

15. Three resistors $R_1 = 3$, $R_2 = 4$, and $R_3 = 12$ ohms respectively are connected in parallel. This combination is connected in series to two other resistors of $R_4 = 3$ and $R_5 = 5$ ohms respectively, and to a 25 volt battery with an internal resistance of 0.5 ohm. Calculate (a) the equivalent resistance of the parallel combination, (b) the resistance of the entire circuit, (c) the current supplied by the battery, (d) the drop in potential across each resistor, and (e) the voltage across the battery.

16. A parallel combination of two resistors 6 ohms and 12 ohms respectively are connected in series to another parallel combination of 10 ohms and 15 ohms respectively. The ends are connected to a battery whose *emf* is 105 volts and internal resistance is 0.5 ohm. Find (a) the current through each resistor and (b) the difference of potential across the battery. (*Ans.* (a) 6.66, 3.33, 6, and 4 amps respectively, (b) 100 v.)

17. Referring to Eq. (49a) show that $IL = Qv$, where Q is the amount of charge free to move in the length L of a conductor, and v is the average speed of these charges when the current flowing through the conductor is I.

18. There are 10^{22} conduction electrons (electrons free to move from atom to atom) per cubic centimeter of copper. Find the average speed of these electrons when a current of one ampere flows through a copper wire 1 sq mm in cross-section. (*Ans.* 0.0624 cm/sec.)

19. An unknown resistor is connected to a Wheatstone bridge and the variable resistances adjusted until the galvanometer G shows no current. See Fig. 49K. The resistors R_1, R_2, and R_3 have values of 100, 650, and 2470 ohms respectively. Find the unknown resistance.

20. An unknown resistor X is connected to a slide wire Wheatstone bridge as shown in Fig. 49J. When the galvanometer G shows no current, $R_1 = 92$ ohms, the wire AB is 100 cm long, and the wire section AD is 65 cm. Find the resistance of X. (*Ans.* 49.5 ohms.)

21. Three resistors of 2, 6, and 4 ohms, respectively, are connected in series. Another three resistors of 5, 8, and 11 ohms, respectively, are connected in series. These two sets are then connected in parallel to a battery of 120 volts. Calculate (a) the current supplied by the battery, (b) the current through each series group, and (c) the IR drop across each resistor.

22. A potential divider is composed of a 200 volt battery and a straight slide wire resistor AB, 100 cm in length. What is the potential difference between any two points on the slide wire (a) 5 cm apart, and (b) 1 cm apart? (*Ans.* (a) 10 volts, (b) 2 volts.)

Electric Field, Potential, and Capacitance
Chapter 50

50.1. The Electric Field. In the space around a charged body is an invisible something called *an electric field*. This field is just another way of describing the action at a distance of one charge upon another. The intensity of *the electric field at any point in the neighborhood of a charged body is equal to the force per unit charge exerted on any charge placed at that point.*

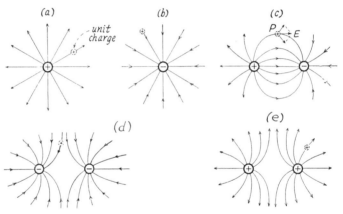

(a) (b) (c)

(d)

(e)

Fig. 50A—Illustrating the electric field and lines of force in the neighborhood of charged bodies.

Since force is a vector quantity, an electric field has magnitude and direction. The field about a positive charge is therefore radially outward as shown in Fig. 50A(a). It is radially outward since a positive charge placed at any point is repelled along a line through the two charges. By a similar reasoning the field about a negative charge is radially inward as shown in diagram (b).

The electric field around two charged bodies is shown in diagrams (c), (d), and (e). Each of these fields may be experimentally mapped by placing a positive charge at any one point and moving it always in the direction of the force F exerted on it. The lines traced out by such a charge are called *electric lines of force.* It is to be noted that as many lines as desired can be drawn and that no two lines ever cross. Furthermore, the lines themselves are imaginary and do not actually exist. They were first introduced by Michael Faraday about 1820 as an aid to the understanding of various electrical phenomena.

The direction of the lines of force is given by the arrowheads and the relative magnitude of the field at any region is given by the relative number of the lines passing through that region. In agreement with Coulomb's law *the intensity of the field at any point near a single charged body is inversely proportional to the square of the distance away.*

Since E, the electric field intensity, is defined as the force per unit charge placed there, F/Q, Coulomb's law may be used to obtain a formula for the field intensity at any point near a small body of charge Q. Transposing Q' to the other side in Eq.(48a) gives

$$\frac{F}{Q'} = k\frac{Q}{d^2}, \qquad \text{or} \qquad E = k\frac{Q}{d^2}. \tag{50a}$$

The charge Q is in *coulombs*, the distance d to the field point is in *meters*, the field E at that point is in *newtons per coulomb*, and $k = 9 \times 10^9$ newton meters^2/coulomb^2. See Eq.(48d). Since E represents the force per unit charge, the force on any charge Q' placed at that point will be

$$F = Q' \times E$$
$$\left(1 \text{ newton} = 1 \text{ coulomb} \times 1 \frac{\text{newton}}{\text{coulomb}}\right). \tag{50b}$$

Example 1. A proton is an atomic particle having a mass of 1.672×10^{-27} kg and a positive charge of 1.602×10^{-19} coulombs. Calculate the force on a proton in an electric field of 5000 newtons per coulomb and compare this with its weight.

Solution. To find the electrical force apply Eq.(50b).

$$F = Q'E = 1.602 \times 10^{-19} \times 5 \times 10^3 = 8.010 \times 10^{-16} \text{ newton.}$$

To find the weight of a proton apply Eq.(6b).

$$W = mg = 1.672 \times 10^{-27} \times 9.80 = 1.638 \times 10^{-26} \text{ newton.}$$

A comparison of these two forces clearly indicates how negligibly small the gravitational force on atomic particles is when compared with the force due to electric fields commonly employed in the laboratory.

Electric field intensity E having both magnitude and direction is a vector quantity. It is to be noted in diagram (c) of Fig. 50A that the field at any point is the vector resultant E of the two fields of force, one due to each charge. Knowing the amount of charge on each body and the distance between them, one can use Eq.(50a) to calculate the field intensity E at any point P.

Example 2. Two charges $Q_1 = -5 \times 10^{-9}$ coulomb and $Q_2 = +16 \times 10^{-9}$ coulomb are located 5 m apart. Find the electric field intensity at a point 3 m from Q_1 and 4 m from Q_2.

Solution. To find the electric field at any point we must find the resultant force per unit charge on any charge placed there. The geometry of this problem becomes that shown in Fig. 50B. Note that the field due to Q_1 is a vector directed toward Q_1 itself while that due to Q_2 is a vector directed away from Q_2 itself. The magnitudes of these two fields, by Eq. (50a) are,

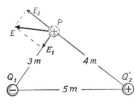

$$E_1 = 9 \times 10^9 \frac{-5 \times 10^{-9}}{3^2} = -5 \text{ newtons/coulomb.}$$

FIG. 50B—Illustrating the electric field intensity at a point P near two charges Q_1 and Q_2.

$$E_2 = 9 \times 10^9 \frac{16 \times 10^{-9}}{4^2} = +9 \text{ newtons/coulomb.}$$

Since the triangle forms a right angle at P, the fields E_1 and E_2 are at right angles to each other and their resultant E is given by

$$E = \sqrt{(-5)^2 + (9)^2} = 10.3 \text{ newtons/coulomb.}$$

50.2. Electrical Potential.

When a body has an excess of electrons (and is not close to other charged bodies), it has a *negative potential*. When it has a deficiency of electrons it is said to have a *positive potential*. There are numerous exceptions to this, however, and it is customary to define positive potential and negative potential in a more general way. This is usually done as follows. If the connection of a body to the ground by an electrical conductor would cause electrons to flow onto the body from the ground, the body is at a *positive potential* (see diagram (a) in Fig. 50C). Conversely if the connection of a body to the ground would cause electrons to flow off the body into the ground, the body is at a negative potential (see diagram (b)).

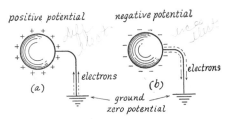

FIG. 50C—Showing the direction of the flow of electrons when a positively or a negatively charged body is connected to the ground by a wire conductor.

In these definitions of positive and negative potential *it is assumed that the earth is at zero potential*. The bodies therefore had positive and negative potentials respectively before they were grounded, but after they were grounded the flow of electrons *to* or *from* the ground brought them to *zero potential*. Electrical potential is analogous to the potential energy of a body in mechanics. In mechanics if a body is raised to a certain height above sea level its potential energy is positive, i.e., it can in returning to the ground perform work. Conversely, a body below sea level has a negative potential energy for in lowering it to that point energy is given up. To raise it again requires the expenditure of energy. Just as sea level is sometimes taken as the zero level of potential energy in mechanics, so the earth's potential is taken as the zero point of potential in electricity.

A quantitative definition of electrical potential is usually given in terms of work or energy. *The electric potential of a body is equal to the amount of work per unit positive charge done in carrying any charge from the ground up to the charged body.* If the work done is large the potential of the body is highly positive. If the work done is negative, i.e., if work is given up, the potential is negative. As a rule this energy is expressed in *volts*, and we speak of a potential of a body as being $+110$ volts, -2500 volts, etc.

It is also proper to speak of the potential of a point located anywhere in the free space around one or more charged bodies. *(The electric potential at any point in an electric field is equal to the work per unit positive charge done in carrying any charge from the ground up to that point.)* To give specific units to this definition, if the unit of charge is one coulomb and the work done is one joule, the potential is one volt.

$$1 \text{ volt} = 1 \text{ joule}/1 \text{ coulomb.}$$

One one-thousandth of a volt is called a *millivolt* (*mv*), one-millionth of a volt a *microvolt* (μv), one thousand volts a *kilovolt* (*kv*), and one million volts a *megavolt* (*Mv*). In the *cgs*, or electrostatic system of units a potential of one *erg/statcoulomb* is called one *statvolt*. 1 *statvolt = 300 volts*.

The work per unit positive charge done in carrying a charge from the ground up to a point near a small body of charge Q is given by

$$V = k\frac{Q}{d} \tag{50c}$$

where d, as shown in Fig. 50D, is the straight line distance from the center of the charged body to the unit test charge, and k is given by $1/4\pi\epsilon_0$. See Eq.(48f).

If the charge is located on a small spherical conductor of radius r the potential at all points outside the sphere is the same as though the charge were concentrated at the center. At all points inside the sphere the potential is the same as it is at the surface, namely

$$V = k\frac{Q}{r}. \tag{50d}$$

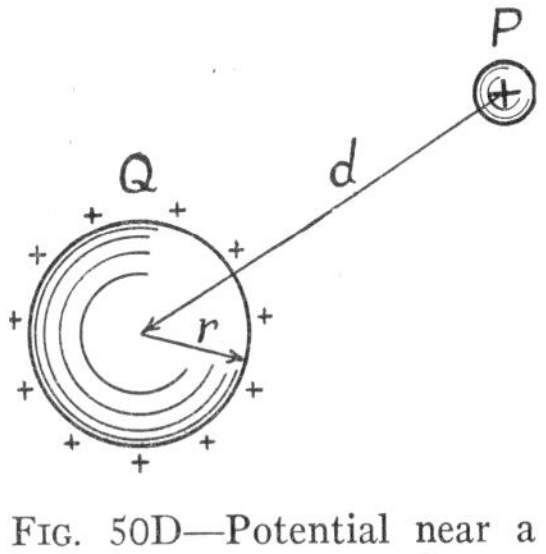

Fig. 50D—Potential near a charged spherical conductor.

The electric intensity at all points inside a charged spherical conductor is zero.

It will be noted from Eq.(50c) that as d is made larger and approaches infinity, V becomes smaller and approaches zero. Mathematically speaking then the ground, referred to in the above definitions and statements, with its arbitrary assigned potential of zero, corresponds in Eq.(50c) to $d = \infty$.

Example 3. A spherical conductor of radius 1 cm has a charge of $+ 25 \times 10^{-10}$ coulombs. Calculate the potential at a point 10 cm from the center.
Solution. Apply Eqs.(50c) and (48d).

$$V = 9 \times 10^9 \frac{25 \times 10^{-10}}{0.10} = 2.25 \text{ volts.}$$

Since energy is a scalar quantity, potential is also a scalar and has no direction. Therefore the potential of a point in space, not far from a number of charged bodies, is given by the arithmetic sum of the potentials at that point due to each of the charged bodies separately.

It follows from the definitions of potential above that if V represents the work per unit charge done in carrying *any charge* from infinity up to some given point or body, the work done W in carrying a charge Q' from infinity to that point or body will be given by

$$W = VQ' \tag{50e}$$

where W represents the stored potential energy and in the *mks* system is measured in *joules*.

50.3. Potential Difference. Since the potential of a body is defined as the work per unit positive charge done in carrying any charge from infinity to that body, *the difference of potential V between two bodies is defined as the work per unit positive charge done in carrying any charge from one of the bodies to the other.* For example, the potential difference between the two terminals of a car storage battery is 6 volts. This means that the work per unit positive charge done in carrying a charge from one terminal to the other is 6 joules per coulomb.

50.4. Uniform Electric Field. In many experimental studies of atomic structure a great deal of knowledge can be obtained by observing the behavior of charged atomic particles traversing a uniform electric field. To obtain such a field, that is, a field constant in magnitude and direction over a specified volume of space, two flat metal plates are set up parallel to each other as shown in Fig. 50E.

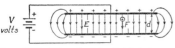

When the terminals of a battery with an electromotive force of V are connected to these plates, as indicated in the diagram, a uniform electric field E is produced between the plates. Outside the plates and near the ends the field is not uniform.

Fig. 50E—The electric field between two parallel charged plates is uniform.

In mechanics *work done* is defined as *force times distance, $W = F \times d$.*

The electrical equivalent of this equation follows, therefore, by direct substitution of the equivalent electrical quantities for W and F. Since work done per unit charge is potential difference V, and the force per unit charge is the electrical field intensity E, see Eqs.(50b) and (50e), the work equation $W = F \times d$ becomes

$$V = E \times d \qquad \text{or} \qquad E = \frac{V}{d}. \tag{50f}$$

If V is in volts and d is in meters, E is in *volts/meter*.

$$1 \ volt/meter = 1 \ newton/coulomb.$$

50.5. The Capacitor and Its Capacitance. A capacitor is an electrical device for storing quantities of electricity in much the same way that a reservoir is a container for storing water, or a steel tank is a container for storing gas. Two plates or sheets of metal when separated by *air, glass, mica,* or some other *dielectric* form a capacitor.

Quantitatively, the capacitance of a capacitor is a measure of its ability to store up electricity. To increase the capacitance of a capacitor one or more of the following things can be done: first, the area of the plates may be increased; second, the plates may be put closer tbgether; and third, a more suitable dielectric may be inserted between the plates. If the plates of a capacitor are small in area and at the same time relatively far apart, the capacitance is small. If the area is large and the plates close together, the capacitance is large.

The principles of the capacitor are illustrated in Fig. 50F. One plate of the capacitor in each diagram is grounded and the other is insulated. To start with, assume that none of the plates are charged. If the insulated plate (the right-hand plate) is now given a positive charge as shown in diagram (a), electrons from the ground are attracted to the other plate. If the insulated plate is given a negative charge as in diagram (b), electrons are repelled from the other plate into the ground. Being always in good electrical contact with the ground, both

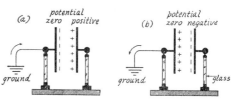

Fig. 50F—Diagrams of simple condensers showing the potentials of the two plates, one of which is grounded.

left-hand plates are by definition at zero potential. The right-hand plate in (a) has a positive potential, since, if connected to the ground, electrons would flow to it neutralizing the positives; whereas the right-hand plate in (b) has a negative potential, since, if connected to the ground, its electrons would escape into the ground.

In both diagrams of Fig. 50F the capacitors are charged. If, while in the charged condition, the two plates of a capacitor are suddenly connected together by a conductor, the negatives can flow through the conductor to the positives, thus neutralizing the charges. The capacitor has thus been discharged.

During the time a capacitor is being charged the plates acquire a greater and greater difference of potential. If in Fig. 50F(b) more electrons are added to the insulated plate the potential difference is increased. The amount of charge stored up in this way is limited only by the breakdown of the dielectric between the two plates. When the charge becomes too great a spark will jump between the plates, thus discharging the capacitor.

Capacitance is not determined by the amount of charge a capacitor will hold before sparking occurs; it is defined as the amount of charge Q on one plate necessary to raise the potential V of that plate one volt above the other. Symbolically,

$$C = \frac{Q}{V}. \tag{50g}$$

The unit of capacitance, the *farad,* named in honor of Michael Faraday is defined as the capacitance of a capacitor of such dimensions that *a charge of one coulomb will give the plates a difference of potential of one volt.*

$$1 \text{ farad} = \frac{1 \text{ coulomb}}{1 \text{ volt}}. \tag{50h}$$

Whether one plate of a 1-farad capacitor is grounded or not, the potential difference between the plates will be one volt when one plate has a positive charge of one coulomb and the other plate has a negative charge of one coulomb. Grounding simply brings that plate to zero potential without changing its charge.

A capacitance of one farad is very large and for practical purposes is not used. The microfarad is more convenient. The smaller unit is one-millionth of the farad and is abbreviated μf. In other words, one million microfarads are equivalent to one farad. A still smaller unit, the micro-microfarad, is sometimes used. One micromicrofarad is one-millionth of one microfarad and is abbreviated μμf.

The charging of a capacitor until the difference of potential is one volt is analogous to raising the level of water in a tank to one foot, whereas the charging of the same capacitor to the point where it sparks over is like filling the tank until water runs over the top. A large capacitance is like a tank of large cross-sectional area, and a small capacitance is like a tank of small area. It takes more charge to raise the potential of a large capacitance one volt, and it takes more water to raise the level in a large tank one foot.

Capacitors in common use today are of various kinds, sizes, and shapes.

Perhaps the most common is the so-called "paper capacitor" used commonly in radios and the ignition system of automobiles. Two long strips of tin foil are glued to the two faces of a strip of thin paper. This paper is then soaked in paraffin or oil and rolled up with another strip of paper into a small compact unit. Each sheet of tin foil becomes one plate of the capacitor and the paper becomes the dielectric separating them.

Another type of capacitor is the variable capacitor commonly used in tuning radios (see Fig. 50G). The capacitance of such a device can be varied in amount at will by the turning of a knob. The turning of a knob moves one set of plates between the other set, thus increasing or decreasing the effective plate area, and hence, the capacitance. The capacitance of such variable air capacitors is from zero to some 4000 μμf.

50.6. Calculation of Capacitance. A general formula for calculating the capacitance of a parallel plate capacitor is the following:

Fig. 50G—Variable capacitor commonly used in radio sets. Capacity 0—500μμf. (*Courtesy General Radio Co.*)

$$C = \varepsilon \frac{A}{d} \qquad (50i)$$

where, as shown in Fig. 50H, A is the area of either of the parallel plates, d is the distance between them in meters, ε a constant of the separating medium, and C is the capacitance in farads.

The constant ε called the *permittivity* is the product of the constant $\varepsilon_0 = 8.85 \times 10^{-12}$ and K the *dielectric constant* or *dielectric coefficient*.

$$\varepsilon = \varepsilon_0 K. \qquad (50j)$$

Values of these two constants are given for a few common dielectrics in the following table.

TABLE 50A. DIELECTRIC CONSTANT K, AND PERMITTIVITY ε AT 0°C.

Dielectric	K	ε	Dielectric	K	ε
Vacuum	1.0000	8.85×10^{-12}	Mica	3-6	$27\text{-}54 \times 10^{-12}$
Air	1.0006	8.85 "	Glycerine	56	500 "
Glass	5-10	45-90 "	Petroleum	2	18 "
Rubber	3-35	22-300 "	Water	81	717 "

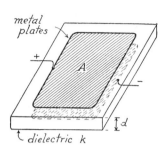

metal plates

A

d

dielectric k

Fig. 50H—Showing the elements of a condenser.

In the *mks* system permittivity has the units of farads/meter or, what is the equivalent, coulombs²/newton meter².

Example. Two rectangular sheets of tinfoil, 20 cm by 25 cm are stuck to opposite sides of a thin sheet of mica 0.1 mm thick. Calculate the capacitance if the dielectric constant is 5.

Solution. The given quantities are $K = 5$, $d = 1 \times 10^{-4}$ m, and $A = 0.20 \times 0.25 = 0.05$ m². By substituting in Eqs. (50i) and (50j), we obtain

$$C = 5 \times 8.85 \times 10^{-12} \frac{0.05}{1 \times 10^{-4}} = 221 \times 10^{-10} \text{ farad} = 0.0221 \ \mu\text{f.}$$

When capacitors are connected in parallel, as shown in Fig. 50I, their combined capacitance is just the arithmetic sum of the individual capacities.

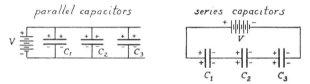

parallel capacitors   *series capacitors*

V C_1 C_2 C_3 V C_1 C_2 C_3

Fig. 50I—Parallel and series connections for capacitors.

When capacitors are connected in series, however, the combined capacitance is given by the reciprocal of the sum of the reciprocals.

Parallel Capacitors   Series Capacitors

$$C = C_1 + C_2 + C_3 + \cdots \qquad \frac{1}{C} = \frac{1}{C_1} + \frac{1}{C_2} + \frac{1}{C_3} + \cdots \quad (50k)$$

It should be noted with care that these two formulas are just the reverse of those for series and parallel resistors. The first of these formulas is derived from the principle that capacitors in a series combination acquire the same charge Q given by $Q = CV$ while $V = V_1 + V_2 + V_3$. The second formula is derived from the principle that capacitors in a parallel combination each have the same potential difference V given by $V = Q/C$, while $Q = Q_1 + Q_2 + Q_3$.

PROBLEMS

1. A small steel ball hangs from a silk thread and is given a negative charge of 2×10^{-7} coulomb. What is the electric field strength at a distance of (a) 1 cm, (b) 5 cm, and (c) 25 cm from the center?

2. A metal bearing ball is supported on the end of a thin glass rod and given a positive charge of 8×10^{-9} coulomb. What is the electric intensity at a distance of (a) 2 cm, (b) 5 cm, and (c) 10 cm from the center? (*Ans.* (a) 1.80×10^5 newtons/coulomb, (b) 2.88×10^4 newtons/coulomb, (c) 7.20×10^3 newtons/coulomb.)

3. Two insulated metal spheres 50 cm apart each have a charge of 5×10^{-8} coulomb. Calculate (a) the field intensity, and (b) the potential at a point 1.2 m from one charge and 1.3 m from the other.

4. A hollow metal ball 20 cm in diameter is given a charge of -5×10^{-8} coulomb. What is the potential at a point (a) 1 m from the center, (b) on the surface of the ball, and (c) inside the ball? (*Ans.* (a) -450 v, (b) -4500 v, (c) -4500 v.)

5. Calculate the work done in carrying a charge of $+6 \times 10^{-8}$ coulomb from the ground to an insulated metal sphere having a charge of $+4 \times 10^{-7}$ coulomb.

6. A metal sphere is suspended by a silk thread and charged positively. If in carrying a plus charge of 5×10^{-8} coulomb from the ground to the metal sphere, an amount of work equal to 6×10^{-5} joules is done. What is the potential of the sphere with respect to the ground? (*Ans.* $+1200$ v.)

7. A potential difference of 5000 volts is applied to two parallel plates 2 cm apart. A small metal sphere with a charge of 1.8×10^{-10} coulomb is located midway between the plates. Find (a) the electric intensity between the plates, and (b) the force on the charged sphere.

8. A potential difference of 500 volts is applied to the two parallel plates of an oscilloscope tube. If the plates are 1 cm apart, what is the force on an electron as it passes through between the plates? The charge on an electron is 1.602×10^{-19} coulomb. (*Ans.* 8.01×10^{-15} newton.)

9. A battery of 7000 volts is applied to the two parallel plates of an air condenser. If the plates are 5 mm apart, what is the force on an electron when it passes between the two plates?

10. A high voltage source of 25,000 volts is applied to two parallel plates 5 cm apart. A small metal sphere when touched to the negative plate acquires a charge of -1.5×10^{-9} coulomb. (a) What is the diameter of the sphere, and (b) how much work is done in carrying this charge across to the other plate? (*Ans.* (a) 1.08 mm, (b) -3.75×10^{-5} joules.)

11. Two sheets of tinfoil 45×66 cm are glued to opposite faces of a glass plate 0.12 mm thick. Find its capacitance. Dielectric constant for glass $= 5.7$.

12. A capacitor is made up of 16 sheets of tinfoil each 6×10 cm, separated by mica sheets 0.25 mm thick. Find the capacitance in microfarads if alternate sheets of tinfoil are connected together. Dielectric constant of mica $= 4.8$. (*Ans.* 1.53×10^{-2} μf.)

13. A variable air capacitor (see Fig. 50G) is made up of 15 semicircular duraluminum plates 8 cm in diameter. Find its maximum capacitance in micromicrofarads if alternate plates are connected together for the rotor and the remaining plates for the stator. Assume the air gap between adjacent plates to be 0.5 mm.

14. Solve problem 13 if the capacitor is immersed in castor oil of dielectric constant 4.6. (*Ans.* 2860 $\mu\mu$f.)

15. Three capacitors 4, 6, and 12 μf respectively are connected in series. Find (a) the capacitance of the combination, (b) the total charge stored by the combination when connected to a 250 volt source, and (c) the charge on each capacitor.

16. Three capacitors 4, 5, and 20 μf are connected in series to a 300 volt battery. Find (a) the capacitance of the combination, (b) the charge on each capacitor, and

(c) the voltage across each capacitor. (*Ans.* (a) 2 μf, (b) 6 $\times$ 10^{-4} coul, (c) 150, 120, and 30 v.)

17. Two capacitors of 5 and 20 μf respectively are connected in series, and the combination is connected in parallel to a third capacitor of 12 μf. The whole combination is connected to a 500 volt source. Find (a) the capacitance of the combination, (b) the charge on each capacitor, and (c) the voltage across each capacitor.

18. Two capacitors of 10 μf each are connected in parallel, and the combination is connected in series with a 5 μf capacitor. The ends of this entire combination are connected in parallel to a 12 μf capacitor. Find (a) the resultant capacitance, (b) the charge on each capacitor if the combination is connected to a 5000 volt battery, and (c) the potential difference across each capacitor. (*Ans.* (a) 16 μf, (b) 0.01, 0.01, 0.02, and 0.06 coul, (c) 1000, 1000, 4000, and 5000 v.)

19. A hollow sphere 5 cm in diameter is charged negatively, and the potential at a point 12.5 cm from the nearest point on the sphere is 10 volts. Find the charge on the sphere.

20. Two metal spheres 10 cm in diameter are insulated from each other. One is given a negative charge of 1 $\times$ 10^{-8} coulomb. What is the potential difference between them? (*Ans.* 3600 v.)

21. Two metal spheres 8 cm in diameter are to be charged by equal amounts, one plus and the other minus, until the potential difference between them is 1000 volts. How much charge should each one have?

22. An electronics technician has three capacitors, 3, 6, and 18 μf respectively. How should these capacitors be connected to obtain a capacitance of (a) 1.8 μf, (b) 6 μf, and (c) 20 μf. (*Ans.* (a) All in series, (b) 3 and 6 in parallel and the combination in series with the 18, (c) 3 and 6 in series and this combination in parallel with 18.)

23. Find all capacitance values that can be obtained with the following capacitors: 4, 8, and 24 μf, respectively.

24. Starting with the formula $Q = CV$, and the left-hand diagram in Fig. 50I, derive the formula for the capacitance of capacitors connected in parallel.

25. Starting with the formula $Q = CV$, and the right-hand diagram in Fig. 50I, derive the formula for the capacitance of capacitors connected in series.

Magnetism   Chapter 51

MAGNETISM was known to the early Greek philosophers. One story goes that Magnes, a shepherd, when on Mt. Ida of the island Crete, was so strongly attracted to the ground by the tip of his staff and the nails in his shoes that he had difficulty in getting away. Upon digging into the ground to find the cause he discovered a stone with the most amazing properties of attracting iron. This stone is now called lodestone or magnetite.

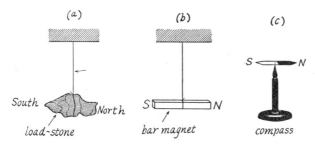

Fig. 51A—Magnetized bodies when free to turn come to rest in a north-south direction.

The idea that a lodestone can be used as a compass is a very old one. There is some evidence that the Chinese had a knowledge of this as far back as A.D. 121. At any rate, a Chinese author writing as early as the beginning of the twelfth century explains that a needle, rubbed with lodestone and suspended free to turn, will point toward the south. This appears to be the first evidence that a piece of iron could be magnetized by a lodestone and used as a compass. The action of a lodestone or a bar magnet when suspended free to turn about a vertical axis is illustrated in Fig. 51A, diagrams (a) and (b).

A compass as it is often made for demonstration purposes consists usually of a straight steel needle which has been magnetized and mounted free to turn on a sharp pointed rod as shown in Fig. 51A(c). In the early days of the mariner's compass it was common to float several small magnet needles on water by mounting them on a block of wood or other light material. In more recent designs a compass needle with a jewel in its center is set upon the sharp point of a hard metal rod, much shorter than that shown in Fig. 51A(c), and placed in a small brass box with a glass top. Such compasses in appearance are familiar to everyone.

51.1. Magnets. Until recent years magnets have been made of hardened

511

steel and molded or rolled into many shapes. Perhaps the most common of these is the horseshoe magnet shown in Fig. 51B, or the straight bar magnet shown in Fig. 51C. The strongest magnets are now made of an alloy containing aluminum, cobalt, nickel, and iron. Small magnets of this alloy are strong enough to lift hundreds of times their own weight.

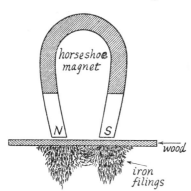

FIG. 51B—The attraction of a magnet for iron acts through all substances.

Pure iron, sometimes called soft iron, when magnetized will not retain its magnetism and is therefore useless in making what are called permanent magnets. Soft iron is used, however, in the construction of electromagnets. These devices will be discussed and demonstrated in another chapter. Of the many practical applications of permanent magnets, the compass, the telephone receiver, and the radio loudspeaker are perhaps the most common.

51.2. The Power of Attraction. Nearly everyone has at sometime or other played with a small horseshoe magnet and discovered for himself that it attracted only things containing iron. Upon drawing the same magnet through the dry sand or dirt you probably discovered that it will pick up small grains of iron ore.

If more extensive experiments are carried out, a magnet can be shown to attract magnetic substances at a distance even though matter lies in the intervening space. In other words, magnetic attraction acts right through matter of all kinds. This can be demonstrated as shown in Fig. 51B by picking up iron filings on one side of a thin wooden board by holding a magnet close to the other side. If a sheet of copper, or brass, or, as a matter of fact, any substance, is placed over the magnet the power of attraction is not destroyed. A small region of space can be partially shielded from magnetic fields if it is entirely surrounded by layers of soft iron.

While a few metals are known to be feebly attracted by a magnet, most substances like aluminum, copper, silver, gold, wood, glass, paper, etc., do not exhibit any noticeable effect. Of those weakly affected, nickel and cobalt are the most important. These two metals, as mentioned above, when alloyed together with other metals in the proper proportions, are found to exhibit stronger magnetic susceptibility than the best grades of iron or steel. As a pure element, however, iron is by far the most strongly magnetic.

51.3. Magnetic Poles. When an ordinary straight bar magnet is dipped into a box of iron filings the tiny bits of iron are observed to cling to the ends as shown in Fig. 51C. These preferred regions of attraction are called *magnetic poles.* If this same magnet is suspended by a thread as shown in Fig. 51A(b), it will come to rest in a position close to the north-south direction. The end toward the north is therefore called the *N* or *north-seeking pole,* and the other end the *S* or *south-seeking pole.*

Fig. 51C—The attraction of iron-filings by a straight bar magnet shows greater attraction near the ends. These regions of greatest attraction are called *magnetic poles.*

That the *N* and *S* poles of a magnet are different may be shown by bringing the magnet close to a compass needle. Such an experiment is illustrated in Fig. 51D. When the *S* pole of the magnet is brought close to the *S* pole of the compass needle as in diagram (a) there is a force of repulsion acting and the compass needle turns away as shown. A similar repulsion occurs between the two *N* poles as shown in diagram (b). If the *N* and *S* poles are brought near to each other, however,

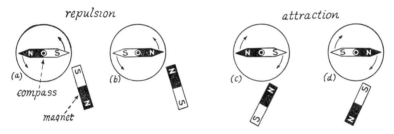

Fig. 51D—When the pole of one magnet is brought close to the pole of another magnet, like poles are found to repel each other and unlike poles to attract.

a very strong attraction arises and the compass needle turns toward the other as shown in diagrams (c) and (d). These experiments show, therefore, that *two kinds of magnetic poles exist* and that *like poles repel and unlike poles attract.*

Permanent magnets can now be made so strong that one magnet can be lifted by the repulsion of another. This is illustrated in Fig. 51E. Unless guide rods of glass or some other substance are used, however, the floating bar will move to one side and then fall. In other words, the

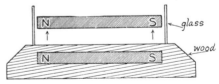

Fig. 51E—One magnet may be suspended in mid-air by the strong repulsion of like poles from another magnet.

forces of repulsion are such that the upper bar is not in stable equilibrium. If the floating magnet is turned end for end, opposite poles become adjacent and the two magnets attract each other. Although the forces may be great enough, no one has ever succeeded in floating a permanent magnet in mid-air, against the pull of gravity and without guide rods, by means of permanent magnets.

It should be pointed out that each magnetic pole in a magnetized body is not confined to a single point but extends over a finite region. From a distance, however, each polar region acts as though it were concentrated at a point, similar to that of the center of mass in mechanics.

51.4. Poles Exist in Pairs. If a magnet is broken in the middle in an attempt to separate the poles one finds new poles formed at the broken ends. If one of these pieces is again broken, each piece is again found to contain two poles of opposite kind. As long as this process is repeated the same result is obtained—a magnetic pole of one kind is always accompanied by a pole of opposite polarity.

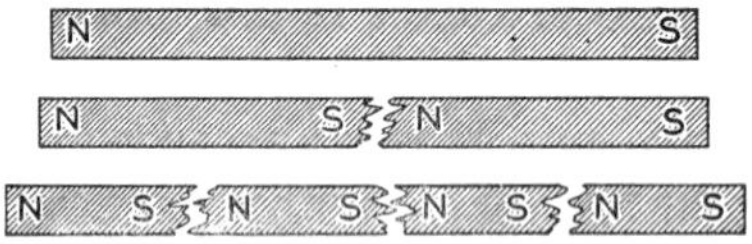

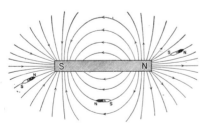

FIG. 51F—The poles of a magnet cannot exist alone. When a bar magnet is broken, poles appear on either side of the break such that each piece has two poles.

This is conveniently illustrated by magnetizing a hack-saw blade and breaking it successively into smaller and smaller pieces as shown in Fig. 51F. Each time a piece is broken each fragment, upon being tested with a compass, is found to have an N pole on one side and an S pole on the other. A hack-saw blade is readily magnetized by stroking it from one end to the other with one of the poles of a magnet.

It is possible to magnetize a bar of steel so that it has three or more polar regions. This is illustrated in Fig. 51G where a hack-saw blade has been magnetized with an N pole at each end and an S polar region in the center. The combined strength of the N poles is seen by the quantity of iron filings to be equal to the S pole strength in the center. We might say, therefore, that the magnet

FIG. 51G—Diagram of a bar magnet with iron filings showing three polar regions. There are two N poles, one at either end, and a doubly strong S pole at the center.

has four poles: an N pole at either end and two S poles at the center.

51.5. The Magnetic Field. In the space surrounding every magnet there exists what is called a magnetic field. Although this field cannot be seen, it can be demonstrated and mapped out in the following way.

FIG. 51H—Diagram of the magnetic field and magnetic lines of force about a straight bar magnet, as obtained with a small compass needle.

If a very small compass is placed at some point near the N pole of a straight bar magnet and then moved always in the direction the compass is pointing, the center of the compass will trace out a smooth line called a magnetic line of force. Starting at various points many such lines may be drawn as shown in Fig. 51H. Each line starts at some point near the *N* pole and ends at a corresponding point near the *S* pole.

These magnetic *lines of force,* as they are called, do not really exist; they are but useful devices that may be used in describing the many different magnetic phenomena to be taken up in later chapters. It should be noted that, where the magnet exerts its strongest attraction near the poles, the lines are closest together and that each line points away from the *N* pole and toward the *S* pole. This latter is an arbitrary assignment, being the direction indicated by the *N* pole of the compass.

A close examination of the iron filings clinging to a magnet (see Figs. 51C and 51G), shows that each tiny needle-like piece of iron lines up in the direction of the magnetic lines of force. The reason for this is that each filing has become magnetized by the magnet, and having its own *N* and *S* poles, acts like a compass. An excellent demonstration of the field and its direction can be performed by laying a plate of glass or a sheet of paper over a magnet and then sprinkling iron filings over the top. By gently tapping the glass or paper the filings turn and line up as shown in the photographic reproduction given in Fig. 51I.

Fig. 51I—Photograph of the iron filings lined up by the magnetic field of a permanent straight bar magnet.

51.6. The Field about Separate Poles. When two magnetic poles are brought close together, the mutual action of the two is such as to produce a

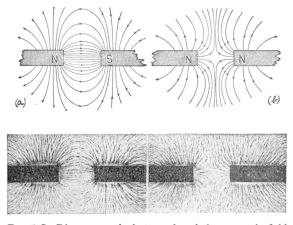

Fig. 51J—Diagrams and photographs of the magnetic field about two magnetic poles placed close together: (a) unlike poles, and (b) like poles.

complicated magnetic field. This is illustrated by compass-made drawings at the top in Fig. 51J and by photographic reproductions of the iron-filing method of observation at the bottom.

A simplified explanation of many electric and magnetic phenomena can be given by assuming that these imaginary *lines of force* are endowed with certain real but simple properties. Lengthwise along the lines they act as though they were stretched rubber bands under constant tension, whereas sideways they act as if they repelled each other. Both of these properties are illustrated in Fig. 51J. When the two poles are of different polarity as in diagram (a), the lines of force acting like stretched rubber bands tend to pull the poles together. In diagram (b) where the poles are alike, the lines repel each other, pushing the poles apart.

51.7. The Earth's Magnetic Field. To Sir William Gilbert we owe the view that the earth is a great magnet. To prove his theory Gilbert shaped a lodestone into a sphere and demonstrated that a small compass placed at any spot of the globe always pointed, as it does on the earth, toward the North Pole.

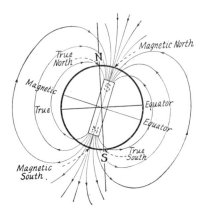

FIG. 51K—Schematic diagram illustrating the earth as a huge magnet surrounded by a magnetic field extending far out into space.

The earth, therefore, has been schematically pictured in Fig. 51K as a large magnetized sphere of iron or as though it contained a huge permanent magnet. Since the magnetic axis is at an angle with the polar axis, the earth's magnetic poles are not at the *true North* and *true South Poles*. The true North and true South Poles are points located on the earth's rotational axis.

The *North Magnetic Pole* is located in far northern Canada, while the *South Magnetic Pole* is located almost diametrically opposite in the Southern Hemisphere. As for polarity, the North Magnetic Pole is an *S* pole and the South Magnetic Pole is an *N* pole. This becomes apparent from the magnetic lines of force which always start from an *N* pole and are directed toward, and end, at an *S* pole.

Although the cause for the earth's magnetism is not completely understood, several reasonable theories have been proposed. The earth is known to contain large iron ore deposits, some of these deposits being almost pure iron. One theory proposes that during the ages past, all these iron deposits gradually became magnetized, in very nearly the same direction, and that together they act like one huge permanent magnet. Another theory, and a very

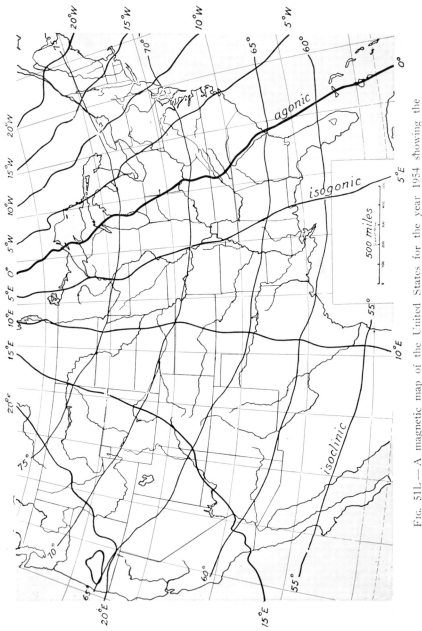

Fig. 51L.—A magnetic map of the United States for the year 1954 showing the declination of a compass from true north and the angle of dip of a dip needle. Such maps are drawn from data assembled by the U.S. Coast and Geodetic Survey.

plausible one, is that the magnetism is due to large electric currents which are known to be flowing around the earth, not only in the earth's crust but also in the air above. These earth currents seem to be connected in some direct way with the earth's rotation. This appears to be corroborated by the fact that the earth is magnetized in a direction almost parallel to the earth's polar axis.

51.8. Magnetic Declination. Since the earth's magnetic and polar axes do not coincide, a compass needle does not in general point toward True North. Because of the influence of the irregular iron deposits near the earth's surface, the magnetic field is not as regular as it is pictured in Fig. 51K and a compass needle may deviate considerably from magnetic north. The angle that a compass needle deviates from true north is called the *angle of declination.*

A map showing the angle of declination for the United States during the year 1954 is shown in Fig. 51L. The more or less vertical set of irregular lines are lines of equal declination and are called *isogonic lines.* At every point along the line marked 20°E, for example, a compass needle actually points 20° east of True North. In the region of San Francisco the declination is seen to be about 18°E, while in the region of New York it is about 11°W. The line through points where a compass points true north, 0°, is named the *agonic line.*

51.9. Magnetic Dip. If a compass needle is mounted free to turn about a horizontal axis as shown in Fig. 51M(b), it will not come to rest in a horizontal position but will dip down at some angle with the horizontal as shown. This direction, called the *dip,* is the angle the earth's field makes

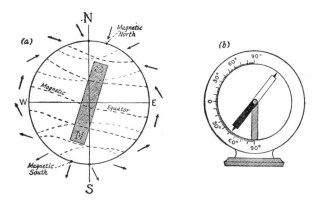

Fig. 51M—Diagram showing (a) the angle of dip of a magnet needle at various points over the earth's surface, and (b) the mounting of a magnetic dip needle.

with the earth's surface at the point in question. Referring to Fig. 51K it is seen that in the far north and south the angle of dip is quite large, whereas near the equator it is quite small. Diagram (a) in Fig. 51M indicates the approximate dip at different latitudes for one cross section of the entire globe.

At a region on the Boothia Peninsula just north of Hudson Bay and 20° from True North, a dip needle points straight down, perpendicular to the earth's surface, and locates the North Magnetic Pole. At a region about 18° from the true South Pole a dip needle points straight up, at 90° from the horizontal, and locates the South Magnetic Pole.

On maps of terrestrial magnetism all points that have equal dip angles are connected by a line called an *isoclinic* line. Such lines for different angles form a set of nearly parallel lines as shown on the map of the United States in Fig. 51L.

In San Francisco the earth's magnetic induction B is about 5.4×10^{-5} webers/meter^2, or 0.54 gauss (see Sec. 51.13 and Eq.(53h)) and the angle of dip about 62°. This gives a horizontal component of 0.25×10^{-4} webers/meter^2 or 0.25 gauss.

Careful and accurate measurements of the *declination* and *dip* show that the earth's magnetic field is continually changing. Although these changes are extremely small they are somewhat periodic and at times quite erratic.

51.10. Magnetization. When a strong magnet is brought close to a piece of soft iron the iron takes on all the properties of a new but somewhat weaker magnet. This phenomenon, called *magnetization*, is illustrated in Fig. 51N(a). As long as the permanent magnet is held close to the soft iron bar the iron filings cling to the end as shown. When the permanent magnet is removed, however, the soft iron immediately loses its magnetism and the iron filings drop off.

When a piece of iron is magnetized, a pole of opposite sign is created at the points of closest approach as shown in the diagrams. If a common iron nail is brought up to the N pole of a permanent magnet it will become magnetized with a S pole at the point of contact and an N pole at the other end as shown in diagram (b). Having two poles, the nail is thus magnetized and will attract another nail and magnetize it in the same way. With a good strong magnet this process can be repeated by adding one nail after the other.

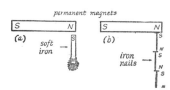

Fig. 51N—Soft iron may be magnetized by (a) induction at a distance, or (b) contact.

It is now clear how iron filings line up with the lines of force of a magnet. Each filing becomes magnetized and, like a small compass, turns parallel to the field in which it is located.

51.11. Molecular Theory of Ferromagnetism. The modern theory of magnetism which is now quite firmly established as being correct is that a piece of iron consists of myriads of tiny elementary magnets. These tiny ultramicroscopic magnets may consist of individual atoms and molecules themselves or of groups of atoms aligned to form small elementary iron crystals. How single atoms can act as magnets will be explained later. Be-

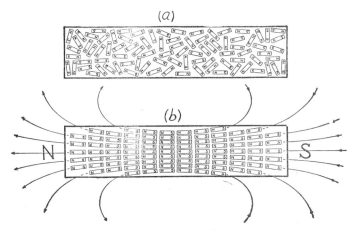

Fig. 510—Schematic diagrams of the elementary magnets within a piece of iron; (upper) unmagnetized, and (lower) magnetized.

fore a piece of iron or steel has been magnetized these elementary magnets may be thought of as being oriented more or less at random throughout the metal as shown in Fig. 510(a).

During the time a piece of iron is being magnetized the elementary magnets are turned around and lined up parallel to each other and to the magnetizing field. This is shown by the schematic representation in diagram (b). Lined up in this way, the small N and S poles are adjacent to each other and cancel each other's effect on external objects. At one end there are many free N poles and at the opposite end an equal number of free S poles.

When a magnet is broken at any point *free S poles* are exposed at one side of the break and *free N poles* at the other. It is therefore clear why poles always exist in pairs and that no matter how many times a magnet is broken each piece will contain an N at one end and an S pole at the other.

When soft iron is magnetized by induction and the permanent magnet taken away, the elementary magnets return to their original random orientations, but, when hardened steel becomes magnetized, they remain lined up after the magnetizing field is taken away.

51.12. Coulomb's Law for Magnetic Poles. For a study of the law of force between magnetic poles, especially designed magnets have been used. The necessity for this is realized when it is remembered that single magnetic poles cannot be isolated by breaking a magnet in two. The special magnets consist of thin steel rods about 18 in. long with a small steel ball on either end. When magnetized the N and S poles become concentrated in the steel balls.

As used in the Hibbert balance shown in Fig. 51P one magnet is balanced on a special set of scales and another is held tightly in an adjustable clamp stand. If the two center poles, when they are brought together, are alike, the repulsion will throw the one magnet off balance. The weight that must

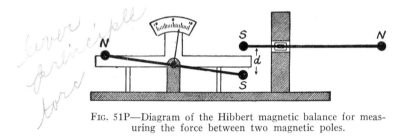

Fᴵɢ. 51P—Diagram of the Hibbert magnetic balance for measuring the force between two magnetic poles.

then be added to the left-hand side to restore balance again is a direct measure of the force of repulsion. Carrying out experiments of a similar nature Coulomb was the first to find that *the force acting between two magnetic poles is inversely proportional to the square of the distance between them.* Having discovered this relation he compared the pole strengths of different magnets with each other and found that *the force between two poles is proportional to the product of the pole strengths.* Combining these two relations Coulomb proposed as a general law for magnetic poles,

$$F = \kappa \frac{mm'}{d^2}, \tag{51a}$$

where F is the force, m and m' are the strengths of the poles, and d is the distance between them. In the *rationalized mks system* used in this text, F is in *newtons,* m and m' are in *ampere meters,* and κ the proportionality constant is

$$\kappa = 10^{-7} \frac{\text{weber}}{\text{amper meter}} \tag{51b}$$

51.13. Magnetic Induction B. It is quite common practice to refer to the strength or the intensity of a magnetic field as the *magnetic induction.*

The magnetic induction B at any point in space may be defined as the force per unit N-pole acting on any pole placed at that point. Algebraically,

$$B = \frac{F}{m'}. \tag{51c}$$

Suppose, for example, that when a unit pole of *1 ampere meter* is placed at a given point in space it experiences a force of *5 newtons*. The magnetic induction *B* at that point is then said to have a magnitude of *5 newtons/ ampere meter*. If a pole with a strength of *m″* ampere meters is placed at this same point where the magnetic induction is known to be *B* newtons/ ampere meter, the force acting on the pole in newtons is

$$F = m'' B. \tag{51d}$$

From the above definition that $B = F/m'$, and Coulomb's law, a relation for the magnetic induction at any point near a single pole of strength *m* may be obtained. When *m′* is transposed to the left side of Eq.(51a),

$$\frac{F}{m'} = \kappa \frac{m}{d^2},$$

or

$$B = \kappa \frac{m}{d^2}, \tag{51e}$$

where *d* is the distance from the field producing pole *m* to the point in question.

While the magnetic induction *B*, as given by Eq.(51c), is in *newtons/ ampere meter*, *B* will be found by Eq.(51e) to be in *webers/meter²*. The two relations are consistent since

$$1 \frac{\text{newton}}{\text{ampere meter}} = 1 \frac{\text{weber}}{\text{meter}^2}. \tag{51f}$$

The preferred units of *B* are *webers/meter²*. (See Sec. 53.1 and Eq.(53h).)

The direction of the magnetic field at any point is the direction of the force acting on an *N* pole placed at that point. This is another way of determining or plotting magnetic lines of force. As illustrated in Fig. 51Q, an *N* pole placed in a position (a), equidistant from the two poles of the magnet, is repelled by the *N* pole with the same force that it is attracted by the *S* pole. The resultant of these two forces is the horizontal force to the right and parallel to the magnet. If an *S* pole were located at the same point, the resultant force would be just oppositely directed. It is therefore clear why a compass placed at (a) turns parallel to the magnet, and why at other points like (b) it turns in another direction. Forces acting on each pole of

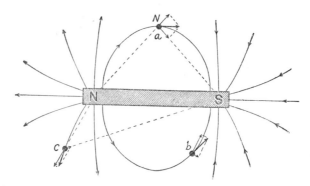

Fig. 51Q—The force acting on a unit N pole placed in a magnetic field gives the magnitude and direction of the magnetic field at that point.

the compass needle turn it into the equilibrium positions found and plotted as the magnetic field in Fig. 51H.

Example 1. Calculate the magnetic induction B at a point 8 cm from an N pole of 48 ampere meters.

Solution. By making direct substitutions of the given quantities into Eq.(51e), we obtain

$$B = 10^{-7} \frac{\text{weber}}{\text{ampere meter}} \times \frac{48 \text{ ampere meters}}{64 \times 10^{-4} \text{ meter}^2} = 7.5 \times 10^{-4} \frac{\text{weber}}{\text{meter}^2}.$$

The direction of B is outward, away from N.

PROBLEMS

1. Two magnetic poles of equal strength are located 2 cm apart. Each exerts a force of 0.004 newton on the other. Calculate the pole strength.

2. Two magnetic S poles of equal strength exert a force of 0.009 newton on each other when they are located 5 cm apart. Find the pole strength. (*Ans.* 15 ampere meters.)

3. Three N poles of 4 ampere meters each are located at the corners of an equilateral triangle 5 cm on a side. Find the resultant force on each pole.

4. Three S poles of 1.2 ampere meters each are located at three corners of a right triangle whose sides are 3 cm, 4 cm, and 5 cm, respectively. Find the force in dynes on the pole at the 90° corner. (*Ans.* 18.4 dynes.)

5. Find the magnitude of the magnetic induction at a point (a) 2 cm from an N pole of 4 ampere meters, (b) 10 cm from an S pole of 3.2 ampere meters, and (c) 1 m from an S pole of 0.8 ampere meter.

6. A straight bar magnet has two poles of 20 ampere meters each, with centers

5 cm apart. Calculate the magnetic induction at a point in line with the two poles, (a) 4 cm beyond the N pole, and (b) 20 cm beyond the S pole. (*Ans.* (a) 1.0×10^{-3} weber/meter^2, directed away from the magnet. (b) 1.8×10^{-5} weber/meter^2, directed toward the magnet.

7. A straight bar magnet has two poles of 50 ampere meters each, spaced 10 cm apart. Find the magnetic induction at a point in line with the two poles, (a) 5 cm from the S pole, and (b) 10 cm from the N pole.

8. A straight bar magnet has two poles, 15 cm apart, each with a strength of 24 ampere meters. Calculate the magnitude of the magnetic induction at a point 9 cm from the N pole and 12 cm from the S pole. (*Ans.* 3.4×10^{-4} weber/meter^2.)

9. Two S poles of 16 ampere meters and two N poles of 40 ampere meters are placed at each of the corners of a square 10 cm on a side. With like poles diagonally opposite each other, what are the forces between (a) one S pole and the other S pole, (b) one N pole and the other N pole, and (c) one N pole and one S pole? What is the resultant force on (d) each S pole, and (e) each N pole?

10. Two N poles of 40 ampere meters and two S poles of 10 ampere meters are placed at each of the corners of a square 10 cm on a side. With unlike poles diagonally opposite each other, what is the magnitude of the magnetic induction (a) at the center of the square, and (b) at the center of the side between the two N poles? (*Ans.* (a) 1.41×10^{-3} weber/meter^2. (b) 1.45×10^{-4} weber/meter^2.)

11. A straight bar magnet has two poles, each of 16 ampere meters and located 10 cm apart. Find the magnitude of the magnetic induction at a point in line with the poles at a distance beyond the N pole of 1, 5, 10, 15, and 20 cm. Plot a graph of B vs x, where x is the distance from the center of the magnet.

12. Solve Prob. 11 if the line along which the chosen field points are located passes through the center of the magnet perpendicular to the magnet axis, and the distances are 0, 5, 10, 15, and 20 cm, as measured outward from the magnet center. (*Ans.* 12.8×10^{-4}, 4.52×10^{-4}, 1.14×10^{-4}, 0.53×10^{-4}, and 0.175×10^{-4} weber/meter^2.)

13. Find the magnetic induction at a point on one side of the square in Prob. 10, midway between an S and an N pole.

14. Find the force exerted on an N pole of 12 ampere meters when it is placed in a field where the magnetic induction is 1.6×10^{-3} weber/meter^2. (*Ans.* 0.019 newton.)

15. Calculate the force in dynes exerted on an N pole of 8 ampere meters when placed in a field where the magnetic induction is 6.5×10^{-4} weber/meter^2.

16. When an S pole of 20 ampere meters is placed 8 cm from another pole of unknown strength, it experiences an attractive force of 5000 dynes. Find (a) the magnetic induction at the point in question, and (b) the strength of the unknown pole. (*Ans.* (a) 0.0025 weber/meter^2. (b) 160 ampere meters; N.)

Effects of Electric Currents   Chapter 52

EVERYONE is more or less familiar with the electrical appliances of the modern household; the electric lights, electric toaster, iron, refrigerator, vacuum cleaner, washing machine, etc. All of these devices depend for their operation upon one or more of four general effects produced by electric currents; these are (1) *the heating effect,* (2) *the magnetic effect,* (3) *the mechanical effect,* and (4) *the chemical effect.* It is the purpose of this chapter to consider the first three of these different phenomena and to take up in some detail the important principles involved.

52.1. The Heating Effect of an Electric Current. When an electron current is sent through a wire, heat is generated and the temperature of the wire rises. If the current is increased, the rate at which heat is generated increases rapidly until the wire itself glows a deep red. A still further increase in current will heat the wire to a yellow or white heat. Beyond this point, if it has not already done so, the wire will reach a temperature where it will melt and become a liquid.

Whether a wire is only warmed by an electron current or heated to incandescence depends upon a number of factors, the two principal ones of which are the current and the resistance. Experiment shows that the heat developed in a wire is directly proportional (1) *to the resistance R,* (2) *to the square of the electron current I,* and (3) *to the time t.*

Expressed as an algebraic equation,

$$\text{Heat} = kI^2Rt, \qquad (52a)$$

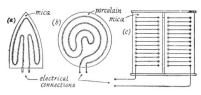

Fig. 52A—Diagrams of the heating elements of various electrical appliances found in some modern homes: (a) electric iron, (b) electric stove, (c) electric toaster.

where k is the proportionality factor and is just the reciprocal of the mechanical equivalent of heat J given in Eq.(33b). To be able to calculate exactly the amount of heat produced in calories the value of k must be known. Experimentally this was first determined by James Joule, an English physicist in 1843, and later by many other experimenters, and found to have the value 0.24 cal/joule. If the electron current is measured in *amperes,* the resistance in *ohms,* and the time in *seconds,* then

$$\text{heat in calories} = 0.24 I^2 Rt. \tag{52b}$$

This is known as Joule's law.

Since heat is a form of energy, Joule's law may be considered as another aspect of the law of conservation of energy. When a given amount of electrical energy I^2Rt is expended or transformed into heat it always produces the same number of calories.

To calculate the heat generated in an electric circuit consider the following simple problem.

Example. If the heating element of an electric toaster has a resistance of 22 ohms and is connected to an ordinary house lighting circuit of 110 volts, how much heat will be generated in one minute?

Solution. From Ohm's law, Eq.(49e), the electron current is first calculated.

$$I = 110/22 = 5 \text{ amperes.}$$

We can now make use of Joule's law by substituting in Eq.(52b).

heat $= 0.24 \times (5)^2 \times 22 \times 60 = 7920$ **calories.**

For some electric appliances heating is a desired effect while in others it is a source of trouble and even danger. In an electric iron, hot plate, or toaster, for example, heat is the main objective of the device. In such appliances a relatively large current of several amperes is sent through a coil or element of special wire having a resistance of several ohms. As a rule the wire is of some alloy, such as nichrome, and of such a size that the heat developed will not raise the temperature higher than red hot. Diagrams of typical heating elements used in three different household appliances are shown in Fig. 52A.

52.2. Electric Energy. When the householder pays his monthly electricity bill, he pays according to the amount of electric energy consumed. To calculate electric energy a general formula involving *current, voltage,* and *time* is usually employed. A battery or generator, in supplying current to any electric system, maintains a constant difference of potential between two ends of the circuit.

In Sec. 50.3 the difference of potential V between any two points is defined as the work per unit charge done in carrying any charge Q' from one point to the other. By returning to Eq.(50e), we observe that to move a total charge Q through a wire will require an amount of work $W = V \times Q$. Since by the definition of electron current, $I = Q/t$, the charge Q may be replaced by It, to give

$$\text{electric energy } W = VIt \tag{52c}$$

If V is in volts, I is in amperes, and t is in seconds, the energy W is in joules. (1 joule $= 10^7$ ergs). Since by Ohm's law, $I = V/R$, direct substitution for I or for V gives two other useful forms of the same equation.

$$W = I^2Rt \qquad\qquad W = \frac{V^2}{R} t \qquad\qquad (52d)$$

The former is the basis upon which Eq.(52a) is derived. The heat developed in a resistance R follows from the mechanical equivalent of heat that 4.2 joules = 1 calorie. Since energy in joules = 4.2 × heat in calories, the heat in calories = 0.24 × energy in joules. Direct substitution of this latter relation in Eq.(52d) gives Eq.(52a).

52.3. Electric Power. Power is defined in mechanics, as well as in electricity, as the rate at which energy is developed or expended. $P = W/t$. Dividing each of the above energy equations by t, gives

$$P = VI \qquad\qquad P = I^2R \qquad\qquad P = V^2/R \qquad\qquad (52e)$$

where P is in watts. These are practical equations since with most electrical equipment the *voltage, current,* and *resistance* are usually known from voltmeter and ammeter readings. The first equation is well worth memorizing: *"power, in watts, is equal to potential difference, in volts, times current, in amperes."* The other two follow by a direct substitution from Ohm's law.

Energy as expressed in Eq.(52c) is power VI multiplied by the time t. *Power in kilowatts multiplied by the time in hours gives the energy in kilowatt-hours.* The kilowatt-hour is the unit of electric energy by which all electric energy is calculated and paid for (1 kilowatt = 1000 watts). The watt-hour meter placed on the premises of every consumer is a slowly revolving motor, having a low resistance winding which is in series with the line and which therefore conducts the current in the line, and a high resistance winding which is across the line and which therefore conducts a small current proportional to V. The time factor t is accounted for by the automatic recording of the total number of rotations of the armature by a small clocklike mechanism with dials and pointers.

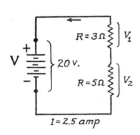

Fig. 52B—The power consumed by any resistance is given by the voltage across it multiplied by the current.

Example. Two resistors of 3 ohms and 5 ohms respectively are connected in series with a battery of 20 volts (see Fig. 52B). Calculate (a) the electron current through the circuit, (b) the potential difference across each resistor, (c) the power consumed by each resistor, (d) the total energy consumed in 2 hr of operation, and (e) the total cost of operation for 40 hr at 3 cents per kw-hr.

Solution. Connected in series the two resistors $R_1 = 3$ ohms and $R_2 = 5$ ohms have a total resistance of $R = 8$ ohms.

(a) If we apply Ohm's law, the electron current through the circuit is found to be

$$I = V/R = 20/8 = 2.5 \text{ amperes.}$$

(b) The drop in potential across any resistor is given by IR.

$$V_1 = I_1R_1 = 2.5 \times 3 = 7.5 \text{ volts}$$
$$V_2 = I_2R_2 = 2.5 \times 5 = 12.5 \text{ volts.}$$

(c) The power consumed is given by VI, the potential drop across each resistor multiplied by the electron current through it.

$$P_1 = V_1I = 7.5 \times 2.5 = 18.75 \text{ watts}$$
$$P_2 = V_2I = 12.5 \times 2.5 = 31.25 \text{ watts.}$$

(d) The power supplied by the battery is VI, the voltage across its terminals multiplied by the total electron current in amperes.

$$P = VI = 20 \times 2.5 = 50 \text{ watts}$$

in agreement with the sum of the two values in (c).
To find the energy, multiply by the time in seconds.

$$W = 50 \text{ watts} \times 7200 \text{ sec} = 360,000 \text{ joules.}$$

(e) The power 50 watts should next be expressed in kilowatts and multiplied by the time in hours, to give

$$W = 0.05 \text{ kw} \times 40 \text{ hr} = 2 \text{ kw-hr.}$$

At 3 cents per kw-hr, the total cost will be 6 cents.

52.4. Magnetic Effect, Oersted's Experiment.

The first discovery of any connection between electricity and magnetism was made by Oersted * in 1820. Often during his lectures, at the University of Copenhagen, Oersted had demonstrated the nonexistence of a connection between electricity and magnetism. His usual custom was to place a current-carrying wire at right angles to and directly over a compass needle and show that there was no effect of one on the other. On this one occasion at the end of his lecture, when several of the audience came up to meet him at the lecture room desk, he placed the wire parallel to the compass needle and, not the least expecting it, saw the needle move to one side

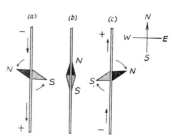

Fig. 52C—Diagrams of Oersted's experiment illustrating the effect of an electric current upon a compass needle.

* Hans Christian Oersted (1777-1851), Danish scientist. Born the son of an apothecary, Oersted spent part of his boyhood teaching himself arithmetic. At the age of twelve he assisted his father in his shop and there became interested in chemistry. Passing the entrance examinations at the University of Copenhagen at the age of seventeen he entered the medical school to graduate six years later with his doctorate in medicine. At twenty-nine he came back to the university but this time as professor of physics. It was at one of his demonstration lectures on chemistry and metaphysics that he discovered the magnetic effect bearing his name. The discovery not only brought him many endowments and prizes but made him one of the most eminent personalities in his own country.

(see Fig. 52C). Upon reversing the current in the wire the needle, to his amazement and perplexity, deviated in the opposite direction. Thus this great discovery was made quite by accident, but, as Lagrange once said of Newton on a similar occasion, "such accidents come only to those who deserve them."

52.5. The Left-Hand Rule. Oersted's experiment is interpreted as demonstrating that *around every wire carrying an electric current there is a magnetic field.* The direction of this field at every point, like that around a bar magnet, can be mapped by means of a small compass or by iron filings. If a wire is mounted vertically through a hole in a plate of glass or other suitable non-conductor and then iron filings sprinkled on the plate, there will be a lining up of the filings parallel to the magnetic field. The result shows that the magnetic lines of force or *lines of induction* are concentric circles whose planes are at right angles to the current. This is illustrated by the circles in Fig. 52D.

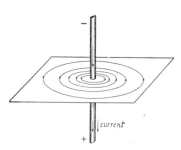

FIG. 52D—Experiment demonstrating the magnetic field about a straight wire carrying an electron current.

The left-hand rule used in electromagnetism can always be relied upon to give the direction of the magnetic field due to an electron current in a wire. Derived from experiment, the rule states that *if the current-carrying wire were to be grasped with the left hand, the thumb pointing in the direction of the electron current, (—) to (+), the fingers will point in the direction of the magnetic induction.*

In other books, using the older convention that current in a wire is from + to —, the *right-hand rule* is used to give the magnetic field the same direction that it has here.

52.6. Magnetic Properties of a Solenoid. Not long after the announcement of Oersted's discovery of the magnetic effect of a current carrying wire, Ampère found that a loop or coil of wire acted as a magnet. This is illustrated by a single loop of wire in Fig. 52E, and by a coil of several turns of wire, in Fig. 52F. A coil of wire of this kind is sometimes referred to as a *solenoid* or as a *helix*. In either case

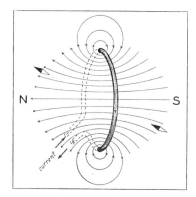

FIG. 52E—Diagram of the magnetic field through and around a single loop of wire carrying an electron current.

the magnetic lines of force are such that one side or end of the coil acts like an *N* magnetic pole and the other side or end like an *S* magnetic pole.

At all points in the region around a coil of wire carrying a current the direction of the magnetic field, as shown by a compass, can be predicted by the left-hand rule. Inside each loop or turn of wire the lines point in one direction, whereas outside they are oppositely directed.

Outside the coil the lines go from *N* to *S* in quite the same way they do about a permanent bar magnet, whereas inside they go from *S* to *N*.

Not only does one coil of wire act like a magnet but two coils may be used to demonstrate the repulsion and attraction of like and unlike poles.

Another left-hand rule which must not be confused with the one in the preceding section, but which follows directly from it, is the following: *if the solenoid were to be grasped with the fingers pointing in the direction of the electron current, around the coil from* (−) *to* (+), *the thumb would point in the direction of the internal field as well as the N pole.*

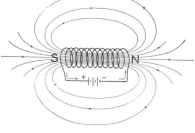

Fig. 52F—Diagram of the magnetic field around a solenoid carrying an electron current.

52.7. The Electromagnet. Five years after Oersted's discovery and Ampère's demonstration of the magnetic properties of a solenoid, William Sturgeon filled the center of a coil of wire with soft iron and thereby pro-

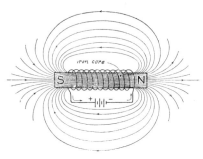

Fig. 52G—Diagram of an electromagnet and the field surrounding it when a current flows through the coil.

duced a powerful magnet. This is illustrated in Fig. 52G. As long as the electron current continues to flow, the addition of the iron core produces a magnet hundreds of times stronger than does the solenoid alone. A nearby compass needle if set oscillating will demonstrate this by vibrating quickly with the iron core in place and slowly with it removed.

Again, with the iron core in the solenoid, a nearby rod of soft iron, magnetized by induction as shown in Fig. 51N, will attract iron filings much more strongly than when the iron core is removed.

52.8. Mechanical Effects of Electric Currents. It was on Christmas day, 1821, that Michael Faraday discovered that when a wire carrying a current is placed in the field of a magnet a mechanical force is exerted on the wire. This, the principle upon which the modern electric motor is based, is illustrated in Fig. 52H.

The dotted circles in diagram (a) represent the circular magnetic lines of force around a straight wire carrying a current into the page, and the solid lines the magnetic lines of force between two opposite poles of the same or different magnets. Each of these sets of lines is drawn independent of the other, for when both the current carrying wire and magnet are present at the same time there can be but one resultant field, one similar in form to that shown in diagram (c). Imagining that magnetic lines of force to act like stretched rubber bands, one can predict from this second diagram that the wire should experience a force *F* toward the left.

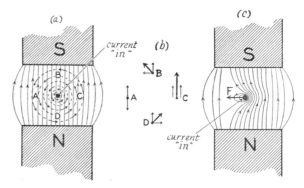

Fig. 52H—Diagrams of the magnetic field around a straight wire carrying an electric current when it is placed between the poles of a magnet.

To understand how such a distorted field can be the result of two symmetrical fields, it must be remembered that the magnetic induction *B* at any point is given by the direction, as well as the magnitude, of the *force per unit N pole* at that same point. Consider, therefore, as examples, the points *A, B, C,* and *D* of diagram (a). At *A*, the magnetic induction *B* due to the current in the wire is down, and that due to the magnet is up. If these two vectors have approximately the same magnitude, they will cancel each other as shown by the small vector diagram at *A* in diagram (b). At *B* the magnetic induction due to the wire is directed toward the left, and that due to the magnet is up. The resultant vector, therefore, slants up and to the left, as is shown in diagram (b). At *C* both vectors are up, reinforcing each other; while at *D* the one is to the right, and the other is up giving a resultant slanting up and to the right. This process, repeated for many other points, will lead to a resultant field, as shown in diagram (c).

It is important to note that *the direction of the current I in the wire, the direction of the magnetic induction B at the wire due to the magnet, and the direction of the force F acting on the wire are all at right angles to each other.* Furthermore, the direction of the force F can be quickly ascertained by applying the left-hand rule to the electron current in the wire. If the wire were to be grasped with the left hand, the thumb pointing in the direction of the electron current ($-$ to $+$), the force is toward the weakened field, that is, toward the region where the fingers are oppositely directed to the field of the magnet.

The existence of a mechanical force may be demonstrated in many ways. One simple experiment is shown in Fig. 52I. Two parallel brass bars fastened to a board are placed over the N pole of a magnet and then connected to a battery. When a round metal rod is now laid across the bars allowing an electron current to flow in the direction shown, the rod experiences a force and rolls to the left. A reversal of either the electron current or the polarity of the magnet will cause the rod to roll to the right. A reversal of both will cause it to roll to the left.

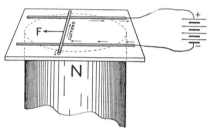

Fig. 52I—An experimental arrangement for demonstrating that a wire carrying a current in a magnetic field experiences a force tending to move it across the field at right angles to the current and at right angles to the field.

It should be emphasized here that this force is exerted on the electrons, the moving charges in the wire, and that they, being confined to the wire, cause it to move. An electron at rest in a magnetic field experiences no force from the magnet. An electron moving across magnetic lines of force experiences a force at right angles to both the field and the direction of motion.

52.9. The Electric Motor. An electric motor is a device by which electrical energy in the form of an electric current is transformed into mechanical energy. The principle of the motor is illustrated in Fig. 52J. A wire carrying an electron current is bent into a loop and placed between two magnetic poles as shown in diagram (a). In this horizontal position the resultant magnetic field is warped as shown in diagram (b), forcing one wire down and the other up. Mounted free to turn about an axis, the loop rotates until it is in a vertical plane. At this point the current in the loop is reversed in direction by means of *sliding contacts* and a *split ring commutator*. The reversal of the electron current reverses the forces so that the side of the loop which was previously pushed up is now pushed down and the side previously pushed down is now pushed up. The loop therefore rotates through half a turn more where the current again reverses. A repetition of this reversing process at each half turn gives rise to a continuous rotation, the left side of

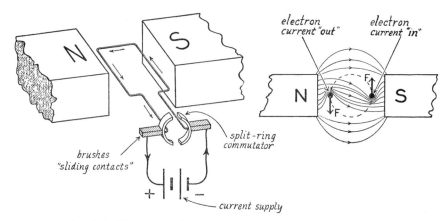

Fig. 52J—Illustrations showing the principle of the electric motor.

the coil or loop always moving down and the right side always moving up.

52.10. Ammeters and Voltmeters. Electrical instruments designed to measure an electric current are called *ammeters,* and those designed to measure potential difference are called *voltmeters.* The principle upon which both of these devices operate is essentially the same as that of the electric motor as shown in Fig. 52J. They differ from the motor, however, in the delicateness of their construction and the restrained motion of the rotating armature.

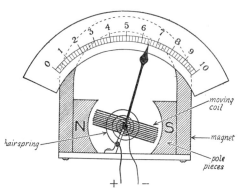

Fig. 52K—Diagram of the essential parts of an ammeter or voltmeter.

A coil of fine copper wire is so mounted between the two poles of a permanent magnet that its rotation, as shown in Fig. 52K, is restrained by a hairspring. The farther the coil is turned from its equilibrium or zero position, the greater is the restoring force. To this coil is fastened a long pointer at the end of which is a fixed scale reading amperes if it is an ammeter or volts if it is a voltmeter. Upon increasing the current through the moving coil of an ammeter or voltmeter the resultant magnetic field between coil and magnet is distorted more and more. The resulting increase in force therefore turns the coil through a greater and greater angle, reaching a point where it is just balanced by the restoring force of the hairspring.

Photographs of two small panel instruments are shown in Fig. 52L. The two connections, necessary in each instrument, are on the back and not shown. On each instrument they lead to the moving coil by means of flexible connections near or through the armature pivots.

Whenever an ammeter or voltmeter is connected to a circuit to measure electron current or potential difference, the ammeter must be connected in series and the voltmeter in parallel. As illustrated in Fig. 52M, the ammeter is so connected that all of the electron current passes through it. To prevent a change in the electron current when such an insertion is made, all ammeters must have a low resistance. Most ammeters therefore have a low resistance wire, called a *shunt*, connected across the armature coil.

FIG. 52L—Photographs of the front face of a typical voltmeter and ammeter. The two electrical connections to each of these panel type instruments are on the back and are not shown. (*Courtesy of the General Electric Co.*)

A voltmeter, on the other hand, is connected across that part of the circuit for which a measurement of the potential difference is required. If the potential difference between the ends of the resistance R_1 is wanted, the voltmeter is connected as shown. If the potential difference across R_2 is desired, the voltmeter connections are made at C and D, whereas if the potential difference maintained by the battery is desired they are made at A and D. In order that the connection of a voltmeter to a circuit does not change the electron current in the circuit, the voltmeter must have a high resistance. If the

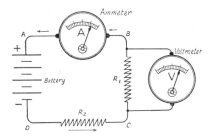

FIG. 52M—Circuit diagram showing the connections for an ammeter and voltmeter.

armature coil does not have a large resistance of its own, additional resistance is added in series.

Very delicate ammeters are often used for measuring very small currents. A meter whose scale is calibrated to read thousandths of an ampere is called a *milliammeter*. One whose scale is calibrated in millionths of an ampere is called a *microammeter* or *galvanometer*.

PROBLEMS

1. The heating element of an electric stove when connected to a 220 volt line draws an electron current of 5 amperes. Find the amount of heat produced in 10 minutes.

2. An electric iron having a resistance of 15 ohms is connected to a 110 volt supply. Find the heat developed in 5 minutes. (*Ans.* 58080 cal.)

3. Calculate the heat developed by a 200 watt electric soldering iron in ten minutes.

4. A tea-kettle containing one gallon of water (3785 cm^3) at a temperature of 10°C is heated on an electric stove. If the heating element draws an electron current of 8 amperes from a 220 volt line, and one half of the heat generated goes to heat the water, how long will it take for the water to reach the boiling point? (*Ans.* 26 min 53 sec.)

5. An electric coffee pot containing 1000 cm^3 of water at 15°C is connected to a 110 volt line. If the electron current drawn is 4.5 amperes and 65 percent of the heat developed goes into the water, how hot will the water be in 8 minutes?

6. Three resistors of 5, 18, and 32 ohms respectively are connected in series to a 110 volt line. Calculate (a) the electron current through the circuit, (b) the power consumed by each resistor, (c) the total energy consumed by each resistor in 5 minutes, and (d) the cost of operation for 10 hours at 1.25 cents per kw-hr. (*Ans* (a) 2 amps, (b) 20, 72, 128 watts, (c) 6000, 21600, 38400 joules, (d) 2.75 cents.)

7. Two resistors of 4 ohms and 12 ohms respectively are connected in parallel and then to a 120 volt line. Find (a) the electron current through each resistor, (b) the power consumed by each resistor, (c) the energy consumed by each resistor in 10 minutes, and (d) the total cost of operation for 3 hours at 1½ cents per kw-hr.

8. During a one-month period an electric refrigerator, connected to the ordinary house lighting circuit of 110 volts, ran for an accumulated time of 150 hrs. (a) If the electron current drawn is 3.2 amperes, what is the total amount of energy consumed? (b) At the rate of 1½ cents per kw-hr what was the total cost of running? (*Ans.* (a) 1.9 × 10^8 joules, (b) 79.2 cents.)

9. A television receiver draws 2.4 amperes from the 110 volt line in a house wiring system. Find the total cost of running a total time of 100 hr at the rate of 1.8 cents per kw-hr.

10. A voltmeter having a resistance of 500 ohms shows a full scale reading when an electron current of 10 milliamperes flows through it. What shunt resistance across this instrument will enable it to be used as an ammeter indicating 5 amperes on full scale deflection? (*Ans.* 1.002 ohm.)

11. A voltmeter having a resistance of 800 ohms shows a full scale reading at 120 volts. What resistance should be connected to this instrument to have it give a full scale reading of 600 volts?

12. What shunt resistance across the voltmeter in Prob. 11 will make an ammeter of it with a full scale deflection reading 10 amperes? (*Ans.* 12.18 ohms.)

Magnetic Induction   Chapter 53

WE HAVE seen in the preceding chapter how an electron current gives rise to a magnetic field surrounding the conductor and also how a current-carrying wire placed in a magnetic field experiences an unbalanced mechanical force tending to move it across the field. We will here give a mathematical formulation of the principles involved in these *magnetic* and *mechanical effects* from which quantitative calculations of practical value can be made. For this treatment we will start with *Ampère's theorem;* a fundamental principle connecting electric currents with the magnetic fields they produce.

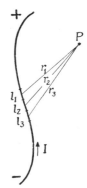

53.1. Ampère's Theorem. Consider a wire of any shape carrying an electron current. The current in each small part of the wire contributes to the magnetic induction at all points around the wire. In Fig. 53A, for example, the small element of wire of length l_1 at a distance r_1 from any chosen point P produces its own magnetic induction contribution at P which, by the left-hand rule for electron currents, is "out" from the page. Similarly, the small element of wire l_2, at a distance r_2 from the same point P, produces

FIG. 53A—The magnetic induction at a point P is due to all current elements of the conductor.

another contribution at P which is out from the page. The resultant magnetic induction at P is, therefore, the vector sum of the contributions from all elements of the wire.

The magnitude of the magnetic induction due to a small current element was first proposed by Biot and Savart in 1820, and later formulated by Ampère, to be given by

$$B = \kappa \frac{Il \sin \theta}{r^2} \tag{53a}$$

where, as shown in Fig. 53B, B is the magnetic induction at a point P, l is the length of a current element of the wire, r is the distance from l to P, θ is the angle between r and l, and κ is a proportionality constant. This equation is usually called *Ampère's theorem.*

The magnitude of the constant κ, like the constant k in Coulomb's law, depends on the choice of units for the other factors. In applying Ampère's theorem to straight wires and circular coils of various kinds, the factor 4π enters so frequently into the formulas that it is convenient to express κ in terms of another constant μ_0, as follows,

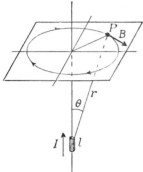

$$\kappa = \frac{\mu_0}{4\pi}.$$

This is analogous to replacing k in Coulomb's law for electric charges by $1/4\pi\varepsilon_0$. See Eq.(48f). Ampère's theorem, therefore, becomes

$$B = \frac{\mu_0}{4\pi} \cdot \frac{Il \ \sin \ \theta}{r^2}. \qquad (53b)$$

If I is in amperes, and r and l are in *meters*,

Fig. 53B—Ampère's Theorem. B is in *webers/meter²* and the constant

$$\mu_0 = 4\pi\kappa = 12.57 \times 10^{-7} \ \text{webers/ampere meter} \qquad (53c)$$

or

$$\kappa = \frac{\mu_0}{4\pi} = 10^{-7} \ \text{webers/ampere meter.} \qquad (53d)$$

From a study of Eq.(53a) and Fig. 53B, it seems reasonable that doubling the electron current I, or doubling the length of the element l, would double the magnetic induction. It is also reasonable by comparison with the field around magnetic poles, and Coulomb's law, that the magnetic induction should vary inversely as the square of the distance r. That the magnetic induction varies as $\sin \theta$, however, was first proved experimentally by Ampère.

To obtain the resultant value of B at any specified point near a current carrying wire, the contributions from all small elements l of the entire circuit must be added together. To do this, a summation process, the *integral calculus*, is usually required. With the calculus, many different calculations are readily carried out, but without it they are, except for the following simple case, difficult.

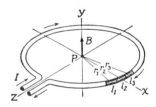

Fig. 53C—Ampère's theorem applied to a single loop of wire.

53.2. The Magnetic Induction at the Center of a Circular Turn.
Consider a circular loop of wire, as shown in Fig. 53C, where each small element l of the wire is perpendicular to the radial distance r, and equidistant from the center P. Since $\theta = 90°$, and $\sin \theta = 1$, Eq.(53b) becomes the same for each element l_i.

$$B_1 = \frac{\mu_0}{4\pi} \cdot \frac{Il_1}{r_1^2}, \qquad B_2 = \frac{\mu_0}{4\pi} \cdot \frac{Il_2}{r_2^2},$$

$$B_3 = \frac{\mu_0}{4\pi} \cdot \frac{Il_3}{r_3^2}, \quad \text{etc.}$$

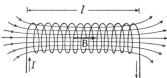

FIG. 53D—A solenoid of N turns of wire.

Summing up the mutually parallel contributions from all elements of the wire, the resultant magnitude of B becomes

$$B = \frac{\mu_0}{4\pi} \left(\frac{Il_1}{r^2} + \frac{Il_2}{r^2} + \frac{Il_3}{r^2} + \ldots \right), \quad \text{or} \quad B = \frac{\mu_0 I}{4\pi r^2} (l_1 + l_2 + l_3 + \ldots).$$

Since the sum $l_1 + l_2 + l_3 + \ldots$ must equal the circumference of the wire loop, the above parenthesis can be replaced by $2\pi r$.

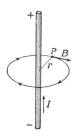

FIG. 53E—Magnetic field B around a straight conductor carrying an electron current.

$$B = \mu_0 \frac{I}{2r} \qquad (53e)$$

where $\mu_0 = 12.57 \times 10^{-7}$ weber/ampere meter, I is in amperes, r is in meters, and B is in webers/meter². Note that B is the magnetic induction at the center only and that its direction is perpendicular to the plane of the loop. For the general shape of the field see Fig. 52E.

If instead of a single loop of wire, the coil has a number of turns, N, each turn contributes the same field at the center, and the resultant magnetic induction will be given by

$$B = \mu_0 \frac{NI}{2r} \qquad (53f)$$

where N is the number of turns.

53.3. The Magnetic Induction Inside a Solenoid. The general shape of the field in a solenoid is shown in Figs. 52F and 53D. When Ampère's theorem is applied to such a coil, the magnetic induction B at the center is found to be given by

$$B = \mu_0 \frac{NI}{l} \qquad (53g)$$

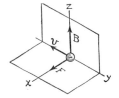

FIG. 53F—Force on a charge moving across a magnetic field.

where l is the length of the solenoid in meters, N is the number of turns, I is the electron current in amperes, and B is the magnetic induction in webers/meter². If the solenoid is long compared to its diameter, the magnetic induction along the center axis will be fairly uniform.

In the *cgs* system, magnetic induction is measured in *maxwells/centimeter²*, or *gauss*.

$$1 \text{ weber/meter}^2 = 10^4 \text{ maxwells/cm}^2 = 10^4 \text{ gauss.} \qquad (53h)$$

53.4. Field Near a Straight Conductor. The magnetic induction around a straight wire is shown in Fig. 52D to be everywhere perpendicular to the wire, and the lines of force to be concentric circles. The magnitude of the induction at any point *P*, close to a long, straight wire, is found from Ampère's theorem to be given by

$$B = \mu_o \frac{I}{2\pi r} \qquad (53i)$$

where, as shown in Fig. 53E, *r* is the perpendicular distance to the point *P* in meters, and *I* is the electron current in amperes.

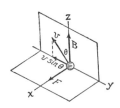

53.5. Force on a Moving Charge. In Sec. 52.8 it was shown how a current-carrying wire, when placed in a magnetic field, experiences a mechanical force tending to move it across the field. This mechanical force is due directly to the force exerted by the magnetic induction upon the individual moving electrons within the conductor. See Fig. 53F.

Fig. 53G—Force on a negative charge moving at an angle to a magnetic field.

A charge *Q*, moving with a velocity *v*, through a magnetic field at right angles to *B*, experiences a force *F* given by

$$F = QvB. \qquad (53j)$$

In the *mks* system, *F* is in *newtons*, *B* is in *webers/meter²*, *v* is in *meters/sec*, and *Q* is in *coulombs*. The vectors *B*, *v*, and *F* are all mutually perpendicular to each other.

If the velocity vector *v* makes an angle *θ* with *B*, as indicated in Fig. 53G, the magnitude of the force *F* is proportional to the component of the velocity perpendicular to *B*.

$$F = QvB \sin \theta. \qquad (53k)$$

If the charge *Q* in Fig. 53G is positive, the force *F* is opposite in direction to the one shown. When a charged particle moves parallel to the field, that is along the magnetic lines, $\sin \theta = 0$, there is no force.

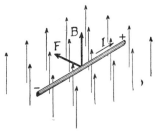

Fig. 53H—The force on a current carrying wire in a magnetic field.

53.6. Force on a Current-Carrying Wire. To find the force on a current-carrying wire in a magnetic field we make use of the above Eq.(53j), $F = QvB$. See Fig. 53H. A single moving charge *Q* constitutes a current

$I = Q/t$. Moving with a velocity v it will, in a time t, travel a distance $l = vt$. Substituting for Q and v in Eq.(53i),

$$F = It \times \frac{l}{t} \times B \qquad \text{or} \qquad F = IlB. \tag{53l}$$

In the *mks* system F is in *newtons*, B is in *webers/meter²*, I is in *amperes*, and l is in *meters*. In the *cgs* system F is in *dynes*, B is in *maxwells/cm²*, I is in *abamperes*, and l is in *cm*. *1 abampere = 10 amperes*, and *1 maxwell/cm² = 1 gauss*.

Like a moving charge in Fig. 53G, a current carrying wire making an angle θ with the field experiences a force proportional to sin θ.

$$F = IlB \text{ sin } \theta. \tag{53m}$$

Example. A wire 40 cm long and carrying an electron current of 2.5 amperes is located in a uniform magnetic field in which $B = 10^{-2}$ weber/meter². Calculate the force on the wire when it makes an angle of 60° with the field direction.

Solution. Since θ is measured from the direction of B, $\theta = 60°$, and substitution in Eq.(53m) gives

$$F = 10^{-2} \times 2.5 \times 0.40 \times 0.866 = 8.66 \times 10^{-3} \text{ newton.}$$

53.7. Total Magnetic Flux and Flux Density.

In Chap. 51 the magnetic field over a region of space is graphically represented by what are called *lines of force*. In order to specify the *strength* or *intensity* of a magnetic field at any point in space, the vector quantity called *magnetic induction B* is there defined. See Sec. 51.13. Since lines of force are frequently used as graphical representations of the variations in the magnetic induction from point to point, they are also called *lines of induction*.

The direction of the magnetic induction B at any point is tangent to the line of induction passing through that point, and its magnitude is given by the number of lines per unit area. The unit area is so chosen that it includes the point in question and is everywhere perpendicular to all lines passing through it.

In the *mks* system, a line of induction is called a *weber*, while in the *cgs* system a line of induction is called a *maxwell*.

The total number of lines of induction passing through a surface is called the magnetic flux and is represented by ϕ. In a region where the field is uniform and the surface area A is normal to the lines of induction,

$$\phi = BA. \tag{53n}$$

Since B is measured in *webers/meter²* and A is in *meters²*, the total flux ϕ is in *webers*. *B is often called the flux density.*

53.8. Magnetic Intensity and Permeability.

Consider a long solenoid bent into the form of a ring as shown in Fig. 53I. Such a coil with closely spaced windings is often called a Rowland ring after H. A. Rowland who first made use of it in his work on electricity and magnetism. When an electron current is sent through a Rowland ring, the magnetic lines of induction B are continuous, and confined entirely within the space enclosed by the winding. If l is the circumference of the ring, the magnetic induction inside is given by Eq.(53g)

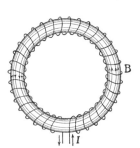

$$B_o = \mu_o \frac{NI}{l} .$$ (53o)

FIG. 53I—Toroidal solenoid, or "Rowland ring."

When the same wire is wound on a ring of ferromagnetic material like iron, the internal field is greatly increased. See Fig. 52G. This large increase in B, over and above the field there previously, is to be ascribed to an additional field B_1 set up by the thousands of tiny elementary magnets that turn to line up with the magnetizing field B_o.

It is now known that the magnetic properties of these tiny magnets are in reality due to the spinning of electrons in the iron atoms themselves. Furthermore the field produced by these spinning negative charges is similar to the field produced by a flow of electrons in a coil of wire. Since the field B_1 set up by the elementary magnets is proportional to the magnetizing field, we may write,

$$B_1 = \chi \frac{NI}{l}$$ (53p)

the proportionality constant χ is called the *magnetic susceptibility.*

The resultant *flux density* B is therefore the sum of the two fields B_o and B_1.

$$B = \mu_o \frac{NI}{l} + \chi \frac{NI}{l} = (\mu_o + \chi) \frac{NI}{l} .$$

Here we introduce and define the *magnetic intensity* H as

$$H = \frac{NI}{l}$$ (53q)

and the *permeability* as

$$\mu = (\mu_o + \chi)$$

Finally we may write,

$$B = \mu H \qquad \text{or} \qquad \mu = \frac{B}{H}$$ (53r)

The permeability of iron, or any other ferromagnetic material, does **not** have a fixed value but varies with different specimens and with the magnetic intensity H. For a vacuum, and practically so for air, χ in Eq.(53p) is zero, and $\mu = \mu_0$. For iron on the other hand μ may go as high as 7×10^{-3} *webers/ampere-meter*, and permalloy (Ni 78.5%, Fe 21.5%) as high as 7×10^{-2} *w/amp-m*.

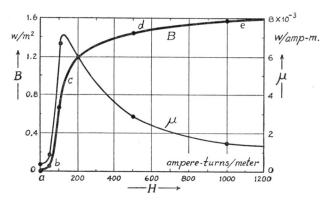

Fig. 53J—Typical magnetization and permeability curves. (For silicon steel.)

Fig. 53J shows a typical magnetization curve for silicon steel, a relatively common material used in motors, transformers, and other electrical equipment. Characteristic of all magnetic substances, the curve rises slowly at first (a to b), then rapidly and uniformly (b to c), and finally turns over and flattens out (d to e). The flattened section represents a saturation condition in which B rises very little as H is increased. In other words, when the tiny elementary magnets are all lined up, B increases only by the amount H contributed by the electron current in the winding.

A table of the important magnetic properties of silicon steel is given in Table 53A.

TABLE 53A. MAGNETIC CONSTANTS OF SILICON STEEL

H amp-turns m	$\mu_0 H$ webers m²	μ webers amp-m	B webers m²	$\dfrac{\mu}{\mu_0}$
0	0	3100×10^{-7}	0	250
50	0.000063	8600 $''$	0.043	680
100	0.00013	67000 $''$	0.67	5300
200	0.00025	60000 $''$	1.20	4700
500	0.00063	28800 $''$	1.44	2300
1000	0.0013	15800 $''$	1.58	1250
10000	0.013	1720 $''$	1.72	137

It will be seen that, when H is small (between 0 and 200 amp-turns/m), μ is very large and practically all of the field is due to the magnetization of the iron. Beyond an H of about 1000 amp-turns/m the permeability decreases to a relatively low value.

PROBLEMS

1. Calculate the magnetic induction at a distance of 1 cm from a long straight wire carrying an electron current of 100 amperes.

2. Two long straight parallel wires 3 cm apart each carry an electron current of 40 amperes. Calculate the magnetic induction at a point between the wires, 1 cm from one and 2 cm from the other, when the currents are (a) in the same direction, and (b) in opposite directions. (*Ans.* (a) 4×10^{-4} w/m², (b) 12×10^{-4} w/m².)

3. A wire 50 ft long is wound into a flat coil 2 in. in diameter. If an electron current of 10 amperes flows through the coil, what is the magnetic induction at the center?

4. A flat coil of 50 turns has a diameter of 4 in. and carries an electron current of 7 amperes. Find the magnetic induction at the center. (*Ans.* 4.33×10^{-3} w/m².)

5. If the magnetic induction at the center of a solenoid 50 cm long is to be 2×10^{-2} w/m² when an electron current of 6 amperes is flowing through it, how many turns must it have?

6. A solenoid 60 cm long has 550 turns of wire. What electron current is required to produce a magnetic induction of 5×10^{-2} w/m² at its center? (*Ans.* 43.4 amps.)

7. A solenoid 30 cm long and 50 turns of wire carries an electron current of 1.2 amperes. (a) Calculate the flux density at the center. (b) What will be the flux density when a bar of silicon steel is inserted as a core? (c) What is the permeability? (See Fig. 53J for part (c).)

8. A flat coil of 20 turns and radius 10 cm carries a current of 6.25 amperes. Find the magnetic induction at its center in gauss. (*Ans.* 7.854 gauss.)

9. A solenoid 50 cm long carries an electron current of 8.5 amperes. How many turns are required if the magnetic induction at the center is to be 100 gauss?

10. A copper wire 100 ft long is wound into a solenoid 2 in. in diameter and 20 in. long. (a) What is the magnetic induction at the center if an electron current of 1.4 amperes flows through the wire? If a silicon steel core is inserted, (b) what is the permeability, and (c) what will be the flux density? (*Ans.* (a) 6.614×10^{-4} w/m², (b) 2.7×10^{-3} w/amp-m, (c) 1.4 w/m².)

11. A straight wire 6 in. long and carrying an electron current of 15 amperes is placed in a field where the magnetic induction is 1 w/m². If the wire and the field are perpendicular to each other, find the force on the wire.

12. An electron moves with one-thirtieth the velocity of light through a magnetic field where the magnetic induction is 2×10^{-4} w/m². If the electron's path is perpendicular to the magnetic induction (a) what force acts on the electron, and (b) what is the radius of the circular path? See Appendix VI. (*Ans.* (a) 3.2×10^{-16} newtons, (b) 2.84 cm.)

13. Solve Prob. 12 if the velocity is one-hundreth the velocity of light and the magnetic induction is 3.5×10^{-5} w/m².

14. A straight wire 25 cm long is placed in a magnetic field where the magnetic induction is 0.10 w/m² so that it makes an angle of 30° with the field. What electron current in the wire will produce a force on the wire of 0.2 newton? (*Ans.* 16.0 amps.)

15. An electron current of 20 amperes flows through a straight wire 15 cm long. If this wire is placed in a field of 2×10^{-2} w/m² making an angle of 60° with the field direction, what is the force on the wire?

Induced Electric Currents   Chapter 54

54.1. Induced Electric Currents. The discovery of induced electric currents goes back more than one hundred years to 1831 and the well-planned experiments of Michael Faraday.* A straight bar magnet plunged into a coil of wire was found to produce an electric current. The experiment is illustrated in Fig. 54A. As the *N* pole of the magnet is plunged into the coil, a galvanometer needle deflects to the *right;* when it is withdrawn the needle deflects to the *left,* indicating a current in the opposite direction. If the *S* pole is moved down into the coil the needle deflects to the *left* and as it is withdrawn the deflection is to the *right.*

The relative motion of the coil and magnet is what produces the current and it makes no difference whether the coil alone moves, whether the magnet alone moves, or

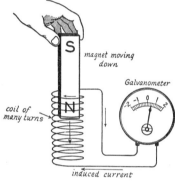

FIG. 54A—Diagram of Faraday's experimental discovery of induced electric currents.

* Michael Faraday (1791-1867), English experimental physicist. Born the son of a blacksmith, Faraday's early life was spent earning his living as a bookbinder's apprentice. Taking time from his work to read some of the books passing through his hands, Faraday became intensely interested in science. With a passionate desire to make science a life work, his chance finally came when he was made a valet and assistant to the great English scientist Sir Humphry Davy of the Royal Institute. As a young man he openly proclaimed that women were nothing in his life, and even wrote and published a poem in criticism of falling in love. At the age of twenty-nine he saw, fell desperately in love with, and married Sarah Barnhard who became a devoted and inspiring companion for the nearly fifty remaining years of his life. Four months after his marriage he made the famous discovery of the motion of a wire carrying a current in the field of a magnet. Since a current-carrying wire would move in a magnetic field, should not the reverse be true and a magnet be made to produce current in a wire? For days he experimented with magnets and coils of wire until in desperation he plunged a magnet down into a coil and observed that a current was generated in the coil. Why had he not discovered this before? The motion was the thing; it was the connecting link he had failed to realize. For this discovery the whole scientific world sought to honor him. So many universities gave him honorary degrees that he soon had to turn down such honors. He refused the presidency of both the Royal Institute and the Royal Society of London, and also refused to be knighted. Like all great scientists he loved his work more than these honors.

whether they both move. In either case, when the relative motion ceases, the current stops. A "somewhat old-fashioned" way of describing the action is to say that only when a wire is cutting the line of force is there an induced emf. A somewhat more acceptable statement at the present time is,

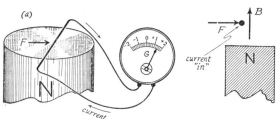

Fɪɢ. 54B—Experimental arrangement for demonstrating induced electron currents.

in effect, that only when the total magnetic flux linking a closed electrical circuit is changing is there an induced emf. To demonstrate this concept, a simple experiment like that shown in Fig. 54B may be performed.

A flexible wire connected to an ammeter, and held in the hands, is moved in various ways across the pole of a magnet. When a straight section of the wire is held over the N pole and moved to the right, an electron current flows in the direction shown by the arrows. If the wire is moved in the opposite direction, the induced emf and current reverses direction. If the wire is moved vertically upward or downward, parallel to the magnetic induction, no current flows. In other words, *there is an induced emf only when the total number of lines of induction through the closed circuit is changing.*

The fact that a current is produced means that electrical energy has been created. It has been created at the expense of mechanical work, for in moving the wire across the field, a force F had to be exerted for a distance s. The faster the wire moves, and the stronger the field through which it moves, the greater is the required force and the greater is the induced emf and the resultant electron current. If the wire stops moving in mid-field, the emf drops to zero. These are the essential principles of the electric generator.

The *left-hand rule* may be used to predict the direction of the induced emf in any section of wire. If we imagine grasping the wire in the left hand, as it moves through the magnetic field, the fingers pointing in the direction of the magnetic induction immediately in front of it, the thumb will point in the direction of the induced emf. See Fig. 54B, diagram (b).

54.2. Induced Electromotive Force. It was shown in Sec. 53.5 how an electric charge Q, moving with a constant velocity v through a magnetic field where the flux density is B, experiences a force F upon it given by

$$F = QvB \qquad (54a)$$

where F, B and v are all mutually perpendicular to each other.

When, therefore, a single wire is made to cross magnetic lines of induction, as shown in Fig. 54C, every atomic charge within the metal experiences a force upon it parallel to the conductor. The direction of the force on the $+$ charges is from J to K, while the force on the $-$ charges is from K to J. Since only the electrons are free to move in a metallic conductor, the negative charges migrate along the wire building up a negative potential at one end and a positive potential at the other.

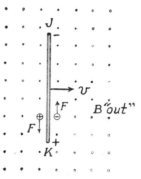

FIG. 54C—Forces on the charges in a conductor moving through a magnetic field.

Consider the straight conductor sliding along a U-shaped conductor to form a closed circuit as shown in Fig. 54D. The potential difference created between the ends force electrons through and around the circuit in the direction indicated. In other words the moving conductor becomes the source of an *electromotive force.*

The electromotive force developed within a moving conductor of length l is defined as the work per unit charge done in carrying any charge from one end to the other. From mechanics we draw upon the principle that work done W is equal to *force times distance* moved. With the force given by Eq.(54a) and the distance moved by l, the work done on a charge Q is

$$W = QvBl$$

If we now divide both sides of the equation by Q, the work per unit charge becomes

$$\mathcal{E} = vBl, \qquad (54b)$$

where $\mathcal{E}$ is the *emf*, or work per unit charge done on the charges in this section of the moving conductor.

In the *mks* system B is in *webers/*

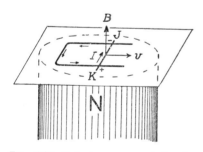

FIG. 54D—Inducing a current by the motion of a conductor.

meter^2, v is in *meters/second*, l is in *meters*, and $\mathcal{E}$ is in *volts*. It should be pointed out that it makes no difference in the above treatment whether the wire moves through a stationary magnetic field or whether the field moves across a stationary conductor. It is the relative motion giving rise to crossing of lines of induction that produces the *emf.*

54.3. Faraday's Law. Faraday's law states that *the electromotive force generated in a conductor is equal to the rate of change of magnetic flux through the circuit.* For example, as the magnet in Fig. 54A is plunged down into the coil the number of lines of induction threading through the coil is increasing, and an induced electron current results. When the magnet is removed, the total flux linking the coil decreases, and again an electron current flows.

Consider again a U-shaped conductor with a slide wire moving with a velocity v across a uniform magnetic field B as shown in Fig. 54E. At one instant the total flux ϕ_1 linking the circuit $JKON$ is BA_1 (see Eq.(53n)). In time t, the wire reaches the position ML where the total flux ϕ_2 linking the circuit $MLON$ has increased to BA_2. The change in flux, therefore, is $\phi_2 - \phi_1 = B(A_2 - A_1)$, where the change in area, $A_2 - A_1 = l \times s$. Hence $\phi_2 - \phi_1 = sBl$. Dividing both sides by t gives

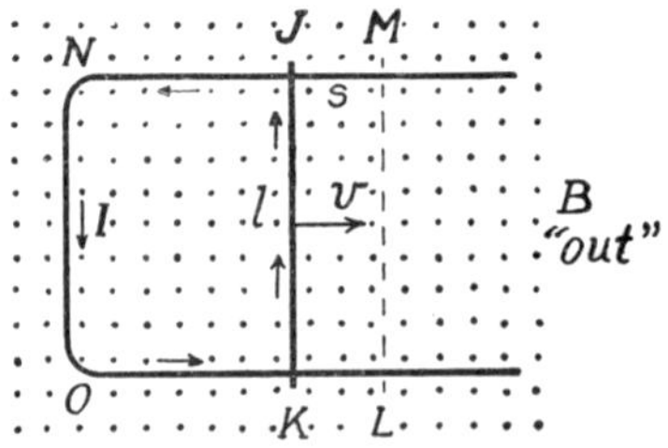

$$\frac{\phi_2 - \phi_1}{t} = \frac{s}{t}Bl = vBl = \mathcal{E}. \quad (54c)$$

Hence, the electromotive force $\mathcal{E}$ is given by

$$\mathcal{E} = \frac{\phi_2 - \phi_1}{t}. \quad (54d)$$

Fig. 54E—The change of magnetic flux through a circuit.

Here we have derived Faraday's law from Eq.(53k), and for the particular case in which there is relative motion between a conductor and a magnetic field. However, the law is equally valid for the case in which the change in flux, $\phi_2 - \phi_1$, is due to a change in the strength of the magnetic field without any relative motion between conductor and flux. If it were not equally valid for this second case, the law of conservation of energy would be violated.

Since Eq.(54d) represents the flux change in a single turn of wire of area A, then an equal flux change in a coil of N turns of wire will induce an overall *emf* N times as great. In the *mks* system ϕ_2 and ϕ_1 are in webers, t is in seconds, and $\mathcal{E}$ is in volts.

54.4. The Electric Generator. An electric generator is constructed the same as an electric motor, with a rotating armature containing coils of wire, pole pieces, field windings, brushes, and a commutator. Instead of supplying an electron current to obtain mechanical rotation, mechanical work is done to turn the armature thus producing an electron current.

If, in the construction of a generator, two solid rings are used as a commutator, as shown in Fig. 54F(a), the current delivered to the brushes flows first in one direction, then in the other. The reversal of current with each half turn of the armature is due to the fact that each wire moves up across

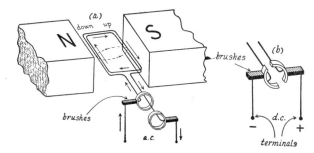

FIG. 54F—(a) Schematic diagram illustrating the principle of
the electric generator. (b) Detail of split ring commutator
necessary for obtaining a direct current.

the field at one instant and down at the next. At one instant the one terminal is positive and the other negative; at the next instant the first terminal
is negative and the second positive. This periodically reversing e.m.f. produces what is called *an alternating emf.*

If a direct current is desired the commutator of the generator must be of
the split-ring type illustrated in diagram (b). It can be seen with this arrangement that one brush is at all times in contact with wires moving up
across the field while the other is in contact with wires moving down across
the field. This produces a uni-directional electron current and the whole
machine is called a *direct-current* (d.c.) *generator.*

It is important to note that a generator does not make electricity. The
electricity, or electric charge, is always in the wire, and a generator sets it
into motion. A generator produces an electric current.

54.5. Direct and Alternating Currents. The difference between a
direct and an alternating current is that a direct current always flows in one
direction, while on alternating current reverses its direction periodically. To
send a direct current through an electric circuit a source capable of developing a constant electromotive force is necessary. For this purpose a battery or
direct current generator is used.

To send an alternating current through a circuit, on the other hand, a
source capable of reversing its *emf* is required. To do this an alternating
current generator is generally used.

Graphical representations of both direct and alternating currents are
given in Fig. 54G for comparison purposes. The two lower curves permit a
comparison of the *electron currents* through a circuit while the upper curves
permit a comparison of the *emf,* or *voltage,* of the source. The horizontal
scale on all diagrams represents the *time.*

Within the short time of one second the generators in most power plants
reverse the *emf* many times. For example, the power supplied to private
homes and public buildings in nearly all cities in the United States is in the

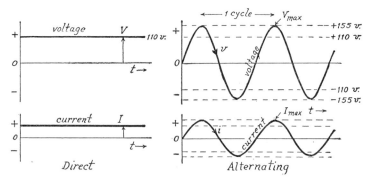

FIG. 54G—Graphs of 110-volt direct and 110-volt alternating currents.

form of alternating current at 25, 50, or 60 cycles per second, and 110 or 220 volts.

A 60-cycle, 110-volt alternating *emf*, for example, is one in which the potential difference reverses direction 120 times per second. The rating of 110 volts specifies a sort of average voltage called the *root mean square emf* and not the so-called *peak emf* of 155 volts.

The magnitude of the emf induced in a coil rotating at uniform speed, as shown in Fig. 54F, may be computed either from the vertical velocities of the wires forming the sides of the coil or by the rate of change of flux through the coil. In either case,

$$\mathcal{E} = NBA\omega \sin \omega t \qquad (54e)$$

where N is the number of turns in the coil, B is the magnetic induction in *webers/meter*^{2}, A is the coil area in *meters*^{2}, ω is the angular speed in *radians/second*, and t is the time in *seconds*. If f represents the *frequency of rotation*,

$$\omega = 2\pi f \qquad (54f)$$

The top curve in Fig. 54G represents the electromotive force $\mathcal{E}$, or the output *emf V*, at any instant, where V_{max} and I_{max} are constants and represent the amplitude or *peak emf* and *peak current* respectively. From Eq.(54e) the *emf* is a maximum when the plane of the coil is parallel to the field and zero when it is perpendicular to the field. In the parallel position the coil sides are cutting across the lines of induction while in the perpendicular position they are moving along the lines of induction. Eq.(54e) is a maximum when $\sin \omega t = 1$. This gives

$$\mathcal{E}_{max} = NBA\omega. \qquad (54g)$$

Example. A rectangular coil of wire having 60 turns with dimensions of 10 cm × 20 cm is set rotating at a constant speed of 1800 rpm in a uniform magnetic field of flux density $B = 0.5$ w/m^2. The axis of the coil is perpendicular to the field. Find the maximum *emf* produced.

Solution. Since ω is $2\pi f$, $\omega = 2\pi \times 1800/60 = 188.5$ rad/sec. Direct substitution in Eq.(54g) gives

$$\mathcal{E}_{max} = 60 \times 0.5 \text{ w/m}^2 \times 0.10 \text{ m} \times 0.20 \text{ m} \times 188.5 \text{ rad/sec.}$$
$$\mathcal{E}_{max} = 113 \text{ w/sec} = 113 \text{ volts.}$$

Since the power dissipated as heat in any resistor at any instant is I^2R, where I is the magnitude of the current at that instant, the average power dissipated when an alternating current flows through the resistor, is the average of I^2R (not the square of the average I) *over* each cycle. Since the average of $\sin^2 \omega t$, as ωt varies from 0 to 2π, is ½ (see Fig. 54H), the average value of I^2 is $\frac{1}{2}(I_{max})^2$. Calling the square root of this average I_{rms},

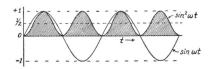

Fig. 54H—The average value of $\sin^2 \theta$ is ½.

$$I_{rms} = 0.707 \ I_{max}. \tag{54h}$$

In a similar averaging process the *root mean square emf* is given by

$$V_{rms} = 0.707 \ V_{max}. \tag{54i}$$

For an *rms* value of 110 volts the maximum is 155 volts.

If an alternating current is applied to circuits containing inductance and capacitance, Ohm's law, as it is used with resistance and direct current, does not apply. In such instances the current and voltage are not in phase with each other, that is, they do not rise to a maximum at the same time or fall to zero at the same time, and more complicated formulas must be used. Such circuits will be treated in Chap. 56.

Alternating currents circuits for which the direct current relations of Ohm's law do hold true are those in which all of the circuit elements are pure resistances. Most electric lights and many heating units are of this class. In applying Ohm's law to pure resistance circuits, it is common practice to use the *rms* voltage V_{rms} and calculate the *rms* current I_{rms}. These values can be used in Eqs.(52c), (52d), and (52e) to calculate energy or power.

PROBLEMS

1. A wire 50 cm long moves with a speed of 5 m/sec through a uniform magnetic field where the flux density is 0.2 w/m². If the wire, field, and motion are all mutually perpendicular to each other, what *emf* is induced in the wire?

2. A wire 6 m long is located in the wing of an airplane making 360 km/hr. If the magnetic induction of the earth's field has a value of 5.4×10^{-5} w/m² and makes an angle of 62° with the airplane's direction of motion, find the emf. Assume the wire perpendicular to the Bv-plane. (*Ans.* 0.0324 volt.)

3. A U-shaped conductor 20 cm wide (see Fig. 54E) is located in a uniform magnetic field where the magnetic induction is 4×10^{-3} w/m². If a straight rod across the loop moves with a speed of 5 m/sec, find (a) the magnitude of the emf, and (b) the rate of change of the flux linking the circuit.

4. A U-shaped conductor 15 cm wide (see Fig. 54E) is located in a uniform magnetic field where the magnetic induction is 500 gauss. Find (a) the magnitude of the emf induced in a rod sliding along the loop at 2 m/sec, and (b) the rate of change of flux. (*Ans.* (a) 15 mv, (b) 0.015 w/sec.)

5. A flat rectangular loop of wire 5 cm by 20 cm is located in a uniform magnetic field where the magnetic induction is 5×10^{-2} w/m² with its plane perpendicular to the flux lines. If the loop is turned to a position where its plane is parallel to the field, in 0.01 sec, what rms emf is induced in the loop?

6. A flat rectangular coil 5 cm by 10 cm contains 200 turns of wire. Located in the earth's magnetic field where the magnetic induction is 5.4×10^{-5} w/m² the coil is turned from a position where its plane is parallel to the field to where it is perpendicular to the field, in 0.05 sec. What average emf is induced? (*Ans.* 1.08×10^{-3} volt.)

7. A flat rectangular coil 10 cm by 20 cm and 50 turns of wire is rotating at the constant speed of 3000 rpm in a magnetic field where the magnetic induction is 0.2 w/m². Calculate (a) the maximum emf produced, and (b) the root mean square voltage.

8. A flat circular coil 10 cm in diameter and containing 200 turns of wire is rotating at 1200 rpm in a magnetic field where the magnetic induction is 0.35 w/m². Find (a) the maximum emf developed, and (b) the root mean square voltage. (*Ans.* (a) 69.1 v, (b) 48.8 v.)

9. An a.c. generator whose terminal root mean square emf is 110 volts is connected to a resistance of 20 ohms. If the internal resistance of the generator is 2.5 ohms, what is the peak electron current?

10. A resistance of 4.5 ohms is connected to an a.c. generator whose internal resistance is 0.5 ohm. If the rms current in the circuit is 10 amps, find the peak emf of the generator. (*Ans.* 70.7 v.)

11. An electric toaster with a resistance of 16 ohms is connected to a 220 volt a.c. line. Find (a) the peak voltage, and (b) the peak electron current.

12. An electric iron with a resistance of 20 ohms is connected to a 120 volt a.c. line. Find (a) the peak voltage, and (b) the peak electron current. (*Ans.* (a) 170 v, (b) 8.5 amps.)

13. Two resistances of 5 and 20 ohms respectively are connected in parallel and the combination in series with a resistance of 8 ohms. The ends of this circuit are connected to a generator supplying an rms emf of 28 volts a.c. at its terminals. Find (a) the peak voltage across the 8 ohm resistance, and (b) the peak electron current through each resistance.

14. A rectangular coil of 200 turns is 10 cm wide and 20 cm long. What is the minimum speed at which this coil can be rotated in the earth's field to generate a peak voltage of 0.10 volt. Assume the magnetic induction to be 5.0×10^{-5} w/m². (*Ans.* 79.5 cycles/sec.)

15. A flat circular coil of 10 turns is 20 cm in diameter. If this coil is located in a uniform magnetic field where $B = 0.2$ w/m², how fast must it rotate about a diameter to generate an rms emf of 28 volts?

16. A flat circular coil of 20 turns is 10 cm in diameter. If an rms voltage of 50 volts and 1000 cycles/sec are to be obtained by rotating this coil in a uniform magnetic field, what must be the value of the magnetic induction? (*Ans.* 0.0717 w/m².)

Transformers Chapter 55

BECAUSE of the widespread use of transformers in long-distance power transmission as well as in telephones, radio transmitters and receivers, television, etc., it is of interest to consider the elementary principles upon which these instruments operate. A transformer is an electrical device by which the *electromotive force* of a source of alternating current may be increased or decreased.

55.1. The Primary Circuit. To study the actions and principles of a transformer we must return to the *solenoid,* or *electromagnet,* treated in Sec.

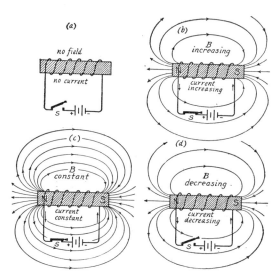

FIG. 55A—Schematic diagrams of the changing magnetic field around an electromagnet when the current is increasing, constant, and decreasing.

52.7. Before an electron current is started through the coil of an electromagnet no magnetic field whatever exists. This is illustrated by diagram (a) in Fig. 55A. When the switch S is first closed, completing the electric circuit, the electron current does not rise immediately to its full value but requires a certain amount of time to "build up" (see Fig. 55B). Starting at zero at the time the switch is closed, the current increases rapidly at first, then more slowly, reaching finally its full value, the value given by Ohm's law.

During the time the electron current is increasing, the magnetic induction B, in and around the solenoid, is increasing as shown in diagram (b) of Fig. 55A. This field continues to grow in strength until the current reaches its maximum value, whereupon both current and field become constant. In most circuits this whole process requires but a small fraction of a second.

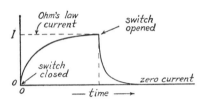

Fig. 55B—Current-time graph for an electromagnet as illustrated in Fig. 55A.

A constant current is indicative, therefore, of a constant unchanging magnetic field as shown in diagram (c).

When the switch is opened, the current will not stop instantly, nor will the surrounding field vanish instantly. The current will decrease with time, as shown in the graph of Fig. 55B, and the magnetic induction will decrease accordingly as shown in Fig. 55A(d). When the current reaches zero, once more the field will simultaneously vanish as in diagram (a). Thus, by opening and closing a switch, a magnetic field of increasing and decreasing strength is produced.

55.2. The Secondary Circuit. If a loop of wire is placed around an electromagnet, as shown in Fig. 55C, and the switch in the circuit is closed and opened as described in the preceding section, an electromotive force, and hence an electron current, will be induced in the loop. Immediately after the switch has been closed and the current and magnetic induction begin to rise, the total flux through the loop increases and we obtain an induced emf. An induced emf means that, if the loop ends are connected together, or to something else, to form a closed circuit, a current will flow in the loop as shown by the arrows in the diagram.

When the electromagnet current reaches a steady state, the field becomes constant. This means that the total flux

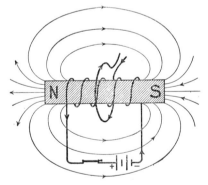

Fig. 55C—Diagram illustrating an electron current induced in a loop of wire placed in the changing field of an electromagnet.

through the loop is no longer changing and the loop current has dropped to zero.

If the switch *S* is opened at this time, allowing the electromagnet current to decrease, the magnetic induction will decrease, and the total flux through the loop will fall. This decreasing flux, linking the loop circuit, induces an electron current opposite in direction to that shown in the diagram. When the current in the electromagnet winding drops to zero, the field vanishes and so does the induced emf. The properly timed closing and opening of a switch can, therefore, induce in a loop of wire one complete cycle of an alternating current.

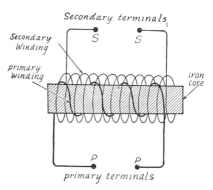

Fig. 55D—Diagram of an "open-core" type of transformer.

To increase the emf in the outside circuit, many loops of wire are usually employed. Such an arrangement becomes similar to that shown in Fig. 55D and is called an *open-core transformer*. The inside winding is called the *primary* and the outside winding is called the *secondary*. As the magnetic induction increases, the total flux through each loop of the secondary increases, and approximately the same emf is induced in each turn of the coil. Since the turns are all in series with each other, the total emf between the outside ends is the sum of the individual emf's for each turn.

It is customary for both the primary and secondary windings of a transformer to be wound with well insulated copper wire and for both windings to be electrically insulated from each other.

55.3. The Induction Coil. When the primary terminals of an open-core transformer are connected to a battery as a source of emf, a current in the secondary is induced only at the instant the circuit is closed and again when it is opened. To derive an alternating current from the secondary winding the primary circuit must be opened and closed continually. When this is done the field will increase and decrease periodically and the secondary will have induced in it, to deliver through the secondary terminals, an alternating current.

An induction coil is an open-core type of transformer with a few turns of large wire in the primary, many turns of fine wire in the secondary, and an automatic circuit *interrupter,* or *vibrator,* as shown in Fig. 55E. When the switch is closed and a current is started through the primary winding *PP,* the iron core becomes magnetized and attracts the iron knob *B.* Mounted on a strip of spring steel *L,* the vibrator bends to the left, breaking the primary circuit at the point *C.* When the current stops and the core loses its magnetism the vibrator springs back to the right, making contact again. Proper adjustment of the thumbscrew *T* will cause the iron knob *B* to vibrate back and forth periodically making and breaking the electric circuit. Each time the circuit is made the magnetic field grows, inducing a current in the secondary winding in one direction; and each time it is broken the field falls, inducing an oppositely directed current. Since

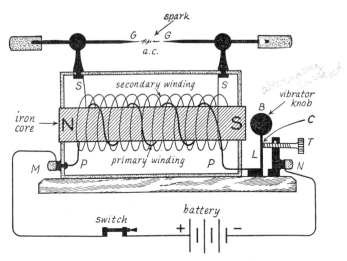

Fig. 55E—Cross-section diagram of a laboratory induction coil capable of producing high voltage sparks at the expense of a small battery.

each vibration of the knob *B* completes one cycle of an alternating current, the frequency of the vibrator determines the frequency of the alternating current delivered at the secondary terminals.

If, as is usually the case, the number of turns of wire in the secondary greatly exceeds the number of turns in the primary, the average voltage of the secondary will be many times higher than the direct current voltage impressed on the primary, and a spark will jump across the gap *GG*.

Perhaps the best place to find a *vibrator type of induction coil* being used today is in the automobile radio. Here a very small induction coil about 1 in in diameter and 3 in long is employed. The function of the coil is to take current from the 6-volt storage battery, with which every car is equipped, and deliver at the secondary terminals an alternating emf of from 200 to 300 volts. This alternating current is then changed into direct current by a single radio tube called *a rectifier* and a system of coils and condensers called *a filter system*. Thus the constant high voltage necessary for the proper operation of the radio receiver is obtained in the roundabout way of first transforming constant low voltage into high voltage alternating emf and then rectifying it to a constant high voltage.

A similar induction coil without a vibrator, called *a spark-coil* or *auto-transformer,* is used in the ignition system of an automobile. Generally, such coils are about 2 in in diameter and 4 in long, and are wound on an open core as shown in Fig. 55D. The primary winding of such coils contains about 100 turns of heavy copper wire and the secondary winding several thousand. The primary is connected to the 6-volt storage battery by wires through the timing system, the purpose of which is to open and close the circuit periodically with the motion of each cylinder of the motor. Each time the circuit is closed and opened, a high voltage induced in the secondary winding is connected to, and is discharged as a spark across, the terminals of one of the motor's spark plugs. The term auto-transformer applies to a transformer where one end of the primary winding is connected by a wire directly to one end of the secondary. This common junction has little effect upon the normal operation of the coil, and is usually connected to the ground. On an automobile the ground connection is made to the metal frame of the car.

55.4. The Closed-Core Transformer. A transformer, like an induction coil, has *a primary winding, a secondary winding,* and *an iron core.* The principal difference between the two is that a transformer does not have a vibrator and it operates on an alternating current supply.

Historically, the first closed-core transformer was made by Michael Faraday in 1831. Two coils of wire, one acting as a primary and the other as a secondary, were wound around opposite sides of an iron ring as shown in Fig. 55F. When a current is started in the primary winding, the magnetic field set up is confined almost entirely to the iron core. In other words, the lines of induction developing in the primary, as a result of the growing primary current, also thread through the secondary inducing an electromotive force and current. The

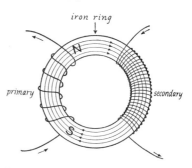

Fig. 55F—Diagram of the first closed-core transformer. (*Designed by Michael Faraday.*)

iron acts like a good conductor of magnetic lines of induction, guiding them through the secondary winding.

When an alternating current is connected to the primary of a transformer, no vibrator is required to start and stop the current; the current rises and falls periodically, satisfying the conditions for a changing magnetic field and induced currents.

Most modern transformers are of the closed-core type, as illustrated in Figs. 55G and H.

55.5. Step-Up and Step-Down Transformer. Nearly all transformers come under one of the two following classes: (a) *step-up,* or (b) *step-down* *transformers.* As shown in Fig. 55G, the step-up transformer is one in which the secondary winding has more turns of wire than the primary. In the step-

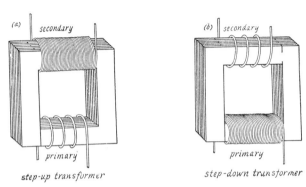

FIG. 55G—Diagram of a closed-core transformer.

down transformer the reverse is true. The importance of this distinction is based upon the general and well-established principle that the ratio of the number of turns of wire in the primary and secondary windings is the same as the ratio of the respective voltages in each. This may be stated as an equation.

$$\frac{\text{Number of primary turns}}{\text{Number of secondary turns}} = \frac{\text{primary voltage}}{\text{secondary voltage}}. \qquad (55a)$$

Thus, if a transformer has 100 turns in the primary and 100,000 turns in the secondary, the voltage delivered at the secondary terminals will be 1000 times the voltage impressed upon the primary. If this same transformer were connected to the ordinary house lighting circuit of 110 volts a.c., the voltage at the secondary terminals would be 110,000 volts a.c.

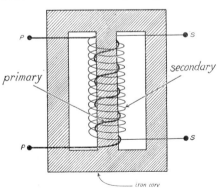

FIG. 55H—Shell type transformer.

The step-down transformer is just the reverse of this; the secondary voltage is lower than the primary voltage. As an illustration, suppose the primary of a transformer has 2000 turns of fine wire and the secondary has 100 turns. Having a turn-ratio of 20 to 1, this transformer connected to the 110 volt a.c. line will deliver at its secondary a difference of potential of one-twentieth of 110 volts, or 5 volts. Such transformers are used in electric welding, for the ringing of doorbells, for the operation of toy electric trains, for lighting the filaments in radio tubes, etc.

Transformers used in the construction of modern radio and television receivers and transmitters are of the shell type shown in Fig. 55H.

55.6. Power. The increase in voltage of an alternating current by means of a step-up transformer appears at first sight to be a violation of the law of conservation of energy, i.e., it appears as though a large amount of energy could be obtained at the expenditure of a smaller amount. This is really not the case, for when the voltage is increased the current is simultaneously decreased by the same proportion.

When, for example, a transformer is used to step up the voltage to 100 times that supplied to the primary, the current in the secondary becomes only one one-hundredth of the current in the primary. Therefore the power ($V_p I_p$) supplied at the primary is just equal to that delivered at the secondary ($V_s I_s$). In general, when the voltage is stepped up by a transformer the current is stepped down by the same proportion.

In practice this is not exactly true because a transformer is not quite 100% efficient. A small amount of electrical energy is continually expended, principally in the form of heat. In a well-designed transformer such losses do not exceed 2 or 3%; so that a transformer is often considered as almost 100% efficient.

55.7. Power Transmission. In the transmission of electrical energy over wires for long distances, transformers are practically indispensable. At the power house in the distant mountains, for example, electric current is generated by huge alternating current generators at the relatively low voltage of several thousand volts. If an attempt were made to transmit this electrical energy, at a voltage of say 2200 volts, over many miles of wire cable to a

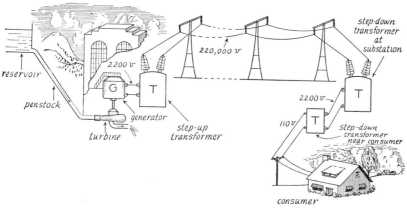

Fig. 55I—Illustrating the use of transformers in the transmission of electrical energy from the power house in the mountains to the consumer in the distant city.

distant city, the current would be so large that nearly all of the energy would be consumed in heating the power line. The heat generated, it should be remembered (see Sec. 52.1), is proportional to the square of the current. (*Heat* $= kI^2Rt$.)

To avoid large heat losses, transformers at the power house (see Fig. 55I) step the voltage up to some 220,000 volts before switching the current onto the power line. Since the voltage in the case cited is increased one-hundred fold, the current drops by the same proportion to one-hundredth. Since the square of 1/100 is 1/10,000, the heat loss along the transmission line is only one ten thousandth of what it would have been had the transformer not been used.

At the city end of the power line a transformer substation steps the voltage down to something like its original value of 2200 volts. From there branch lines distribute the power to various sections of the city where smaller transformers, one near each group of several houses, steps it down again to the relatively safe voltage of 110 to 220 volts.

PROBLEMS

1. A step-up transformer has 125 turns in the primary coil and 25,000 turns in the secondary coil. If the primary is connected to a 220 volt a.c. line, find the voltage delivered at the secondary terminals.

2. The primary of a step-up transformer having 260 turns is connected to a house lighting circuit of 115 volts a.c. If the secondary is to deliver 15,000 volts, how many turns must it have? (*Ans.* 33,913.)

3. The secondary of a step-down transformer has 50 turns of wire, and the primary is connected to a 110 volt a.c. line. If the secondary is to deliver 2.5 volts at its output terminals, how many turns should the primary have?

4. The primary of a step-down transformer has 600 turns and is connected to a 120 volt a.c. line. If the secondary is to supply 5 volts at its terminals and an electron current of 3.5 amp, find (a) the number of turns in the secondary, and (b) the electron current in the primary. (*Ans.* (a) 25 turns, (b) 0.146 amp.)

5. A step-up transformer with 160 turns in the primary is connected to a 120 volt a.c. line. The secondary delivers 10,000 volts at its terminals and a current of 50 milliamps. (a) How many turns are in the secondary? (b) What is the current in the primary? (c) What power is drawn from the line?

6. The primary of a step-up transformer is connected to a 220 volt a.c. line. The secondary with 7200 turns delivers 5000 v and a current of 20 milliamp. Calculate (a) the number of turns in the primary, and (b) the current drawn from the line. (c) What is the power? (*Ans.* (a) 317, (b) 0.454 amp, (c) 100.0 watts.)

7. A step-down transformer with 1200 turns in the primary is connected to a 115 volt a.c. line. If the transformer is to have three separate secondaries to give 2.5, 5.0, and 7.5 volts respectively, how many turns should each have?

Alternating Currents   Chapter 56

56.1. Self-Induction. When a battery is first connected to the ends of a long straight copper wire the electron current rises quickly to the value given by Ohm's law. When the same wire is wound into a coil or solenoid, however, the current rises more slowly as shown by curve (b) in Fig. 56A. If an iron core is inserted to make of the solenoid an electromagnet the current rises much more slowly as shown in curve (c).

The cause for this lagging of the current is attributed to an emf induced in the wire which is opposed in direction to the rising current. This *back emf*, as it is sometimes called, is extremely small if the wire is straight, is large if it is a coil, and still larger if a soft-iron core is inserted. To explain the existence of a back emf, consider a small section of one turn of wire in a solenoid of many turns. As the current rises in this

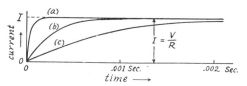

Fig. 56A—Current-time graph for a long copper wire in the form of (a) a straight wire, (b) a coil, and (c) a coil with an iron core.

section the growing magnetic induction developing around it threads through neighboring loops of wire inducing in them an emf. These induced emf's and their corresponding currents run counter to the impressed emf and current. This property is called *self-induction*.

The unit by which one measures the self-induction of a coil is called the *henry* in honor of the American scientist, Joseph Henry.* *A coil having an inductance of one henry is one in which a change in the current of one ampere per second produces a back emf of one volt.* A coil with a large

---

* Joseph Henry (1797-1878), American physicist and scientific administrator, was born in Albany, New York, in 1797. Henry attended a country school, but quit at the age of thirteen. Later he attended the Albany Academy. Becoming interested in electricity and magnetism he invented the magnetic telegraph, the electric relay, and discovered the phenomenon of self-induction. In 1832 he became professor of natural philosophy at Princeton and in 1842 was elected by Congress as first secretary of the Smithsonian Institution in Washington, D.C. In this capacity he founded the U. S. Weather Bureau and inaugurated the idea of distributing scientific publications to libraries and scientific bodies all over the world. He was the principal figure in the organization of the National Academy of Sciences of which he was the second president. By general consent Henry was the foremost American physicist of his time.

number of turns is one that has a large inductance L, whereas one with but a few turns has a small inductance. The higher the inductance the more slowly does the current rise or fall within the coil.

The establishment of a steady current in an inductance requires work, since the back emf's must be overcome. Not all of the electrical energy expended in reaching the steady-current state is lost. Some is stored up in the form of a magnetic field. When the source emf is disconnected from the circuit, the magnetic induction decreases, thereby inducing an oppositely directed emf and corresponding current.

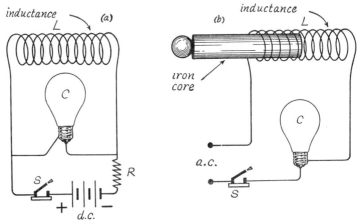

Fig. 56B—Two experiments illustrating the self-induction of a coil of wire. The circuit (b) is commonly used as a dimmer for electric lights.

Two experiments demonstrating the property of self-induction are illustrated in Fig. 56B. In diagram (a), a solenoid of many turns of wire is connected in parallel with an electric light to a 110-volt battery B. When the switch S is closed, the light flashes bright for an instant and then becomes dim. When the switch is opened, the light again flashes bright for a moment and then goes out. When the switch was closed, the back emf in the inductance prevented the current from building up rapidly through the inductance. The inductance therefore acted as though it had a very high resistance so that practically all of the current went through C. When the current became steady there was no back emf in L, and part of the current flowed through C and part through L. When the switch was opened, the magnetic field fell off, inducing a current in L. This current flowing through the lamp C caused it to light up momentarily to full brightness.

The second experiment, as illustrated in diagram (b), demonstrates an increase in the self-induction of a coil due to a soft-iron core. Connected to an alternating emf the light is bright when the iron core is out and dim when it is in place inside the solenoid. When the iron is inside, the back emf induced in the coil at each rise and fall of the current is very much greater than before, since the waxing and waning magnetic field is strengthened by its presence. The increased inductance therefore prevents the current reaching a very high value before the current stops again and reverses its direction. The effect on the brightness of the lamp is the same as if the inductance were replaced by a variable resistance whose value is greatest when the iron core is inside the solenoid.

When a current is started in an electromagnet, the tiny elementary magnets within the iron core (these are the elementary magnets referred to in Sec. 51.11.) turn around from their random orientations and line up with each other to make a single magnet of the entire core. In turning around, the field of each elementary magnet threads through the coil windings, inducing an emf opposing the rising current. This is another way of accounting for the back emf of self-induction.

56.2. Calculation of Inductance. In many instances the inductance of a solenoid can be calculated from its geometry. For a long solenoid of uniform cross-section, or a Rowland ring as shown in Fig. 53I, the inductance L, in *henries*, is given by

$$L = \mu \frac{N^2 A}{l} \tag{56a}$$

where N is the number of turns of wire, A is the cross-sectional area of the core in *square meters*, μ is the permeability of the core in *webers/ampere-meter*, and l is the length of the coil in meters.

Example. A round iron bar 4 cm in diameter and 20 cm long is wrapped with one layer of copper wire to form a solenoid. The coil has 200 turns and the permeability of the iron is 2×10^{-3} *w/amp-m*. Find the inductance.
Solution. The given quantities are just those occurring on the right in Eq.(56a). $N = 200$, $\mu = 2 \times 10^{-3}$, $l = 0.20$ m, and $A = \pi r^2 = 0.00126$ m².

$$L = \frac{2 \times 10^{-3} \times (200)^2 \times 0.00126}{0.2} = 0.504 \text{ henry.}$$

Without the iron core the solenoid above would have a very much smaller inductance. For an air core, μ would be equal to $\mu_o = 12.57 \times 10^{-7}$, and the inductance would be only 0.316 millihenry. *The millihenry* (abbr. mh) *is a smaller unit of inductance and is equal to one-thousandth of a henry*, while a still smaller unit, *the microhenry* (abbr. μh) *is equal to one-millionth of a henry*.

It should be noted that if the core is air, or a vacuum, L is a constant independent of the electron current and magnetizing field H. If the core is a ferromagnetic material, however, L will vary because the permeability varies.

56.3. Time Constants. When a capacitance C is connected in series to a resistance R and a battery emf V (see Fig. 56C), an electron current flows for a short period of time because it takes time for the plates of the capacitor to acquire their full charge Q. The rate at which a capacitor charges up is shown graphically in Fig. 56D. If now the switch S is opened disconnecting the battery, and then the switch K is closed, the capacitor will discharge, and again an electron current will flow through R.

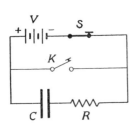

FIG. 56C—Series circuit containing capacitance and resistance.

The time taken for the charge on the capacitor to reach within $\frac{1}{e}th$ of its full charge Q while charging, and the time taken to drop to $\frac{1}{e}th$ of its full charge while discharging is called the circuit *time constant*.

$$\text{time constant} = RC. \quad (56b)$$

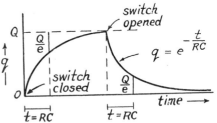

FIG. 56D—Capacitance time constant.

The constant e equals 2.718, ($1/e = 0.369$), and is the base of natural logarithms. The greater the resistance and the larger the capacitance the greater is the time required to charge or discharge a capacitor.

When an inductance L is connected in series with a resistance R and a battery of *emf* V (see Fig. 56E), it takes time for the electron current I and the accompanying magnetic field to build up to a steady state. When the switch S is opened and the switch K closed, the field decreases and the electron current falls approaching zero as t approaches infinity. The time constant of the circuit, that is, the time for the electron current to rise to within $\frac{1}{e}th$ of its final value (see Fig. 56F), is given by

$$\text{time constant} = \frac{L}{R}. \quad (56c)$$

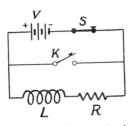

FIG. 56E—Series circuit containing inductance and resistance.

56.4. Stored Electrical Energy. When a capacitor like that shown in Fig. 56C is fully charged, electrical energy is stored in the form of an electric field. If W represents the stored energy in *joules*,

$$W = \tfrac{1}{2}CV^2 \quad (56d)$$

where C is in farads and V is in volts.

Similarly, when a steady electron current is maintained in an inductance *L,* as shown in Fig. 56E, electrical energy is stored up in the surrounding magnetic field to the amount,

$$W = \tfrac{1}{2}LI^2 \qquad (56e)$$

where *L* is in *henries,* *I* is in *amperes,* and *W* is in *joules.*

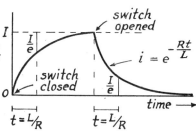

FIG. 56F—Inductance time constant.

56.5. Inductive and Capacitive Reactance. All electrical devices connected to a source of alternating *emf* contain a certain amount of *resistance, inductance,* and *capacitance.* If the total inductance and capacitance of the circuit are small compared with the resistance, Ohm's law can be applied to find the current in the various parts.

If the inductance and capacitance are not relatively small, they will introduce phase differences, or time lags, between current and voltage and Ohm's law will not apply in the ordinanry way. Such a circuit is shown schematically in Fig. 56G.

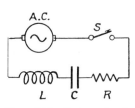

FIG. 56G—Series circuit containing inductance, capacitance and resistance.

Since an *emf* suddenly applied to an inductance requires a certain time for the electron current to build up to a fixed value (see Fig. 56A), the application of an *alternating emf* finds the current lagging behind the voltage in its rapid changes and reversals. Furthermore, if the frequency is very high there isn't time enough for the electron current to rise very far from zero toward its Ohm's law value.

Because the inductance effect reduces the electron current, it may be thought of as something analogous to a resistance. The measure of this effect is called *inductive reactance,* to distinguish it from a true resistance where electrical energy is converted into heat.

$$\text{Inductive reactance} = X_{\mathrm{L}} = 2\pi f L \text{ ohms} \qquad (56f)$$

where *f* is the frequency or cycles per second.

When a capacitor is inserted into a *d.c. circuit,* the plates charge up, and the electron current drops to zero. The capacitor thereafter acts as though it were an infinite resistance. Connected to an alternating emf, however, it may act quite differently. As the frequency *f* rises in an *a.c. circuit,* the resistive effect of a capacitor decreases. The reversing of the *emf* reverses the flow of electrons to and from the plates of the capacitor, and the alternating flow of charge constitutes an *alternating current.* Because a capacitor differs from a pure resistance in that it stores electrostatic energy, its resistive effect is called *capacitive reactance.*

$$\text{Capacitive reactance} = X_C = \frac{1}{2\pi fC}. \qquad (56g)$$

56.6. A.C. Series Circuit. When an inductance L, capacitance C, and a resistance R, are connected in series to an a.c. generator as shown in Fig. 56G, the electron current in the circuit can be determined by the following equation,

$$I = \frac{V}{\sqrt{R^2 + (X_L - X_C)^2}} \qquad (56h)$$

where I and V are the electron current and voltage respectively. The quantity $X_L - X_C$ in this equation is often called the *reactance* and is represented by X,

$$X = X_L - X_C, \qquad \text{so that} \qquad I = \frac{V}{\sqrt{R^2 + X^2}}.$$

The whole denominator is called the *impedance* and is represented by Z.

$$Z = \sqrt{R^2 + (X_L - X_C)^2} \qquad \text{and} \qquad I = \frac{V}{Z}. \qquad (56i)$$

Note the identical form of this last equation to Ohm's law for direct currents. The resistance R in Ohm's law has here been replaced by the impedance Z.

The relations between R, X_L and X_C and the resultant impedance Z of a series circuit containing them may be represented graphically by treating all quantities as vectors. As shown in Fig. 56H, the resistance R is represented by a vector along the x-axis, the reactances X_L and X_C by vectors up and down on the y-axis, and the impedance Z as the vector resultant of X and R. In practice, R includes the resistance of the inductance winding as well as all connecting wires of the circuit.

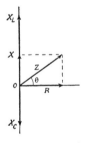

56.7. Phase Relations Between I and V. The effect of an inductance and a capacitance on an *a.c. series circuit* is such as to alter the phase of the electron current I with respect to the applied alternating emf or voltage. If the inductive reactance X_L is greater than the capacitive reactance X_C, the electron current will lag behind the impressed voltage, while if $X_C > X_L$ the electron current will lead the impressed voltage.

FIG. 56H—Impedance diagram for a.c. circuit.

The amount the electron current lags or leads is given by the phase angle θ, where θ is given by

$$\tan \theta = \frac{X}{R} \cdot \qquad (56j)$$

In Fig. 56H, θ is seen to be the angle between Z and R. In one complete cycle of either the current or voltage the phase angle has changed by 2π radians, so that a phase lag of 45 degrees means that the electron current is one-eighth of a cycle behind the voltage. A graphical representation of this example is given in Fig. 56I.

56.8. Power Factor. With direct current circuits the power is given by the product $V \times I$, and is measured in *volt-amperes*, or *watts*. In alternating current circuits the instantaneous rate at which energy is supplied is equal to the product of the instantaneous voltage and the instantaneous current. Since both of these are sometimes zero, it is clear that the power consumption varies

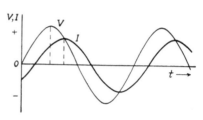

FIG. 56I—Graph showing current lagging 45° behind voltage.

over each cycle and that some sort of average power must be taken.

The average power supplied to any a.c. circuit is equal to the rms voltage times the rms electron current multiplied by the cosine of the angle of lag.

$$P = VI \cos \theta. \qquad (56k)$$

The quantity $\cos \theta$ is called the *power factor*. A low power factor in *a.c. circuits* is to be avoided since for a given supply voltage V a large current would be needed to transmit appreciable electrical energy. Because heat losses are given by I^2R currents should be held to a minimum by making the power factor as near unity as possible. This means that θ should be as near zero as possible.

Examination of the impedance diagram Fig. 56H, will show that a circuit containing a relatively large inductive reactance should contain an equally large capacitive reactance to make $\theta = 0$, and the power factor $\cos \theta = 1$.

Example. A 60 ohm resistor is connected in series with a 0.25 henry inductor, a 50 μf capacitor, and an a.c. generator delivering 110 volts (rms) at 60 cycles. Find (a) the reactance, (b) the impedance, (c) the electron current in the circuit, (d) the power factor, and (e) the power.

Solution. By direct substitution in Eqs.(56f), (56g), (56h), and (56i)

$$X_L = 2\pi fL = 2\pi \times 60 \times 0.25 = 94.25 \text{ ohms}$$
$$X_C = 1/2\pi fC = 1/2\pi \times 60 \times 50 \times 10^{-6} = 53.05 \text{ ohms}$$
(a) $\quad X = X_L - X_C = 94.25 - 53.05 = 41.20 \text{ ohms.}$
$$Z = \sqrt{R^2 + X^2} = \sqrt{(60)^2 + (41.2)^2} = 72.8 \text{ ohms.}$$
(c) $\quad I = V/R = 110/72.8 = 1.51 \text{ amp.}$

Fig. 56H is drawn to scale as a graphical solution for part of this problem. By direct substitution in Eq.(56j),

(d) $\tan \theta = \dfrac{X}{R} = \dfrac{41.2}{60} = 0.687$ or $\theta = 34.5°$

$\cos \theta = 0.824 =$ power factor.

By Eq.(56k),

(e) $P = VI \cos \theta = 110 \times 1.51 \times 0.824 = 137$ watts.

The power expended in a circuit containing inductance and capacitance cannot be measured with a voltmeter and ammeter. To measure power one uses a *wattmeter*. Such an instrument takes emf, current, and power factor into account and reads directly the power. By reading a wattmeter, an ammeter, and a voltmeter, the power factor of a circuit can be determined by Eq.(56k).

$$\text{power factor} = \cos \theta = \frac{P}{VI}. \qquad (561)$$

56.9. Lenz's Law. When a conductor moves through a magnetic field, the induced current in the wire is in such a direction that its own magnetic field generated by that current acts on the original magnetic field in a way opposing the motion. Stated for the first time by H. Lenz in 1833, this is known as Lenz's law. The action of the two magnetic fields upon each other is always such as to oppose the motion or any change in conditions already existing, for if they assisted the change we would have perpetual motion and a violation of the law of conservation of energy.

If the N pole of a straight bar magnet is approaching a solenoid (see Fig. 54A), the induced electron current in the coil is in such a direction as to produce an N pole at the nearest face of the coil. The two N poles therefore repel each other, tending to stop the motion. To keep the current flowing a force F must continually be supplied to the moving magnet. It is this force F moving through a given distance that determines the amount of mechanical work done in producing a given current. If now the N pole is withdrawn from the solenoid, the induced current in the coil reverses in direction and produces an S pole at the nearest face. The opposite poles therefore attract each other, tending to stop the motion. Again to keep the current flowing a force F must be continually supplied and thus work is done.

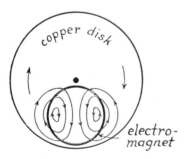

Fig. 56J—Eddy currents in a moving plate conductor.

There are numerous ways of demonstrating Lenz's law. One common experiment is to move a flat copper or aluminum plate rapidly through a strong magnetic field. As each part of the plate enters the field a strong opposing force tends to stop it. What happens electrically is that strong eddy currents of electricity are produced in the metal as shown in Fig. 56J. The magnetic field arising from these eddy currents opposes the field through which it is moving. If the plate is held in the hand the sensation is that of movement through thick molasses.

Another interesting demonstration is illustrated in Fig. 56K. A coil of wire with an extra long iron core is set on end and a solid metal ring or band slipped over the top as shown. At the instant an alternating emf is applied to the coil, the metal ring is thrown upward several feet into the air. The explanation is not difficult since the arrangement is quite the same as a *step-down transformer;* the solenoid acts as a primary of many turns and the ring acts as a secondary of only one turn. As the current first starts to flow in one direction in the primary the expanding magnetic field induces an oppositely directed current in the ring. The field set up by tion in the primary, the growing magnetic field induces an oppositely directed like poles pushes the ring upward. When the primary current reverses, the second-

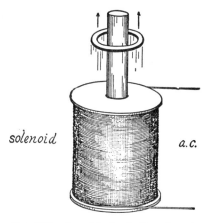

FIG. 56K—A metal ring is flipped up in the air by means of induced currents. A demonstration of Lenz's law.

ary current also reverses, and again there is a repulsion. To demonstrate the existence of a large current, the ring, if held down over the core, will soon become hot.

56.10. Levitation. The phenomenon known as levitation is another illustration of Lenz's law. A metal bowl *B,* as in Fig. 56L(a), is supported in stable-equilibrium in the mid-air just above an electromagnet *M* of special design. Top and side views of the iron core and coil windings are shown in diagrams (b) and (c). Excited by an alternating current, the raised iron knobs labeled *N* and *S* reverse their polarity periodically with the current. As the electron current builds up in the direction indicated in diagram (b), the magnetic induction grows as in diagram (c). With the aluminum bowl in place as in diagram (d), the growing field induces strong eddy currents in the aluminum conductor. These currents in turn give rise to opposing fields. Since the primary field being created by an alternating current increases and decreases rapidly, the bowl always experiences an upward force.

Should the bowl move to one side, as for example to the left in diagram

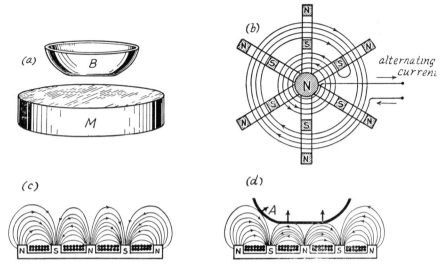

FIG. 56L—Diagrams illustrating the application of Lenz's law to produce *levitation*. A metal bowl floats in mid-air.

(d), the changing field at A will induce stronger electron currents on that side of the bowl and give rise to an increased repulsion, pushing the bowl back toward the center as indicated. The strong induced currents give rise to so much heat that the bowl soon becomes hot.

Because the coil windings of a levitator have a relatively large inductive reactance, a fairly large capacitance must be inserted in the a.c. circuit to raise the power factor close to unity and thereby keep the current in the levitator coils at a maximum and the current supplied by the source at a minimum.

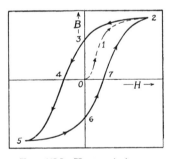

FIG. 56M—Hysteresis loop.

56.11. Hysteresis. In Sec. 53.8, it was shown how a rising electron current in a coil containing iron gives rise to a magnetization curve as shown in Fig. 53J. When an alternating current is applied to such an inductance, thereby reversing the magnetizing field H with each half cycle, the magnetization B lags behind as shown in Fig. 56M. As the elementary magnets within the iron try to line up with H, first one way then the other, the tendency to turn around gives rise to mechanical stresses in the iron and these in turn produce heating. This wasted energy due to the cyclic magnetization is given by the area within the *hysteresis loop* in Fig. 56M and is called *hysteresis loss.*

Hysteresis losses are not to be confused with other losses due to eddy currents set up in the iron core (see Fig. 56J). To reduce these eddy currents to a minimum, thereby reducing heat losses, the iron core is laminated, that is, built up from layers of thin iron sheets.

PROBLEMS

1. A capacitor of 6 μf is connected in series with a 5×10^4 ohm resistor. Calculate the time constant of this combination.

2. What resistance connected in series with a capacitance of 0.2 μf will give the combination a time constant of 0.5 sec? (*Ans.* 2.5 megohms.)

3. What resistance connected in series with an inductance of 6 mh will give the combination a time constant of 0.25 sec?

4. An inductor of 20 μh is connected in series with a 2000 ohm resistor. Find the time constant. (*Ans.* 1×10^{-8} sec.)

5. An oscillator coil is wound on a glass tube 4 cm in diameter and 20 cm long. How many turns of copper wire must it have to give it an inductance of 250 μh?

6. A round iron bar 4 cm in diameter and 20 cm long is wound with copper wire to form a solenoid. If the iron has a permeability of 12.57×10^{-4} w/amp-m, and the inductance is 0.45 h, how many turns of wire does it have? (*Ans.* 239 turns.)

7. A solenoid 2.0 cm in diameter and 50 cm long has 420 turns of wire. Find its inductance when it has (a) an air core, and (b) an iron core of permeability 2.5×10^{-3} w/amp-m.

8. A small solenoid 1 cm in diameter and 10 cm long has 500 turns of fine wire. Calculate its inductance when it has (a) an air core, and (b) an iron core of permeability 2263×10^{-7} w/amp-m. (*Ans.* (a) 247 μh, (b) 0.444 h.)

9. A capacitance of 3 μf is connected to a d.c. voltage supply of 10,000 volts. Find (a) the stored charge, and (b) the stored electrical energy.

10. A capacitance of 25 μf has a charge of 5×10^{-2} coulombs. Calculate (a) the potential difference across the terminals, and (b) the stored electrical energy. (*Ans.* (a) 2000 v, (b) 50 joules.)

11. An electron current of 5 amps flows through an inductance of 2.5 μh. How much energy is stored in the surrounding magnetic field?

12. What steady electron current will store up 0.25 joules of energy in an inductance of 100 μh? (*Ans.* 70.7 amps.)

13. An inductance of 60 μh is connected to a 60 cycle a.c. line. Calculate the inductive reactance.

14. A capacitance of 250 μf is connected to a 60 cycle a.c. line. Find the capacitive reactance. (*Ans.* 10.6 ohms.)

15. A capacitance of 15 μf, in series with a resistance of 100 ohms is connected to a 400 cycle generator supplying a rms voltage of 27 volts at its output terminals. Calculate (a) the capacitive reactance, (b) the impedance, (c) the rms electron current in the circuit, and (d) the power factor.

16. An inductance of 50 mh, in series with a resistance of 100 ohms is connected to a 400 cycle generator supplying a rms voltage of 24 volts at its output terminals. Calculate (a) the inductive reactance, (b) the impedance, (c) the rms electron current, and (d) the power factor. (*Ans.* (a) 125.7 ohms, (b) 160.6 ohms, (c) 0.149 amp, (d) 0.623.)

17. A 0.5 h inductor is connected in series with a 0.4 μf capacitor and a 500 cycle

generator delivering an rms voltage of 1000 v at its output terminals. If the resistance of the circuit is 1000 ohms, find (a) the reactance, (b) the impedance, (c) the rms electron current, (d) the power factor, and (e) the power expended.

18. A 5.0 μf capacitor is connected in series with a 0.06 h inductor and a 400 cycle generator delivering a rms voltage of 30 v at its terminals. If the resistance of the circuit is 90 ohms, find (a) the reactance, (b) the impedance, (c) the rms electron current, (d) the power factor, (e) the power expended. (*Ans.* (a) 71.2 ohms, (b) 114.8 ohms, (c) 0.261 amp, (d) 0.784, (e) 6.14 watts.)

19. An inductance of 5 mh is connected to a 1000 cycle/sec a.c. line. Calculate the inductive reactance.

20. An inductance of 240 μh is connected to a 500 cycle/sec a.c. line. Calculate the inductive reactance. (*Ans.* 0.75 ohm.)

21. A capacitance of 180 μf is connected to a 500 cycle/sec a.c. line. Find the capacitive reactance.

22. If a capacitor, when connected to a 60 cycle/sec line, has a capacitive reactance of 40 ohms, what is its capacitance? (*Ans.* 66.2 μf.)

23. An inductance of 40 mh, in series with a resistance of 10 ohms, is connected to a 60 cycle/sec generator supplying a rms voltage of 120 v at its output terminals. Calculate (a) the inductive reactance, (b) the impedance, (c) the rms electron current, and (d) the power factor.

24. A capacitance of 60 μf, in series with a resistance of 50 ohms, is connected to a 60 cycle/sec generator supplying an rms voltage of 120 v at its output terminals. Calculate (a) the capacitive reactance, (b) the impedance, (c) the rms electron current in the circuit, and (d) the power factor. (*Ans.* (a) 44.2 ohms, (b) 66.7 ohms, (c) 1.80 amps, (d) 0.75.)

25. A 125 μf capacitor is connected in series with a 50 mh inductor and a 60 cycle/sec generator delivering an rms voltage of 120 v at its terminals. If the resistance of the current is 10 ohms, find (a) the reactance, (b) the impedance, (c) the rms electron current, (d) the power factor, and (e) the power expended.

Electric Waves and Oscillations

Chapter 57

THERE is little doubt that *wireless, radio,* and *television* are among the greatest miracles of modern science. Traveling with the speed of light, code signals, the human voice and music can be heard around the world within the very second they are produced in the broadcasting studio. Through television, world events can be observed in full color at the same moment they occur hundreds of miles away.

The more we learn of the fundamental principles of radio and its operation the more amazing does their reality become. It is the purpose of this chapter to introduce some of the earlier fundamental principles of wireless telegraphy in the approximate chronological order in which they were discovered and developed, and in so doing gain some familiarity with ideas now being used to create and transmit *electromagnetic waves.*

57.1. The Leyden Jar. A cross section of a "Leyden jar" of the type invented by the Dutch scientist Musschenbroek in 1746 is shown in Fig. 57A. Two metallic conductors forming the plates of a condenser are separated by a glass bottle as a dielectric insulator. When such a capacitor is connected to a source of high potential, one plate will become positively charged and the other will be negative. If the source voltage is high enough, an electric spark will jump between the terminals indicating a sudden discharge of the condenser, and an electron current will surge first one way then the other around the circuit.

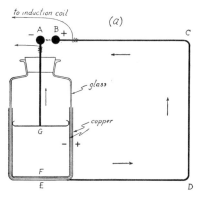

FIG. 57A—A Leyden jar discharge is oscillatory.

This oscillatory current was first postulated by Joseph Henry, then derived from theory by Lord Kelvin and later proved experimentally by Fedderson. Fedderson, looking at a condenser discharge with a rotating mirror, observed that each initial breakdown spark was followed by a succession of fainter sparks. The initial spark ionizes the air making of it a good conductor and of the entire system *ABCDEFGA* a complete electrical circuit.

57.2. The Oscillatory Circuit. The Leyden jar circuit in Fig. 57A contains, in addition to a *capacitance,* an *inductance* as well. The single loop

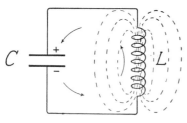

FGABCD and *E* forms practically one turn of a coil. An inductance and capacitance, connected as shown in simplest, schematic form in Fig. 57B, form the necessary elements of all oscillating circuits.

If initially the capacitance is charged as indicated, the surplus electrons on the plate below cause a surge of negative charge counterclockwise around the circuit to neutralize the positives and, in so doing, set up a magnetic field in and around the inductance. When the posi-

FIG. 57B—Schematic diagram of a resonant electrical circuit containing a condenser of capacity *C* and a coil of inductance *L*.

tives become neutralized and the electron current tends to cease, the magnetic flux linking the circuit decreases and keeps the current flowing in the same direction. Once this field has vanished and the current has ceased, the capacitance is found to be in a charged condition, the upper plate negative and the lower plate positive.

Having reversed the charge on the capacitance, the above process will repeat itself, this time the electron current surging clockwise around the circuit. Thus the current rushes first in one direction then the other, oscillating back and forth in an electrical way just as any spring pulled to one side and released vibrates in a mechanical way (see Fig. 57C).

When a straight spring is pulled to one side and released the kinetic energy it gains upon straightening keeps it moving and it bends to the other side. Just as the vibration amplitude of the spring slowly decreases because of *friction,* so also does the current in the electrical circuit decrease because of *electrical resistance.* A graph showing how current slowly dies out in an electric circuit is given

(b)

FIG. 57C—A vibrating spring is a mechanical analogue of an oscillating electrical circuit.

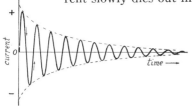

FIG. 57D—Graph of the damped oscillations of an electric circuit.

in Fig. 57D. These are called *damped vibrations,* or *damped oscillations.* If the resistance of the circuit is high, the damping is high and the current quickly dies out after but few oscillations. If the resistance is low, however, the damping is small, the amplitude decreases slowly, and there are many oscillations.

To calculate the frequency of an oscillating circuit either of the following formulas may be used:

$$T = 2\pi\sqrt{LC} \qquad\qquad f = \frac{1}{2\pi\sqrt{LC}}, \qquad (57a)$$

where L is the inductance in henries, C is the capacitance in farads, T is the time for one complete oscillation in seconds and f is the number of oscillations per second. T is the period and f the frequency. The formula at the left is to be compared with the analogous formula for the period of a vibrating spring.

$$T = 2\pi\sqrt{m/k}. \qquad (57b)$$

The mass m for the spring is analogous to the inductance L for the circuit, and the stiffness $1/k$ is analogous to the capacitance C. An increase of the inductance L, or capacitance C, or both, increases the period and decreases the frequency of the oscillating circuit.

Example. A Leyden jar with a small capacitance of 0.01 μf is connected to a single turn of wire (about 6 in. in diameter) having an inductance of 1 microhenry. Calculate the natural frequency of the circuit.

Solution. Since 1 henry $= 10^6$ microhenries and 1 farad $= 10^6$ microfarads, direct substitution for L and C in Eq.(57a) gives

$$f = \frac{1}{2\pi\sqrt{LC}} = \frac{1}{2\pi\sqrt{1 \times 10^{-6}\,\text{h} \times 1 \times 10^{-8}\,\text{f}}} = 1{,}590{,}000 \text{ cyc/sec}$$

or 1.59 megacycles/sec.

57.3. Electrical Resonance. One of the earliest experiments on electrical resonance is due to Sir Oliver Lodge,* and is known as Lodge's experiment. The phenomenon is analogous to the sympathetic vibrations of two tuning forks demonstrated with sound in Sec. 36.9. Two similar electrical circuits, each containing a Leyden jar of the same capacity, are set up parallel to each other and some 5 to 10 ft apart as

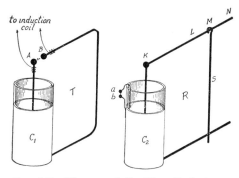

Fig. 57E—Diagram of Sir Oliver Lodge's experiment demonstrating electrical resonance.

* Sir Oliver Lodge (1851-1926), English physicist, was born at Staffordshire, on June 12, 1851. Educated at University College, London, he became professor of physics at Liverpool. He conducted researches and wrote several books on lightning, electrolysis, electromagnetic waves, and wireless telegraphy. After 1910 he became interested in psychical research and became a strong believer in the possibility (now considered nonsense by most intelligent people) of communicating with the dead. He was knighted in 1902 and in 1919 received the Albert Medal of the Royal Society of Arts for his pioneer work in wireless telegraphy.

shown in Fig. 57E. The circuit T on the left acts as a source of oscillations or transmitter and the circuit R on the right acts as a resonator or receiver.

Connected to a source of high potential, the capacitance C_1 charges, and sparks are seen jumping the gap AB. If the crossbar S of the receiver is moved to position M, resonance will occur and small sparks will also be observed jumping the gap ab. If S is moved toward L or N, however, no sparks are observed at ab. In other words, to respond to the oscillations the receiver R must be tuned to the same frequency of the transmitter T.

With the first rise of the current in the transmitting circuit, a magnetic field develops in and around the loop T. With each reversal of the current the field falls off and builds up again in the opposite direction just as it does with the primary winding of a transformer. Reaching out in all directions from T, this changing field induces a weak but alternating current in R. If the natural vibration frequency of R is the same as that of the induced current, the amplitude of the oscillations will quickly rise to a high value and cause sparks to jump the gap ab.

57.4. Maxwell's Electromagnetic Wave Theory. In 1856 James Clerk Maxwell wrote his now famous theoretical paper on electromagnetic waves. In this scientific publication, he proposed the possible existence of electromagnetic waves and at the same time postulated that if such waves could ever be produced, they would travel through free space with the speed of light.

Light itself, said Maxwell, is propagated as an electromagnetic wave, and electrically produced waves should differ from light only in their wave length and frequency. Because Maxwell gave no clues as to how such waves might be generated or detected, their real existence was not discovered until thirty-two years later when Heinrich Hertz made his important discovery.

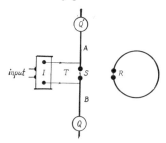

FIG. 57F—Schematic diagram of the apparatus with which Hertz produced and detected the first radio waves.

57.5. Hertzian Waves. In 1888 a young German scientist, Heinrich Hertz,* began a series of experiments in which he not only produced and detected electromagnetic waves but also demonstrated their properties of reflection, refraction, and interference. One of his experimental arrangements is diagramed in Fig. 57F.

* Heinrich Rudolf Hertz, (1857-1894). German physicist born at Hamburg, February 22, 1857. Studied physics under Helmholtz in Berlin, at whose suggestion he first became interested in Maxwell's electromagnetic theory. His researches with electromagnetic waves that made his name famous were carried out at Karlsruhe Polytechnic between 1885 and 1889. As professor of physics at the University of Bonn, after 1889, he experimented with electrical discharges through gases and narrowly missed the discovery of x-rays described by Roentgen a few years later. By his premature death science lost one of its most promising disciples.

The transmitter consists of two spheres QQ' located near the ends of two straight rods AB separated by a spark gap S. With the two rods connected to an induction coil I, sparks jump across the gap S, giving rise to oscillating currents in AB. That such a generator is an oscillating circuit can be seen from the fact that the spheres QQ' form the plates of a capacitor and the rods form the inductance.

The receiver, or detector, consists of a single loop of wire with a tiny spark gap at R. This circuit too is an oscillating circuit with the spark gap as a capacitance C and the loop as an inductance L. Tuning the transmitter frequency to that of the receiver is accomplished by sliding the spheres Q along the rods AB, resonance being indicated by the appearance of sparks at R.

With apparatus of this general type Hertz was able to transmit signals a distance of several hundred feet. He found that large metal plates would reflect the radiation, and that at normal incidence the reflected waves would interfere with those coming up to set up standing waves with nodes and loops. As the receiver was moved slowly away from the reflector, nodes and loops were located by the appearance of sparks only at equally spaced intervals.

With a large prism of paraffin he demonstrated refraction and with a lens made of pitch he focused the waves as a glass lens focuses visible light.

57.6. Electromagnetic Waves. To visualize the production of waves by an Hertzian oscillator, consider the schematic diagram in Fig. 57G. Let the rods AB and spheres Q_1 and Q_2 be charged initially as indicated and consider the electrostatic action of the charges on a small charge C located

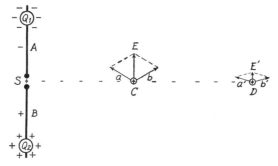

Fig. 57G—Illustrating the origin and development of electromagnetic waves from a Hertzian dipole oscillator.

some distance away. The negative charge Q_1 attracts C with a force a and the positive charge Q_2 repels it with a force b. Since by symmetry these two forces are of equal magnitude, their resultant CE is parallel to AB. If the isolated charge is farther away as at D, the resultant force is also parallel to AB but weaker. In other words, the electric field E at points C and D is up and parallel to AB, decreasing in intensity as the distance from the transmitter increases.

Suppose that a spark jumps the gap S and oscillation sets in. One-half cycle after the condition shown in Fig. 57G, electrons have surged across the gap charging Q_1 positively and Q_2 negatively. With reversed charges the resultant force on C and D will be down instead of up. Thus it is seen how oscillations in the transmitter, which constitute a surging of electrons back and forth between A and B give rise to a periodically reversing electric field at distant points.

In addition to an electric field at C and D the surging electrons in AB give rise to a magnetic field as well. When the electron current is down (using the conventional left-hand rule), the magnetic intensity H at C or D is perpendicular to and into the plane of the page, and when the electron current is up the magnetic intensity is out from the page. The surging of the charges therefore gives rise to a periodically reversing magnetic intensity, the direction of which is at right angles to the electric intensity at the same points.

According to Maxwell's theory, the E and H fields do not appear instantly at distant points; time is required for their propagation. The speed of propagation, according to Maxwell (and this has been confirmed by numerous experiments) is the same as the speed of light. The changing E and H fields at C therefore lag behind the oscillating charges in AB, and those at D lag behind still farther.

Fig. 57H is a graph of the instantaneous values of the electric and magnetic fields as they vary with distance from the transmitter. At certain points the fields are a maximum and at other points they are zero. As time goes on these electric and magnetic waves move away from the transmitter with a speed of 186,300 mi/sec.

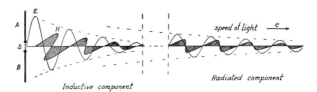

Fig. 57H—The electromagnetic waves from an antenna travel outward with the speed of light.

The mathematical theory of electromagnetic radiations shows that close to the transmitter the E and H fields, called the *inductive components*, are $90°$ out of phase and that their magnitudes fall off very rapidly with distance. Farther out, however, the two get in step with each other and their amplitudes fall off more slowly as shown in the diagram. The latter are called the *radiated components* and are the ones detected at great distances.

Suppose now that a series of sparks are made to occur in the gap *S* of a transmitter as in Fig. 57I. Each spark will give rise to a damped oscillation in *AB* which in turn sends out a damped electromagnetic wave. The succession of sparks sends out a train of such waves which, as they leave the

Fig. 57I—Damped electromagnetic waves from an Hertzian oscillator.

antenna, decrease rapidly in magnitude at first, then more slowly as they get farther away. Only the electric component of such waves is shown in the diagram.

If an electrical conductor is located at some distant point the free electrons within it will, as such waves go by, experience up and down forces tending to set them in oscillation. If the conductor is an oscillating circuit whose natural frequency is that of the passing waves, resonance will occur and large currents will be set up.

57.7. Air-Core Inductances and Transformers. When a high-frequency alternating current is sent through a solenoid with an iron core or the primary of an iron core transformer, the back emf is so large that the current as well as the magnetic induction cannot build up to any appreciable value before it reverses in direction. This is made evident by curve (c) in Fig. 56A which shows how the iron core tends to hold the current back. The result is that in one ten-thousandth of a second or less the current hardly gets started in one direction before it stops and reverses. Eq.(56f) shows that a high frequency emf impressed upon a large inductance gives rise to a very large inductive reactance.

In an iron core transformer the back emf in the primary winding so retards the building up of strong fields that little or no induced currents can be "drawn" from the secondary. To overcome this difficulty the iron core is done away with and we have what is called an *air-core transformer.* In the absence of any iron the current in the coil may, as illustrated by curve (b) in Fig. 56A, rise to an appreciable value each time it changes in direction. The rapidly increasing and diminishing flux linking both circuits induces a current in the secondary of exactly the same frequency.

Air-core transformers, consisting of nothing more than two coils of a few turns each, a primary winding and a secondary winding, are used extensively in radio and television transmitters and receivers. In these instances the alternating currents with frequencies of thousands and even millions of cycles per second are usually referred to as *radio frequencies* and the transformers are referred to as *radio frequency transformers*.

57.8. The Tesla Coil. The Tesla coil, designed by the American inventor Nikola Tesla, is an instrument for producing high-frequency high-voltage electric currents. The device, as shown in Fig. 57J, is a kind of *step-up air-core transformer* with a primary winding of but a few turns of heavy copper wire and a secondary winding of many turns of fine copper wire.

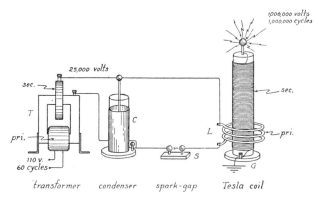

Fig. 57J—Tesla coil and circuit for producing high-frequency, high-voltage electric sparks.

As commonly set up in the laboratory, 110-volt, 60-cycle alternating current from the house lighting circuit is stepped up by means of a transformer to about 25,000 volts where it is used to charge a capacitor of relatively low capacitance. The capacitor is connected to a spark-gap and the Tesla coil primary to form an oscillating *LC* circuit. When during one-half cycle of the applied 25,000 volts the capacitor becomes charged, a spark occurs at *S* completing the circuit and damped oscillations of a very high-frequency, perhaps 1,000,000 cycles or higher, take place. The increasing and decreasing magnetic flux induces a high voltage in the secondary of several hundred thousand volts.

Such high-frequency potentials as these are often used as spectacular displays of electricity. Sparks from the top of such a coil jumping onto the unprotected hand or into a metal rod held in the hand are not the least harmful to the body. The reason for this is that such high frequency currents as these travel over the surface of conductors like the body and not through it. Care should be taken, however, to see that the operator under no circumstances touches any other parts of the circuit *TCS* or *L* as the low-frequency 60-cycle potentials may prove fatal. Low-frequency currents pass through the body and through the heart and blood stream, thereby producing harmful effects.

PROBLEMS

1. Calculate the frequency and period of an oscillating circuit containing two 3 μf capacitors and an inductance of 3.4 μh if all three are connected in parallel.

2. What inductance connected to a capacitor of 0.25 μf will give the circuit a natural frequency of 4 megacycles/sec? (*Ans.* 0.00633 μh.)

3. What capacitance if connected in parallel to an inductance of 6 μh will give an oscillating circuit a frequency of 250 kilocycles/sec?

4. Determine the frequency of an oscillating circuit composed of two capacitors and one inductor, all connected in parallel: $C_1 = 2$ μf, $C_2 = 3.5$ μf, and $L = 6.6$ μh. (*Ans.* 26.4 kc/sec.)

5. Two capacitors of 10 μf each are first connected in series and then the combination connected across an inductor of 2 μh. Calculate the period of the oscillating circuit.

6. Calculate all of the possible frequencies that can be obtained by combining two or more of the following to form an oscillating circuit: $C_1 = 3$ μf, $C_2 = 6$ μf, $L = 5$ μh. (*Ans.* 23.7, 29.0, 41.0, and 50.3 kc/sec.)

7. A 5 mh inductor is connected in parallel with a 50 μf capacitor. What is the natural frequency of this circuit?

8. A 50 μh inductor is connected across a 40 μf capacitor. What is the frequency of the third harmonic of the oscillating circuit thus formed? (*Ans.* 3.56 kc/sec.)

9. What capacitance connected in parallel to an inductance of 0.5 μh will produce an oscillating circuit with a fundamental frequency of 1 megacycle/sec?

10. What inductance connected in parallel to a capacitance of 5.0 μf will produce an oscillating circuit with a fundamental frequency of 50 kilocycles/sec? (*Ans.* 2.0 μh.)

The Discovery of the
Electron

Chapter 58

HISTORICALLY, a study of electrical discharges through gases and the discovery of the electron mark the beginning of a new branch of physical science called *"modern physics."* Modern physics, dealing principally with atoms, molecules, and the structure of matter, has developed at such a tremendous rate within the past three score years that it now occupies the center of attention of many leading scientists the world over. It is not exaggeration to state that recent discoveries in atomic physics have had and will continue to have a tremendous influence on the development of civilization. Because the subject of atomic physics is relatively new it is logical to treat the subject matter associated with each major discovery in a more or less chronological order.

58.1. Electrical Discharge Through a Gas. In 1853, an obscure French scientist by the name of Masson sent the first electric spark from a high-voltage induction coil through a partially evacuated glass vessel and discovered that instead of the typical spark observed in air the tube was filled with a bright glow. Several years later, Heinrich Geissler, a German glass blower in Tübingen, developed and began the manufacture of gaseous discharge tubes. These tubes, made in diverse sizes, shapes, and colors of glass, and resembling the modern neon and argon signs used in advertising, attracted the attention of physicists in the leading scientific institutions and universities of the world, who purchased many of these "Geissler tubes" and used them for study and lecture demonstrations.

In 1869 W. Hittorf of Munster, with improved vacuum pumps, observed a dark region near one electrode of the electrical discharge which grew in size as the exhaustion was continued. This is but one of a number of phases of the study of electrical discharge through gases observed and studied a few years later by Sir William Crookes.*

---

* Sir William Crookes (1832-1919), English physicist and chemist. At twenty-two he became an assistant at the Radcliff Observatory in Oxford. He was knighted in 1897, received the Order of Merit in 1910, and was president of the Royal Society from 1913 to 1915. He invented and made the first focusing type of x-ray tube. His experiments with electrical discharges through rarefied gases led to his discovery of the dark space which now bears his name.

In Fig. 58A a long glass tube about 4 cm in diameter and 150 cm long is shown connected to a mercury diffusion pump and a mechanical vacuum pump. The purpose of the pumps is to enable one to observe continuously

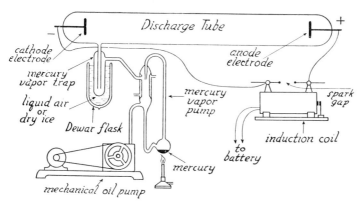

FIG. 58A—Diagram of a gaseous discharge tube showing the electrical connections as well as the vacuum pumps and accessories.

the changes in the electrical discharge as the air is slowly removed from the tube. The purpose of the *trap* is to freeze out any mercury vapor and prevent it from reaching the discharge. High voltage from an induction coil is shown connected to the two electrodes, one at either end of the tube.

Although an induction coil does not deliver direct current, its characteristics are such that the potentials are higher on half of the alternations than they are on the other and, the two electrodes act nearly the same as if a high-voltage direct current were used. The negative electrode under these circumstances is called the *cathode* and the positive electrode the *anode*.

As the long tube is slowly pumped out, an emf of 10,000 to 15,000 volts will produce the first discharge when the pressure has dropped to about one-hundredth of an atmosphere, i.e., at a barometric pressure of about 10 mm of mercury. This first discharge, as illustrated in diagram (a) of Fig. 58B, consists of long thin bluish-colored streamers. As the gas pressure drops

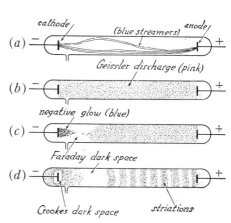

FIG. 58B—Sketches of the general appearance of a high-voltage electric discharge through rarefied air at various stages of evacuation.

to about 5 mm of mercury, sometimes called a Geissler-tube vacuum, the discharge changes to pink and at the same time widens until it fills the whole tube as shown in diagram (b). At a still lower pressure of about 2 mm a dark region called the *Faraday dark space* appears in the region of the cathode, dividing the bright discharge into two parts, a long pinkish section called the *positive column* and a short bluish section called the *negative glow*. As the pressure drops still further the Faraday dark space grows in size and the negative glow moves away from the cathode, producing another dark space between it and the cathode. With the appearance of this second dark region, called the *Crookes dark space,* the positive column divides into a number of equally spaced layers called striations.

As the pumping proceeds the striations and the negative glow grow fainter, and the Crookes dark space widens until finally at a pressure of about 0.01 mm it fills the whole tube. At this point a new feature appears; the whole glass tube itself glows with a faint greenish light.

58.2. Cathode Rays. The green glow in the final stage of the gaseous discharge just described was soon found to be a *fluorescence of the glass produced by invisible rays emanating from the cathode itself.* These *cathode rays,* as they are called, believed by Sir William Crookes to be an "ultra gaseous state" and by Johann W. Hittorf to be a "fourth state" of matter, turn out to be tiny corpuscles which we now call *electrons.* In the relatively free space of a highly evacuated tube, cathode particles, torn loose from the atoms of the cathode, stream down the length of the tube, seldom colliding with a gas molecule until they hit the glass walls.

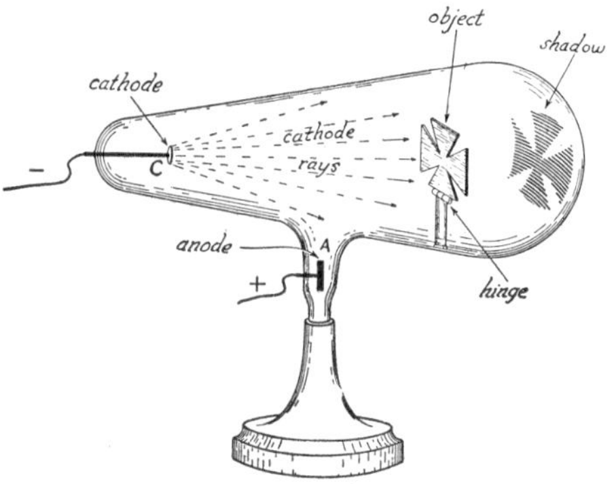

The first important discovery concerning the nature of cathode rays was that they travel in straight lines. This was first revealed by Hittorf in 1869 by casting shadows of objects placed inside the discharge tube. This is usually demonstrated by a tube of special design as shown in Fig. 58C.

Where the rays strike the walls of the tube the glass fluoresces green, while in the shadow it remains dark. Under continuous bombardment of the walls by cathode rays the fluorescence grows fainter because of a fatigue effect of the glass. This is demonstrated by tipping the object down on its hinge, permitting the rays to strike the fresh glass surface. Where

Fig. 58C—A Crookes' discharge tube for demonstrating that cathode rays travel in straight lines.

the shadow appeared previously, a bright green image of the object is clearly visible.

That *cathode rays have momentum and energy* was first demonstrated by Crookes in 1870 using a tube of special design as illustrated in Fig. 58D. Leaving the cathode and acquiring a high speed on their way toward the anode, the rays strike the mica vanes of a small pinwheel and exert a force, causing it to turn and thus roll along a double track toward the anode. When it reaches the end of the track a reversal of the potential, making the right-hand electrode the cathode, will send it rolling back toward the anode, now at the left. From this experiment Crookes concluded that cathode particles have *momentum,*

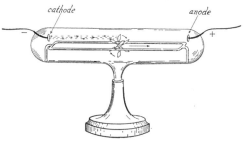

FIG. 58D—Demonstration of experiment showing that cathode rays have momentum and energy. Cathode rays striking the vanes of a small pin wheel cause it to roll from one end of the tube to the other.

and that therefore they have *mass, velocity,* and *kinetic energy* $\frac{1}{2}mv^2$.

That *cathode rays are negatively charged particles* was first discovered in Paris in 1895 by Jean Perrin. A discharge tube of special design usually

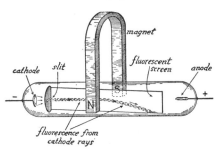

FIG. 58E—The bending of a beam of cathode rays in the field of a magnet demonstrates that cathode rays are negatively charged particles.

used to demonstrate this property is illustrated in Fig. 58E. A beam of cathode rays is narrowed down to a thin pencil or ribbon of rays by a narrow slit near the cathode. The path of the rays is made visible by allowing them to strike a long strip of metal painted with zinc sulfide, a fluorescent paint. By placing a horseshoe magnet over the outside of the tube as illustrated, the path of the cathode rays is bent down. If the polarity of the magnet is reversed the path is bent up. The bending shows they are charged, and the direction of bending shows the kind of charge. Being charged, a stream of particles is like an electric current. From the direction of the magnetic field, the direction of the current, and applying the left-hand rule (see Sec. 52.8), the charge is found to be *negative.* (Remember that the left-hand rule applies to a current from $(-)$ to $(+)$.)

The penetrating power of cathode rays was first demonstrated by Hein-

rich Hertz and his assistant P. Lenard by passing cathode rays through thin
aluminum foils. Out in the air the rays were found to retain sufficient power
to cause fluorescence and phosphorescence.

58.3. J. J. Thomson's Experiments. Knowing cathode rays to be
negatively charged particles the question immediately arose as to whether
they were all alike. To determine this it was clear that two things would
have to be done: one to measure the mass of the particles, and the other to
measure the amount of their charge. Although the first attempts to do this
were not entirely successful, J. J. Thomson* did succeed, in 1897, in determining the velocity of the rays and in measuring the ratio between their
charge e and their mass m.

The discharge tube designed for these experiments is drawn in Fig. 58F.
Cathode rays originating at the left-hand electrode and limited to a thin
pencil of rays by two pinholes in diaphragms DD are made to pass between

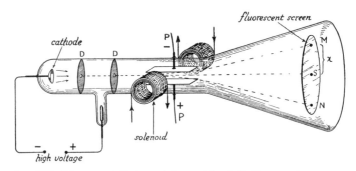

Fig. 58F—Diagram of discharge tube used by J. J. Thomson to measure
the velocity of cathode rays.

two parallel metal plates and the magnetic field of two external solenoids to
a fluorescent screen at the far side. When the two metal plates P are connected to a high potential, the particles experience a downward force and
their path is bent to strike the screen at N. Without a charge on the plates
the beam passes straight through undeviated and strikes the screen at S.

When the magnetic field alone is applied so that the magnetic lines are
perpendicular to the plane of the page, the path of the rays is bent upward to
strike the fluorescent screen at some point M. If both the electric field and
the magnetic field are applied simultaneously, a proper adjustment of the

* Sir Joseph John Thomson (1856-1940), English physicist, educated at Owens College,
Manchester, and at Trinity College, Cambridge. He was appointed Cavendish professor at
Cambridge in 1884, and professor of physics at the Royal Institution, London, in 1905. He
was awarded the Nobel Prize in physics in 1906, was knighted in 1908, and elected to the
presidency of the Royal Society in 1915. He became master of Trinity College in 1918 and
helped to develop at Cambridge a great research laboratory attracting scientific workers from
all over the world.

strength of either field can be made so that the deflection downward by the one is exactly counteracted by the deflection of the other upward. When this condition is attained, a measurement of the magnetic induction B and the electric intensity E permits a calculation of the velocity of cathode rays.

In Sec. 50.1 on the theory of electricity it is shown that if e is the charge in coulombs on a particle of matter in an electric field of strength E, the force exerted on the particle is given by Eq.(50b)

$$F_E = eE. \qquad (58a)$$

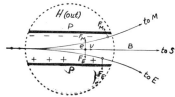

As illustrated in Fig. 58G, this force acts straight down parallel to the field and causes the particle to traverse a parabolic path the same as a projectile does under the pull of gravity. In Sec. 53.5 it is shown that, if a charged particle is moving in a

FIG. 58G—Detailed diagram of center section of J. J. Thomson's cathode ray tube.

magnetic field, the force on it in newtons depends upon the velocity by the relation given in Eq.(53j),

$$F_M = evB. \qquad (58b)$$

Since this force is always at right angles to both the magnetic induction and the direction of motion, the particle will traverse a circular path. By counterbalancing the two forces F_E and E_M, i.e., by making them equal in magnitude and opposite in direction, the two relations can be set equal to each other.

$$eE = evB. \qquad (58c)$$

By canceling the charge e on both sides of this equation, we obtain

$$E = vB \qquad \text{from which} \qquad v = \frac{E}{B} \qquad (58d)$$

where E is in volts per meter, B is in webers per square meter, and v is in meters per second. Inserting the known values of E and B *the velocity v can be calculated.* The results show that cathode rays generally travel with a speed of several thousand miles per second, about *one-fifth the velocity of light.* Furthermore, the velocity is not always the same but depends upon the voltage applied between the anode and cathode. By increasing this voltage the velocity of the rays is increased (see Sec. 65.1).

It is of interest to point out here that tubes used for scanning and observing moving pictures by modern television receivers are quite similar in shape and principle to J. J. Thomson's cathode ray tube of Fig. 58F.

58.4. The Ratio of Charge to Mass, e/m. The next step taken by

Thomson was to measure the deflection of the cathode beam produced by a magnetic field alone and from this calculate the ratio between the charge e and the mass m of the electron. To do this he reasoned that, if a charged particle moving through a uniform magnetic field has a force exerted on it at right angles to its direction of motion, causing it to move in the arc of a circle, the force is of the nature of a centripetal force. Calling F_H a centripetal force (see Eqs.(58b) and (14h)), we obtain

$$F_M = m\frac{v^2}{r}, \quad \text{or} \quad Bev = m\frac{v^2}{r}. \tag{58e}$$

Transposing m to the left side and B and v to the right side in the second equation, there results

$$\frac{e}{m} = \frac{v}{Br},$$

where r is the radius of the circular arc in meters through which the particles are deviated, v is the velocity of the particles in meters per second, as measured in the last section, m is the particle mass in kilograms, and B is the magnetic induction in webers per meter². With all of these known, the value of e/m can be calculated. It is found to be

$$e/m = 1.7589 \times 10^{11}\frac{\text{coulombs}}{\text{kg}}. \tag{58f}$$

Such a large number means that the mass of a cathode ray particle in kg is extremely small as compared with the charge it carries in coulombs. If now it were possible by some experiment to measure the charge e alone the value could be substituted in Eq.(58f) and the mass m calculated.

58.5. Millikan's Oil-Drop Experiment. Millikan* began his experiments on the electronic charge e in 1906. His apparatus is illustrated by a simple diagram in Fig. 58H. Minute oil drops from an atomizer are sprayed into the region just over the top of one of two circular metal plates E^+ and E^-. Shown in cross section, the upper plate is pierced with a tiny pinhole P through which an occasional oil drop from the cloud will fall. Once between the plates such a drop, illuminated by an arc light from the side, is observed by means of a low-powered microscope.

---

*Robert Andrews Millikan (1868-1953), American physicist, educated at Oberlin College and Columbia University, for twenty-five years professor of physics at the University of Chicago and for thirty years president of the Norman Bridge laboratory at the California Institute of Technology in Pasadena. He served during World War I in the research division of the Signal Corps with the rank of lieutenant colonel. His principal contributions to science have been his measurement of the charge on the electron, his photoelectric determination of the energy in a light quantum, and his precision study of cosmic rays. He was the second American to be awarded the Nobel Prize in physics (1923). He has also been awarded the Edison Medal, the Hughes Medal of the Royal Society, the Faraday Medal, and the Mattenci Medal.

With the switch S in the "up" position, the condenser plates are grounded so that they are not charged. Under these conditions the oil drop falling under the pull of gravity has a constant velocity. This *terminal velocity,* as it is called, is reached by the drop before it enters the field of view and is of such a value that the downward pull of gravity, F_G, in Fig. 58I(b), is

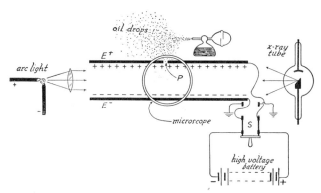

FIG. 58H—Schematic diagram of Millikan's oil-drop experiment. From this experiment the charge of the electron was determined.

exactly equalized by the upward resisting force of the air. By measuring this velocity of fall the force F_G can be calculated and from it the mass of the oil drop determined. The velocity of the drop can be determined by using a stop watch and measuring the time required to fall the distance between the two cross hairs illustrated in diagram (a) of Fig. 58I.

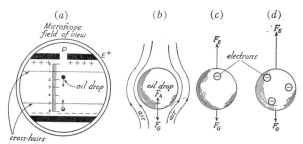

FIG. 58I—Detailed diagrams showing (a) oil drop as seen in the field of view of the microscope; (b), (c) and (d) the forces acting on the same oil drop at different times of observation.

As the drop nears the bottom plate the switch S is thrown "down," charging the two parallel plates positive and negative. If now the drop has a negative charge, as illustrated in diagram (c), there will be an upward electrostatic force F_E acting to propel the drop up across the field of view.

The drop will move upward with a constant velocity if F_E is greater than the gravitational force F_G. Again using the stop watch, this time to measure the velocity of rise, the upward force F_E can be calculated. Knowing the force, and the voltage on the condenser plates, the charge on the drop can be computed.

As the drop nears the top plate the switch S is thrown "up" and the plates are again grounded. Under these conditions the drop falls again under the pull of gravity alone. Upon nearing the bottom plate the switch is again thrown "down" and the drop rises once more. When this process is repeated, a single drop may be made to move up and down many times across the field of view. Each time it falls the velocity is measured and the mass computed, while each time it rises the velocity is measured and the charge computed.

Millikan found that if x-rays were allowed to pass through the apparatus while an oil drop was being observed, the charge on the drop could be increased or decreased almost at will. One time on rising, the velocity would be low due to a small charge, see diagram (c) in Fig. 58I, while the next time the velocity would be high due to a larger change, as in diagram (d). Regardless of the amount of charge, the rate of fall for a given drop is always the same. The reason for this is that the total mass of a number of electrons is so small compared with the mass of the oil drop that their added mass is not perceptible.

Millikan, and numerous other experimenters who have repeated these experiments, have found that the charge on a drop is never less than a certain minimum value, and is always some integral multiple of this value. In other words, any one electron is like every other electron, each carrying this minimum charge called e.

$$e = -1.6019 \times 10^{-19} \text{ coulombs.} \qquad (58g)$$

This is the most recent and probable value of the electronic charge.

58.6. The Mass of the Electron. From Millikan's determination of the charge on the electron and Thomson's measurement of e/m, the mass of the electron can be calculated by dividing one value by the other. Using the most accurately known values for both e and e/m, we obtain

$$m = \frac{e}{e/m} = \frac{1.6019 \times 10^{-19} \text{ coulomb}}{1.7589 \times 10^{11} \text{ coulombs/kg}} = 9.1072 \times 10^{-31} \text{ kg.}$$

that is,

$$m = 9.1072 \times 10^{-31} \text{ kg,} \quad \text{or} \quad m = 9.1072 \times 10^{-28} \text{ gm.} \qquad (58h)$$

This mass is unbelievably small; yet its value has been determined many times and by many experimenters, and it is always the same.*

PROBLEMS AND QUESTIONS

1. Electrons with a velocity of one-tenth the velocity of light enter a uniform magnetic field at right angles to the magnetic induction. What will be the radius of their circular path if $B = 2.0 \times 10^{-3}$ weber/meter^2?

2. Electrons entering a uniform magnetic field where $B = 4$ gauss, in a direction at right angles to the lines of induction, have a velocity of 6.5×10^8 cm/sec. Calculate the radius of their circular path. See Eq.(53h). (*Ans.* 9.24 cm.)

3. Two flat parallel metal plates 20 cm long and 4 cm apart (see Fig. 56G) are connected to a 50 volt battery. If electrons enter this field with a velocity of 2×10^9 cm/sec, how far will they be deviated from their original straight line path by the time they reach the other end?

4. In J. J. Thomson's experiment shown in Fig. 58F, a magnetic induction field of 1.9×10^{-2} webers/meter^2 is employed. If electrons entering this field have a velocity of 2×10^9 cm/sec, what potential difference applied to the parallel plates will keep their path straight? Assume the plates to be 0.5 cm apart. See Eq.(50f). (*Ans.* 1900 volts.)

5. Electrons moving in a uniform magnetic field where $B = 10$ gauss follow a circular path of 46.5 cm radius. Calculate their velocity. See Eq.(53h).

6. Electrons moving in a uniform magnetic field $B = 4.5 \times 10^{-4}$ webers/meter^2 follow a circular path of 20 cm radius. Find their velocity. (*Ans.* 1.58×10^7 m/sec.)

7. If one gram of free electrons could be bound together on the moon and another gram of electrons on the earth, what would be their force of repulsion? Earth-moon distance is 239,000 mi.

8. Make a diagram and briefly explain the experiment by which J. J. Thomson measured the velocity of electrons.

9. Make several diagrams showing the main features of an electrical discharge through a gas filled tube as the pressure is lowered.

10. Diagram and briefly explain the three experiments given in this chapter to demonstrate that cathode rays, (a) travel in straight lines, (b) have momentum and energy, and (c) are negatively charged particles.

11. Explain, and give a diagram of, Millikan's oil-drop experiment. What conclusions were reached by Millikan in this experiment?

12. Electrons are injected with a speed of 5×10^7 m/sec into a uniform magnetic field at right angles to the lines of force. If the magnetic induction is 2×10^{-3} weber/meter^2, find the diameter of the circular path. (*Ans.* 28.4m.)

13. If a beam of electrons, moving with a speed of 3×10^7 m/sec, enter a uniform magnetic field at right angles to the lines of force and describe a circular path with a 10 cm radius, calculate the magnetic induction.

14. A 100 volt battery is connected to two flat parallel metal plates 15 cm long and 2 cm apart. If electrons enter this field from one end, moving with a constant velocity of 3×10^7 m/sec, how far will they be deviated from their original straight line path by the time they reach the other end? (*Ans.* 1.1 cm.)

* For a more complete and elementary treatment of these early experiments see "Electrons + and —," by R. A. Millikan, University of Chicago Press.

Atoms and the Periodic Table

Chapter 59

ALTHOUGH no one has ever seen an atom there is no doubt in the mind of the true scientist that such particles really exist. To the physicists and chemists who have built up and established the present-day theories of the structure of matter, atoms are as real as any material objects large enough to be seen with the eyes or to be felt with the hands. Their reality is evidenced by hundreds of laboratory experiments that can be planned and executed in the research laboratory.

As the subject of atomic physics is developed in this and the following chapters, it will become more and more apparent that, although a physicist requires an extremely imaginative mind, the accumulated knowledge of atoms, their structure, and their behavior under a multitude of conditions, are based upon exact results of experiments performed with the greatest of accuracy and precision.

59.1. The Discovery of Positive Rays. During the latter part of the nineteenth century, when many physicists were investigating the various properties of cathode rays, Goldstein designed a special discharge tube and with it discovered new rays called *canal rays*. The name "canal rays" is de-

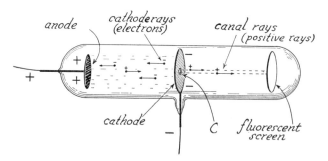

FIG. 59A—Experiment illustrating canal rays, discovered by Goldstein in a discharge tube.

rived from the fact that the rays, traveling in straight lines through a vacuum tube in the opposite direction to cathode rays, pass through and emerge from a canal or hole in the cathode. A tube designed to illustrate this is shown in Fig. 59A.

Shortly after the measure of the electronic charge by J. J. Thomson in 1896, W. Wien deflected a beam of canal rays in a magnetic field and came to the conclusion that the rays consisted of positively charged particles. Due to this and other experiments, canal rays have become more commonly known as *positive rays*.

Since the time of Goldstein's discovery, positive rays have been found to be charged atoms of different weights. The origin of the charge carried by such atoms is explained briefly as follows. As the electrons from the cathode stream down the tube toward the anode they occasionally collide with the atoms and molecules of the small quantity of remaining gas, knocking electrons from them. This process, called *ionization*, is illustrated by a schematic diagram of a single oxygen atom in Fig. 59B. Before the collision, the atom as a whole, with its eight electrons and eight equal positive charges on the nucleus, has no net charge. After one of the electrons is removed by collision it has but seven electrons and therefore a net positive charge equivalent in amount to the charge of one electron.

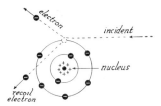

Fig. 59B—Schematic diagram of an oxygen atom in the process of becoming ionized by a collision with a high-speed electron.

Since the atom is now positively charged, the anode repels and the cathode attracts such atoms, accelerating them toward the cathode. There exists, therefore, between the anode and cathode, two streams of particles: electrons moving toward the anode, and positively charged atoms or molecules moving toward the cathode.

Of the many particles striking the cathode, in Fig. 59A, the ones moving toward the small opening *C*, constituting the observed canal rays, pass straight through to the fluorescent screen. As each atom or molecule strikes the screen a tiny flash of light is produced. These tiny flashes, which can be seen individually in the field of view of a microscope, are called *scintillations*.

Any process by which an electron is removed from an atom or molecule is called *ionization*, and the resulting charged particle is called a *positive ion*. The amount of charge carried by an electron is a unit called *the electronic charge*.

59.2. The Thomson Mass Spectrograph. Ever since the time canal rays were shown to be positively charged atoms or molecules of the gas contained within the discharged tube, physicists have tried to determine with ever-increasing accuracy the mass and charge of the individual ray particles. Although the charge and mass of every electron were known from

Thomson's and Millikan's experiments to be the same as that for every other electron, it could be postulated that the mass of the positive rays should be different for the atoms of different chemical elements. The further postulation could be made that if each positive ion is produced by the removal of one electron from a neutral atom, all positive ions should have the same amount of charge. This in part is anticipating what is now known.

In 1911 J. J. Thomson developed a method of measuring the relative masses of different atoms and molecules by deflecting positive rays in a magnetic and an electric field. The apparatus he developed for doing this is shown schematically in Fig. 59C and is called *Thomson's mass spectrograph.*

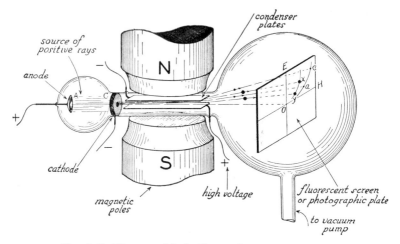

Fig. 59C—Diagram of J. J. Thomson's mass spectrograph.

The entire spectrograph, enclosed in an airtight glass chamber, is first thoroughly evacuated, and then a small quantity of the gas, the masses of whose atoms are to be measured, is admitted to the bulb at the left. When a high voltage is applied to this chamber, electrons from the cathodes ionize atoms and molecules in the region between the anode A and the cathode C. Traveling to the right, many of these positively charged particles pass through the narrow hole in the cathode, thus forming a very narrow pencil of rays. Leaving the cathode with a constant velocity they then pass between the poles of an electromagnet and the parallel plates of a condenser, and thence to a fluorescent screen at the far end of the chamber.

The two condenser plates, when charged, exert an upward force on the particles, deflecting them from the point O toward E. The magnetic field, on the other hand, with its magnetic lines vertically downward and in the plane of the page, exerts a force at right angles to this, deflecting the particles "into" the page from the point O toward H.

Suppose now that the apparatus contains a pure gas like helium, all of the atoms of which have exactly the same mass. Of these atoms, the ones that are ionized in a region near the cathode C cannot attain a very high velocity before reaching the cathode. Remaining longer in the deflecting fields, their paths are bent considerably up and back to a point such as c on the screen. Particles ionized near the anode A, on the other hand, attain a high velocity upon reaching the cathode and, being under the influence of the deflecting fields for a shorter time, have their paths bent only a little, to a point like a on the screen. Since the velocities of the particles vary considerably, a bright streak or line of fluorescence will appear on the screen. From a calculation of the forces exerted by both fields it is found that the line on the screen should have the shape of a parabola.

If the gas in the apparatus is not pure but contains two kinds of atoms, the positive ions passing through the cathode will have two different masses. Although each ion will contain the same positive charge and will therefore experience the same electric and magnetic forces when passing through the fields, the heavier particles will not be deflected as much as the lighter ones. The net result is that the heavier particles form one parabolic curve like xy, and the lighter particles another curve like ac.

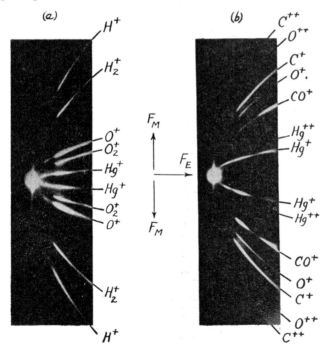

FIG. 59D—Reproductions of the photographs of parabolas made with Thomson's mass spectrograph.

By substituting a photographic plate for the fluorescent screen and exposing it to the rays for several minutes, photographs like those reproduced in Fig. 59D are obtained. The continual bombardment of the photographic plate by atoms and molecules has the same effect as does light, and images are produced upon development. The upper half of each picture is taken with the connections as shown in Fig. 59C and the lower half by reversing the polarity of the electromagnet, and exposing for an equal length of time.

When photograph (a) was taken the spectrograph contained *hydrogen, oxygen,* and *mercury,* and the magnetic field was relatively weak. From the known strengths of both the electric and magnetic fields and the assumption that each atom carries a unit positive charge, the mass of the atoms producing each parabola can be calculated. The results of these calculations show that the two largest parabolas are due to ionized hydrogen atoms (H^+) of mass 1, and ionized hydrogen molecules (H_2^+) of mass 2. The next three are due to ionized atoms (O^+) of mass 16, ionized oxygen molecules of mass 32, and ionized mercury atoms (Hg^+) with a mass of approximately 200.

When photograph (b) was taken the mass spectrograph contained carbon monoxide gas and mercury vapor, and the magnetic field was relatively strong. Upon calculating the masses of the particles producing the different parabolas, the four intense lines were identified as due to ionized carbon atoms (C^+) of mass 12, ionized oxygen atoms (O^+) of mass 16, ionized carbon monoxide molecules (CO^+) of mass 28, and ionized mercury atoms (Hg^+) of mass about 200. The three faint parabolas which show in the original photograph but probably not in the reproduction, are due to doubly ionized atoms of *carbon, oxygen,* and *mercury.*

A doubly ionized atom or molecule is one which has lost two electrons in place of one and, having a net positive charge of two units, is designated by two ($^+$) signs as superscripts. Since the particles have double charges the electric and magnetic forces exerted on them are double those for singly ionized atoms and they, undergoing greater deflections, produce larger parabolas.

The principal conclusions to be drawn from Thomson's experiments are (1) *that positive rays or canal rays are charged atoms or molecules of whatever gas is present in the apparatus,* (2) *that hydrogen and oxygen molecules have twice the weight of their single atoms and are therefore diatomic,* (3) *that a chemical compound like carbon monoxide is composed of diatomic molecules CO, each with a weight equal to the sum of the weights of the separate atoms.*

It is significant to point out that, while Thomson found many atoms could be doubly and some even triply ionized, hydrogen could never be found more than singly ionized and helium more than doubly ionized. The reason for this, as will be seen later, is that neutral hydrogen atoms have but one electron and neutral helium atoms but two. All other elements have more than two electrons.

59.3. The Periodic Table of Elements. From present-day knowledge of physics, chemistry, and astronomy, it is quite certain that the entire universe is made up of 80 to 90 stable elements. By an element is meant a substance composed of atoms having identical chemical properties. All but two or three of these elements have been found in the earth's crust, some of them in much greater abundance than others. Silicon and iron are examples of abundant elements, whereas platinum is an example of a rare element.

Long before the Thomson mass spectrograph had been devised and used to measure the relative masses of atoms, the chemist had arranged all of the elements in a table according to their atomic weights. The most common form of this arrangement is given in Appendix IV. Divided as they are into eight separate groups, all elements in the same column have similar chemical properties. In Group I, for example, the elements Li, Na, K, Rb, and Cs, known as the *alkali metals,* have one set of chemical properties, whereas the elements Be, Mg, Ca, Sr and Ba in Group II, known as the *alkaline earths,* have another set of chemical properties. The largest group of elements having similar chemical properties are the fourteen rare earth elements listed by themselves at the bottom of the table.

The names of the elements are all indicated by one-letter and two-letter symbols. (The full names are given in the second column of Appendix IV.) The number preceding each abbreviation is the order number of that element and is called *the atomic number.* The average weight of atoms of that element, called *the atomic weight,* is given in the last column.

The atomic weights of all elements are based upon the weight of oxygen as 16. This is purely an arbitrary selection of a unit of weight but one which has considerable significance when it is noted that the weights of the first 25 elements, with the exception of chlorine (Cl), atomic number 17, are very close to whole numbers. This suggests the possibility that the weights of all atoms are really whole number units of the unit of weight, the hydrogen atom, and that those weights of an element which differ considerably from whole numbers are incorrectly determined values. On the strength of this, Prout was the first to propose the hypothesis that all elements are made of hydrogen atoms as building stones. These suppositions, as will be seen later, are only partly true.

59.4. Thomson's Discovery of Isotopes. In 1912 Thomson, in comparing the mass of the neon atom with the known masses of other elements, discovered two parabolas for neon in place of one. Upon computing the masses of the particles involved, the stronger of two parabolas was found to be due to particles of mass *20* and the other, a fainter parabola, to particles of mass *22*.

Since the atomic weight of neon was then known to be *20.2*, Thomson expressed the belief that neon is composed of two kinds of atoms, 90% of which have a mass of *20* and the other 10% a mass of *22*. Because these two kinds of atoms exist as a mixture and cannot be separated chemically, their atomic weight, when measured by chemical methods, is found to be their average value *20.2*.

The discovery of two kinds of neon atoms, identical chemically but differing in atomic weight, suggested the possibility that all other elements whose atomic weights were not whole numbers might also be mixtures of atoms which do have whole number weights. Not only has this been confirmed by experiment but a large majority of the elements have been found to be mixtures of from two to ten different kinds of atoms.

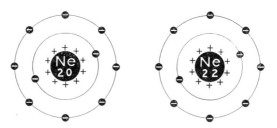

Fɪɢ. 59E—Schematic diagrams of the two different kinds of neon atoms, one of mass 20 and the other of mass 22. The external electron structure of two such isotopes are identical.

To all atoms of different weight belonging to the same element Soddy gave the name *isotopes*. The external structure of all isotopes of a given element are identical. The two atoms Ne-20 and Ne-22, shown in Fig. 59E, are neon isotopes. Each of these neutral atoms, before it is ionized to become a positive ray, has ten external electrons and ten positive charges on the nucleus. They differ only in the weight of the nucleus.

59.5. Aston's Mass Measurements. Immediately following World War I in 1919, F. W. Aston* developed a new and improved type of mass spectrograph. Employing both electric and magnetic fields, the device presented the chief improvement over Thomson's mass spectrograph of

---

*Francis Wm. Aston (1877-1945), British scientist, was born in Birmingham and educated at Malvern College and Cambridge University. He became assistant lecturer in physics at the Birmingham University in 1909, and received the Mackenzie Davidson Medal of the Röntgen Society in 1920. In 1922 he was awarded the Hughes Medal of the Royal Society and the coveted Nobel Prize in chemistry for his work on atomic mass measurements. He has written an authoritative book entitled "Isotopes," in which a full account of his work is given.

"focusing" the rays of different velocities to the same point on the screen or photographic plate. This had two important effects: (1) it made it possible to observe rare isotopes which might otherwise escape detection, and (2) it produced sharper images of the different masses on the photographic plate, so that their masses could be more accurately measured.

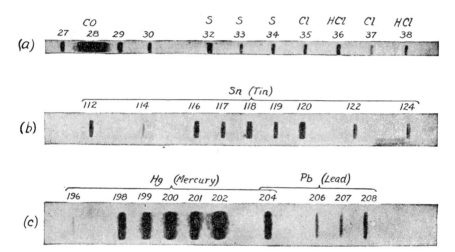

FIG. 59F—Photographs taken with a mass spectrograph illustrating the linear shift of atoms differing by one unit of mass. (a) Carbon monoxide, sulfur, chlorine, and argon lines (after Aston). (b) and (c) Isotopes of mercury, tin and lead (*after Bainbridge and Jordon*).

An Aston mass spectrogram is reproduced at the top of Fig. 59F. In taking this particular photograph Aston had introduced into his apparatus, among other things a little *hydrochloric acid* (HCl), *carbon monoxide* (CO), and *sulfur dioxide* (SO₂). Being close together in the periodic table these elements furnish an excellent demonstration of the linear shift of atoms and molecules, differing in mass by one unit. It is found from this and other photographs that sulfur has three isotopes with masses *32, 33,* and *34,* and that chlorine has two isotopes of mass *35* and *37.*

Since the atomic weight of chlorine is *35.46,* then for every atom of mass *37* in a given quantity of chlorine gas there are four of mass *35.* Mixed together in these proportions they give an average mass of *35.4.*

The photographic lines corresponding to masses *28, 36,* and *38* are due to diatomic molecules CO and HCl, each molecule having the combined weight of its constituent atoms. Since there are two relatively abundant chlorine isotopes there are two kinds of HCl molecules. One type, H¹Cl³⁵ has a mass of *36,* and the other type H¹Cl³⁷ a mass of *38.*

A CO molecule of the type producing the strong line at mass *28* in Fig. 59F(a) is shown schematically in Fig. 59G. As a neutral molecule there are

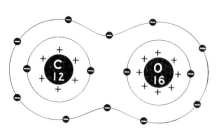

just as many electrons surrounding the two bound atoms as there are positive charges on the nuclei (six on the carbon nucleus and eight on the oxygen nucleus). When the molecule becomes ionized and is moving through the apparatus as a positive ray, it contains one less electron than the number shown. Since the mass of the electrons is negligibly small the mass of the molecule is 12 + 16 or 28 mass units.

FIG. 59G—Schematic diagram of a diatomic molecule, carbon monoxide, CO.

So successful was Aston with his mass measurements and his determination of isotopes of different elements that he attempted an investigation of the entire periodic table. All of the known elements are listed in Appendix IV, with all of their observed isotopes. In each case the most abundant isotope is given in heavy type, while the very rare isotopes, i.e., those present to less than 1%, are given in parentheses. Where more than one isotope is given in heavy type the isotopes occur with almost equal abundance. The masses given in italics represent unstable atoms which are responsible for *radioactivity*, the subject of Chap. 61. Recent developments in mass spectroscopy have made it possible to detect exceptionally rare isotopes. In neon, for example, an isotope of mass number 21 has been found, making three in all, with relative abundances as follows:

Isotope	Ne-20	Ne-21	Ne-22
Abundance, %	90.4	0.6	9.0

In a pure carbon monoxide gas all of the molecules are diatomic and alike in every respect except for mass. Since there are two carbon isotopes, *12* and *13*, and three oxygen isotopes, *16, 17*, and *18* (see Appendix IV), there are six different combinations of atoms to form molecules. These are $C^{12}O^{16}$, $C^{12}O^{17}$, $C^{12}O^{18}$, $C^{13}O^{16}$, $C^{13}O^{17}$, and $C^{13}O^{18}$. The relative abundances of all but the C^{12} and O^{16} isotopes are so small, however, that more than 90% of the molecules in a given quantity of gas are of the type $C^{12}O^{16}$, with a mass of *28*.

59.6. Isobars. Another mass spectrograph of remarkably high precision was devised in 1933 by an American physicist, K. T. Bainbridge.

Two photographs taken with this instrument are shown in Fig. 59F. The middle picture (b) shows the many isotopes of tin, and the lower plate (c) the isotopes of mercury and lead. The rare lead isotope *204* falls on top of the strong mercury isotope *204*. Such coincidences are called *isobars*.

Atoms having the same mass but belonging to different chemical elements are called isobars. The first pair of isobars, see Appendix IV, occurs in argon and calcium. The principal isotope of argon, atomic number 18, has a mass of 40, as does also the principal isotope of calcium, atomic number 20. Other examples are Cr54 and Fe54, Ge76 and Se76, Rb87 and Sr87, Zn92 and Mo92. The isobars Hg204 and Pb204 are illustrated in Fig. 59F(c).

59.7. Unit Mass, and the Hydrogen Atom. Until 1927 all oxygen atoms were thought to have the same mass and were arbitrarily chosen to be the standard by which all atomic masses were measured. At this time Giauque and Johnson discovered the existence of two rare oxygen isotopes with masses 17 and 18. So rare are these heavier particles that in every ten thousand oxygen atoms only sixteen of them have a mass of 18, and only three a mass of 17.

The arbitrary choice of unit atomic mass is therefore taken to be one-sixteenth of the mass of the oxygen isotope 16. On this basis very accurate mass spectrographic measurements give, for the mass of the hydrogen atom 1.008, a value nearly 1% higher than unity. This apparent discrepancy is real, however, and, as we shall see in a later chapter on nuclear disintegration, it plays an important role in the sun and stars as a source of *atomic energy.*

To compare the masses of atoms with the mass of an electron, it is convenient to know the mass of the atom in kilograms. This mass can be calculated by knowing its equivalence in atomic mass units, *unit atomic mass being defined as one-sixteenth the mass of an oxygen sixteen atom.* This unit mass is found by experiment to be

$$M = 1.660 \times 10^{-24} \text{ gm} = 1.660 \times 10^{-27} \text{ kg.} \tag{59a}$$

This number multiplied by the "atomic weight" of any atom will give its mass in kilograms.

Compared with the mass of the electron, namely,

$$m = 9.1072 \times 10^{-28} \text{ gm} = 9.1072 \times 10^{-31} \text{ kg} \tag{59b}$$

an atom of unit mass would be 1824 times as heavy. The hydrogen atom is slightly heavier than one unit mass and is about 1840 times as heavy as the electron. This latter number is convenient to remember for it is often quoted to illustrate the enormous difference between the mass of the nucleus of a hydrogen atom and the mass of its one and only electron.

Atomic number is defined as that number ascribed to an element specifying its position in the periodic table of elements. See Column 1, Appendix IV.

Mass number is defined as that whole number nearest the actual mass of an isotope measured in atomic mass units. See column four.

Atomic weight is defined as the average weight of all the isotopes of an element weighted according to relative abundance and expressed in atomic mass units.

PROBLEMS AND QUESTIONS

1. The atomic weight of aluminum is 26.97. Find the mass in grams of one aluminum atom.

2. If the atomic weight of cobalt is 58.94, how many atoms are there in one gram of cobalt metal? (*Ans.* 1.022×10^{22} atoms.)

3. The atomic weight of manganese is 54.94. How many atoms are there in one gram of manganese metal?

4. If the atomic weights of carbon and oxygen are 12.00 and 16.00 respectively, find the mass in grams of a carbon dioxide molecule. See Fig. 23A. (*Ans.* 7.30×10^{-23} gm.)

5. The atomic weights of hydrogen, carbon, and oxygen, are 1.01, 12.00, and 16.00 respectively. How many ethyl alcohol molecules are there in one gram of ethyl alcohol? See Fig. 23A.

6. Define or briefly explain the meaning of the following: (a) isotopes, (b) isobars, (c) positive rays, (d) atomic weight, and (e) unit atomic mass.

7. Name five of each of the following: (a) alkali metals, and (b) alkaline earths.

8. What chemical element has the greatest number of isotopes? See Table IV in the Appendix.

9. Make a list of elements having (a) atoms of one mass only, and (b) only two isotopes.

10. Carbon has two isotopes, 12 and 13, while oxygen has three, 16, 17, and 18. Find the mass in kilograms for each of the six possible CO molecules. (*Ans.* $C^{12}O^{16} = 4.65$, $C^{12}O^{17} = 4.81$, $C^{12}O^{18} = 4.98$, $C^{13}O^{16} = 4.81$, $C^{13}O^{17} = 4.98$, $C^{13}O^{18} = 5.15 \times 10^{-26}$ kg.)

11. Nitrogen has two isotopes, 14 and 15. Calculate the mass in kilograms for each of the three possible kinds of diatomic molecules.

12. The two stable isotopes of chlorine have masses of 35 and 37 atomic mass units. The normal mixture of these atoms has an atomic weight of 35.49. What percentage of any given amount of the normal gas is composed of O^{35} atoms? (*Ans.* 75.5 per cent.)

13. The fifth element in the periodic table, boron, has two stable isotopes with masses of 10 and 11 atomic mass units respectively. The normal mixture of these atoms has an atomic weight of 10.82. Calculate the percentage of any given amount of the normal boron composed of B^{10} atoms.

X-rays $\qquad$ *Chapter 60*

ONE of the most interesting episodes in the history of modern science began with the accidental discovery of x-rays by Wilhelm Röntgen* in 1895. While studying the green fluorescent stage of an electrical discharge in a Crookes tube, Röntgen observed the bright fluorescence of some nearby crystals of barium platino-cyanide. Even though the discharge tube was in a darkened room and entirely surrounded with black paper to prevent the escape of visible light, a distant screen covered with crystals would fluoresce brightly, when the discharge was turned on. Röntgen reasoned, therefore, that some kind of invisible yet penetrating rays of an unknown kind were being given out by the discharge tube. These rays he called *x-rays,* the letter *x* meaning, as it so often does in algebra, an unknown.

In the short series of experiments that followed his discovery, Röntgen found that the unknown rays were coming from the glass walls of the tube itself and, in particular, from the region where the most intense part of the cathode ray beam was striking the glass. So great was the importance of this discovery that within but a few weeks of Röntgen's announcement, x-rays were being used as an aid to surgical operations in Vienna. This, along with other practical applications and uses to be made of a single scientific discovery, is a good example of the role played by modern science in the rapid advancement of civilization.

60.1. X-ray Tubes. The Crookes tube with which Röntgen made his discovery bears very little resemblance to the modern x-ray tube. In form it had somewhat the appearance of the tube shown in Fig. 58C. Within a short period of time after Röntgen's discovery quite a number of noteworthy improvements upon tube design were made. The first important contribution in this direction came immediately following the discovery that it is the sudden stopping of electrons that gives rise to x-rays.

* Wilhelm Konrad von Röntgen (1845-1923). Born at Lennep on March 27, 1845, Röntgen received his education in Holland and Switzerland. His scientific career began at the age of twenty-five when he became an assistant in the physics laboratory at Würzburg, Germany. After a teaching period extending over a period of twenty-five years, which carried him to the University of Strasbourg, then to Hohenheim, back to Strasbourg, then to Giessen and finally to Würzburg again, he discovered x-rays in his laboratory at Würzburg in 1895. For this discovery he received the Rumford Medal of the Royal Society in 1896 and the first Nobel Prize in physics in 1901. Röntgen also conducted researches in light, heat, and elasticity, but none of these works compare in importance with his discovery of x-rays.

In x-ray tubes of early design, the electrons from the cathode were not allowed to strike the glass walls but were directed toward the anode as a target, as shown in Fig. 60A. By curving the cathode like a concave mirror it was found possible to focus the electrons on one spot on the target, thus making of that spot a localized source of x-rays. Radiating outward in all possible directions these Röntgen rays, as they are sometimes called, have no difficulty in passing through the glass walls of the tube.

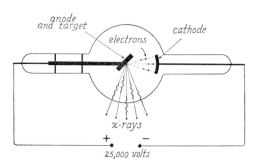

Fig. 60A—Diagram of early form of x-ray tube.

The biggest improvement in x-ray tube design was made by Coolidge, an American physicist, in 1913. In the Coolidge tube, now a commercial product (see Fig. 60B), a tungsten wire filament is placed at the center of the cathode and heated to incandescence by a storage battery or low-voltage

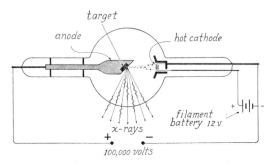

Fig. 60B—Diagram of a Coolidge x-ray tube employing a hot cathode.

transformer. This filament, being a copious source of electrons, gives rise at the target to a far more intense source of x-rays than was previously possible with a cold cathode. Under the terrific bombardment of the target by so many electrons, most metals will melt. To overcome this difficulty a metal, with a high melting point, like tungsten or molybdenum, is imbedded in the face of a solid copper anode to become the target. Copper, being a good heat conductor, helps to dissipate the heat.

The early sources of high voltage applied to the anode and cathode of x-ray tubes were supplied by induction coils of various descriptions. Although some of these sources are still in use, they have been almost entirely supplanted by a more efficient high-voltage transformer. The emf generated by these transformers varies between 50,000 and 2,000,000 volts. The normal emf used for surgical work is about 100,000 volts, whereas for the treatment of diseases the higher emf's are employed. The high-voltage alternating emf supplied by a transformer is not applied directly to the x-ray tube but is first changed into direct current by means of rectifier tubes.

60.2. Penetration of X-rays. Four useful and important properties of x-rays are their ability (1) to penetrate solid matter, (2) to cause certain chemical compounds to fluoresce, (3) to ionize atoms, and (4) to affect a photographic plate. The penetration of x-rays depends upon two things: first, the voltage applied between the anode and cathodes of the x-ray tube; and second, the density of the substance through which the rays must travel. The higher the voltage applied to the tube the greater is the penetration. *X-rays of great penetrating power are called hard x-rays, whereas those having little penetrating power are called soft x-rays.*

The relation between density and penetration may be illustrated in several ways. When x-rays are sent through a block of wood containing nails, or a closed leather purse containing coins, a clear and well-defined image of the nails, or coins, can be formed and observed on a fluorescent screen. The experimental arrangement is the same as that shown in Fig. 60C. When x-rays are sent through the hand or any part of the body to obtain photographs of the bones it is the difference in penetration between the flesh and the bones that permits a picture to be made. Materials like paper, wood, flesh, etc., composed principally of light chemical elements like those at

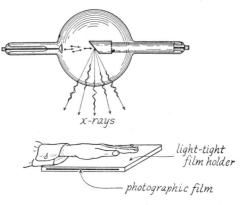

Fig. 60C—Arrangement for taking x-ray photographs of the bones of the hand.

the beginning of the periodic table, are readily penetrated by x-rays. In other words, they are poor absorbers of x-rays. For materials like brass, steel, bone, gold, etc., composed partly of heavy elements, like those farther along and near the end of the periodic table, the penetration of x-rays is very poor. Hence heavy elements, or dense substances, are good absorbers.

The bones of the body, containing large amounts of calcium, are relatively good absorbers of x-rays, whereas the flesh, composed principally of much lighter elements—hydrogen, oxygen, carbon and nitrogen—are poor absorbers. This explains the general appearance of x-ray photographs. X-ray pictures like the ones in Fig. 60D are similar to shadows cast by the objects being photographed. The focus point on the x-ray target, being bombarded by high-speed electrons, acts as a point source of rays. These spread out in straight lines as shown in Fig. 60C. On passing through the hand to the photographic film more x-rays are absorbed by the bones than by the flesh. The shadow cast by the bones is therefore very weak in x-rays and the photographic film develops out clear.

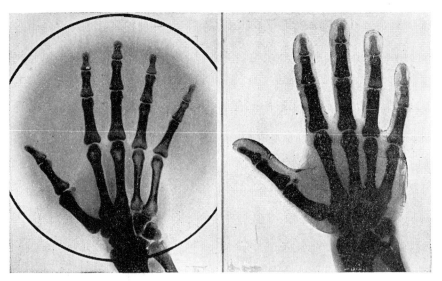

Fig. 60D—X-ray photographs of the wrist bones of the hand. (a) With hand in water. (b) With lead-oxide ointment spread on hand. (*Courtesy of the Stamford Research Laboratories American Cyanamid Co.*)

Where only flesh is traversed the x-rays penetrate through to the photographic film, causing it to develop out black. The bones therefore appear white against a darker background. If this "negative film," as it is called, is printed on paper as in Fig. 60D, it becomes a "positive" with the bones appearing black.

If the photographic film is placed farther away from the hand than shown in the diagram, the shadow picture will be larger and less distinct. The best pictures are obtained by placing the film as close in contact with the object to be photographed as is physically possible. Whenever a film is being exposed for an x-ray picture, it is mounted in a black paper envelope or thin aluminum box. This prevents visible light from reaching the film but allows the x-rays to pass through.

60.3. Ionizing Power. As x-rays pass through matter in the solid, liquid, or gaseous state, they are found to *ionize* atoms and molecules. This can be shown by charging a gold-leaf electroscope positively or negatively and placing it some 10 to 15 ft away from an x-ray tube. When the x-ray tube is turned on (see Fig. 60E), the gold leaf falls, showing discharge.

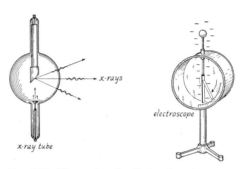

The explanation of this experiment is as follows: x-rays pass through the electroscope and ionize the air by removing electrons from many of the oxygen and nitrogen molecules. Leaving these particular molecules with a net positive charge, the freed electrons move about until they are picked up by other neutral molecules, thus giving them a net negative charge. The result is that the passage of x-rays through matter produces both *positively charged* and *negatively charged ions*. If the electroscope is negatively charged it attracts the positively charged ions to the gold leaf, neutralizing the charge and repelling the negatively charged ions to the "grounded" walls where they, too, become neutralized. If the electroscope is positively charged it attracts the negative ions to it, again neutralizing the charge. The positive ions in this case are repelled to the walls. In either case, whether the electroscope is positively or negatively charged, the gold leaf falls, showing discharge.

Fig. 60E—Illustrating the discharging of an electroscope by x-rays. This demonstrates the property of ionization.

It is the ionization of atoms and molecules in a substance that limits the penetrating power of x-rays. Heavy elements contain more electrons than light elements, thus placing more electrons in the path of the x-rays to stop them. The stopping power of a thin sheet of lead, for example, is equivalent to the stopping power of a sheet of aluminum several times thicker. Lead atoms each contain 82 electrons, whereas aluminum atoms each contain only 13.

60.4. Practical Applications. During the first few weeks following Röntgen's discovery of x-rays, reports from all over the world were received by the editors of scientific journals telling of how the new rays could be put to practical use. A few examples of the first applications were (1) the location of a bullet in a patient's leg, (2) the observation and photography of the healing of a broken bone, (3) the detection of contraband in baggage, (4) the distinction between artificial and real gems, (5) the detection of pearls in oysters, and (6) the examination of the contents in parcel post. In 1897 Dr. Morton in New York exhibited an x-ray picture of the entire skeleton of a living and fully-clothed adult.

The biological effects became important when it was found that x-rays killed off some forms of animal tissue more rapidly than others. This makes them a possible means of cure for certain skin diseases. The application in particular to the treatment of well-known forms of cancerous growths in animals and human beings has yielded amazing results, and oftentimes a cure. When an internal cancer is treated by sending a beam of x-rays directly through the body the cancerous tissue as well as the normal tissue is slowly killed off. It is principally because the normal tissue grows in again more rapidly than the cancerous tissue that it is possible to bring about a cure. Periodic radiation allows the normal tissue to build up in the intervals.

Although only certain diseases can be successfully treated by x-rays a great deal of research work is still being carried on with extremely high-voltage x-rays in the hope of discovering new and more effective medical aids. It is generally believed that the killing off of cell tissue by x-rays is due primarily to the ionization of the molecules within the individual cells.

The importance of x-rays in some phases of the field of engineering cannot be overestimated. This can be appreciated when it is realized that metal castings or welded joints sometimes contain internal flaws or blowholes that otherwise escape detection. Because of the diastrous results which might occur by the insertion of defective castings or welded joints into a bridge or building, many such metal parts are examined by x-rays before being used.

60.5. X-rays Are Waves. Not long after Röntgen's discovery of x-rays, there arose in scientific circles two schools of thought concerning the nature of these penetrating rays. The one school held to the belief that x-rays are high-speed particles like cathode rays but more penetrating, and the other school held to the idea that they are electromagnetic waves of extremely high frequency. Although many experiments were performed to test these two hypotheses, several years passed before the wave theory was proved to be correct.

The crucial experiment came in 1912 when Von Laue* suggested to his associates W. Friedrich and P. Knipping that they try diffracting x-rays by sending them through a thin crystal. Believing that the ultramicroscopic structure of a crystal is a three-dimensional array of regularly spaced atoms, Von Laue reasoned that the equally spaced layers of the atoms would act

---

* Max von Laue (1879-   ). Born near Coblenz, Germany, in 1879, young Max was educated in the German Universities of Strasbourg, Göttingen, and Munich. Following this his teaching and research work carried him to the University at Munich, Zurich, Frankfurt on the Main, and finally Berlin. Being interested in theoretical physics, his early attentions were confined to various phases of Einstein's theory of relativity, and to Bohr's quantum theory of atomic structure. His chief contribution to physics, however, was the instigation and supervision of experiments leading to the diffraction of x-rays by crystals. For this work, which proved the wave-nature of x-rays, he was granted the Nobel Prize in 1914.

like a diffraction grating. (For details of the action of a diffraction grating on light waves see Sec. 46.7.)

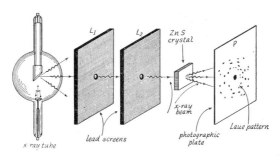

Fig. 60F—Experimental demonstration of the wave property of x-rays. Diffracted by the atoms in a crystal, a Laue pattern is photographed.

The experiment, as it was performed, is shown diagrammatically in Fig. 60F. X-rays from a cold cathode x-ray tube, and limited to a narrow pencil of rays by a pinhole in each of the two lead screens L_1 and L_2, are shown passing through a thin crystal to a photographic film of plate at P. In addition to the central beam, the major part of which goes straight through to produce a blackened spot at the center of the film, there are many other weaker beams emerging in different directions to produce other spots on the same film. The pattern of spots obtained in this way is always quite symmetrical and is referred to as a *Laue pattern*.

Photographs of two Laue patterns obtained with single crystals are reproduced in Fig. 60G. The small number of spots in (a) is indicative of a relatively simple crystal structure for zinc sulfide, ZnS, and the large number of spots signifies a relatively complex crystal structure for sugar, $C_{12}H_{22}O_{11}$. While the picture for

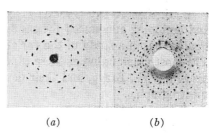

(a)　　　　(b)

Fig. 60G—X-ray diffraction patterns from crystals, (a) Zinc sulfide crystal (face centered cubic crystal), (b) Sugar crystal (a complex crystal structure).

sugar was being taken the central beam was masked off by a small lead disk placed just in front of the film to prevent excessive blackening. Simple Laue patterns in general arise from simple crystal structures. Common salt is an example of a simple crystal, containing, as shown in Fig. 23E, sodium atoms (Na) and chlorine atoms (Cl) in equal numbers arranged in a three-dimensional cubic lattice. Fig. 60H is a cross section through such a crystal showing the alternation of atoms in two of the three directions. Here in this two-dimensional array, the origin of the different spots on a Laue pattern is illustrated.

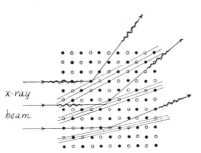

Each spot arises from the reflection of some of the incident x-rays from one of the various sets of parallel crystal planes, three of which are shown by the sets of parallel lines. Always the rays obey the law of reflection that the angle of incidence equals the angle of reflection. While the reflection planes shown in the diagram are all perpendicular to the plane of the page, there are many

FIG. 60H—Illustrating the reflection of x-rays from the various atomic planes in a cubic crystal lattice.

other planes in a three-dimensional lattice to reflect the rays off in other directions.

The success of the Laue experiment proves the correctness of two postulates: (1) that x-rays are light rays of very short wave length, and (2) that the atoms of a crystal are arranged in a regular three-dimensional lattice. These are the results for which Von Laue was granted the Nobel Prize in physics in 1914. As a direct result of the Laue experiment two new and important fields of experimental physics were opened up: (1) the study and measurement of x-ray wave lengths, and (2) the study of crystal structures by their action on x-rays.

60.6. The X-ray Spectrograph. No sooner had Von Laue, Friedrich, and Knipping announced the results of their experiments than many investigators began a study of the various phases of *x-ray diffraction* by crystals. The most outstanding of these experiments are those of W. H. Bragg,* and his son W. L. Bragg, and their development of the x-ray spectrometer and spectrograph.

A diagram of an x-ray spectrograph is shown in Fig. 60I. Instead of having pinhole screens, as in Fig. 60F, and sending a narrow pencil of rays through a crystal, the early spectrographs used screens with narrow slits and reflected the rays from one face of a crystal. The crystal is not fixed tightly in place but can be turned back and forth about a pivot C at the center of the front face. As this rocking motion takes place, the crystal acts somewhat

---

* Sir William Henry Bragg (1862-   ), British physicist and professor at the University of London. Bragg's researches on radioactive phenomena brought him early recognition from scientific societies at home and abroad. Joint work with his son, William Lawrence Bragg (1890-   ), on the arrangement of atoms in crystals, and the development of the x-ray spectrograph are his greatest scientific contributions. In 1915 father and son were jointly granted the Nobel Prize in physics, as well as the Barnard Gold Medal from Columbia University.

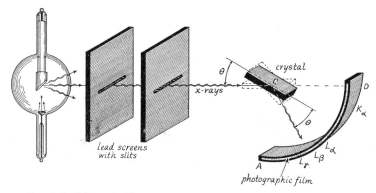

FIG. 60I—Schematic diagram of a Bragg x-ray crystal spectrograph.

like a mirror and causes the reflected x-ray beam to sweep back and forth along the photographic film from one end to the other. After the photographic film has been exposed to the rays for some time and then developed, it is found to have the general appearance of the reproduction in Fig. 60J. This unusually clear photograph was originally taken by de Broglie using an x-ray tube containing a tungsten metal anode target. Instead of a general blackening from end to end, the film shows *bands* and *lines*, indicating that at certain orientation angles of the crystal the reflected rays were unusually intense while at others there

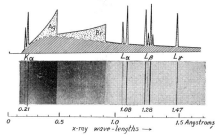

FIG. 60J—X-ray spectrogram taken with an x-ray tube containing a tungsten metal target. (*After de Broglie.*)

were apparently none. The lines, which are particularly noticeable at points marked K_a, L_a, L_β, and L_γ, are called *x-ray spectrum lines*.

The origin and interpretation of these spectrum lines are illustrated by a detailed diagram in Fig. 60K. To reflect x-rays of one given wave length from a crystal a certain relation must exist between the direction of the incident rays and the distance d between surface layers of the crystal. This relation, known as *the Bragg rule*, re-

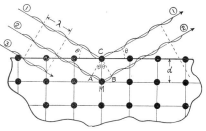

FIG. 60K—Illustrating the Bragg rule of reflection for x-rays from the surface layers of a crystal.

quires the waves to be incident on the crystal face at such an angle θ that the crests of the waves reflected from adjacent atomic layers move off together. This occurs when the additional distance traveled by ray (2), *AMB* in the diagram, is exactly one whole wave length greater than that traveled by the ray (1) next above it. When the angle is adjusted so that this is true, other rays like (3), belonging to the same wave train as (1) and (2), will be reflected from the third crystal layer to be "in step" with the others.

Suppose now that the x-ray tube in Fig. 58I emits x-rays of only one wave length; then, as the crystal rocks back and forth, there will be no reflection except at one particular angle θ and this will occur where the conditions of Bragg's rule are satisfied. At this particular position on the photographic plate a single dark line will appear. If now the distance d between crystal layers is known and the angle θ for the x-ray line measured, the wave length of the x-rays can be calculated. One wave length, it will be noted in Fig. 60K, is equal to twice the length of the side *AM* of the right triangle *AMC*. Thus, with one side and two angles of a triangle known, either of the other sides can be calculated. Bragg's rule therefore becomes

$$2d \sin \theta = \lambda \tag{60a}$$

Since several spectrum lines appear in the photograph of Fig. 60J, there are several different wave lengths emitted by the same x-ray tube. The two fluted appearing bands between the K and L x-ray lines are not of interest here because they appear on all x-ray spectrograms and are due to the strong absorption of x-rays of many other wave lengths by the silver and bromine atoms in the photographic plate itself. Had the original photographic film been exposed for a much longer time the spectrogram would have shown a general blackening over the whole plate. This blackening, illustrated by the shaded area in the curve above, is due to x-rays of all different wave lengths being emitted by the x-ray tube, and it is these which, although not very intense, strongly affect the photographic plate at the two bands, *Ag* and *Br*. An explanation of this continuous x-ray spectrum is given in Sec. 68.8.

To be able to calculate the wave lengths of x-rays it is necessary to know the distance between the atomic layers of the crystal being used in the spectrograph. As one illustration of how this has been done, consider the simple case of a crystal of rock salt, NaCl which, from the appearance of its Laue pattern, is known to be a cubic lattice as shown in Fig. 23E. Since the atoms are of two kinds, in equal numbers, it is necessary to determine the average weight of an atom. Taking 35.4 as the atomic weight of Cl and 23.0 as the atomic weight of Na, the average atomic weight is 29.2. This, multiplied by the weight in grams of one atomic mass unit (see Eq.59a), gives the average weight of one atom as

$$M = 29.2 \times 1.66 \times 10^{-24} = 48.4 \times 10^{-24} \text{ gm.}$$

Since 1 cm³ of a salt crystal can be weighed directly and is known to have a mass of 2.16 gm, the same cube must therefore contain

$$n = \frac{2.16}{48.4 \times 10^{-24}} = 4.46 \times 10^{22} \text{ atoms.}$$

Now if d is the distance between one atom and the next, along one edge of the cube, there are $1/d$ atoms in a row 1 cm long. In a 1-cm cube, therefore, there are $1/d^3$ atoms. If we write

$$n = 1/d^3$$

and solve for d, the lattice spacing comes out to be

$$d = 2.81 \times 10^{-8} \text{ cm,}$$

or $d = 2.81$ angstroms, or $d = 0.0000000281$ cm.

It will be seen from Fig. 60K that this small distance is about the same order of magnitude as the wave length of x-rays.*

PROBLEMS AND QUESTIONS

1. Briefly explain why an x-ray photograph of the hand shows the bones more clearly than the flesh surrounding them.

2. An x-ray photograph of a closed leather purse will readily show silver coins or other metal articles inside. Explain.

3. How and by whom were x-rays discovered?

4. Diagram a modern x-ray tube of the type developed by Coolidge.

5. X-rays sent through a Bragg crystal spectrometer using a rock salt crystal are reflected at an angle of 20.5°. What is the wave length of the x-rays?

6. X-rays sent through a Bragg crystal spectrometer show three spectrum lines at 6.41°, 8.16°, and 8.70°, respectively. If the crystal used is rock salt, what are the wave lengths of the x-rays? (*Ans.* 0.627, 0.798, 0.850.)

7. X-rays of wave length 1.45×10^{-8} cm are diffracted by a Bragg crystal spectrograph at an angle of 12.4°. Find the effective spacing of the atomic layers in the crystal.

8. X-rays having a wave length of 0.6×10^{-8} cm are diffracted at an angle of 3.2° in a Bragg crystal spectrograph. Find the effective spacing of the atomic layers in the crystal. (*Ans.* 5.38A.)

9. When a molybdenum target is used in an x-ray tube, the two shortest wave lengths emitted are found with a Bragg crystal spectrograph to be diffracted at angles of 6°24′ and 7°15′, respectively. Find their wave lengths. Assume a crystal spacing of 2.81×10^{-8} cm.

10. When a tungsten target is used in an x-ray tube, the two shortest wave lengths emitted are found with a Bragg crystal spectrograph to be diffracted at angles of 1°51′, and 2°8′, respectively. Find their wave lengths. Assume a crystal spacing of 2.81×10^{-8} cm. (*Ans.* 0.182A and 0.210A.)

* For a more complete treatment of x-rays see, "X-RAYS" by A. H. Compton and S. K. Allison, D. Van Nostrand Co., Inc.

Radioactivity   Chapter 61

RADIOACTIVITY may be defined as a spontaneous disintegration of the nucleus of one or more atoms. The phenomenon was discovered originally by Becquerel * in 1896 and is confined almost entirely to the heaviest elements in the periodic table, elements 83 to 96. What Becquerel discovered was that uranium, element 92, gave out some kind of rays that would penetrate through several thicknesses of thick black paper and affect a photographic plate on the other side. When the same phenomenon was confirmed several months later by Pierre and Marie Curie,** these rays became known as Becquerel rays.

61.1. Discovery of Radium. Unlike the discovery of many new phenomena the discovery of radium by Pierre and Madame Curie in 1898 was brought about intentionally by a set of carefully planned experiments. Having found that pitchblende was active in emitting Becquerel rays, the Curies treated chemically a ton of this ore in the hope of isolating from it the substance or element responsible for the activity. The first concentrated radioactive substance isolated was called *polonium* by Madame Curie, a name chosen in honor of her native country, Poland. Five months later came the isolation of a minute quantity of *radium,* a substance which was a powerful source of Becquerel rays. Continued experiments by the Curies,

* Antoine Henri Becquerel (1852-1908), French physicist. Born in Paris on December 15, 1852, Antoine succeeded to his father's chair at the Museum of Natural History in 1892. In 1896 he discovered radioactivity, the phenomenon for which he is most famous. The invisible but penetrating rays emitted by uranium and other radioactive elements are now called Becquerel rays. For these researches he was granted the Nobel Prize in physics in 1903.

** Pierre Curie (1859-1906) and Marie Curie (1867-1936), French physicists. Pierre Curie was educated at Sorbonne where he later became professor of physics. Although he experimented on piezoelectricity and other subjects, he is chiefly noted for his work on radioactivity performed jointly with his wife, Marie Sklodowska, whom he married in 1895. Marie was born in Poland on November 7, 1867, where she received her early scientific training from her father. Becoming involved in a students' revolutionary organization, she left Poland for Paris where she took a degree at the university. Two years after the discovery of radioactivity by Becquerel, Pierre and Madame Curie isolated polonium and radium from pitchblende by a long and laborious physical-chemical process. In 1903 they were awarded the Davy Medal of the Royal Society, and (jointly with Becquerel) the Nobel Prize in physics. Professor Curie, who was elected to the Academy of Sciences in 1905, was run over and killed by a carriage in 1906. Succeeding him as professor at the university, Madame Curie in 1911 was awarded the Nobel Prize in chemistry. She has the unique distinction of having had a share in the awards of two Nobel Prizes.

and others, soon led to the isolation of many other substances now recognized as radioactive elements. Some of the more common of these are *ionium, radon,* and *thorium.*

61.2. The Properties of Becquerel Rays. It is to the experimental genius of Rutherford * that we owe the complete unraveling of the mystery surrounding the nature of Becquerel rays. As the result of an extensive series of experiments Rutherford and his coworkers discovered that these

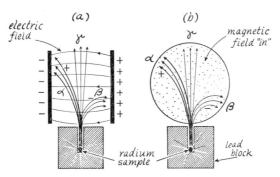

FIG. 61A—Illustrating the bending of Becquerel rays in
(a) an electric field, and (b) a magnetic field.

penetrating rays are of three quite different kinds. A simplified experiment demonstrating this is illustrated in Fig. 61A. A small sample of radium is dropped to the bottom of a small drill hole made in a block of lead. This produces a narrow beam of rays emerging from the top of the block since those rays entering the walls of the lead are absorbed before reaching the surface. When electrically charged plates are placed at the side of this beam as shown in diagram (a), the paths of some rays are bent to the left, some to the right, and some not at all. A magnetic field as shown in diagram (b) exhibits the same effect. Those paths bending to the left indicate positively charged particles called α-*rays* or α-*particles,* those bending to the right indicate negatively charged particles called β-*rays* or β-*particles,* and those going straight ahead indicate no charge and are called γ-*rays* or *photons.*

Rutherford, by a series of experiments, was able to show that each α-*ray* is in reality a *doubly ionized helium atom,* i.e., a helium atom with both of

* Lord Rutherford (1871-1937), British physicist, was born in New Zealand where he attended the university. In 1898 he became Macdonald professor of physics at McGill University, Montreal, Canada, and in 1907 professor of physics at Manchester University. In 1919 he became professor and director of experimental physics at the University of Cambridge, and in addition held a professorship at the Royal Institution in London. He is most famous for his brilliant researches establishing the existence and nature of radioactive transformations and the electrical structure of the atom. For this work and until the time of his death in 1937 he was acclaimed by many as the greatest living experimental physicist. He was awarded the Nobel Prize in chemistry in 1908, and was knighted in 1914.

its electrons gone. Such a particle is nothing more than a bare helium nucleus with double the positive charge of a hydrogen nucleus or proton, and a mass number or atomic weight four times as great. The β-*rays* he found are ordinary electrons with a mass of 1/1840th the mass of a *proton* or 1/7360th the mass of an α-*particle*, while γ-*rays* are electromagnetic waves of about the same or a little higher frequency than x-rays. Although γ-rays all travel with exactly the velocity of x-rays and visible light, α-rays are ejected with a speed of from one-tenth to one-hundredth the velocity of light. β-particles move faster than α-particles, some of them traveling with 99% the velocity of light.

61.3. Ionizing Power. When Becquerel rays penetrate matter in the gaseous, liquid, or solid state, they do not continue to move indefinitely, but are brought to rest slowly by ionizing atoms all along their path. Being ejected from their radioactive source with tremendously high speeds, all three types of rays collide with electrons and knock them free from atoms. They are, therefore, *ionizing agents*. The relative number of ionized atoms created along the path of an α-particle, however, is much greater than the number created by a β-particle or γ-ray. If, in traveling the same distance in a given material, a γ-ray produces one ionized atom, a β-particle will, on the average, produce approximately one hundred, and an α-particle will produce about ten thousand. Thus α-particles are powerful ionizing agents, while γ-rays are not.

As stated above, an α-particle, ejected from a radioactive atom, is but the nucleus of a helium atom and lacks the two electrons necessary to make of it a neutral atom. As this particle speeds through matter it picks up and loses electrons at a rapid rate. No sooner does an electron become attached than it is swept off again by other atoms. Finally upon coming to rest, however, each α-particle collects and retains two electrons, becoming a *normal helium atom*.

61.4. Penetrating Power. At each collision with an atom, Becquerel rays lose on the average only a small part of their initial energy. Usually an α-particle or β-particle will make several thousand collisions before being brought to rest. At each collision some of the kinetic energy is expended in ionizing the atom encountered while giving that same atom a certain amount of kinetic energy. Since α-particles produce the greatest number of ions in a given path they penetrate the shortest distance and therefore have the poorest penetrating power. The penetrating powers of the three kinds of rays are roughly inversely proportional to their ionizing power.

	α	β	γ
Relative ionizing power	10,000	100	1
Relative penetrating power	1	100	10,000

61.5. Methods of Detecting Becquerel Rays. There are several well-known methods for detecting and measuring radioactivity; the first of these is the gold-leaf electroscope, the second is the Wilson cloud chamber, and the third is the Geiger-Mueller tube counter. We have already seen how x-rays passing through an electroscope cause the charge to disappear and the gold leaf to fall. This same action may be demonstrated with α, β, and γ-rays. The stronger the source of rays or the nearer the sample is brought to the electroscope the more rapid is the discharge. Experiments show that if the walls of the electroscope are too thick only the γ-rays get through to produce ionization on the inside. For this reason specially designed electroscopes made with thin windows of light material like aluminum are used for measuring α and β-rays.

61.6. The Wilson Cloud Chamber. In 1912 C. T. R. Wilson devised a method by which one may actually observe the paths of α and β-particles. As will be seen in the following chapters this method is used extensively in modern atomic physics as a means of studying many different atomic processes. The device by which this is accomplished consists of an expansion chamber in which water vapor is made to condense upon ions produced by the high-speed particles that have previously passed through it.

To begin with, the conditions under which water in the vapor state will condense into fogdrops are quite critical. These conditions are: *first,* there must be water vapor present; *second,* there must be dust particles or ions on which the drops can form; *and third,* the temperature and pressure must

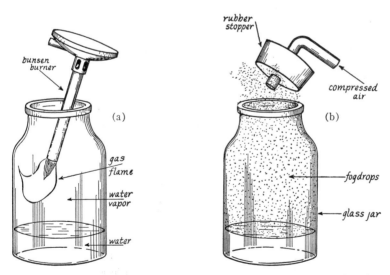

Fig. 61B—Experiment demonstrating the formation of fogdrops on ions in a glass jar.

be brought to a definite value. That water drops will condense only upon ions or dust particles can be demonstrated with an ordinary glass jar containing a little water as shown in Fig. 61B. If allowed to stand for a short period of time, some of the water will evaporate and fill the bottle with vapor. Ions are next formed in the bottle by momentarily inserting a small gas flame as shown in diagram (a). Compressed air is then injected into the bottle through a tube so that when the stopper is quickly removed the sudden expansion will produce a dense fog as shown in diagram (b). If the flame is not first inserted to produce ions no appreciable fog can be formed.

The purpose of the compressed air and subsequent expansion of the chamber is to lower the temperature, thus causing the air to become supersaturated with water vapor. Under these conditions the vapor will condense on all ionized molecules present.

When an α or β-particle "shoots" through the air, positive and negative ions are formed all along its path. The removal by collision of each electron from a neutral atom or molecule leaves a positively charged ion. The electron attaching almost immediately to another neutral atom or molecule forms a negatively charged ion. If immediately after an α-particle has gone through a cloud chamber, an expansion takes place, fogdrops will form on the newly created ions, revealing clearly the path the particle has taken. As illustrated by the photographs in Fig. 61C such α-ray tracks are straight and quite dense, whereas the β-ray tracks are crooked and sparsely lined

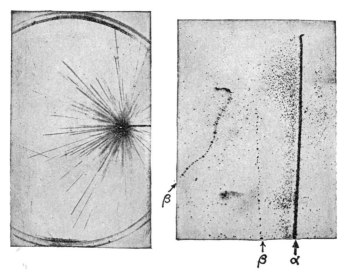

Fig. 61C—(a) α-ray tracks from radium as seen in a Wilson cloud chamber. (b) One α-ray and two β-ray tracks. (*After C. T. R. Wilson, Proceedings of the Royal Society of London, Vol. 87, 1912, p. 292.*)

with drops. The β-rays being very light particles are easily deflected by collision, while the relatively heavy α-particles "plow" right through thousands of atoms with only an occasional deflection.

Gamma rays are never observed in a cloud chamber since they produce so few ions. In passing through several feet of air a single γ-ray will, on the average, produce only one or two ions. This is not enough to produce a recognizable cloud track. If a very strong source of γ-rays is available, however, their presence can be observed in a cloud chamber by the chance collisions some of them have made with electrons. These recoiling electrons, as shown in Fig. 67D, are called "Compton electrons" and will be explained in Sec. 69.2.

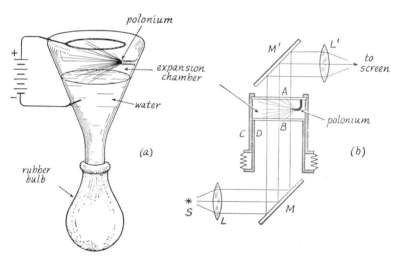

Fig. 61D—Wilson cloud chambers used for demonstrating α-ray tracks from radioactive elements. (a) Small chamber for individual observers. (b) Chamber used for projecting tracks on a large screen.

Diagrams of two types of Wilson cloud chamber are shown in Fig. 61D. The arrangement in (a) is made from an ordinary flat-bottomed flask with a rubber bulb attached to the neck. A tiny deposit of radium or polonium is inserted in the end of a thin-walled glass tube as indicated. When the rubber bulb is squeezed to compress the air in the top, and then released to cause an expansion, fogdrops will form on the ions created by the α-particles. The battery and the wires leading to the wire ring in the top of the chamber and the water below are for the purpose of quickly removing ions previously formed in the chamber. This clears the field of view for newly formed tracks.

For projection purposes a cloud chamber designed as shown in diagram

(b) is quite successful. Light from a source S and lens L is reflected by a mirror M up through the two glass plates A and B of the expansion chamber. By a second mirror M' and lens L' this light is made to focus an image of the polonium support and tracks on the distant screen. The expansion is produced by a sudden pull downward on the movable piston D.

The third type of instrument used for the detection of Becquerel rays is known as the Geiger-Mueller tube counter, or more briefly as the Geiger counter. This device will be described in detail in Chap. 71 dealing with cosmic rays.

61.7. Transmutation by Spontaneous Disintegration. A careful study of radioactivity indicates that α, β, and γ-rays originate from within the nucleus of the atom. When a radium atom disintegrates by ejecting an α-particle the nucleus loses a net positive charge of two. Since the number of positive charges on the nucleus determines the exact number of electrons outside of the atom and this in turn determines the chemical nature of an atom, the loss of an α-particle, with two positive charges, leaves a new chemical element. Thus a *radium atom*, for example, in disintegrating, changes into a new atom called *radon*. We say there has been a *transmutation*. Not only does a nucleus lose a double charge by emitting an α-particle and thereby *drop down two places in atomic number*, but it also loses a weight of four units and thus *drops down four units in atomic weight, or mass number*.

When a nucleus like *radium B* disintegrates by ejecting a β-particle (an electron) to become *radium C*, the nuclear positive charge *increases by one unit*. Such a transmutation yields a new element one atomic number higher in the chemical table. Since an electron weighs only 1/1840th part of a hydrogen atom or proton, the change in mass due to a β-particle leaving a nucleus is too small to change the mass number. Although the loss in weight is measurable, it changes the atomic weight so slightly that for most purposes of discussion it can be and is neglected. A γ-ray, like the β-ray particle, changes the weight of a nucleus by a negligible amount and, since it has no charge, it does not alter either the atomic number or the mass number. These changes, if not clearly understood now, will be explained in more detail in Chap. 73.

61.8. Half-life. *The half-life of a radioactive element is the time required for half of a given quantity of that element to disintegrate into a new element.* For example, it takes 1600 years for half of a given quantity of radium to change into radon. In another 1600 years half of the remainder will have disintegrated, leaving one-quarter of the original amount. The half-life of radium is therefore said to be 1600 years.

The rate at which a given quantity of a radioactive element disintegrates, that is, *decays,* is found by observing the activity of a given sample over a period of time and plotting a graph of the type shown in Fig. 61E. Here for *polonium* the activity drops to half of its original value in 140 days. In another 140 days it again drops to half value, etc. The term activity may be defined as the number of rays given off per second of time, or as the number of ionized atoms produced each second by the rays.

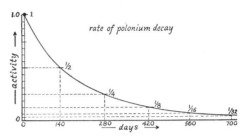

The only difference between the decay curve of one element and that of another is the horizontal time scale to which they are plotted. To turn Fig. 61E into a decay curve for radium the

Fig. 61E—Decay curve for the radioactive element, polonium. Polonium has a half-life of 140 days.

times 140, 280, 420 days, etc., need only to be changed to read 1600, 3200, 4800 years, etc., respectively. Since, therefore, all radioactive decay curves follow the same law, one does not have to wait for half of a given sample to disintegrate to be able to calculate how long it will be before half will have changed. This would require too many years of waiting for some elements.

61.9. Range. The *range* of an α-particle is defined as the distance such a particle will travel through dry air at normal atmospheric pressure. In a partial vacuum where there are fewer air molecules per centimeter to bump into, the distance traveled before coming to rest will be greater, whereas in air under higher than normal atmospheric pressure there are more molecules per centimeter and the distance will be diminished. Experiments show that some radioactive elements eject α-particles with a higher speed than others.

Fig. 61F—Wilson cloud chamber tracks from thorium C and C'. (*After Rutherford, Chadwick and Ellis, Courtesy of Cambridge University Press.*)

The higher the initial speed the greater is the range. The range of the α-particles from *radium* is 3.39 cm, whereas the range of those from *thorium C'* is 8.62 cm.

The ranges of α-particles in general have been determined in three different ways: *first,* by the Wilson cloud chamber, *second,* by the number of ions produced along the path, and *third* by scintillations produced on a fluorescent screen.

In the Wilson cloud chamber photograph of Fig. 61F, α-particles of two different ranges are observed. The radioactive sample used to obtain this picture was a mixture of *thorium C* and *thorium C'*. The shorter tracks with a 4.79 cm range are due to the α-particles from *thorium C* disintegrating to become *thorium C″*, and the longer tracks of 8.62 cm range are due to the α-particles from *thorium C′* disintegrating to become lead (see the last chart in Appendix IV).

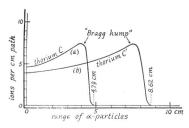

Fig. 61G—Graphs of the relative number of ions produced at various points along the path of an α-particle (a) from thorium C, and (b) from thorium C′.

When one measures the number of ions produced along the path of an α-particle, curves similar to those shown in Fig. 61G are obtained. At the end of each track the number is seen to reach a maximum and then drop to zero within a very short distance. This maximum on the graph is called the "Bragg hump" in honor of W. H. Bragg who discovered the phenomenon. The maximum number of ions is therefore produced just before the particles are stopped, i.e., where they are moving at relatively low speeds. The point at which the ion density drops rapidly to zero gives the range as shown in the figure. Although the experimental method by which ion density is usually determined will not be presented here, another method

Fig. 61H—Enlarged photograph of a cloud chamber track showing individual fogdrops. (*After Brode and Corson.*)

will be. This is the well-known method of counting fogdrops. An enlarged photograph of a cloud track, as reproduced in Fig. 61H, reveals the individual fogdrops separated sufficiently to enable the number of drops per centimeter of path to be counted. In measurements of this kind it is assumed that each ion produces one fogdrop.

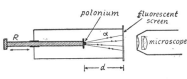

Fig. 61I—Experimental method of measuring the range of α-particles.

The third method used in measuring the range is illustrated in Fig. 61I. When each α-particle strikes a fluorescent screen, a tiny flash of light is produced. These flashes, called *scintillations*, are observed by means of a microscope. When the sample is moved farther and farther away, by pulling the rod *R* back, a point is reached where scintillations are no longer observed. The distance d where the α-particles just fail to reach the screen is a direct measure of the range.

The range of β-rays is seldom given since their velocity of ejection even for the atoms of the same element varies considerably. Why this is so is still a mystery in atomic theory.

61.10. Radioactive Series. It was Rutherford and his colleagues who discovered that when one radioactive atom disintegrates by ejecting an α or β-particle, the remaining atom is still radioactive and may sooner or later eject another particle to become a still different atom. This process they found to continue through a series of elements, ending up finally with a type of atom that is stable and not radioactive. It is now known that nearly all natural disintegration processes, occurring among the heaviest elements of the periodic table, finally end up with *stable lead atoms,* atomic number 82.

There are at least four known radioactive series or chains of elements, one starting with uranium-238, a second with thorium-232, a third with uranium-235, and a fourth with plutonium-241. The first and fourth of these series are given in Tables 61A and 61B. All four series are given in a graphical tabulation in Appendix IV.

When a uranium atom of mass number 238 and atomic number 92 disintegrates by ejecting an α-particle the remainder is a new atom, *uranium*

TABLE 61A. RADIOACTIVE SERIES OF ELEMENTS

URANIUM 238 SERIES

Element	Symbol	Atomic Number	Mass Number	Particle Ejected	Range in Air	Half-life
Uranium I	UI	92	238	α	2.70 cm	2×10^9 yr
Uranium X_1	UX_1	90	234	β	..	24.5 days
Uranium X_2	UX_2	91	234	β	..	1.14 min
Uranium II	UII	92	234	α	3.28	3×10^5 yr
Ionium	Io	90	230	α	3.19	83,000 yr
Radium	Ra	88	226	α	3.39	1600 yr
Radon	Rn	86	222	α	4.12	3.82 days
Radium A	RaA	84	218	α	4.72	3.05 min
Radium B	RaB	82	214	β	....	26.8 min
Radium C	RaC	83	214	α, β	....	19.7 min
Radium C'	RaC'	84	214	α	6.97	10^{-6} sec
Radium C''	RaC''	81	210	β	....	1.32 min
Radium D	RaD	82	210	β	....	22 yr
Radium E	RaE	83	210	β	....	5 days
Polonium	Po	84	210	α	3.92	140 days
Lead	Pb	82	206	stable	....	infinite

X_1, of mass number 234 and atomic number 90. When an uranium X_1 atom disintegrates by ejecting a β-particle to become *uranium X_2*, the mass number remains unchanged at 234, while the atomic number increases by one to become 91. This increase of one positive change is attributed to the loss of one negative charge. These processes of successive disintegration continue until *lead, a stable* atom, is all that is left.

It is common practice among physicists to designate all atomic nuclei in an abbreviated form. The nucleus of radium, for example, is written $_{88}Ra^{226}$. The subscript to the left of the chemical symbol gives the *atomic number*, i.e., the number of positive charges on the nucleus, and the superscript on the right gives the *mass number,* or weight.

As explained in Sec. 59.4, all atoms with the same atomic number but different mass number are called isotopes of the same element. For example, $_{82}RaB^{214}$, $_{82}ThB^{212}$, $_{82}AcB^{211}$, $_{82}RaD^{210}$, $_{82}Pb^{209}$, $_{82}Pb^{208}$, $_{82}Pb^{207}$, and $_{82}Pb^{206}$ are isotopes of the same chemical element, lead (see Appendix IV). Even though the first five of these are radioactive, i.e., unstable, the other three are stable. Chemically they behave exactly alike and are separated only with difficulty. The isotopes 214, 210, and 206 belong to the uranium-238 series, 212, and 208 to the thorium series, 211 and 207 to the uranium-235 series, and 209 to the neptunium series.

TABLE 61B. NEPTUNIUM SERIES†

Element	Symbol	Atomic Number	Mass Number	Particle Ejected	Range in air	Half-life
Plutonium	Pu	94	241	β	. .	
Americium	Am	95	241	α	4.1*	500 yr
Neptunium	Np	93	237	α	3.3*	2.25×10^6 yr
Protoactinium	Pa	91	233	β	. .	27.4 da
Uranium	U	92	233	α	3.3*	1.63×10^5 yr*
Thorium	Th	90	229	α	3.3	7×10^3 yr
Radium	Ra	88	225	β	. .	14.8 da
Actinium	Ac	89	225	α	4.4	10 da
Francium	Fa	87	221	α	5.0	4.8 min
Astatine	At	85	217	α	5.8	0.018 sec
Bismuth	Bi	83	213	β(94%) α(4%)	4.6	47 min
Polonium	Po	84	213	α	7.7	10^{-6} sec
Lead	Pb	82	209	β	. .	3.3 hr
Bismuth	Bi	83	209	stable	. .	Infinite

† See F. Hagemann, L. I. Katzin, M. H. Studier, A. Ghiorso, and G. T. Seaborg. Physical Review, August, vol. 72, 252, 1947.

* See "Radioactivity and Nuclear Physics" by J. M. Cork, D. Van Nostrand.

The disintegration of radioactive nuclei may be written in the form of simple equations, as follows:

For radium, $\quad\quad {}_{88}Ra^{226} \rightarrow {}_{86}Rn^{222} + {}_2He^4$; $\quad\quad$ (61a)

for polonium, $\quad\quad {}_{84}Po^{210} \rightarrow {}_{82}Pb^{206} + {}_2He^4$ $\quad\quad$ (61b)

and for radium B, $\quad\quad {}_{82}RaB^{214} \rightarrow {}_{83}RaC^{214} + {}_{-1}e^0 + \gamma\text{-ray}$ $\quad\quad$ (61c)

In each equation the sum of the subscripts on the right side of the equation is equal to the subscript on the left. The same is true for the superscripts. The designation ${}_2He^4$ represents the α-particle, and ${}_{-1}e^0$ represents the β-particle. In nearly all radioactive disintegrations where a β-particle is emitted one finds a γ-ray also. In such cases, as shown by the example in Eq.(61c), *radium B* ejects a β-particle and a γ-ray to become *radium C*, a nucleus higher in atomic number by unity but with the same mass number.*

PROBLEMS AND QUESTIONS

1. If the activity of a radioactive sample drops to $\frac{1}{16}$th of its initial value in 10 hrs and 40 min, find its half-life.

2. The activity of a radioactive sample drops to $\frac{1}{8}$th of its initial value in 2 days and 6 hrs. Find its half-life. (*Ans.* 18 hrs.)

3. How long will it take for the activity of a sample of radon 222 to decrease to 1%? Determine your answer by graphing the time decay curve.

4. How long will it take for the activity of a sample of polonium 210 to decrease to $\frac{1}{10}$th of one percent? (*Ans.* 1405 days.)

5. What radioactive atoms are isotopes of bismuth? See Appendix IV. Give symbols, atomic numbers, and mass numbers.

6. When and by whom were the following discovered: (a) polonium, (b) radium, (c) radioactivity, and (d) the nature of radioactive rays?

7. Name the three kinds of radioactive rays and carefully explain the nature of each.

8. Define or briefly explain each of the following: (a) scintillations, (b) the Bragg hump, (c) penetrating power, (d) ionizing power, and (e) an ionized atom.

9. Make a table by listing the alpha active atoms in the uranium series of elements in Table 61I. Make six columns for values to be listed under the following headings: (a) element, (b) element abbreviation, (c) reciprocal of the half-life, (d) logarithm of the reciprocal of the half-life, (e) the range, and (f) the logarithm of the range.

10. Plot a graph of the values given in Column (d) of Problem 9, vs the values given in Column (f). The result should be a fairly straight line and illustrates the so-called Geiger-Nuttall Law.

* For a more complete treatment of radioactivity, see "The Particles of Modern Physics," by J. D. Stranathan, Blakiston.

Sources of Light
and Their Spectra
Chapter 62

62.1. The Tungsten Filament Lamp. The most common source of light today is the *tungsten filament lamp* used in house lighting. The light is produced by sending an electric current through a very fine tungsten wire placed at the center of a glass bulb as shown in Fig. 62A. The purpose of

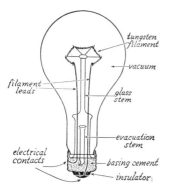

FIG. 62A — Cross-section of a common tungsten filament lamp used in house lighting.

the current is to heat the wire to a very high temperature. The light comes from the hot solid tungsten wire and not from the electric current. The tungsten filament of most light bulbs, if examined with a magnifying glass, will be found to be made of very fine wire wound in a spiral-like coil or spring. Being closely wound with about two hundred turns to the inch, this spiral appears to the naked eye as a larger but straight solid wire.

Tungsten filament lamps ranging from about 0.03 candle power (0.17 watts) up to 120,000 candle power (50,000 watts) have been made. A *photoflood lamp* used by photographers is a regular tungsten filament lamp designed for 70 volts. When operated on 110 volts, the filament is heated to an excessively high temperature and, although it gives off an intense light (about 500 candle power for example), its life is only about 2 hr.

The *photoflash lamp* is a bulb containing shreds of aluminum foil and oxygen gas at a pressure of about 20 cm of mercury. When set off by a small filament, the oxygen and aluminum combine chemically with the liberation of an intense light; about 5 million candle power lasting almost one-tenth of a second.

62.2. The Carbon Arc. Perhaps next in importance to the tungsten filament lamp as a source of light is the carbon arc. These very bright sources were at one time used for street lighting. Today they are used in moving picture projectors, in searchlights, lighthouses, and wherever a very bright and concentrated source is required.

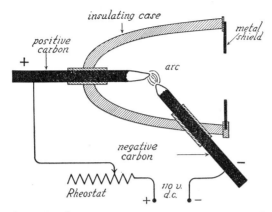

Fig. 62B—Cross-section of a carbon arc showing connections to a rheostat and a direct current source of 110 volts.

An ordinary laboratory arc consists of two carbon rods connected to the positive and negative sides of a battery or generator supplying anywhere from 50 to 250 volts. As shown in Fig. 62B a resistance is connected "in series" to keep the current down to about 10 amperes for normal operation. The arc is started by bringing the ends of the rods together and pulling them apart. This striking of the arc produces a flame of burning carbon. It is through this flame that the electric current passes from one carbon tip to the other. Because of the high temperature, carbon is vaporized, chiefly at the *positive carbon tip,* supplying the arc flame with gaseous ions necessary for conduction. The tip of the positive carbon reaches a temperature of about 4000°K, whereas the negative carbon reaches about 3500°K. Most of the visible light comes from the positive carbon and relatively little from the vapor in the arc flame.

The reason high-current carbon arcs are used in moving picture projectors and searchlights is that they produce a greater amount of light in a smaller spot than is possible with a tungsten filament. Briefly, because of greater surface temperature, a far higher surface brightness is attained.

62.3. Neon Lights. The neon signs so commonly used for advertising purposes consist of long nar-

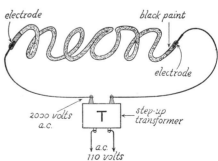

Fig. 62C—Diagram of a neon sign showing electrodes in each end of the glass discharge tube and the transformer connections.

row tubes partially filled with neon, a rare gas. The tubes, after being bent into the required shape, are thoroughly evacuated and a small amount of gas is admitted to bring up the gas pressure inside to about one-fortieth of an atmosphere. By means of a high-voltage transformer and small wires sealed into both ends of each tube, an electric current is sent through the rarefied gas. The electrical connections are shown in Fig. 62C. The passage of the electric current through *neon gas* produces the characteristic red light with which everyone is familiar. The action of the electric current in producing the light is called an electric discharge.

If *helium* or *argon gas* is used in place of *neon,* the light produced is pinkish or bluish white. With the addition of a little mercury vapor these same tubes will produce a greenish-white light. Most colors other than white or the neon red are produced by using colored glass tubes filled with mixtures of the rare gases, helium, neon, argon, and krypton, along with a little mercury. For example, a yellow glass tube with helium gas alone will give yellow, whereas with argon and neon mixed it produces green. Krypton gas alone in a clear glass tube gives a deep blue color.

62.4. Luminescence. Any substance which gives out light by itself, without heating from outside, is said to be luminescent. In many cases like the glowing of phosphorus, or of a firefly, the source of energy is in all probability a chemical action. Besides luminescent materials there are many substances that glow brilliantly when ultraviolet light shines on them. This property to give out light of one color by absorbing light of a different color is called *fluorescence* and *phosphorescence.*

A fluorescent substance is one which glows with a light of its own when light of a shorter wave length falls on it. When the incident light is turned off, the glowing ceases. Various salts of uranium are good materials for demonstrating fluorescence, and *mercury discharge tubes with special black glass filters* are excellent sources of ultraviolet light. It was while studying the excitation of some uranium salts that Becquerel discovered radioactivity in 1896.

A phosphorescent substance is one which acts the same as a fluorescent substance but differs in that it continues to glow for some little time after the exciting light has been turned off. The explanation of the phenomena is quite complex but, in simple words, the incident light in being absorbed causes a temporary deformation in the molecules of the material. Sooner or later, however, this deformation is restored, with the simultaneous re-emission of light of a greater wavelength. The only difference between fluorescent and phosphorescent substances is the time required for the deformed molecules to restore themselves.

Some few luminescent paints have been developed that fluoresce one color under ultraviolet light, but phosphoresce another color upon its removal. Luminescent paint containing minute quantities of radium have been used to paint the hands and dials of clocks, the buttons of light switches, etc. In these paints the radium atoms emit penetrating rays that energize the fluorescent material and thus cause it to emit visible light continuously. Because of the scarcity of radium these paints are costly and due to the dangers of radium poisoning during manufacture they are not widely used.

Many substances are known which absorb ultraviolet light of one wave length and re-emit ultraviolet light of a greater wavelength. The chemical art of producing better fluorescent and phosphorescent paints developed rapidly during World War II. One of the results is a phosphorescent paint which, when applied to any surface, stores up energy from the daylight and continues to glow all night. In many instances these paints eliminate the need for using radium impregnated phosphors.

Another group of phosphors, energized by visible light, or β-rays from radium, retain the stored energy until released later on by infrared light. When infrared light falls on such a charged phosphor, visible light is emitted. These phosphors have been used to make special telescopes and field glasses, thus enabling objects illuminated only by invisible infrared light to be clearly seen in the dark.

62.5. Medical Applications. Luminescence has been applied to many medical problems. Because most fluorescent materials light up brightly when radiated by x-rays, thin screens painted with such phosphors as zinc sulfide are used to make x-ray images visible to the naked eye. Similar screens placed in contact with x-ray film speed up the taking of x-ray photographs. (See Chapter 60 on x-rays.) Another useful application of fluorescence is to be found in the medical diagnosis of various skin diseases. Melanin and heme pigments in the skin, when radiated by an ultraviolet lamp, decrease or prevent fluorescence; whereas ringworm, the result of infection with fungi, gives an intense yellow or green fluorescence.

Natural teeth fluoresce brilliantly while artificial teeth, as a rule, do not. Different parts of the brain fluoresce differently, and blood sera show many different colors ranging from yellow to violet. Poisons as well as many useful drugs can be detected by their characteristic fluorescence. Vitamin A is fluorescent and may be demonstrated in body tissue by reflecting ultraviolet light through a microscope. These are but a few examples of an ever-growing field of medical diagnosis made possible through fluorescence under ultraviolet radiation.

62.6. Fluorescent Lights. In recent years fluorescent materials have been used for general illumination purposes. Long glass tubes, containing argon and nitrogen gas and a small drop of mercury, are painted on the inside with luminescent paint. When an electric current is sent through such a tube the strong ultraviolet light emitted by the mercury vapor is absorbed by the luminescent coating and re-emitted as visible white light. The net result is a lamp with greater efficiency, that is, greater output of visible light for each unit of electrical power consumed.

A comparison of the figures given in the last column of the following table confirms this statement. The first column gives the electrical power

TABLE 62A. RELATIVE EFFICIENCY OF VARIOUS KINDS OF LIGHTS

	Watts	Candle Power	Eff. = c.p./watt
Tungsten filament	60	66	1.10
Mercury lamp (H-4)	100	278	2.78
Sodium vapor	145	477	3.29
Fluorescent	40	167	4.17

input to the lamps in watts, and the second column the amount of visible light emitted in candle power.

A section diagram of all essential parts and electrical connections of a standard fluorescent lamp is shown in Fig. 62D. When the switch is closed, applying 110 volts from the house lighting circuit, the voltage at the *automatic starter* terminals *F* and *G* is sufficient to produce a glow discharge between the U-shaped *bimetal strip* and the straight contact. The heat generated by the glowing argon gas inside causes the bi-metallic strip to bend over, bringing the contacts together. Contact stops the glow and at the same time completes the entire lamp circuit to allow full current to flow through the lamp heater filaments *D* and *I* and *ballast coil*. The function of the heaters is to vaporize the mercury in the fluorescent tube. Because the starter glow is shorted out, the contacts soon open the circuit and the sudden col-

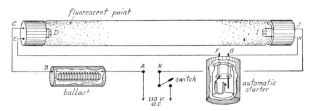

FIG. 62D—Section diagram of a fluorescent light and accessories.

lapsing magnetic field of the ballast gives a high voltage "kick" that starts the glow in the fluorescent tube. The voltage at the starter is insufficient thereafter to cause the switch to operate, so the starter consumes no energy during lamp operation.*

* For a more general and detailed study of light sources see "Measurement of Radiant Energy," by W. E. Forsythe, McGraw-Hill Book Co., Inc.

62.7. The Spectrum. When a block of metal like iron or copper is heated slowly to incandescence, the first noticeable change in its appearance occurs at a temperature of about 1000°K. At this temperature the metal appears with a dull red glow. As the temperature continues to rise the color changes slowly to orange, then to yellow, and finally to white.

If the slowly heating metal is observed through a prism the first appearance of visible light will be found at the extreme red end of the spectrum. As the temperature rises the light spreads slowly out across the spectrum until, at white heat, the entire band of visible colors from red to violet is seen. At the orange stage where the temperature is about 1500°K the pure spectrum colors contain red, orange and yellow, and when the yellow stage is reached where the temperature is about 2000°K the spectral green is included. When the white stage is reached at about 3000°K, and the spectrum is complete, a further rise in temperature continues to increase the intensity of each color without a noticeable change in color.

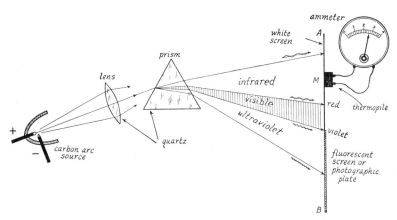

Fig. 62E—Experiment demonstrating the existence of the ultraviolet and infrared rays beyond the visible spectrum.

What the prism has done in such an experiment is to separate all of the light waves according to their wave lengths, the longest waves of red light at the one side, the shortest waves of violet light at the other, and the intermediate waves at their proper places in between. The fact that the color is continuous from red through violet is characteristic of the spectrum of all solids and liquids and means that there is a continuous set of different wave lengths present.

To demonstrate the existence of an ultraviolet and infrared spectrum an experiment of the type illustrated in Fig. 62E may be performed. The visible light from a carbon arc lamp is made to pass through a quartz lens and prism to be focused on a nearby screen.

If at the violet end of the spectrum the screen is painted with luminous paint, a bright fluorescence will be observed for some little distance beyond the visible violet. When the screen is replaced by a photographic plate, the exposed and developed picture will again show the extension of the spectrum into the ultraviolet.

To detect the presence of the infrared radiations a thermopile* is conveniently used as shown at the top of the screen. Connected to an ammeter a thermopile measures the amount of light energy falling upon its front face. If the thermopile is first placed to receive violet light and slowly moved

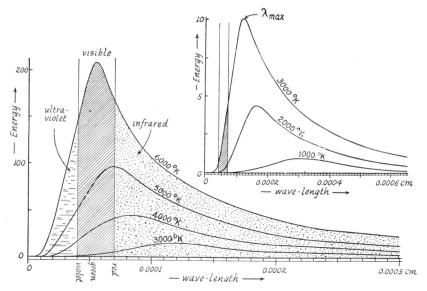

FIG. 62F—Distribution of the energy emitted by a hot solid at different temperatures.

across the visible spectrum and out into the infrared region beyond, the ammeter will show a steady rise in current. The current will continue to rise until a maximum is reached at a point in the region of M and then it will drop off slowly as the thermopile approaches the end of the screen at A. A graph of the energy from the carbon arc source, for the different parts along the screen, is shown by the 3000°K curve in Fig. 62F.

Each curve represents the amount of energy given out over the entire spectrum by a solid at different temperatures. Studying these curves it will be observed that at low temperatures very little light is emitted in the visible spectrum. At 1000°K only the visible red is seen and even that is very faint. At 2000°K the brightness of the red not only increases but the other colors,

* For the principles of the thermopile see Sec. 29.3.

orange, yellow, and green, appear. At 3000°K, the temperature of a low-current carbon arc or tungsten filament light, all of the visible spectrum is emitted, but the maximum radiation is in the infrared. At 6000°K, the temperature of the surface of the sun, the maximum energy is radiated in the green of the visible spectrum, with an appreciable amount of ultraviolet light on the one side and the infrared on the other. Thus the visible spectrum as seen by the human eye is but a small band out of all the waves emitted by a body as hot as the sun.

It is an interesting fact that the maximum energy radiated by a hot body shifts to shorter and shorter waves as the temperature rises. To be more exact, if the temperature of a body is doubled the radiated energy maximum, λ_{max}, shifts to half the wave length. If the temperature is tripled the energy maximum shifts to one-third the wave length, etc. This is known as Wien's* displacement law, and is written as an algebraic equation

$$\lambda_{max}T = C, \tag{62a}$$

where C is a constant, found by experiment to have a value of 0.2897 cm-degrees, T is the absolute temperature, and λ_{max} the wave length in cm at which the maximum energy is radiated. By substituting the constant C in Eq.(62a) the wave-length maximum radiated by a hot body can be calculated for any temperature.

The total energy radiated by a hot solid body is proportional to the fourth power of the absolute temperature. This law, known as the *Stefan-Bolzmann law*, is treated in Sec. 31.8.

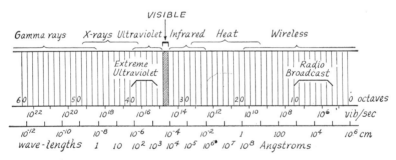

Fig. 62G—Complete wave-length and frequency chart of the electromagnetic spectrum as it is now known.

62.8. The Complete Spectrum. *Visible, ultraviolet,* and *infrared* light waves do not represent all of the known kinds of electromagnetic radiation.

* Wilhelm Wien (1864-1928), German physicist, chiefly known for important discoveries with cathode rays, canal rays, and the radiation of light. He was awarded the Nobel Prize in physics in 1911 for his discovery of the displacement law of heat radiation named in his honor.

A complete chart of the known spectrum is shown in Fig. 62G. Beyond the visible and infrared toward longer wave lengths we find the *heat waves* and the *wireless waves,* while beyond the ultraviolet toward shorter wave lengths we find the *x-rays* and the *gamma rays.*

In spite of the tremendous expanse of wave lengths ranging all the way from the longest wireless waves several miles in length to γ-ray waves one-million-millionth of a centimeter in length, all electromagnetic waves travel with the same velocity in vacuum, 186,300 mi/sec, or 3×10^{10} cm/sec.

Although their velocities in a vacuum are all the same, the properties of the various waves differ considerably. One striking illustration of these differences is found in the response of the human eye. Of the entire spectrum only one very narrow band of waves can be seen, all the rest being invisible. Another illustration is the passage of light waves through the atmosphere. With the exception of the band of waves known as the extreme ultraviolet the air is fairly transparent to all electromagnetic waves. To waves of the extreme ultraviolet the air is quite opaque. *Fog is opaque to all but the wireless waves.*

62.9. The Angstrom as a Unit of Length. Because the wave lengths of light are so very small, the physicist has adopted a smaller unit of length than the centimeter or millimeter. This unit is called the angstrom after the Swedish scientist by that name. In 1868 Angstrom published a map of the visible spectrum of the sun, and on this map he labeled the wave lengths in ten-millionths of a millimeter. Since that time light waves have been specified in these units.

In one centimeter there are 100,000,000 angstroms.

$$1 \text{ cm} = 10^8 \text{ A.}$$

In light, just as in sound, the velocity c in a vacuum is given by

$$c = \nu\lambda, \tag{62b}$$

where ν is the vibration frequency and λ is the wave length. From this we see that the longer the wave length the lower is the frequency, and the shorter the wave length the higher is the frequency. It is common practice among physicists to designate the wave length of light waves by the Greek letter λ (*lambda*) and the frequency by the Greek letter ν (*nu*).

62.10. Diffraction Grating Instruments. As already explained in Chapter 46, and illustrated in Figs. 46M to 46Q, a diffraction grating is a device capable of separating white light into a spectrum. The essential difference between this spectrum and the one from a prism is that the diffraction grating produces several images of the same spectrum, whereas a prism confines all of the light to one.

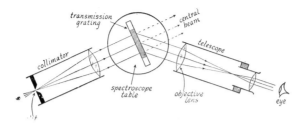

Fɪɢ. 62H—Diagram of a diffraction grating spectroscope
used in observing the visible spectrum.

A glass transmission grating is shown in Fig. 62H mounted on the center table of a laboratory spectroscope. As the telescope is rotated to a position on either side of the central beam, the various colors and wave lengths emitted by the source can be observed in the *first order spectrum,* the *second order spectrum,* etc. (see Figs. 46O and 46Q).

Transmission gratings were first made by Fraunhofer, a German physicist, in 1819, and the first reflection gratings were made by H. A. Rowland,* an American physicist, in 1882. Although Rowland's first gratings were ruled on flat surfaces his best ones were ruled upon the polished surfaces of concave mirrors.

62.11. Classification of Spectra. A spectrum may be defined as a wavelength analysis of a source of light. As illustrated in Sec. 62.7, such an analysis is usually made with a prism spectrograph or a diffraction grating. Different sources produce different wave lengths of light and hence reveal different spectra. All spectra may be grouped into four main classes:

    (*a*) *Continuous emission spectra*
    (*b*) *Line emission spectra*
    (*c*) *Continuous absorption spectra*
    (*d*) *Line absorption spectra*

The first of these, *continuous emission spectra,* has already been treated in detail in Sec. 62.7. There it was demonstrated that when light from a hot *solid* like the tungsten filament of an electric light, or the positive carbon of an arc, is sent through a prism, a continuous band of color from red to violet is observed (see color plate Fig. 62I). The intensity of such a spectrum depends upon the temperature and upon the hot body itself. All hot solids raised to the same temperature give very nearly the same continuous emission spectrum.

---

* Henry A. Rowland (1848-1901), American physicist, is noted principally for his ruling of the first high quality diffraction gratings and his publication of a large and detailed photograph of the sun's spectrum. He was the recipient of many honors, including the Rumford Medal and the Draper Medal.

62.12. Line Emission Spectra. When the slit of a spectrograph is illuminated by the light from a mercury arc, a sodium lamp, or a neon discharge tube, a number of bright lines appear on the photographic plate in place of a continuous spectrum.

It is important to realize that line spectra derive their name from the fact that a slit is used whose image constitutes a line. If a small circular opening were used in place of a slit a disk image would appear in the place of each line.

The most intense sources of spectrum lines are obtained from metallic arcs and sparks. The flame of a carbon arc may be used for demonstration purposes by previously soaking the *positive carbon rod* in various chemicals. (An experimental arrangement for projecting the spectrum on a large screen is shown in Fig. 62J.) Common salt water (sodium chloride in solution) gives a brilliant yellow line characteristic of sodium. Solutions of strontium or calcium chloride will show other strong spectrum lines in the red, green, and blue.

While a continuous emission spectrum arises from hot solids, *a line spectrum always arises from a gas at high temperatures*. It is the gas flame of the carbon arc that gives rise to the line emission spectrum, in the above experiment.

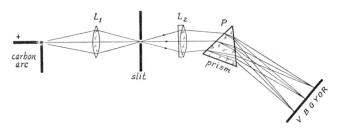

Fig. 62J—Experimental arrangement used in demonstrating spectrum lines in emission.

62.13. Continuous Absorption Spectra. Continuous absorption spectra are usually produced by passing a continuous emission spectrum through matter in the solid or liquid state. Good demonstrations can be performed by allowing white light to pass through colored glass. When the light is later dispersed by a prism, the missing colors will in general cover a wide band of wave lengths. The same experiment was described in Chapter 45 to demonstrate *body color* and *color mixing*.

62.14. Line Absorption Spectra. Line spectra in absorption are produced by sending continuous white light through a gas. Experimentally the gas or vapor is inserted in the path of the light as shown in Fig. 62K. Light from a carbon arc, after passing as a parallel beam through a glass tube

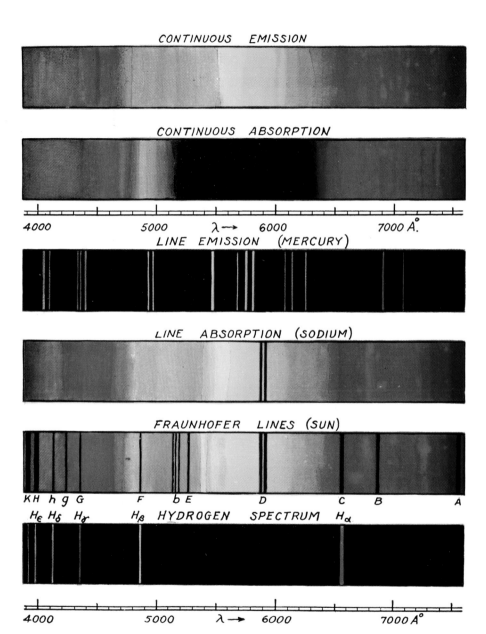

CONTINUOUS   EMISSION

CONTINUOUS   ABSORPTION

4000   5000   λ→   6000   7000 Å.

LINE   EMISSION   (MERCURY)

LINE   ABSORPTION   (SODIUM)

FRAUNHOFER   LINES   (SUN)

K H   h g   G   F   b E   D   C   B   A

H_ϵ H_δ H_γ H_β HYDROGEN   SPECTRUM H_α

4000   5000   λ→   6000   7000 Å°

FIG. 621 — Illustrations of continuous and line spectra.

containing sodium vapor, is brought to a focus at the slit C. From there the light passes through a lens L_3 and a prism P to form a spectrum on the observing screen.

Sodium is chosen as an example for demonstration purposes because of

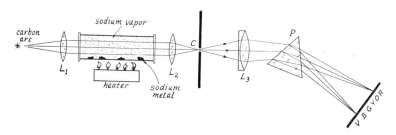

F$_{IG}$. 62K—Experimental arrangement for demonstrating the line absorption spectrum of sodium vapor.

its convenience. The vapor is produced by inserting a small amount of metallic sodium in a partially evacuated glass tube and heating it with a small gas burner. As the metal vaporizes, filling the tube with sodium vapor, a dark line will appear in the yellow region of the spectrum (see color plate Fig. 62I).

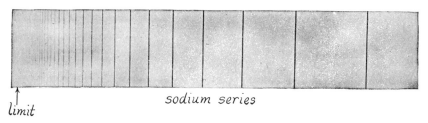

F$_{IG}$. 62L—Absorption spectrum of sodium vapor. The principal series of sodium. (*After Jenkins.*)

If a photograph is taken of this absorption, and the photographic plate is long enough to extend into the ultraviolet, many absorption lines as shown in Fig. 62L are detected. A systematic array of absorption lines like this occur only with a few elements, principally with the alkali metals, lithium, sodium, potassium, rubidium, and caesium. All elements in the gaseous state, however, give rise to a number of absorption lines, usually in the ultraviolet region of the spectrum.

62.15. The Sun's Spectrum. The solar spectrum, consisting of a bright colored continuous spectrum interspersed by thousands of dark lines, was first observed by Wollaston in 1802 and independently discovered and studied by Fraunhofer in 1817. Fraunhofer mapped out several hundred of these lines and labeled eight of the most prominent lines by the first letters of the alphabet. The strongest of these lines, now called Fraunhofer lines, are illustrated in Fig. 62M.

In 1882 the American physicist, H. A. Rowland, ruled the first diffraction grating and from photographs made with it published a large map of the

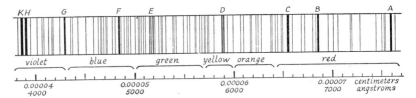

Fig. 62M—Diagram of the solar spectrum indicating the most prominent lines labeled as they first were by Fraunhofer with the first letters of the alphabet.

sun's spectrum. These lines are explained as being due to the absorption of light by the solar atmosphere. The surface of the sun at a temperature of 6000°K emits light of all wave lengths, i.e., a continuous emission spectrum. As this light passes out through the cooler gas layers of the solar atmosphere (see Fig. 62N) certain wave lengths are absorbed. Because the absorbing

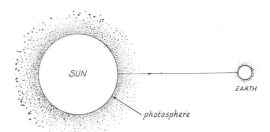

Fig. 62N—Light from the sun must pass through the solar atmosphere and the earth's atmosphere before reaching an observer on the earth's surface.

medium is in the gaseous state, the atoms and molecules there do not absorb all wave lengths equally but principally those wave lengths they would emit if heated to a high temperature. Thus the atoms of one chemical element with their own characteristic frequencies absorb certain wave lengths, whereas the atoms of other elements absorb certain other wave lengths.

Before the sunlight reaches the earth's surface to be examined by an observer with a spectroscope it must again pass through absorbing gases, this time the earth's atmosphere. Here, too, certain wave lengths are partially absorbed, producing other dark lines.

That the missing wave lengths correspond to definite chemical elements is illustrated by diagram in Fig. 62O. The center strip (b) represents a small

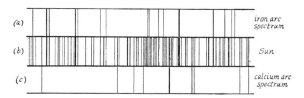

(a) iron arc spectrum

(b) Sun

(c) calcium arc spectrum

FIG. 62O—Schematic diagram illustrating the comparison of laboratory spectra from different elements with the many-line spectrum of the sun.

section of the visible spectrum as obtained with sunlight entering the slit of a spectroscope. The upper and lower strips, (a) and (c), represent the bright line spectrum observed when an iron arc and a calcium arc are successively placed in front of the same slit. Where each calcium line occurs in the laboratory source an absorption line is found in the sun's spectrum. The same is true for each iron line. The remaining lines, not matched by an iron or calcium line, are due to other elements.

It has been possible by spectrum photographs of this kind to identify about two-thirds of the known chemical elements as existing on the sun. The reason why not all ninety or more elements are found is that some are too rare to produce absorption, whereas others existing within the sun in large enough quantities find the temperature either too high or too low to bring out their lines.

Eight prominent Fraunhofer lines labeled in Fig. 62M have been identified as follows:

A, oxygen .. $\lambda = 7594 \times 10^{-8}$ cm   E, iron .... $\lambda = 5270 \times 10^{-8}$ cm
B, oxygen .. ” $= 6870$ ”   F, hydrogen ” $= 4861$ ”
C, hydrogen ” $= 6563$ ”   G, iron .... ” $= 4308$ ”
D, sodium .. ” $= 5893$ ”   H, calcium . ” $= 3968$ ”

62.16. The Balmer Series of Hydrogen. The first successful attempt to obtain a formula which represents the hydrogen series was made by Balmer in 1885. Since that time these lines have become known as the Balmer series of hydrogen. Balmer's formula is written

$$\frac{1}{\lambda} = 109{,}678\left(\frac{1}{4} - \frac{1}{n^2}\right), \tag{62c}$$

where n is a whole number, 3, 4, 5, 6, . . . etc. If the number 3 is substituted for n in the above formula the wavelength λ of the first line of the series is calculated. Likewise, if the number 4 is substituted in its place the wave length of the second line can be calculated, etc. When these calculations are carried out, the following results are obtained for the first four lines,

H_a, $\lambda = 0.000065647$ cm (red) H_γ, $\lambda = 0.000043417$ cm (blue)

H_β, $\lambda = 0.000048627$ cm (blue green) H_δ, $\lambda = 0.000041029$ cm (violet).

These wavelengths, as well as those calculated for other lines of the series, agree exactly with the measured values. Balmer did not derive his formula from any theory but simply formulated it from the measured wave length for each series line.

The wavelengths of the hydrogen lines are usually given in angstroms in place of centimeters. Moving the decimal point eight places to the right, in each of the above values, gives

$$H_a, \lambda = 6564.7 \text{ A} \qquad H_\gamma, \lambda = 4341.7 \text{ A}$$
$$H_\beta, \lambda = 4862.7 \text{ A} \qquad H_\delta, \lambda = 4102.9 \text{ A} \qquad (62d)$$

PROBLEMS AND QUESTIONS

1. At what wavelength will the maximum energy be radiated by a solid piece of metal heated to a temperature of 2800°C?

2. Find the wavelength at which the maximum energy is radiated from a block of black carbon at a room temperature of 27°C. What kind of light is it? (*Ans.* 9.66 × 10⁴ A. Infrared.)

3. The wavelength range of the light of the visible spectrum extends from 4000 angstroms in the violet to 7500 angstroms in the red. What are these same wavelength limits in centimeters?

4. X-rays from a certain x-ray source have a wavelength of 0.25 angstrom. What is the wavelength in meters? (*Ans.* 2.5 × 10⁻⁹ m.)

5. Find the frequency of violet light of wavelength 4200 A.

6. What is the frequency of x-rays if the wavelength is 2.4 A? (*Ans.* 1.25 × 10¹⁸ vib/sec.)

7. Calculate the wavelength maximum for light radiated by a body at 20 million degrees absolute. To what kind of light is this equivalent?

8. Calculate to four figures the wavelength of the sixth line of the Balmer series of hydrogen. (*Ans.* 3890 A.)

9. Briefly describe an experimental arrangement by which a line emission spectrum is produced.

10. Briefly describe an experimental arrangement by which a line absorption spectrum is produced.

11. Find the wavelength of the tenth line of the Balmer series of hydrogen.

12. Calculate the wavelength of the fifth line of the Balmer series of hydrogen. (*Ans.* 3971 A.)

13. Determine the wavelength of the series limit of the Balmer series of hydrogen. (Note $n = \infty$.)

Vacuum Tubes and Radio   Chapter 63

EARLY in the summer of 1895 a young Italian inventor, Guglielmo Marconi,* happened upon a scientific article describing Hertz's experiments with electromagnetic waves (see Chap. 57), After reading the article with great interest Marconi, then only twenty-one years of age, conceived the idea of using Hertzian waves as a means of communication. Beginning experiments immediately, he soon found that (1) by increasing the power of the transmitter, (2) by stretching a wire high in the air for an antenna, and (3) by improving upon Hertz's methods of detection, distances over which signals could be transmitted and received could be greatly increased. So successful was he with these improvements that by 1898 he had spanned a distance of 12 mi and by 1900 had communicated successfully with another station 200 mi away.

With successes like these it is not surprising that wireless companies were soon formed and Wireless Telegraphy became a commercially profitable business. The U. S. Navy too became interested in the possibility of inter-ship communications as a means of greater cooperation and effectiveness. Between the experimentation carried on by commercial stations in England, Germany, and the United States and the amateur wireless enthusiasts everywhere, progress in wireless telegraphy went forward by leaps and bounds.

The most important contributions made during the turn of the century were (1) the invention of the coherer by Branley in 1892 and its subsequent improvement for use in wireless by Marconi, (2) the invention of the vacuum tube receiver by Fleming in 1904, (3) the invention of the crystal detector by General Dunwoody of the U. S. Army in 1906, and (4) the invention of the audion vacuum tube by Lee DeForest in the same year. These were important discoveries because they involve the fundamental principles upon which radio, television, and radar were later developed.

The first authentic broadcast of the human voice by wireless waves took

* Guglielmo Marconi (1874-1939), Italian inventor, famous for establishing wireless telegraphy on a commercial basis, was born at Bologna on April 25, 1874. Privately educated, he became interested in electrical phenomena at the age of twenty. During his lifetime he initiated many new ideas in wireless telegraphy, each one of which contributed to greater and greater range. In World War I he served in the Italian Army and Navy as a technical expert. In 1909 Marconi, jointly with Ferdinand Braun, was awarded the Nobel prize in physics, the Albert Medal of the Royal Society of Arts and, in the United States, the Franklin and the John Fritz Medals.

place on Christmas day in 1906. The feat was accomplished by Prof. F. A. Fessenden of the University of Pittsburgh. Using the continuous oscillating currents from a high-frequency electrical generator of his own design, instead of the damped oscillations of a discharging condenser circuit, he was able to broadcast music from an experimental station at Brant Rock, Massachusetts, and have it heard by U. S. Naval Warships nearby. It is a most incredible fact that the importance of this great event and its future possibilities were not generally recognized.

63.1. The Vacuum Tube Rectifier. While the great American inventor, Thomas A. Edison, was striving by a process of trial and error to produce a satisfactory electric light bulb, he made an accidental discovery, the importance of which was first recognized and used successfully by Sir John Fleming. Now called a vacuum tube rectifier or diode, the Fleming valve is used in nearly every radio and television transmitter and receiver to change alternating current into direct current.

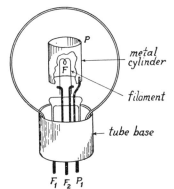

Fig. 63A—Diagram of a Fleming valve or rectifier tube. Such tubes are now called "diodes."

The Fleming valve, as shown in Fig. 63A, consists of a highly evacuated glass bulb containing a wire filament that is heated electrically to incandescence. Surrounding the filament and connected to the outside through the tube base and a prong P_1 is a cylindrical metal plate P. When the filament is heated to incandescence it gives off large quantities of electrons in much the same way that water, when heated to the boiling point, gives off steam.

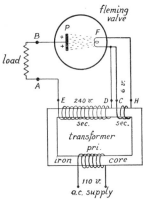

Fig. 63B—A diagram showing how a Fleming valve is used as a rectifier of electric current.

The emission of electrons by a hot body is called *thermionic emission* and is due to the high temperature and not to the electric current. Heating a metal by any other means will produce the same effect.

The principal action of the *filament F* and *plate P* is explained by means of a typical electric circuit shown schematically in Fig. 63B. The circuit consists of a *transformer* having *two secondary windings*, a *Fleming valve*, and a *load*. The latter, shown as a resistance, represents any electrical device requiring unidirectional current for its operation. With an alternating current of 110 volts supplied to the primary, a high voltage, 240 volts for example, is delivered by one secondary to the terminals *ED* and a low voltage of 5 volts alternating current is delivered by the other secondary to the terminals *CH*. The latter, called the *filament winding,* is for the purpose of heating the filament.

When for a fraction of a second the plate *P* of the tube is positively charged and the filament *F* is negatively charged, the electrons from *F* are attracted to the plate *P* and constitute a current flowing across the vacuum space *PF* and through the load from *B* to *A*. One-half cycle later, when the potential is reversed and *P* becomes negatively charged and *F* positively charged, the electrons from *F* are repelled by *P* and very little current flows.

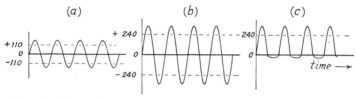

FIG. 63C—Alternating current as rectified by a Fleming valve or diode.

The emfs in each part of the rectifier circuit are shown by graphs in Fig. 63C. The primary emf of 110 volts is shown in (a), the secondary emf of 240 volts in (b) and the *rectified* or *pulsating emf* through the load *AB* in (c).

63.2. Full Wave Rectifier. A full wave rectifier tube, sometimes called a *duo-diode,* is essentially a double Fleming valve with two plates and two

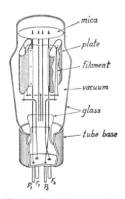

FIG. 63D—Cross-section
of a full-wave rectifier
tube.

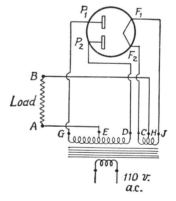

FIG. 63E—Circuit for full-wave
rectifier tube.

filaments. (See Fig. 63D.) The two prongs F_1 and F_2 in the base are connected to both filaments in series while the prongs P_1 and P_2 are connected one to each plate.

A schematic diagram of a rectifier circuit employing such a tube is shown in Fig. 63E. Here an iron core transformer with one primary and two secondary windings is used, differing from the single phase rectifier in Fig. 63B in that the center of each secondary winding is now connected to the load. *CHJ* is the filament winding and supplies current to both filaments (shown as one bent wire) while *GED* is the high voltage winding. The latter supplies an alternating potential to the plates so that when P_1 is $+$ and P_2 is $-$, electrons from the filament are attracted to P_1, and when a moment later P_1 is $-$ and P_2 is $+$, electrons from the filament are attracted to P_2.

In the first instance a current flows around the circuit $F_1P_1GEABHJF_1$, and in the second it flows around the circuit $F_2P_2DEABHCF_2$. In each case the current has gone through the load *AB* in the same direction and has pulsating characteristics as shown in Fig. 63F.

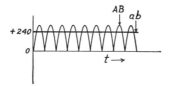

Fig. 63F—Pulsating direct current from full-wave rectifier circuit.

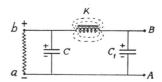

Fig. 63G—Electrical "filter circuit for smoothing out" pulsating direct current.

If such a pulsating current were used to supply the direct current needed in every radio receiver a loud objectionable hum with a frequency of 120 cycles would be heard. To make this current a steady smooth direct current as illustrated by the straight line in the same graph, and thus eliminate the hum, a *filter circuit* as shown in Fig. 63G is used. The terminals *A* and *B* are connected to and replace the load *A* and *B* in Fig. 63E. *K* is an iron core inductance and C_1 and C_2 are condensers of large capacity.

As the current through *AaLbB* starts to flow, the condensers become charged as shown and a magnetic field is created around *K*. This has a retarding action and prevents the current from reaching its otherwise peak value. When a moment later the filament to plate current drops to near zero, the condensers discharge and the field around *K* collapses, thus sending a current through *AB*. This process is repeated with each pulse of electrons from either plate of the tube and the current through *ab* remains steady. Large capacities and large self-inductance deliver more constant voltage.

63.3. De Forest's Audion. Although the Fleming valve was originally developed for the purpose of detecting wireless waves, its operation as such did not prove to be very satisfactory until, in 1906, De Forest * invented the *audion*. By inserting a *grid* wire between the *plate* and *filament* of a

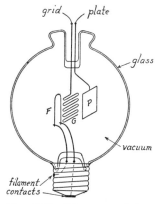

Fleming valve, he created a device capable not only of detecting wireless waves but of amplifying the signals as well. The purpose of the grid (see Fig. 63H) is to control the flow of electrons from the hot filament F to the plate P.

A circuit diagram showing how the audion may be used as a one-tube receiver of radio waves is given in Fig. 63I. The filament F is heated by a 6-volt battery A, and the plate P is maintained at a positive potential of 45 volts or more by the *B-battery*. The condenser C and inductance L form an *oscillation circuit*, the natural frequency of which may be varied by changing the capacity of C. The arrow indicates a condenser of variable capacity.

Fig. 63 H—Diagram of De-Forest's audion. This is the first triode tube ever made.

Co-axial with L is another inductance L' (shown beside each other in the diagram), one end of which is connected to a wire in the air called the *antenna*, and a sliding contact S near the other end is connected to a metal conductor embedded in the ground. The antenna and ground form the two plates of a condenser C' with the air as a dielectric. This capacity C' with the variable inductance L' forms a second oscillation circuit whose natural frequency is varied by the sliding contact S.

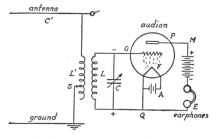

Fig. 63I—One-tube radio receiver using a DeForest-audion.

By varying the frequency of the $L'C'$ circuit until it matches the frequency of any passing wave (shown as a damped wireless wave in the diagram), an oscillating current and magnetic field occurs in L'. By tuning the LC circuit to this same frequency, resonance is set up and the oscillating current imposes alternate $(+)$ and $(-)$ charges on the grid G. During the time the grid G is negative, electrons from the filament are repelled and are

* Lee De Forest (1873-   ), American scientist; Ph.D. from Yale University, 1899. Most famous for the audion, considered by many to be the most important invention ever made in radio. He designed and installed the first five high-power radio stations for the U. S. Navy. After 1921 he devoted his time to the development of talking motion picture film. He was awarded gold medals at the St. Louis exposition in 1904, the Panama Pacific Exposition in San Francisco in 1915, and the Institute of France in 1923. He received the Cresson Medal of the Franklin Institute in 1921 for his important contributions to wireless.

unable to reach the plate *P*. When the grid is positive, however, the electrons from the filament are accelerated toward the plate and constitute a flow of current clockwise around the circuit *PMEQFP*.

Not only does the grid act as a rectifier valve and let the electron current flow in one direction only, from filament to plate, but it acts as an amplifier allowing large currents from the high voltage *B*-battery to flow through when it is slightly positive and practically no current when it is slightly negative.

Voltage graphs for the two parts of the receiver circuit are given in Fig. 63J. Diagram (a) represents the oscillating potentials in the *LC* circuit connected to the grid, and diagram (b) the current through the plate and earphones. Since the frequency of this rectified current is far too rapid for the electromagnets in the earphones, their metal diaphragms over the pole

Fig. 63J—(a) Input and (b) output voltage curves, for DeForest audion used in wireless receiver, Fig. 63I.

tips move up and down with the dotted line in (b) and is heard as a single audible click. A succession of damped waves is then heard as a noise with each damped wave producing a single vibration of the receiver diaphragms.

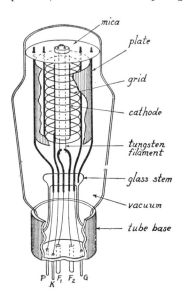

Fig. 63K—Modern radio tube with a caesium coated cathode as a source of thermal electrons. The filament serves only to heat the cathode.

63.4. Modern Vacuum Tubes. Every radio enthusiast today knows there are hundreds of different kinds of radio tubes. Some contain two filaments and two plates, while others contain as many as three or four separate grids. Although a treatment of such complex tubes is out of place here, the fundamental principles of all of them are little different from DeForest's audion. One important difference, however, is illustrated in Fig. 63K, and that is the employment in some tubes of a cathode in place of a filament as a source of thermal electrons.

A fine tungsten wire filament is threaded through two small holes running lengthwise through a porcelain-like insulating rod. Fitting snugly around this rod is the cathode, a metal cylinder coated on the outside with a thin layer of thorium, strontium or caesium oxide. These particular oxides are copious emitters of electrons when heated to a dull red heat. Insulated from the cathode the filament as a source of heat can be, and generally is, connected directly to an appropriate transformer winding.

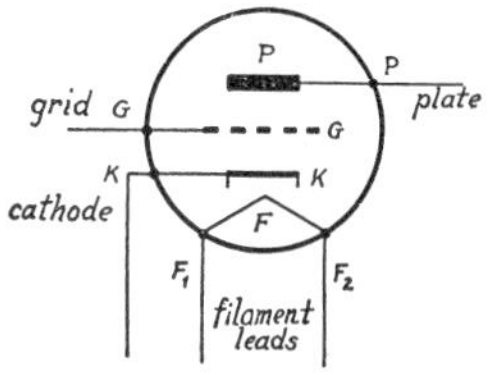

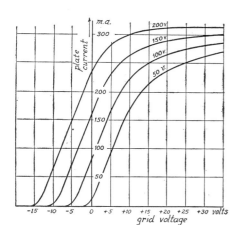

FIG. 63L—Schematic diagram of a cathode type of radio tube.

A schematic diagram of the cathode type of tube containing one plate and one grid is given in Fig. 63L. A circuit diagram showing the electrical connections and instruments needed to measure the *grid-voltage* vs *plate-current* curve for vacuum tubes in general is given in Fig. 63M. A constant voltage is applied to the plate *P* by a *B*-battery, and a variable voltage is applied to the grid *G* by a *C*-battery, connected to a potential divider. The various applied grid potentials are read from the voltmeter *V* and the corresponding plate current is read from a milliammeter *A*.

Four characteristic curves taken with the above circuit connections are reproduced in Fig. 63N, one for each of four plate voltages 50, 100, 150, and 200 volts respectively.

The flattening out of all the curves at the top indicates that, when the grid is highly positive, practically all of the electrons leaving the filament get to the

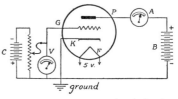

FIG. 63M—Laboratory circuit for determining the grid-voltage vs. plate-current characteristics of a vacuum tube.

plate and no further increase in plate current can occur. Should the cathode be heated to a higher temperature, however, more electrons will be emitted and the saturation current will occur at higher plate currents than those shown. The foot of each curve, near -2, -6, -11, and -16 volts, indicates what negative voltage on the grid will stop all electrons and prevent them from reaching the plate. The higher the $+$ potential on the plate, the more negative must be the grid to stop the electrons.

FIG. 63N—Grid voltage—plate current curves for normal grid controlled vacuum tube.

63.5. Vacuum Tube Oscillator.

To broadcast the human voice by radio, a generator of alternating current of extremely high frequency and constant amplitude is required. In commercial broadcasting stations and amateur transmitters this function is performed by a vacuum tube and circuit of relatively simple design.

One type of oscillator circuit is shown in Fig. 63O. When the switch S is closed connecting the B-battery to the plate of the tube an electron current from the cathode K to the plate P starts a current in the circuit $PRVL_3K$. This growing current in L_3 creates an expanding magnetic field, which cutting across L_2 induces a current in the grid circuit in such a direction that the grid becomes negative. A negative charge on the grid, as shown by the characteristic curves in Fig. 63N, causes the plate current to decrease. This decreasing

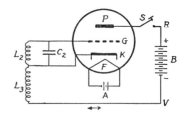

FIG. 63O—Vacuum tube oscillator circuit for generating radio waves of constant amplitude.

current causes the field about L_3 to collapse, thus inducing a reversed current in the grid circuit and therefore a positive charge on the grid. Such a charge increases the plate current and the above process is repeated.

If the two circuits L_2C_2 and $PRVL_3$, are properly tuned by adjusting C_2 resonance will occur and energy from the B-battery will be continuously supplied to keep the oscillations going with constant amplitude. The graph of the continuous oscillations shown in Fig. 63P represents the voltage across L_3 as it varies in time. The L_2C_2 circuit controls the frequency by controlling the grid potential while the large voltage and current fluctuations take place in the L_3 circuit.

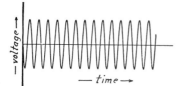

FIG. 63P—Continuous oscillations in a vacuum tube oscillator circuit like Fig. 63O.

63.6. Radio Transmitter. To use an oscillating tube circuit, of the kind described above, as part of a radio transmitter the high frequency oscillations in the L_2C_2 circuit must be modified by sound waves and then applied to an antenna and ground system for

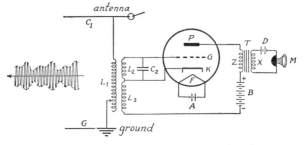

FIG. 63Q—Radio transmitter employing a microphone and only one tube as an oscillator.

broadcasting as electromagnetic waves. A simplified circuit diagram showing one of the many ways of doing this is given in Fig. 63Q. There are three parts to this particular "hook up," (1) *the microphone circuit* containing a battery D and a transformer T, (2) *the oscillator circuit* in the middle, and (3) *the antenna circuit* C_1L_1G at the left.

By talking or singing into the microphone the diaphragm inside moves back and forth with the sound vibrations, thus altering the steady current previously flowing around the circuit DMX. An illustration of the pulsating current is shown in Fig. 63R (a). Current pulsations in X, the transformer primary, cause similar pulsations in Z, the secondary circuit carrying the plate current. The effect of the relatively low frequency audio currents on the high frequency oscillations already there is to alter their amplitude as shown in diagram (c).

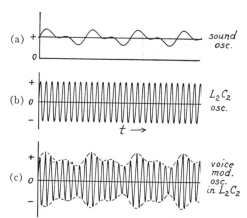

Through the *coupling* of L_3 with L_1 the modulated oscillations are induced in the antenna circuit by resonance, and are radiated as electromagnetic waves of the same frequency and form. The continuous wave produced by the radio-frequency oscillations alone is called the *carrier wave*, and the alteration of its amplitude by *audio-frequencies* is called *modulation*. Although radio transmitters with one vacuum tube have been used by radio amateurs, it is customary to find transmitters with half a dozen or more tubes. The principal function of additional tubes in receivers as well as transmitters, is to amplify currents wherever they are needed and thereby give greater transmitting range and clearer reception.

Fig. 63R—Graphs of (a) sound waves, (b) continuous oscillations in $L_2 C_2$, and (c) voice modulated oscillations in $L_2 C_2$.

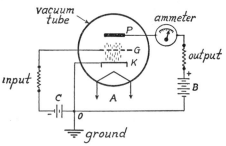

Fig. 63S—Amplifier circuit with one vacuum tube.

63.7. Vacuum Tube Amplifier.
One of the most important functions of the vacuum tube is its use as an *amplifier* of radio frequency or audio frequency currents as shown in Fig. 63S. The *input* resistor represents some part of any circuit in which

a weak but varying current is flowing and the *output* resistor represents another circuit to which a stronger current of the same form is delivered. In some cases these are resistors as shown but in others they are the primary and secondary windings of separate transformers. The source of the additional energy is the *B*-battery plate supply.

In amplifying any given signal current a faithful reproduction of the *wave form* must be carried out, otherwise *distortion* will result; musical sounds from a radio will be harsh or pictures from a television receiver will be blurred. To amplify without distortion a tube must be used that has a long straight section in its *characteristic curve*, see Fig. 63N, and it should be operated at the center of this straight portion. Such operation is shown by the graph in Fig. 63T. To make the tube operate at *M* a small battery, called a *C*-battery or *C*-bias, is inserted in the grid circuit to maintain the grid at a negative potential. For the curve and tube shown this requires —5 volts, while for other types of tubes it might well require greater or smaller potentials.

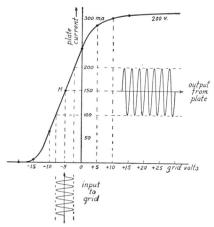

Fig. 63T—Graph showing amplifier operation.

When no input signal potentials are imposed the grid is held at —5 volts and a steady current of 150 milliamperes flows through the plate and output circuit. If now an alternating current like a radio frequency of constant amplitude is impressed across the input terminals, the grid potential will rise and fall in the same way, and an undistorted but amplified current will flow in the plate and output circuit. The time variations in grid potential are shown below in Fig. 63T and the corresponding plate current oscillations at the right and center. If the input radio frequency is voice modulated, the amplified current will also be voice modulated without distortion. It should be noted that if the impressed grid voltage variations are too large, say —20 to +10 volts, the amplified currents will reach the curved portions of the curve above and below and *distortion* of the *wave form* will result. As long as the tube is operated on the straight portion of the curve, plate current is directly proportional to the impressed grid potential, and faithful amplification takes place.

63.8. The Dynamic Loud-Speaker. A loud-speaker of conventional design is shown in cross section in Fig. 63U. Its function is the same as that of a telephone receiver, to change audio-frequency currents from the last amplifier in a radio receiver or public address system into sound waves of the same form.

There are three main parts to every loud-speaker. First, there is a strong shell-type magnet whose function it is to provide a field radially outward from a central *N* pole, across a narrow air gap, to a ring-like *S* pole. In small speakers this field is provided by an *alnico permanent magnet*, whereas in larger high quality units an *electromagnet*, like the one shown, is employed. The second element is a small cylindrical *voice coil* consisting of a dozen or so turns of wire fixed near the apex of a *paper cone* and centered in the narrow field gap by a springy fiber disk called a *spider*. The third is a *step-down transformer*, the low voltage, high current winding of which is connected by flexible wires to the voice coil.

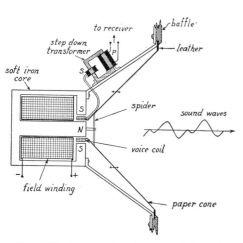

FIG. 63U—Cross-section diagram of dynamic loud-speaker.

When a varying current from the "output" transformer passes through the voice coil, varying forces are exerted which cause it to vibrate back and forth along its axis. As the cone is driven back and forth it acts like a plunger, its large area setting considerable air into vibration. The walls of the room or cabinet behind which the speaker is mounted acts as a *baffle* preventing sound waves from the back surface of the cone from getting around to interfere destructively with the waves from the front surface. A good demonstration is to be had by removing a speaker from its normal mounted position and listening to the distorted sounds it seems to produce. The low-pitched sounds in particular are noticeably absent.

Large sized speakers with a suitably large baffle area are particularly good at reproducing and dispersing low-pitched sounds. Due to *diffraction* and *interference*, however, high-pitched sounds are emitted in a narrow beam and in a forward direction only. Speakers with small cones, on the other hand, are particularly good on the high-pitched notes but are generally poor at reproducing the "lows." *

* For a detailed treatment of the principles of radio see, "Basic Radio," by J. Hoag, D. Van Nostrand Co., Inc.

63.9. A Radio Receiver. To combine the various functions of vacuum tubes as already described in this chapter, a radio receiver employing four tubes will here be described. See Fig. 63V. The first tube on the left of the circuit diagram amplifies the radio frequency currents supplied by the antenna circuit. The second tube, with its two plates, is a *duo-diode* detector and acts as a *full wave rectifier* to change radio frequencies into audio frequencies. The third tube amplifies the audio frequency current before delivery to the loud speaker while the fourth tube is a full wave rectifier supplying high and low voltages to the two amplifier tubes.

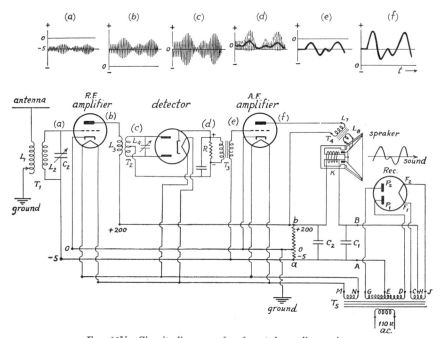

Fig. 63V—Circuit diagram of a four-tube radio receiver.

The transformer T_5 and the rectifier tube at the lower right hand corner are to be compared with Fig. 63E and the accompanying filter circuit of condensers C_1 and C_2, choke K, and *load* resistance ab are to be compared with Fig. 63G. The loud speaker winding K serves two purposes, one as a choke coil for smoothing out the current to b, and the other as an electromagnet supplying a strong magnetic field for the voice coil.

The load resistor ab is a potential divider (see Fig. 49L) from which desired voltages are obtained for the two amplifier tubes. The point O is grounded to bring that point to zero potential, the top end to about $+200$ volts, and the bottom end to about -5 volts. Since the first and third tubes are operated as amplifiers, their plates are given a potential of $+$ 200 volts by connecting them, through L_3 and L_7, to the point b, and the grids are given a potential of -5 volts by connecting them to the point a.

Reception from a distant station is obtained by varying the capacity C_2 in the grid circuit of the first tube until the antenna and L_2C_2 circuit resonate to the passing carrier wave. When this occurs the grid of the first tube obtains a potential varying in a manner similar to graph (a) directly above. The amplifier plate current is shown directly above in graph (b). This current flowing through L_3, the primary of an air core transformer, induces a similar current in the secondary L_4 and delivers to the plates of the detector a potential varying as in diagram (c). The rectifying action of the tube gives a cathode current like the dotted curve in graph (d).

An iron core transformer like T_3 will not operate on radio frequencies of several hundred thousand cycles, but only on audio frequencies up to about 15,000 cycles. The reason is that the primary winding with its iron core acts like a choke coil for the radio frequency with the net result that the "smoothed" out current through it rises and falls with the audio signal as shown by the solid line in graph (d). The secondary of T_3, therefore, has induced in it a current similar to graph (e).

With such an audio frequency potential on the grid of the third tube an amplified audio current flows in the plate circuit as in graph (f). The audio frequency is then delivered to the speaker where it is changed into a sound wave of the same form. T_1 and T_2 are air-core transformers since they must operate at radio frequencies.

QUESTIONS

1. Draw from memory a schematic wiring diagram of a full wave rectifier showing the vacuum tube, transformer, and load.

2. Make a schematic diagram of a full wave rectifier and filter circuit consisting of a transformer, vacuum tube, choke coil, two capacitors, and a load.

3. Draw from memory a wiring diagram of a one tube radio receiver as shown in Fig. 63I but using a cathode type of vacuum tube in place of a De Forest audion.

4. Diagram the circuit of a vacuum tube oscillator for generating high radio frequencies of constant amplitude.

5. Draw from memory an amplifier circuit with one vacuum tube.

6. Make a wiring diagram of a half-wave rectifier showing a vacuum tube containing a filament, a cathode, and plate, along with a transformer with a filament winding, and a load.

7. Make from memory a drawing of (a) a Fleming valve, and (b) a De Forest audion.

The Photoelectric Effect

THE photoelectric effect was discovered by Heinrich Hertz in 1887 when he observed that ultraviolet light, falling on the electrodes of a spark gap, caused a high-voltage discharge to jump greater distances than when it was left in the dark. One year later Hallwachs made the important observation that ultraviolet light falling on a negatively charged body caused it to lose its charge, whereas a positively charged body was not affected. Ten years later J. J. Thomson and P. Lenard showed independently that the action of the light was to cause the emission of free negative charges from the metal surface. Although these negative charges are no different from all other electrons it is customary to refer to them as photoelectrons.

64.1. Photoelectrons. The photoelectric effect in its simplest form is demonstrated in Fig. 64A. Light from a carbon arc is focused by means of a quartz lens onto a freshly polished plate of zinc metal. When the plate is

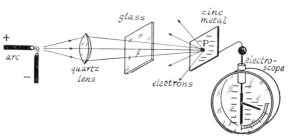

Fɪɢ. 64A—Experimental arrangement for demonstrating the photoelectric effect. When the glass plate is inserted the effect stops.

charged negatively, and the light is turned on, the gold leaf of the attached electroscope slowly falls. It falls because the electrons, under the action of the light, leave the zinc plate at the illuminated spot P. When the plate is positively charged the gold leaf does not fall, showing that the plate retains its charge. The same result of no discharge is observed if the zinc plate is negatively charged and a sheet of glass is inserted as shown in the figure. When the glass is removed the gold leaf again falls. Since common glass transmits visible and infrared light but not ultraviolet we conclude from the latter result that electrons are liberated only by ultraviolet light. This is also generally true for nearly all of the known metals.

A few elements, namely the alkali metals, *lithium, sodium, potassium, rubidium* and *caesium,* are exceptions to this, for they will eject photoelectrons when visible light falls on them. For this reason the *alkali metals* are often used in the manufacture of photoelectric cells.

64.2. The Photoelectric Cell. Photoelectric cells are usually made by depositing a thin layer of an alkali metal on the inner surface of a small vacuum tube (see Fig. 64B). If the cell is to operate in ultraviolet light it is made of quartz, whereas if it is to be used in visible light it is made of com-

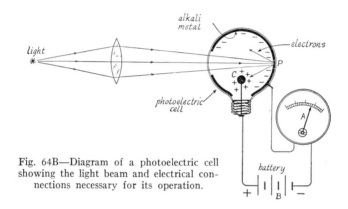

Fig. 64B—Diagram of a photoelectric cell showing the light beam and electrical connections necessary for its operation.

mon glass. The cell must be thoroughly evacuated as the oxygen content of the air will combine chemically with the active metal layer, contaminating its surface and making it insensitive to visible light. A small section of the cell is always left clear to serve as a window for the incoming light. Photoelectrons, upon leaving the metal surface, are attracted and collected by the positively charged electrode C. The negative charge on the metal film and the positive charge on the central collector electrode are maintained at a constant potential by the battery B.

A beam of light shining through the window of a photoelectric cell acts like a switch which completes an electric circuit. When the light strikes the metal P there is a flow of electrons to the collector C, thus causing a current to flow around the circuit. This current can be measured by means of an ammeter at A. If the intensity of the light increases, the number of photoelectrons increases and the current therefore rises. When the light is shut off the photoelectric action ceases and the current stops. If the metal film is positively charged the cell becomes inactive to light since electrons attempting to leave the plate are held back by electrostatic attraction. All of these factors are readily demonstrated by a simple electrical circuit arranged as shown in the figure.

64.3. Practical Applications. Talking motion pictures, television, and burglar alarms are but three of the hundreds of practical applications of the photoelectric cell. The simplest of these is the burglar alarm in which a beam of infrared light (invisible to the eye) is projected across the room into a photoelectric cell connected as shown in Fig. 64B. When an intruder walks through the beam, thus interrupting the light for an instant, the photoelectric current ceases momentarily. An electric relay in place of the ammeter at A in the circuit moves, causing another electric circuit to be completed and thereby ringing an electric bell.

During the filming of talking motion pictures a "sound track" is produced photographically on the side of the master motion picture film. Such sound tracks are shown in Fig. 64C. In strip (a), which is just a sample of one of the several kinds of sound tracks, the sound vibrations on the stage are converted into electrical vibrations by the stage microphone and then carried over wires to the camera taking the pictures. There the electrical impulses are made to move one of the jaws of a narrow slit through which a beam of light passes to the edge of the film. Loud sounds open the slit wide with each vibration, allowing a large amount of light through.

When the film is developed and positives are made for distribution, the loud sounds show up as periodic bands with considerable contrast as at L in strip (b).

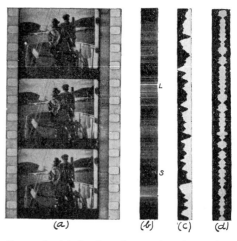

Fig. 64C—(a) Section of a moving picture film from MGM's "Spawn of the North," showing the *single variable density sound track*. (b) Enlarged section of sound track from (a). (c) Section of a *unilateral variable area sound track*. (d) Section of a *bilateral variable area sound track*.

The latter strip is an enlarged section of the *single variable density* sound track seen on the right in photograph (a). Weaker sounds produce bands with less contrast as at S. Strips (c) and (d) are enlarged sections of two other types of sound track used in other patented recording systems.

When a sound film is projected on the screen in the theater (see Fig. 64D), the film for the pictures themselves must of necessity move intermittently through the projection system P of the projection machine. As the film moves downward, each picture (frame) stops momentarily in front of the condensing lenses L and then moves on for the next frame. While the film is moving, the light is cut off by a rotating shutter S, and while it is at rest the light passes through to the screen. Thus the continuous motion seen on the screen is the result of a number of still pictures projected one after the other in rapid succession. To make this motion seem smooth, and not jumpy, it is standard practice to project 24 frames each second.

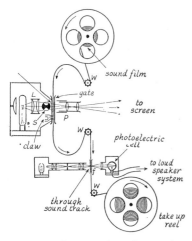

Fig. 64D—Cross section of a motion picture projector with sound attachment.

To produce the sound a small subsidiary beam of light, shown in detail in Fig. 64E, shines through the sound track at a point 25 frames farther along on the film where the motion is no longer intermittent, but smooth. As the sound track moves through the focus line *f* of the subsidiary light at constant speed, the transmitted light falling on the photoelectric cell fluctuates exactly as the sound track interrupts it. The photoelectric cell then changes the fluctuating light beam into a fluctuating electric current with the same variations. When transmitted to the radio amplifier and loudspeaker the fluctuating current is changed into sound vibrations. Thus sound vibrations have been carried over a light beam from the photographic film to the photoelectric cell and then by means of a loud-speaker system reproduced as sound.

64.4. Sound Over a Light Beam. The sending of voice and musical sounds for several miles over a light beam is readily accomplished with a suitable light source as transmitter and a photoelectric cell as a receiver. A convenient laboratory demonstration can be made by using a small ¼ watt neon glow lamp as a source of light, as shown in Fig. 64F.

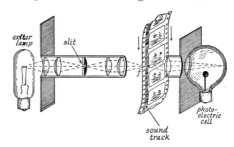

Fig. 64E—Detail of sound "pick-up" system of a moving picture projector showing the exciter lamp, sound track, and photoelectric cell.

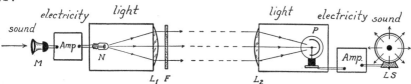

Fig. 64F—Voice and musical sounds can be sent long distances over a beam of light.

Sound waves entering the microphone M produce electric current fluctuations which, after being strengthened by a 2-stage amplifier, cause the intensity of the neon glow lamp N to fluctuate accordingly. Made into a parallel beam by a lens L_1, the light travels across the room to a second lens L_2 and a photoelectric cell where the light is changed back into a varying electric current. This faint signal is then amplified by a 2-stage amplifier before it is delivered to the loud-speaker.

If the microphone is replaced by a phonograph "pick-up," records can be played at the transmitter end and excellent reproduction can be obtained from the loud-speaker. The light beam can be made completely invisible by placing an infrared filter in the light beam at F. Talking several miles over a beam of invisible light was developed to quite a high state of perfection during World War II. One system employs the infrared light from a glow discharge tube containing caesium, while several others, modulated by mechanically vibrating mirrors, employ the infrared from a tungsten filament lamp. Another system employs the invisible ultraviolet light from a glow discharge tube containing gallium.

64.5. The Velocity of Photoelectrons. The first measurements of the velocity of photoelectrons led to the very startling discovery that the velocity does not increase as the intensity of the light increases. Increasing the intensity of the light increases the number of photoelectrons but not their velocity. This discovery, as we shall see later, has had far reaching implications in its result, for it has played an important role in the development of our modern concepts of light and atomic structure.

Lenard's experiments, performed as far back as 1902, showed that to increase the velocity of photoelectrons one must increase the frequency of the light, i.e., use shorter wave lengths. The shorter the wave length of the light used, the higher are the velocities of the electrons.

64.6. Einstein's Photoelectric Equation. Following an earlier idea of Planck's that light waves consist of tiny bundles of energy called *photons* or *quanta,* Einstein proposed an explanation of the photoelectric effect as early as 1905. His ideas are expressed by one simple relation, an algebraic equation, destined to become famous in the annals of physics. Two Nobel Prizes, one to Einstein in 1921 and one to Millikan in 1923, have been granted on this, the photoelectric equation,

$$h\nu = W + \tfrac{1}{2}mv^2. \tag{64a}$$

The first term $h\nu$ represents the total energy content of a single quantum of light incident on a metal surface, as shown in Fig. 64G. The letter h is a constant called *Planck's constant of action* which has the same value for all light waves regardless of the frequency ν. At or beneath the surface of the

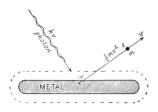

FIG. 64G—A light quantum (photon) of energy hv, incident on a metal surface ejects an electron with a velocity v given by Einstein's equation.

metal this *light quantum,* better known as a *photon,* is completely absorbed and, in disappearing, imparts its total energy to a single electron. Part of this energy W is consumed in getting the electron free from the atoms and away from the metal surface, and the remainder is used in giving the electron kinetic energy $\frac{1}{2}mv^2$, and therefore a velocity. For some metals like platinum, the energy required to pull an electron away from the surface is large, whereas for other metals like the alkalies it is quite small. W is called the *work function* of the metal.

64.7. Millikan's Measurement of h. The letter h in Einstein's photoelectric equation is important because it is fundamental to the structure of all matter and therefore *a universal constant.* Having first been introduced by Planck in 1901, the name *Planck's constant* has become firmly attached to this symbol h. The first experimental confirmation of Einstein's photoelectric equation came in 1912 when A. L. Hughes, and independently O. W. Richardson and K. T. Compton, observed that the energy of photoelectrons increased proportionately with the frequency. The constant of proportionality they found to be approximately equal to a constant, Planck's constant h.

Subsequently Millikan carried out extensive experiments which established the photoelectric equation so accurately that his work is now considered to give one of the most trustworthy values for h.

To do this it was necessary to measure the three factors v, W, and $\frac{1}{2}mv^2$, and calculate h as the unknown quantity in Eq.(64a). The most recent value obtained for this universal constant, is

$$h = 6.62 \times 10^{-34} \text{ joule sec} = 6.62 \times 10^{-27} \text{ erg sec.} \tag{64b}$$

Since the frequency of visible light is about 6×10^{14} vib/sec, the energy in a single photon or quantum of visible light is the product of these two numbers or 3.936×10^{-12} erg. In other words, it would take about 250,-000,000,000 photons to do one erg of work.

It should be pointed out in passing that the photon in ejecting an electron from a metal surface as in the photoelectric effect, disappears completely, i.e., it is annihilated. This is exactly the reverse of the process of the production of x-rays, where a high-speed electron, upon hitting a metal target and being suddenly stopped, creates and emits a photon of high frequency.

64.8. The Photoelectric Threshold. The photoelectric threshold v_0 is defined as the frequency of light which, falling on a surface, is just able to liberate electrons without giving them any additional kinetic energy. For such a frequency the kinetic energy $\frac{1}{2}mv^2$ in Einstein's equation is zero and the energy of the photon, $h\nu_0 = W$. Eq.(64a) can therefore be written in the form

$$h\nu = h\nu_0 + \tfrac{1}{2}mv^2. \tag{64b}$$

The meaning of ν_0 in this new equation is quite clear; it means that for frequencies lower than ν_0, electrons are not liberated, whereas for frequencies greater than ν_0 they are ejected with a determined velocity.

The photoelectric threshold for most metals lies in the ultraviolet where the frequencies are relatively high. For the alkali metals the threshold lies in the visible and near infrared spectrum. In other words, it takes photons of less energy to free electrons from the alkali metals than it does to free them from most other metals.

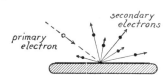

64.9. Secondary Electrons. When electrons strike the surface of a metal plate, they knock additional electrons free from the surface. These are called *secondary electrons* and the process is called *secondary emission* (see Fig. 64H). As the speed of a

Fig. 64H—The impact of a single electron liberates additional electrons from a metal surface.

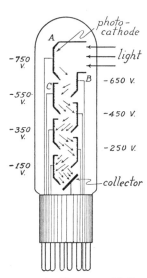

Fig. 64I—Photo multiplier tube with six stages. Caesium-oxide, silver-coated photo cathode.

primary or incident electron increases from zero to a few hundred volts, the number of secondaries increases toward a definite maximum. For most metal surfaces this maximum is in the neighborhood of two, while for certain alkali metal films it may be as great as eight or ten. In general it is greatest for surfaces having a *low work function*.

64.10. Photo-Multiplier Tubes. The process of secondary electron emission is widely used in a special type of photoelectric cell used most effectively in detecting faint light. A cross-section diagram of such a photo-multiplier tube is given in Fig. 64I.

The number of photoelectrons from the photocathode A is proportional to the intensity of the incident light. These are attracted toward the next plate B, more positive by 100 volts, where upon impact additional electrons are liberated. Attracted to the next more positive plate C, still more electrons are liberated. By the time the collector plate has been reached, a small avalanche of electrons has developed and a correspondingly large charge and current are led off through that electrode to a suitable recording device.

If each electron on impact releases n secondaries, then in a tube with k stages, the number arriving at the collector would be n^k. For example, if $n = 6$, and if $k = 5$, then $n^k = 7776$ electrons. This is an enormous gain over the signal obtained from a standard photo tube. Photo-multiplier tubes have been used most successfully with faint light, not only with visible light but with infrared and ultraviolet as well.

64.11. Scintillation Counters. When charged atomic particles or γ-rays pass through certain crystals, fluorescent radiation, characteristic of the substance, is emitted. For many crystals this fluorescent light is blue or violet in color and therefore in a region of the spectrum to which phototubes are most sensitive. By placing a block of fluorescent material—such as (a) zinc sulfide, for α-particles, (b) anthracene, for β-particles, or (c) thallium activated sodium iodide, for γ-rays—close to the photocathode of a photo-multiplier tube, a sensitive detector called a *scintillation counter* is obtained.

The principal advantages of scintillation counters over other detectors of nuclear radiation are: first, they operate in air or in a vacuum; second, they deliver an electrical impulse which is roughly proportional to the energy lost by the traversing particle; and third, they can count at amazingly high speeds because of their extremely short resolving time of 10^{-5} to 10^{-9} sec.

QUESTIONS AND PROBLEMS

1. Find the energy equivalent to a γ-ray whose wavelength is 1×10^{-3} A.

2. Calculate the energy in joules of a visible light photon of wavelength 5500 A. (*Ans.* 3.57×10^{-19} joules.)

3. If the photoelectric threshold of metallic copper is at $\lambda = 3200$ A, and ultraviolet light of wavelength 2536 A falls on it, find (a) the maximum kinetic energy of the photoelectrons ejected, (b) the maximum velocity of the photoelectrons, and (c) the value of the work function in ergs.

4. If light of wavelength 5000 A falls on a metal surface and emits photoelectrons with a velocity of 1.5×10^7 cm/sec, what is the wavelength of the photoelectric threshold? (*Ans.* 5132 A.)

5. If x-rays with a wavelength of 0.42 A falls on a metal plate, what would be the maximum velocity of the photoelectrons emitted? The work function can be assumed to be negligibly small.

6. Find the overall gain of a ten-stage photo-multiplier tube if the average number of secondary electrons produced by each primary electron is five. (*Ans.* 9.76×10^6.)

7. A six-stage photo-multiplier tube has an overall gain of 15,625. Find the average number of secondary electrons produced by each primary electron.

8. Make a diagram showing how a photoelectric cell could be used to count the number of cars passing a given point on a highway in a single day.

9. When x-rays with a wavelength of 1.5 A fall on a copper plate, what would be the maximum velocity of the photoelectrons emitted? Assume the work function to be negligible.

Electron Optics   Chapter 65

THERE exists a remarkable similarity between optical systems of prisms and lenses as they act upon light rays and electric and magnetic fields as they act upon streams of electrons. It is the purpose of this chapter to consider some of these similarities and to treat several practical applications of *electron optics*. To begin with it is convenient to present one of the standard methods of producing a beam of electrons, and to give the formula for calculating electron velocity.

65.1. An Electron Accelerator. A schematic diagram of an electron accelerator is shown in Fig. 65A. The source of electrons is a caesium-oxide-coated cathode K, heated by a filament F. The cathode and filament are

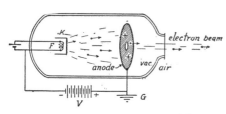

FIG. 65A—Electrons are accelerated by an applied potential V.

connected to the negative terminal and the circular disk at the center to the positive terminal of a high-voltage battery V. Starting from rest at the cathode, the electrons are accelerated along the electric lines of force acquiring at the anode A a velocity v.

By connecting the $(+)$ terminal to the ground, the anode is brought to the potential of the surrounding walls of the room and the electrons are not attracted back toward A but continue on with constant velocity. With a thin aluminum foil at the end and a high applied voltage V, electrons may be projected into the air beyond.

One of the results of J. J. Thomson's experiments with cathode rays was the discovery that the velocity of electrons depends upon the potential applied between the anode and the cathode. The higher the voltage the higher is the electron velocity. Since the energy required to carry an electric charge Q through a difference of potential V is given by $Q \times V$ (see Eq. 50e), the kinetic energy acquired by an electron of charge e falling through a difference of potential V will be $V \times e$. If we equate this product to the kinetic energy $\frac{1}{2}mv^2$,

$$Ve = \tfrac{1}{2}mv^2, \tag{65a}$$

where V is the applied accelerating potential in volts, m is the mass in kg,

v the velocity in meters per second and e the charge on the particle in coulombs.

Example. Calculate the velocity of electrons accelerated by a potential of 10,000 volts. (The electronic charge $e = 1.60 \times 10^{-19}$ coulombs, and $m = 9 \times 10^{-31}$ kg.)

Solution. Direct substitution in the above equation gives

$$10,000 \times 1.6 \times 10^{-19} = \tfrac{1}{2}(9 \times 10^{-31}) \times v^2$$

from which

$$v = \sqrt{\frac{10,000 \times 1.6 \times 10^{-19} \times 2}{9 \times 10^{-31}}} = 0.6 \times 10^8 \text{ m/sec.}$$

This is just one-fifth the velocity of light. (Velocity of light $c = 3 \times 10^8$ m/sec.)

Instead of calculating the velocity of electrons in meters per second it is customary to refer to their kinetic energy in terms of the applied voltage. For example, in the problem above the energy gained by the electrons is said to be 10,000 *electron volts*, (abbr. 10,000 *ev*). They are also sometimes referred to as 10,000 volt electrons.

65.2. Refraction of Electrons. When a moving electron, entering an electric field, makes an angle with the electric lines of force, it is bent in its

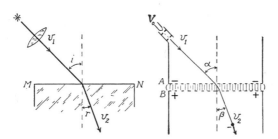

FIG. 65B—Refraction of light is analogous to the bending of an electron path.

path according to *Bethe's law of refraction* (see Fig. 65B). A correlation of this law with Snell's law in optics (see Eq.41b) is indicated by the following parallel equations.

Snell's law	Bethe's law	
$\dfrac{\sin i}{\sin r} = \dfrac{v_1}{v_2}$	$\dfrac{\sin \alpha}{\sin \beta} = \dfrac{v_2}{v_1}$	(65b)

Note the reverse order of the velocities v_1 and v_2. When a ray of light enters a more dense medium it is slowed down and at the same time bent toward the normal. Electrons, on the other hand, are deflected toward the normal when, in crossing a potential layer, they are speeded up. If the grid potentials are reversed the electrons will be retarded in crossing the potential layer and they will be deflected away from the normal. In other words, *re-*

verse the direction of the electrons, keeping their speed the same and they will retrace their paths exactly. Such a behavior is analogous to the very useful principle in geometrical optics that *all light rays are retraceable.*

To carry the refraction analogy a little further, consider the bending of electron paths by electrically charged bodies as shown below in Fig. 65C.

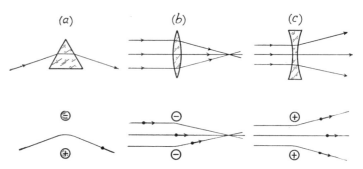

Fig. 65C—Comparison of light optics with electron optics.

Attraction by the positively charged wire and repulsion by the negative produces a prism-like action in case (a). A negatively charged metal ring produces a converging lens-like action in case (b) and a positively charged ring produces a diverging lens action in case (c).

Since by Eq.(65a), $v^2 \propto V$ and $v \propto \sqrt{V}$, the velocities v_1 and v_2 in Bethe's law of electron refraction may be replaced by $\sqrt{V_1}$ and $\sqrt{V_2}$ respectively, giving

$$\frac{\sin \alpha}{\sin \beta} = \sqrt{\frac{V_2}{V_1}}. \qquad (65c)$$

V_1 and V_2 are the potentials of the two grids A and B in Fig. 65B, taken with respect to the cathode source of electrons in the electron gun as zero.

65.3. Equipotential Surfaces. The refracting layer in Fig. 65B is formed by two equipotential surfaces, all points over the grid A being at one potential and all points over grid B at another potential. The electric lines of force are everywhere normal to the equipotential surfaces. Because the bending takes place in this potential layer it is convenient to generalize the subject of electron refraction by diagraming and briefly describing equipotential surfaces in and around various shapes of charged bodies.

Three configurations of commonly used charged bodies are shown in cross section in Fig. 65D. Diagram (a) represents two small charged wires (end on view), diagram (b) parallel metal plates, and diagram (c) parallel disks with circular holes through their centers. The *electric lines of force are shown by thin solid lines and the equipotential surfaces*, everywhere at right angles to the lines of force, are shown dotted. These latter are not wire grids, but imaginary surfaces of equipotential.

At all points on any given equipotential surface the potential is the same and has a value given by the amount of work per unit charge done in carrying any charge from the grounded body to that surface. The grounding of

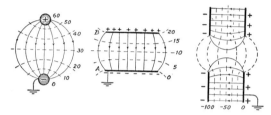

Fig. 65D—Equipotential surfaces (dotted) are everywhere perpendicular to electric lines of force (solid).

one charged body in each case brings that potential surface to zero potential. The potentials of other surfaces, arbitrarily chosen, increase or decrease, reaching at the other metallic conductor whatever voltage has been applied to the system.

65.4. Electron Lenses. An electron lens, known as a double aperture system, is shown in Fig. 65E, and is to be compared in its action to parallel rays of light incident on a converging glass lens as shown at the lower right. While both are converging systems, the essential difference between the two is that whereas light rays are bent only at the two surfaces, electrons are refracted continuously as they pass through the potential layers.

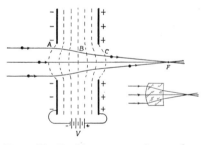

Fig. 65E—Double aperture electron lens and its optical analogue.

The focal length of a glass lens is fixed in value by the radius of curvature of its two faces and the refractive index for the light used, but the focal length of an electron lens can be varied at will by altering v, the velocity of the electrons, and V, the voltage applied to the system. In this respect the latter can be compared to the crystalline lens of the eye where the focal length can be changed by altering the lens curvature.

In the diagram, refraction for the upper path is greatest near A and, although it changes sign at some point near B, the gain in velocity due to the electric field produces a lesser deviation over the second half of the path, thereby causing convergence. If the electrons are reversed in direction on the right they will retrace their paths and emerge parallel at the left but, if the electric field is reversed in direction, the electron paths will not be the same but the system will still act as a converging lens.

Another type of electron lens, known as a single aperture system, is shown in Fig. 65F and is to be compared with the refraction of light by a single spherical surface as shown at the lower right. Three metal disks, *A, B,* and *C,* in a vacuum tube, are arranged in line and given potentials as shown. Plate *A,* called a guard ring, contains an electron source at its center while plate *B* contains a circular aperture *E* through which the electrons are focused.

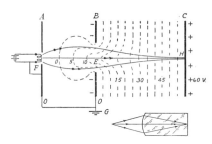

Because the surrounding walls to the left of *B* are at ground potential, the equipotential surfaces between *B* and *C* bulge into the open space giving rise to a lens-like action. This raises the potential at the aperture center above the potential of the disk itself. By proper adjustment of the voltage applied between *B* and *C* the electrons can be brought to a sharp focal point on the metal plate at *H.*

FIG. 65F—Single aperture electron lens and its optical analogue.

A third type of electron lens, known as a double cylinder system, is shown in Fig. 65G. In passing through the potential gap the electric field

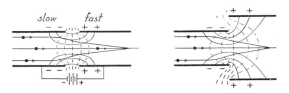

FIG. 65G—Double cylinder electron lenses.

has a converging action for the first half of the distance and a diverging action during the second half. Because they spend a greater time in the first half of the converging field, and the force on a charged particle is independent of velocity, the impulse (force × time) is greater for the convergence interval than it is for the divergence interval.

By making the second cylinder larger than the first the electric lines of force spread out more in the second cylinder. Such spreading weakens the field in the larger cylinder and reduces the divergent action to bring the electrons to a shorter focus.

65.5. An Electron Gun. A narrow beam of high-speed electrons, all having as nearly as possible the same velocity, has many practical applications in the field of electronics and atomic research. A device for producing such beams is called an "electron gun" (see Fig. 65H).

Electrons from a small filament-heated-cathode K are accelerated by a difference of potential V applied to the cylinders of an electrostatic lens system A_1 and A_2. The purpose of the guard ring maintained at the potential of the cathode is to improve the properties of the lens action of the first aperture and thereby collect a maximum number of emitted electrons into the collimated beam.

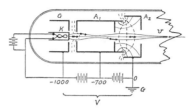

Fig. 65H—Electron gun.

The function of the second lens is to converge the bundle toward a focus and then introduce enough divergence to straighten the beam out into a narrow pencil. The velocity of the emergent beam is given by Eq.(65a) where V is the over-all voltage from cathode K to anode A_2.

65.6. The Cathode Ray Oscilloscope. One of the simplest applications of an electron gun is to be found in every *cathode ray oscilloscope,* an instrument whose purpose it is to reveal the detailed variations in rapidly changing electric currents, potentials, or pulses (see Fig. 65I). In appearance this device looks like J. J. Thomson's cathode ray tube (see Fig. 56F), and is actually the important element in one type of television receiver.

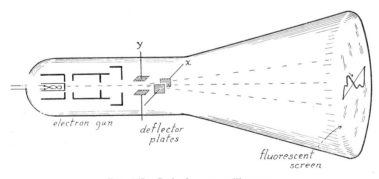

Fig. 65I—Cathode ray oscilloscope.

A cathode ray oscilloscope is a vacuum tube containing *an electron gun* at one end, two pairs of *deflector plates* (or magnetic coils) near the middle and a *fluorescent screen* at the other end. When an alternating potential is applied to the *x-plates* the electron beam bends back and forth from side to side and, when applied to the *y-plates,* it bends up and down. The luminous spot produced where the beam strikes the fluorescent screen traces out a horizontal line in the first instance and a vertical line in the second.

It is customary to apply a *saw-tooth potential* to the *x*-plates (see Fig. 65J(a)) and the unknown potential to be studied, (b), to the *y*-plates. The saw-tooth potential supplied by a special radio tube circuit called a "sweep circuit" causes the beam spot to move from left to right across the screen at constant speed and then jump quickly back from right to left to repeat the motion, (c). When the vertical deflections occur at the same time

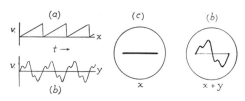

Fig. 65J—Potentials applied to cathode ray tube and graphs appearing on fluorescent screen.

the spot draws out a graph of the varying potential as in diagram (d). By varying the sweep circuit frequency until it matches the frequency of the studied signal repeated graphs will be drawn out, one on top of the other, and persistence of vision and the fluorescent screen will present a stationary graph.

Green fluorescent screens are used for visual observation since the eye is most sensitive to this color; blue screens are used for photographic purposes since films and plates are most sensitive to blue.

The oscilloscope has many practical applications and is to be found in every research laboratory as well as in every radio and television and repair shop. Its principal function is to analyze, or diagnose, rapidly changing potentials whose frequencies may be as low as a fraction of a cycle per second or as high as thousands of megacycles per second. Periodic or transient potentials as small as a fraction of a microvolt may also be studied by first amplifying them with standard vacuum tube circuits. (See Sec. 63.7.)

Another valuable feature of the oscilloscope is provided by its ability to measure time intervals between electrical impulses less than a microsecond apart. One microsecond is equal to one-millionth of a second.

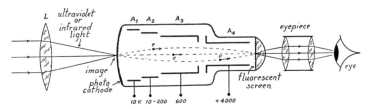

Fig. 65K—Ultraviolet and infrared telescope employing an electron image tube.

65.7. Infrared Telescope. A telescope for seeing objects illuminated in the dark by infrared light is diagramed in Fig. 65K. An image of the object to be observed is focused on the photo-cathode of the vacuum tube by means of an ordinary glass lens *L*. The caesium-oxide-coated cathode under infrared illumination emits photoelectrons which, accelerated to the right by $A_1A_2A_3$ and A_4, are brought to a focus on the green fluorescent screen at the right. The visible light they produce there by their impact is then observed by means of a magnifying eyepiece.

Electron focusing is accomplished by varying the potential applied to the second anode A_2, the infrared light image is focused by moving the lens *L*, and the visible light image is focused by moving the eyepiece.

65.8. Magnetic Lenses. When electrons cross a magnetic field, and their paths make an angle with the magnetic lines, they are deflected in spiral-like paths which, if properly controlled, may bring them to a focus. Such focusing properties of magnetic fields, illustrated by the cross section of a flat-coil in Fig. 65L, were first demonstrated and proved mathematically by Busch in 1926. It can be shown that the focal length of such a lens, the magnetic field strength and the electron velocity fit into well-known formulas in optics.

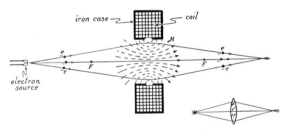

Fig. 65L—Magnetic lens for electrons. (Optical analogue right.)

By encasing a flat coil in a hollow iron ring the magnetic field becomes more concentrated and the refraction of electrons becomes more abrupt as they pass through the field. As a consequence the refraction more nearly resembles that of optical lenses. Still greater concentration is brought about by providing a small narrow gap on the inside of the iron casing as shown in the diagram.

If electron paths diverge too far from the principal axis of a coil-lens, aberrations of the kind described for light in Chap. 43 arise. For this reason *diaphragms* are often used to confine electron beams to the center of the coil the same as an *iris diaphragm* is used to confine light rays to the center of a lens.

65.9. Electron Microscope. The electron microscope, like the optical microscope, is an instrument used principally in the research laboratory for magnifying small objects to such an extent that their minutest parts may be observed and studied in detail. The importance of this device in the field of medical research cannot be overestimated. To illustrate, many viruses known to medical science as being responsible for certain human diseases lie beyond the range of the optical microscope. With the electron microscope, magnifications of from 10 to 100 times that of the finest optical microscopes make many of these viruses and some of their detailed structure visible to the eye. While the highest magnification obtained with the best optical microscope is about 2000X, electron microscopes have already been made that give magnifications as high as 100,000X.

A schematic diagram of an electron microscope employing magnetic lenses is shown in Fig. 65M. At the bottom a source of electrons is concentrated on the object (small arrow) by a condenser coil. Passing through or around the object, these electrons focus a magnified image of the object just below the projector coil. Only a small central section of these electrons pass into the projector coil to be brought to focus in a further magnified image at the top. There the image of only a small section of the object can be seen directly on a fluorescent screen or can be photographed with ordinary photographic plates. Fig. 23H shows reproductions of photomicrographs taken in this way.

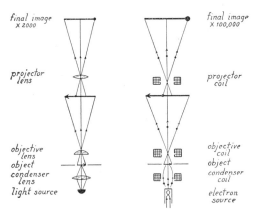

FIG. 65M—Optical microscope compared with electron microscope.

Electrons, like light waves, are stopped by metallic films and only when they are extremely thin can transmitted rays be employed. For opaque objects the light, or electrons, may be reflected from the surface and only surface structures may be observed.*

65.10. The Electrocardiograph. When two small metal electrodes are placed at random on the skin of the human body small continuously changing potential differences are found to exist between them. When these varying

---

* For a more complete treatment of electron optics see "Electron Optics," by V. K. Zworykin and others, John Wiley and Sons.

potentials are carefully measured and compared with muscular activity many of them can be correlated directly with certain activities of the body organs.

Each muscular action within the body is preceded and accompanied by an electrical impulse the magnitude of which depends upon many factors.

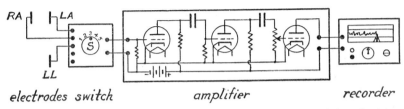

electrodes switch   amplifier   recorder

FIG. 65N—Schematic diagram for an electrocardiograph as used by physicians and surgeons.

Such impulses accompanying the beating of the heart for example are exceedingly large (of the order of one millivolt) and are of such importance to the medical profession that special instruments have been devised and successively used to graphically record their intricate and minute variations. Such an instrument is called an *electrocardiograph*.

A schematic wiring diagram of one type of electrocardiograph is shown in Fig. 65N. *RA*, *LA*, and *LL* represent three metal electrodes that are taped to the patient's *right arm, left arm,* and *left leg* respectively. Varying potentials created between any pair of electrodes are selected by the switch box *S* and, after being amplified, are applied to the vertical deflector plates of an oscilloscope or to the ink stylus of a recorder. The latter draws out the potential changes on a moving strip of paper to make what is called an *electrocardiogram*.

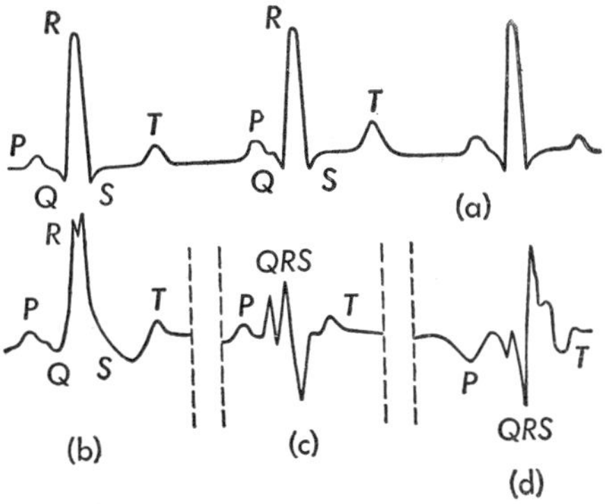

Small sections of electrocardiograms are shown in Fig. 65O. Curve (a) is characteristic of a normal

FIG. 65O—(a) Electrocardiogram of a normal heart. (b), (c) and (d) Waves showing three types of abnormalities.

heart action. After a relaxation period *T—P* an electrical pulse *P*, associated with activity of the right and left atrium is recorded. This stimulates the right and left ventricles (see Fig. 28I) and their response results in the *QRS* section of the curve. Between *S* and *T* both ventricles are still activated, the pulse *T* indicating a restoration to the relaxed condition.

Although an electrocardiogram is only a record of a series of complex electrical events, it does indicate the time relations and magnitudes of certain muscular activity. In (b), (c), and (d) single period sections of abnormal electrocardiograms are shown as samples of the thousands of different curves found in practice. If, as an illustration, the electrical conduction to one ventricle is poor the *QRS* section of the curve is delayed as well as modified. If, on the other hand, there is a larger than normal heart muscle the *QRS* curve widens, etc.

65.11. Electroencephalography. When small metal electrodes are placed on the scalp, potentials of the order of from one to fifty microvolts are found to exist between any given pair. The predominant frequencies of these varying potentials are lower than 100 cycles per second and are called "brain waves." Instruments used to record these waves are essentially the same as those used in electrocardiography and are called *electroencephalographs*. See Fig. 65N.

At the present time it is common practice to use a dozen or more electrodes on one patient in order to localize with precision tumors and other abnormalities. Potential waves from any three or more selected points are often recorded simultaneously to provide additional information by correlation. Reproductions of two electroencephalograms (*abbreviated EEG*), are shown in Fig. 65P. It will be noted that there is a marked difference between (a) the waves from a normal patient's record, and (b) those from a patient in epileptic seizure.

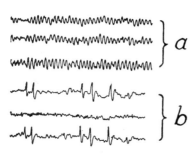

Fig. 65P—Electroencephalograms (EEG), (a) normal, (b) epileptic seizure.

When EEG recordings are analyzed into their component waves, as is done with complex sound waves, various frequencies can be identified and associated with recognized abnormalities. Very low frequencies up to about 8 cyc/sec are called *delta waves;* those around 10 cyc/sec, *alpha waves;* and those in the range 10 to 60 cyc/sec, *beta waves.* Of the many brain disorders detectable from EEG records the most familiar are: *epilepsy; cerebral thrombosis; encephalitis* and *meningitis;* and *brain tumor.*

65.12. The Mass of the Electron Increases with Speed. In the last few chapters we have seen how the electron makes its appearance in nearly every phenomenon in atomic physics. Electrons first appeared in Chapter 58 as cathode rays, then in Chapter 59 as the constituents of the atom; next they appeared in Chapter 61 as β-rays ejected by naturally radioactive elements, then in Chapter 63 as thermo-electrons, and finally in Chapter 64 as photoelectrons. That we are dealing with the same particles having the same charge in all of these cases there can be no doubt. As to their having the same mass, however, there must be an explanation.

Soon after the discovery of the electron by Thomson in 1898 the famous Dutch physicist H. A. Lorentz proposed an electron theory of matter in which he found it necessary to assume that the mass of an electron increases as its velocity increases, according to the following equation:

$$m = m_0/\sqrt{1 - (v/c)^2}. \tag{65d}$$

A few years later this same equation was again derived, this time by Einstein from his restricted theory of relativity. Although the equation has been tested most thoroughly with high-speed electrons, it applies to all bodies large or small. The symbol m_0 stands for the mass of a body when at rest, m for its mass when moving with a velocity v, and c for the velocity of light.

In words, this equation states that as the velocity of an electron (or any other body) increases, its mass increases ever so gradually at first and then more rapidly as the velocity approaches the velocity of light. Should the velocity of a body be equal to the velocity of light, v in the equation becomes equal to c, and the mass m becomes infinite. Since this is an impossibility we conclude that *no material body, not even an electron, can travel with the speed of light.*

To test the above equation experimentally it is necessary to employ bodies moving with high speeds. For this purpose Bucherer, Neumann, and others performed the very elegant experiment of measuring the increased mass of high-speed β-rays from radioactive elements. Some β-rays are known to be emitted with a velocity of 99% the velocity of light. The apparatus used in these experiments was quite similar to that used originally by J. J. Thomson for cathode rays (see **Fig. 58F**).

For electrons ejected at very low speeds the mass was found to be the same as Thomson's value 9×10^{-31} kg, while for electrons ejected at the highest speeds the mass was several times larger. When the experimentally determined masses were compared with the relativity formula, Eq.(65d), almost perfect agreement was found. The following values indicate the relative increase in mass for any material object when it moves with an extremely high velocity.

Velocity v/c, (in per cent) ..	1%	10%	50%	90%	99%
Relative mass m/m_0	1.000	1.005	1.15	2.3	7.1

At 1% of the velocity of light (1863 mi/sec) the mass of a body is the same as when it is at rest to one two-hundredth of 1%. At 50% the velocity of light, however, the mass has increased 15%; whereas at 99% the velocity of light, it has jumped up to over seven times its rest mass.

1. What voltage applied to an electron gun will give electrons a velocity of 3×10^9 cm/sec?

2. If 8000 volts is applied to an electron gun, what will be the velocity of the electrons? (*Ans.* 5.31×10^9 cm/sec.)

3. Make a table of electron velocities for the following accelerating voltages: $V = 10, 50, 100, 200, 500$ and 1000 volts.

4. What voltage applied to an electron gun will produce electrons having a speed of 60 mi/hr? (*Ans.* 2.05×10^{-9} volt.)

5. The moon weighs 1.62×10^{23} lbs, is 139,000 mi from the earth's center, and makes one trip around the earth in its orbit in about 28 days. Find its apparent increase in mass due to this motion.

6. A meteorite with a 5 kg rest mass passes the earth with a speed of 181,500 mi/sec. What is its apparent mass? (*Ans.* 22.2 kg.)

7. Electrons accelerated by a potential $V_1 = 1000$ volts enter an electric field between two grids as shown in Fig. 65B. If the angle of incidence is 35°, and the potential across the grids is 500 volts, find the angle of refraction.

8. If in Prob. 7 the voltage across the grids is reversed, find the angle of refraction. (*Ans.* 54.3°.)

9. Electrons accelerated by a potential of 300 volts enter an electric field as shown in Fig. 65B. If the angle of incidence is 45°, and the angle of refraction is 32°, find the potential difference between the grids.

10. If the angles are reversed in Prob. 9, find the potential difference between the grids. (*Ans.* 131 volts.)

11. Electrons from an electron gun enter a uniform magnetic field perpendicular to the lines of induction. If their circular path has a diameter of 20 cm, and a potential of 200 volts is applied to the gun, find the magnetic induction B.

12. Electrons are to be accelerated by an electron gun and then allowed to enter a uniform magnetic field. If the magnetic induction is 5×10^{-4} weber/m², and the circular path is to have a radius of 10 cm, what voltage should be applied to the gun? (*Ans.* 220 volts.)

13. Electrons accelerated by a potential $V = 500$ volts enter a uniform magnetic field in which the magnetic induction is 4×10^{-4} weber/m². Moving at right angles to the field, what is the radius of their circular path?

Frequency Modulation and Television

Chapter 66

66.1. Long-Distance Reception. It has long been known that radio waves travel farther at night than they do in the daytime. During daylight hours programs heard on standard broadcast bands, 550 to 1500 kilocycles/sec, are generally received at distances up to 10 to 100 mi (see Fig. 66A).

$$1000 \, \frac{\text{cycles}}{\text{sec}} = 1 \, \frac{\text{kilocycle}}{\text{sec}} \qquad 1,000,000 \, \frac{\text{cycles}}{\text{sec}} = 1 \, \frac{\text{megacycle}}{\text{sec}}.$$

At night, however, signals can be heard at 10 to 100 times these distances but with intensities often varying in an erratic manner. Such nocturnal variations are due to changing atmospheric conditions and are known as

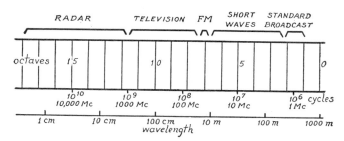

Fig. 66A—Frequency and wave-length bands for radio waves.

"fading." Fading is more pronounced at greater distances but improves considerably after the first hour or two after sundown, only to become worse again shortly before sunrise.

Short radio waves in the range 1.5 to 40 megacycles travel great distances day or night but are strongly susceptible to changing atmospheric conditions. One time of day, for example, communications between two greatly distant stations may be carried on over 20 m waves but not over 40 m waves. Later during the day the reverse may be true.

It is now known that the great distances spanned by radio are due to the reflection (actually refraction) of waves by a layer of electrically charged atoms and molecules in the upper atmosphere. The possible existence of such a layer was first postulated by O. Heaviside and A. E. Kennelly in 1902 to account for the propagation of waves around the earth's curved surface.

673

The existence of such a layer was first demonstrated experimentally in 1925 by G. Breit, M. Tuve, and others, and its elevation shown to vary from 50 to 150 mi.

As illustrated in Fig. 66B, waves radiated upward from a transmitter *T* are bent back toward the earth where they are again reflected upward. The diagram indicates how the entire earth's surface might be covered with radio waves, the intensity of which should decrease with distance from the transmitter. At short distances of only a few miles a "ground wave," *T* to *G* in the figure, is heard as a strong steady signal day and night.

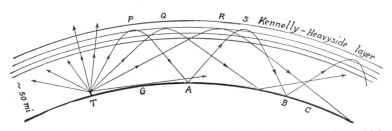

Fig. 66B—Radio waves are refracted (reflected) by the ionized gas layers high in the earth's atmosphere.

For some reason the Kennelly-Heaviside layer does not reflect the ultra high frequency waves used in *television* and *radar*. For this reason both are restricted to short-range operation, the waves traveling only in straight lines like visible light. To receive radar or television signals, therefore, the receiver antenna must be within sight of the transmitting antenna, and to cover a large area the transmitting antenna should be located high in the air atop a building, hill, or mountain peak.

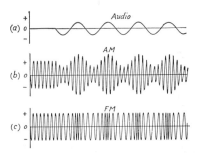

Fig. 66C—Graphs comparing amplitude modulation (*AM*) with frequency modulation (*FM*) of radio waves.

66.2. Frequency Modulation. A majority of the standard broadcasting stations, as well as amateur and commercial radio stations, still employ *amplitude modulation* (abbr. *AM*) as described in a previous chapter. The audio-frequency currents from the microphone are used to vary the amplitude of the continuous oscillations and waves from the transmitter.

In frequency modulation (abbr. *FM*), the audio-frequency currents from the microphone are used to vary the frequency of the carrier wave yet keep its amplitude constant. Louder sounds with *AM* mean greater variations in amplitude while with *FM* they mean greater changes in frequency. The two are compared graphically in Fig. 66C.

While just as good reproduction of voice and music can be accomplished with *AM* as is possible with *FM*, the latter has the advantage of eliminating "static." Static is the term applied to those noises in radio reception directly attributed to local atmospheric disturbances. Frequent minor lightning discharges in the air induce undesirable current pulses in any radio receiving antenna. When the receiver is designed to receive *AM*, these current pulses are amplified along with the broadcast and are heard as sharp cracking sounds or sometimes as a kind of "frying" noise. Where the receiver is designed for *FM*, however, the sudden current pulses picked up by the antenna do not change the frequency in any way and do not get through the *frequency discriminator circuit* to the audio amplifier. The resulting quietness to radio reception is remarkable and must be heard on a well-designed receiver to be fully appreciated.

66.3. Width of Radio Bands. The above discussion should not imply that the frequency of a carrier wave is unaltered by *AM*. Theory, confirmed by experimentation, shows that if a carrier wave of N cycles per second is amplitude modulated by a sound wave of n cycles per second, two new frequencies are produced, one $N - n$ and the other $N + n$. The first one is the beat note or difference frequency (see Sec. 36.10), whereas the other is a summation frequency not easily visualized from a graph like Fig. 66C. When, for example, a carrier of 1 million cycles is modulated by a sound of 5000 cycles, a receiver tuned to the carrier must also respond to 995,000 cycles and 1,005,000 cycles, and to hear all other sound frequencies between zero and 5000 cycles must respond to all frequencies between these two limits. Hence a frequency range of 10,000 cycles ($N \pm 5000$ cycles) is required to transmit sounds from zero to 5000 cycles.

Transmitting stations must have their carrier frequencies 10,000 cycles apart to avoid interfering with each other; and receivers, when tuned to a given carrier, must not respond to frequencies of more than 5000 cycles up or down. To obtain higher quality reception 10,000 and even 15,000 cycles should be used. The latter would require a band width of 30,000 cycles and broadcasting stations would have to be at least 30,000 cycles apart. The desirability of high fidelity suggests shifting of all standard broadcast bands into the short-wave region (see Fig. 66A) where there is ample space for numerous stations 30,000 cycles apart.

66.4. The Scanning Process in Television. For years the sending of pictures by wire or radio has been an everyday occurrence. The fundamental principle involved in this process, and illustrated in Fig. 66D, is known as *scanning*. Every picture to be transmitted is scanned by an *exploring spot* which, starting at the top, moves in straight lines over the entire picture. The spot first moves from *A* to *B*, then from *C* to *D*, then *E* to *F*, etc., until the entire picture has been covered. Each time the spot reaches the right-hand side it jumps back to the left and starts on the next line.

The exploring spot in any scanning device is so constructed that it generates an electric current proportional to the brightness of its instantaneous position. Such a pulsating current, called the *video signal,* is transmitted

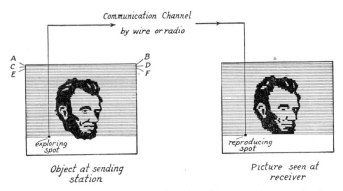

FIG. 66D—Illustrating the scanning of a picture and its reproduction.

over wires or radio waves to the receiving station. There in a specially designed instrument a *reproducing spot,* whose brightness is proportional to the video signal amplitude, moves over a viewing screen in a path similar to that of the exploring spot. In this way the reproducing spot reconstructs the original picture.

It will be realized that the smaller the scanning and reproducing spots and the greater the number of lines the better will be the details of the scanned picture being reproduced at the receiving end. The diagram shown here includes only 50 lines per picture as compared with 525 lines used in some standard (black and white) broadcasts.

If a single picture is to be sent by wire, as is generally the case in the *telephotographic newspaper service,* the scanning process requires from 10 to 20 min. In television, however, it is standard practice to scan and transmit thirty distinct and separate pictures every second of time. At the receiving station these pictures are rapidly flashed one after the other upon a viewing screen. All are still pictures differing progressively one from the next so that, due to persistence of vision, the motions seem smooth and continuous, just as with moving pictures.

To avoid spurious shadows and images, the process of *interlacing* is employed. By this process each picture is scanned twice, first by running the exploring spot over the odd numbered lines 1, 3, 5, 7, etc., and then over the even numbered lines 2, 4, 6, 8, etc.

In many respects the apparatus used in television differs very little from that used in radio broadcasting. The varying current from the exploring element of a scanning device, called a *televisor,* takes the place of the voice currents from a microphone. In other words, instead of modulating the carrier wave of a radio transmitter with the voice currents due to sound waves it is modulated with the *video current* from the light of a picture image in a televisor. Except for the *televisor tube* used in the transmitter, and a similar device called a *kinescope* used in the receiver, television equipment consists of numerous electrical circuits containing radio tubes similar to those in any radio receiving set.

66.5. The Televisor. The most important element in any television transmitter is the televisor or "pick-up tube," an instrument used in the broadcasting studio or in the field to convert light images into electric currents. Although many televising systems involving numerous principles have been devised, nearly all of them are to be classified as either mechanical or electronic in nature. Because mechanical systems have proved to be more cumbersome, electronic systems are now used almost exclusively. Among those classified under the latter heading, the "image orthicon" developed by the Radio Corporation of America, and the "dissector tube" developed by the Farnsworth Television and Radio Corporation, are among the most successful.

66.6. The Kinescope. In many respects the construction of a television receiver and its operation is similar to an ordinary radio receiver. The car-

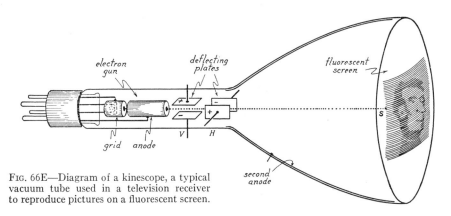

Fig. 66E—Diagram of a kinescope, a typical vacuum tube used in a television receiver to reproduce pictures on a fluorescent screen.

rier wave from a nearby transmitter after being tuned in, detected, and amplified with conventional radio tube circuits, is fed as a video signal into a kinescope in place of a loud-speaker. A kinescope is a large vacuum tube used for scanning and viewing the transmitted pictures.

A kinescope using electrostatic deflection plates for scanning is shown in Fig. 66E. Electrons from an electron gun at the left travel down the length of the tube to where, impinging upon a fluorescent screen, they produce a bright luminescent spot S. The purpose of the deflecting plates V and H is to deflect the electron beam with the identical frequency and scanning motion of the transmitting station. Two special oscillator tubes and circuits in the receiver supply saw-tooth potentials (see Fig. 66F) to these plates; the high-frequency potentials to the H-*plates* for horizontal scanning and the lower frequency potentials to the V-*plates* for vertical scanning.

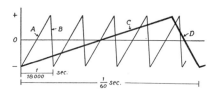

FIG. 66F—Saw-tooth potentials applied to plates of the television tube to produce horizontal scanning *A* and *B*, and vertical scanning *C* and *D*. *A* horizontal deflection, *B* horizontal return, *C* vertical deflection, and *D* vertical return.

The proper fluctuations in the intensity of the luminescent spot are brought about by applying the video signal shown in Fig. 66G to the *grid* of the electron gun. This grid controls the flow of electrons through to the anode in the same way that the grid controls the current to the plate in an ordinary three-element radio tube.

For a small fraction of a second, between successive pictures being scanned for transmission, current pulses of a certain type and frequency are sent out from the sending station as part of the video signal. These, picked up by the receiver, act as a trigger-like mechanism to bring the reproducing spot to the top left of the screen at the proper time to start the next picture.

In other words the transmitter sends out signals that enable the receiver to automatically keep "in step" with the pictures as they are sent.

FIG. 66G—Video signal current from a television tube.

66.7. Television in Full Color.

To produce television pictures in full color the *additive method of color mixing* is employed (see Sec. 45.6).

Several all electronic color television receivers have been invented in recent years. One of the simplest and most promising of these is that originated by E. O. Lawrence. The fundamental principles of the color producing elements of this receiver are shown in Fig. 66H. Instead of the fluorescent screen being coated with one fluorescent pigment as in the black and white tubes, Fig. 66E, a separate flat glass plate just inside the large end of the tube becomes the screen and is coated with three fluorescent pigments. These three pigments *R, G,* and *B,* under electron bombardment fluoresce with the additive primary colors *red, green,* and *blue,* respectively. These *fluors* are painted on the

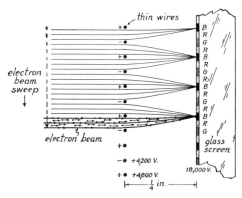

FIG. 66H—Illustrating the principles of the "chromatron" an all-electronic color-television-receiver-tube and screen.

glass in the form of hundreds of narrow vertical ribbons as indicated in the diagram.

About one quarter of an inch beyond the fluorescent screen, and electrically insulated from it, are about 400 fine equally spaced wires mounted parallel to and with twice the spacing as the color fluor lines. With alternate wires at about $+4200$ and $+4800$ volts respectively, and the screen at about 18,000 volts, the narrow incoming beam is brought to a focus as indicated.

The beam from the single electron gun (to the left of the diagram but not shown), sweeping across the screen several hundred times in a fraction of a second, scans and produces a green picture. When the wire potentials are reversed, the electron beam sweeping across the screen is brought to focus on only the blue fluor stripes and produces an all blue picture. When the wires are all automatically switched to the same potential ($+4500$ volts) the electrons are brought to a focus on the red stripes midway between the wires, and the beam "paints" an all red picture. By controlling the electron beam intensity from the gun all colors can be produced. A yellow object being televised, for example, will appear in both red and green pictures but not in the blue picture. A short distance away the eye blends the additive mixture as *yellow*.

The scanning method of presenting a complete blue picture, followed by a complete green picture, and then a complete red picture, is called *field-sequential-scanning*. This is to be distinguished from a *line-sequential-scanning* process in which first a blue line, then a green line, and then a red line are presented at the top of the picture, followed by another blue, then a green, and another red line, and so on down the screen.

The "chromatron" is also capable of dot-sequential scanning, a process in which sequences of dots are presented in rapid succession; a blue dot, then a green dot, then a red dot, then a blue, then a green, then a red, etc., filling up each line in turn and each entire picture frame with colored dots.

66.8. Television Requires Ultra High Frequencies. Extremely high-frequency radio waves are required in television because of the enormous frequency at which the intensity of a scanning spot must be able to change. To scan a picture with 525 lines to the frame, intensity fluctuations of 525 per line are also required in order to give equal picture definition in both directions. With a requirement of 30 complete pictures per second, and a minimum of 5 carrier frequency cycles on which a single variation can be registered (see Fig. 63R), we arrive at a minimum frequency of

$$525 \times 525 \times 30 \times 5 = 41,343,750 \text{ cycles/second.}$$

Therefore, to permit several stations to operate and cover the same metropolitan area, broadcast frequencies should be at least 8 megacycles apart. To bring this about requires going to ten to one hundred times this frequency, i.e., 80 to 800 megacycles or higher (see Sec. 66.3).*

QUESTIONS AND PROBLEMS

1. Make a diagram from memory showing the principles of a black-and-white television receiver tube. Label each essential part and briefly explain how it works.

2. Make from memory a wavelength and frequency chart showing the bands used for (a) standard radio broadcasts, (b) short wave radio, (c) frequency modulation broadcasts, (d) television, and (e) radar.

3. A radio station broadcasts on 1500 kilocycles/sec. What is the minimum band width a receiver must have to detect and reproduce audio frequencies of 6750 cycles/sec?

4. Calculate the minimum frequency required to transmit television pictures with 1000 lines to the frame. Assume 30 frames per second and a minimum of 5 cycles for light intensity variations. (*Ans.* 150 Mc/sec.)

5. Find the minimum frequency required to transmit television pictures with 500 lines to the frame, if 30 frames per second are to be produced and if 5 cycles are allowed for light intensity variations.

6. If 30 frames per second are to be transmitted by a television transmitter using a carrier frequency of 5 Mc/sec, how many scanning lines can be used? Assume 5 cycles/sec are needed for light variations. (*Ans.* 182 lines.)

* "Television," by V. K. Zworykin and G. A. Morton, John Wiley and Sons.

Radar   Chapter 67

RADAR is one of the most important electronic developments of World War II and may be defined as the art of determining by means of *radio echoes* the presence, distance, direction, and velocity of distant aircraft, ships, land masses, cities, and other objects. RADAR derives its name from the longer title "Radio Detection And Ranging." While its importance in naval and military operations has been demonstrated in many phases of modern warfare, its peacetime potentialities have already proved to be very great. The principal advantage of ultra short radio waves over visible or invisible light for locating and observing objects is their ability to penetrate dense fog and clouds.

It was Hertz who in 1888 demonstrated with damped waves from an electric spark (see Sec. 57.5) that electromagnetic waves travel in straight lines, can be reflected from various surfaces, refracted by prisms, and under proper conditions made to interfere as in standing waves. Recently vacuum tubes have been developed which oscillate at frequencies as high as 60,000 megacycles or more and generate powerful waves of continuous amplitude. These continuous waves in combination with the above-mentioned optical phenomena constitute an important part of the fundamental elements of radar.

67.1. The Fundamental Principle. Basically a complete radar station consists of a *transmitter*, a *receiver*, and an *indicator*. As shown by a schematic diagram in Fig. 67A, the transmitter sends out high-frequency radio

FIG. 67A—Illustrating the principles of radar detecting and ranging.

waves which, traveling outward with the velocity of light, are reflected from a distant object. That small portion of the reflected waves returning toward the station is picked up and amplified by the receiver. The signal is then fed into any one of a number of indicating devices, some of which are so complete as to give continuously the instantaneous distance, direction, and relative velocity of the object. With one type of air-borne unit, ground objects can be observed on the screen of a kinescope even though fog or clouds intervene. Such systems are extremely useful in reducing flying hazards always present during inclement weather.

Because the travel distance of radar waves is large and the reflecting power of most objects is low, the power radiated by any transmitter must be very great and the receiver must be capable of detecting the faintest of signals. Since the signal intensity arriving at any object falls off as the square of the distance from the transmitter, and the reflected intensity arriving at the receiver falls off as the square of the distance from the object, the intensity of the echo signal received from the transmitter is inversely proportional to the fourth power of the distance. In other words, when any given object moves to twice its distance from a radar station the signal received drops sixteen fold.

In spite of this rapid falling off of signal intensity with increased distance, instances of "tracking" planes several hundred miles away are well known, and in 1946 radar signals were, for the first time, sent to the moon and back. In this latter case the distance is large but so is the reflecting area.

67.2. The Pulsed System. Since a powerful transmitter must operate side by side with a supersensitive receiver, some provision is always made whereby the power from the transmitter is blocked out of the receiver. In most radar equipment this is accomplished by means of intermittent transmission commonly called the "pulsed system." According to this system the transmitter is turned *on* for only a fraction of a second to send out a train of waves while the receiver is made very insensitive. When the transmitter goes *off* the receiver is turned *on* to full sensitivity to receive the faint echo signal returning. When the receiver goes *off* the transmitter comes *on* again to send out another wave train and repeat the above process hundreds of times per second.

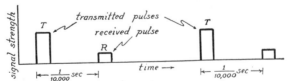

Fig. 67B—Graph of transmitted pulses showing received pulse, or "echo," from an object 9 mi. distant.

A graph of the received pulses from an object 9 mi away is shown in Fig. 67B. Since the velocity of radio waves is 186,300 mi/sec, the same as light, the time interval between each transmitted pulse T and its echo R returning is a direct measure of the distance. If a frequency of 30,000 megacycles is used, the waves are only 1 cm long and each pulse will contain thousands of waves. Rectified by the receiver, an entire wave train appears as a voltage pulse as in the graph.

One type of *indicator* used for determining this time interval is a *cathode ray, oscilloscope,* or *kinescope,* of the type shown in Fig. 66E. While the scanning spot is kept at constant intensity a saw-tooth potential is applied to the horizontal sweep to make it move with constant speed across the fluorescent screen.

Electrical circuits are so arranged that the spot starts at the left just prior to the transmitter's emission of a pulse. When, a fraction of a second later, a pulse is initiated, a small part of the energy is applied as a vertical deflection of the spot, thereby producing a trace T as shown in Fig. 67C. When the returning echo signal arrives at the receiver it too is applied as a vertical deflection and a peak like the one at R_1 is produced. Upon reaching the right-hand end of the screen the spot is extinguished and returned to the left where it is again turned on and the above process repeated. As the spot retraces the same line many times every second, persistence of vision gives rise to the appearance of a steady trace.

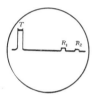

Fig. 67C—Trace of spot on cathode ray tube as used in radar ranging.

If several different objects reflect waves of sufficient intensity to be picked up by the receiver, several peaks R_1, R_2, etc., will be seen on the indicator screen. In radar parlance, each such peak on the trace is called a "pip" and its distance along the horizontal line from T is a direct measure of the time required for the signal to go out and return and is therefore a measure of the range of the object that caused it. Various methods of accurately measuring the distance interval have been developed.

If an object is coming toward or receding from a radar station, the frequency of the waves reflected from it will be increased or decreased respectively as in the Doppler Effect. Hence by measuring the frequency change between the waves going out and those coming back, the velocity of approach or recession becomes known.

67.3. Transmitting Antennae. Considerable increase in the range and general usefulness of radar systems is brought about by concentrating as much of the radiated energy from the transmitter as possible into a narrow searchlight kind of beam. In the most common systems in use today the antenna source is located at the focus of a paraboloidal metal reflector as shown in Fig. 67D. Diagram (a) shows an arrangement in which the high-frequency oscillations from as oscillator tube source are fed through a coaxial cable C to a single dipole, or Hertzian doublet D. Radiated waves from the doublet are reflected into a parallel beam by the mirror. Since the over-all length of a dipole must be equal to one-half a wave length, the two small rods for 10 cm waves would each be 2.5 cm, or 1 in., long.

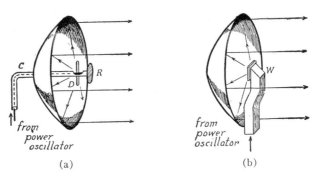

(a)   (b)

Fig. 67D—Radar antennas using paraboloidal reflectors with, (a) coaxial cable and dipole, (b) hollow rectangular wave guide.

Diagram (b) shows a similar reflector with the waves emerging from the opening at the end of a hollow rectangular pipe called a *wave guide*. For 3 cm waves this pipe W would have a cross section and an opening approximately one-half by 1 in.

67.4. Wave Guides. The term wave guide is generally applied to a special class of metallic conductors having the property of conducting high-frequency oscillations from one place to another. To be more specific it is a radio transmission line by which power generated at an oscillator can be transmitted to some utility point with little or no loss along the line.

The three types of wave guide most commonly used at present are shown in Fig. 67E. The first, called a *coaxial cable* or *concentric line*, consists of a

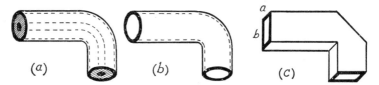

(a)   (b)   (c)

Fig. 67E—Wave guides commonly used in radar and television transmission lines. (a) coaxial cable, (b) and (c) hollow conductors.

wire conductor insulated from and running lengthwise through the center of a tubular conductor. Power from any high-frequency source, when connected to the central wire and tubular sheath, is propagated as waves through the dielectric between the two conductors.

The second is a hollow cylindrical pipe and the third a hollow rectangular pipe. Power introduced as electromagnetic waves at one end is guided by the conducting walls to the other end. Each conductor is shown with a 90° bend to show that waves can be guided around corners.

While there is no limit to the frequency transmitted by coaxial lines there is a lower limit for hollow wave guides. This lower limit, called the *cut-off frequency* or critical frequency, is the limiting case of a so-called *dominant mode* of vibration inside the guide, and is analogous in some respects to the *fundamental vibration* of a given air column in sound. The dominant mode occurs in a long round pipe when the diameter is about six-tenths of one wave length, and in a rectangular pipe when the wider of the two dimensions b is one-half a wave length. The narrow dimension of the latter is not critical but in practice is made to be about $\frac{1}{2}b$.

Since wave guides are comparable in cross section to the waves they propagate, and a coaxial cable will transmit any frequency no matter how low, the latter is generally used for waves longer than 10 cm, whereas hollow pipes are used with waves shorter than 10 cm. The power capacity of a hollow pipe, transmitting at its dominant mode, is greater than a coaxial cable of the same size.

Two commonly used methods of feeding waves into one end of a wave guide, or withdrawing them at the other end, are shown in Fig. 67F. *Probe coupling* illustrated at (a) and (d) shows the center wire of a coaxial cable protruding into a rectangular guide a short distance from the end. *Loop*

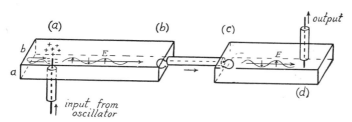

Fig. 67F—Illustrating probe and loop coupling between wave guides and coaxial cables.

coupling illustrated at (b) and (c) shows a single loop of wire protruding through the end wall of the guide. The size and position of the probe and loop are critically determined for each separate installation.

In probe coupling as at (a) the protruding wire becomes alternately positive and negative. By attraction and repulsion of electrons the metal surface above the probe acquires an opposite charge thereby giving rise to a periodically changing electric field E parallel to the probe. The surging charges in the probe simultaneously produce magnetic field lines B around the probe, perpendicular to the electric lines, hence the propagation through the guide of electromagnetic waves with E and H perpendicular to each other (see Fig. 57H). The probe location is such that waves reflected from the end will be "in step" with those already moving down the guide. The reverse process takes place at (d) where the probe acts like a radio receiver antenna set into oscillation by the incoming waves.

In loop coupling (b) the surging charge in the loop constitutes a changing current that sets up magnetic lines of force threading through it. This changing magnetic field induces electric currents in the metal walls such that the bunching of charges above and below gives rise to a simultaneously reversing electric field E. The net result is the same as with probe coupling, electromagnetic waves are propagated through the guide.

67.5. **Wave Propagation in Guides.** In sound, the resonance of an air column is described as the result of two waves traveling in opposite directions and stationary nodes and loops are formed. The propagation of elec-

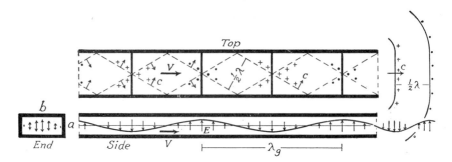

Fig. 67G—Illustrating the propagation of microwaves through a rectangular wave guide.

tromagnetic waves in a wave guide, on the other hand, may be described in terms of two wave trains crisscrossing each other as they reflect back and forth between the walls of the conductor. For one of these modes, the so-called *dominant mode,* see Fig. 67G.

The dotted lines in the "top" view represent wave fronts of the field E, *dots* for the wave crests where the field is *up* out of the page, and *crosses* for the troughs where the field is *down* into the page. These two waves, traveling normal to their wave fronts with the velocity of light c, form resultant waves traveling lengthwise down the tube with a velocity V. The velocity V is always greater than the velocity of light and the wave length λ_g in the guide is always greater than the wave length λ outside. $V = \nu \lambda_g$.

As the b-dimension of the guide is reduced, the oblique wave fronts stay the same normal distance apart while the wave length λ_g and the velocity V

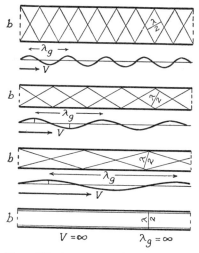

FIG. 67H—As a wave guide is narrowed down the wave length and wave velocity inside increases, becoming infinite when the critical width $b = \frac{1}{2}\lambda$.

increase, becoming infinite when $b = \frac{1}{2}\lambda$ (see Fig. 67H). Under this latter condition the two component wave fronts are parallel to the wave guide and the electric field at all points in the guide is rising and falling together. This is the resonant condition of the dominant mode, and the guide width b is at its minimum allowable value.

67.6. Scanning. In a majority of radar installations the receiver uses the same antenna as the transmitter, thereby requiring a rapid switching mechanism that connects the transmitter to the antenna when a pulse is to be radiated and then to the receiver to pick up a possible echo signal (see Fig. 67I). Such dual use of one antenna saves space and weight and eliminates the mechanical difficulty of making two directive antennas point in exactly the same direction while they are moved about.

In certain types of radar installation the transmitter beam is made to sweep back and forth across the ground or sky with a scanning motion similar to that used in television. In one system a spiral scanning motion adapts

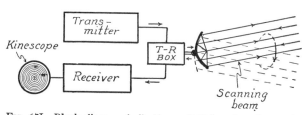

FIG. 67I—Block diagram indicating a T-R box for alternately connecting the antenna reflector to the transmitter and receiver. Conical, or spiral scanning is also indicated.

itself to total coverage of a given area. When the beam crosses the path of any reflecting object, an echo signal returns to the receiver where it is amplified and applied to the cathode beam of a kinescope. As the transmitter beam carries out its scanning motion the cathode ray spot on the kinescope is made to traverse a similar path and at that instant when an echo signal returns, the spot brightens and its location on the screen locates the relative position of the object in the scanning field.

Because the reflector is rotated mechanically, the radar scanning speed is considerably slower than in television. Its usefulness, however, is unquestionable, for high above the clouds in a plane it is possible to observe the positions and shapes of many landmarks on the ground below.

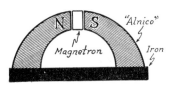

FIG. 67J—Diagram showing how a magnetron power tube is mounted in the strong field of a permanent magnet.

67.7. The Magnetron. The magnetron is a vacuum tube known to radar engineers as a powerful source of electromagnetic waves. A tube no larger than a man's hand, for example, is capable of delivering 100 kilowatts in the form of 1 cm waves. A typical arrangement is shown in Fig. 67J where the vacuum tube itself, in the shape of a pill box, is mounted between the poles of a small permanent magnet.

Diagrams showing the resonant cavities inside the tube are given in Fig. 67K. Electrons emitted by the hot cathode K are accelerated toward the ring-like plate by a potential of several thousand volts. The magnetic field urges the electrons to follow a spiral-like path, and at the same time causes them to bunch into clouds shaped like the arms of a windmill. These radial arms of spiraling electrons sweep clockwise around the main central cavity several billion times per second.

As the electron arms whirl around they repel the free electrons in the interstices between the small cavities, causing them to move alternately clockwise, then counterclockwise around their respective openings. These oscillatory surges of negative charge make the metal

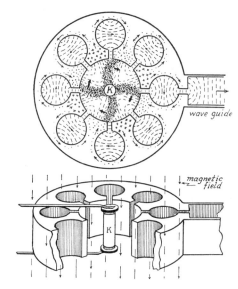

FIG. 67K—Details of magnetron tube showing resonant cavities and their action on electrons and electric lines of force.

interstices alternately positive, then negative, and at the same time set up electric and magnetic lines of force in the cavities and slots as shown. These fields extending into the central cavity, slow down some electrons and speed up others to bunch them as stated above.

The high-frequency oscillating fields in each of the eight cavities constitute electrical energy which can be tapped through any one of the cavities by an opening leading into a wave guide as shown at the upper right. By pulsing the cathode to plate voltage thousands of times per second, bursts of microwaves are sent along the wave guide channel to some antenna system. Since the dominant mode of a cylindrical cavity occurs when the diameter is about 0.7λ the smaller the diameter of the magetron cavities, the shorter is the wave length of the generated waves.*

67.8. Diathermy. It has long been known that if the human body is subjected to direct or low frequency alternating currents of any appreciable magnitude and duration detrimental and all too often lethal effects will result. It was in 1890 that the French physicist d'Arsonval, and a year later Nikola Tesla, discovered that relatively large alternating currents with a frequency of ten kilocycles per second or more could be carried by the body without detrimental effects of any kind. Today it is common practice in the well equipped hospital to deliberately use very high frequency currents to produce beneficial, internal, heating effects in various parts of the body. This practice is called *diathermy*.

The earliest machines used in diathermy employed a step-up transformer and Tesla coil (see Fig. 57J) and were equipped with a variety of metal plates, needles, and moistened pads to apply the high frequency currents to the proper parts of the body. In more recent machines continuous high voltage with frequencies of from 25 to 100 megacycles per second are produced by vacuum tubes and oscillator circuits, and the disagreeable electrodes and needles are replaced by a flexible insulated wire that

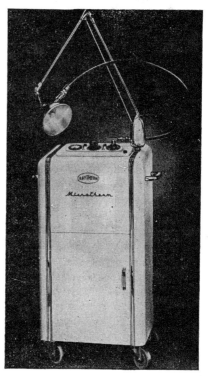

Fig. 67L—The "Microtherm," a generator used in micro-wave therapy. *Courtesy of Raytheon Manufacturing Co.*

can be wound lightly around an extremity, or wound into a flat coil and laid upon a pad against the body area to be heated. A high frequency current sent through such a coil produces an oscillating magnetic field of the same frequency. When the coil is close to the body these fields induce localized eddy currents of the same frequency within the body tissue and these in turn are dissipated as localized heat.

* "Principles of Radar by M.I.T. Radar School Staff," McGraw-Hill Book Co., Inc.

A photograph of an up-to-date microwave diathermy generator, designed to operate at a frequency of 2450 Mc/sec is shown in Fig. 67L. Being in the wavelength range employed in radar, energy in the form of microwaves is guided and directed by reflectors to the exact region to be heated. In penetrating the body, these waves set molecules into oscillation and bring about a more uniform heating of the fatty and vascular tissues. The localization of such heat is particularly effective in the treatment of *sprains, bruises, neuritis, arthritis,* and *congestion of all kinds.* In spite of claims to the contrary, experimental evidence and theory agree that the only effect these high frequencies have upon the body is a heating effect and that no organ responds to a particular range.

PROBLEMS

1. Radar waves of frequency 6×10^3 megacycles per second are reflected from a paraboloidal metal reflector. Calculate the overall length of the dipole used at its focal plane.

2. The dipole of a radar transmitter has an overall length of 1.63 cm. Calculate the frequency in Mc/sec. (*Ans.* 9200 Mc/sec.)

3. A rectangular wave guide has a vertical opening of width $b = 1.8$ cm. If waves of frequency 1.0×10^{10} vib/sec travel through the guide as shown in Fig. 67G, find the wavelength λ_g and the wave velocity V.

4. A rectangular waveguide as shown in Fig. 67G has a vertical dimension $b = 1.5$ cm. If waves of frequency 1.5×10^{10} vib/sec travel through the guide, find the wavelength λ_g and the wave velocity V. (*Ans.* (a) 2.68 cm. (b) 4.02×10^{10} cm/sec.)

5. A television transmitter broadcasts on a frequency of 82 Mc/sec. Find the length of the dipole of the transmitting antenna.

6. A television receiver uses a straight dipole with an overall length of 2.5 m. What is its natural frequency? (*Ans.* 60 Mc/sec.)

7. A cross-section of a rectangular wave guide has an opening of 5 mm by 12 mm. If waves of frequency 15,000 Mc/sec are sent through the guide, find (a) the wavelength λ, and (b) the wave velocity V.

The Structure
of the Atom

Chapter 68

THE continual search of the scientist for some knowledge of the ultimate particles in to which all matter may be subdivided has led within the last fifty years to the discovery of the *molecule,* the *atom,* and the still smaller element of negative electricity, the *electron.* These discoveries are but the first steps toward solving the age-old mystery of why all solids, large or small, hold together and do not fall apart.

68.1. Rutherford's Scattering Experiments. As early as 1903 P. Lenard sent cathode rays through thin films of metal and measured their penetration and absorption in matter. He concluded from his experiments that the mass associated with solid matter is not distributed uniformly throughout the body but is concentrated upon myriads of tiny isolated centers which he called *dynamids.* It was for these experiments that he was awarded the Nobel Prize in physics in 1905.

During the following decade Sir Ernest Rutherford, and his collaborators H. Geiger and E. Marsden, performed a series of ingenious experiments on the scattering of α-particles, the results of which implied that the positive charge and mass of every atom is confined to a particle smaller than 10^{-12} cm in diameter. Historically this marks the beginning of the idea of a nuclear atom proposed formally by Niels Bohr several years later. A schematic diagram of the scattering experiments is given in Fig. 68A.

High-speed α-particles from the radioactive element radon, confined to a narrow beam by a hole in a lead block *L,* were made to strike a very thin gold foil *F.* While most of the α-particles go straight through the foil as if there were nothing there, some of them collide with atoms of the foil and bounce off at some angle. The latter phenomenon is known as *Rutherford scattering.*

The observations and measurements made in the experiment consisted of counting the number of particles scattered off at different angles θ. This was done by the scintillation method of observation. Each α-particle striking the fluorescent screen *S* produces a tiny flash of light, called a *scintillation,* and is observed as such by the microscope *M.* With the microscope fixed in one position the number of scintillations observed within a period of several minutes was counted, then the microscope was turned to another angle and the number again counted for an equal period of time.

In the schematic diagram (b) of Fig. 68A, α-particles are shown passing through a foil three atomic layers thick. Although the nuclear atom was not known at the time the experiments were performed, each atom is drawn in the figure with the positively charged nucleus at the center and surrounded by a number of electrons. Since most of the film is *free space*, the majority of the α-particles go through with little or no deflection as indicated by ray (1). Other α's like (2) passing relatively close to an atom nucleus are deflected at an angle of a few degrees. Occasionally, however, an almost *head-on collision* occurs as shown by (4) and the incoming α-particle is turned back toward the source.

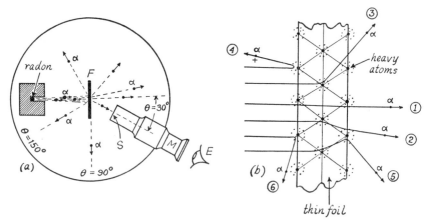

Fig. 68A—Diagram illustrating the Rutherford, Geiger, and Marsden scattering experiment.

Repeated experiments with different films made of light and heavy elements like copper, silver, and gold, showed that the relative number of the wide-angled deflections increases with atomic weight. From all of these results and numerous calculations, Rutherford came to the following conclusions: (1) *that all of the positive charge of an atom is confined to a particle smaller than 10^{-12} cm in diameter;* (2) *that practically all of the weight of an atom is confined to this same particle; and* (3) *that the amount of positive charge in atomic units is approximately equal to half the atomic weight.*

As an α-particle approaches an atom, as represented by ray (6) in diagram (b), it is repelled by the heavy positively charged nucleus and deflected in such a way as to make it follow a curved path. The magnitude of the repulsive force is at all times given by Coulomb's law, see Eq.(48a).

$$F = kQQ'/r^2. \tag{68a}$$

Whatever the force of repulsion may be at one distance r, it becomes four times as great at half the distance, nine times as great at one-third the distance, sixteen times as great at one-quarter the distance, etc. We see, therefore, that at very close range the mutual repulsion of the two particles on each other increases very rapidly and finally becomes so great that the lighter α-particle is turned away. The repelling force, still acting, gives the particle a push, causing it to recede with the same velocity as that with which it approached. The actual trajectory is in every case an hyperbolic orbit with the nucleus at the focus.

Although an α-particle (atomic weight, 4) is light compared with an atom of a metal like gold (atomic weight, 197) it is 7000 times heavier than a single electron. For this reason the electrons surrounding the atomic nucleus are pushed to either side as the α-particle goes speeding through and they have little effect upon the shape of the trajectory.

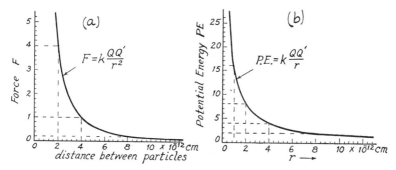

Fig. 68B—Graphs representing the repulsion between a positively charged nucleus and an α-particle. (a) Coulomb's law giving the repelling force F, and (b) potential curve giving the energy.

A graph representing the force of repulsion between an α-particle and a positively charged nucleus is illustrated in Fig. 68B. Diagram (a) shows the rapid increase in force as the distance decreases, while diagram (b) shows the rapid rise in potential energy. The potential energy between electric charges is analogous to the potential energy of a body in mechanics, for just as we multiply the force F by the distance moved d to get potential energy in mechanics, so in electrostatics we multiply the force F by the distance r between the charges to get the potential energy PE. See Sec. 50.2. Multiplying Eq.(68a) by r, gives

$$\text{potential energy } PE. = kQQ'/r. \tag{68b}$$

The reason for giving this equation, and the potential energy curve in Fig. 68B, is that from it an interesting mechanical model for demonstrating

Rutherford scattering can be derived. Such a model is illustrated in Fig. 68C, where the circular peak at the right represents the nucleus of an atom and has a form generated by rotating curve (b) of Fig. 68B, about its vertical axis at $r = 0$.

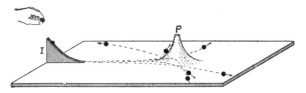

FIG. 68C—Mechanical model of an atomic nucleus for demonstrating Rutherford scattering.

Marbles, representing α-particles, roll down a chute and along a practically level plane where they approach the potential hill. Approaching the hill at various angles the marbles roll up to a certain height and then off to one side or the other. The paths they follow, if watched from above, are *hyperbolic* in shape. Approaching the hill in a head-on collision, the ball rolls up to a certain point, stops, then rolls back again. Thus the potential energy of the α-particle close to the nucleus is analogous to the potential energy of a marble on the hillside, and the electrostatic force of repulsion is analogous to the component of the downward pull of gravity. In a later chapter this same model will be used to demonstrate the disintegration of atomic nuclei.

68.2. Bohr's Theory of the Hydrogen Atom. In 1913 Niels Bohr * proposed a theory of the hydrogen atom which marked the beginning of a new era in the history of physics. With his theory Bohr not only gave a satisfactory explanation of the Balmer series of hydrogen (see Fig. 62I) but a model for the structure of all other atoms as well.

As a young physicist of twenty-seven, Bohr became intrigued by Rutherford's scattering experiments and set about trying to construct in his own mind a model of the atom which would be consistent with Rutherford's conclusions as stated in the preceding section. Since the atomic number of the

---

* Niels Bohr (1885-), Danish physicist, was born at Copenhagen, the son of Christian Bohr, professor of physiology at the University of Copenhagen. After taking his Ph.D. degree at Copenhagen in 1911 he studied for one year under J. J. Thomson at Cambridge, and one year under Ernest Rutherford at Manchester. Returning to Copenhagen in 1913, with the results of the Rutherford scattering experiments fresh in his mind, he worked out and published his now famous theory of the hydrogen atom. In 1920 Bohr was appointed head of the institute for theoretical physics at the University of Copenhagen. In 1921 he was awarded the Hughes Medal of the Royal Society and in 1922 the Nobel Prize in physics. Today he is the most honored Danish scientist and the father of a fine family. In 1937 he proposed the waterdrop theory of the atomic nucleus, which, at the time this is being written, is meeting with considerable experimental confirmation.

lighter elements is approximately equal to half the atomic weight (see **Appendix IV**), Bohr postulated that the positive charge carried by every atom is numerically equal to the atomic number Z. Hydrogen therefore should have one positive charge, helium two positive charges, lithium three positive charges, beryllium four, etc.

Since, to be neutral, every normal atom must contain one electron for every unit positive charge, a second postulate was made that the number of electrons retained by every natural atom is numerically equal to the atomic number Z.

Starting with what should be the simplest of all atoms, Bohr assumed that a hydrogen atom, $Z = 1$, consists of a nucleus with one positive charge $+e$, and a single electron of charge $-e$ revolving around it in a circular orbit of radius r (see Fig. 68D). Because it is 1840 times heavier than the electron, the nucleus could be assumed at rest.

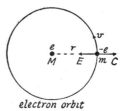

electron orbit

Fig. 68D—Orbital diagram of the hydrogen atom according to the Bohr theory.

To keep the electron in its orbit and prevent it from spiraling in toward the nucleus, or away from it to escape, Bohr next assumed that the inward centripetal force E is due to and, therefore, equal to the inward electrostatic force E. From Eq.(14h) the centripetal force is mv^2/r, and from Eq.(68a), Coulomb's law, the electrostatic force is kee/r^2. Equating these two gives

$$mv^2/r = kee/r^2. \tag{68c}$$

If the atom is to be stable this equality must always hold true.

At this point in the development Bohr introduced a *quantum hypothesis* similar to the one employed by Planck to explain the radiant heat from hot bodies and later by Einstein to explain the photoelectric effect (see Sec. 64.6). The electron, he assumed, cannot move in any sized orbit, stable under the conditions of the above equation, but in just *certain definite and discrete orbits*. The sizes of these orbits are governed by Eq.(68c) and the rule that 2π times the angular momentum of the electron, mvr, is equal to an integer n times Planck's constant h.

$$2\pi \ mvr = nh. \tag{68d}$$

In this equation n is called the *principal quantum number* and because it can take only whole number values 1, 2, 3, 4, etc., it fixes the sizes of the allowed orbits. To find the radius of these Bohr circular orbits, Eq.(68d) is solved for v, then squared and substituted in Eq.(68c) to give

$$r = \frac{n^2h^2}{4\pi^2me^2k}. \tag{68e}$$

Putting into this equation the known value of the electronic charge e from Millikan's oil-drop experiment, the electronic mass m from J. J. Thomson's cathode ray experiment, and Planck's constant h from Millikan's photoelectric experiment, the orbits shown in Fig. 68E are calculated. The innermost orbit has a radius $r = 0.000,000,005$ cm, or 0.5A, and a diameter of 1A. The second orbit is four times as large and the third is nine times. etc. (see Fig. 68E).

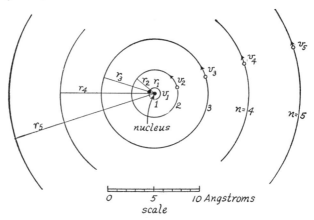

FIG. 68E—Scale diagram of the Bohr circular orbits of hydrogen.

The velocity of the electron, when it is in any one orbit, can be determined from Eq.(68d). In the innermost orbit, $n = 1$, the velocity v is 1/137th the velocity of light. In the second orbit the speed is only half as great and in the third only one-third as great, etc. With such small orbits and such high velocities the number of revolutions per second becomes very high. In the second orbit the frequency comes out to be 10^{15} rps. This, by comparison with the frequency of vibration of visible light waves, is of the same order of magnitude.

It should be noted that the one and only electron in each hydrogen atom can occupy only one orbit at any one time. If the electron changes its orbit it must move to one of the allowed orbits and never stop in between.

68.3. Bohr's Electron-Jumps. Bohr's final assumption regarding the hydrogen atom concerns the emission of light. Bohr postulated that light is not emitted by an electron when it is moving in one of its fixed orbits, but only when the electron jumps from one orbit to another, as illustrated in Fig. 68F. The frequency of this light, he said, is not determined by the frequency of revolution but by the difference in energy between the initial and final orbit.

$$E' - E'' = h\nu, \tag{68f}$$

where E' is the energy of the *initial orbit*, E'' the energy of the *final orbit*, h is Planck's constant, and ν is the frequency of the light.

To illustrate this let E_1, E_2, E_3, E_4, etc., represent the total energy of the electron when it is in the orbits $n = 1$, 2, 3, 4, etc., respectively. When for example the electron is in orbit $n = 3$ where its energy is E_3, and it jumps to orbit $n = 2$ where the energy is E_2 (see Fig. 68F), the energy difference $E_3 - E_2$ is ejected from the atom in the form of a light wave of energy $h\nu$ called a *photon*. Here then is the origin of light waves from within the atom.

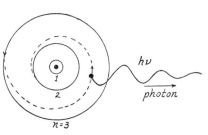

FIG. 68F—Schematic diagram of Bohr's quantum hypothesis of the radiation of light from an hydrogen atom.

The success of Bohr's theory is not to be attributed so much to the mechanical picture or model of the atom just proposed but rather to the development of an equation which agrees exactly with experimental observations.

The energy of the electron in any one of the allowed circular orbits is fixed by the quantum conditions imposed by Eq.(68d), and found by Bohr to be

$$E_\text{n} = -\frac{2\pi^2 m e^4 k^2}{n^2 h^2}. \tag{68g}$$

In the *mks* system, m is in *kg*, e is in coulombs, h is in joule sec, and $k = 9 \times 10^9$ newton-meter^2/coulomb^2.

The minus sign comes from the fact that the electron's energy is greater when it is in the larger of two orbits. By substituting Eq.(68g) in Eq.(68f), the frequency ν of an emitted light wave becomes

$$\nu = \frac{2\pi^2 m e^4 k^2}{h^3}\left(\frac{1}{n''^2} - \frac{1}{n'^2}\right), \tag{68h}$$

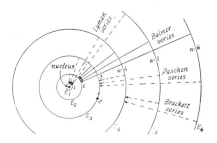

FIG. 68G—Diagram of the Bohr circular orbits of hydrogen showing the various electron-jumps giving rise to the emission of light waves of different frequency.

where n' represents the quantum number of the orbit from which the electron jumps and n'' represents the quantum number of the orbit to which it jumps.

When the known values of m, e, and h are substituted in the above equation, it gives exactly the observed frequencies of the Balmer series of hydrogen (see Fig. 62I). Remembering that in any wave motion the velocity of waves equals the frequency times the wave length, $c = \nu\lambda$, the frequency ν can be replaced by c/λ above, and there results

$$\frac{1}{\lambda} = \frac{2\pi^2 m e^4 k^2}{ch^3}\left(\frac{1}{n''^2} - \frac{1}{n'^2}\right). \tag{68i}$$

If the wave length λ is in cm, the evaluation of the factors in front of the parenthesis gives 109,678, the value in Balmer's formula, Eq.(62c).

Balmer's complete formula is obtained by setting $n'' = 2$, and $n' = 3, 4,$ 5, etc., in Eq.(68i). The first line of the series H_a, at 6564A, is produced by atoms in which the electron jumps from the 3rd to the 2nd orbit, the second line H_β, at 4863A by a jump from the 4th to the 2nd orbit, the third line H_γ, at 4342A, by a jump from the 5th to the 2nd orbit, etc. These transitions are illustrated schematically by arrows in Fig. 68G.

68.4. Normal and Excited Atoms. When the single electron of an hydrogen atom is in the innermost orbit, $n = 1$, the atom is said to be in its normal state. As the name implies, this is the condition of most free hydrogen atoms in a gas under normal room temperature and pressure. If an electrical discharge is sent through a vessel containing hydrogen gas, cathode rays (electrons) moving at high speed make frequent collisions with electrons, knocking some of them out of the atom completely and some of them into one of the outer allowed orbits, $n = 2, 3, 4$, etc.

When the electron is completely removed from the atom, the atom is said to be *ionized;* whereas, when it is forced into an outer orbit, the atom is said to be *excited*. Once in an excited state an atom will not remain that way long, for the electron, under the attraction of the nucleus, will jump to an inner orbit. By jumping to an inner orbit the electron loses all or part of the energy it had gained.

When an electron is excited it does not necessarily return to the innermost orbit by a single jump but may return by several different jumps. Starting from the 4th orbit, for example, it may return: (1) by three successive jumps from 4 to 3, then 3 to 2, and 2 to 1; (2) by two successive jumps from 4 to 2, and 2 to 1, or from 4 to 3, and 3 to 1; or (3) by one jump from 4 to 1. It takes thousands of excited atoms performing the same jump of the electron to register an observable effect on the photographic plate or on the retina of the eye.

68.5. Bohr's Newly Predicted Series. Bohr's orbital model of the hydrogen atom not only accounts for the Balmer series of hydorgen, but also predicts new series of lines, many of which have been observed.

By substituting $n'' = 1$ and $n' = 2, 3, 4$, etc., in Eq.(68i), Bohr predicted a series of spectrum lines in the extreme ultraviolet region of the spectrum. These lines were first photographed by T. Lyman of Harvard University, and the wave lengths were found to check exactly with Bohr's predictions.

This series, now called the *Lyman series,* which can only be photographed in a vacuum spectrograph, is reproduced in Fig. 68H. On the orbital picture of Fig. 68G, the Lyman series of lines arises from electron jumps from any outer orbit directly to the innermost orbit, the normal state.

Lyman Series of Hydrogen

Fig. 68H—Photograph of the extreme ultraviolet series of hydrogen, predicted by Bohr's theory and first observed by Lyman.

If in Eq.(68i), n'' is set equal to 3, and n' to 4, 5, 6, etc., the calculated frequencies predict spectrum lines in the infrared spectrum. These lines were looked for and observed, exactly as predicted, by F. Paschen, and the series is now known by his name. Another series of lines arising from electron jumps, ending on orbit $n = 4$, was predicted and observed in the far infrared by Brackett.

68.6. Bohr-Stoner Scheme of the Building Up of Atoms. Bohr and Stoner proposed an extension of the orbital model of hydrogen to include all of the chemical elements. As shown by the examples in Fig. 68I, each atom is composed of a positively charged nucleus with a number of electrons around it.

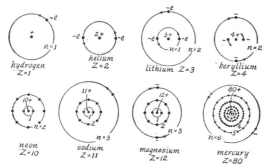

Fig. 68I—Bohr-Stoner orbital models for the light and heavy atoms of the periodic table.

Although the nucleus is a relatively small particle less than 10^{-12} cm in diameter it contains almost the entire mass of the atom, a mass equal in *atomic mass units* to the *atomic weight*. The positive charge it carries is equal numerically to the atomic number, and it determines the number of electrons located in orbits outside. A helium atom, atomic number $Z = 2$, has two positive charges on the nucleus and two electrons outside. A lithium atom, atomic number $Z = 3$, contains three positive charges on the nucleus and three electrons outside. A mercury atom, atomic number 80, contains 80 positive charges on the nucleus and 80 electrons outside.

The orbits to which the electrons are confined are the Bohr orbits of hydrogen with $n = 1, 2, 3$, etc., and are called electron shells. Going from element to element in the atomic table, starting with hydrogen, electrons are added one after the other, filling one shell and then another. A shell is filled only when it contains a number of electrons given by $2n^2$. To illustrate this, the first shell $n = 1$ is filled when it has 2 electrons, the second shell $n = 2$ when it has 8 electrons, the third shell $n = 3$ when it has 18 electrons, etc. $2 \times 1^2 = 2$, $2 \times 2^2 = 8$, $2 \times 3^2 = 18$, etc.

Quantum number	$n = 1$	$n = 2$	$n = 3$	$n = 4$	$n = 5$	$n = 6$
No. of electrons	2	8	18	32	50	72

Among the heavier elements there are several departures from the order in which the shells are filled. Although these departures are not important from the present standpoint their nature is illustrated by the mercury atom, Fig. 68I. The four inner shells $n = 1, 2, 3$, and 4, are entirely filled with 2, 8, 18, and 32 electrons respectively, while the 5th shell contains only 18 electrons and the 6th shell 2 electrons. The reasons for such departures are now well understood and are indicative of the chemical behavior of the heavy elements.

It is important to note that, as the nuclear charge increases and additional electrons are added in outer shells, the inner shells, under the stronger attraction by the nucleus, shrink in size. The net result of this shrinkage is that the heaviest elements in the periodic table are not much larger in diameter than the lighter elements. The schematic diagrams in Fig. 68I are drawn approximately to the same scale.

The experimental confirmation of these upper limits to the allowed number of electrons in each shell is now considered one of the most fundamental principles of nature. A sound theoretical explanation of this principle of atomic structure was first given by W. Pauli in 1925 and is commonly referred to as the *Pauli exclusion principle.**

68.7. The Sodium Atom. Guided by the simple appearing series of spectrum lines known to arise from the alkali metals, lithium, sodium, potas-

---

* For a more detailed treatment of atomic structure see, "Introduction to Atomic Spectra," by H. E. White, McGraw-Hill Book Co., Inc.

sium, rubidium, and caesium, Bohr and Stoner proposed that the filling of each new shell of electrons starts with these elements. This means that each alkali atom has one electron outside all the others and in an orbit by itself. This is illustrated for sodium, atomic number $Z = 11$, in Fig. 68I, and again in Fig. 68J.

In all normal sodium atoms the outer electron, called the *valence electron*, is located in orbit $n = 3$. When an electric discharge is sent through sodium vapor many of the atoms become excited and subsequently emit light waves in a manner similar to the hydrogen atom illustrated in Figs. 68G and 68F. In each excited atom the

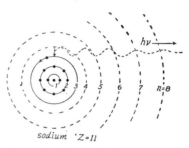

Fig. 68J—Schematic diagram of an atom showing the virtual orbits.

valence electron is in one of the outer virtual orbits $n = 4, 5, 6,$ etc. Jumping back to the normal state $n = 3$ a photon of frequency ν is emitted.

The energy content of each photon is governed by the quantum theory expressed by Eq. (68f). A series of jumps from outer orbits all ending on the normal state $n = 3$ give rise to a series of spectrum lines as shown in Fig. 62L. A jump from $n = 4$ to $n = 3$ gives rise to the first line of the series; a jump from $n = 5$ to $n = 3$, the second line of the series, etc.

The absorption of light by sodium atoms is the reverse process of emission. When a light wave or photon of just the correct frequency approaches a normal sodium atom it will be absorbed by the atom and the energy used to raise the outer electron from its normal orbit $n = 3$ to some outer orbit. This is a process of excitation of atoms by the absorption of light. In returning to the normal state the electron may emit the light again.

68.8. The Origin of X-rays. X-rays, like visible light, originate from the jumping of an electron from one orbit to another. When high-speed electrons from the cathode of an x-ray tube strike the target they ionize many of the atoms comprising the surface layers of the metal.

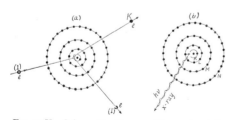

Fig. 68K—Schematic diagram illustrating (a) the ionization of an atom by a high-speed electron and (b) the subsequent jumping of an inner electron with the simultaneous emission of an x-ray.

Due to their very high speeds (about one-tenth the velocity of light) the electrons penetrate the atoms and remove an electron from the inner shells by collision. This is illustrated in Fig. 68K where an electron is knocked out of the K-shell. The designations $K, L, M, N, O, P,$ etc., for the various electron shells originated with the x-ray spectroscopist and are identical with the quantum numbers $n = 1, 2, 3, 4, 5, 6$, etc. When an electron is missing in the innermost K-shell, a nearby electron from the next shell beyond jumps into the vacant space, simultaneously emitting a photon of energy $h\nu$. Such x-rays arising from millions of atoms produce the K-lines shown in Fig. 60J.

Since the L-shell now has one less electron, an M electron can jump into the L-shell vacancy, with the consequent emission of another but different x-ray frequency. These are the L-lines in Fig. 60J. The jumping process continues until the outermost shell is reached, where an electron jumping in gives rise to visible light. Thus we see how it is possible for a single atom to emit x-rays of different wave lengths.

The continuous x-ray spectrum, illustrated by the shaded area under the curve in Fig. 60J, is due to another phenomenon often referred to as "Bremsstrahlung." These radiations are due to the slowing down of high-speed electrons as they pass close to the nuclei of the atoms within the target of the x-ray tube. The process is illustrated in Fig. 68L.

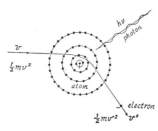

FIG. 68L — Diagram illustrating the production of a photon by a high-speed electron as it passes through an atom close to the nucleus. "Bremsstrahlung."

As the electron passes through the atom it is attracted by the positive charge of the nucleus and deflected in its path.

During the deflection of the electron in the strong electric field of the nucleus a light wave of energy $h\nu$ is emitted. Since the law of conservation of momentum must hold for such a collision the electron is deflected off to one side of the atom and the photon off to the other. Since the law of conservation of energy must hold, some of the energy of the incoming electron $\frac{1}{2}mv^2$ is given up to the newly created photon $h\nu$, and the remainder $\frac{1}{2}mv'^2$ is retained by the electron. Thus the electron is slowed down to a velocity v' by the encounter. The closer the electron comes to the nucleus the greater is its loss in velocity and energy and the greater is the frequency and energy of the radiated photon. By the conservation of energy,

$$\tfrac{1}{2}mv^2 - \tfrac{1}{2}mv'^2 = h\nu. \tag{68j}$$

The highest frequency that is possible is one in which the electron is completely stopped by the atom. In this special case,

$$\tfrac{1}{2}mv^2 = h\nu_{max}. \tag{68k}$$

68.9. Molecules Emit Light. Like the electrons in atoms, the electrons associated with molecules are also confined to *shells*. The innermost electrons are usually confined to one atom alone while the outer ones are shared with two or more. When an electrical discharge is sent through a gas containing diatomic molecules the outer electrons of some of the molecules are not only excited to outer orbits but the molecules as a whole are made to *vibrate* and *rotate* as illustrated in Fig. 68M.

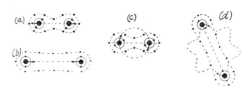

The frequency and amplitude of vibration and the frequency of rotation are restricted by the quantum theory in much the

Fig. 68M—Schematic diagram of the vibration and rotation of a diatomic molecule.

same way that the electrons are restricted to definite orbits in the Bohr atom. In other words, a molecule cannot vibrate or rotate with any frequency but with certain definite frequencies only. A change from one frequency of vibration to a lower frequency of vibration gives rise to the emission of a photon. If at the same time this occurs the rotational frequency of the molecule also changes, the frequency of the emitted photon will be changed by a small amount.

PROBLEMS AND QUESTIONS

1. Calculate the potential energy of an alpha-particle when it is only 4×10^{-11} cm from the nucleus of a lead atom, $Z = 82$.

2. Find the potential energy of a proton when it is only 2.5×10^{-12} cm from the nucleus of a mercury atom, $Z = 80$. (*Ans.* 7.38×10^{-13} joules.)

3. Find the force on an alpha-particle when it is only 3×10^{-12} cm from the nucleus of a gold atom, $Z = 79$.

4. Calculate the force on a proton when it is only 6.5×10^{-12} cm from the nucleus of a plutonium atom, $Z = 94$. (*Ans.* 5.13 newtons.)

5. Calculate the wave-lengths of the first two spectrum lines of the Paschen series of hydrogen. See Eq.(68i).

6. Calculate the wave-length of the first spectrum line of the Brackett series of hydrogen. See Eq.(68i). (*Ans.* 40,540A.)

7. Find the radius of the 25th orbit of the electron in a hydrogen atom.

8. If a source of 15,000 volts is applied to an x-ray tube, what is (a) the maximum frequency of the x-rays produced, and (b) the corresponding wave-length? See Eqs. (65a) and (68k). (*Ans.* (a) 3.48×10^{18} sec^{-1}, (b) 0.862A.)

9. If the shortest wave-length x-rays produced by an x-ray tube is 2.0×10^{-10} cm, find the voltage applied to the tube. See Eqs.(65a) and (68k).

10. Make a diagram of an argon atom according to the Bohr-Stoner scheme.

11. Make a diagram of a krypton atom showing the number of electrons in each shell according to the Bohr-Stoner scheme.

12. Determine the wave-length of the third line of the Brackett series of hydrogen. (*Ans.* 21,660A.)

13. Calculate the highest possible x-ray frequencies emitted when 50,000 volts is applied to an x-ray tube. See Eqs. (65a) and (68k).

Photon Collisions and
Atomic Waves
Chapter 69

In the preceding chapters we have seen that light waves consist of small finite bundles of energy called *quanta* or *photons,* and that they too, like atomic particles, may be made to collide with atoms of one kind or another. This was the case both in the *photoelectric effect,* Chapter 64, and in the production of *x-rays,* Chapter 60. The first part of the present chapter deals with the *corpuscular nature of light* and the last part of the chapter with the *wave nature of atomic particles.*

This last statement suggests a sort of "Dr. Jekyll and Mr. Hyde" existence for light waves as well as for atoms. Under some conditions light and atoms may both act as though they were waves, whereas under other conditions they may both act like small particles.

69.1. The Photoelectric Effect with X-Rays. When a beam of x-rays is allowed to shine on the surface of a thin sheet of metal, like gold, several different phenomena may be observed to take place. Acting like waves, the x-rays may be scattered at different angles to produce a diffraction pattern (see Fig. 60F), or acting like particles they may collide with atoms and eject electrons as in the photoelectric effect (see Chapter 64).

Even though a beam of x-rays may contain waves all of the same frequency, not all of the ejected photoelectrons acquire the same velocity,

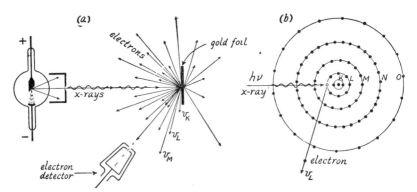

Fig. 69A—(a) Photoelectric effect produced with x-rays gives rise to electrons with several different velocities. (b) Detail of an x-ray ejecting an *L* electron from a heavy atom.

but are divided into several well-defined groups. These different groups are illustrated schematically by the lengths of the arrows in Fig. 69A.

Careful measurements of the velocities of the photoelectrons, first made by Robinson and his collaborators in 1914, have shown that each velocity group is to be associated with the various shells of electrons within the atoms. The slowest electrons, all with the same velocity v_K, are ejected from the K-shell, the next faster group with a velocity v_L from the L-shell, the next group with a velocity v_M from the M-shell, etc.

The closer an electron is to the nucleus (see diagram (b)), the greater is the attracting force and the greater is the force and energy necessary to liberate it from the atom. The velocity of the electrons in each group is given by Einstein's photoelectric equation,

$$h\nu = W + \tfrac{1}{2}mv^2, \tag{69a}$$

where W, the work function, is the energy necessary to free an electron from any one of the different electron shells (see Sec. 64.7).

While all of the incident x-ray photons have the same energy $h\nu$, more energy W will be used in liberating a K electron than there will be in liberating an L electron. This being the case, a photon liberating a K electron will have less energy left over for the electron than would another photon liberating an L electron from a similar atom. This experiment shows as well as one could wish that electrons exist in shells within the atom.

It should be pointed out that the energy W, used up in ejecting a photoelectron, is not lost by the atom but is later given out again in the form of x-rays of various frequencies. In atoms where a K electron has been ejected, an L electron may jump into the vacated K-shell, with the simultaneous emission of a K x-ray. This may be followed immediately by an M electron jumping into the vacated L-shell and the emission of an L x-ray (see Fig. 58J).

69.2. The Compton Effect. While making a spectroscopic study of scattered x-rays in 1923, A. H. Compton * discovered a new phenomenon now known as the Compton effect. After considerable controversy with other experimenters Compton proved quite conclusively that an x-ray may collide with an electron and bounce off with reduced energy in another direction. This is analogous to the collision between two billiard balls.

---

* Arthur H. Compton (1892-   ), American physicist, was born in Wooster, Ohio, on September 10, 1892. He received the degree of Doctor of Philosophy at Princeton University in 1916, and became head of the department of physics at Washington University in St. Louis, Mo., in 1920. In 1923 he discovered the change in wave length of x-rays when scattered by carbon, the phenomenon now known as the Compton effect. In recognition of this important discovery he was awarded in 1927, jointly with C. T. R. Wilson, of England, the Nobel Prize in physics. He is at present Chancellor of the Washington University, St. Louis, Missouri.

Compton's historic experiment is illustrated schematically in Fig. 69B. X-rays from a tube T were made to strike one face of a small carbon block and scatter out in various directions. With an x-ray spectrograph at one side of the block he measured the wave length of the x-rays S scattered in a direction θ. These wave lengths he then compared with those of the incident beam P.

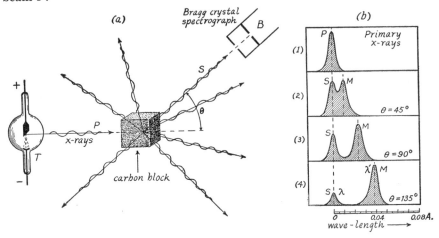

FIG. 69B—The Compton effect. (a) Schematic diagram of Compton's experiment, and (b) graphs of the x-ray spectrum lines observed with a Bragg crystal spectrograph.

The comparisons are illustrated by graphs in diagram (b). The top curve (1) represents the wave length λ of the x-rays in the beam P, before striking the block. The other three curves (2), (3), and (4), represent the two wave lengths, λ and λ', observed when the spectrograph is located at the angles $\theta = 45°$, $\theta = 90°$, and $\theta = 135°$ respectively. These graphs show that some of the scattered x-rays have changed their wave lengths whereas others have not. They further show the important result that as the angle increases, the change in wave length of the modified rays M increases.

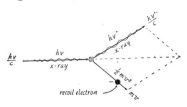

FIG. 69C—Vector diagram for the collision between an x-ray photon and an electron. The Compton effect.

To explain the modified wave lengths M, Compton invoked the quantum theory of light and proposed that a single x-ray photon acting as a material particle may collide with an electron and recoil off as though it were a perfectly elastic sphere (Fig. 69C). Applying the law of conservation of energy to the collision, Compton assumed that the energy $\frac{1}{2}mv^2$ imparted to the recoiling electron must be supplied by the incident x-ray quantum $h\nu$. Having lost energy the x-ray moves off in some new direction with a lower frequency ν' and energy $h\nu'$. By applying conservation of energy, we obtain

$$h\nu = h\nu' + \tfrac{1}{2}mv^2. \tag{69b}$$

As with two perfectly elastic balls, Compton also applied the law of conservation of momentum and derived an equation from which he could calculate the change in wave length λ' of the scattered x-ray. These calculated changes were found to agree exactly with those observed by the experiment. For those x-rays that are scattered at an angle of 90°, the observed or calculated change in wave length amounts to 0.0243 angstrom and is the same for all x-ray wave lengths.

The fact that a beam of light has the equivalent of a momentum mv, and can exert a pressure on a wall on which it falls, has long been known. According to the quantum theory the momentum of a single photon is given by the energy $h\nu$ divided by the velocity of light c,

$$\text{momentum of a photon} = h\nu/c. \tag{69c}$$

Compton's experiment is considered a proof of this equation. The momentum of the x-ray before impact is $h\nu/c$, while its momentum after impact is $h\nu'/c$, and the momentum of the electron is mv.

The discovery and early observations of the Compton effect were confined to the change in wave length of the scattered x-rays and not to the recoiling electrons predicted by theory. Compton's success is to be attributed to the exact agreement he found between the wave-length shift calculated from his application of the quantum theory and the values measured by experiment.

FIG. 69D—Recoil electrons from x-rays passing through the air in a Wilson cloud chamber. The Compton effect *(after C. T. R. Wilson.)*

The first discoveries of the recoil electrons from the Compton effect were made by C. T. R. Wilson, and by Bothe and Becker. The existence of these collision products is readily shown by sending a beam of x-rays through a Wilson cloud chamber just prior to its expansion. The result is a photograph similar to the one reproduced in Fig. 69D. The irregular and random shapes of the tracks as well as the relatively few drops found along the path are characteristic of electrons as well as of β-rays.

69.3. De Broglie's Electron-Waves. In 1924 De Broglie, a French theoretical physicist, derived an equation predicting that all atomic particles have associated with them waves of a definite wave length. In other words, a beam of electrons or atoms should, under the proper experimental conditions, act like a train of light waves or a beam of photons. The wave length of these waves, as predicted by De Broglie, depends upon the mass and velocity of the particles according to the following relations:

$$\lambda = \frac{h}{mv}. \qquad (69d)$$

This is known as *De Broglie's wave equation.* For an electron moving at high speed the denominator *mv* is large and the wave length is small. In other words, the faster an election moves, the shorter is the wave length associated with it.

To acquire some concept of the relative wave lengths of electrons moving with different velocities, several values have been computed from De Broglie's equation and given in Table 69A. The velocities are listed in miles per second in column 2 and in per cent of the velocity of light in column 3. The potentials listed in column 1 are the voltages required by Eq.(65a) to give an electron any one of the velocities listed in columns 2 and 3. It will be noted that the wave lengths at the bottom correspond closely to those for x-rays and γ-rays.

TABLE 69A. WAVE LENGTHS ASSOCIATED WITH ELECTRONS MOVING WITH DIFFERENT VELOCITIES ACCORDING TO DE BROGLIE'S WAVE EQUATION

$V \left(\begin{array}{l} \text{Applied} \\ \text{Voltage} \end{array} \right)$	$v \left(\begin{array}{l} \text{velocity} \\ \text{in mi/sec} \end{array} \right)$	$\dfrac{v}{c} \left(\begin{array}{l} \text{velocity} \\ \text{in per cent} \end{array} \right)$	$\lambda \left(\begin{array}{l} \text{wave length} \\ \text{in angstroms} \end{array} \right)$
1	370	0.20	12.23
10	1,100	0.62	3.87
100	3,700	1.98	1.22
1,000	18,000	6.26	0.38
10,000	36,000	19.50*	0.12
100,000	100,000	54.80*	0.03
1,000,000	175,000	94.10*	0.01

* These values take into account the increase in mass of the electron due to the theory of relativity. (See Sec. 65.10).

69.4. The Davisson-Germer Experiment. The first experimental proof of the wave nature of atomic particles was demonstrated in 1927 by two American physicists, C. J. Davisson and his collaborator, L. H. Germer. Their experiment is illustrated schematically in Fig. 69E. Electrons from a hot filament F are accelerated toward an anode P where, upon passing through a system of pinholes, they emerge as a narrow beam as indicated. This source acts as an "electron gun" from which electrons of any desired velocity may be obtained by applying the proper potential V.

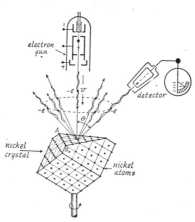

Upon striking one of the polished faces of a nickel crystal the electrons, acting like waves, are diffracted off in certain preferred directions. These preferred directions are located by means of a detector in which the electrons are collected and their accumulated charge measured. The detector is mounted so that it may be turned to any angle θ and the crystal is mounted so it may be turned about an axis parallel to the incident beam.

FIG. 69E—The Davisson-Germer experiment. Electrons striking the surface layers of a crystal are diffracted at different angles just as if they were waves with a very short wave-length.

With the electron beam incident perpendicular to the crystal surface shown in Fig. 69E, the preferred direction of diffraction for 54-volt electrons was found to be 50°. Under these conditions the surface rows of atoms parallel to AB act like the rulings of a diffraction grating, producing the first-order spectrum of 54-volt electrons at $\theta = 50°$. This is illustrated in a cross-section detail in Fig. 69F. The waves reflected from one row of atoms M must travel one whole wave length farther than the waves from the adjacent row N.

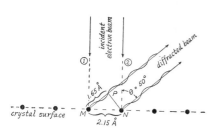

FIG. 69F—Diagram of electron diffraction from the surface layer of a nickel crystal. The regular spacing of the atoms acts like a diffraction grating.

69.5. Electron Diffraction Patterns. Experiments analogous to von Laue's x-ray diffraction experiments (see Fig. 60F) were first performed in 1928 by the English physicist, G. P. Thomson, and independently by the Japanese physicist, Kikuchi. A schematic diagram of their experimental apparatus is given in Fig. 69G. Electrons of known velocity from an "electron gun" are projected at the front face of a thin metal film or crystal at C. A short distance farther on the diffracted electrons strike a photographic

plate where they produce patterns of the type reproduced in Fig. 69H.
Kikuchi's photograph (b) was made by projecting 68,000-volt electrons
through a thin mica crystal. In this instance we have the exact analogue to

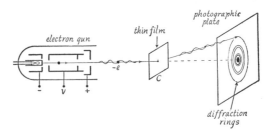

FIG. 69G—Experimental arrangement for observing
the diffraction of electron waves by thin films or
crystals.

the x-ray diffraction patterns of Friedrich, Knipping and von Laue (see
Figs. 60F and 60G). The electrons, in passing through the crystal, are diffracted by the atom centers in such a way that the various crystal planes
act like mirrors to reflect them the same as they do with x-rays of an equivalent wave length. Because high-speed electrons had to be used to penetrate
the crystal, the diffraction spots are closer together. The reason for this
latter is that the equivalent electron wave length, $\lambda = 0.047A$, is about one-
fiftieth of the crystal spacing.

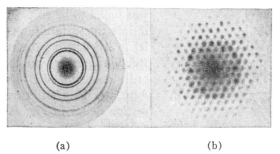

(a)   (b)

FIG. 69H—Photographs of electron diffraction patterns
demonstrating the wave nature of electrons. (a) 36,000
volt electrons from a thin silver foil *(after G. P. Thomson)* (b) 68,000 volt electrons from a thin mica crystal
(after Kikuchi.)

69.6. Electron Waves Within the Atom. The most recent development in the theory of atomic structure has shown that the Bohr picture of
the atom with sharply defined electron orbits is not correct. The new theory
does not discard the Bohr theory entirely but only modifies it to the extent

that the electron does not behave as though it were a particle. The electron behaves as if it were made up of waves (sometimes called De Broglie waves) of the type described in the previous sections.

The new theory of the hydrogen atom was worked out independently by the two German theoretical physicists, W. Heisenberg and E. Schrödinger, in 1925 and was later modified and improved by the English theoretical physicist, P. Dirac, in 1928.* Schrödinger, making use of De Broglie's idea of electron waves, pictures the single electron in the hydrogen atom as moving around the nucleus as a sort of *wave packet*. This wave packet, as it is called, is formed in somewhat the same way that standing waves are set up and maintained in sound waves.

To set up these standing waves, according to Schrödinger, the length of the path of an electron around the hydrogen nucleus must be a whole number of wavelengths. Since the circumference of a circle is $2\pi r$, and the De Broglie wavelength $\lambda = h/mv$, the conditions to be satisfied by the new theory are

$$n \frac{h}{mv} = 2\pi r, \qquad (69e)$$

where $n = 1, 2, 3$, etc. This is exactly the condition proposed by Bohr in his orbital theory presented in Eq.(68d), since transposing the momentum to the other side of the equation gives $2\pi mvr = nh$. It is not surprising, therefore, that the new theory also gives exactly the Bohr equation, Eq.(68h), for the wave lengths, and frequencies of the hydrogen spectrum.

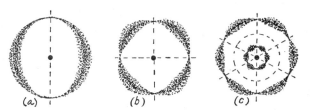

(a) $\qquad$ (b) $\qquad$ (c)

FIG. 69I—Schematic diagram of the waves of the orbital electron in a hydrogen atom.

One method of representing the electron in the atom is to picture an electron wave as one having a considerable length so that it extends to standing waves. These may be illustrated schematically as shown in Fig. 69I. In the first figure there are two radial nodes, in the second four radial nodes, and in the third six radial nodes and one spherical node. In this representation the electron is not thought of as a particle located at some point within

* For their contributions to the new theory of atomic structure Heisenberg was granted the Nobel Prize in physics for the year 1932, while Schrödinger and Dirac were jointly granted the Prize one year later.

the atom but as though its mass and charge were spread out symmetrically throughout the space immediately surrounding the nucleus of the atom. It is interesting to point out that, while the Bohr circular orbits were confined to a plane, the wave model allows the electron distribution to be three-dimensional.

Even though the new theory of the hydrogen atom is an improvement upon the older Bohr orbit theory and gives a more satisfactory explanation of all known phenomena, it is more difficult to form a mental picture of what an atom might look like. Indeed, the modern theoretical physicist goes on far as to say that the question, "what does an atom look like?" has no meaning, much less an answer. There are others, however, who still maintain that only those things that can be pictured are the things that are understood and that all mental thought processes are made in terms of things we detect by sight or touch. For this reason an interpretation is often given to the theory and its resultant equations that the amplitude of the electron waves within an atom represents the distribution of the electronic charge and mass. At

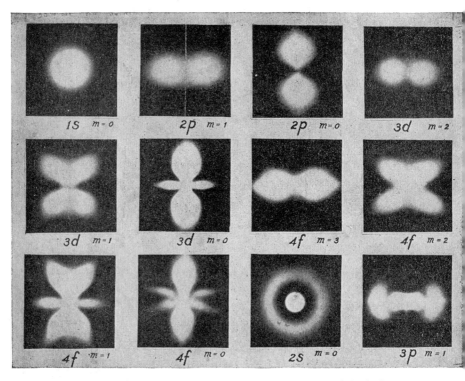

Fig. 69J—Density figures representing the single electron states of the hydrogen atom.

the nodes where the motion is practically zero there is assumed to be little or no charge, while at the loops there is a maximum amount of charge.

Photographs representing a few of the possible states of the single electron in hydrogen are shown in Fig. 69J. These are not pictures of real atoms but are made to represent them. They are made by photographing a specially designed mechanical top. Where the electronic charge density is large the figure is white, and where it is practically zero at the nodes it is dark. The three-dimensional distributions can be visualized by imagining each figure as rotating about a vertical axis, illustrated by the white line in the second figure. This particular figure in three dimensions would have a shape similar to a smoke ring.

69.7. The New Atomic Picture. Although the Bohr atom has been replaced by the more satisfactory model of *a nucleus surrounded by electron waves,* it is still customary, for convenience only, to talk about electron *shells* and *orbits.* The reason for this is that there is a close analogy between the old and new models. When the Bohr-Stoner scheme of the building-up of the elements is extended to the new theory of electron waves, the electrons are found to distribute their charge in such a way that something analogous to shells are formed.

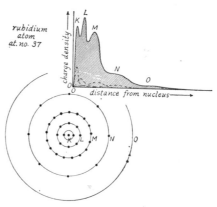

This is illustrated by the graph for a rubidium atom, atomic number 37, in Fig. 69K. The shaded area above represents the distribution of the charge of 37 electrons on the new theory, and the lower orbital model represents the electron shells on the old theory. The new model is represented by a graph because it is spherically symmetrical in space, while the old model is represented by orbits because it is confined to one plane. Proceeding out from the nucleus it is seen that the charge rises to several maxima at distances corresponding closely to the discrete K, L, M, N, and O shells of the orbital model. In other words, the new atom also has a shell-like structure.

FIG. 69K—Diagrams comparing the new and the old theories of atomic structure, according to the wave mechanics and the Bohr-Stoner model.

PROBLEMS AND QUESTIONS

1. Find the wavelength associated with an electron moving with one tenth the velocity of light.

2. Calculate the wavelength associated with a proton moving with one tenth the velocity of light. (*Ans.* 1.31×10^{-12} cm.)

3. Find the wavelength of an alpha-particle accelerated by a potential difference of 10,000 volts.

4. The equivalent wavelength of a moving electron is 0.42×10^{-8} cm. What voltage applied between two grids will bring it to rest? (*Ans.* 848 volts.)

5. If 2000 volts is applied to an electron gun, what is the equivalent wavelength of the electrons?

6. The electron beam in a small television receiver tube is accelerated by 5000 volts. What is the De Broglie wavelength of the electrons? (*Ans.* 0.173A.)

7. Briefly explain the Davisson-Germer experiment. What was observed and what were the conclusions?

8. Give a brief description of the Compton effect. Make a diagram.

9. Write down the De Broglie wave equation and explain what it means.

10. Make a Bohr-Stoner diagram of the electron shells of an argon atom. From the numbers of electrons in the shells, make a sketch of charge density as you think it is distributed according to wave mechanics. See Fig. 69K.

11. Calculate the momentum of each photon in a beam of visible green light, $\lambda = 5000$ A.

12. Find the momentum of each photon in a beam of red light, $\lambda = 6000$ A. (*Ans.* 1.10×10^{-17} kg m/sec.)

13. Find the speed of an electron whose wavelength is equivalent to 1 A.

14. X-rays of wavelength 1.5 A fall on a metal plate. Find the wavelength associated with the photoelectrons emitted. Neglect the work function of the metal. (*Ans.* 0.14 A.)

15. A beam of X-rays falls on a metal plate and emits photoelectrons. Find the equivalent wavelength of the electrons if the X-rays have a wavelength of 0.5 A. Neglect the work function of the metal.

Atomic Collisions and
Nuclear Disintegrations
Chapter 70

THE discovery of the disintegration and transmutation of stable elements by controlled experiments is attributed to the great experimental genius of Lord Rutherford. Outsiders might say that the discovery was an accident, but to those who knew him well it was the result of a long series of well-planned experiments. True, he did not predict the phenomenon and then discover it, but his long experience with radioactivity and his keen insight enabled him to recognize the meaning and importance of the phenomenon when it was first observed. Due credit must also be given to the admirable work of his collaborators and to experimenters in other laboratories who have since carried the work much further.

70.1. Elastic Collisions Between Atoms. Collisions between free atomic particles were first studied by Rutherford with apparatus as shown in Fig. 70A. A long glass tube, containing a small sample of radioactive material R, was first thoroughly evacuated by means of a vacuum pump and

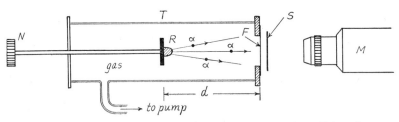

FIG. 70A—Rutherford's apparatus used in observing atomic collisions between α-particles from radium and the atoms of a gas like hydrogen, helium, nitrogen, oxygen, etc.

then filled with a gas of known constitution. Alpha-particles from the radioactive source were then permitted to travel through the gas to the other end of the tube where, upon passing through a thin aluminum foil to a fluorescent screen S, they could be observed as scintillations in the field of view of a microscope M. This is exactly the arrangement used by Rutherford in measuring the range of α-particles from different radioactive elements (see Sec. 61.9).

With air in the tube T and *radium C'* as a source of α-particles, scintillations could be observed with the screen as far back as 7 cm. With hydrogen in the tube it was found that the distance d could be greatly increased. Inserting thicker and thicker aluminum foils between F and S in front of the fluorescent screen, the range of the particles was calculated to be equivalent to 28 cm of air. The conclusion Rutherford drew from this result was that an α-particle occasionally collides with a hydrogen atom, much the same as a large ball collides with a lighter one, imparting to it a greater velocity and hence a greater penetrating power. Of the many recoil hydrogen atoms from collisions with α-particles, some of them undergo "head-on" collisions and go shooting off in a forward direction with over half again (more accurately 1.6 times) the speed of the incident α-particle.

The enormous increase in range is due principally to a higher velocity. Each hydrogen nucleus, called a *proton,* is stripped of its orbital electron, and, with but a single positive charge, produces fewer ions per centimeter path than an α-particle with its double positive charge. Curiously enough, protons or α-particles having the same velocity would have about the same range. The reason for this is that, whereas an α-particle has double the charge of a proton and produces more ions per centimeter of its path, tending to slow it down more rapidly, it also has four times the mass and therefore four times the energy. Later, in Fig. 70H, we will see that for *protons* and *α-particles* with the same kinetic energy, the protons have about ten times the greater range.

A more convincing study of such atomic collisions can be made with a Wilson cloud chamber. Out of thousands of cloud chamber photographs of the ion tracks made by α-particles from radioactive elements one occasion-

(a)   (b)   (c)

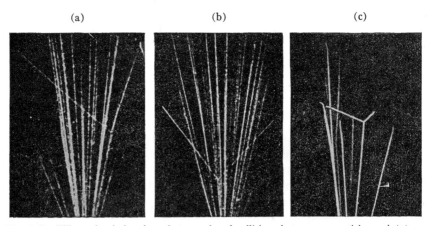

Fɪɢ. 70B—Wilson cloud chamber photographs of collisions between α-particles and (a) an hydrogen atom, (b) a helium atom, and (c) an oxygen atom. (*After Rutherford, Chadwick, and Ellis.*)

ally observes forked tracks of the type reproduced in Fig. 70B. When each of these pictures was taken the cloud chamber contained different gases. For photograph (a) the cloud chamber contained hydrogen, for (b) it contained helium, and for (c) it contained oxygen. Schematic diagrams of these same collisions are illustrated in Fig. 70C. Note in (b) that the angle between the two recoiling particles is 90°, a right angle.

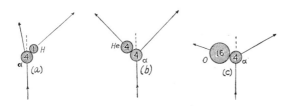

Fig. 70C—Diagrams of collisions between α-particles and other nuclei of different mass.

Most elastic collisions between atoms are not "head-on" collisions but ones in which the incident particle strikes the other a glancing blow. When an α-particle having a mass of 4 units collides with an hydrogen atom of 1 unit, the α-particle is deviated only a little from its path, whereas the hydrogen atom nearly always recoils off at quite a large angle. This is in agreement with the laws of conservation of energy and momentum applied to two perfectly elastic spheres.

When an α-particle collides with a helium atom, both particles have the same mass of 4 units each, and the two always glance off at right angles to each other. The laws of mechanics show that for a "head-on" collision between perfectly elastic spheres of equal mass, one moving and one at rest, the incident particle is stopped by the collision and the second body goes on in the forward direction with all of the velocity.

When an α-particle collides with an oxygen atom having a mass of 16 units, the oxygen atom recoils to one side with a relatively low velocity and the α-particle glances off to the other side with a high or low velocity depending upon the angle of recoil. The oxygen atom with its greater mass and charge ionizes more particles per centimeter path and therefore leaves a heavier track.

It should be pointed out that atomic collisions involving such high velocities take place between the heavy nuclei of the atoms and are little affected by the light orbital electrons. If a nucleus is hit hard by a collision it will be partially or wholly denuded of its electrons. When it comes to rest it will soon pick up enough electrons to make it a neutral atom again.

70.2. The Discovery of Nuclear Disintegration. Upon repeating the range experiments illustrated in Fig. 70A, with a heavy gas in the tube *T*, Rutherford in 1919 made a new and startling discovery. When nitrogen gas (atomic weight, 14) was admitted to the tube, scintillations could be observed at a distance of 40 cm or more from the source. No such long-range particles had ever been observed before. What were these long-range particles? They could not be electrons or γ-rays, for these are not capable of producing visible scintillations. Rutherford allowed the new rays to pass through a magnetic field and from their deflection discovered that they had the mass and charge of protons. In other words, the long-range particles were hydrogen nuclei.

Rutherford was not long in coming forward with the correct explanation of the phenomenon. An α-particle, near the beginning of its range where its velocity is high, may make a "head-on" collision with a nitrogen nucleus and be captured. This capture is then followed immediately by a disintegration in which a proton is ejected with high speed. The process is illustrated in Fig. 70D, and the transformation can be represented by the following simple reaction.

$$_2\mathrm{He}^4 + {}_7\mathrm{N}^{14} = ({}_9\mathrm{F}^{18}) = {}_8\mathrm{O}^{17} + {}_1\mathrm{H}^1. \tag{70a}$$

When the α-particle with a charge of $+2$, and mass 4, collides with the

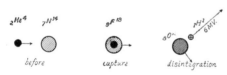

FIG. 70D—Illustrating the disintegration of a nitrogen nucleus by a high speed α-particle.

nitrogen nucleus with a charge of $+7$ and mass 14, they form a single particle with a charge of $+9$ and mass 18. Since an atom with a nuclear charge of $+9$ would be expected to have all the chemical properties of *fluorine,* atomic number 9, the newly formed nucleus is labeled ${}_9\mathrm{F}^{18}$.

An examination of the table of isotopes, however (see Table IV in the Appendix), shows that no such isotope exists in nature. The reason becomes apparent when it is realized that such a combination of particles is not stable. A fluorine nucleus of mass 18 is unstable and disintegrates by discharging a proton, a particle with a charge of $+1$ and a mass of 1. This leaves behind a residual nucleus with a charge of $+8$, and a mass of 17. Under atomic number 8 in the same Table IV, an oxygen isotope of mass 17 is seen to have been found in nature.

Thus the above disintegration process started with two stable nuclei, *helium* and *nitrogen,* and out of them were created two new stable nuclei, *oxygen* and *hydrogen.* This is called a transmutation of elements. Because the intermediate step indicates but a momentary existence of a fluorine nucleus,

$_9F^{18}$, this step is often omitted from any discussion of the above process and the disintegration reaction simply written

$$_2He^4 + _7N^{14} = _8O^{17} + _1H^1. \tag{70b}$$

Such transformation reactions are like equations and must balance: first, the total amount of charge must remain the same, and second, the mass numbers must balance. The first of these is accomplished by having the sum of the subscripts on one side of the reaction equal to the sum of the subscripts on the other side, and the second by having the sum of the superscripts the same on both sides. In every known atom the subscript, representing the nuclear charge, is the sole factor determining the chemical element to which the atom belongs.

70.3. Chadwick's Identification of the Neutron. In 1932 Chadwick, in England, performed an experiment for which he was later awarded the Nobel Prize in physics in 1935. As diagramed in Fig. 70E his experiment con-

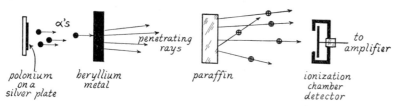

Fɪɢ. 70E—The experiment by which Chadwick discovered the neutron. The penetrating rays are neutrons and γ-rays.

sisted of bombarding a beryllium target with α-particles. Penetrating particles emerging from the beryllium were permitted to impinge upon a block of paraffin from which protons were found to emerge with high speed. From energy calculations he was able to show that the penetrating rays were uncharged particles with the mass of protons, and these he called *neutrons*. The disintegration taking place in the metal target is the following (see Fig. 70F):

$$_2He^4 + _4Be^9 = _6C^{12} + _0n^1. \tag{70c}$$

The α-particle, $_2He^4$, makes a collision and unites with a beryllium nucleus, $_4Be^9$, causing a disintegration; whereupon a neutron, $_0n^1$, is expelled with high velocity. The residual particle with a charge of $+6$ and mass of 12 units is a stable carbon nucleus such as found in nature.

Fɪɢ. 70F—Discovery of the neutron.

The penetrating rays from the beryllium block in Fig. 70E are mostly neutrons which, in bombarding the paraffin block, collide elastically with hydrogen atoms, knocking them out on the other side. An elastic "head-on" collision between two particles of the same weight, like a neutron and proton, finds the entire velocity of one transferred to the other; the neutron is stopped and the proton goes on. The protons, having a positive charge, can be observed by their tracks in a Wilson cloud chamber, whereas neutrons cannot.

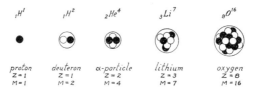

$_1H^1$ $\quad$ $_1H^2$ $\quad$ $_2He^4$ $\quad$ $_3Li^7$ $\quad$ $_8O^{16}$

proton	deuteron	α-particle	lithium	oxygen
Z = 1	Z = 1	Z = 2	Z = 3	Z = 8
M = 1	M = 2	M = 4	M = 7	M = 16

Fig. 70G—Diagrams showing the number of protons (black) and neutrons (white) in the nuclei of hydrogen, deuterium, helium, lithium, and oxygen.

The reason fast neutrons have such a high penetrating power is that they are not slowed down by ionizing atoms as they pass close by them. A proton, electron, or α-particle has a charge and can ionize atoms by attracting or repelling electrons from a distance, but a neutron without a charge cannot do this. It must make a direct collision with another particle to be slowed down or stopped.

Neutrons can now be produced in such intense beams that they are often used in place of x-rays wherever radiations of high penetrating power are desired.

TABLE 70A. SHOWING THE NUMBER OF NEUTRONS AND PROTONS IN THE NUCLEI OF A FEW ELEMENTS

Atom	Protons	Neutrons	Atom	Protons	Neutrons
$_1H^1$	1	0	$_5B^{11}$	5	6
$_1H^2$	1	1	$_7N^{13}$	7	6
$_2He^4$	2	2	$_8O^{16}$	8	8
$_3Li^6$	3	3	$_{11}Na^{23}$	11	12
$_3Li^7$	3	4	$_{29}Cu^{65}$	29	36
$_4Be^9$	4	5	$_{80}Hg^{200}$	80	120
$_4Be^{10}$	4	6	$_{92}U^{238}$	92	146

70.4. The Nucleus Contains Neutrons and Protons. Since the time of Chadwick's identification of the neutron as an elementary particle our ideas concerning the nucleus of the atom have had to be modified. We now believe that the nucleus contains but two kinds of particles, neutrons and protons.

Each neutron has a mass of one unit and no charge, whereas each proton has a mass of one unit and a positive charge of one unit. This differs from the older idea that the nucleus contains protons equal in number to the atomic weight, and enough electrons to neutralize the surplus charge in excess of the amount specified by the atomic number.

Since only the proton has a charge, any given nucleus of atomic number Z and mass number M is now believed to have Z protons and M-Z neutrons, and that in a neutral atom the number of protons is equal to the number of orbital electrons. The nuclear particles of a few of the elements of the periodic table are given in Table 70A, as examples.

Schematic diagrams of the nucleus of five different atoms are given in Fig. 70G.

70.5. Mass Is a Form of Energy. Einstein, in working out the theory of relativity, arrived at a number of simple equations concerning the nature of the physical world. One of these equations, having to do with the increase in mass of a moving object, was presented in Sec. 65.12. It is important at this point to consider another of these equations, since its proof can be demonstrated by, and is needed to explain, atomic disintegration experiments. The relation referred to is known as Einstein's mass-energy equation. In its simplest form this equation is written,

$$E = mc^2, \qquad (70d)$$

where m is the mass, c is the velocity of light, and E is the energy equivalence of the mass.

This relation would predict that mass can be turned into energy, or energy into mass. In other words, mass is a form of energy, for if a quantity of mass m could be annihilated, a definite amount of energy E would be available in some other form. To illustrate this, suppose that a 1-gm mass could be completely annihilated and the liberated energy given to another body in the form of kinetic energy.

$$E = 1 \times 3 \times 10^{10} \times 3 \times 10^{10} = 9 \times 10^{20} \text{ ergs.} \qquad (70e)$$

In foot pounds of energy this is equivalent to 7×10^{13} ft-lb, or enough energy to propel the largest battleship around the world.

The annihilation of mass then is a source of undreamed of energy. Disintegration is one means, however, whereby mass can be annihilated or created more or less at the will of the experimenter.

If an atom, a part of an atom, or an electron is annihilated, the energy may either be transformed into kinetic energy and given to another atomic particle in the form of a velocity or it may appear as a γ-ray of specified frequency ν and energy $h\nu$. To find the equivalence between mass energy, γ-ray energy, and kinetic energy, all of the following quantities are equated to each other.

$$E = mc^2 = h\nu = \tfrac{1}{2}mv^2 = Ve. \tag{70f}$$

It is customary among physicists to express each of these energies in terms of V in volts. Thus one speaks of a million volt γ-ray, a three million volt electron, or a 12.5 million volt proton, etc. This terminology is used for convenience only, and denotes the value of V in the above equation which, with the electronic charge substituted for e, gives the energy of the γ-ray photon, or of the moving atomic particle.

To give several examples, suppose that an electron were to be annihilated and we wished to express the liberated energy in volts. To calculate V we make use of the equality between the second and last terms of Eq.(70f); that is,

$$mc^2 = Ve. \tag{70g}$$

Substituting the known electronic mass $m = 9.1 \times 10^{-31}$ kg, $e = 1.60 \times 10^{-19}$ coulombs, and $c = 3 \times 10^8$ m/sec, we obtain $V = 500,000$ volts.

Annihilation energy of 1 electron $= 0.5109$ Mev.   (70h)

This means that if the energy liberated by the annihilation of an electron could be given to another electron in the form of kinetic energy, that electron would have a velocity equivalent to half a million volts. In other words, it would have the same velocity and energy as an electron which has been accelerated by a potential of 500,000 volts in a tube of the kind shown in Fig. 65A.

In certain processes to be described in the next chapter atomic mass is sometimes converted into a gamma-ray. To calculate the frequency of such a γ-ray we make use of the second and third terms in Eq.(70f), that

$$mc^2 = h\nu, \tag{70i}$$

from which we find $\nu = 1.2 \times 10^{20}$ vib/sec. Such a frequency is 200,000 times that of visible green light and the wave length about two hundredths of an angstrom unit. As a proof of Eq.(70i), experiments show that γ-rays of twice this frequency, or higher, will produce electron pairs by collision (see Fig. 71I), whereas those of lower frequency will not.

As a third and last example we may calculate the energy liberated by the annihilation of one *atomic mass unit*, that is, the energy equivalent to one sixteenth the mass of an ordinary oxygen atom. Substituting the known values of m, c, and e, in Eq.(70g), the following is obtained.

Annihilation energy of 1 atomic mass unit $= 931.33$ Mev.   (70j)

This is a useful number to memorize, for it is frequently used in the following chapters. Atomic mass unit is abbreviated *amu.*

70.6. Atomic Masses Are Not Whole Numbers. When an α-particle collides with the nucleus of an atom and produces a disintegration as shown in Fig. 70D, the total energy before collision must be equal to the total energy after collision. To verify this, all forms of energy involved in the process must be included; namely, (1) *the kinetic energy of all particles,* (2) *the energy of a γ-ray if one is involved,* and (3) *the mass-energy.* The latter is necessary since disintegration experiments show that the total mass of the two colliding particles is not in general equal to the total mass after disintegration. To test this change, it is necessary that we know the exact masses of all atoms individually.

Recent mass spectrographic measurements by Aston, Bainbridge, and others (see Chap. 59), show that the masses of atoms are not exactly whole number values as previously suspected and given in Appendix IV. A list of the most recent mass determinations of some of the lighter elements of the periodic table is given in Appendix V. These values are all based upon the oxygen isotope 16 as having a mass of exactly 16.0000.

70.7. Conservation of Energy in Nuclear Disintegrations. To illustrate the law of conservation of energy as it applies to nuclear disintegrations, consider Rutherford's first experiment, shown in Figs. 70A and 70D, where α-particles from *radium C'* passing through nitrogen gas make collisions with and disintegrate nitrogen nuclei. The total energy of any two particles before impact will be the sum of the masses of the two nuclei, $_2He^4 + _7N^{14}$, plus their kinetic energy E_1. The total energy after impact will be the sum of the masses of the two nuclei, $_8O^{17}$ and $_1H^1$, plus their kinetic energy E_2, or,

$$_2He^4 + _7N^{14} + E_1 = _8O^{17} + _1H^1 + E_2. \tag{70k}$$

It is customary to express the energies E_1 and E_2 in *mass units* or in million electron volts, Mev. Now the kinetic energy before impact is confined to the α-particle from radium C', which has been measured and found to be equivalent to 7.7 Mev. Dividing this value by 931, from Eq.(70j), gives the equivalent of 0.00827 mass unit. Adding mass-energy for both sides of Eq.(70k), we must obtain the same total.

$_2He^4 =$	4.00387	$_8O^{17} =$	17.00453
$_7N^{14} =$	14.00751	$_1H^1 =$	1.00814
$E_1 =$	0.00827	$E_2 =$	?
Total	18.01965		18.01965

(711)

Simple addition and subtraction show that, to give the proper sum for the right-hand column, E_2 must be equal to 0.00698 mass unit. Multiplying by 931 gives, this time, 6.50 Mev as the energy liberated. This is the liberated energy utilized in the "explosion" which drives the proton and oxygen nuclei apart.

In general, when an atomic nucleus disintegrates by splitting up into two particles, the annihilation energy is divided between them. Experiments show that this division takes place according to the ordinary laws of mechanics, that the kinetic energies of the two particles are approximately inversely proportional to their respective masses.

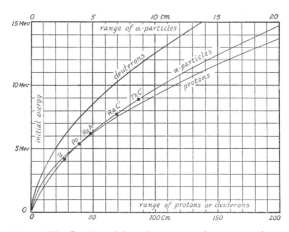

Fig. 70H—Graphs giving the range of protons, deuterons, and α-particles for different initial energies in million electron volts.

When, in the above example, the available energy is divided between an oxygen nucleus of mass 17 and a proton of mass 1, the $_8O^{17}$ nucleus acquires an energy of 0.36 Mev, and the proton an energy of 6.18 Mev. A proton with this kinetic energy and velocity has a range of 49 cm in air. Recent repetitions of Rutherford's experiment give measured ranges of 48 cm and an energy of 6 Mev, in good agreement with the calculation.

Graphs showing the ranges of protons, deuterons and α-particles for different energies are drawn in Fig. 70H. These three curves are extremely useful in disintegration work, for knowing the range of a particle, its initial energy becomes known, or knowing the initial energy, the range becomes known. It is interesting to note that for the same energy a proton has ten times the range of an α-particle.* Deuterons will be considered in detail in succeeding chapters.

* "Radioactivity and Nuclear Physics," by J. M. Cork, D. Van Nostrand Co., Inc.

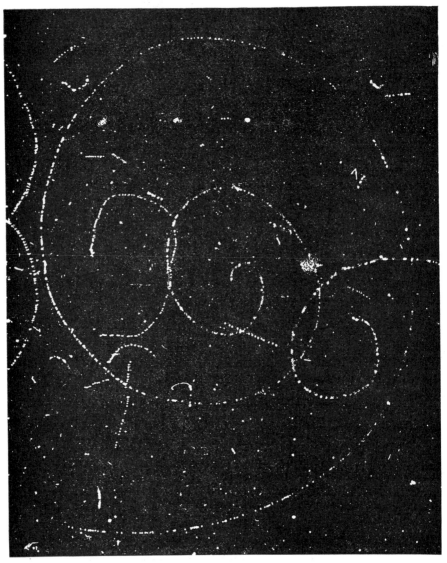

F<small>IG</small>. 70I—Bubble chamber photograph showing electron tracks in liquid hydrogen at −247°C and in a strong magnetic field. (*Courtesy of L. W. Alvarez*)

70.8. The Bubble Chamber. The discovery by D. A. Glaser that bubbles will form on ionized atoms and molecules in a super-heated liquid has led to the development of a most useful instrument known as *the bubble chamber*. The phenomenon involved is brought about by applying pressure to a liquid and then heating the liquid to very nearly its new boiling point. When the pressure is suddenly reduced, boiling sets in with the formation of tiny bubbles. Thus, any ion tracks produced by the previous traversal of the liquid by charged particles can be seen and photographed. See Fig. 70I and frontispiece.

PROBLEMS AND QUESTIONS

1. If the following masses could be annihilated, how much energy, in Mev, is created? (a) 0.0045 atomic mass unit, (b) 0.0145 atomic mass unit.

2. If one kilogram of water could be completely annihilated, how many joules would be produced? (*Ans.* 9×10^{16} joules.)

3. Calculate the mass equivalent to an energy of (a) 15 Mev, (b) 24 Mev, (c) 3.5 Mev.

4. Complete the following disintegration reactions:

$$_1H^2 + {}_8O^{16} \rightarrow {}_7N^{14} + ? \qquad\qquad _1H^2 + {}_5B^{10} \rightarrow {}_6C^{11} + ?$$
$$_2He^4 + {}_{13}Al^{27} \rightarrow {}_{14}Si^{30} + ? \qquad\qquad _1H^1 + {}_3Li^6 \rightarrow {}_2He^4 + ?$$

(*Ans.* $_2He^4$, $_1H^1$, $_0n^1$, $_2He^3$.)

5. From the known masses of the atoms in the reactions of Prob. 4, find the energy liberated by each disintegration in Mev. Assume the incident energy of the lighter nucleus in each reaction to be 20 Mev.

6. From the graphs plotted in Fig. 70H, write down the ranges of the following particles: (a) 8 Mev protons, (b) 12 Mev protons, (c) 10 Mev α-particles, (d) 14 Mev deuterons, and (e) 2 Mev α-particles. (*Ans.* (a) 78 cm, (b) 158 cm, (c) 10.5 cm, (d) 122 cm, (e) 1.0 cm.)

7. If the following mass is annihilated and 90% of it goes into kinetic energy of an α-particle, find the range of the particle in air at normal atmospheric pressure: (a) 0.0123 amu, (b) 0.0039 amu.

8. Briefly explain the experiment by which Chadwick discovered the neutron. Make a diagram.

9. Give a brief description of the Rutherford experiment in which the first nuclear disintegrations were discovered.

10. Make a table of the following atoms giving the number of protons and neutrons in each nucleus: Ba^{138}, Ca^{44}, Fe^{56}, I^{127}, Au^{197}.

11. The range of protons in air are found to have the following values: (a) 5 cm, (b) 12 cm, (c) 75 cm, and (d) 200 cm. Find their energies in Mev.

12. Deuterons from a radioactive source are found to have three definite ranges: (a) 12 cm, (b) 65 cm, and (c) 120 cm. Determine their energies from Fig. 70H. (*Ans.* (a) 3.6 Mev, (b) 9.9 Mev, (c) 13.9 Mev.)

13. Alpha-particles from a radioactive material are found to have three ranges: (a) 2.5 cm, (b) 7.2 cm, and (c) 17.0 cm. Find their energies using Fig. 70H.

14. In a nuclear disintegration process a mass of 0.01800 amu is annihilated and 90 per cent of the liberated energy is imparted as kinetic energy to an α-particle. Find (a) its energy in Mev, and (b) its range. (*Ans.* (a) 15.08 Mev, (b) 21 cm.)

Cosmic Rays   Chapter 71

KARL K. DARROW has described the subject of cosmic rays "as unique in modern physics for the minuteness of the phenomena, the delicacy of the observations, the adventurous excursions of the observers, the subtlety of the analysis, and the grandeur of the inferences." * It is impossible for anyone to say when and by whom cosmic rays were first studied. From the time of the discovery of radioactivity by Becquerel (in 1896) and the discovery of radium by the Curies but a few months later, the radioactive rays from the ground, air and outer space have been investigated by many scientists. Extending over a period of some fifty years these investigations have led to some of the most interesting and important discoveries in the structure of atomic nuclei.

71.1. Early Experiments. It has long been known that a charged electroscope, if left standing for some little time, will discharge regardless of how well the gold leaf is insulated. Realizing that the rays from radioactive materials can be stopped by a sufficient thickness of heavy matter, Rutherford and Cooke (in Canada, 1903) surrounded an electroscope with a thick wall of brick and found very little decrease in the rate of discharge. McLennan and his co-workers (also in Canada) lowered an electroscope into a lake hoping that the thick layer of water would screen off the rays. This experiment, like the other, failed. In 1910 Glockel, with an electroscope, rose nearly 3 mi in a balloon in order to get away from the ground radiation, but to his astonishment he found that the rate of discharge did not decrease but increased the higher he went. The same effect was observed by Hess (in Austria, 1911) and Kolhörster (in Germany, 1914). Rising to heights as great as 5½ mi, both of these observers independently found that the intensity of these unknown radiations became greater the higher they went. Because in one of his scientific publications concerning these results Hess suggested the possibility that some kind of penetrating rays were entering the earth's atmosphere from outer space, he is usually credited with the discovery of cosmic rays. For this reason he was granted the Nobel Prize in physics for the year 1936.

71.2. Millikan and Bowen's Discovery. Soon after World War I

---

* This quotation is from a monograph on cosmic rays by Karl K. Darrow, American physicist and contemporary writer of modern physics at the Bell Telephone Laboratories.

(1922), R. A. Millikan, with the help of I. S. Bowen, constructed several small self-recording string electroscopes. Making use of their war time experiences with sounding balloons, they sent these electroscopes high into the stratosphere by fastening each one to two sounding balloons. As shown in Fig. 71A, the string electroscope *E* consists of two gold-covered quartz fibers insulated and mounted with their ends together. When they are charged the fibers spread apart due to mutual repulsion, and as they discharge they slowly come together.

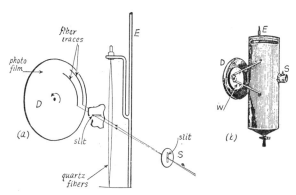

Fig. 71A—Diagrams of one of the sensitive electroscopes sent up into the stratosphere by Millikan and Bowen to measure cosmic rays (a) Schematic diagram, (b) Scale drawing of entire instrument 6 in high.

Daylight, passing through a narrow vertical slit *S* in the instrument case, casts a shadow of the center section of the fibers on a rotating disk *D* containing a photographic film. As the film turns slowly and the fibers come together they leave a double trace as indicated in the diagram. On the same film a small oil manometer recorded the height of ascent and a small thermometer recorded the temperature. The film was driven by a watch *W*, the whole apparatus weighing only 7 oz. On one of the best record flights only one of the balloons burst at a height of 10 mi and the other brought the instruments safely to earth. Like the earlier results obtained by other experimenters, Millikan and Bowen found the ionization to increase with increasing altitude. After extending the observations of previous workers to higher altitudes Millikan and Bowen became convinced, and announced their belief, that the rays were coming from interstellar space.

71.3. The Penetration of Cosmic Rays. In order to determine the nature of the new rays, Millikan and his co-workers, Otis, Cameron, and Bowen, in the fall of 1922, began an extensive study of the penetrating power of cosmic rays. Since cosmic rays penetrate our atmosphere of many miles of air, how far might they penetrate beyond?

Self-recording electroscopes were lowered to various depths in snow-fed lakes as illustrated schematically in Fig. 71B. Measurements taken at Arrowhead Lake in Southern California (at an elevation of 5100 ft) agreed approximately with those taken at Muir Lake near Mt. Whitney (at an elevation of 11,800 ft), provided one took into account the increased air path for the lower elevation. The extra mile and a quarter of air is equivalent in weight to 6 ft of water. As cosmic rays penetrate deeper and deeper

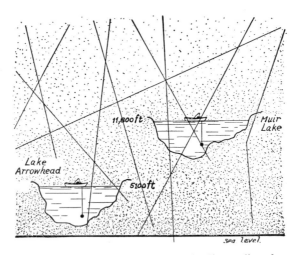

Fig. 71B—Illustrating the lowering of self-recording electroscopes into deep snow-fed lakes to measure the absorption of cosmic rays by the water.

below the surface of water their number decreases, until at a depth of 100 ft the intensity is reduced to about one-ten-thousandth of that at the surface. With very sensitive electroscopes cosmic radiation capable of penetrating 2000 ft of water has more recently been detected. This is a far greater penetrating power than that possessed by any known x-rays, or γ-rays from radioactivity.

71.4. The Geiger-Mueller Tube Counter. There are in general four methods of observing and measuring cosmic rays. These are (a) *Geiger-Mueller tube counters*, (b) *Wilson cloud chambers*, (c) *ionization chambers*, (d) *photographic emulsions* and scintillation counters. The latter is described in Sec. 64.11.

The Geiger-Mueller tube, named after its inventors, is one of the simplest electrical instruments ever designed (see Fig. 71C). It

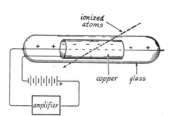

Fig. 71C—Diagram of a Geiger counter, quite commonly used to detect cosmic rays.

consists of an open-ended copper cylinder from 1 to 25 in long fitted inside a thin-walled glass cylinder with a fine tungsten wire stretched along the middle. After the tube has been partially evacuated (a pressure of from 5 to 10 cm of mercury is convenient), a potential of about 1000 volts is applied, the positive to the center wire and the negative to the cylinder.

When a single cosmic ray or high-speed particle from a radioactive source goes through a Geiger-Mueller tube, ions are created by the freeing of electrons from air molecules. These freed electrons are attracted by the positively charged wire and move toward it, acquiring within a very short distance a high velocity of their own. Because of this velocity they, too, can ionize other atoms, thus freeing more electrons. This multiplication of charges repeats itself in rapid succession, producing within a very short interval of time an *avalanche of electrons toward the central wire.* This sudden surge of charge is equivalent to the flow of a small current impulse along the electrical circuit. When this current has been intensified by an amplifier it may be made to operate an electric switch, a radio loud-speaker, or any kind of an electrical device.

Quite frequently the impulses of a Geiger-Mueller tube are made to operate a small counting device. Each cosmic ray particle passing through the tube is therefore counted automatically. The number of counts received per second depends upon the size of the counter tube. An average-sized tube 1 in. in diameter and several inches long, at sea level, gives from 50 to 100 counts per minute.

71.5. Directional Effects. To observe the direction of the greatest cosmic ray intensity, a cosmic ray telescope is used. Such a telescope is made by connecting two or more Geiger-Mueller tubes *in coincidence,* and mounting them on a common support some distance apart. Tubes in coincidence are so connected electrically that a current will flow in the accompanying electric circuit only when both tubes discharge at the same time. When the tubes are set above the other, as shown in Fig. 71D(a), a single cosmic ray on going through both cylinders will cause a current to flow and a count to be made. If, however, a particle goes through one and not the other, no count is recorded. Experiments at sea level show that when the telescope is mounted in the horizontal position (b) few counts are made, whereas when it is mounted in a vertical direction, many more counts are recorded. The interpretation to be made, therefore, is that cosmic rays come principally from overhead.

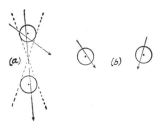

Fig. 71D—Diagram of two Geiger counters. Connected together they form a cosmic ray telescope.

As a verification of the telescope method, a Wilson cloud chamber is frequently inserted between two Geiger counter tubes as shown in Fig. 71E and a photograph of each cosmic ray is taken. Thousands of such photographs are made automatically by having a single cosmic ray take its own picture. This is accomplished by allowing the sudden electric current from the counter tubes, produced by a ray in transit, to open and close a camera shutter, to cause the cloud chamber to expand, and to flash a light, illuminating the fog track that forms.

In the reproduction of Fig. 71E, either one of the two cosmic rays would have tripped the electrical devices and taken the picture. It should be noted that both rays passed right through a 0.5 in lead plate without being deviated. Cloud chamber pictures are not photographs of cosmic rays but of the path traversed by the rays.

71.6. The Altitude Effect. The results of airplane and balloon flights into the stratosphere have shown that the intensity of cosmic rays increases up to a height of from 12 to 15 mi and then decreases again. In 1935 Stevens and Anderson,* for example, rose to a height of nearly 14 mi carrying with them, among other scientific instruments, Geiger-Mueller tube counters. With these instruments they measured the cosmic ray intensity at various altitudes on both their ascent and descent.

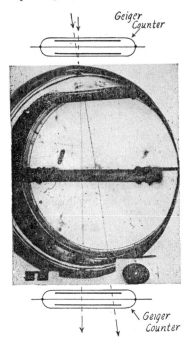

FIG. 71E — With a Wilson cloud chamber mounted between two Geiger tubes connected in coincidence the cosmic rays are made to take their own picture. (*After Brode.*)

The compiled experimental results of various observers taken at different elevations are illustrated by the curves in Fig. 71F. Near the city of Omaha, at a latitude of 51°N, the maximum is found at a height of 15 mi where an intensity 170 times as great as that at sea level has been measured. From that altitude to the highest points that observations have been made, about 17 mi, there is a gradual decrease in total intensity.

The four different curves in the figure show, from altitude measurements made by observers all over the world, that in nearing the magnetic equator the cosmic ray intensity decreases at high altitudes as well as at sea level.

71.7. Primaries and Secondaries. Experimental observations show that the cosmic rays entering our atmosphere are almost entirely composed

---

* Capt. A. W. Stevens and O. A. Anderson, *National Geographic Magazine,* Vol. LXIX, 1936, p. 693.

of positively charged atomic nuclei. About two-thirds of these so-called *primary cosmic rays* are protons, and the other third (by mass) are about 90% α-particles and 10% heavier nuclei like carbon, nitrogen, oxygen, iron, etc.

Upon entering the atmosphere, a high energy primary particle soon collides with another atomic nucleus, splitting one or both particles into a number of smaller nuclear fragments, each one of which carries away some of the primary's energy. These high-speed particles in turn collide with other nuclei further dividing their energy to produce other high speed particles. All of these with the exception of the primary particle are called *secondary cosmic rays*.

One of the results of cosmic ray collision processes is the creation of very high frequency and highly penetrating gamma rays. These photons, too, are included in the classification *Secondary Cosmic Rays*.

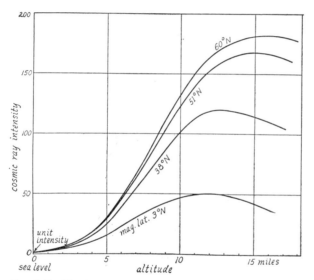

Fig. 71F—The intensity of cosmic rays increases with altitude up to a height of 10 to 15 mi and then decreases.

At a height of some 15 mi, about ten to fifteen times as many secondary cosmic rays exist as have entered the atmosphere as primaries. At this level, where more than nine-tenths of the earth's atmosphere still lies below, as many rays are observed moving in a horizontal direction as in the vertical. From the diagram presented in Fig. 71G it becomes quite clear why the primaries are difficult to distinguish from the far greater number of secondaries.

At lower altitudes the total intensity decreases since many of the secondaries produced above are stopped by collision. In other words, so much energy is lost by successive collisions that the energy is gradually absorbed as heat motion by the air molecules. By the time sea level is reached the remaining rays consist principally of a few high-speed secondaries and primaries. Even at sea level some of these have enough energy left to penetrate several hundred, and even several thousand feet of earth and water.

It should be borne in mind that between collisions of the type indicated in Fig. 71G each cosmic ray particle is continually being slowed down as it

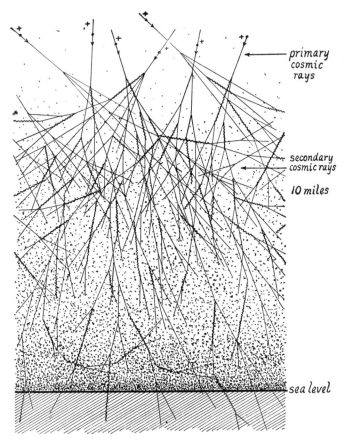

primary cosmic rays

secondary cosmic rays

10 miles

sea level

Fig. 71G—Schematic illustration of secondary cosmic rays produced from primaries entering the earth's atmosphere.

"plows through" thousands of air molecules, knocking electrons free to produce ions. These are the ions on which fogdrops form, revealing the path in a cloud chamber.

Although γ-rays also lose energy by collisions with atoms to produce Compton electrons, the γ-rays themselves do not leave visible tracks in a Wilson cloud chamber. The reason for this is that collisions are few and far between and the resulting fogdrops are too far apart.

71.8. Effect of the Earth's Magnetic Field. The decrease in cosmic ray intensity at the earth's magnetic equator (see Fig. 70F) is now explained as being due to the earth's magnetic field. This is illustrated in Fig. 71H. The paths of all charged particles crossing the earth's magnetic field are bent by a force which is perpendicular to the direction of the field. The result is that some rays entering the earth's field are deflected back into free space without ever reaching the earth's surface. At the magnetic equator where the magnetic lines of force are more nearly perpendicular to the incoming particles the deflecting force is a maximum. The curved paths shown in the diagram are not confined to the plane of the page. Only those of high energy which enter nearly straight down have much chance of ever reaching the earth's surface.

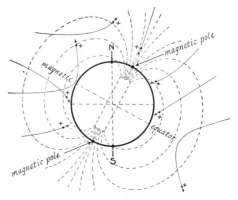

FIG. 71H—Illustrating the effect the earth's magnetic field has upon primary cosmic rays.

At the magnetic poles, particles coming straight down run nearly parallel to the field and experience no deflecting force. These have a better chance of getting through to the earth's surface.

71.9. Discovery of the Positron. The positron, or positive electron, was discovered by Anderson in 1932 by photographing the tracks of cosmic rays in a Wilson cloud chamber. Under the influence of a strong magnetic field applied perpendicular to the face of the cloud chamber, positively charged particles should bend to the right and negatively charged particles should bend to the left. In order to be certain that those bent one way were not all coming from above and those bent the other way were particles of the same kind and charge coming from below, Anderson inserted a block of lead in the chamber to slow down the particles. Under these conditions photographs similar to the one shown in (a) of Fig. 71I were obtained. Here Anderson could be quite certain, from the curvature of the track on each side of the lead, that the particle entered from the side shown above, for in pass‑ing through the lead plate it could only have been slowed down and not speeded up. Knowing the direction of motion, the direction of the field, and the direction of bending, Anderson concluded that such a particle had a posi‑

tive charge. Comparing the track with well-known electron tracks and alpha-particle tracks, he concluded that the new particle had about the same mass as the electron. Later experiments continued to give more positive proof of the existence of a positive electron. Now very strong beams of positrons can be produced in the laboratory.

It should be pointed out here that near sea level most cosmic rays come from above, whereas a few come from other angles and the horizontal and some even from below.

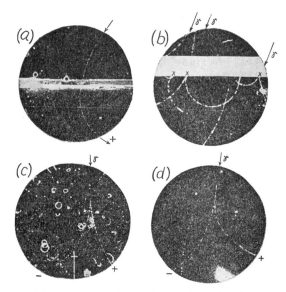

Fig. 71I—Wilson cloud chamber photographs of pair production. X-ray coming close to the nucleus of an atom produces a pair of electrons, one positive and one negative. (a) Discovery of a positron (*after Anderson*), (b) Three pairs of electrons produced by X-rays (*after Anderson*), (c) Pair produced in air by X-rays (*after Lauritson and Fowler*), (d) Pair produced in air by X-rays from Thorium C″ (*after Simons and Zuber*).

71.10. Creation of Electron Pairs. Soon after Anderson's discovery of the positron J. R. Oppenheimer attempted to calculate the conditions under which a positron might exist in nature. An extension of the quantum theory of the electron, proposed earlier by P. Dirac, led him to the prediction that if a high energy photon, i.e., a high-frequency γ-ray, were to come close enough to the nucleus of an atom, the electric field of the nucleus would be strong enough to annihilate the γ-ray and create in its place a *pair of particles, an electron and a positron.* These two particles, the theory predicts, should have the same mass, and equal but opposite charges. A schematic diagram of pair production is given in Fig. 71J.

Blackett, Anderson, and others looking for such pairs in a cloud chamber soon found them exactly as predicted. γ-rays, from a radioactive element like *thorium C″*, in passing through matter were observed to produce pairs of electrons. Three photographs of such incidents are shown in Fig. 71I. In (b) three different pairs are seen emerging from the points marked *X* on the lower side of a lead plate, and in (c) and (d) a pair is seen having been produced apparently in mid-air. As usual the γ-rays that produced these pairs do not show up in the cloud chamber.

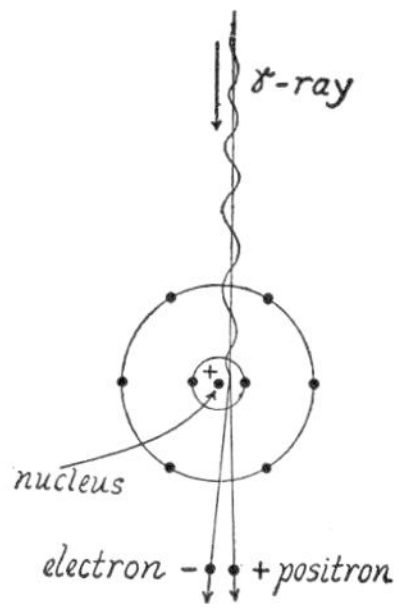

When an electron pair is created, *conservation of energy and momentum* require the two particles to move almost straight forward. Without a magnetic field applied to the cloud chamber the particles travel side by side in almost parallel paths, but with a magnetic field the path of the positron bends to one side and that of the electron to the other.

The reason positrons were not discovered earlier in the history of physics is that they do not exist long in the free state. As soon as a positron meets with an electron, the two are annihilated.

Experiments indicate that all electrons and positrons spin around an axis through their center of mass. There is good evidence that when a positron and an electron come close together they frequently combine by revolving around each other like a double-star, with their spin axes parallel to one another. As such a pair they are called *positronium*. Positronium is very short lived for soon the two particles disintegrate completely and in their place γ-rays are created. If the particles were spinning in the same direction, they would disintegrate into three γ-rays of different energies, whereas, if they were spinning in opposite directions, they would produce two γ-rays. Conservation of energy and momentum require these latter to each have an energy of ½ Mev. (See Eq.(70h).)

71.11. Cosmic Ray Showers. Out of hundreds and hundreds of cloud chamber photographs of cosmic rays, the experimenter is occasionally rewarded with a picture of a cosmic ray shower. Instead of one or two tracks in the picture in this instance one finds anywhere from half a dozen or more to several hundred. As shown by the photographs in Fig. 71K most of the tracks of a shower seem to come from one localized region usually within a solid piece of matter like a lead plate or the wall of the cloud chamber.

An extensive study of showers by both the experimental and theoretical

Fig. 71J—Schematic diagram of pair production. A high energy γ-ray passing close to the nucleus of an atom is annihilated and in its place a pair of electrons, one plus and one minus are created.

physicists has led to the conclusion that each shower is produced by a single high energy cosmic ray. A charged particle of very high energy upon entering a solid block of matter where atoms are packed very close together carries out the multiple collision process illustrated in Fig. 71G. Here within a short distance of 1 or 2 cm of lead enough atoms are encountered to yield many secondaries. These secondaries emerging from the lower face of the metal result in the observed photographs. In a thin sheet of metal, relatively small showers are usually found, whereas with a thick metal block showers of many tracks are occasionally photographed. The first five photographs in Fig. 71K were taken without a magnetic field and the tracks are all straight, while the last photo was taken with a magnetic field. The bending of three tracks to the right and three to the left indicates equal numbers of both positrons and electrons.

In photograph (a) a single high-speed particle is seen to enter the lead plate from above and to produce some twenty or more secondary particles, each with enough energy to get through and into the air space below. In (b) two small showers of particles enter the top surface of the lead plate, whereas a single larger shower emerges from the bottom. Apparently one or

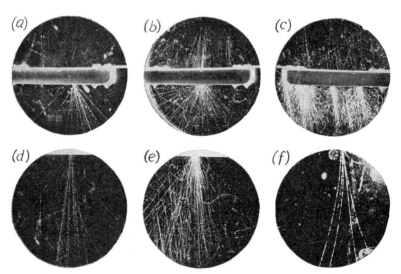

Fɪɢ. 71K—Wilson cloud chamber photographs of cosmic ray showers. (*The first three photographs are reproduced through the courtesy of R. B. Brode and the last three through the courtesy of C. D. Anderson and the Physical Review.*)

two of the particles at the center of the one shower above have the necessary high energy to produce the lower shower, whereas the others of lower energy are stopped by the lead. Note particularly the fanning out of the rays below. In (c) a small shower of very high energy particles enters the chamber from above, having been produced far above the cloud chamber in a shower producing process, probably by a single particle of extremely high energy. As some of these secondaries pass through the lead each produces a shower of its own.

Direct evidence that some showers originate with a single high energy particle is shown in Fig. 71L. Here in a cloud chamber with five equally spaced lead plates a relatively large shower is seen to have grown from but one or possibly two particles at the top. Not only does this avalanche grow in numbers with each traversal of a lead plate but the relatively small spread of the tracks indicates how nearly each new particle recoils along with the others in the forward direction. In this picture one observes in the small space of several inches the process that, in Fig. 71G, requires several miles of air.

71.12. Mesons. The presence in cosmic rays of charged particles having a mass several hundred times that of an electron, yet considerably lighter than a proton, was discovered by Anderson and Nedermeyer in 1938. These particles now called *mesons* are of several kinds, and experimental data taken in balloons and airplanes show that most of them are produced high in the atmosphere by the collisions of primary cosmic rays with air nuclei.

In these collisions positively and negatively charged π-mesons are produced along with neutral π-mesons, protons, and neutrons as shown in Fig. 71M. The π-mesons, each with a mass of about 275 m_e, along with other nuclear particles, recoil forward with speeds close to that of light. (m_e = mass of an electron.) The term nuclear particles is here applied to only those particles believed to exist in atomic nuclei and consist of protons, neutrons, deuterons, and alpha-particles.

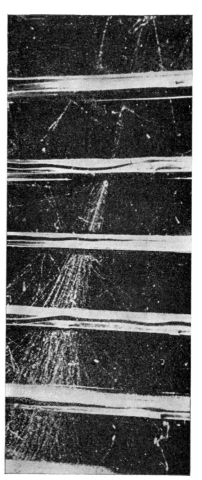

Fig. 71L—Photograph showing cascade shower growth of cosmic rays in five layers of lead. (*Taken on Mt. Evans, Colo., by W. Powell.*)

The possible existence of, and the spontaneous disintegration of mesons was first predicted by Yukawa* in 1935, and first photographed by Williams

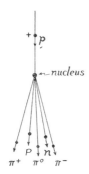

Fig. 71M—Primary cosmic ray produces π-mesons by nuclear collision.

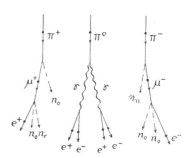

Fig. 71N—π-mesons disintegrate into μ-mesons, γ-rays, electrons, and neutrinos.

and Roberts in 1940. All charged π-mesons seem to have a half-life of 2×10^{-8} sec, and each one decays into a charged μ-meson and a light-weight neutral particle called a neutrino. The charged μ-meson in turn decays, with a half-life of 2×10^{-6} sec, into an electron and two neutrinos as shown in

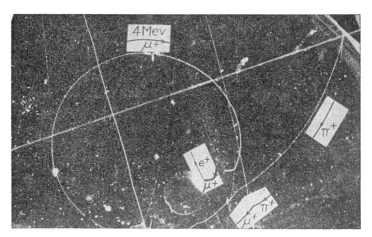

Fig. 71O—Wilson cloud chamber photographed in a magnetic field of 8000 gauss showing decay of π-meson into a μ-meson and the μ-meson into a positron. *Courtesy W. Powell.*

Fig. 71N and Fig. 71O. The neutrino n_o is an uncharged particle, not yet observed or detected by anyone, but postulated by physicists in order to ex-

* Yukawa, Proceedings Physical and Math. Society, Japan, **17**, 48, 1935.

plain nuclear phenomena in keeping with the fundamental laws of the conservation of energy and of momentum.

The uncharged π-mesons are very unstable. With a half-life of less than 10^{-14} sec they decay into two γ-rays. In the upper atmosphere these γ-rays create cascade showers of electrons by electron pair-production and bremsstrahlung. See Fig. 71L. Many of the charged μ-mesons, with their mass of about 210 m_e, traverse the atmosphere before decaying, and reach the surface of the earth. At sea level the charged cosmic rays are nearly 70% μ-mesons and 29% electrons and positrons, with about 1% heavier particles like protons, deuterons, α-particles, etc.

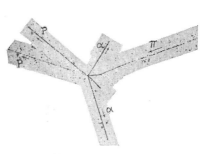

FIG. 71P—"Star" in photographic emulsion showing the explosion of a nucleus resulting from the capture of a slow π-meson. *Courtesy of C. F. Powell's laboratory, University of Bristol, England.*

In traversing solid matter negatively charged π-mesons frequently slow down to such a speed that upon an encounter with a nucleus they are attracted by the + charge, and captured. In this process the meson mass is transformed into energy exciting the nucleus to such a state that it literally explodes by shooting out a number of heavier particles like protons, deuterons, α-particles, etc. Fig. 71P shows such a "star" event in a photographic emulsion.

Recent studies of cosmic ray tracks made in photographic emulsions and cloud chambers indicate the presence of particles with masses of about (a) 966 m_e called *τ-mesons*, (b) 1200 m_e called *κ-mesons*, and (c) 2200 m_e called *V-particles*. How these all fit into the structure of matter is but one of the many mysteries of modern physics that only future experimentation can reveal.

QUESTIONS

1. Make a diagram of a Geiger-Mueller tube counter and briefly explain how it is able to be used to detect atomic particles of high energy.
2. Who was awarded the Nobel Prize in physics for the discovery of cosmic rays? What was his experimental observation?
3. How does the intensity of cosmic rays vary with altitude?
4. Explain why the intensity of cosmic rays is a minimum near the equator. Make a diagram.
5. How was the positron discovered and by whom?
6. Under what conditions are electron pairs created?
7. What is a cosmic ray telescope and how is it made?
8. What are primary cosmic rays and of what are they composed?
9. What are secondary cosmic rays and of what are they composed?
10. Make a list of all the atomic particles found in cosmic rays.

Atomic Accelerators   Chapter 72

72.1. The Cockcroft-Walton Experiment. Believing that the disintegration of atomic nuclei might be accomplished by using other than α-particles as projectiles, Rutherford instigated in 1930 the construction of a high-voltage, direct-current generator at the Cavendish laboratory. The purpose of this *million volt* source of potential was to accelerate hydrogen nuclei, *protons*, to high speeds and then cause them to strike known substances. In this way he hoped to produce new and various kinds of disintegrations.

Becoming impatient with the relatively slow progress of the project, however, Rutherford suggested to Cockcroft and Walton that lower voltages be tried in the meantime to see if by chance disintegrations might occur. In 1932 Cockcroft and Walton announced that they had successfully disintegrated lithium atoms with protons accelerated by relatively low voltages. Their apparatus is schematically represented in Fig. 72A.

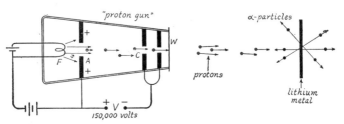

Fig. 72A—Schematic diagram of the Cockcroft-Walton experiment. Lithium is disintegrated by 150,000 volt protons.

Electrons from a hot filament F, passing through hydrogen gas in the region of A, ionize many hydrogen atoms. These protons with their positive charge are then accelerated toward the other end of the tube by a potential V of 150,000 volts. Upon passing through the opening C and a window W, they emerge from the acceleration chamber as a narrow beam of protons.

This tube, acting as a "proton gun," is aimed at a target consisting of lithium metal. Cockcroft and Walton observed and measured α-particles emanating from the metal with a range of 8 cm, an energy equivalent to 8.5 Mev. Considering the relatively low energy of the bombarding protons of only 0.15 Mev, this is a tremendous release in atomic energy. The transmutation taking place here is written as follows:

$$_1H^1 + {}_3Li^7 + E_1 = {}_2He^4 + {}_2He^4 + E_2. \qquad (72a)$$

This reaction, illustrated in Fig. 72B, shows a proton, $_1H^1$, of energy E_1 = 0.15 Mev, entering a lithium nucleus, $_3Li^7$, to form a new but unstable beryllium nucleus, $_4Be^8$. Being unstable this compact structure of eight particles splits up into two a-particles which are driven apart with great violence. Since the measured energy of each a-particle is equivalent to 8.5 Mev, each disintegration involves the liberation of 17.0 Mev energy. The source of energy is to be found in the annihilation of a part of the total atomic mass.

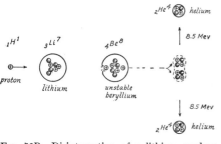

FIG. 72B—Disintegration of a lithium nucleus by a proton of 0.15 Mev. energy. The Cockcroft—Walton experiment.

The loss in mass can be calculated from the table of atomic weights, given in Appendix V. List the involved masses in two columns and add.

$$_1H^1 = 1.00814$$
$$_3Li^7 = 7.01822 \qquad _2He^4 = 4.00387$$
$$E_1 = 0.00016 \qquad _2He^4 = 4.00387$$
$$\overline{8.02652} \qquad \qquad \overline{8.00774}$$

E_1 is the mass equivalent to the energy of the incident proton and is obtained by dividing 0.15 Mev by 931 (see Eq.(70j)). The difference between the two sums, $8.02652 - 8.00774 = 0.01878$ mass unit, represents the loss in mass by the disintegration. When multiplied by 931, this gives 17.48 Mev as the liberated energy, a value in good agreement with the experimentally determined value of 17.0 Mev.

It might be thought that such a disintegration as the one described above could be used as a source of energy but as yet it has not been feasible to do so. While each nuclear collision and disintegration liberates at least one hundred times as much energy as that supplied to the proton, it takes many particles to make a few collisions. In other words, only a small percentage of the proton bullets hit the tiny nuclear targets as they pass through matter. Most of them are slowed down by electron collisions and the ionization of atoms. To a proton bullet the lithium nuclei as targets in the lithium metal present an area millions of times smaller than the space between them.

72.2. The Lawrence Cyclotron. At the time Cockcroft and Walton were performing their first disintegration experiments, E. O. Lawrence,* an American physicist, was developing a new type of atomic accelerator which soon attracted the attention of the leading physicists the world over. So successful was this "atomic machine gun" in producing high-speed atomic projectiles for disintegration experiments that a new and larger cyclotron was soon constructed and put into operation. Now a cyclotron of considerable size occupies a most prominent position in many of the leading physics laboratories of the world.

One of the cyclotrons located at the University of California, and called the "sixty-inch," is an instrument capable of producing intense beams of protons, deuterons or α-particles having energies of 10, 20, and 40 Mev respectively. The purpose of these high-speed particles, as is the case with all such instruments, is to subject various known substances to bombardment and thus produce disintegrations and transmutations of all kinds.

Although the operation of a large cyclotron requires an elaborate outlay of apparatus and equipment, the principles upon which it operates are quite simple. As a means of explaining these principles, cross-section diagrams of a cyclotron are shown in Fig. 72C.

The very heart of the instrument consists of two short, hollow, half cylinders D_1 and D_2, mounted inside of a vacuum chamber V, between the poles of a powerful electromagnet, and connected on the outside to the two terminals of a high-frequency alternating current generator. It is interesting to point out that this generator is really a short-wave radio transmitter supplying energy to the dees (D_1 and D_2) instead of to the antenna. When a trace of hydrogen gas is admitted to the evacuated chamber the hot wire filament F ionizes some of the hydrogen atoms, thereby producing the protons to be used as atomic bullets. At the particular instant when D_1 is charged positively and D_2 is charged negatively, a proton in the neighborhood of F will be accelerated toward D_2. Moving through the strong magnetic field of the huge magnet this positively charged particle traverses a

---

* Ernest O. Lawrence (1901-   ), American experimental physicist. Deriving his early education in South Dakota, Lawrence obtained the A.B. degree at the University of South Dakota in 1922, the master's degree at Minnesota in 1923, and the Ph.D. at Yale University in 1925. After two years as National Research Fellow he became, at the early age of twenty-six, Assistant Professor of Physics at Yale University. The following year he was appointed Associate Professor of Physics at the University of California, and in 1930 was made full Professor. Having built up the Radiation Laboratory at the same institution he became its Director in 1936. In 1937 he was awarded the Comstock Prize of the National Academy of Sciences, the Cresson Medal of the Franklin Institute, and the Hughes Medal of the Royal Society of London. Lawrence is a member of the National Academy of Sciences and is noted principally for his invention and development of the cyclotron and its application to the production of induced radioactivity. It is for these discoveries that he was granted the Nobel Prize in 1939. During World War II he directed one of the main research projects leading to the isolation of uranium 235 used in atomic bombs.

circular path as shown in the diagram. If, after making a half turn, the potential is reversed so that D_1 becomes negatively charged and D_2 positively charged, the proton will be attracted by one and repelled by the other causing it to increase its speed. With added speed it therefore moves in the arc of a larger circle as shown. After this second half turn the potential again reverses, making D_1 positive and D_2 negative, and again the proton speeds up. Thus, as the potential reverses periodically, the proton travels faster and faster, moving in ever-expanding circles, until, reaching the outer edge, it passes through a narrow open window W.

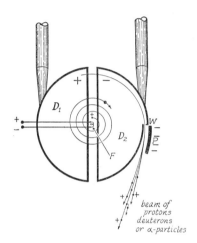
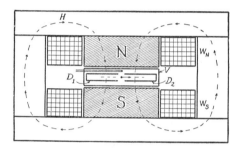

Fig. 72C—Diagram of the principal elements of a cyclotron.

Upon leaving W all protons must pass close to a negatively charged plate P where, by attraction, their paths are straightened out and they become a separated beam of projectiles. Whatever substance is to be bombarded is then placed in this beam, and the disintegrated fragments are studied by means of various detecting devices.

The fundamental principle that makes the cyclotron work at all is the fact that *the time required for a charged particle to make one complete turn within the dees is the same for all speeds.* The faster a particle travels the larger is the circle it must traverse, thus keeping the time constant. Hence with a constant frequency of the alternating current supply, some particles may be just starting their acceleration near the center while others farther out have already acquired higher speeds. The result is a more or less continuous stream of protons emerging from the window W.

If the alternating current voltage applied between the *dees* of the cyclotron is 200,000 volts, with each half turn a particle obtains an added velocity equivalent to 200,000 volts. If a proton makes twenty-five complete revolu-tions before leaving the chamber at *W*, it will have acquired a velocity equivalent to 200,000 times 25 times 2, or 10,000,000 volts. Here, then, is a beam of 10 Mev protons acquired by the application of a potential only one-fiftieth as great.

When hydrogen in the evacuated chamber of the 60-in. cyclotron is re-placed by *deuterium* and the magnetic field strength is doubled, a beam of high-energy deuterons is obtained. Having twice the mass but the same charge as protons these particles acquire twice as much energy. If helium gas is used in place of deuterium, many of the atoms become doubly ionized at the source and after acceleration emerge from the cyclotron window with an energy of about 40 Mev. By increasing or decreasing the frequency of the potential applied to the dees and properly adjusting the magnetic field protons, deuterons, or α-particles of 10, 20, and 40 Mev respectively can be produced.

Some of the details of the cyclotron shown in Figs. 72C and 72D are as follows: The dimension, 60 in., refers to the diameter of the poles of the cyclotron magnet, and this in turn limits the size of the dees and therefore the maximum energy available in the form of atomic projectiles. Most of the instrument's total weight of 200 tons lies in the solid core *I,* and the pole pieces located inside the field windings. The latter, consisting of many turns of thick copper wire, are encased in tanks W_S and W_N through which cool-ing fluid is continually circulated.

The cut-away diagram in Fig. 72D shows the dee supports as long hollow

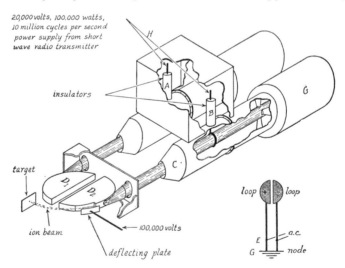

FIG. 72D—Assembly diagram showing the D's and their mounting supports, the deflecting plate, and the electrical supply connections.

tubes rigidly clamped and grounded at the one end G. The high voltage a.c. applied through vacuum tight joints AB sets each of the freely suspended dees into electrical oscillation.

Like Hertzian oscillators these two long rods resonate with a *voltage node* (zero potential) at the clamped end G and a *voltage loop* or peak at each of the dees. (See lower right-hand diagram, and Fig. 57G.) With the connections made at E, about one-fifth of the distance from G the peak potential at the dees reaches approximately five times that of the peak voltage applied. The electrical oscillations are analogous to the vibration of the prongs of a tuning fork. The applied voltage is approximately 20,000 volts, whereas each dee reaches approximately 100,000 volts. In some respects this step-up in voltage is similar to a step-up transformer.

Fig. 72E—Photograph by Paul Donaldson of an 11 Mev deuteron beam from the Harvard cyclotron. *(Courtesy of the Harvard University Press and A. K. Solomon.)*

A photograph of an 11 Mev deuteron beam from the Harvard University cyclotron is shown in Fig. 72E. From the point where they emerge from the cyclotron window at the left center to where they come to rest in mid-air at the lower right the high energy particles ionize the air molecules and atoms causing them to emit visible light.

72.3. Theory of the Cyclotron. The theory of the cyclotron involves simple classical laws describing the motion of a charged particle in a uniform magnetic field. By Eq.(53j), the force on a particle in a magnetic field is given by evB, and this is equal to the centripetal force mv^2/r.

$$evB = \frac{mv^2}{r}. \qquad (72b)$$

Here e is the charge on the particle in coulombs, m is its mass in kilograms, v is its velocity in meters per second, and r is the radius of its circular path in meters. To find the time required for any charged particle to make one complete circle the formula $s = vt$ from mechanics is employed. The distance traveled in one turn is represented by s, and T represents the time.

$$T = \frac{s}{v} = \frac{2\pi r}{v}. \qquad (72c)$$

By solving Eq.(72b) for v, and substituting in Eq.(72c), we obtain

$$v = \frac{Ber}{m} \quad \text{and} \quad T = \frac{2\pi}{B} \cdot \frac{m}{e}. \qquad (72d)$$

The latter shows that the *period* T is independent of r and v and for like particles, that is the same e and m, varies with the magnetic induction B. The alternating potential E applied to the cyclotron dees must therefore match in frequency the particles' motion due to the field B. It is customary in practice to apply a fixed frequency to the dees and adjust the current in the magnetic field coils until resonance occurs. In the 60-in. cyclotron $B = 1.6$ webers/meter^2 or 16,000 gauss.

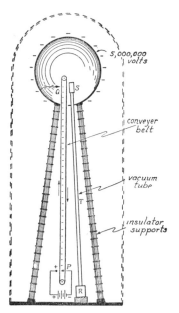

72.4 **The Van de Graaff Generator.** This machine developed in 1931 by R. Van de Graaff at Princeton University employs the principle of the electrostatic generator discovered many years ago. A typical installation, as shown in Fig. 72F, consists of a large hollow sphere, supported on insulating columns and charged by a belt conveying electrical charges from a battery at ground potential and depositing it inside the sphere. The fabric conveyor belt, a foot or more in width, and running over well aligned rollers, travels about 60 mi/hr.

As the belt passes between the metallic surface and row of needle points at P, elec-

Fig. 72F—Diagram of a Van de Graaff generator of high voltage.

trons from the points jump toward the positive electrode and are caught by the belt. Upon entering the sphere at the top the electrons jump to the needle points Q where they go quickly to the outside surface of the sphere. The "spraying" of electrons *to* and *from* the points is assured by keeping the battery potential high (about 50,000 volts) to maintain a "brush discharge." As more and more electrons arrive at the sphere its negative potential rises higher and higher until leakage into the surrounding air and through the insulators becomes equally fast.

Atomic particles to be accelerated are generated inside a vacuum tube source S inside the sphere. Starting at the top of a long straight vacuum tube T, electrons are accelerated downward toward ground potential, where, acquiring the full energy of the available voltage, they are allowed to bombard whatever target is being studied. Where installations are designed for accelerating protons, deuterons, or α-particles, the battery potential is reversed and the sphere acquires a high positive potential.

72.5. The Betatron. The *betatron*, invented in 1941 by D. W. Kerst at the University of Illinois, is an electron accelerator capable of producing electron beams of high energy as well as x-rays of extremely high penetrating power. This ingenious device differs from the cyclotron in at least two fundamental respects; first, the electrons are accelerated by a rapidly changing magnetic field, and second the circular orbit of the particles has a constant radius.

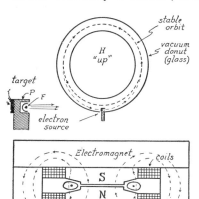

A cross-section diagram of a 20 Mev betatron is shown in Fig. 72G. A glass vacuum tube in the shape of a *doughnut*, and containing an *electron gun,* is mounted between the poles of an electromagnet. An alternating current (180 cycles/sec) applied to the coils causes some of the magnetic lines of force to pass through the vacuum tube at the electron orbit and the

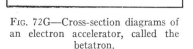

Fig. 72G—Cross-section diagrams of an electron accelerator, called the betatron.

remainder through the orbit center as shown below. Electrons are injected only at the beginning of each quarter cycle when the field begins to increase in the "up" direction. The increasing field through the center of the orbit gives rise to an electromotive force, tangent to the orbit, speeding up the electrons, whereas the increasing field at the orbit is just sufficient to increase the centripetal force and keep the electrons from spiraling outward. The stability of such an orbit is brought about by properly shaping the pole faces of the magnet, adjusting the frequency and strength of the magnetic field, and injecting the electrons at the proper voltage at the appropriate time.

During World War II a 350-ton betatron was constructed by the General Electric Company and put into use as a source of extremely penetrating x-rays. In this instrument electrons accelerated to 100 Mev energy, and impinging upon a target, give rise to x-rays capable of penetrating many feet of solid iron and lead.

72.6. The Synchro-Cyclotron. The firm belief that new and fundamental discoveries in nuclear physics can be made with atomic projectiles having greater and greater energies has lead scientists and engineers in various institutions to combine their efforts in groups to design and construct larger and larger atomic accelerators. One such instrument is the giant 4000-ton synchro-cyclotron at the University of California capable of producing deuteron beams of 200 Mev and α-particles of 400 Mev. The following specifications and the photograph in Fig. 72H will give some idea of the size of this modern instrument of experimental research.

Total weight of iron	3700 tons	Weight of copper	300 tons
Length of magnet	56 ft	No. of turns	2600
Pole tip diameter	184 in.	Conductor size	4 in. $\times \frac{1}{4}$ in.
Pole force	250 tons	Conductor length	30 mi
Pole gap	20 in.	Conductor resistance	1.4 ohms

A cut-away diagram in Fig. 72I shows the principal mechanical features of the instrument. The fundamental differences between this and the orthodox cyclotron is the employment of one dee in place of two and of an applied alternating-current potential whose frequency is made to rise and fall periodically instead of remaining constant. The principles of operation are illustrated in Fig. 72J. Starting at the center, protons, deuterons, or α-particles, are made to move in circles of increasing radius, the acceleration taking place as they enter and leave the lips of the dee. At the outer edge they are deflected out of the field as in the cyclotron or allowed to strike a suitable target inside the vacuum chamber.

The theory of the synchro-cyclotron * is based upon "phase stability," a principle fundamental to nearly all high energy accelerators. This relatively new idea can be derived from the well-founded theory that, as a particle is accelerated and approaches the speed of light, continued acceleration increases the mass while the speed approaches a nearly constant value. In

---

* The theory of phase stability of atomic accelerators of high energy was first developed in 1945 by V. Veksler (*Journal of Physics*, USSR, Vol. 9, 1945, p. 153), and independently by E. M. McMillan (*Physical Review*, Vol. 68, 1945, p. 143.)

FIG. 72H—Photograph of the 184 in., 4000 ton, synchro-cyclotron at the University of California.

other words, as more and more energy is given to a particle, more and more of it is stored as *increased mass* and less and less as *increased speed*.

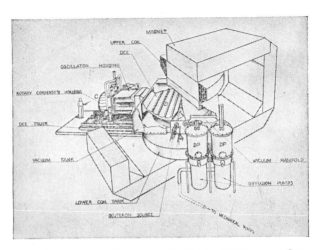

Fig. 72I—Cut-away diagram of the 184 in., 4000 ton, synchro-cyclotron.

To apply this principle to an accelerator like the synchro-cyclotron, consider the conditions that exist when a positively charged particle in a uniform magnetic field is moving with constant speed in an orbit of constant radius and at the same time in synchronism with an applied high-frequency potential. Such an orbit is represented by the dotted circle in Fig. 72J, with the particle entering and leaving the lips of the dee at A and B when

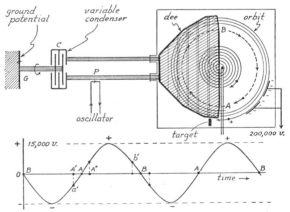

Fig. 72J—Illustrating "phrase stability" as it applies to the synchro-cyclotron.

the potential (see graph below) is zero. By Eq.(72b), $evB = mv^2/r$. Since from mechanics, angular velocity $\omega = v/r$, and the frequency of revolution $f = \omega/2\pi$, direct substitution in Eq.(72b) gives $m = Be/2\pi f$. Multiplying both sides of this equation by the square of the speed of light c^2 gives

$$mc^2 = \frac{Bec^2}{2\pi f},$$

where mc^2 represents the total energy E of the particle,

$$E = \frac{Bec^2}{2\pi f}. \tag{72e}$$

It may be seen from these equations that mc^2 includes the *rest mass* $m_o c^2$ of the particle, and that to increase E the magnetic induction can be *increased* as in the betatron and synchrotron (see Sec. 72.7), or *the frequency can be decreased* as in the synchro-cyclotron.

Returning now to the high-speed but stationary orbit AB in Fig. 72J, assume that a particle is a little early in entering the dee. Arriving there as shown by A' in the graph below the dee has a negative potential a' and the particle is accelerated by attraction. Being accelerated the mass increases with little increase in speed. Due principally to increased mass the particle now describes a larger circle and the next time around has dropped back to arrive more nearly at the time of *zero potential*. Hence if the magnetic induction B were to be increased or the frequency f were to be decreased the particle might be made to continually enter and leave the dee ahead of the zero phase and receive acceleration each time around.

If a particle gets behind the zero phase (A to A'' in the graph), it will not be accelerated and, moving with more nearly constant or diminished speed, will permit a decreasing frequency of an applied potential to catch up and get ahead again. Hence phase stability is assured and acceleration will occur as the particle spirals outward with increasing energy.

In the 184-in. synchro-cyclotron, the high-frequency potential is applied to the dee stem at P (see Fig. 72J), whereas the variable condenser C, composed of a fast rotating set of "fan blades" passing between a set of stationary blades, varies the frequency up and down through relatively wide limits. In producing 200 Mev deuterons the frequency of the dee potential rises and falls 120 times/sec between the limits of 12.5 and 8.5 megacycles/sec.

The positive ions are pulsed into the center of the dee when the frequency is 11.3 megacycles and they arrive at the outer edge when it has dropped to about 9.6 megacycles. Having made 10,000 turns around the chamber in a period of only one-thousandth of a second the deuterons have an energy of

200 Mev. The target, located inside the vacuum chamber, is therefore bombarded by pulses coming at the rate of 120 per sec.

A drop from 11.3 to 9.6 megacycles decreases f (see Eq. 72e) by about 15% thereby increasing a deuteron's energy E and mass m by 15%, or 0.3 atomic mass unit (abbr. amu). Such an increase, by Eq.(70j), is equivalent to 200 **Mev**.

72.7. The Synchrotron. This device is an electron accelerator employing the principles of the *cyclotron*, and *phase stability*. A cut-away diagram of a 350-ton synchrotron, constructed at the University of California, is shown in Fig. 72K. As in the betatron, electrons are injected into a dough-nut-shaped vacuum chamber by an electron gun. Operating first as a betatron the electrons are accelerated, in an orbit of fixed radius, by a rapidly increasing magnetic field. The rising field is produced by discharging a large condenser bank through the magnet coils. Part of the field goes through the relatively small *flux bars* near the orbit center and part through the pole faces and vacuum chamber.

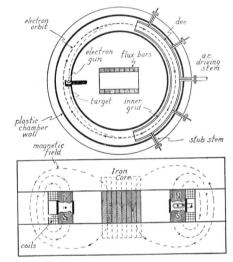

As the electrons quickly approach the speed of light, their mass begins to increase rapidly and from about 2 Mev on they move at almost constant speed (between 98 and 100% the speed of light). Increasing energy is added in this *second phase* by an

Fig. 72K—Cross-section diagrams of a 300 Mev synchrotron.

alternating potential applied to the *sector dee* shown in the diagram. Instead of decreasing the frequency, as in the synchro-cyclotron, the magnetic induction B is increased (see Eq. 72e), and as the electron *mass* increases the stronger field maintains the beam orbit constant.

Upon reaching a maximum energy of 300 Mev the electrons with a mass some 600 times their *rest mass*, are caused to spiral inward to strike a tungsten target where they produce 300 Mev x-rays.

72.8. The Linear Accelerator. Although linear accelerators were proposed as early as 1929, and several were constructed, they have never proved satisfactory until recently. Applying the principles of tubular wave guides and resonant cavities, L. Alvarez and his collaborators have constructed at the University of California the first section of a linear accelerator whose eventual possibilities seem almost unlimited.

A cut-away diagram of part of the apparatus is given in Fig. 72L. Protons are initially produced and accelerated to 4 Mev by a pressure Van de Graaff Generator (see Fig. 72F) and then injected at that energy into one end of a 40-ft tank as shown at the upper left. Once inside they are further accelerated as they pass through a series of "drift tubes," and arrive at the other end with an energy of about 40 Mev.

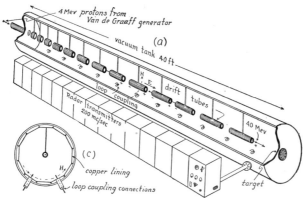

FIG. 72L—Diagrams showing the first section of a linear accelerator.

The tank cavity within the copper lining, fed by 30 radar transmitting oscillators, is set resonating at its *dominant mode* at a frequency of 200 megacycles. The "standing-wave" conditions set up are such that the electric field E is parallel to the tube axis and is everywhere rising and falling together. The lengths of the drift tubes gradually increase so that the protons cross each gap when the field E is to the right, and are inside the tubes, in a field free space, when the field is to the left. It now seems possible that additional tank sections can be added end to end to this system to obtain almost any desired energy. Calculations indicate about 1 Mev per lineal foot can be expected from such a system.

72.9. Billion Electron Volt Accelerators. The design and construction of an instrument capable of accelerating particles to energies of billions of electron volts (*Bev*) involve many problems. Not the least of these is the economic factor concerned primarily with the cost of such an instrument as well as its subsequent maintenance.

Four accelerators designed to reach the billion volt energy mark are now or soon will be in operation: (1) a 1-Bev electron synchrotron at the California Institute of Technology, in Pasadena, (2) a 1.3-Bev proton accelerator at Birmingham, England, (3) a 2 to 3-Bev proton accelerator at Brookhaven National Laboratory, Long Island, N. Y., and called a *cosmotron*, and (4) a 6-Bev proton accelerator at the University of California, Berkeley, and called a *bevatron*.

The basic design of the largest of these instruments, the bevatron, stems from proposals of W. M. Brobeck. The magnet arrangement was first proposed by H. R. Crane and consists of four quadrant segments spaced so that the particle orbits are quarter-circles connected by 20 ft straight sections.

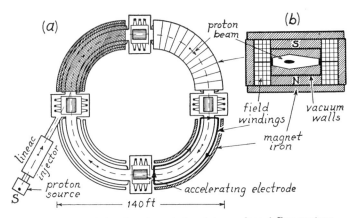

Fig. 72M—Berkeley Bevatron designed to produce 6 Bev protons.

The electrical power supplied to the 10,000 ton magnet is provided by a motor generator with a large flywheel. During buildup of the magnetic field a peak power of 100,000 kilowatts will be drawn from the flywheel and stored in the magnet. As the field is reduced between beam pulses the generator acts as a motor and returns energy to the flywheel.

The protons from a source S, as shown in Fig. 72M, are first accelerated to 10 Mev by a linear accelerator and then injected into the 385 ft race track proper. As they pass through the accelerator electrode in one of the straight sections and are speeded up by the high-frequency potentials the magnetic field increases at the proper rate to keep the beam in the same orbit. The output beam consists, as it does in all high energy accelerators, of a series of pulses. From the time of injection each pulse of protons takes about 2 seconds to acquire its final speed, and in so doing makes about 4 million revolutions of the orbit and travels about 300,000 miles.

PROBLEMS AND QUESTIONS

1. If the frequency of the potential applied to the dees of a cyclotron is 8×10^6 cycles/sec, what must be the magnetic induction B to accelerate α-particles?

2. Calculate the frequency of the oscillating potential that must be applied to a cyclotron in which deuterons are accelerated and the magnetic induction has a constant value of 1.0 weber/m². (*Ans.* 7.63 Mc/sec.)

3. The frequency applied to the dees of a cyclotron is 9.4 megacycles/sec. What must be the magnetic induction if protons are to be accelerated?

Transmutation of the Elements

Chapter 73

73.1. Proton and Deuteron Disintegrations. When high-energy protons or deuterons are used to bombard different known elements, various disintegration products are formed. An experimental arrangement in which the cyclotron acts as the source of high-speed particles is shown in Fig. 73A. To determine the nature of the disintegration taking place within the substance under bombardment it is common practice to identify the penetrating rays emerging from the other side by the use of suitable detectors.

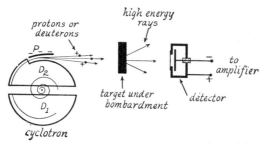

Fig. 73A—Experiment arrangement generally used for bombarding known substances with high-speed deuterons from the cyclotron, and detecting the disintegration products with an ionization chamber as a detector.

Numerous experiments have shown that the disintegration products to be looked for may be *protons, α-particles, neutrons, γ-rays,* or even *electrons* and *positrons.* For some of these penetrating rays one kind of detector may be more suitable than another. The *Geiger counter,* for example (see Fig. 71C), is particularly useful in detecting γ-rays and electrons, whereas the *Wilson cloud chamber* and *ionization chamber* are useful in detecting protons, α-particles, or neutrons.

The detector shown at the right in Fig. 73A represents a so-called "shallow ionization chamber." This device consists of a small copper box filled with air or some other suitable gas. When a proton or α-particle passes through the thin metal foil window at the front of the box it produces numerous ions inside. The positive ions are attracted toward a negatively charged plate at the center, where they give rise to minute electric currents

755

along a wire to a radio tube amplifier. The amplifier in turn can be made to operate a high-speed counting device, or to activate a loud-speaker from which each impulse can be heard and counted. By inserting thin foils one after the other between the target and detector the nature and energy of the incoming particle can be determined.

When a Wilson cloud chamber is used to identify disintegration products, charged particles can be identified by the density of their fog tracks and their energy can be determined by the curvature of the tracks when a magnetic field is applied. This is illustrated in Fig. 73G for positrons. Once the nature of the emerging rays from a bombarded target is known, the recoil product of the disintegration also becomes known by writing down a reaction equation. Six examples of such reaction equations are given by the following:

$$_1H^1 + _9F^{19} = _8O^{16} + _2He^4 \qquad Q = 8.1 \text{ Mev} \qquad (73a)$$

$$_1H^1 + _5B^{11} = _6C^{12} + \gamma\text{-ray} \qquad Q = 15.8 \text{ Mev} \qquad (73b)$$

$$_1H^2 + _7N^{14} = _6C^{12} + _2He^4 \qquad Q = 13.6 \text{ Mev} \qquad (73c)$$

$$_1H^2 + _8O^{16} = _7N^{14} + _2He^4 \qquad Q = 3.1 \text{ Mev} \qquad (73d)$$

$$_1H^2 + _3Li^6 = _3Li^7 + _1H^1 \qquad Q = 5.0 \text{ Mev} \qquad (73e)$$

$$_1H^2 + _4Be^9 = _5B^{10} + _0n^1 \qquad Q = 4.4 \text{ Mev} \qquad (73f)$$

It is customary to omit the *mass energy* of the bombarding particle from the left-hand side of all reaction equations and to designate the total energy liberated by the disintegration as shown at the right above. The values of Q given above therefore represent the experimentally determined values of the energy over and above that supplied by the incident projectile.

Consider the fifth reaction which can be taken to represent an experiment in which a beam of two million volt deuterons from the cyclotron bombards a target of lithium metal. From the other side of the target a stream of high-energy protons would be detected. If they are sent through a Wilson cloud chamber in a magnetic field, for example, their tracks could be identified as proton tracks and their energy determined by the curvature of the tracks to be 6.0 Mev. The lithium atoms in the target recoil with about 1 Mev. When the accurate weights of the four nuclei involved are taken into account, there is a total loss of 0.00540 mass unit. Multiplying by 931 this is equivalent to 5.0 Mev energy. This value plus the energy of the incident bombarding particle gives 7.0 Mev. The unaccounted for energy of 1.0 Mev has gone into the recoil of the $_3Li^7$ nucleus inside the target.

As a second example consider Eq.(73f) in which deuterons, bombarding beryllium metal, produce high-speed neutrons and recoiling boron nuclei. This particular disintegration is important experimentally because it is used as a means of obtaining intense beams of neutrons for use as projectiles in other disintegrations. The nuclear changes are illustrated schematically in Fig. 73B. The available energy from the loss in mass alone is equivalent to

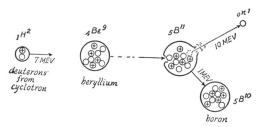

Fig. 73B—Deuteron disintegration of a beryllium nucleus to produce high-speed neutrons.

4.4 Mev; so that, if deutrons with an energy of 7 Mev are used to bombard the beryllium target, the available energy becomes about 11 Mev, 1 Mev going to the recoil boron nucleus and approximately 10 Mev to the neutron.

73.2. Multiple Disintegrations. A study of certain disintegration experiments shows that some of the unstable nuclei created by the capture of a proton or deuteron by a stable nucleus split up into more than two stable nuclei. Examples of this arise when boron is bombarded by protons and when nitrogen is bombarded by deuterons. In the case of boron (see Fig.

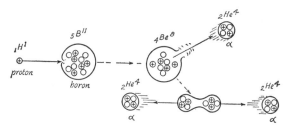

Fig. 73C—Diagram of the disintegration of a boron nucleus of mass 11 by a proton to produce three α-particles.

73C), the proton is first captured by a $_5B^{11}$ nucleus to form an unstable carbon nucleus, $_6C^{12}$. This composite structure disintegrates by the expulsion of an α-particle with several million volts energy, leaving behind a beryllium nucleus, $_4Be^8$.

$$_1H^1 + {_5B^{11}} = {_4Be^8} + {_2He^4} = {_2He^4} + {_2He^4} + {_2He^4}. \qquad (73g)$$

This nuclear combination is still unstable and splits apart into two more α-particles. When the phenomenon was first observed it was thought that all three α-particles came apart simultaneously, but further observations showed that first one and then two were ejected. The total energy liberated has been measured to be about 11 Mev and checks almost exactly with the value obtained from the loss in mass.

73.3. Branch Disintegrations. It so happens that, when certain atoms are bombarded with high-speed particles, two or more disintegration processes may subsequently take place. As an illustration of this phenomenon of *branch disintegration,* consider the proton bombardment of beryllium in which the following two types of disintegration have been identified:

$$_1H^1 + {}_4Be^9 = {}_3Li^6 + {}_2He^4 \qquad Q = 2.1 \text{ Mev} \qquad (73h)$$

$$_1H^1 + {}_4Be^9 = {}_5B^{10} + \gamma\text{-ray} \qquad Q = 6.0 \text{ Mev.} \qquad (73i)$$

When a proton is captured by a beryllium nucleus to form an unstable boron nucleus, $_5B^{10}$, there are two ways in which it may split up. The instability of the boron in the first place is due to the presence of too much mass. Such an atom is said to be in an *excited state,* for by the emission of a γ-ray it gives up its surplus energy and becomes a stable $_5B^{10}$ nucleus, or by splitting up into two particles it gives up its surplus in the form of kinetic energy to become $_2He^4$ and $_3Li^6$, two stable nuclei.

73.4. Discovery of Induced Radioactivity. The discovery of induced radioactivity was made in 1934 by F. Joliot and I. Curie Joliot.*

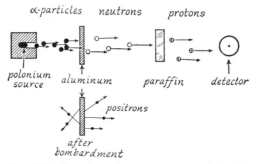

Fig. 73D—Experimental arrangement used by the Curie-Joliots when they discovered induced radioactivity.

For years the Curie-Joliots, as they are now often called, had been exposing various substances to the α-rays from naturally radioactive elements

* Irene Curie, daughter of the most famous woman physicist, is the wife of Frederick Joliot. Because of the now famous name of Curie, the physicists of the world hyphenate the name and call them Mme. Curie-Joliot and M. J. F. Joliot, or for short the Curie-Joliots. It is not so strange a coincidence that induced radioactivity was discovered by these observers since for years they had worked with radioactive substances in the famous laboratory of the late Mme. Marie Curie at the Radium Institute in Paris.

and had been studying the various disintegrations that took place. In the specific instance referred to above they bombarded aluminum with *α-particles from polonium* and measured the energies of the ejected neutrons by the recoiling of protons from paraffin (see Fig. 73D). They observed that even after the polonium source was taken away the detector continued to respond to some kind of penetrating radiation. Upon investigating the nature of these rays they found positively charged electrons coming from the aluminum.

Repeating the experiments to make certain of the results, they came to the conclusion that, under the bombardment of α-particles, the aluminum had become radioactive in its own right. What was happening has since been verified; α-particles striking aluminum nuclei are captured, and the resulting nuclei disintegrate with the violent ejection of neutrons.

$$_2\text{He}^4 + {}_{13}\text{Al}^{27} = {}_{15}P^{30} + {}_0\text{n}^1. \tag{73j}$$

The newly created recoil particles, with a charge of $+15$ and mass 30 have been identified as phosphorus nuclei which are not stable but radioactive. Spontaneously disintegrating, these radioactive phosphorus nuclei $_{15}P^{30}$ shoot out positrons, leaving behind them stable silicon atoms of charge $+14$ and mass 30.

$$_{15}P^{30} = {}_{14}\text{Si}^{30} + {}_1\text{e}^0. \tag{73k}$$

The *half-life* of this activity, which measures the rate of decay of the phosphorus into silicon (for the meaning of half-life see Sec. 61.8), is only 2.5 min.

Although the mass of the electron is not zero it is so small compared with unit mass (the mass of one electron, it will be remembered, is 1/1840th of one mass unit) that e is written with a zero superscript. According to this notation a positron is written $_1\text{e}^0$ and an electron $_{-1}\text{e}^0$.

Because the phosphorus does not all disintegrate immediately it has been possible to identify the activity as coming from the newly created phosphorus atoms in the following way. A piece of aluminum metal, immediately after being bombarded, is dissolved in hydrochloric acid together with some ordinary inactive phosphorus and a standard chemical separation made. Testing each part separately, the radioactivity is found to be present with the phosphorus residue and not with the aluminum.

73.5. The Discovery of Radioactive Sodium. Immediately after the discovery of induced radioactivity by the Curie-Joliots, Lawrence bombarded sodium with 2 Mev deuterons from the cyclotron and found that it too, like aluminum, became radioactive (see Fig. 73E). Upon testing for the nature of the rays given off during bombardment, Lawrence found protons with an energy of about 7 Mev. When the sodium target was removed from the deuteron beam, as shown in diagram (b), and then tested for activity it

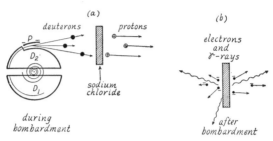

Fig. 73E—Experimental arrangement used by Lawrence in discovering radioactive sodium.

was found to be emitting both electrons and γ-rays. The bombarding reaction, therefore, is

$$_1H^2 + {}_{11}Na^{23} = {}_{11}Na^{24} + {}_1H^1 \tag{73l}$$

followed by the radioactive decay of the unstable sodium nuclei,

$$_{11}Na^{24} = {}_{12}Mg^{24} + {}_{-1}e^0 + \gamma\text{-ray.} \tag{73m}$$

The first stage of the disintegration process is shown at the left in Fig. 73F, and the radioactive decay is shown at the right.

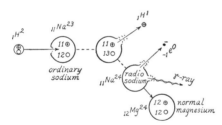

Fig. 73F—Diagrams illustrating the production and disintegration of radio-sodium.

The residual nucleus $_{11}Na^{24}$ of the first disintegration is called *radio-sodium*. Having a charge of $+11$ and mass of 24, it must be an isotope of sodium not found in nature. Since measurements of the activity of radio-sodium give a *half-life* of only 15 hr, it is clear why such atoms are not found in nature. If they were formed some time in the ages past, they would have all disintegrated by this time.

Up to the present time more than two hundred different kinds of radioactive atoms have been produced in the laboratory. Two examples in addition to those already given are illustrated by the following reactions:

$$_1H^2 + {}_{15}P^{31} = {}_{15}P^{32} + {}_1H^1, \qquad {}_{15}P^{32} = {}_{16}S^{32} + {}_{-1}e^0 \tag{73n}$$

$$_1H^2 + {}_6C^{12} = {}_7N^{13} + {}_0n^1, \qquad {}_7N^{13} = {}_6C^{13} + {}_1e^0. \tag{73o}$$

The first of these reactions forms *radioactive phosphorus* $_{15}P^{32}$ which is *electron active* with a half-life of 15 days.

A cloud chamber photograph of the positrons emitted by radioactive nitrogen $_7N^{13}$ is reproduced in Fig. 73G. The magnetic field bends all the rays in the same direction, indicating all are positive charges. The low-density fogdrops forming the tracks indicate particles with the mass of an electron.

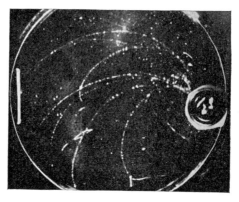

73.6. Neutron Projectiles Produce Disintegrations. The first disintegrations produced by high-speed neutrons as atomic projectiles were announced in 1932 by the English physicist, Feather. Immediately following Chadwick's discovery of these neutral particles, Feather allowed neutrons from beryllium (see Fig. 71E) to enter a Wilson cloud chamber containing pure nitrogen gas. Numerous expansions of the chamber and the simultaneous clicks of a camera shutter gave many photographs of the ion tracks left by recoiling nitrogen atoms.

FIG. 73G—Photograph of the Wilson cloud chamber tracks of positrons ejected by radio nitrogen, $_7N^{13}$

Although most of the photographs indicated elastic collisions between nitrogen atoms and neutrons, an occasional photograph showed a forked track, indicating a disintegration of a nitrogen nucleus.

$$_0n^1 + {}_7N^{14} = {}_6C^{14} + {}_1H^1. \tag{73p}$$

Three photographs of several such disintegrations are reproduced in Fig.

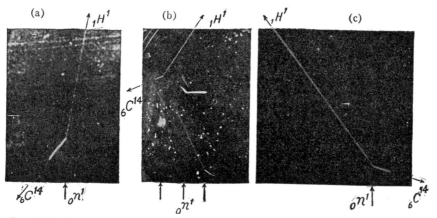

FIG. 73H—Cloud track photographs of neutron disintegrations of nitrogen. (a) *After Feather;* (b) *after Kurie and Kamen;* (c) *after Rasetti.*

73H. Although hundreds of neutrons enter the cloud chamber every second they do not ionize atoms as charged particles do, and hence leave no tracks. When a head-on nuclear collision occurs, however, the disintegrated nuclei, possessing as they do high speeds and positive charges, leave a trail of ions behind them. The fork in (a) shows a proton track of considerable length originating at the same point as the more dense, short-ranged track of the recoiling carbon nucleus.

The second photograph (b) is an extremely rare picture showing three separate nitrogen disintegrations. The center disintegration occurred slightly before the others and the fog tracks have had time to spread out and appear as heavy tracks. The third photograph, like the first, shows a long thin track of the proton and a short heavy track of a heavier carbon recoil nucleus.

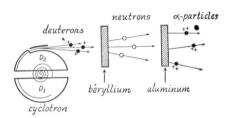

FIG. 73I—Experimental arrangement for producing intense beams of neutrons by bombarding beryllium with deuterons. The neutrons are then used as projectiles for further disintegrations as illustrated here for aluminum.

Strong sources of neutrons are produced by inserting a thin plate of beryllium metal in the intense beam of deuterons coming from the cyclotron as shown in Fig. 73I. The disintegration process, giving rise to the neutrons, is the reaction Eq.(73f).

Into such a beam of chargeless particles numerous substances of known chemical constitution have been inserted and the disintegration products studied with suitable detectors. To illustrate by an example, suppose that a thin sheet of aluminum is inserted into the beam of neutrons as shown in the figure. In this particular instance α-particles are observed emerging from the aluminum, thus enabling one to write down the following neutron reaction,

$$_0n^1 + {}_{13}Al^{27} = {}_{11}Na^{24} + {}_2He^4. \tag{73q}$$

Thus *radioactive sodium*, produced originally by the deuteron bombardment of ordinary sodium, is here produced by a different reaction. As proof of the result the bombarded aluminum target is found to be β-ray and γ-ray active with a half-life of 15 hr (see Eq.(73l). There are at least two other known disintegration processes by which radio-sodium is produced: one by the neutron bombardment of silicon, and the other by the α-particle bombardment of magnesium.

This is but one example of the many known radioactive elements that can be manufactured in four different ways. As a matter of fact, with sufficiently energetic atomic bullets it is now possible to produce hundreds of new atomic nuclei not found in nature.

Examples of other neutron disintegrations are illustrated by the following reactions,

$$_0n^1 + _9F^{19} = _7N^{16} + _2He^4 \tag{73r}$$

$$_0n^1 + _{20}Ca^{42} = _{19}K^{42} + _1H^1$$
$$_{19}K^{42} = _{20}Ca^{42} + _{-1}e^0. \tag{73s}$$

Eq.(73s) represents a typical case of the capture of a neutron to form a radioactive isotope $_{19}K^{42}$ which, by the ejection of an electron, reverts back to the original stable element $_{20}Ca^{42}$. Many such reactions are known, particularly among the heavier elements in the first half of the period table

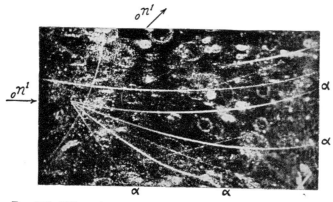

FIG. 73J—Wilson cloud chamber photo showing the result of a 100 Mev neutron impact on an oxygen nucleus. *(Courtesy W. Powell.)*

When 100 to 200 Mev deuterons from the large 184 in cyclotron strike almost any target, neutrons with energies of 100 Mev or more are produced. Fig. 73J is a Wilson cloud chamber photo showing the result of a 100 Mev neutron impact with an oxygen nucleus. The paths of the recoiling fragments, four α-particles, are bent in the magnetic field.

Not all disintegration processes liberate more energy than that required to produce them. This is illustrated by the following example:

$$_0n^1 + _6C^{12} = _4Be^9 + _2He^4 \qquad Q = -5.7 \text{ Mev.} \tag{73t}$$

To carry out this disintegration the bombarding neutrons must have an energy of 5.7 Mev or greater. The sum of the masses produced are greater by this amount than those which went to make them. This is an example of what is called a fast neutron reaction. It is interesting to point out that this reaction is the reverse of the reaction by which neutrons were first produced in large quantity. (See Sec. 70.3 and Eq.(70c).)

73.7. Slow Neutron Disintegrations. The fact that neutrons, slowed down to very low speeds, have the ability to disintegrate certain atoms was first discovered and investigated by the Italian physicist, Enrico Fermi, and his collaborators. A neutron approaching the nucleus of an atom does not experience a repulsive force, as does a proton, deuteron, or α-particle, and consequently its chances of penetration into, and of being captured by, a nucleus is relatively large. It is for this reason that slowly moving neutrons are able to bring about disintegrations that slowly moving charged particles cannot.

The customary method of producing *slow neutrons* is to surround a source of fast neutrons with paraffin or some material containing large quantities of hydrogen or deuterium. As neutrons pass through this "moderator" material, elastic collisions with hydrogen nuclei continually slow them down until at a distance of several centimeters from the source most of them have lost all of their original energy. What little energy they do have is picked up by regular thermal collisions with other atoms. Their resultant motions become quite the same as the random motions of atoms or molecules in a gas.

For his experimental discoveries of disintegration, induced by *slow neutrons,* Fermi was granted the Nobel Prize in physics for 1938.

73.8. Internal Conversion. When, in the disintegration of atomic nuclei, γ-rays are emitted, they frequently collide with orbital electrons of their respective atoms and liberate them by a kind of *photoelectric process.* This disappearance of a γ-ray and the appearance of a photoelectron within the same atom is called *internal conversion.* If an electron is ejected from the innermost *K*-shell, leaving a vacancy there, another electron from the *L*-shell or *M*-shell falls in to take its place and in so doing emits an *x-ray.* Confirmation of such a process is assured since the wave lengths of such x-rays are identical with those emitted by the same element in an x-ray tube.

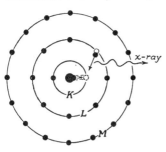

73.9. K-Capture. Many radioactive nuclei, when created by some collision process, are unstable to the extent of one extra positive charge. Although many such nuclei disintegrate and become stable by the emission of a positron, others draw to them an orbital electron from the *K*-shell of the same atom. Inside the nucleus this negative charge neutralizes a

Fig. 73K—Unstable nucleus captures an electron from the *K*-shell of orbital electrons. As a consequence an x-ray is emitted.

positive charge, whereas outside an *L* or *M*-electron jumps into the *K*-shell vacancy with the simultaneous emission of a characteristic x-ray (see Fig.

73K). Beryllium 7, and gallium 65, are specific examples of unstable nuclei in which *K-capture* occurs.

$$_4Be^7 + {}_{-1}e^0 = {}_3Li^7 \qquad\qquad _{31}Ga^{65} + {}_{-1}e^0 = {}_{30}Zn^{65}. \qquad (73u)$$

73.10. Abbreviated Notation. An abbreviated notation for nuclear reactions is illustrated by the following examples taken from this chapter:

$$_1H^1 + {}_9F^{19} = {}_8O^{16} + {}_2He^4 \qquad \text{Abbr.} \qquad F^{19}\ (p,\ a)\ O^{16}$$
$$_1H^2 + {}_7N^{14} = {}_6C^{12} + {}_2He^4 \qquad \text{``} \qquad N^{14}\ (d,\ a)\ C^{12}$$
$$_1H^2 + {}_3Li^7 = {}_2He^4 + {}_2He^4 + {}_0n^1 \qquad \text{``} \qquad Li^7\ (d,\ 2an).$$

73.11. Medical Applications. Since the time of its discovery radio-sodium has found numerous and important applications in many branches of science. It has, for example, been used as a means of tracing certain organic and inorganic chemicals passing through the human body, through plants, and through chemical experiments of one kind or another. To give a simple example, one can show, by drinking water containing radio-sodium in the form of common table salt (NaCl), that within 2 min some of it has entered the blood stream and has been distributed to all parts of the body. The presence of the salt in the finger tips or the toes can be demonstrated by detecting the electrons and γ-rays from the sodium with a Geiger counter. Similar experiments can be performed with trees and plants to see how rapidly their roots take up certain plant foods and distribute them to the leaves and branches. At the present time radio-phosphorus 32, because of its chemical properties and its comparatively long *half-life,* is being used in a number of medical researches as a possible cure for certain diseases, as well as for tracing the migration of phosphorus through the body.

One useful medical technique is the use of radioactive elements to obtain *radio-autographs.* A plant or animal is given a single dose of liquid contain-

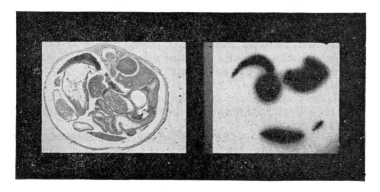

Fig. 73L—Radio-autograph of the type used in medical studies. Shows selective absorption of phosphorus by the liver and spleen.

ing the "tagged" atoms and at various times thereafter *thin sections of tissue* from the plant or animal are placed in direct contact against a photographic film. After several hours of exposure to any possible rays from "tagged"

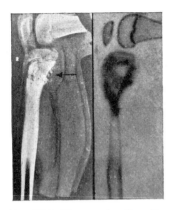

atoms in the section, the film is developed. Fig. 73L shows at the left a thin cross-section of the mouse, previously fed radio-phosphorus (see Eq. 73n), and at the right the resulting autoradiograph of this same section. The dark areas indicate the uptake of phosphorus by the *spleen* and *liver* sections and nowhere else.

Fig. 73M shows an *x-ray* and *strontium radio-autograph* of a section of an amputated leg from a patient with osteogenic sarcoma (bone cancer). The patient received radio-strontium orally two days before removal of the extremity. The x-ray shows the bone tumor at the upper end of the tibia, while the radio-autograph shows selective deposits of strontium in the tumor with small amounts in

Fig. 73M—X-ray and radio-auto-graph of a human leg. *(Courtesy of Dr. J. G. Hamilton.)*

the surrounding bone and relatively little in the soft tissues. These studies indicate that radio-strontium may prove useful in clinical therapy.

References. 1. "Radioactivity and Nuclear Physics," by James Cork, D. Van Nostrand Co., Inc.

2. "Introduction to Atomic Physics," by Henry Semat, Farrar and Rinehart.

PROBLEMS

1. When 5 Mev α-particles bombard Na^{23}, protons are observed being ejected. (a) Write down the disintegration equation, and (b) find the energy liberated.

2. If a 5 Mev deuteron on C^{12} produces a proton, what is the energy liberated? Assuming 92% of the energy goes into the proton what will be its maximum energy, and (b) its range in air? See Fig. 70H. *(Ans.* (a) 7.86 Mev, (b) 63 cm.)

3. When 10 Mev deuterons bombard B^{10}, protons, neutrons, and α-particles are observed as disintegration products. Assuming these are branch disintegrations write down the three reactions and give the liberated energies.

4. If 10 Mev deuterons on O^{16} produce N^{14} and α-particles, (a) how much energy is liberated? If the available energy is divided between the two particles in the inverse ratio of their respective masses what is (b) the maximum energy of the α-particles, and (c) their range in air?

5. If 5 Mev protons are incident on Be^9, α-particles are observed emitted as high speed disintegration products. (a) Write down the reaction, and (b) find the energy liberated. If the liberated energy is divided between the disintegration products in the inverse ratio of their respective masses what is (c) the energy of the α-particles, and (d) their maximum range in air?

Inside the Atomic Nucleus   Chapter 74

74.1. What Holds the Nucleus Together? Although the disintegrations of different nuclei give rise to some half dozen different kinds of particles or units of energy, it now seems quite probable that we need assume only two kinds of particles existing within the nucleus—*neutrons* and *protons*. If this is correct our task becomes the difficult one of explaining not only the disintegration mechanism of an unstable nucleus but the binding forces which hold a stable nucleus together. An answer to the latter question will serve as a starting point for the following presentations.

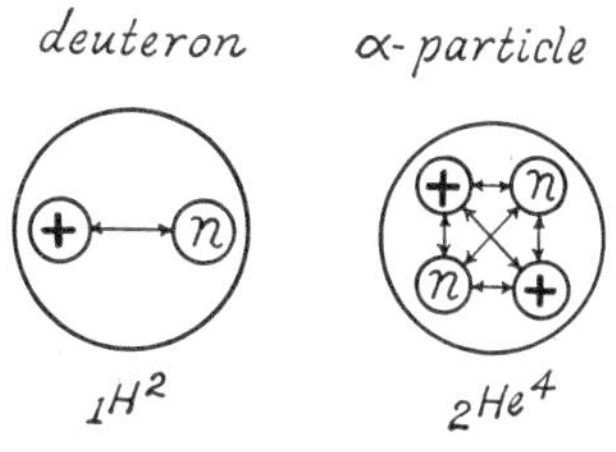

FIG. 74A—Schematic diagrams of the nucleus of (a) a deuterium atom, and (b) a helium atom.

According to the *neutron-proton theory* of the atomic nucleus (see Fig. 74A), the deuteron nucleus contains but one neutron and one proton. Let us compare, therefore, the mass of one free proton and one free neutron with their mass when combined as a deuteron (for masses see Appendix V).

$$\text{Neutron mass,} \quad _0n^1 = 1.00898$$
$$\text{Proton mass,} \quad _1H^1 = 1.00814$$
$$\text{Sum} = \overline{2.01712}$$
$$\text{Deuteron mass,} \quad _1H^2 = 2.01474$$

The difference in mass of 0.00238 atomic mass unit (*abbr.* amu) is not due to inaccurate measurements of mass but is a real difference to be accounted for as the annihilation energy which binds the two particles together. When a neutron and proton come together to form a deuteron a small part of their mass—namely 0.00238 amu (equivalent to 2.2 Mev energy)—is radiated from the newly formed nucleus. At close approach, in other words, the two particles attract each other so strongly that once together it takes the equivalent of a little more than two million volts of energy to pull them apart. This has been confirmed by a nuclear photoelectric effect, an experiment in which γ-rays of 2.2 Mev energy or greater are found to break up deuterium nuclei into their constituent parts, while γ-rays of lower energy have no effect. How neutrons and protons attract each other when very close together is a question of great importance for we now realize that the stability of all the universe as we know it depends upon these forces.

Consider, as a second example, the attractive forces between the four particles of a helium nucleus, i.e., the two neutrons and two protons contained in an α-particle as shown in Fig. 74A. By combining the masses of the various free particles $_0n^1$, $_1H^1$, $_1H^2$ and $_1H^3$, in various ways and comparing them with the mass of the helium nucleus we obtain the following:

$_1H^1 + {}_1H^3 = 4.02514$	$_1H^2 + {}_1H^2 = 4.02948$	$2_0n^1 + 2_1H^1 = 4.03424$
$_2He^4 = 4.00387$	$_2He^4 = 4.00387$	$_2He^4 = 4.00387$
Diff. 0.02127	Diff. 0.02561	Diff. 0.03037
Energy 20 Mev	Energy 24 Mev	Energy 28 Mev

The first mass difference shows that to pull one proton $_1H^1$, out of a helium nucleus requires the tremendous energy of 20 Mev. The second and third mass differences show that to split the α-particle into two deuterons requires 24 Mev, while to separate all four particles a total energy of 28 Mev must be supplied. These large forces are to be explained as due to the binding forces of the several particles and to their close proximity to each other. As shown by the arrows in the diagram, the removal of a proton requires the breaking of three bonds, while the removal, as a unit, of a deuteron requires the breaking of four bonds.

To find the average binding energy of a single proton or a single neutron to the nucleus of a heavier atom, we need only compare the masses of two heavy nuclei differing from each other by only one proton or one neutron. Among the heavier atoms in Appendix V, it will be seen that consecutive nuclei differ from each other, on the average, by unity. Therefore, to remove a proton or neutron from the average nucleus we must supply enough energy to increase the mass from 1.00000 to 1.00814 for a proton, or 1.00898 for a neutron. That means we must supply an energy equivalent to about 8 Mev.

We need not be alarmed that these tremendous forces of attraction between protons and neutrons exist, for without them the universe would fall apart. That they do not obey our previous ideas of the repulsion of like charges need not bother us either, for not until the atomic nucleus was investigated have we ever had an opportunity to test Coulomb's law for such small charges so close together. We must be satisfied, therefore, by stating that Coulomb's law applies only to charges spaced some distance apart.

74.2. The Nuclear Potential Barrier. Early in the development of ideas concerning nuclear disintegration Gamow proposed a model by which one might represent the atomic nucleus. This model is based upon the forces acting between two positive charges and is an extension of the nuclear model described in Sec. 68.1, and illustrated in Figs. 68B and 68C.

Picture again a proton or α-particle, with its positive charge, approaching a positively charged nucleus. As the two charges come closer and closer together, they repel each other with greater and greater forces as given by Coulomb's law. Graphically the increasing repulsion is represented by the dotted curve in diagram (a) of Fig. 74B. This repulsion cannot continue to increase all the way to zero separation, however, for as the two charges come very close together we know, from what has been said in the preceding section about the attraction between neutrons and protons in the nucleus, that there must be an

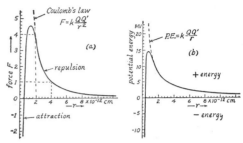

FIG. 74B—Graph representing the force between an α-particle and a positively charged nucleus at various distances apart. (b) Graph of the potential energy for the same two particles.

attraction. Gamow proposed, therefore, that at close approach there is a departure from Coulomb's law and the curve turns over and drops almost straight down as shown by the solid curve in the diagram. All points of this curve lying above the horizontal axis correspond to *repulsion,* whereas those lying below correspond to *attraction.*

If each value of the force F in diagram (a) is multiplied by the corresponding distance r, the result is a potential curve like that shown in diagram (b). Such a curve represents what is called the *potential barrier* of the nucleus. The highest point of the barrier is frequently called the edge of the nucleus which, for heavy atoms in the periodic table, occurs at, and gives a nuclear radius of, about 1×10^{-12} cm. For lighter nuclei the radius is several times smaller.

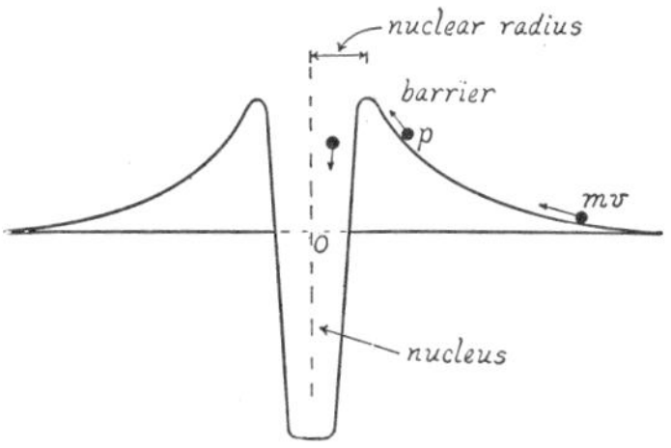

For want of a mechanical model of the nucleus we can pattern a surface having the form of the crater of a volcano similar to the surface obtained by rotating diagram (b) around the vertical axis (see Fig. 74C). By such an analogy the electrical potential energy V between the two positively charged particles is analogous to the potential energy of a ball at any point on the crater model, and the *electrostatic force of repulsion* is analogous to the *force of gravity.*

FIG. 74C—A graphical model of the atomic nucleus as proposed by Gamow. The potential barrier of a nucleus to an approaching positive charge is analogous to the crater of a volcano.

If now a small marble, representing a proton or α-particle, approaches the nuclear barrier it will roll up the hill as shown in the diagram. Experiencing a rapidly increasing force down the hill, the ball may be turned back, or off to one side, and we have elastic scattering of the kind observed by Rutherford (see Fig. 68C). If the initial velocity is high enough, however, the ball may go over the top of the barrier and drop down inside, representing a capture. What happens inside the nucleus and the disintegration that follows is the subject of the following sections of this chapter.

74.3. Bohr's Nuclear Model. In 1937 Niels Bohr, the famous Danish physicist, made another outstanding contribution to modern physics when he improved Gamow's model of the nucleus by extending what is sometimes called the *waterdrop model* of the nucleus. Bohr, and his collaborator Kalkar, imagines the many particles in a heavy nucleus as moving about within a spherical inclosure with motions analogous to the molecules in a drop of water. The surface of the spherical enclosure, which is the top of the potential barrier as represented in Fig. 74C, is analogous to the surface tension which holds a small waterdrop to its spherical form.

Just as the rapid motion of the molecules in water is a measure of the temperature, so Bohr speaks of the rapid motion of the neutrons and protons within the spherical boundary of the nucleus as a sort of pseudo-temperature. To explain disintegration, the analogy is drawn that *the ejection of a particle from the nucleus is like the evaporation of a water molecule from a drop of water.* Just as a rise in temperature brings about a more rapid evaporation of water, so an increase in the motions within the nucleus gives rise to a higher probability of disintegration.

In a stable nucleus, the particles within are moving about with very little kinetic energy, and are in the analogous state of a relatively low temperature. When a high-speed particle from outside penetrates through the potential barrier it is accelerated toward the center of the nucleus and acquires a very high kinetic energy before it collides with one or more of the particles inside. Soon the energy becomes divided among the many particles and the nucleus takes on a higher temperature state.

Now as the particles move about inside there is a certain probability or chance that, within a given interval of time, some one particle will be hit by several particles, giving it a sufficiently high velocity in an outward direction to permit an escape through the potential barrier. The more rapid the internal motions, that is, the higher the temperature, the greater is this chance of escape.

A direct disintegration may be described in this way: if upon entering the nucleus a high-speed particle like a proton adds sufficient energy to give the nucleus a high temperature, another particle like a neutron or α-particle may be ejected immediately. Since such an ejected particle has to be supplied with a certain minimum energy to get free, the remaining particles will be slowed down, and the nucleus will have a lower temperature.

Potential barrier models of stable and unstable nuclei are shown in Fig. 74D. For a stable atom the particles are moving slowly about at the bottom of the volcano pit as in diagram (a). When a proton or α-particle from outside comes over the barrier and drops down inside regaining its original speed, it collides with other particles and sets them into a more rapid state of motion. If one of the particles near the outside is hit hard enough, it may acquire a sufficient

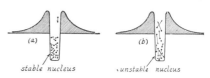

stable nucleus , *unstable nucleus*

Fig. 74D—Diagrams representing stable and unstable atomic nuclei.

energy to escape over the barrier. This is the analogue of disintegration and radioactivity.

74.4. Nuclear Demonstration Models. A demonstration model illustrating the capture of a high-speed proton or α-particle by a nucleus, prior to disintegration, is shown in Fig. 74E. Marbles rolled down the incline represent the speeding up of atomic projectiles by an accelerator like the cyclotron. Approaching the potential barrier a marble may roll part way

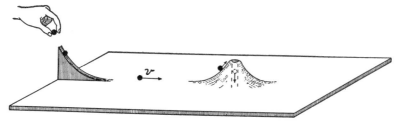

Fig. 74E—Mechanical model of a nucleus for demonstrating the capture of a high-speed proton, deuteron, or α-particle, prior to disintegration.

up and then be deflected off to one side, illustrating an elastic collision without capture; or it may roll up the side and drop into the crater opening at the top, representing a capture prior to disintegration.

A demonstration of what happens inside the nucleus is illustrated by another model as shown in Fig. 74F. In this case the vertical scale of the

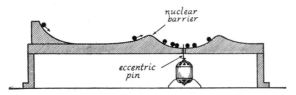

Fig. 74F—Mechanical model of a nucleus for demonstrating (a) the increased kinetic energy of nuclear particles after a capture, and (b) the chance probability of radioactive decay or disintegration by the ejection of a particle.

barrier has, of necessity, been reduced, i.e., flattened out. When a marble is rolled down the incline and into the group of marbles at the center of the barrier there may be several collisions before another particle usually goes bouncing out on the other side. This corresponds to a direct disintegration where one particle like a proton goes in and a neutron comes out.

If a single particle does not emerge, most of the particles inside take on random motions, colliding with each other much the same as do the molecules or atoms in a gas or liquid. To prevent friction from stopping them (there is no friction in an atom), the marbles are continually agitated by a small pin protruding through from underneath the barrier. This pin is mounted slightly off center at the end of the shaft of a small electric motor. If the motor is left running for some time a single marble will eventually be hit by several particles moving in the same direction and will recoil with sufficient speed to carry it over the barrier and out. This corresponds to a disintegration or radioactive decay, which takes place according to the laws of chance, and to the resultant drop in temperature of the nucleus.

The faster the motor runs, the greater is the internal agitation and chance of ejection, and the shorter is the so-called *half-life* of the element.

74.5. Nuclear Model for Neutron Disintegrations. When a neutron approaches a nucleus prior to a disintegration it does not encounter a potential barrier of the type already described for protons and α-particles. A neutron has no charge so that at large distances it is not repelled by the positively charged nucleus. It may, therefore, approach a nucleus with very little speed of its own and be captured when it comes too close. At very close range a strong attractive force sets in, drawing the two together.

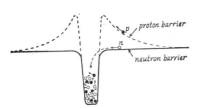

To an approaching neutron the nucleus acts as though it were a pit into which the particle will fall. This is illustrated by the

FIG. 74G—A graphical model of the nucleus as it is presented to an approaching neutron or proton.

flat potential curve in Fig. 74G. The marble rolling along the horizontal plane toward the pit represents the influence of the nucleus upon the neutron's motion, whereas the marble rolling up the hill (dotted line) represents the influence of the same nucleus upon the motion of a proton.

74.6. The Origin of Gamma Rays. It is often observed that the emission of α-particles or β-particles from a nucleus is accompanied by γ-rays. The appearance of these high-frequency light waves, or photons, is now known to occur after the primary process of α- or β-disintegration and to represent a settling down of the excited residual nucleus to its normal state. The internal nuclear process giving rise to γ-rays has an explanation similar to that of the emission of visible light by the electrons in the outer structure of the atom.

The protons and neutrons within the nucleus are probably not moving about with quite the freedom pictured above but are very likely confined in their motions to shells analogous to the electron structure in the outer part of the atom.

When a projectile from the outside passes through the potential barrier and into the nucleus it may supply the system with more than enough energy to emit an α-particle. If this is the case and an α-particle is ejected, one or more of the remaining particles may acquire a certain amount of energy and be held momentarily in an outer nuclear orbit. Then upon jumping into an orbit or shell nearer the center the energy is given up and radiated as a γ-ray. The energy $h\nu$ of this γ-ray is equal to the difference in energy between the two energy states.

In some cases the capture of a particle from the outside is followed by the emission of a γ-ray with all of the available energy, while in others it is divided between say an α-particle and a γ-ray as described above.

74.7. The Origin of Beta Rays. For years the emission of electrons from radioactive elements has been a puzzle and a challenge to the best minds in physical science. Although many theories have been proposed, none appears to be entirely acceptable. From experimental evidence one thing seems quite certain and that is that the appearance of a high-speed electron is the result of some violent disruption of the nucleus. Among all of the heavy radioactive elements, natural or induced, electrons but no positrons are observed as a product of disintegration, whereas from the induced radioactivity of the lighter elements both positrons and electrons are found.

On numerous occasions it has been suggested that the neutron is a composite particle made up of one proton and one electron. The fact that the mass of a free neutron (1.00898) is slightly greater than the mass of a free proton (1.00814) and that the charge is zero would tend to confirm this. A β-ray might therefore be explained as the result of a disintegration in which one of the neutrons in the nucleus splits apart with a violent ejection of an electron, the remaining particle, a proton, staying with the nucleus to increase its charge by unity.

A theory similar to this was proposed early to explain positron emission. According to this hypothesis, the proton is a composite particle, being made up of a positron and a neutron.

Since the difference in mass between the neutron and proton would seem to make one of these hypotheses wrong, it is assumed that both are incorrect. The difficulty is explained away by recalling that the average mass of neutrons and protons within the nucleus is unity and assuming that, so confined, both particles have the same mass and differ only in their charge. To explain electron or positron emission by a radioactive nucleus the electron has been assumed to be created at the expense of one half million volts of energy. Once a sufficient amount of energy is acquired by a certain nucleus, a neutron simply acts as an agent capable of (1) changing about $\frac{1}{2}$ Mev energy into a particle having the mass of an electron, and (2) of creating a negative charge for the electron and itself absorbing an equal positive charge to become a proton. Similarly, in the nucleus of another type of atom a proton may act as an agent capable of changing energy into a positron and itself becoming, by the absorption of the complementary negative charge, a neutron.

While in many ways this theory seems to be quite plausible, in view of all the known experimental observations, it violates the law of conservation of angular momentum. Although a detailed explanation of the difficulty is out of place here, one phase of it will be briefly explained. According to experimental observations, as well as the predictions of the quantum theory, every elementary particle, electron, positron, neutron, and proton has an angular momentum of $\frac{1}{2} \times \frac{h}{2\pi}$, where h is Planck's constant. When, therefore, one of these particles, by a disintegration, is ejected away from a nucleus with a definite amount of angular momentum, the angular momentum of the remaining nucleus should change by the same amount, i.e., by one-half a unit of angular momentum.

Experimental observations confirm this for proton or neutron emission, but not for electron emission. The angular momentum of a nucleus before and after electron emission is found to have remained the same or to have changed by a whole number of units, 1, 2, 3, etc.

To surmount this difficulty the theoretical physicists have proposed the existence of the neutrino (small neutron), a chargeless particle with a mass much smaller than that of an electron. The existence of these tiny hypothetical neutrinos has been assumed in order that they may take up the extra angular momentum necessary for positron or electron emission.

When an electron, or positron, with its spin angular momentum of $\frac{1}{2} \times \frac{h}{2\pi}$ is ejected from a nucleus, a neutrino, with the same amount of spin and little or no mass, is ejected simultaneously. Because neutrinos have, as yet, escaped detection, this theory is still looked upon by some with scepticism. We therefore leave this particular phase of radioactivity by saying it is still one of the many unsolved mysteries of nature.

While the half-life of a neutron in free space appears to be of the order of several minutes, its probability of capture by some nucleus when in solid matter, reduces its life to about one millisecond (1×10^{-3} sec). In free space a neutron presumably decays into a proton, an electron, and a neutrino.

PROBLEMS AND QUESTIONS

1. Calculate the total energy in Mev required to separate a Li^7 nucleus into individual protons and neutrons.

2. Find the energy in Mev required to separate an O^{16} nucleus into individual neutrons and protons. (*Ans.* 127.4 Mev.)

3. By what other name are each of the following known: (a) electron, (b) proton, (c) deuteron, (d) α-particle, (e) positron, (f) x-ray, (g) γ-ray, and (h) photon?

4. How much energy in Mev would be liberated if the proper number of neutrons and protons could be brought together to make an A^{40} nucleus? (*Ans.* 343 Mev.)

5. Make a table of all the elementary particles you can think of. In different columns give (a) the particle name, (b) symbol, (c) the charge in units of the electronic charge *e*, and (d) the mass in units of the electronic mass.

6. Draw the potential barrier representing a nucleus of a heavy atom (a) when an α-particle approaches it in collision, and (b) when a neutron approaches it.

7. Give a brief description of the water-drop model of a heavy nucleus like uranium.

8. Briefly explain nuclear disintegration in terms of the water-drop model of the nucleus.

9. How does one explain the origin of β-rays when electrons do not exist as such in the nucleus?

10. Calculate the energy required to separate a $_4Be^9$ nucleus into separate protons and neutrons. (*Ans.* 58.1 Mev.)

11. How much energy is required to separate a $_3Li^6$ nucleus into separate neutrons and protons?

12. Find the energy required to separate a $_5B^{10}$ nucleus into individual protons and neutrons. (*Ans.* 64.4 Mev.)

13. How much energy would be required to separate a $_6C^{12}$ nucleus into individual protons and neutrons?

14. A $_{92}U^{235}$ nucleus has a mass of 235.128 amu. How much energy would be required to separate a nucleus into separate neutrons and protons? (*Ans.* 1.90 Bev.)

Atomic Energy   Chapter 75

75.1. A New Discovery. In 1937 Fermi, Segré, and their collaborators subjected uranium to the bombardment of neutrons and from the radio-activity produced believed they had succeeded, for the first time, in produc-ing a series of new elements, 93, 94, 95, etc., beyond uranium 92. The reason for their belief was that the uranium, after bombardment, gave off electrons with a number of different half-lives. Attributing these different half-lives to the successive disintegrations of the same atoms, a single nu-cleus should emit several electrons one after the other. With each emission the nuclear charge would increase by unity, thus producing an atom of higher and higher atomic number.

Although similar observations were later made by the Curie-Joliots, all observers seemed to have misinterpreted the phenomenon because, in 1939, Hahn made a new and important discovery. After bombarding uranium with neutrons, Hahn and his collaborators carefully performed a series of

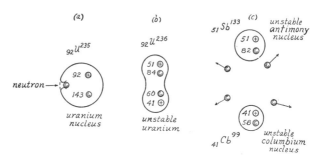

Fig. 75A—Diagram illustrating the fission of a uranium nucleus into two almost equal parts.

chemical separations of the uranium sample to determine the element to which the newly produced radioactivity belonged. To their amazement they found the radioactive atoms to be identical chemically to a number of differ-ent elements, nearly all of which are near the center of the periodic table. In other words, a uranium nucleus, after the capture of a single neutron, seemed to be splitting apart into two nearly equal fragments as illustrated in Fig. 75A.

In the few weeks that followed this discovery, many observers in differ-ent laboratories the world over not only confirmed the results but extended the observations by studying in detail the products of the disintegrations. To explain the phenomenon in simple words, consider the details of the process illustrated in Fig. 75A. An original uranium nucleus, $_{92}U^{235}$, with its 92 protons and 143 neutrons is shown at the left as it captures a slow moving neutron.

In the center diagram (b) the newly formed nucleus is unstable and starts to separate into two nearly equal parts. This separation process is called *fission*. In coming apart the uranium nucleus, behaving like the analogous waterdrop, splashes out small drops, this time neutrons not needed

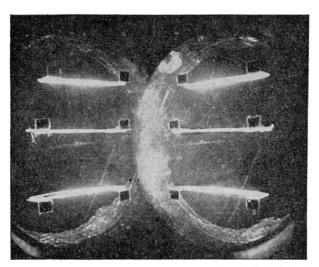

Fig. 75B—Wilson cloud chamber photographs of the "fission" of a uranium nucleus. *(After Corson.)*

by the two fragment nuclei. So great is the energy liberated by this explosion of the nucleus that each of the two heavy nuclei fly apart in opposite directions. That they do so has been confirmed by many Wilson cloud chamber photographs, one of which is reproduced in Fig. 75B. This particular picture is a stereoscopic photograph of the same pair of tracks (two pictures taken at slightly different angles). The cloud chamber contained three thin foils coated with uranium. The fission of one uranium nucleus in the lower film shows two tracks of the same density, formed in opposite directions.

Not all of the uranium nuclei divide into *antimony* and *columbium* as shown in diagram but into any one of a number of pairs of fragments corresponding to elements near the center of the periodic table. The experimental evidence seems to favor pairs of slightly unequal mass, accompanied by

from one to five or more neutrons as shown in Fig. 75A(c). The two fragments with nearly equal positive charges (+51 and +41 in the figure) are
in general not stable nuclei, for they still contain an excess of neutrons.
(For the stable isotopes of these elements, see Appendix IV.)

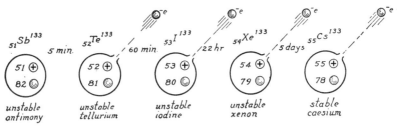

| $_{51}Sb^{133}$ | $_{52}Te^{133}$ | $_{53}I^{133}$ | $_{54}Xe^{133}$ | $_{55}Cs^{133}$ |
| 5 min. | 60 min. | 22 hr | 5 days | |

51 ⊕	52 ⊕	53 ⊕	54 ⊕	55 ⊕
82 ◎	81 ◎	80 ◎	79 ◎	78 ◎
unstable antimony	*unstable tellurium*	*unstable iodine*	*unstable xenon*	*stable caesium*

FIG. 75C—Disintegration series starting with unstable antimony, one of the fragments of the fission of a uranium 235 nucleus.

To become stable each nucleus starts a series of β-ray emissions as indicated in Fig. 75C, finally ending up with a stable nucleus. Starting at the
left in the diagram with the unstable antimony nucleus of charge +51 and
mass 133 the successive emission of four electrons raises the nuclear charge
by four unit steps ending with a stable caesium nucleus, $_{55}Cs^{133}$. The other
fragment, $_{41}Cb^{99}$, in Fig. 75A(c), carries out a similar series of β-ray emissions ending up with $_{44}Ru^{99}$.

As proof that the above series are produced by fission, previously bombarded uranium has been chemically analyzed for elements near the center
of the periodic table. After each chemical separation is performed a test of
the β-ray activity is made by a measurement of the *half-life*. A comparison
of this measured *half-life* with the values already known for the same element from other disintegration experiments has made it possible to identify
some of the radioactive nuclei produced. Such tests, for example, have been
made by Wu * for the series of four elements in Fig. 75C. Note the increasing half-lives she identified for this series, indicating increased stability as
the *stable* nucleus *caesium* is approached.

75.2. Spallation. When elements near the middle of the periodic table
are bombarded by 400 Mev α-particles, or 200 Mev deuterons, the nuclei do
not undergo fission and break up into two more or less equal parts as do many
of the heavier elements. On the other hand these nuclei emit from twenty to
forty nucleons leaving behind any one of a number of nuclei of lower atomic
number and mass number. This phenomenon, now called spallation, was discovered by G. T. Seaborg, I. Pearlman, and their collaborators at the University of California Radiation Laboratory.

---

* C. S. Wu, *Physical Review*, Vol. 58, 1940, p. 925.

When heavy nuclei like bismuth, lead, gold, and uranium are bombarded by high energy particles, a number of nucleons are often emitted as in spallation, but the resulting nucleus is still so unstable that it undergoes fission.

75.3. Uranium-235 as an Explosive. Not long after the discovery of fission it became evident to many scientific groups in America and in Europe that, if a sufficient quantity of pure uranium-235 (U-235) could be isolated from its more abundant isotope uranium 238 (U-238), it might have explosive powers many times greater than anything heretofore known. The reasons for believing this appeared at the time to be somewhat as follows. Suppose that a given mass of uranium metal, all composed of U-235 atoms, was brought together into one lump. The first cosmic ray that penetrated this mass and produced a neutron might well set off the chain reaction shown schematically in Fig. 75D. A U-235 nucleus would capture the neutron and in splitting apart with great violence liberate one or more additional neutrons. These in turn would be quickly absorbed by other nearby atoms which in turn would split up and at the same time liberate other neutrons. Hence a rapidly growing kind of avalanche might occur, a kind which, if fast enough, would have the characteristics of an explosion. A graph showing the rate of growth of such a chain process is given

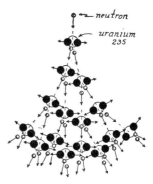

Fig. 75D—Schematic diagram of chain reaction in pure uranium-235.

in Fig. 75E. Since even the slowest of neutrons in solid matter will have speeds of hundreds of thousands of centimeters per second, and since many neutron collisions will, on the average, occur within several millimeters, the graph shows how quickly the growth reaches gigantic proportions. (The *time* scale is of the order of microseconds.)

The escape of neutrons from any quantity of uranium is a *surface effect* depending on the area of the surface, whereas fission capture occurs throughout the body and is therefore a *volume effect*. If the assembled mass of uranium is too small the probability that most neutrons liberated by fission would escape through the surface before being captured might well be so large that a growing chain reaction could not occur. Since the volume of a sphere increases with the cube of the radius while the surface area increases with the square of the radius, the *probability of escape* would decrease with increasing

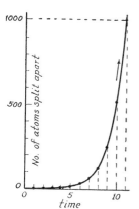

Fig. 75E—Growth curve of fission in pure uranium-235.

size. In other words, if the uranium mass were too small the growth process shown in Figs. 75D and 75E would be cut off before it became very large, and only if the mass were greater than some critical value would an explosion take place.

Visualize therefore a large quantity of U-235 in units smaller than the critical size, separated either by distance or by neutron absorbing material like cadmium metal. Suddenly by some mechanical process all is made as one single mass considerably greater than the critical value. A few neutrons created within this system should set off the chain reaction resulting in explosion.

75.4. Atomic Energy Calculated. As explained in Sec. 75.1, the fragments of every nucleus that undergoes fission consist of two atoms near the center of the periodic table, several neutrons, few if any electrons, and a considerable amount of kinetic energy. Electron mission from the two radioactive atoms are emitted some time after fission is completed and their effect can be neglected from the calculations.

The energy in which we are primarily interested arises during the fission process by the annihilation of a small part of the original atomic mass. As an illustration, consider the following totals for the particles shown in Figs. 75A and 75C.

$$_{55}Cs^{133} = 132.942 \text{ amu}$$
$$_{44}Ru^{99} = 98.933 \text{ ''}$$
$$3 \text{ neutrons} = 3.027 \text{ ''}$$
$$\overline{\text{Total} = 234.902 \text{ ''}}$$

$$_{92}U^{235} = 235.117 \text{ amu}$$
$$\text{Total} = 234.902 \text{ ''}$$
$$\overline{\text{Diff.} = 0.215 \text{ ''}}$$

The incident neutron is omitted from both sides of the calculation since its effect cancels out. The difference between *the mass of a single U-235* nucleus and the sum of the masses of the products of fission seem to be of the order of 0.215 amu or about one-tenth of 1% of the initial U-235 atom.

If, therefore, all the atoms in a kilogram of U-235 undergo fission, the mass annihilated will be approximately one-tenth of 1% of 1000 gm, or 1 gm. By Einstein's equation, $E = mc^2$, 1 gm amounts to an energy of 9×10^{20} ergs and is approximately equal to the energy liberated by the explosion of 20,000 tons of TNT.

75.5. The Calutron. The first successful attempt to separate sizable quantities of U-235 from U-238 was made with a *mass spectrograph* in December, 1941, by E. O. Lawrence and his co-workers at the University of California. Encouraged by their initial successes and with financial support from the United States Government, this group designed and constructed a special electromagnet in which the uranium isotopes were separated by deflecting them in a magnetic field. Many of these instruments now called "calutrons" were later built and put into operation at Oak Ridge, Tennessee by a government sponsored project called the "Manhattan District."

In 1945 sufficient U-235 was separated by these instruments to permit the assembling and setting off of an atomic bomb. During peacetime the calutron has a scientific and practical application, for with it usable quantities of most any isotope of any element can be isolated in a relatively pure state.

A schematic diagram illustrating the fundamental principles of the calutron is shown in Fig. 75F. A vacuum chamber *C* containing the detailed parts of the separation system is located between the *N* and *S* poles of a strong electromagnet. There in the strong magnetic field, atoms of any inserted element are ionized at the *source,* then accelerated toward a *slit S,* held in circular paths by the uniform field *B,* and finally collected in separate compartments at *T.* If the isotope desired belongs to an element containing lighter as well as heavier isotopes the ion paths will be similar to those shown in the right-hand diagram. The greater the mass of the ion the greater is the diameter of its circular path.

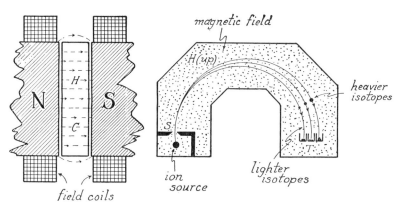

Fig. 75F—Schematic diagram of the Calutron, a magnetic spectrograph for separating the different isotopes of any element.

75.6. New Elements. Just prior to and during World War II, great strides were made in the study of nuclear structure and atomic energy. Not only were methods developed for separating large quantities of U-235 from natural uranium mixtures but a number of new elements, among them plutonium (Pu) 239, were produced and identified.

Technetium (Tc), element 43, was first discovered by Perrier and Segré in 1937 by bombarding molybdenum with neutrons, or deuterons. For example, a neutron captured by $_{42}Mo^{98}$ produces $_{42}Mo^{99}$, a radioactive nucleus which, by β-decay, becomes $_{43}Tc^{99}$. While a number of other radioactive isotopes of technetium have since been made, well-known regularities in nuclear structure indicate *no stable nuclei with charge 43 should exist.*

Astatine (*At*), element 85, was manufactured by Corson, MacKensie, and Segré in 1940. One of its known radioactive isotopes At-211 may be made by α-particles bombarding *bismuth* metal.

$$_2\text{He}^4 + {}_{83}\text{Bi}^{209} \longrightarrow {}_{85}\text{At}^{211} + {}_0\text{n}^1 + {}_0\text{n}^1.$$

Although other radioactive isotopes are known, *no stable isotopes with charge 85 are found and none are expected to exist.*

Francium (*Fa*), element 87, was discovered by Mlle. Perey as a rare disintegration product in the decay of actinium, ${}_{89}\text{Ac}^{227}$. Normally this nucleus decays, as shown in Appendix IV, by β-emission, but on rare occasions a nucleus decays by α-emission giving ${}_{87}\text{Fa}^{223}$. Other radioactive isotopes of Fa are now known but no stable isotopes are known and none are expected to exist.

Neptunium (*Np*), element 93, was first detected and identified by Abelson and MacMillan in 1939. A slow neutron captured by ${}_{92}\text{U}^{238}$ forms ${}_{92}\text{U}^{239}$ which is followed by β-emission to give ${}_{93}\text{Np}^{239}$. This is but one of several known radioactive isotopes. Np^{237} is an α-emitter with a half-life of 2.2×10^6 yr.

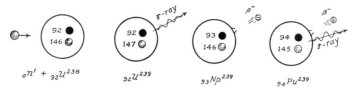

Fig. 75G—Neutron capture by uranium 238 produces, by radioactive β-decay, neptunium and plutonium.

Plutonium (*Pu*), element 94, first identified by Kennedy, MacMillan, Seaborg, Segré, and Wahl, arises from the spontaneous β-emission of neptunium. Reactions giving rise to Pu-239, the isotope used in atomic bombs, are the following:

$$_0\text{n}^1 + {}_{92}U^{238} \longrightarrow {}_{92} U^{239} + \gamma\text{-ray} \xrightarrow{23 \text{ min}} {}_{93}Np^{239} + {}_{-1}e^0$$

$$_{93}Np^{239} \xrightarrow{2.3 \text{ da}} {}_{94}Pu^{239} + {}_{-1}e^0 + \gamma\text{-ray}.$$

Schematic diagrams of these processes are shown in Fig. 75G.

Americium (*Am*), element 95, and *Curium* (*Cm*), element 96, were discovered in 1944 by Seaborg, James, Morgan, and Ghiorso, in collaboration with Hamilton. A sizable quantity of ${}_{94}Pu^{239}$ was bombarded in the Berkeley cyclotron by 40 Mev helium nuclei and two isotopes, ${}_{96}Cm^{240}$ and ${}_{96}Cm^{242}$, formed by (α,n) and $(\alpha,3n)$ reactions. These nuclei are α-emitters with half-lives of one month and five months respectively. $_{95}Am^{241}$ was first discovered as arising from a relatively long-lived β-emitter, $_{94}Pu^{241}$, and emits α-particles with a half-life of about 500 yr.*

Berkelium (*Bk*), element 97, was discovered in 1949 by Thompson, Ghiorso, and Seaborg. Am^{241} bombarded by 35 Mev α-particles yields Bk^{243}. K-capture with a half-life of 4.7 hrs turns 99.9% of these nuclei into Cm^{243}, with 0.1% emitting α-particles to become Am^{239}.

Californium (*Cf*), element 98, was discovered in 1950 by Thompson, Street, Ghiorso, and Seaborg. $_{96}Cm^{242}$ bombarded by 35 Mev α-particles yields $_{98}Cf^{244}$. With a half-life of 45 min $_{98}Cf^{244}$ ejects α-particles with an energy of 7.1 Mev to produce $_{96}Cm^{240}$.

It is now known that all heavy nuclei starting approximately with Th-232 are fissionable, i.e., under proper excitation conditions they split apart with great violence into almost equal pair fragments. Some of them, like U-233, U-235 and Pu-239 fission by the capture of a slow neutron, whereas others like U-238 and Pu-241 fission only by the capture of fast neutrons. The capture of a slow neutron by U-238 is followed by β-decay to produce Np and Pu, whereas fast neutron capture is followed by fission.

Not all of the neutrons liberated by fission are fast neutrons and therefore only those nuclei fissionable by slow neutrons are suitable as atomic explosives. Experiments show that bombs made of Pu-239 explode with greater violence than those made with U-235.

75.7. The Uranium Pile. The uranium pile is a kind of atomic furnace in which U-235 is the "fuel burned" and many useful atomic by-products are produced. A schematic diagram of a pile constructed of solid carbon blocks surrounded by thick absorbing walls of concrete is shown in Fig. 75H. Long cylindrical holes through the carbon blocks provide space for the insertion of all materials and controls needed for proper operation. Chemically pure uranium in tightly sealed aluminum containers is inserted in alternate rows of blocks, while water flows through pipes to keep the temperature of the entire mass from rising dangerously high.

When within the uranium metal a few U-235 atoms undergo fission, fast neutrons are liberated. Entering the surrounding medium, these neutrons collide frequently (about every 2.5 cm) with carbon atoms and are slowed down. Eventually entering uranium metal again as slow neutrons, some are captured by U-235 nuclei to produce fission and hence more neutrons. Since each fission produces several neutrons, the total number in the pile will increase continuously and the temperature will rise from the recoiling energy of the carbon atoms. The whole process is a self-sustaining chain

* For the discovery of neptunium and plutonium, E. M. MacMillan and G. T. Seaborg were jointly awarded the 1951 Nobel Prize in chemistry.

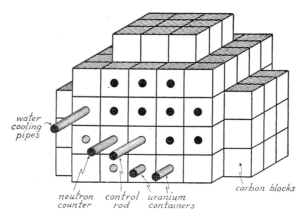

water
cooling
pipes

neutron   control   uranium   carbon blocks
counter   rod   containers

FIG. 75H—Uranium pile of carbon blocks used to produce
plutonium-239 and many other radioactive atomic nuclei.
(Concrete protective walls are not shown.)

reaction only if a sufficient number of the neutrons produced find their way
into U-235 nuclei before being lost or absorbed by some other process.

The other processes referred to are (1) absorption by U-238 nuclei to
produce U-239, (2) absorption by carbon atoms, (3) absorption by impurities, and (4) loss by escape through the furnace walls. The first of
these, if not too large, is a desirable process as it leads to the production of
Pu-239 (see previous section). The second is small since carbon is used as
furnace material in preference to so many other substances because of its
relatively low neutron capture probability. Small quantities of impurities
initially present, as well as those resulting as fission fragments, are unavoid-
ably present. The fourth loss is minimized by making the pile sufficiently
large, thereby increasing the volume-to-wall-area ratio (see Sec. 75.3).

Since cadmium atoms are strong absorbers of neutrons, a solid cadmium
rod inserted into the pile will absorb many neutrons and, acting as a damper,
limit the neutron density as well as the temperature within the pile. Activity within the pile is measured with a boron trifluoride counter inserted
through one of the holes.

After many hours running, the uranium samples are removed and chemical separation processes are carried out to segregate the various products.
The unused uranium is separated out to be used again, while the plutonium
and other elements, all highly radioactive, are used for numerous other experiments. Such large quantities of radioactive elements are produced in
the pile that all handling and chemical processing must be carried on by
remote control methods. The dangers to operators will be realized when it
is pointed out that one milligram of plutonium is a lethal dose to the average human being.

Rare isotopes in quantities large enough for all future scientific work (medical, chemical, etc.) are now obtainable by the insertion of common materials into the pile where under the intense neutron radiation rapid transmutation takes place.

Thorium-232, found quite abundantly in the earth's crust, is not fissionable with slow neutrons, but, when placed in a uranium pile where it is bombarded by neutrons, it can be changed into $_{92}U^{233}$ which is fissionable by slow neutrons. U-235 is of course the fuel burned in the pile and the neutrons released change U-238 into Pu-239, and Th-232 into U-233.

$$_0n^1 + {}_{90}Th^{232} \longrightarrow {}_{90}Th^{233} \longrightarrow {}_{91}Pa^{233} + {}_{-1}e^0$$
$$\longrightarrow {}_{92}U^{233} + {}_{-1}e^0.$$

75.8. Power Reactors or Nuclear Power Plants. The idea that the natural heat developed in a uranium or plutonium pile might be utilized as a source of great power has long been recognized as a feasible enterprise. The basic principles of one type of "power reactor" are shown in Fig. 75I. A quantity of enriched uranium, or plutonium, in the form of a pure metal, or in the form of a solution of soluble salt in water, forms the center of the heat energy source.

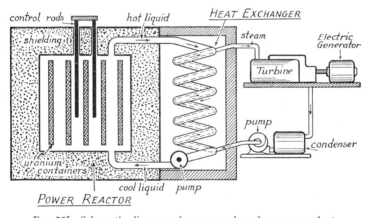

Fig. 75I—Schematic diagram of a proposed nuclear power plant.

The energy released by fission produces great quantities of heat and the rising temperature is regulated to a predetermined value by cadmium rods. To reduce the fission rate, and thereby lower the temperature, the central rods are pushed in a little farther to absorb more neutrons, while to raise the temperature they are pulled out a little farther.

Because of the harmful effects of the intense neutron radiation to men and equipment it is not reasonable to vaporize a liquid directly as in a steam boiler; it is better to circulate a fluid through the shielded reactor and heat exchanger as shown in the diagram.

The hot liquid flowing through the heat exchanger vaporizes a more volatile liquid like water and the resulting hot gas or steam under pressure drives a turbine of special design. The turbine in turn drives an electric generator developing power that can be used to light our cities and factories, or to drive ships and submarines through the water and large planes through the air.

One of the problems connected with such power reactors concerns the effect of the intense neutron radiation on the metal structures. The neutrons change some atoms and permanently displace others from their normal positions in the crystal lattice of the solids and as a result weaken certain crucial mechanical parts. Intensive studies of the properties of various materials under conditions likely to be encountered in power reactors are continually carried on in our research laboratories.

Another important problem concerns the nature of the *coolant;* it must be able to withstand high temperatures, not absorb neutrons and become radioactive to any appreciable extent, and yet it must be efficient in the transfer of heat in both the reactor and the heat exchanger. Certain metals with low melting points appear to be most promising in these and other respects.*

75.9. The Sun's Energy. Measurements of solar radiation reaching the earth each day not only make it possible to calculate the surface temperature of the sun but also to determine its total radiation. The fact that the sun, over a period of many years, shows no signs of cooling off, has long been an unsolved mystery. With the discovery of nuclear disintegration and the development of methods of producing many new types of atoms, this mystery has in a measure been recently solved.

Although there is no direct way known of observing the interior of a star like our sun, mathematical calculations based upon well-established physical laws show that down deep within such a mass the temperature is so extremely high that matter must be a conglomeration of atoms, electrons, and light waves all moving about at tremendously high speeds.

Near the center of the sun where the temperature is about 20 million degrees, the atoms are stripped of their electrons and the light waves produced there are of such high frequencies that they should be classified as γ-rays and x-rays. Here, where the average particle velocity is so high, nuclear reactions must be taking place on a large scale and the liberated energy must be filtering up through to cooler and cooler layers as light waves of lower and lower frequency. At the surface most of the radiations

---

* For a more complete treatment of nuclear energy see "Atomic Energy" by S. Glasstone, pub. by D. Van Nostrand.

escaping are of sufficiently low frequency to be classified as *visible, ultraviolet,* and *infrared.*

A careful study of all known nuclear reactions led Bethe in 1938 to propose the following set of chain processes as those most probably responsible for the generation of energy at the sun's central core.

$$(1) \quad {}_1H^1 + {}_6C^{12} = {}_7N^{13} + \gamma\text{-ray}$$
$$(2) \quad\quad\quad\quad {}_7N^{13} \longrightarrow {}_6C^{13} + {}_1e^o$$
$$(3) \quad {}_1H^1 + {}_6C^{13} = {}_7N^{14} + \gamma\text{-ray}$$
$$(4) \quad {}_1H^1 + {}_7N^{14} = {}_8O^{15} + \gamma\text{-ray}$$
$$(5) \quad\quad\quad\quad {}_8O^{15} \longrightarrow {}_7N^{15} + {}_1e^o$$
$$(6) \quad {}_1H^1 + {}_7N^{15} = {}_6C^{12} + {}_2He^4.$$

By summing up the equations it will be seen that four hydrogen atoms are consumed and that two positrons, three γ-rays, and one helium nucleus, are created. The other nuclei cancel out since the original carbon atom in the first reaction is returned unaltered in the last reaction. Hence hydrogen is burned and helium is liberated. The loss in mass for each such cycle of reactions is, therefore, as follows:

$$4_1H^1 = 4.03256 \quad\quad {}_2He^4 = 4.00387 \quad\quad 2_1e^o = 0.00109.$$

Subtracting gives $4.03256 - 4.00387 - 0.00109 = 0.02761$ amu.

This is equivalent to 27.6 Mev energy.

More recent experiments and calculations* indicate that the *proton-proton cycle* given below is of even greater importance in the creation of solar and stellar energy than the above *carbon cycle.*

$$_1H^1 + {}_1H^1 \longrightarrow {}_1H^2 + {}_1e^o + 0.93 \text{ Mev.} \quad\quad (75a)$$

$$_1H^1 + {}_1H^2 \longrightarrow {}_2He^3 + \gamma\text{-ray} + 5.5 \text{ Mev.} \quad\quad (75b)$$

$$_2He^3 + {}_2He^3 \longrightarrow {}_2He^4 + 2_1H^1 + 12.8 \text{ Mev.} \quad\quad (75c)$$

The net result is the same as before, four hydrogen atoms have been converted into one helium atom. Note that since two ${}_2He^3$ nuclei are involved in the reaction Eg.(75c), two proton-proton reactions of the type Eg.(75a) are required to form one ${}_2He^4$ nucleus.

The rates at which these reactions should take place are not only consistent with the temperature of 20 million degrees, calculated from other considerations, but hydrogen and helium are known to be the most abundant elements of which stars are made.

In order for the sun to radiate 3.8×10^{33} ergs of energy per second,

---

* See "Nuclear Reactions in Stars," by E. E. Salpeter, *Physical Review,* 88, 547, 1952.

Einstein's equation $E = mc^2$ shows that mass must be annihilated at the rate of 4.2×10^{12} gm/sec (or 4,500,000 tons/sec). While this result indicates that the sun is losing mass at a tremendous rate, the amount is small when compared with the sun's total mass of 1.98×10^{33} gm. To illustrate, in one million years the sun should lose one ten-millionth of its total mass.

75.10. Fusion and the Hydrogen Bomb. We have just seen how the sun, and other stars, by means of certain nuclear reaction cycles and temperatures of millions of degrees, are able to fuse hydrogen nuclei into helium with the simultaneous emission of great quantities of energy. While all of the elements needed in these reactions are plentiful on the earth's surface and can be purified and assembled in the research laboratory, the temperature of several million degrees required to cause them to fuse cannot be produced by any of the standard laboratory methods.

Here the atomic bomb, with its heavy elements employing the process of fission, comes to our aid and makes such temperatures possible. When an atomic bomb, containing uranium-235 or plutonium-239, explodes, the temperature reached at the central core, although it may last for only a small fraction of a second, is comparable to that reached at the center of the sun.

Let us "go along" with some of those who are "outsiders," in this "top secret" business of building and testing atomic weapons and make some guesses as to how an hydrogen bomb might be constructed. We may begin by writing down a number of well established nuclear reactions involving the lightest of elements and from them select several that look promising from an energy standpoint. Among others we might select, for example, four reactions involving the hydrogen isotopes deuterium and tritium, as well as the lighter of the two lithium isotopes, lithium-6.

$$_1H^2 + {_1H^2} \longrightarrow {_2He^3} + {_0n^1} \qquad + 3.3 \text{ Mev} \qquad (75d)$$

$$_1H^2 + {_1H^3} \longrightarrow {_2He^4} + {_0n^1} \qquad + 17.6 \text{ Mev} \qquad (75e)$$

$$_1H^2 + {_3Li^6} \longrightarrow {_2He^4} + {_2He^4} \qquad + 22.4 \text{ Mev} \qquad (75f)$$

$$_0n^1 + {_3Li^6} \longrightarrow {_2He^4} + {_1H^3} \qquad 4.8 \text{ Mev} \qquad (75g)$$

Lithium is relatively abundant on the earth, and lithium-6 can be separated in reasonable quantities from its more abundant isotope lithium-7. Tritium, on the other hand, is not found in nature because of its relatively short half-life of twelve years, and it is only produced in quantities in a nuclear reactor at considerable expense.

Our hypothetical hydrogen bomb may now take the schematic form shown in Fig. 75J. A small concentrated core of hydrogen isotopes, deuterium and tritium, is surrounded by pellets of plutonium. Outside of this atomic bomb with its booster *core* is a shell of deuterium and lithium-6 atoms in the concentrated chemical form of lithium deuteride.

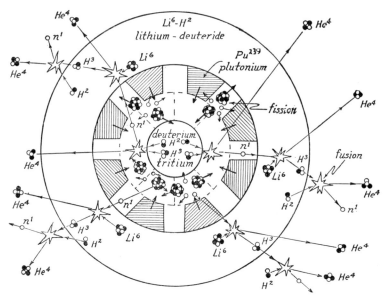

FIG. 75J—Schematic diagram of a hydrogen bomb.

We initiate the explosion process of the bomb by the sudden implosion, i.e., the sudden bringing together, of the isolated plutonium pellets into one spherical mass, whereupon a chain reaction of fission processes occurs (see Fig. 75D), raising the temperature to several million degrees. At this high temperature the very active deuterium-tritium reaction takes place and the resulting boost to still higher temperatures makes possible the very energetic lithium-deuteride reactions. All this takes place in an extremely short period of time with a tremendous explosion.

Note in the schematic diagram how neutrons on lithium-6 form helium and tritium nuclei, thus regenerating the active tritium ingredient of the core, and how most of the fusion processes end up with stable helium nuclei. Considerable quantities of radioactive elements, however, are liberated as by-products of the plutonium. (See Fig. 75C.) *Since great quantities of neutrons are produced by the fissioning of plutonium, neutron reactions with lithium-6 to make tritium might well eliminate the need for the expensive tritium ingredient as an initial booster.* Such an elimination is of paramount importance, since concentration requirements necessitate liquefaction of the hydrogen core with all of its maintenance, and excessive weight and space difficulties. With or without such a liquid core the device can be referred to as a "wet bomb" or a "dry bomb," respectively.

The importance of the H^2H^3 reaction is due not so much to the 17.6 Mev liberated, but to the large size of the tritium nucleus. Tritium nuclei behave as though their cross-sectional area is about one hundred times that of the average nucleus. It is because they present such large targets for the random flying deuterons that a fast chain reaction ensues.

The relative abundance of deuterium in ordinary hydrogen is about one in five thousand, and lithium-6 in ordinary lithium is about one in thirteen (see Appendix V). One pound of these two isotopes in a bomb should react with the explosive effect of 23,000 tons of TNT, and it would appear that any amount could be set off by an atomic blast.

Tritium is made in an atomic reactor at the expense of neutrons on Li^6 (see Eq. 75g). Since neutrons are the essential commodity paid for in the operation of an atomic reactor, every neutron used to produce a tritium nucleus means one less neutron available for transforming U^{238} into Pu^{239}. Since each Pu^{239} nucleus liberates about 200 Mev when it fissions, and H^3 liberates 17.6 Mev when fusing with H^2, it would be economically unsound to use tritium unless it is absolutely necessary.

The question of whether in the foreseeable future the fusion of the lightest elements such as hydrogen and lithium into helium can be controlled and used continuously as fuel in a power plant appears now to be more than just a possibility. Although a continuously high temperature of several million degrees cannot be maintained in the laboratory, the high atomic velocities needed to carry out the reactions may be brought by the intense radiations inside a power reactor, or by intense beams from specially designed atomic accelerators.

It is the hope of every true scientist that the stockpiles of powerfully destructive atomic weapons now on hand will never be used in warfare and that the knowledge gained from their test firings may be utilized in the design of power machines that can certainly be utilized in useful ways to bring about a more abundant life for all mankind.

QUESTIONS AND PROBLEMS

1. Write from memory the carbon cycle of reactions from which the sun and stars derive part of their radiant energy.

2. If α-particles on Pu^{239} give Cm^{240}, what elementary particles are liberated? (*Ans.* 3 neutrons.)

3. Plutonium-239 bombarded by α-particles produces Cm-242 which is α-active with a half-life of one month. Write down the reactions for these changes.

4. If the deuteron on Li^6 reaction is sufficiently rapid for a hydrogen bomb explosion, how much energy would be released by each nuclear reaction? (*Ans.* 22.2 Mev.)

5. Americium-241 bombarded by 35 Mev α-particles porduces Bk-243. This latter nucleus is unstable, and undergoing K-capture with a half-life of 4.7 hrs becomes Cm-243. Write down the reactions.

Appendix 1

1929 De Broglie, Louis V. (1892-   ), French. *Wave Character of Electrons.*
1930 Raman, Sir Chandrasekhara V. (1888-   ), Hindu. *Raman Effect.*
1932 Heisenberg, Werner (1901-   ), German. *Creation of Quantum Mechanics.*
1933 Schroedinger, Edwin (1887-   ), German, and
         Dirac, P. A. M. (1902-   ), English. *Atomic Theory.*
1935 Chadwick, James (1891-   ), English. *Discovery of the Neutron.*
1936 Hess, Victor F. (1883-   ), Austrian. *Discovery of Cosmic Rays.*
         Anderson, Carl D. (1905-   ), American. *Discovery of Positron.*
1937 Davisson, Clinton J. (1881-   ), American, and
         Thompson, George P. (1892-   ), English. *Electron Diffraction by Crystals.*
1938 Fermi, Enrico (1901-   ), Italian. *Slow Neutron Reactions.*
1939 Lawrence, Ernest O. (1901-   ), American. *Development of Cyclotron.*
1940, 1941, 1942, not awarded
1943 Stern, O. (1888-   ), German. *Magnetic Moment of Proton.*
1944 Rabi, I. I. (1898-   ), American. *Magnetic Moments of Nuclei.*
1945 Pauli, W. (1900-   ), German. *Pauli Exclusion Principle.*
1946 Bridgman, P. W. (1882-   ), American. *Physical Effects of High Pressures.*
1947 Appleton, Sir Ed. V. (1892-   ), English. *Exploration of the Ionosphere.*
1948 Blackett, P. M. S. (1897-   ), English. *Discoveries in Cosmic Radiation.*
1949 Yukawa, H. (1907-   ), Japanese. *Theoretical Prediction of Mesons.*
1950 Powell, C. F. (1903-   ), English. *Photographic Cosmic Ray Studies.*
1951 Cockcroft, Sir J. D. (1897-   ), English, and
         Walton, E. T. S. (1903-   ), English. *First Transmutation of Atomic Nuclei.*
1952 Bloch, Felix (1905-   ), American. *Nuclear Magnetic Moments.*
         Purcell, Ed. M. (1912-   ), American. *Radio Astronomy.*
1953 Zernike, Frederik (   ), Dutch. *Phase Contrast Microscope.*
1954 Born, Max (1882-   ), German. *Quantum mechanics, and wave functions.*
         Bothe, Walter (1892-   ), German. *Quantum mechanics, and wave functions.*

THE GREEK ALPHABET

A	α	*Alpha*	H	η	*Eta*	N	ν	*Nu*	T	τ	*Tau*
B	β	*Beta*	Θ	θ	*Theta*	Ξ	ξ	*Xi*	Υ	υ	*Upsilon*
Γ	γ	*Gamma*	I	ι	*Iota*	O	o	*Omicron*	Φ	φ	*Phi*
Δ	δ	*Delta*	K	κ	*Kappa*	Π	π	*Pi*	X	χ	*Chi*
E	ε	*Epsilon*	Λ	λ	*Lambda*	P	ρ	*Rho*	Ψ	ψ	*Psi*
Z	ζ	*Zeta*	M	μ	*Mu*	Σ	σ	*Sigma*	Ω	ω	*Omega*

Appendix II

Trigonometry of the Right Triangle. Of the mathematics to be encountered in this book none involves more than the simplest equations in algebra and the three most common functions in trigonometry, *sine, cosine,* and *tangent.* These, however, are quite generally used and a brief review of the trigonometric functions is not out of place here. The principal use of the sin, cos, and tan occurs in problems where the solution requires the solving of a right triangle.

As shown in Fig. 1 the small letters a, b, and c represent the lengths of the sides of the triangle and the capital letters A, B, and C represent their corresponding opposite angles. Angle $C = 90°$.

By definition

$$\sin = \frac{\text{side opposite}}{\text{hypotenuse}}, \quad \cos = \frac{\text{side adjacent}}{\text{hypotenuse}},$$

$$\tan = \frac{\text{side opposite}}{\text{side adjacent}}.$$

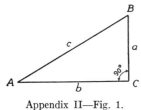

Appendix II—Fig. 1.

(It would be well to memorize these definitions and from them and Fig. 1 practice writing down the following equations:)

(1) $\sin A = \dfrac{a}{c}$ (2) $\cos A = \dfrac{b}{c}$ (3) $\tan A = \dfrac{a}{b}$

(4) $\sin B = \dfrac{b}{c}$ (5) $\cos B = \dfrac{a}{c}$ (6) $\tan B = \dfrac{b}{a}$.

Each of these equations is a relation between one angle and two sides of the triangle. By transposing they take on another useful form. Eqs. (1) and (2), for example, become

(7) $a = c \sin A$ (8) $b = c \cos A$.

If two of the sides of any right triangle are known, the other side and the two acute angles can be calculated from the above equations. This is done by making use of trigonometric tables of sin, cos, and tan given in the following table for all angles between 0° and 90°.

Example: For a given right triangle, angle $C = 90°$, the side $a = 6$ cm, and side $c = 12$ cm. Find angle A, angle B, and side b.

Solution: Using Eq.(1) and substituting, sin $A = 6/12 = 0.5$. Looking up 0.500 in the sin column of Appendix III, the angle 30° is read. Since the sum of the three angles in any triangle is 180°,

(9) $A + B + C = 180°$.

793

Subtraction gives angle $B = 60°$. Applying Eq.(8), $b = c \cos A$, we look up the cos of 30° in the tables and find 0.866, which substituted for cos A gives $b = 12 \times 0.866 = 10.39$ cm.

When two of the sides of a right triangle are known, the other side can also be calculated from the theorem that the square on the hypotenuse equals the sum of the squares on the other two sides.

$$(10) \quad c^2 = a^2 + b^2.$$

When in a right triangle, one of the acute angles is known, only the length of one side need be known to calculate the lengths of the other two sides.

From the definitions of the sin, cos, and tan in Eqs. (1), (2), and (3) it will be noted that the tan is equal to the sin divided by the cos.

$$(11) \quad \tan \theta = \frac{\sin \theta}{\cos \theta}.$$

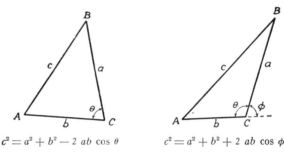

$$c^2 = a^2 + b^2 - 2\,ab \cos \theta \qquad c^2 = a^2 + b^2 + 2\,ab \cos \phi$$

Appendix II—Fig. 2.

Solution of Any Triangle. Many times in the solving of a physics problem it becomes necessary to solve an oblique triangle (see Fig. 2). Where two sides and the included angle of such a triangle are known, the **Law of Cosines** may be used to calculate the other side.

$$(12) \quad c^2 = a^2 + b^2 - 2ab \cos \theta.$$

If the included angle is less than 90° as shown in diagram (a), the values of a and b and cos θ are substituted directly into Eq.(12) and the value of the side c calculated. .f the angle θ is greater than 90°, as in diagram (b), the supplementary angle ϕ is found and Eq.(13) used.

$$(13) \quad c^2 = a^2 + b^2 + 2ab \cos \phi.$$

In reality Eqs. (12) and (13) are one and the same equation since $\phi = 180° - \theta$. In the special case $\theta = 90°$, the cosine term becomes zero, since cos 90° = 0, and both formulas reduce to Eq.(10), as they should.

In words, the *Law of Cosines* states: *the square of any side of a triangle is equal to the sum of the squares on the other two sides minus twice their product multiplied by the cosine of the included angle.*

When three sides of a triangle are known, the angles can all be determined from Eq.(12). Transposing all but cos θ to the same side of the equation,

$$(14) \quad \cos \theta = \frac{a^2 + b^2 - c^2}{2ab}.$$

With this as a general formula for angle θ, similar equations for all three angles of any triangle may be written,

$$(15) \quad \cos A = \frac{b^2 + c^2 - a^2}{2bc}, \qquad \cos B = \frac{c^2 + a^2 - b^2}{2ca},$$

$$\cos C = \frac{a^2 + b^2 - c^2}{2ab}.$$

A negative value for the cosine calculated from these equations means that the angle is greater than 90°. Its value can be found by looking in the tables for the angle whose sine has the same positive value, and then add 90°. For example, suppose $\cos A$ equals —0.5. Looking up the angle whose sine is +0.500 we find 30°. Angle A is therefore 30° + 90° or 120°.

If two angles and the included side of an oblique triangle are known, the other two sides are readily calculated from the well-known **Law of Sines.**

$$(16) \quad \frac{a}{\sin A} = \frac{b}{\sin B} = \frac{c}{\sin C}.$$

Any two terms from these equalities give an equation with only one unknown.

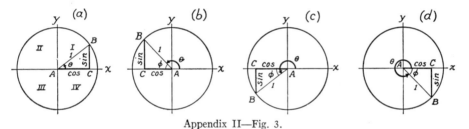

Appendix II—Fig. 3.

The trigonometric functions sin, cos, and tan apply not only to angles between 0° and 90° but to larger angles as well. How they apply is illustrated in Fig. 3 where four circles of unit radius are drawn. Diagram (a) shows a right triangle ABC with angle θ in the first quadrant. It follows from the definitions of the sin, and cos given by Eqs. (1) and (2) that

$$\sin \theta = BC/AB, \qquad \text{and} \qquad \cos \theta = AC/AB.$$

Since $AB = 1$, the sin θ becomes just the length of the line BC. From Eq.(11), the tan $\theta = BC/AC$.

All angles between 90° and 180° lie in the second quadrant, and are represented by θ in diagram (b). Similarly, angles between 180° and 270° lie in the third quadrant as illustrated in diagram (c), and angles between 270° and 360° lie in the fourth quadrant as illustrated in diagram (d). In all quadrants the length of the line $BC = \sin \theta$, the length of the line $AC = \cos \theta$, and the ratio $BC/AC = \tan \theta$.

To find the numerical values of the functions for all angles greater than 90°, the angle ϕ is first determined by finding the difference between θ and 180° and/or 360°, as the case may be. The values of sin ϕ, cos ϕ, and tan ϕ are then read from the Tables in Appendix III. In the second quadrant the sin, being in the + direction, is positive, whereas the cos, being in the —x direction, is negative. In the third quadrant the sine and cosine are both negative, whereas in the fourth quadrant the sine is negative and the cosine positive.

Examples: let $\theta = 150°$. Find sin θ, cos θ, and tan θ. Subtracting from 180° gives $\phi = 30°$. From the Tables in Appendix III sin 30° = 0.500, cos 30° = 0.866, and tan 30° = 0.577, giving sin 150° = 0.500, cos 150° = −0.866 and tan 150° = −0.577.

Problems in Trigonometry

1. Find the number of degrees in the following angles: (a) sin θ = 0.446, (b) sin θ = 0.518, (c) cos θ = 0.350, (d) cos θ = 0.833, (e) tan θ = 0.854, and (f) tan θ = 2.950.

2. Find the sin, cos, and tan for the following angles: (a) 28.2°, and (b) 78.7°. (*Ans.* (a) 0.473, 0.881, 0.536, (b) 0.981, 0.196, 5.013.)

3. Find the sin, cos, and tan of the following angles: (a) 122°, (b) 234°, and 304°.

4. Find the angle θ for each of the following: (a) cos θ = −0.165, (b) sin θ = −0.454, and (c) tan θ = −2.246. (*Ans.* (a) 99.5° or 260.5°, (b) 207° or 333°, (c) 114° or 294°.)

5. One of the acute angles of a right triangle is 24° and the shortest side is 10 in long. Find the length of the other two sides and the remaining angle.

6. One of the acute angles of a right triangle is 54° and the hypotenuse is 5 in long. Find the other angle and the lengths of the other two sides. (*Ans.* 36°, 2.94 in, 4.05 in.)

7. A right triangle has sides of length 5 ft, 12 ft, and 13 ft. Make a diagram to scale and measure the angles. Calculate the angles and compare with those measured.

8. If the hypotenuse of a right triangle is 20 ft long and one side is 6 ft long, what is the length of the remaining side and the size of the two acute angles? (*Ans.* 19.08 ft, 17.5°, and 72.5°.

9. From a point on the level ground 200 ft from the base of a flag pole an observer sights the top at an elevation angle of 42°12'. How high is the flag pole?

10. A base line 500 ft long is measured along the beach and from its ends a rock can be seen some distance from shore. If the angles which the lines of sight make with the base line are 90° and 86.5°, how far from shore is the rock? (*Ans.* 8175 ft.)

11. A base line 45 ft long is measured along the bank of a river and from its ends a tree on the opposite bank is sighted. If the angles which these lines make with the base line are 79° and 87° what is the width of the river? Make a diagram to scale.

12. To find the distance to a mountain peak a base line 8 mi long is measured out on level ground in the valley below. From each end of this line the peak is sighted through a surveyor's telescope and the lines of sight found to make angles of 46° and 54° with the base line. Find the distance to the peak from the ends of the base line. Make a diagram to scale. (*Ans.* 5.84 mi, 6.57 mi.)

13. A ship in distress is sighted from two lighthouses 5 mi apart. The first lighthouse finds the line of sight to the ship makes an angle of 110° with the line of sight to the second lighthouse, while the second finds the line of sight to make 59° with the line of sight to the first lighthouse. How far is the ship from the nearest lighthouse? Make a diagram to scale.

14. When the sun is 62° above the horizon the shadow of a tall tree is found to be 41 ft long, as measured along the level ground from the base of the tree. How high is the tree? (*Ans.* 77.11 ft.)

15. The two sides of a triangle are 4.5 ft and 6.9 ft respectively, and the included angle is 34°. Find the length of the other side and the values of the other two angles.

16. Two sides of a triangle are 14 ft and 26 ft respectively, and the included angle is 109°. Find the length of the other side and the values of the other two angles. (*Ans.* 33.3 ft, 23.3° and 47.7°.)

Appendix III

TRIGONOMETRIC FUNCTIONS (*Natural*)

Angle	Sine	Cosine	Tangent	Angle	Sine	Cosine	Tangent
0°	0.000	1.000	0.000				
1°	.018	1.000	.018	46°	.719	.695	1.036
2°	.035	0.999	.035	47°	.731	.682	1.072
3°	.052	.999	.052	48°	.743	.669	1.111
4°	.070	.998	.070	49°	.755	.656	1.150
5°	.087	.996	.088	50°	.766	.643	1.192
6°	.105	.995	.105	51°	.777	.629	1.235
7°	.122	.993	.123	52°	.788	.616	1.280
8°	.139	.990	.141	53°	.799	.602	1.327
9°	.156	.988	.158	54°	809	.588	1.376
10°	.174	.985	.176	55°	.819	.574	1.428
11°	.191	.982	.194	56°	.829	.559	1.483
12°	.208	.978	.213	57°	.839	.545	1.540
13°	.225	.974	.231	58°	.848	.530	1.600
14°	.242	.970	.249	59°	.857	.515	1.664
15°	.259	.966	.268	60°	.866	.500	1.732
16°	.276	.961	.287	61°	.875	.485	1.804
17°	.292	.956	.306	62°	.883	.470	1.881
18°	.309	.951	.325	63°	.891	.454	1.963
19°	.326	.946	.344	64°	.899	.438	2.050
20°	.342	.940	.364	65°	.906	.423	2.145
21°	.358	.934	.384	66°	.914	.407	2.246
22°	.375	.927	.404	67°	.921	.391	2.356
23°	.391	.921	.425	68°	.927	.375	2.475
24°	.407	.914	.445	69°	.934	.358	2.605
25°	.423	.906	.466	70°	.940	.342	2.747
26°	.438	.899	.488	71°	.946	.326	2.904
27°	.454	.891	.510	72°	.951	.309	3.078
28°	.470	.883	.532	73°	.956	.292	3.271
29°	.485	.875	.554	74°	.961	.276	3.487
30°	.500	.866	.577	75°	.966	.259	3.732
31°	.515	.857	.601	76°	.970	.242	4.011
32°	.530	.848	.625	77°	.974	.225	4.331
33°	.545	.839	.649	78°	.978	.208	4.705
34°	.559	.829	.675	79°	.982	.191	5.145
35°	.574	.819	.700	80°	.985	.174	5.671
36°	.588	.809	.727	81°	.988	.156	6.314
37°	.602	.799	.754	82°	.990	.139	7.115
38°	.616	.788	.781	83°	.993	.122	8.144
39°	.629	.777	.810	84°	.995	.105	9.514
40°	.643	.766	.839	85°	.996	.087	11.43
41°	.656	.755	.869	86°	.998	.070	14.30
42°	.669	.743	.900	87°	.999	.052	19.08
43°	.682	.731	.933	88°	.999	.035	28.64
44°	.695	.719	.966	89°	1.000	.018	57.29
45°	.707	.707	1.000	90°	1.000	.000	∞

Appendix IV

COMPLETE LIST OF THE STABLE ISOTOPES OF THE CHEMICAL ELEMENTS

At. No.	Element	Sym.	Isotopes, Mass. No.	At. Wt.
1	hydrogen	H	1, (2)	1.0078
2	helium	He	4, (3)	4.002
3	lithium	Li	6, 7	6.940
4	beryllium	Be	9	9.02
5	boron	B	10, 11	10.82
6	carbon	C	12, (13)	12.01
7	nitrogen	N	14, (15)	14.008
8	oxygen	O	16, (18), (17)	16.000
9	fluorine	F	19	19.000
10	neon	Ne	20, (21), 22	20.183
11	sodium	Na	23	22.997
12	magnesium	Mg	24, 25, 26	24.32
13	aluminum	Al	27	26:97
14	silicon	Si	28, 29, 30	28.06
15	phosphorus	P	31	31.02
16	sulfur	S	32, 33, 34	32.06
17	chlorine	Cl	35, 37	35.457
18	argon	A	(36), (38), **40**	39.944
19	potassium	K	39, (40), 41	39.096
20	calcium	Ca	40, (42), (43), 44	40.08
21	scandium	Sc	45	45.10
22	titanium	Ti	46, 47, **48**, 49, 50	47.90
23	vanadium	V	51	50.95
24	chromium	Cr	50, **52**, 53, 54	52.01
25	manganese	Mn	55	54.93
26	iron	Fe	54, **56**, 57, (58)	55.84
27	cobalt	Co	59	58.94
28	nickel	Ni	58, 60, 61, 62, (64)	58.69
29	copper	Cu	63, 65	63.57
30	zinc	Zn	64, 66, 67, 68, (70)	65.38
31	gallium	Ga	69, 71	69.72
32	germanium	Ge	70, 72, 73, **74**, 76	72.60
33	arsenic	As	75	74.91
34	selenium	Se	(74), 76, 77, 78, **80**, 82	78.96
35	bromine	Br	79, **81**	79.916
36	krypton	Kr	(78), 80, 82, 83, **84**, 86	83.7
37	rubidium	Rb	**85**, 87	85.48
38	strontium	Sr	(84), 86, 87, **88**	87.63

798

COMPLETE LIST OF THE STABLE ISOTOPES OF THE CHEMICAL ELEMENTS

At. No.	Element	Sym.	Isotopes, Mass. No.	At. Wt.
39	yttrium	Yt	89	88.92
40	zirconium	Zr	**90**, 91, 92, 94, 96	91.22
41	columbium	Cb	93	92.91
42	molybdenum	Mo	92, 94, 95, 96, 97, **98**, 100, 102	96.0
43	technetium	Tc	*99*	97.8
44	ruthenium	Ru	96, 98, 99, 100, 101, **102**, 104	101.7
45	rhodium	Rh	103	102.91
46	palladium	Pd	(102), 104, 105, **106**, 108, 110	106.7
47	silver	Ag	**107**, 109	107.88
48	cadmium	Cd	106, (108), 110, 111, **112**, 113, 114, 116	112.41
49	indium	In	113, **115**	114.76
50	tin	Sn	112, (114), (115), 116, 117, 118, 119, 120, 122, 124	118.70
51	antimony	Sb	**121**, 123	121.76
52	tellurium	Te	(120), 122, 123, 124, 125, 126, **128**, **130**	127.61
53	iodine	I	127	126.92
54	xenon	Xe	(124), (126), 128, **129**, 130, 131, 132, 134, 136	131.3
55	caesium	Cs	133	132.91
56	barium	Ba	(130), (132), 134, 135, 136, 137, **138**	137.36
57	lanthanum	La	139	138.92
58	cerium	Ce	(136), (138), **140**, 142	140.13
59	praseodymium	Pr	141	140.92
60	neodymium	Nd	142, 143, **144**, 145, 146, (148), (150)	144.27
61	prometeum	Pm		146.0?
62	samarium	Sa	144, 147, 148, 149, 150, **152**, 154	150.43
63	europium	Eu	**151**, 153	152.0
64	gadolinium	Gd	155, **156**, 157, **158**, 160	156.9
65	terbium	Tn	159	159.2
66	dysprosium	Dy	161, 162, 163, **164**	162.46
67	holmium	Ho	165	163.5
68	erbium	Er	**166**, 167, 168, 170	167.64
69	thulium	Tm	169	169.4
70	ytterbium	Yb	171, 172, 173, **174**, 176	173.04
71	lutecium	Lu	175	175.0
72	hafnium	Hf	176, 177, 178, 179, **180**	178.6
73	tantalum	Ta	181	180.88
74	tungsten	W	182, 183, **184**, **186**	184.0
75	rhenium	Re	185, **187**	186.31
76	osmium	Os	186, (187), 188, 189, 190, **192**	191.5
77	iridium	Ir	191, **193**	193.1
78	platinum	Pt	(192), 194, **195**, 196, 198	195.23
79	gold	Au	197	197.2
80	mercury	Hg	(196), 198, 199, 200, 201, **202**, 204	200.61

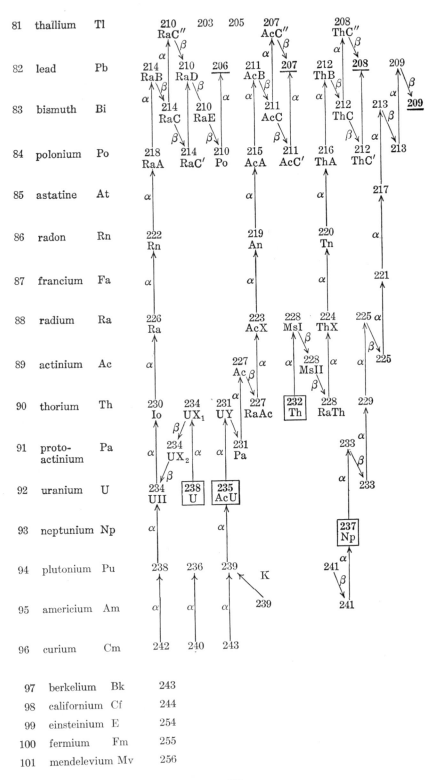

Appendix V

TABLE OF ATOMIC WEIGHTS FOR ISOTOPES OF THE LIGHT ELEMENTS

s = seconds. m = minutes. hr = hours. d = days. y = years.

Isotope Symbol	Relative Abundance and Half-life		Atomic Weight	Isotope Symbol	Relative Abundance and Half-life		Atomic Weight
$_0n^1$	β^-	10^{-6}s	1.00898	$_9F^{17}$	β^+	70s	17.00749
$_1H^1$	99.98		1.00814	$_9F^{18}$	β^+	112m	18.00667
$_1H^2$	0.02		2.01474	$_9F^{19}$	100		19.00446
$_1H^3$	β^-	31y	3.01700	$_9F^{20}$	β^-	12s	20.00635
$_2He^3$			3.01698	$_{10}Ne^{19}$	β^+		19.00792
$_2He^4$	100		4.00387	$_{10}Ne^{20}$	90		19.99886
$_2He^6$	β^-	0.8s	6.02047	$_{10}Ne^{21}$	0.27		21.00059
$_3Li^6$	7.5		6.01702	$_{10}Ne^{22}$	9.73		21.99827
$_3Li^7$	92.5		7.01822	$_{10}Ne^{23}$	β^-	43s	23.00168
$_3Li^8$	β^-	0.88s	8.02502	$_{11}Na^{21}$	β^+	23s	....
$_4Be^7$	K, γ	43d	7.01915	$_{11}Na^{22}$	β^+, γ	3y	22.00132
$_4Be^8$	2α		8.00785	$_{11}Na^{23}$	100		22.99714
$_4Be^9$	100		9.01504	$_{11}Na^{24}$	β^-, γ	14.8h	23.99865
$_4Be^{10}$	β^-, γ	10^3y	10.01671	$_{11}Na^{25}$	β^-, γ	62s	24.99779
$_5B^{10}$	18.4		10.01611	$_{12}Mg^{23}$	β^+	11.6s	23.00111
$_5B^{11}$	81.6		11.01279	$_{12}Mg^{24}$	77.4		23.99270
$_5B^{12}$	β^-	0.02s	12.01816	$_{12}Mg^{25}$	11.5		24.99381
$_6C^{10}$	β^+	8.8s	10.02060	$_{12}Mg^{26}$	11.1		25.99087
$_6C^{11}$	β^+	20m	11.01492	$_{12}Mg^{27}$	β^-, γ	10.2m	26.99295
$_6C^{12}$	98.9		12.00380	$_{13}Al^{26}$	β^+	7s	25.99619
$_6C^{13}$	1.1		13.00747	$_{13}Al^{27}$	100		26.99014
$_6C^{14}$	β^-	10^3y	14.00768	$_{13}Al^{28}$	B$^-$, γ	2.4m	27.99083
$_7N^{13}$	β^+, γ	9.9m	13.00986	$_{13}Al^{29}$	β^-	6.7m	28.98975
$_7N^{14}$	99.62		14.00751	$_{14}Si^{27}$	β^+	4.9s	26.99525
$_7N^{15}$	0.38		15.00486	$_{14}Si^{28}$	89.6		27.98584
$_7N^{16}$	β^-	8s	16.01074	$_{14}Si^{29}$	6.2		28.98572
$_8O^{15}$	β^+	126s	15.00777	$_{14}Si^{30}$	4.2		29.98331
$_8O^{16}$	99.76		16.00000	$_{14}Si^{31}$	β^-	170m	30.98521
$_8O^{17}$	0.04		17.00453	$_{15}P^{29}$	β^+	4.6s	28.98962
$_8O^{18}$	0.20		18.00487	$_{15}P^{30}$	β^+	2.5m	29.98817
$_8O^{19}$	β^-	31s	19.00948	$_{15}P^{31}$	100		30.98362
				$_{15}P^{32}$	β^-	14.3d	31.98409

Isotope Symbol	Relative Abundance and Half-life			Atomic Weight	Isotope Symbol	Relative Abundance and Half-life	Atomic Weight
$_{16}S^{31}$	β^+		3.2s	30.98886	$_{82}Pb^{208}$		208.04140
$_{16}S^{32}$		95.1		31.98226			
$_{16}S^{33}$		0.74		32.98196	$_{83}Bi^{209}$		209.04550
$_{16}S^{34}$		4.2		33.97877			
$_{16}S^{35}$	β^-		87d	34.98035	$_{84}Po^{218}$		218.07676
$_{16}S^{36}$		0.016		. . . .			
					$_{86}Rn^{222}$		222.08663
$_{17}Cl^{33}$	β^+		2.4s	. . . .			
$_{17}Cl^{34}$	β^+		33m	33.98100	$_{88}Ra^{226}$		226.09574
$_{17}Cl^{35}$		75.4		34.98018			
$_{17}Cl^{36}$	β^+, K, β^-			35.97996	$_{90}Th^{232}$		232.11034
$_{17}Cl^{37}$		24.6		36.97762	$_{92}U^{234}$		234.11379
$_{17}Cl^{38}$	β^-, γ		33m	37.98004	$_{92}U^{235}$		235.11704
					$_{92}U^{238}$		238.12869
$_{18}A^{35}$	β^+		1.9s	. . . .			
$_{18}A^{36}$		0.31		35.97893	$_{93}Np^{237}$		237.12158
$_{18}A^{37}$				36.97850			
$_{18}A^{38}$		0.06		37.97488	$_{94}Pu^{239}$		239.12653
$_{18}A^{39}$	β^-		4m	. . . .			
$_{18}A^{40}$		91.63		39.97510	$_{98}Cf^{244}$		244.14211
$_{18}A^{41}$	β^-, γ		110m	40.97776			

Appendix VI

VALUES OF THE GENERAL PHYSICAL CONSTANTS (AFTER DU MOND)

Planck's constant of action. . . . . $h = 6.6238 \times 10^{-34}$ joule sec

Electronic charge. . . . . $e = 1.6019 \times 10^{-19}$ coulombs

Electronic charge. . . . . $e = 4.8022 \times 10^{-10}$ e.s.u.

Specific electronic charge. . . . . $e/m = 1.7589 \times 10^{11}$ coulombs/kg

Specific proton charge. $e/M_p = 9.5795 \times 10^7$ coulombs/kg

Electronic mass. . . . . $m = 9.1072 \times 10^{-31}$ kg

Mass of atom of unit atomic weight. . . . . $M = 1.6600 \times 10^{-27}$ kg

Mass of proton. . . . . $M_p = 1.6722 \times 10^{-27}$ kg

Ratio mass proton to mass electron. . . . . $M_p/m = 1836.1$

Wien's displacement-law constant. . . . . $C = 0.28976$ cm deg.

Velocity of light. . . . . $c = 299,790$ km/sec

$c^2 = 8.9874 \times 10^{10}$ km^2/sec^2

THE PERIODIC TABLE OF CHEMICAL ELEMENTS

I	II	III	IV	V	VI	VII	VIII			(0)
1 H 1.0078										2 He 4.002
3 Li 6.940	4 Be 9.02	5 B 10.82	6 C 12.01	7 N 14.008	8 O 16.000	9 F 19.000				10 Ne 20.183
11 Na 22.997	12 Mg 24.32	13 Al 26.97	14 Si 28.06	15 P 31.02	16 S 32.06	17 Cl 35.57				18 A 39.944
19 K 39.096	20 Ca 40.08	21 Sc 45.10	22 Ti 47.90	23 V 50.95	24 Cr 52.01	25 Mn 54.93	26 Fe 55.84	27 Co 58.94	28 Ni 58.69	
29 Cu 63.57	30 Zn 65.38	31 Ga 69.72	32 Ge 72.60	33 As 74.91	34 Se 78.96	35 Br 79.916				36 K 83.7
37 Rb 85.48	38 Sr 87.63	39 Yt 88.92	40 Zr 91.22	41 Cb 92.91	42 Mo 96.0	43 Tc	44 Ru 101.7	45 Rh 102.91	46 Pd 106.7	
47 Ag 107.9	48 Cd 112.41	49 In 114.8	50 Sn 118.7	51 Sb 121.8	52 Te 127.6	53 I 126.9				54 Xe 131.3
55 Cs 132.9	56 Ba 137.4	57 La 138.9	72 Hf 178.6	73 Ta 180.88	74 W 184.0	75 Re 186.3	76 Os 191.5	77 Ir 193.1	78 Pt 195.2	
79 Au 179.2	80 Hg 200.6	81 Tl 204.39	82 Pb 207.18	83 Bi 209.00	84 Po 210.	85 At				86 Rn 222.
87 Fa	88 Ra 225.95	89 Ac 227	90 Th 232.15	91 Pa 234	92 U 238.17	93 Np	94 Pu	95 Am	96 Cm	

58 Ce 140.2	59 Pr 140.9	60 Nd 144.3	61 Il 146.0	62 Sa 150.4	63 Eu 152.0	64 Gd 156.9	65 Tb 159.2	66 Ds 162.5	67 Ho 163.5	68 Er 167.6	69 Tm 169.4	70 Yb 173.0	71 Lu 175.0
90 Th	91 Pa	92 U	93 Np	94 Pu	95 Am	96 Cm	97 Bk	98 Cf	99 E	100 Fm	101 Mv		

803

Author and Subject Index

804

Index